VOLUME 7

THE PAPERS OF JOSEPH HENRY

January 1847–December 1849

The Smithsonian Years

Joseph Henry (1797–1878), from a daguerreotype presumably taken in the late 1840s. Courtesy of the Division of Photographic History, National Museum of American History, Smithsonian Institution.

The Papers of
JOSEPH HENRY

Editor: Marc Rothenberg
Associate Editor: Paul H. Theerman
Assistant Editor: Kathleen W. Dorman
Assistant Editor: John C. Rumm
Research Assistant: Deborah Y. Jeffries

VOLUME 7

January 1847–December 1849
The Smithsonian Years

SMITHSONIAN INSTITUTION PRESS
WASHINGTON AND LONDON

ENDPAPERS: *The north facade of the Smithsonian Institution Building, constructed between 1847 and 1855. Henry and his family occupied an apartment on the second floor of the east wing from 1855 until his death. Photograph by Jeff Tinsley, 1984. Courtesy of the Office of Prints and Photographs, Smithsonian Institution.*

Library of Congress Cataloging-in-Publication Data

Henry, Joseph, 1797–1878.
  The papers of Joseph Henry.
  Editor for v. 6–7: Marc Rothenberg.
  Includes bibliographical references and indexes.

  Contents: v. 1. December 1797–October 1832: the Albany years. — v. 2. November 1832–December 1835: the Princeton years. — v. 7. January 1847–December 1849: the Smithsonian years.
  1. Henry, Joseph, 1797–1878. 2. Smithsonian Institution—History—Sources. 3. Science. 4. Science—United States—History—Sources. 5. Physicists—United States—Biography. I. Reingold, Nathan, 1927–   ed. II. Rothenberg, Marc, 1949–   . III. Title.
Q113.H43   537′.092′4   72-2005
ISBN 0-87474-123-8 (v. 1)
     0-87474-164-5 (v. 2)
     0-87474-174-2 (v. 3)
     0-87474-792-9 (v. 4)
     0-87474-793-7 (v. 5)
     1-56098-112-1 (v. 6)
     1-56098-533-X (v. 7)

British Library Cataloguing-in-Publication Data is available

Manufactured in the United States of America
03 02 01 00 99 98 97 96   5 4 3 2 1

⊗ *The paper used in this publication meets the minimum requirements of the American National Standard for Permanence of Paper for Printed Library Materials Z39.48–1984.*

❧ CONTENTS ❧

for Smithsonian—On being secretary: "I dislike the noteriety of the position and the executive duties which it involves" (Doc. 91); cooperation with Great Britain on meteorology—Richard A. Tilghman on Faraday as a lecturer—Lightning protection for Independence Hall and the Capitol Building—Former student's proposal for science journalism and tribute to Henry as a teacher—Thoughts on the heat of the moon and experiments on heat reflected from ice—Visits to Francis Wayland and Zachariah Allen in Providence; meeting of Association of American Geologists and Naturalists in Boston—Matthew F. Maury questions Henry's conduct.

Contents

criticism of Owen's building—Scientific discussion with Lane—Recommendations for Virginia's chair of natural philosophy—Resignation from Princeton—Honorary degree for Squier—Gray's publication problems—Request for examination of commercial product (Argillo).

❧ ILLUSTRATIONS ❧

xi

This volume marks the inauguration of the third and last phase of Henry's life, his thirty-two years as secretary of the Smithsonian Institution. Although he never ceased thinking of himself as a research scientist and educator, hereafter his chief roles were those of science administrator and advisor.

When Henry accepted the office of secretary from the Smithsonian Board of Regents in December 1846, he faced a challenge unprecedented in the history of American science. He became head of an institution established by an act of Congress but funded entirely by the enigmatic bequest of a foreigner. Congress had passed the legislation only after years of debate,[1] during which contradictory interpretations of the language of James Smithson's will, "to found at Washington under the name of the Smithsonian Institution, an Establishment for the increase and diffusion of knowledge among men," had been presented. The vagueness of the bill and its passage in the final hours of the session reflected the difficulty of reaching a consensus. While the legislation called for the construction of a building to accommodate various anticipated functions of the institution—natural history and geology collections, a library, an art gallery, and a laboratory—it left almost every other detail of the Smithsonian's program to the Board of Regents. In electing Henry, the regents apparently endorsed his vision of the Smithsonian—a vision of the Smithsonian as a supporter of research and publication[2]—as it had been presented to them by his close friend and colleague, Alexander Dallas Bache, a member of the Board of Regents and superintendent of the United States Coast Survey. Henry's goal was to launch an institution which, in his own words, would "call forth the original talent of the country and put those who are capable of increasing the sum of human knowledge in bold relief."[3]

As secretary of the Smithsonian, Henry faced three equally daunting tasks: first, to construct a program which in his own mind satisfied the charge given in Smithson's will; second, to acquire support for his program among the regents, Congress, the American scientific community, and, to a certain extent, the American public; and last, to implement his program. An additional challenge was to do all these without the luxuries of precedents, experience, adequate funds, or sufficient staff.

Henry had a clear sense of what he wanted the Smithsonian to be. Because Smithson was a scientist, he argued, "he [Smithson] intended by the expression 'for the increase of knowledge' an organization which should promote original scientific research."[4] The appropriate role of the Smithsonian, therefore, was to support basic research and to disseminate the results of that research through scholarly publication. Henry was less certain about Smithson's views on diffusion, but was confident that the donor did not want the Smithsonian to serve only local or even national needs, but rather to function as an international institution ("among men"), albeit in a national context. The primary form of diffusion would be through journals providing accounts of the "progress of the different branches of knowledge as compiled from all the journals of the world."[5]

As envisioned by Henry, the Smithsonian was to be part of the larger program he and Bache envisioned to upgrade science in the United States. They had long been concerned about the lack of support for basic research in this country. As Henry wrote:

> Practical Science will always meet with encouragement in a Country like ours. It is the higher principles—those, from which proper practice naturally flows that require to be increased and diffused.[6]

Elsewhere he lamented that "our country has produced but one Franklin to five hundred Fultons."[7] He and Bache had complained for years about the lack of standards in American scientific publications, difficulties in getting access to the current literature, the lack of time and funds for research, problems in international communication, lapses in scientific ethics, and the ignorance and gullibility of the public and Congress when faced with scientific questions. He had not only a firm conviction of the rightness of his vision, but also an invaluable ally in Bache, who had defined the job of secretary and had engineered Henry's election to it.

Unlike Henry, with his sureness of purpose deriving from his interpretation of Smithson's will, the fifteen members of the Board of Regents had varied ideas of the purpose of the institution. These derived from the legislation and also from the many years of debate prior to the founding of the institution. Despite the election of Henry, among the regents were men who still hoped to use Smithson's bequest to establish a national library, or a school to train teachers, or to erect a monumental building designed for activities to entertain and educate the citizens of

Washington. These were uses Henry opposed, because "their influence would be local and would not carry out the wishes of the Donor in the best manner."[8] Henry had been elected by only a slim majority and that majority had been achieved through a deal arranged by Bache in which Rufus Choate and other supporters of a large library "concurred"[9] in Henry's appointment if Henry would include a library in his program and would name Charles Coffin Jewett assistant secretary in charge of the library. As a result of the differing visions of Henry and a divided board, the early months of Henry's tenure were marked by a great deal of uncertainty.

Henry began imposing his vision in his reworking of Robert Dale Owen's "Report of the Organization Committee of the Smithsonian Institution." Originally presented to the regents on December 1, 1846, two days before Henry's election, the report had been referred back to the committee on December 21.[10] Although the revised report, presented to the Board of Regents on January 25, 1847, and adopted the next day, still appeared under Owen's name, it bore Henry's extensive input. In contrast to the original, which dealt almost entirely with how the Smithsonian could diffuse knowledge, the revised report made clear that the institution's mission would also be to increase knowledge. It included Henry's specific plans for a scholarly series of refereed papers, "containing positive additions to the sum of human knowledge,"[11] and for appropriations for original research.

Henry came to realize he could convince the board to endorse his program for the Smithsonian only by compromising and establishing what was in a sense a dual track program. His strategy during these early months was very complex and subtle. On one hand, he often used language that was rigid and uncompromising. This has led Wilcomb Washburn, in his ground-breaking study of Henry's conception of the Smithsonian, to use terms like "single-minded devotion" and "religious fervor" to describe Henry's commitment to his plan.[12] However, Henry also took the half-loaf, formed alliances, and otherwise proved to be a skilled politician. Rigidity and confrontation frequently gave way to adroit compromise. Henry's letters throughout the first half of 1847 are filled with phrases that indicate that the compromises adopted provided him with less than he had wanted, but as much as he had reasonably hoped for, and more than enough to satisfy him for the moment. Moreover, Henry suspected that as time went on, the regents would tire of managing the Smithsonian and leave him alone. Indeed, by May 1848, Henry could brag that "the members who were in the Board [of Regents] at the time of my election are fast passing out and those which remain are either my fast friends or take but little interest in the affair."[13]

An example of Henry accepting the half-loaf was the major compromise which marked the regents' debates during January 1847. After much give-and-take, the regents voted to divide the annual income—once the building was complete—between the library and museum collections on the one hand, and research and publications (Henry's program) on the other. Three factions competed on the Board of Regents: proponents of a large library, led by Choate; champions of Owen's position that the institution take on educational and utilitarian roles, who were allied with those Washingtonians who wanted the institution to focus on local activities; and the Bache-led supporters of Henry's belief that the Smithsonian should support basic research in science. The Henry-Bache faction based their position on a particular interpretation of Smithson's will rather than any mandate in the congressional legislation and on the regents' discretionary authority granted them in the legislation. As with any compromise, each interested party gave something up but found some satisfaction in the outcome. Choate relinquished his dream of devoting most of the institution's income to a large library, but succeeded in getting Henry to nominate Jewett as assistant secretary and librarian. Owen, for his part, found nothing in the compromise to prevent the construction of the grand Smithsonian building he envisioned. Henry, though disappointed that half of the institution's annual income was to go to the library and museum, nonetheless was pleased that the regents appropriated the other half for his programs.

Much of Henry's energy throughout the remainder of 1847 centered on his developing a formal program of organization and getting it adopted by the regents. Although Henry carried out the regents' instructions to consult "with men of eminence, in the different branches of literature and science,"[14] the surviving documentation is too slim to specifically identify the contributions of others. Henry did credit Regent William C. Preston with many of the ideas and language of the first page. Adopted by the regents in December 1847, the "Programme of Organization of the Smithsonian Institution" was divided into two sections. The first included those activities which Henry saw as arising from Smithson's will. To promote the increase of knowledge, these encompassed scholarly publication and direct support of research. Under diffusion of knowledge, Henry included annual reports of the state of current knowledge in a variety of fields, and various original historical expositions or translations. Under a second heading—"in accordance with the terms of the resolutions of the Board of Regents"—and making it unmistakable that here the program was responding to the legislation, Henry included the library and museum collections in art and science.[15]

In gaining approbation for his views among larger and larger external circles, Henry repeatedly demonstrated his skills as a diplomat and politician, no doubt having been carefully tutored by Bache. He was unyielding in his fight for what he perceived as the core issues, but gracefully yielded or compromised on peripheral issues. He understood the significance of personal contact. His days, and especially his evenings, were filled with visits to people important for the Smithsonian's success. The selection of a new regent was almost immediately followed by a personal call by Henry and a briefing on the issues at hand. He kept in touch with the leadership of both political parties. Whether through inclination or a sense of duty, Henry was socially active in Washington. He also understood the importance of a positive press, and attempted on occasion to mold public opinion through it. Finally, he knew that even in a democracy, some voters are more important than others. In dismissing some expressions of support for the Smithsonian, he noted that the endorsers were "uninfluential . . . . The remarks thus far have all been favorable; but they are from persons unknown the value of opinions should be estimated by weight as well as by number."[16] College presidents, senior professors, the membership of learned societies—these were the supporters that Henry successfully sought. Even one of Henry's critics, who argued that "very few will read and fewer still will understand your publications," conceded that Henry had obtained unanimous approval from "great numbers of the most distinguished literary men of the Union."[17] Ironically, one of the strongest arguments against those who branded the Smithsonian as elitist came from a Massachusetts farmer who captured the essence of Henry's vision:

It [the Smithsonian] must, it will become a fountain from which ten thousand streams will flow out in all directions to refresh and gladden the hearts of all who will partake its bounty. I say all. Not that I infer that every one will ever visit the establishment or become direct owners of all or any of its published documents, for in the present state of things it is questionable whether one in five hundred of our whole population would care to do either, unless indeed it were for any other object rather than to acquire information, yet, from those who search its tomes or investigate its researches, other streams will flow forth, whose influence, though silent as the dewfall of a breezeless morning, will scatter intellectual health and happiness into every mind.[18]

That man understood what Henry was trying to do: to stake out a place for elite science in a democracy.

Of course, Henry's "Programme of Organization" was only a skeleton. The true test would come when Henry attempted to put his ideas into practice. As other historians have noted, the Smithsonian had relatively little money to spend each year. To maximize the institution's impact, Henry adopted a "seedbed" approach, taking on responsibilities others could or would not assume, but withdrawing support when "the seedlings were transplanted elsewhere or became self-sustaining."[19]

Henry began implementation of his program almost immediately upon the approval of the revised Owen report in January 1847. During the years covered by this volume, one can identify at least seven distinct elements in the Smithsonian's operations—Smithsonian Contributions to Knowledge, limited research and publication subventions, the meteorological network, popular publications, the library, collections, and lectures. He enthusiastically promoted those elements that derived from his interpretation of Smithson's will, while reluctantly carrying out functions deriving from the congressional legislation.

Dominating Henry's time through the end of 1848 was the establishment of the Smithsonian Contributions to Knowledge, which he considered the most important element of his program. This series was his attempt to publish significant scholarly monographs, which were expensive to print and had limited audiences. Natural historians, whose work often required expensive illustrations, had particular problems in getting work published. His colleagues had told him that for many scientists "the illustrations of their labours frequently cost more than they can afford to expend on them and on this account many valuable articles never see the light."[20] The Smithsonian Contributions to Knowledge was to be a highly prestigious series, with all submissions subject to peer review. Fully aware that it would establish a precedent, he took great care with the first volume, E. G. Squier and E. H. Davis's *Ancient Monuments of the Mississippi Valley: Comprising the Results of Extensive Original Surveys and Explorations* (1848), worrying about everything from the quality of the paper to the layout of the pages. Henry acted with calculated intent, selecting a topic in archeology for the first volume in order to emphasize the breadth of the Smithsonian's interests. He backdated and manipulated correspondence to establish a precedent for submission and refereeing for future contributions. He restricted content to ensure that the volume met the highest standards of scientific research, insisting to Squier that the monograph be "as free as possible from every thing of a speculative nature and that your positive addition to the sum of human knowledge should stand in bold relief unmingled with the labours of others."[21] He even arranged an honorary degree for Squier from Princeton to enhance his standing in the scholarly community.

Henry quickly followed up on his initial success with a second volume in the series. In press by the end of 1849 (although it did not appear until 1851), this volume contained monographs in the fields of astronomy, biology, geography, archeology, chemistry, and education. Among the authors were Louis Agassiz, Robert Hare, Sears Cook Walker, and Francis Lieber.

The second part of Henry's program, begun in 1848 once he had paid for most of the Squier and Davis publication, supported research as well as publication. Recognizing that Smithsonian funds were limited, Henry decided against assembling a faculty or research staff at the Smithsonian and instead awarded small research grants and publication subventions to individual researchers. Such grants might be used to pay for specimen collecting trips, or for the services of artists or engravers. Again, Henry carefully established precedent in terms of application and refereeing. For example, he instructed referees "to mention [in their formal reports] that the researches cannot be properly prosecuted unless with the aid required from the Smithsonian Institution."[22] Henry also supported researchers through the acquisition of specimens for their use. He either purchased specimens from collectors or underwrote a collector's expenses in exchange for a share of the specimens gathered.

Once the Smithsonian Contributions to Knowledge was successfully launched, Henry turned to meteorology where he hoped to contribute to "solving the problem of American storms."[23] He had called for the Smithsonian's involvement in gathering meteorological data in his very first ruminations on the institution in September 1846,[24] and continued to identify it as a potential activity for the institution in subsequent discussions. Not only did Henry have a personal interest in coordinating widespread meteorological observations, dating back to his days at the Albany Academy,[25] but it was one of the great problems in the physical sciences, with both theoretical and applied implications. It was also a problem which necessitated a large-scale, coordinated effort, which the Smithsonian was in a position to provide.[26] Collaborating with James P. Espy, whose meteorological program in the Navy Department Henry had lobbied hard to save, the Smithsonian established a network of volunteer meteorological observers in November 1848. It was intended as part of an international meteorological network covering all of North America. By the end of 1849, approximately one hundred and fifty regular observers were sending data to the Smithsonian. In addition, the meteorological network run by the Regents of the University of the State of New York, begun in 1825, conformed itself to the Smithsonian program and contributed its data.

In terms of Henry's goals for the Smithsonian, his greatest failure during these early years was his inability to launch a series of popular publications. As envisioned by Henry, these reports would be written by leading American scientists, but would provide non-technical summations of various disciplines. For example, he initially proposed an account of agricultural chemistry by Lewis C. Beck, one by Asa Gray on the forest trees of the United States, one by either Benjamin Peirce or Elias Loomis on recent discoveries in astronomy, and one by himself on lightning. The authors he chose, though experts in their fields, were already overwhelmed with other projects and, with the exception of Loomis, did not complete their manuscripts. The Loomis volume gave evidence that such a project was fraught with difficulties. As with Smithsonian Contributions to Knowledge, Henry concerned himself about details in order to establish precedents. After all, anything published with Smithsonian sponsorship could and would be seen as an authoritative account. After receiving Loomis's completed manuscript, Henry assigned the part dealing with the discovery of Neptune to Benjamin Apthorp Gould because he felt Loomis's account was inadequate (and perhaps not free enough in its praise of Benjamin Peirce). He did not inform Loomis for six months, at which time he wrote not only that he had reassigned a portion of the book to someone else, but that the rest of the manuscript was inadequate and needed a major revision. Although the documentation does not survive, we suspect that as a direct result of Henry's actions, Loomis chose to publish his book elsewhere.[27]

Henry was less enthusiastic about the three elements of his program that derived from the legislation, notably a library, a museum, and a lecture series. Although he recognized the benefits of libraries and museums to scholarship, he considered both a national library and a national museum of government collections to be more properly supported by the federal government than by the bequest of an Englishman. He doubted that the Smithsonian's limited operating funds would be sufficient to create and to maintain these activities let alone the rest of his program. (Henry's resolve to limit the Smithsonian library may also have been strengthened by events at the British Museum, where the librarian and the scientific staff were clashing over cataloging and access.[28]) Although Henry was not able to completely shed responsibility for a library and a national museum, in the early years of the Smithsonian he nonetheless endeavored to limit them.

In terms of a library, his options were limited. In addition to the library concessions Bache had made to ensure Henry's election, the Smithsonian legislation made the institution a copyright depository, thus ensuring a steady flow of recently-published books to the institution. Although Henry could not forestall Jewett's hiring, he tried to contain and direct Jewett's energy and enthusiasm, while trying to gain acceptance for his position that the Library of Congress should become *the* national library and that the Smithsonian library should be only a small scientific research collection. Although the Library of Congress was the fourth largest library in the nation in 1850, behind Harvard, the Library Company of Philadelphia, and Yale, its importance was limited by its obsolete cataloging system and lack of staff.[29] The decision to draw out the construction of the Smithsonian Building worked in Henry's favor by delaying the assembling of a library. In the meantime, Jewett planned his future purchases, worked to gather statistics on the nation's public libraries, and began preparing a union catalog of the holdings of all American public libraries.

Henry was even more hesitant to have the Smithsonian take responsibility for the voluminous national collections, including those of the United States Exploring Expedition. Henry investigated various ways to frustrate the transfer from the Patent Office building, from arguing that these were national collections properly supported by the federal government, to delaying the construction of the building so that he would have nowhere to house the collections. He did, however, accept the rationale for having "working" collections for research and by 1849 had accumulated some ten thousand natural history specimens, acquired to provide "material for an interesting series of memoirs on physiology, embryology, and comparative anatomy."[30] Considerably more to his liking, Henry collected a "museum of physical instruments," which consisted primarily of scientific apparatus purchased by the Smithsonian or donated to the institution by Hare upon his retirement. These instruments were to serve for "experimental illustration and original research, and . . . as models to workmen as well as to illustrate the general progress of inventions in this line."[31] Henry thought that these instruments would "induce a pilgrimage to Washington of all the quid nunc professors in our country to enlighten themselves as to the progress of science and to witness the new phenomena."[32]

Henry was very ambivalent about the sponsorship of popular lectures. After his December 1846 meetings with the Board of Regents, he grudgingly accepted that they were necessary for political reasons: "the edification of members of Congress."[33] His reflections after the first officially-sponsored lectures in March 1849 were considerably more positive, however, as he realized that these lectures could truly diffuse knowledge, albeit locally:

> I think courses of lectures in Washington will tend to do much good there are in the several offices of the city many intelligent gentlemen with small salaries who will attend with their families provided the lectures are free.[34]

He also appreciated the lectures' high visibility at a time when many of the other Smithsonian activities were less obvious to the public. Rather than inviting "mere popular lecturers, whose chief recommendation is fluency of speech or powers of rhetorical declamation," Henry preferred "all who have distinguished themselves in literature or science."[35] Reflecting his ambivalence, however, the budget for lectures was small, with many speakers offered only their expenses.

Overshadowing all the programmatic activities of the Smithsonian, at least in terms of its budget, was the construction of the building. It had been Henry's fervent belief that the Smithsonian did not need and could not afford an elaborate and expensive building. Aware of similar cases—notably the Girard College for Orphans in Philadelphia—Henry lobbied hard against the large building which had virtually been approved before his election. In this case, the sentiment among a majority of the regents was the opposite of Henry's. They wanted a distinct physical presence in Washington. As Henry related to his wife, Harriet, "nothing but a large building immediately erected will satisfy the Washingtonians"; indeed, "the very salvation of the integrity of the union of the states is thought to be connected with a large building at Washington."[36] Faced with such fervor, Henry yielded, telling Gray that "I have concluded not to attempt to stop the erection but to endeavour to control the expenditure."[37]

His attitude toward the building came from his concern for the Smithsonian's finances. The original bequest was over $515,000, but the only guaranteed source of operating funds was the interest on that amount, which at six percent was just under $31,000 per year. Henry's $3,500 salary alone took over one-tenth of that amount. (By way of comparison, the Smithsonian budget was only one-quarter of the Coast Survey's expenditure in 1847.) Henry advocated increasing his annual operating funds by adding to the principal of $515,000 as much as possible of the $242,000 interest which had accumulated during the eight years Congress had debated what to do with the bequest. Bache devised a plan to do this by deliberately spreading the construction of the building over five years and thereby preserving more of the building fund so it could continue to earn interest.

Nonetheless, the building was expensive. For example, in 1849 the total operating budget of the Smithsonian, excluding expenses related to the building, but including all salaries, was $17,350. Over three times that amount was spent on the building. For the period 1846–1850, total Smithsonian expenditures in all categories were over $244,000. Expenditures for the building itself, the grounds, and furniture and fixtures totaled some $169,000. In contrast, Henry spent less than $18,000 on publications, research, and lectures.[38]

Henry's anxiety over the building was lessened in part by his managing to gain control over the design of the interior through an adroit move by Bache just prior to the signing of the construction contract. He had a clause inserted that allowed the Board of Regents to modify the construction contract at will, as long as the contractors received suitable compensation. Subsequently, Henry redesigned much of the interior to suit his programmatic needs. (The architect of the building, James Renwick, Jr., did not object as "all the interior of the building"[39] had been designed by Robert Dale Owen and his brother, David Dale Owen.)

To implement his program and oversee the construction of the Smithsonian Building, Henry had to learn to carry on the day-to-day work of the Smithsonian. He had no executive experience or inclination, as some had pointed out before his election. He was chosen as secretary because of his plans for the institution and his international reputation as one of the country's leading scientists. Henry brought prestige, a coherent vision of the Smithsonian based on years of thought about the needs of American science, and extensive knowledge of both the American and European scientific communities, but whether he had the skills to run an organization was unknown at the time.[40] Although he was initially very optimistic about his ability to handle "the official duties of my office," claiming that "a little common sense will stand a man in place of much knowledge of a merely technical kind,"[41] the volume of correspondence and the details of administration quickly threatened to overwhelm him. For the first two years, the Smithsonian was essentially a one-man institution. In the early months he continued to live in Princeton, commuting to Washington to attend meetings of the Board of Regents or confer with the executive committee. When in Washington, Henry set up shop in the office of the vice-president in the Capitol Building. Once he permanently relocated to Washington, he operated from his lodgings or a tiny office in the Patent Office Building, finally moving into an office in the Smithsonian Building in April of 1849. The staff consisted originally of only him and a messenger, William McPeake, to be joined in March of 1847 by Charles P. Russell to handle the copyright correspondence. For his other correspondence, he had only minimal clerical assistance, rendered at various times by his wife, one of his former students, and even Jewett, who had joined the staff part-time in December 1847. Not until the hiring of Edward Foreman in January 1849 could Henry rely upon the full-time services of a clerk able to handle routine correspondence on his own. Moreover, it quickly became apparent that Henry was stretching both the human and financial resources of the Smithsonian very thinly. In 1849 he described himself as "man of all work for the last two years."[42] Concerned as he was about the establishment of precedents, Henry worried over the details of every Smithsonian program. Correspondents began to complain about unpaid bills and unfulfilled promises. Some of the criticisms were mild: "he is not at all a man of business."[43] But the attacks could be quite violent. Writing in confidence to a friend, George P. Marsh, a regent, wrote:

> In all matters of business, Prof. H. is as imbecile a person as I ever met, & a man more utterly unfit for his place could hardly be found. . . . I can easily understand, that it must be very difficult for a person of common sense, & reasonable acquaintance with men, to agree with Prof. H. in anything.[44]

In one 1849 letter, Squier characterized Henry as "careless and neglectful," and "altogether the <u>reverse</u> of a business man, and of what the Sect. of the Smithsonian Inst. <u>Should</u> be."[45] In another, he claimed that "everybody here, who has had the slightest connection with [Henry], is thoroughly disgusted . . . . The sooner he <u>resigns</u> and takes to his gallipots the better."[46] But these relatively few complaints (and Squier was not a dispassionate observer, having repeatedly clashed with Henry over details of his publication) must be balanced against Henry's accomplishments with almost no staff and "several thousands" of incoming letters during just the first three years of the Smithsonian's existence.[47]

*   *   *   *   *

One very important aspect of Henry's secretaryship was his relationship with the United States government. Because of the unique status of the Smithsonian, Henry had a degree of freedom of action denied other Washington scientists. This freedom was manifested in a number of ways.

First, the Smithsonian did not have an explicit mission restricting it to a particular area such as surveying, astronomy, or technological evaluation. In contrast, government scientists at the Coast Survey and the Patent Office, for example, had specific responsibilities prescribed by law.

Second, the Smithsonian was relatively insulated from partisan politics. The regents came from both parties and the senior executives, notably the secretary, were not appointed by the president. The report of the committee on organization of the Board of Regents had recommended that no Smithsonian lecture or publication should deal with "party politics." It went on to state that

> they [the members of the committee of organization] would deeply regret to see party tests and party wranglings obtrude themselves on the neutral ground of science and education; jeoparding, as such intrusions surely would, the tranquility of the Institution, disturbing the even tenor of its action, perhaps assaulting its welfare, certainly contracting the sphere of its usefulness.[48]

Despite differences in political affiliation, congressional Smithsonian regents almost inevitably became strong supporters of the Smithsonian, its programs, and its independence from the political wars.

Adding to Henry's independence was his freedom from congressional appropriations. Congress did not vote on his budget, nor did the president or any of the department heads have direct control over his activities. To ensure the Smithsonian's continuing independence and his own freedom of action, Henry wanted to have nothing to do with the appropriations process. In 1849 he summed up his attitude towards the possibility of closer ties with the government:

> I am fully convinced that the true policy of the Institution is to ask nothing from Congress except the safekeeping of its funds; to min-

gle its operations as little as possible with those of the general government, and to adhere in all cases to its own distinct organization, while it co-operates with other institutions in the way of promoting knowledge; and on the other hand, that it is desirable that Congress should place as few restrictions on the Institution as possible, consistent with a judicious expenditure of the income, and that this be judged of by a proper estimate of the results produced.[49]

The Smithsonian was also free of direct congressional oversight. Time and again during Henry's early tenure, the possibility of either direct oversight or the imposition of congressional will upon the Board of Regents was considered, and every time it was rejected. In December 1847, and again in January 1848 and December 1848, the House of Representatives rejected resolutions to add a "Smithsonian Committee, whose duty it shall be to superintend the affairs of the Smithsonian Institution" to the list of standing committees.[50] Isaac Walker introduced a resolution in the Senate in January 1851 calling upon the Board of Regents to explain why the Smithsonian had not yet taken responsibility for the national collections, as required by the legislation. Led by Senator and Regent Jefferson Davis, supporters of the Smithsonian successfully argued that "the Board of Regents . . . should not be compelled to accept of this donation, and . . . that under the law as it now is they can not be compelled to accept it."[51] When the Board of Regents' decision to uphold Henry's firing of Jewett was appealed to Congress in 1855, the independence of the board was reconfirmed. The Senate Committee on the Judiciary endorsed the regents' actions and the House select committee split, but with a plurality supporting the regents. Both houses rejected the need for further action.[52]

Underpinning this freedom was the consensus among Henry's contemporaries that the Smithsonian was not part of the federal government, but a private institution, for which the government served as the trustee. When the Senate Committee on the Judiciary discussed accepting the Smithson bequest in 1836, it concluded that

> the fund given to the United States by Mr. Smithson's will is nowise and never can become part of their revenue. They can not claim or take it for their own benefit. They can only take it as trustees, to apply to the charitable purpose for which it was intended by the donor.[53]

Twelve years later, the National Institute, a Washington-based learned society, characterized the Smithsonian as "a private establishment . . .

intended to increase the fame and perpetuate the name of a private individual."[54] In his 1851 response to Walker, Davis contended that "the Smithsonian Institution is not a department of the Government."[55] Henry himself wrote that "the institution is not a national establishment, in the sense in which institutions dependent on the government for support are so."[56] It is in this context that A. Hunter Dupree has concluded that prior to the inauguration of an annual appropriation for the national museum in 1858, "the government's control [of the Smithsonian] was limited to its position as trustee of the fund and to the officers who served ex officio on the board of regents."[57]

Complementing this freedom were Henry's long and mutually beneficial relationships with politicians, going back to his youth in Albany. He felt comfortable with them, had friends among politicians on the local and national levels from both the Democratic and Whig parties, and discussed issues of scientific importance with them. Henry was carefully non-partisan. As his confidential secretary put it: "He [Henry] belongs to the party that is in power, & can do most for the Institution."[58] He carefully cultivated his personal ties with members of Congress. Henry believed that politicians could be educated as to the importance of science and would respond positively to requests by the scientific community:

> If the scientific men of the country will only be properly united they can do much for the advance of their persuits through assistance from Congress. Politicians as a class are timid except when they have an object which they know is worthy and in the advocating of which they are sure of being sustained by authority."[59]

Henry had a unique status in Washington. Although he had intimate ties with the federal establishment, both scientific and political, he was not an employee of the federal government. He walked a tightrope, rigorously safeguarding the Smithsonian's independence, while actively involving the Smithsonian and himself in federal scientific activities. He took advantage of the flexibility of the Smithsonian's private funding to fill gaps in federal support of science. The Smithsonian, for example, supplemented the Navy Department's meager and unreliable support of Espy's meteorological observation program by establishing its own observation network in cooperation with Espy and operating it until Henry convinced the United States Army Signal Office to take it over in 1874. When Beck undertook the first federally funded investigation of food adulteration, Henry offered Smithsonian support if federal funding fell through. Henry also worked to expand existing federal programs and activities to include science. In the spring of 1847 he convinced the secretary of the treasury to have geomagnetic observations included in the geological surveys of federal mineral reserves in Michigan and the Wisconsin Territory and provided some of the instruments. Likewise Henry persuaded the commissioner of the General Land Office to have his surveyors make observations on the variation of the compass in the course of their surveying. Alluding to these two initiatives, Henry boasted that "without expending but little of the funds of the Smithsonian I find I can here do a good deal for the cause of american science."[60]

Others in the American scientific community quickly recognized Henry's role as a de facto advisor to both the executive and legislative branches of government on all aspects of science and technology. As his correspondence demonstrates, the careers of individual scientists, the livelihoods of inventors, and the future of certain government scientific activities came to depend at least in part upon his support and his ability to sway members of Congress or cabinet members. His effectiveness as an advocate was becoming more important than his skills as an experimental physicist.

Henry was often asked to intervene with the government on behalf of individual scientists or scientific projects. After the Mexican War, several geologists and naturalists asked him to urge the government to add an investigation of the mineral resources of California to the federal surveys of the area and requested his support for their applications. When Squier decided he could extend his ethnological work into Central America by receiving a diplomatic appointment, he asked Henry to confer with the secretary of state and convince him of the importance of the research. After receiving an impassioned letter from the geologist Charles T. Jackson asking him to intercede with the secretary of the interior to save his job as head of the Lake Superior survey, Henry wrote a firm appeal. He also wrote the secretary to urge continued support for Henry R. Schoolcraft's six-volume study of Native Americans.

*   *   *   *   *

In becoming secretary of the Smithsonian Institution, Henry entered a new environment, one familiar in some ways and different in others. In leaving Princeton for Washington, he was exchanging an intellectual community for a political one, a private persona for a public role, research for administration, and a sphere of action in which he was uniformly revered and respected for one in which he was occasionally the target of public criticism.

Henry's colleagues at Princeton had warned him that, given his need for "freedom from anxiety & unusual responsibility,"[61] Washington would be dangerous for his mental health and that one of his "high noble spirit"[62] would suffer greatly from being subjected to the "harassing questionings of coarse & incompetent men."[63] Having spent years in the New York state capital, however, Henry was familiar with a city in which politics was a preoccupation. Now, of course, he had a position of responsibility whereas in Albany he had been a protégé. Surprisingly, however, Henry found that his health actually improved when he went to Washington, in part due to the greater amount of walking he had to do to get around the city.[64] Although he missed the contemplative quiet of Princeton, he was stimulated by Washington, a city "where every one does as he chooses."[65] Finding Washington a magnet for visitors, he enjoyed chance encounters with former students and acquaintances from Albany. He realized he would "be spattered by the News papers in various ways & served up for good and for evil"[66] but resolved to ignore such coverage as long as he felt he was "in the line of my duty"[67] and unless his honor was "impeached."[68]

Founded in 1800 to be the seat of the national government, Washington was a small city, much larger than the quiet town of Princeton, but smaller than Albany and only the fifteenth largest city in the country in 1850.[69] According to one historian of Washington, "the antebellum capital reflected the kind of institutional impoverishment that resulted from the stalemated sectionalist politics of the period."[70] With the administration changing every four years in this period, federal employment was unstable and office seekers flooded into town after each election.[71] The latest manifestation of a local learned society, the National Institute, was moribund when Henry arrived. One of Henry's correspondents in 1847 questioned his decision to remain in the "desert of Washington."[72] Henry noted, however, in an early annual report, that there was an audience for the type of lectures the Smithsonian offered, an audience whose needs were presumably not before met "in a city . . . commonly thought to be exclusively devoted to politics and amusement."[73] Although he was philosophically opposed to using Smithson's bequest for local purposes, the Smithsonian became a "beachhead of sorts" for the reformers of intellectual life in Washington.[74]

Henry arrived in Washington at a time when the federal bureaucracy was still relatively small. There were only six cabinet officers: the secretaries of state, war, navy, and the treasury, and the postmaster-general and attorney-general. Although most interaction was still on a personal level, the government already had its own bureaucratic procedures and codes of conduct. Henry complained that "all matters pertaining to the operations of the Government require constant pushing"[75] and that "government is no respecter of persons."[76] The crush of business was becoming sufficient to force even Henry to work through the bureaucracy. He complained:

> To obtain a single interview with one of the heads of Departments during the session of Congress members having precedence of all others sometimes costs me several calls. Most of the business has to be transacted at this season of the year by letter and these answered by clerks.[77]

In 1849, the cabinet grew with the establishment of the Interior Department.

In terms of scientific activity, the nation's capital was a distinct fourth to Boston, Philadelphia, and New York.[78] Although the federal government was spending a relatively large percentage of its budget on science—perhaps twenty-five to thirty-three percent during the years 1840–1860—most of that funded expeditions on land and sea.[79] Relatively few of the scientists employed by the federal government actually resided in Washington.[80] Most of those that did were at the Coast Survey headquarters, the Naval Observatory, the Patent Office, and the topographical and engineering bureaus of the army. It would take the expansion of the federal government during the Civil War to "vitalize Washington, D.C., as a scientific center."[81]

Like Princeton, with its rhythm of alternating periods of activity when classes were in session and quiet when they were not, Washington was a city of two personalities—"the season" when Congress was in session, and the rest of the year when it wasn't. "The season"—beginning in December and lasting three to eight months—was marked by hustle and bustle: throngs of people crowded the streets and public meeting-places; the social calendar was filled with dances and dinner parties; shops, hotels, and other businesses that catered to visitors prospered. During these months, Henry reported "no want of excitement."[82] When Congress adjourned, Washington reverted to a slower tempo: the streets were emptier and social life lagged. For Henry, the two phases of Washington's year meant two very different work patterns, analogous to the alternating periods of teaching and research at Princeton. While Congress was in session, Henry called on important people, arranged lectures, and maneuvered through the bureaucracy. With Congress gone, Henry traveled, reflected, and planned. He could do all three by going to whatever Coast Survey field station Bache was working at, a frequent escape during the miserable Washington summers.

At first, however, Henry was not certain that he would stay in Washington for more than one season. When he accepted the secretaryship of the Smithsonian in December 1846 he retained his professorship at Princeton. With the full cooperation of the administration of the College of New Jersey, which was eager to keep him, he did not move his family out of the house provided by the college or give up his teaching responsibilities. His family did not move down to Washington until January 1848. Not until June 1848 did he finally submit his resignation to Princeton.

Why the apparent indecision? Part of Henry's psychological strength during the many debates among the regents as to the program of the Smithsonian was his willingness to walk away from the institution if he felt he would be unable to fulfill the charge of Smithson's will to increase and diffuse knowledge. If he and Bache could not convince the board to endorse Henry's plan of the Smithsonian, then Henry would resign.

The uncertainty surrounding the Smithsonian was only partly responsible for Henry's hesitation. Harriet Henry's reluctance to move to Washington undoubtedly played a part. To Harriet, Washington was an alien place, devoid of family, containing few friends, and rumored to be unhealthy. Henry worked hard to persuade her that her fears about Washington were exaggerated. His letters to her included such phrases as "I think the transfer to Washington when once it is made will be much less disagreeable than you immagine"[83] and "I think when you are once settled here you will be pleased with the place."[84] He reassured her that the rumors about the unhealthiness of Washington were false: "I also learn that the most health part of the city is on the mall where the Smithsonian Hall is to be erected."[85] He even saw advantages in the transience of the population of Washington. Inhabitants came and went as the fortunes of political parties or individuals changed. Henry comforted Harriet that "your position will if you chose give you standing and the constant changes in the inhabitants will enable you to choose to mingle or not in society."[86] His trump card was that Washington was a much more desirable environment to raise their three daughters than Princeton. The latter had too many young men and too few educational opportunities for young women.

During these uncertain early months, a great temptation arose. On May 10, 1847, Hare resigned as professor of chemistry at the University of Pennsylvania School of Medicine. The job was Henry's for the asking.

Hare's chair was probably the best position in American academia, combining high income, limited responsibilities, great visibility, and an exciting metropolitan venue. As Henry told his brother: "This is a situation I have long looked forward to as the most desirable in our country for a scientific man."[87] He wrote Hare that the position "would be on many accounts much more agreeable to myself and my family, than the one I now hold."[88] Henry carried on an intensive debate with himself, writing Bache that he felt "like the ass between two bundles of hay."[89] Adding to the pressure was his knowledge that his wife preferred Philadelphia to Washington. Henry's sense of obligation and duty, however, ultimately swayed him. Not only did he have an opportunity to change the face of science in America, he and Bache continued to fear that the bequest would be squandered in the hands of others. Going against his perceived self-interest, (he had written Harriet earlier that "in comming to Washington I may not consult my own ease"[90]) he decided to stay, "sink or swim live or die."[91] On reflection, he concluded:

> I have made a sacrifise for the cause of American science and though I may not succeed in rendering the Institution what it ought to be yet I shall at least deserve some credit for the attempt.[92]

With his rejection of Hare's chair, it became clear to all, including Henry's supporters and opponents, that he would be staying.

*   *   *   *   *

Given Henry's preoccupations, it is not surprising that his efforts as a researcher during these three years were limited. In 1847 he conducted some experiments to test the conclusions of Count Rumford of nearly a half-century earlier regarding the role of non-combustibles in increasing the heat output of a fire. Add to that some observations on optics and others on lightning and you have the sum of Henry's work. His scientific publications for the period consist of abstracts of papers he presented at the meeting of the Association of American Geologists and Naturalists in 1847, and before the American Philosophical Society in 1847 and 1849, and comments made at meetings of the American Association for the Advancement of Science in 1848 and 1849.[93] In many ways, the documents in this volume foreshadow Henry's future as a research scientist. Applied research, often in the service of his government, would increasingly take precedence over the basic research and almost random observations which were so characteristic of his research efforts in the early 1840s.

Although his own research was limited, Henry continued to be in demand as a consultant or expert witness, largely by virtue of his expertise in applied electricity. Vice-President George M. Dallas, for example, asked him whether James Crutchett's plan for illuminating the Capitol Building and grounds by a gaslight mounted atop the dome made the building more vulnerable to lightning. When some prominent Philadelphians became concerned that Independence Hall was not adequately protected from lightning, they consulted Henry. The commissioner of the Patent Office called on him to evaluate the originality of an application of electro-chemistry, specifically whether the addition of Glauber's salt to the sulfuric acid in a galvanic battery was a patentable improvement. Much more surprising was an appeal by a doctor, a former student, for help in microscopic analysis of evidence in a Baltimore rape trial.

Commercial parties were also interested in Henry's expertise, or at least his endorsement. An old friend from Albany seeking a government contract wrote for an evaluation of a substance to replace marble in public buildings. A former neighbor from Princeton sought an endorsement from Henry, to be used in advertising, for a process of insulating telegraph wires, offering that if "we effect A Contract, I Shall feel bound for this and past favors to Send you by Mail A one hundred dollar bill."[94] Henry indignantly rejected the proposed bribe.

Less troublesome ethically—but in the long run much more annoying—was Henry's involvement in patent cases concerning S. F. B. Morse's telegraph. In 1842, Henry credited Morse with inventing a very effective and practical form of the electromagnetic telegraph.[95] He repeatedly contended, however, that Morse should not be granted patent rights for all forms of the electromagnetic telegraph. In particular Henry had stated that neither the telegraphs invented by Alexander Bain nor the one by Royal E. House violated Morse's patents. By the late 1840s the relationship between Henry and Morse was hostile, fueled by their differing views on the roles each had played in the development of the telegraph. In defending his patents, Morse was defending his livelihood. Henry was affirming something less tangible, but no less important: his scientific reputation and place in history. Yet despite his eagerness to have full recognition of his contributions to the science and to the development of the invention, Henry claimed a reluctance to become involved in a public dispute with Morse, writing Gray that "I gave my testimony in the telegraph case [*Morse* v. *O'Reilly*] unwillingly and as I stated in the introduction only in obedience with the authority of the law."[96]

* * * * *

Henry's correspondence during this period grew dynamically in volume and broadened both in its range of correspondents and in its subject matter. Because Henry and his wife were separated a great deal in the early years of the Smithsonian, particularly in 1847, we also have more of the candid, soul-searching letters which he wrote to his wife in such circumstances.

Henry's correspondence with his wife is essential to our understanding of his early tenure as secretary of the Smithsonian. These letters are useful in two ways. Often, they supply the only surviving account of Henry's activities. Second, they are a singular window into his private thoughts and feelings regarding his public life and into his decision-making process. (His surviving desk diaries, which begin in 1849, record meetings and correspondence but only rarely his private thoughts and plans.) Because we lack Harriet's side of the correspondence, we do not know if Henry was simply using these letters to think out loud or using her as a sounding board and advisor. On at least one occasion, however—the dispute over the terms of the contract for the Smithsonian Building in March 1847—Henry consulted with Harriet and proceeded to take an aggressive position upon her advice and with her "concurrence."[97]

In addition to insights into Henry's professional life, the correspondence with Harriet also includes philosophical musings, declarations of love, and unique accounts of their relationship, at least from the husband's perspective. Lonely and under tremendous pressure in Washington, Henry needed to reveal his thoughts to Harriet:

> I cannot refrain from scribbeling a few lines to you though I have nothing to say. . . . I have been scribling near an hour and can scarcely recollet without an effort what I have written. I can however assure you that my pen has only served to give expression to the genuine feelins of my heart though as you know my fingers are not adequate to the task of expressing as much as I feel.[98]

He also had to release some of his guilt. Like many men before and after, he acknowledged that obligations outside the home had preoccupied him, leaving Harriet with the responsibility for raising the children. He recognized that the lot of a woman was not necessarily a happy one, even in a middle-class marriage where the wife was loved and respected and experienced no real material want.

These private letters also make it clear that one of Henry's sources of strength during the vicissitudes of these years was his acceptance of one's fate or destiny. Whether confronting opposing forces on the Board of Regents, a cholera epidemic, or the news that his sister-in-law had died, Henry consistently acknowledged the uncertainty of life and the inability of humans to predict events:

> but every think in life is uncertain, and when we think we are standing on the firmest earth the hiden fire may be burning beneath us. The sailor boy on the bending mast often lives through the storm while the landsman in fancied security is crushd with his falling house.[99]

Nevertheless, he was certain the universe ran according to a plan: "Well all things are ordered by a Power which controlls events and over rules them for good to those who put their trust in Him."[100]

Of course, Henry had a wide range of correspondents beyond Harriet. When he wrote, he was filling one of two very different roles, and the correspondence reflects those differences. To some, he wrote as Secretary Henry, an official of the Smithsonian writing on official issues. These letters were often formal, sometimes with each word weighed carefully. To old friends or colleagues, he could be less careful about phrasing and possible implications. As Henry noted in a letter to Gray, "I may however write to you with less care than to others and consequently with less expense of time."[101]

Among his old friends from his Princeton or Albany days, Bache was his most important correspondent. When Henry was at Princeton or Bache at a Coast Survey field station, they wrote each other long, candid letters giving and seeking advice, support, and sympathy. Bache and Henry held powerful institutional positions in American science, forming what Robert V. Bruce has called "the most potent duumvirate in government science,"[102] and were poised to institute reforms in that enterprise. Responsible for Henry's election, Bache continued to support him with advice and maneuvering on the Board of Regents. Henry, in turn, learned the ways of Washington from Bache, listened to his laments about "such storms as howl about these high places,"[103] and produced heartfelt arguments about the merits of the Coast Survey whenever necessary.

The other familiar names among Henry's correspondents are Gray of Harvard, probably Henry's closest professional advisor next to Bache, John Torrey, Loomis, Benjamin Silliman, Sr., and Espy. Among the new correspondents are regents, cabinet officers, politicians, and various members of the general public. A number of important figures in American science also appear as correspondents for the first time in this volume, including Agassiz, Matthew Fontaine Maury, and Spencer Fullerton Baird.

One of the more interesting of Henry's new correspondents was George P. Marsh, a lawyer, scholar, and representative from Vermont who became a regent in late 1847. Although Marsh had advocated using the Smithson bequest for a library during the congressional debates prior to the founding of the Smithsonian, Henry came to consider him, according to Jewett, "one of his most trustworthy & judicious advisors."[104] Marsh played the matchmaker for Henry and Squier and not only mediated when they disagreed, but even proofread the volume. In an unusual transaction, Henry used Smithsonian funds to help Marsh recover from business losses by agreeing to buy part of Marsh's fine arts library, thereby giving Marsh enough money to leave the country when he was named minister to Turkey in 1849. Remembered as a forefather of the conservation movement in this country, Marsh was a mentor to both Jewett and Baird and in fact introduced Baird to Henry.[105]

Of Henry's new correspondents, it was Baird who was the most important for the long-term development of the Smithsonian. He first appeared in the late winter of 1847 as an applicant for the position of curator, armed with letters of support from a number of American naturalists, including James Dwight Dana, John James Audubon, and Gray. By 1848, he had become one of the scientists Henry supported with small research grants. A year later, Henry maneuvered to ensure that Baird received the appointment as "naturalist to the Institution," characterizing him as "an original investigator and not a mere curator of a museum."[106] In December 1849, Henry wrote Baird:

> I can assure you that it would give me much pleasure to nominate you to the office . . . . I have told you that you are my choice and if nothing occurs to change my opinion of your character of which I see not the slightest prospect I shall nominate you to the Board in due time. You most recollect howev (and I know you do) that in all the appointments I must be governed by what I conceive to be the best for the Institution. I shall know no friendship in the choise and if you are elected it will be because, all things considered you are the best man; you will therefore owe your election to your own reputation—though I shall nominate you with the understanding that you will assist in carrying out the plan of organization of the Institution set forth in the Programme.[107]

Introduction

As the next volume of *The Papers of Joseph Henry* will document, Henry hired Baird in 1850. In doing so he changed the future course of the Smithsonian. Ultimately, his subordinate and future successor would place the Smithsonian on a path much different from that chosen by Henry. Disciplinary balance and grants to individual scientists would gradually give way to an emphasis on natural history and museum exhibitions. Ironically, Henry planted the seeds of the destruction of his dream.

* * * * *

The staff of the Joseph Henry Papers Project has relied upon the assistance of many others to produce this volume. The Joint Committee of the Sponsoring Institutions has provided consistent support and welcome guidance. The Richard Lounsbery Foundation provided valuable financial support, as did the Ida Hornstein Reingold Memorial Fund. The members of our Editorial Advisory Board read our manuscript and raised many issues which improved the final product immensely. Many colleagues in the Smithsonian Institution helped in the day-to-day operation of the project. In particular, we are indebted to the staffs of the Office of the Assistant Secretary for Science, the Office of the Assistant Secretary for Arts and Humanities, the Smithsonian Institution Libraries, and the Office of Information Resource Management. Special thanks go to the staff of the Office of Smithsonian Institution Archives, which provides us with an administrative home in the Division of Institutional History. The leadership and support of Pamela M. Henson, the director of the division, has been invaluable and indispensable. Thank you!

During the editing of this volume we have called upon numerous archivists, librarians, historians, and curators throughout the world for assistance. In some cases we have acknowledged their assistance in our annotations. But whether explicitly recognized or not, the help of these colleagues has been invaluable. A project such as this could not hope to succeed without it. In particular, we wish to express our gratitude to the holders of the originals of the documents published in this volume:

> Academy of Natural Sciences of Philadelphia
> Adams Papers, Massachusetts Historical Society
> American Antiquarian Society
> American Philosophical Society
> Bailey-Howe Library, University of Vermont

Beinecke Rare Book and Manuscript Library, Yale University
John Carter Brown Library at Brown University
Carl E. Coy, Sr.
Wesley A. Crozier
Milton S. Eisenhower Library, Johns Hopkins University
Gray Herbarium Library, Harvard University
Houghton Library, Harvard University
Hunt Institute for Botanical Documentation, Carnegie Mellon University
Huntington Library
Library of Congress
F. K. Mitchel
National Archives and Records Administration
New York Botanical Garden Library
New-York Historical Society
New York State Archives
Penfield Library, State University of New York at Oswego
Princeton University Libraries
Public Record Office, London
Royal Greenwich Observatory
Royal Society of London
Smithsonian Institution Archives
University of Michigan Library
University of Pennsylvania Libraries
Yale University Library

We benefitted greatly from the skill of our temporary research assistant, Joel C. Hodson, and are grateful as always for the careful deciphering over the years of our volunteer transcribers. We are also in debt to the following students for their various contributions while they were interns with us: Heather N. Dean, David Diamond, Eliza D. Hetherington, and Silvia L. Simpson.

---

1. See *Henry Papers*, 6:463–471.
2. For Henry's initial ideas about the Smithsonian, see *Henry Papers*, 6:493–503.
3. Doc. 54.
4. *Henry Papers*, 6:497.
5. *Henry Papers*, 6:624.
6. Doc. 63.
7. Doc. 312.
8. *Henry Papers*, 6:624.
9. Doc. 11.
10. See *Henry Papers*, 6:557n–558n.

11. Rhees, *Journals*, p. 26.
12. "Joseph Henry's Conception of the Purpose of the Smithsonian Institution," in *A Cabinet of Curiosities: Five Episodes in the Evolution of American Museums*, ed. Walter M. Whitehill (Charlottesville, 1967), pp. 163–165.
13. Doc. 177.
14. *Smithsonian Report for 1847*, p. 172.
15. Doc. 130.
16. Doc. 234.
17. Doc. 306.

18. Doc. 307.

19. Bruce, *American Science*, pp. 199–200 (quotations on p. 200).

20. Doc. 115.

21. Doc. 142.

22. Doc. 182.

23. "Programme of Organization," "Section I," part II, paragraph 4.

24. *Henry Papers*, 6:496.

25. *Henry Papers*, 1:435–436.

26. For a summary of the arguments in favor of Smithsonian involvement, see Elias Loomis's letter to Henry, printed as Appendix No. 2 in *Smithsonian Report for 1847*, pp. 193–207.

27. It appeared as *The Recent Progress of Astronomy; Especially in the United States* (New York, 1850).

28. See Doc. 318.

29. Charles C. Jewett, *Notices of Public Libraries in the United States* (Washington, 1851), pp. 139, 192.

30. *Smithsonian Report for 1849*, p. 19.

31. *Smithsonian Report for 1849*, p. 18.

32. Doc. 37.

33. *Henry Papers*, 6:624.

34. Doc. 277.

35. *Smithsonian Report for 1849*, p. 21.

36. Doc. 10.

37. Doc. 177.

38. Rhees, *Journals*, pp. 53, 490–491.

39. Doc. 322.

40. *Henry Papers*, 6:553–554.

41. Doc. 13.

42. Doc. 253.

43. Doc. 204.

44. Doc. 160.

45. E. G. Squier to Brantz Mayer, March 1, 1849, Gratz Collection, Historical Society of Pennsylvania.

46. E. G. Squier to George Perkins Marsh, March 1, 1849, Marsh Papers, Bailey/Howe Library, University of Vermont.

47. Rhees, *Journals*, p. 479.

48. *Report of the Organization Committee of the Smithsonian Institution* (Washington, 1847), p. 16.

49. *Smithsonian Report for 1849*, p. 21.

50. Rhees, *Documents* (1901), 1:444–463 (quotation on p. 444).

51. Rhees, *Documents* (1901), 1:471–477 (quotation on p. 474).

52. Rhees, *Documents* (1901), 1:511–591.

53. Rhees, *Documents* (1901), 1:128–129.

54. Memorial of the National Institute, November 14, 1848, signed by Peter Force et al., Petitions and Memorials Referred to the Committee on the Library, 31st Congress, Records of the United States Senate, RG 46, National Archives.

55. Rhees, *Documents* (1901), 1:471.

56. *Smithsonian Report for 1847*, p. 178.

57. Dupree, *Science in the Federal Government*, p. 86.

58. C. W. Hodge to Sarah Hodge, November 17, 1848, Charles Hodge Papers, Manuscripts Division, Department of Rare Books and Special Collections, Princeton University Libraries.

59. Doc. 267.

60. Doc. 39.

61. *Henry Papers*, 6:572.

62. *Henry Papers*, 6:577.

63. *Henry Papers*, 6:572.

64. *Henry Papers*, 6:617.

65. Doc. 49.

66. *Henry Papers*, 6:578.

67. *Henry Papers*, 6:578.

68. *Henry Papers*, 6:586.

69. *The American Almanac and Repository of Useful Knowledge for the Year 1853* (Boston, 1853), p. 210.

70. Michael J. Lacey, "The World of the Bureaus: Government and the Positivist Project in the Late Nineteenth Century," in *The State and Social Investigation in Britain and the United States*, ed. Lacey and Mary O. Furner (Cambridge, 1993), p. 128.

71. Leonard D. White, *The Jacksonians: A Study in Administrative History, 1829–1861* (New York, 1954), pp. 101–102, 302–307.

72. Doc. 93.

73. *Smithsonian Report for 1852*, p. 28.

74. Lacey, p. 128.

75. Doc. 193.

76. Doc. 228.

77. Doc. 253.

78. Robert V. Bruce, "A Statistical Profile of American Scientists, 1846–1876," in *Nineteenth-Century American Science: A Reappraisal*, ed. George H. Daniels (Evanston, Illinois, 1972), p. 80; Bruce, *American Science*, p. 50.

79. William H. Goetzmann, "Exploration and Early American Culture," *Proceedings of the American Antiquarian Society*, 1988, 2:225.

80. Bruce, "A Statistical Profile of American Scientists, 1846–1876," pp. 80, 91, 94; Bruce, *American Science*, p. 50.

81. Bruce, *American Science*, p. 343.

82. Doc. 16.

83. Doc. 51.

84. Doc. 16.

85. Doc. 16.

86. Doc. 49.

87. Doc. 81.

88. Doc. 59.

89. Doc. 66.

90. Doc. 49.

91. Doc. 72.

92. Doc. 72.

93. The abstract of the 1847 presentation to the American Association for the Advancement of Science appeared under the title "On Heat," in *Silliman's Journal*, 1848, 2d ser. 5:113–114.

For the presentations to the American Philosophical Society, see APS *Proceedings*, 1843–1847, *4*:370, and 1848–1853, *5*:108. Henry's comments upon the papers of others appear in AAAS *Proceedings*, 1848, *1*:94; 1849, *2*:11–12, 18, 105, 127–128, 220, 374–376, 377.

94. Doc. 298.

95. *Henry Papers*, *5*:151.

96. Doc. 332.

97. Doc. 25.

98. Doc. 49.

99. Doc. 15.

100. Doc. 13.

101. Doc. 177.

102. Bruce, *American Science*, p. 170.

103. Doc. 117.

104. Doc. 217.

105. E. F. Rivinus and E. M. Youssef, *Spencer Baird of the Smithsonian* (Washington, 1992), p. 42.

106. Doc. 324.

107. Doc. 351.

Selection of Documents

The Papers of Joseph Henry is a highly selective edition. The fifteen volumes projected will include less than five percent of the approximately one hundred thousand Henry documents the editors expect to identify. The percentage selected for publication will vary from volume to volume, but will in general be less for volumes documenting Henry's last dozen years when the surviving documentation is greater. This is partly a function of Henry's greater public role later in life. It is also, however, the direct result of the fire in the Smithsonian Building on January 24, 1865, which destroyed most of the official Smithsonian correspondence to that date, as well as some of Henry's private correspondence and scientific notes. Over eighty-five thousand pages of correspondence were lost.

In this volume, we are printing 12.3 percent of the 2,898 documents datable to the years 1847–1849 written by, to, or about Henry which we have located. In deciding what documents to publish, the editors used general criteria rather than specific rules. Because we are documenting the life of Henry, rather than the history of American science in the mid-nineteenth century or the history of the Smithsonian Institution, we have selected the documents which throw the most light on Henry's private life and his professional career. In doing so, however, we publish documents which explicate central issues in the development of the Smithsonian and the institutional framework of American science more generally. Of highest priority are documents which Henry authored. Incoming correspondence is included when it is essential for understanding the context of Henry's letters. We include third party letters if, and only if, they throw unique light on Henry.

Copies of all unselected documents may be consulted, by appointment, in the office of the Joseph Henry Papers Project, Office of Smithsonian Institution Archives, Smithsonian Institution.

Organization

Documents are given in chronological order and numbered consecutively. If a specific date is not given or is not ascribable, the document is placed at an appropriate place within the chronology, as determined by internal evidence from the document (for example, the dates of events mentioned in the letter) or from the date of related correspondence (the incoming letter or response, whichever is appropriate).

Preliminaries to the Documents

Each document is preceded by a document number and a heading. In the case of correspondence, the heading indicates the author and recipient. If a letter is to or from Henry, we only give the other correspondent's name. For example:

TO BENJAMIN SILLIMAN, SR.

If Henry is neither the author nor the recipient, both correspondents are specified. In the case of noncorrespondence, we use the title given on the original. If there is no title, or if the given title is noncommunicative, the editors will devise a title.

In a few instances we will provide a headnote immediately after the date. A headnote serves either to introduce a document or group of documents, or to stand instead of a document or group of documents when the document or documents in question are too lengthy for publication. In rare instances, a headnote may be used to discuss an event in Henry's life when there is no specific document to mark the occasion.

Copy Text

When multiple copies of a document are extant, we will print one version, and, with the exception of obvious copyist errors, report variations in text notes (see below). Our preferred copy text is an autograph signed copy. If that has not been located, our order of preference is a signed retained copy; unsigned retained copy; draft; Mary Henry Copy (see explanation, below, under *Text*); printed copy.

Date and Place

In correspondence, the date and place are situated at the top, right-hand side preceding the body of the text, in block format, regardless of location or format in the original. Dates in non-correspondence items will generally be retained in their original locations. If the date has been moved from another location in the letter, a text note will indicate the original location. Missing dates are supplied in brackets, with a text note explanation.

If not given, places of composition may be supplied in brackets and discussed in an editorial note.

Notes on Style

The Henry Papers utilizes the "expanded transcription" method. Some changes, specified below, are made silently in the interest of clarity. Otherwise, we either retain original spelling, punctuation, capitalization, grammar, and paragraph division, or report any changes in text notes.

We do not try to duplicate the original word-spacing, line-division (except in openings, inside addresses, and closings) or format. All complimentary openings and inside addresses are placed at the left margin. All paragraphs are indented, except for numbered paragraphs, which begin at the left margin. Where an author has not provided terminal punctuation for a sentence, but a sentence is clearly indicated (for example, the text ends with a gap and is followed by a capitalized letter), we silently supply a period. Author's square brackets will be silently changed to parentheses to prevent confusion with square brackets added by the editors. Catch-words at the turn of a page, author's page numbers (and other words such as "over" that refer to the physical layout of the page), and non-contemporary annotations to the manuscript are silently deleted. Hastily written words whose ends dribble off to illegibility are expanded to full, correct endings without any editorial comment.

Our transcription conventions include:

~~strikeouts~~	author's deletion
[---]	illegible author's deletion; unless otherwise noted, one or two words
[?~~strikeout~~]	conjectured author's deletion
↑added words↓	author's interlineations and other additions: material added at beginning or ending of lines, words squeezed in between existing words, or words moved by caret
[word or letter]	editorial insertion because of lost material or material omitted by author
[?word]	conjectured words or parts of words
[...]	missing material due to physical deterioration of manuscript, illegibility of undeleted matter, or blank left in manuscript by author; unless otherwise noted, one or two words

All legible, contemporary alterations of the text in which letters or words have been written over by other letters or words will be signaled by a text note, with the original version given in the note. If the original letters or words are illegible, they will be silently ignored.

Mary Henry, one of Henry's daughters, gathered a large collection of documents after Henry's death in anticipation of writing a biography of her father. She transcribed a number of letters or portions of letters, and sometimes discarded the originals. From surviving originals, we know that these transcriptions are sometimes inaccurate and that she often edited the language to conform with later standards of spelling, punctuation, and capitalization. In cases where only the Mary Henry Copy survives but the letter meets our standards of selection, we will use her transcription, signaling it in the provenance note as "Mary Henry Copy." We resolve textual uncertainties in her transcriptions by opting for modern usage.

Foreign language documents will be published in the original language, except when we have evidence that Henry read a translation rather than the original, and that translation is extant. In such cases, we will publish the translation and not the original document. When in doubt, we will publish the original and include the translation in the volume's appendix.

Illustrations

Illustrations within documents have been photographically reproduced, with varying reductions in size, from the originals.

Closing Material

Closing sentiments and signature are printed as a block, preserving the order and line division of the words.

Provenance Note

This is the first unnumbered note immediately following the text and briefly gives the type of document, if other than an autograph letter or autograph letter signed, and the location of the original.

General Text Note

This is an unnumbered note which follows the provenance note. It includes general comments on any unusual physical characteristics of the original; information on the existence and location of other copies (other than Mary Henry Copies) or drafts and on any previous publication (including microform) known to the editors; identification of the handwriting, if not that of the author; file notations and indications of date of receipt or transmittal to another person or agency, if important to the understanding of the document; information on a reply if any is known; and other information dealing with the document as a whole.

Editorial Notes

Editorial notes follow the general text note. They are numbered consecutively within each document.

Text Notes

Text notes are indicated by superscript capital letters, alphabetically within each document, with duplication within a document where appropriate. They are used to signal, and sometimes to explain, author's alterations or overt editorial emendations of the text or to discuss specific physical characteristics of the paper and ink. Included in the text notes are indications of the movement of a date from another location in the document; explanations for a supplied date; the original text when there have been alterations by either the author or an amanuensis; descriptions of specific damage to the paper, such as a hole or tear; contemporary annotations; and notations of punctuation added by the editors.

In reporting author's alterations, we do not distinguish between alterations of a letter or letters and the imposition of one or more letters over other letters. Nor do we indicate which specific letter or letters were altered or written over. All changes by the author are signaled in the same way. In all cases, the phrase "Altered from" in a text note indicates an author's alteration *from* whatever follows that phrase *to* what appears in the text. Most forms of alterations are corrections of misspellings, false starts, and capitalization. For example, the following hypothetical line:

He copied passages[A] from his[B] Lady's Swedish[C] textbook.

would be reported as follows:

A. Altered from *paggases*

B. Altered from *L*

C. Altered from *swedish*

This can be reconstructed to indicate that the author initially wrote "paggases" and corrected it to "passages"; began to write "from Lady" but altered the initial "L" in the second word to an "h" and wrote "his" instead; and first wrote "Swedish" as "swedish".

The text notes appear at the end of the book, preceding the index.

AAAS *Proceedings*	*Proceedings of the American Association for the Advancement of Science.*
APS *Proceedings*	*Proceedings of the American Philosophical Society.*
BDAC	*Biographical Directory of the American Congress, 1774–1949* (Washington, 1950).
British Association Report for . . .	*Report of the . . . Meeting of the British Association for the Advancement of Science . . .* (London, 1833–).
Bruce, *American Science*	Robert V. Bruce, *The Launching of Modern American Science, 1846–1876* (1987; Ithaca, 1988).
Coast Survey Report for 1847	U.S. Senate, 30th Congress, 1st Session, *Report of the Superintendent of the Coast Survey, Showing the Progress of the Work during the Year Ending October, 1847,* Senate Executive Documents, No. 6 (1847).
Coast Survey Report for 1848	U.S. Senate, 30th Congress, 2d Session, *Report of the Superintendent of the Coast Survey, Showing the Progress of the Work for the Year Ending November 13, 1848,* Senate Executive Documents, No. 1 (1848).
Coast Survey Report for 1849	U.S. Senate, 31st Congress, 1st Session, *Report of the Superintendent of the Coast Survey, Showing the Progress of the Work for the Year Ending November, 1849,* Senate Executive Documents, No. 5 (1849).
DAB	*Dictionary of American Biography.*
Desk Diary	A set of thirteen manuscript volumes in Boxes 14 and 15 of the Henry Papers, Smithsonian Archives.
DNB	*Dictionary of National Biography.*
DSB	*Dictionary of Scientific Biography.*
Dupree, *Gray*	A. Hunter Dupree, *Asa Gray, 1810–1888* (1959; New York, 1968).
Dupree, *Science in the Federal Government*	A. Hunter Dupree, *Science in the Federal Government: A History of Policies and Activities to 1940* (1957; New York, 1980).

Elliott, *Dictionary*

Clark A. Elliott, *Biographical Dictionary of American Science: The Seventeenth through the Nineteenth Centuries* (Westport, Connecticut, 1979).

Elliott, *Index*

Clark A. Elliott, compiler, *Biographical Index to American Science: The Seventeenth Century to 1920* (Westport, Connecticut, 1990).

Fleming, *Meteorology*

James Rodger Fleming, *Meteorology in America, 1800–1870* (Baltimore, 1990).

Goode, *Smithsonian*

George Brown Goode, editor, *The Smithsonian Institution, 1846–1896: The History of Its First Half Century* (Washington, 1897).

Hageman, *Princeton*

John F. Hageman, *History of Princeton and Its Institutions,* 2d ed., 2 vols. (Philadelphia, 1879).

Henry Papers

Nathan Reingold et al., editors, *The Papers of Joseph Henry,* vols. 1–5 (Washington, 1972–1985).

Marc Rothenberg et al., editors, *The Papers of Joseph Henry,* vols. 6– (Washington, 1992–   ).

Henry Pocket Notebook

Designates one of a set of small manuscript notebooks in Box 13 of the Henry Papers, Smithsonian Archives. Each notebook is referred to by the number assigned to it in the project's document control system.

Henry Pocket Notebook [13272]
   Date: archival label "Circa. 1847" on spine
   Size: 6.8 × 10.5 cm
   First line: "Bagleys Steel pens"

Henry Pocket Notebook [13279]
   Date: archival label "Circa. 1848" on spine
   Size: 8 × 12 cm
   First line: "Rev. Charles P Russell Washington DC"

King, *Electrical Technology*

W. James King, *The Development of Electrical Technology in the 19th Century: 1. The Electrochemical Cell and the Electromagnet; 2. The Telegraph and the Telephone; 3. The Early Arc Light and Generator,* 1962, Bulletin of the United States National Museum, no. 228, pp. 231–271, 273–332, 333–407.

Kohlstedt, *AAAS*

Sally Gregory Kohlstedt, *The Formation of the American Scientific Community: The American Association for the Advancement of Science, 1848–60* (Urbana, Illinois, 1976).

National Union Catalog

The National Union Catalog, Pre-1956 Imprints, 754 vols. (London, 1968–1981).

Phil. Trans.	*Philosophical Transactions of the Royal Society of London.*
Poggendorff	J. C. Poggendorff, compiler, *Biographisch-Literarisches Handwörterbuch zur Geschichte der Exacten Wissenschaften.*
Princeton Catalogue	*General Catalogue of Princeton University, 1746–1906* (Princeton, 1908).
"Record of Experiments"	Henry's three-volume laboratory notebook in Box 21, Henry Papers, Smithsonian Archives.
Rhees, *Documents* (1879)	William J. Rhees, editor, *The Smithsonian Institution: Documents Relative to Its Origin and History,* 1879, Smithsonian Miscellaneous Collections, vol. 17 (Washington, 1880).
Rhees, *Documents* (1901)	William Jones Rhees, compiler and editor, *The Smithsonian Institution: Documents Relative to Its Origin and History,* 2 vols., 1901, Smithsonian Miscellaneous Collections, vols. 42 and 43 (Washington, 1901).
Rhees, *Journals*	William J. Rhees, editor, *The Smithsonian Institution: Journals of the Board of Regents, Reports of Committees, Statistics, Etc.,* 1879, Smithsonian Miscellaneous Collections, vol. 18 (Washington, 1880).
SI Contributions	Smithsonian Contributions to Knowledge.
Silliman's Journal	*American Journal of Science and Arts.*
Smithsonian Daybooks	Daybooks, Box 110, Smithsonian Institution Fiscal Records, Private, 1846–1859, RU 100, Smithsonian Archives.
Smithsonian Report for . . .	*Annual Report of the Board of Regents of the Smithsonian Institution* (Washington, 1847–). The short title refers to the year covered by the report (e.g., *Smithsonian Report for 1855*). The only exception is the first report, which consists of the journal of proceedings of the regents from September 7, 1846, through March 1, 1847, but is cited as *Smithsonian Report for 1846.*
Squier and Davis	E. G. Squier and E. H. Davis, *Ancient Monuments of the Mississippi Valley: Comprising the Results of Extensive Original Surveys and Explorations,* 1848, Smithsonian Contributions to Knowledge, vol. 1 (Washington, 1848).
U.S. Statutes at Large	*Statutes at Large of the United States of America, 1789–1873,* 17 vols. (Washington, 1850–1873) and *United States Statutes at Large* (1874–).

THE PAPERS OF JOSEPH HENRY

1. FROM LOUIS AGASSIZ[1]

Cambridge the 2 Jan. 1847.[A]

Prof. Henry in Washington
My dear Sir,

As I happen to be in Cambridge at the receipt[B] of a letter from D[r] Torrey[2] explaining to D[r] Gray[3] your views about the Smithsonian Institute[4] I can not help writing a few lines to you to congratulate you and your country upon the prospect of a well established national scientific Institute. I think your view of printing Transactions of approved, valuable memoirs is especially important, as nothing will put the Institute on a higher level among scientific men, than such a publication, which will undoubtedly rise ↑raise↓ it more in the estimation of foreigners than any palace in which it could be established. Besides the publication of such transactions would at once supply you with the most convenient means for securing the published Transactions of all scientific societies in Europe;[5] and I have little doubt that the value of the Memoirs you will receive in exchange ↑for↓ of yours will partly repay the expense of printing and engraving your illustrations. Annual Reports of the state of things in science and arts I consider also as of first rate importance; but they should be printed in a more pocketable form, then the original Transactions, which necessarely require the 4° forme on account of the plates. I know too well the deficiencies and advantages of our european scientific institutions (as) not to consider with you helping scientific men in their original researches, where they can make no money by them, as a duty ↑of↓ to any liberal government or large scientific Institution;[6] but there is a difficulty in doing it by permanent appointments of the men. The best plan is to help them as long they are at work, but not give them sinecures for doing nothing.[7] The case is quite different with teachers, who have their every day's business to perform and must be permanent in their position.

I understand that you do not wish to have the charge of Natural history specime[n]s and such things. Pray let me insist upon the necessity of having them. I have seen the Collection of the Expl. Exp. and I can testify that I have seen no where larger and better collections arising from a single Journey round the world.[8] The naturalists of that expedition who have had the charge of making these collections deserve the greatest credit; especially two[C] departments stand above all praise.[9] Now I consider that it would be very creditable to Your Institution if these collections where properly arranged according the actual state

3

of our knowledge,[10] ↑which↓ what is nowhere the case in our ancient Museums, which have been successively enlarged, without being ever rearranged and adapted to the newer views of the subject.[11]

As You contemplate also the introduction of a large library, let me remind you of the difficulties I have seen ↑arising↓[D] everywhere with us, from the mere fact that they attempted to unite ↑the books of↓[D] all departments in one library. Incessant quarrels about the increase of this or that branch are unavoidable; whilst limiting yourself to Sciences and arts you could at once establish your library on the most respectable footing, by having from the beginning every thing which is published in these[E] departments and leaving for the future to supply the books of past times and of mere historical value.[12]

Excuse my liberty in adressing you so freely upon a subject upon which my opinion has not been asked; but I feel so much interest in the prospect of a truly scientific national Institute, established in a contry where every[F] thing is done in a highly liberal way, that I thought it allowed to one who has spend his whole live in the devotion to science, to introduce a few remarks upon the subject.

> Beleive me,
> My dear Sir,
> most sincerely Yours
> J L Agassiz

Henry Papers, Smithsonian Archives.
Enclosed in Doc. 2. Interlineations and parentheses, possibly written by someone other than Agassiz, are in pencil except as noted.

1. An eminent Swiss-born naturalist, Agassiz was currently delivering a course of lectures at Boston's Lowell Institute. He was soon to become professor of natural history at Harvard University's Lawrence Scientific School. *Henry Papers*, 6:530n.

2. Professor of chemistry and botany at the New York College of Physicians and Surgeons, and professor of chemistry and natural history at Princeton, John Torrey was one of Henry's closest friends. *Henry Papers*, 1:159n.

3. Asa Gray, Fisher Professor of Natural History at Harvard, was another of Henry's close friends. *Henry Papers*, 2:281n.

4. While Torrey's letter has not been found, its summary of Henry's plans presumably resembled that which Henry had provided in other recent letters, such as those to Gideon Hawley and James H. Coffin; see *Henry Papers*, 6:610–615 and 623–625.

5. As early as 1694, the Royal Library of France began trading duplicate volumes for foreign materials; other European libraries and, after 1846, the Library of Congress, also relied on international exchanges to build up their holdings. Leading learned societies adopted a similar approach, exchanging their transactions with other societies. In the United States, the American Philosophical Society, the American Academy of Arts and Sciences, and the Academy of Natural Sciences of Philadelphia all sent their transactions to foreign societies.

An international exchange of the Smithsonian's publications did not figure in Henry's earliest ideas for the Smithsonian (for which see *Henry Papers*, 6:493–501, 607–609, 611–619, 623–625). However, it was included—perhaps owing to Agassiz's prompting—in the revised report issued by the committee of organization and approved by the Board of Regents on January 25, 1847, which formed the basis for Henry's "Programme of Organization."

George H. Boehmer, "History of the Smithsonian Exchanges," *Smithsonian Report for 1881*, pp. 703–810, especially pp. 703–711; A. Hunter Dupree, "The National Pattern of American Learned Societies, 1769–1863," in *The Pursuit of Knowledge in the Early American Republic*, ed. Alexandra Oleson and Sanborn C. Brown (Baltimore, 1976), p. 24; Patsy A. Gerstner, "The Academy of Natural Sciences of Philadelphia, 1812–1850," in Oleson and Brown, pp. 178–179; Murphy D. Smith, *Oak from an Acorn: A History of the American Philosophical Society Library, 1770–1803* (Wilmington, Delaware, 1976), pp. 12–13, 36–39, 42–43; Rhees, *Documents* (1879), p. 939; Rhees, *Documents* (1901), p. 434.

6. Agassiz spoke from personal experience on the value of financial assistance for those engaged in original research. While at work on his *Recherches sur les poissons fossiles* (Neuchâtel, 1833–1844), he received support from scientific institutions, governments, and private individuals, including some £240 from the Geological Society of London and the British Association for the Advancement of Science, and several research grants from the Prussian government. Such assistance also enabled Agassiz to provide means for his personal artist, Joseph Dinkel, whom he had hired to make illustrations of specimens in museum collections. Edward Lurie, *Louis Agassiz: A Life in Science* (1960; Chicago, 1966), pp. 90–91.

7. In September 1846, in his earliest statement on the organization of the Smithsonian, Henry had proposed the creation of a corps of researchers, the elected members of which would receive support for their research from the institution. By December 1846 he had abandoned this idea, instead proposing that the institution would pay for original memoirs and award premiums to the authors of the best submissions. *Henry Papers*, 6:496–497, 613–614, 623–624.

8. Agassiz was referring to the voluminous natural history collections gathered by the United States Exploring Expedition, which, together with an assortment of other scientific, art, and ethnological specimens belonging to the government, were housed in a gallery of the Patent Office known as the "National Gallery." The act establishing the Smithsonian stated that these collections should be turned over to the institution after a building had been erected to contain them. Fearful that the expense of housing and caring for the collections would drain so much of the income from the Smithsonian fund that nothing would be left for other programs, Henry was deeply opposed to the plan of having the institution take charge

of them. See *Henry Papers*, 6:466–467, 471, 604, 608, 611–612.

9. During a visit to Washington in October 1846, Agassiz saw the exploring expedition collections at the Patent Office. Their richness impressed him; "in some departments," he wrote, "the collection at Washington surpasses in beauty and number of specimens all that I have seen." He singled out for particular praise the work done by the expedition's chief zoologist, Charles Pickering (*Henry Papers*, 3:106n), and its geologist, James Dwight Dana (*Henry Papers*, 3:126n). Elizabeth Cary Agassiz, *Louis Agassiz: His Life and Correspondence*, 2 vols. (Boston, 1885), 2:420–421 (quotation on p. 420).

10. Section 5 of the act establishing the Smithsonian had termed the collections at the Patent Office "the national cabinet of curiosities." This was an apt characterization. While some of the exploring expedition collections had been scientifically arranged—notably the small mammals and fishes—others, including the insects, birds, quadrupeds, and plants, were still awaiting arrangement. Section 6 of the act directed the Smithsonian to see that these collections were "arranged in such order, and so classed, as best [to] facilitate the examination and study of them." Douglas E. Evelyn, "The National Gallery at the Patent Office," in *Magnificent Voyagers: The U.S. Exploring Expedition, 1838–1842*, ed. Herman J. Viola and Carolyn Margolis (Washington, 1985), pp. 226–241, especially pp. 237, 239.

11. Agassiz's assessment was overly harsh. Curators at leading European museums who hoped to rearrange their collections confronted problems such as the weight of tradition, backlogs of existing specimens and the continual infusion of new accessions, and shortages of space. Still, some efforts were being made, particularly by enterprising curators who took advantage of opportunities as they arose. At the British Museum, for example, John Edward Gray (*Henry Papers*, 3:229n), since 1840 keeper of the zoological department, used the occasion of the removal of the collections to a new building in 1845 to make changes in their arrangement. Reflecting current interests in "the ancestry of living forms," Gray took fossil shells—formerly under the care of the mineralogical department—and arranged them in a series with contemporary specimens. Albert E. Gunther, *A Century of Zoology at the British Museum through the Lives of Two Keepers, 1815–1914* (Kent, England, 1975), pp. 98–100 (quotation on p. 100); Gunther, *The Founders of Science at the British Museum, 1753–1900* (Suffolk, England, 1980), pp. 83, 87–91.

After failing to convince Henry that the

Smithsonian should take custody of the exploring expedition collections, Agassiz adopted a new course: he began lobbying for the policies which he felt the institution should follow in collecting and arranging its own museum specimens. He urged the institution to pursue two approaches. First, it should assemble a large collection of living and fossil shells which could be used to study the influence of climate upon organisms during different eras. Second, it should assemble developmental series of common animals, such as the cat or the pig, from the embryo to the adult. "Taking care that such series be put up in the Smithsonian Institution," Agassiz wrote, "would at once give to the collections of that establishment the stamp of a true progressive scientific museum." "Communication from Professor Agassiz, Relative to the Formation of a Museum," *Smithsonian Report for 1849*, pp. 24–26 (quotation on p. 25).

12. Henry firmly rejected the idea that the Smithsonian bequest should be used to create a national library and instead favored using only a portion of the income to establish a small working library. See *Henry Papers*, 6:471, 498, 565n, 612, 624.

2. FROM ASA GRAY

Cambridge. January 4, 1847.[A]

My Dear Sir

On Saturday I had a letter[1] from our friend D[r]. Torrey which contained some account of your views on the plans proper to be pursued in regard to the Smithsonian Institute.

Let me say, hastily that I think they will in the highest degree approve themselves to the real men of science in the country & throughout the world. The idea of 'Memoirs accepted & published by the Smithsonian Institute' is admirable, and would do great good. So is that of Reports, like the German Jahresberichten.[2] It seems to me too that a general library is nearly an impossibility,—at least,[B] if attempted, it would aborb all your funds in the purchase & care of books and the erection of buildings;—while a special library of Science & Arts—taken in the most extensive meaning—is attainable, falls into your general plan well, and would be of real utility. I think you are wrong, however, if I understand you to go against a National Cabinet, or Museum. That you should have, and the Expl. Exped. Collections as the[C] nucleus.[D] But surely you may insist that the Government should not whelm you with a present, that will absorb all the income of your foundation to provide for and take care of. I think you would have a right to insist that the Government who impose upon you this charge should provide a building for their reception. You might then properly assume the curatorship, which would be well provided for by one or two such ~~subord~~ subordinates as Breckenridge[3] (who has now charge of the live plants) with a single well-qualified curator, like Pickering.

I read a part of D[r] T.' letter to Agassiz, who was with me when it came. His approval of those[E] views was so hearty that I asked him to put them on paper, which he did at once—in the form of the letter I enclose.[4] I thought the opinion of a person so highly qualified to give one on such a subject would be of some weight.[F]

I had a conversation with Pickering, who was much gratified when I told him that you would strenuously endeavor to prevent the absorption of large funds in buildings,—impoverishing yourselves with grandeur. (At Boston, we are experiencing the good effects of the late Mr. Lowell's wise provision on this subject.— A copy of his will, establishing the Lowell Institute, might be useful[G] to you—it could be had by application.)[5]

Pickering thought that, if you could stave off all appointments and all pledges or encouragements there to, you would do well, while a contrary course would soon swamp the whole. But I need not mention this, as I am sure that you have already formed a decided opinion on this subject. I shall take the liberty to confer with Prof. Peirce[6] in reference to your views, as far as expressed in Dr Torrey's letter. I am sure he will approve them as decidedly as I do.

On your return from Washi[ng]ton,[H] can you not make us a visit. When you can, come direc[t][H] to my house, where I need not say you will be a mos[t][H] welcome guest and confer a great favor by coming.

Yours ever
A Gray

Henry Papers, Smithsonian Archives.

1. Not found.

2. Gray may have had in mind Friedrich Link's *Jahresbericht über die Arbeiten für physiologische Botanik*, which he reviewed in 1844 for *Silliman's Journal* (47:205), praising its "almost indispensable summaries." Henry was familiar with other foreign-language reports of this kind, such as the *Jahres-Bericht über die Fortschritte der physischen Wissenschaften*, commenced in 1821 by Jöns Jacob Berzelius (*Henry Papers,* 2:189), which had carried notices of his own publications (see *Henry Papers,* 5:29, 133–134). Henry referred specifically to Berzelius's reports in the explanation of his "Programme of Organization," terming it "a desideratum in the English language" for the Smithsonian to publish its own series, "posting up all the discoveries in science from time to time, and giving a well digested account of all the important changes in the different branches of knowledge" (*Smithsonian Report for 1847,* p. 182). For his earlier thinking along this line, see *Henry Papers,* 6:499, 501, 614n.

3. William Dunlop Brackenridge (1810–1893), assistant botanist on the United States Exploring Expedition, and later author of its report on ferns, was now tending the botanical collections in a greenhouse near the Patent Office. Gray and other naturalists regarded him more as a gardener than a botanist. Elliott, *Dictionary;* Richard H. Eyde, "Expedition Botany: The Making of a New Profession"; Douglas E. Evelyn, "The National Gallery at the Patent Office," both in *Magnificent Voyagers: The U.S. Exploring Expedition, 1838–1842,* ed. Herman J. Viola and Carolyn Margolis (Washington, 1985), pp. 28, 33, 234, 236, 238.

4. Doc. 1.

5. Under the terms of his will, John Lowell, Jr., established a trust—amounting to some $250,000—to support a program of lectures. He clearly stipulated that none of this fund was to be expended on a building or for any other program that might detract from his intended purpose. See *Henry Papers,* 4:297.

6. Benjamin Peirce, Perkins Professor of Mathematics and Astronomy at Harvard University. *Henry Papers,* 5:306.

7

January 6, 1847

3. TO HARRIET HENRY

[January 6, 1847][A]
New York Wednesday
11 o'clock PM.

My dear H.

I have been much engaged all day in calling on persons and studying the plan which has been adopted by the Regents for the Smithsonian.[1] You may recollect that Bache[2] informed me that the plan of young Renwick[3] had been adopted with the direction that he should cut it down.[4] This plan will make a beautiful building the only objection is the cost. I fear with all the cutting down it will cost nearly 200 thousand—I may perhaps succeed in getting it down to 170.[5] I visited with young Renwick Grace church which he has just finished this is the most beautiful sample of the Gothic[B] I have seen in this country.[6] The remainder of the day was spent with Dr Torrey Mr Redfield[7] and Prof Loomis[8]—the last two gentlemen have adopted my vews relative to the smithsonian very warmly— Mr Loomis is to give a paper for the first no. of the Proceedings or as they are to be called Smithsonian Contributions.[9] Also I have reason to beleive that Mr Galletan will ~~also~~ furnish a paper on on Ethnography[10]— I have not yet seen James Alexander[11] nor called on Mr Furness.[12] I purpose calling on these gentlemen tomorrow. I stopped at Stewards the candy makers[13] and have promised to meet Dr Torrey there at dinner tomorrow. I intend if I can get through with my engagements to s[t]art for home in the evening train.[14] If I should not arrive you need not however be uneasy as it is possible that I may not get away.

Kiss the children for me and believe that I remain as ever

Yours

Family Correspondence, Henry Papers, Smithsonian Archives.

1. Henry traveled to northern New Jersey and New York City "to confer with gentlemen of learning and intelligence on the practicability of the plans I had submitted" for the Smithsonian. While in New York he also attended a meeting of the New-York Historical Society. Henry to Harriet Henry, [January 5, 1847], Family Correspondence, Henry Papers, Smithsonian Archives; quotation from Henry's reminiscences, beginning "By the advice of my friend Bache," n.d., n.p., Folder "Smithsonian Institution Miscellaneous Notes and Papers," Box 30, Henry Papers, Smithsonian Archives.

2. Alexander Dallas Bache, superintendent of the Coast Survey, a Smithsonian regent, and one of Henry's closest friends. *Henry Papers,* 2:108.

3. James Renwick, Jr. (1818–1895), the son of James Renwick, Sr. (*Henry Papers, 1:*59), professor of natural philosophy and experimental chemistry at New York's Columbia College, was a civil engineer and self-trained architect whose commissions included numerous churches and public buildings. His early designs—including those for the Smithsonian Institution Building—were marked by their use of the Gothic and Romanesque Revival styles. *DAB.*

4. At its meeting of November 30, 1846, the

building committee of the Board of Regents reported that it had selected two of the thirteen designs submitted for the Smithsonian Building. Both were Renwick's: one was Gothic, the other Norman. The building committee preferred the latter plan. The board filed the committee's report and did not take up the matter again until January 20, 1847.

The regents' minutes from November 30 through January 20 do not indicate that Renwick was directed to "cut down" his plan (that is, to trim it back from three stories to two). He may have been advised to do so, however, by the chairman of the building committee, Robert Dale Owen, representative from Indiana (*Henry Papers*, 6:465n, 470). On January 1, Owen told Isaiah Rogers, another architect who had submitted a plan, that the regents "had selected Mr. Renwick's plan and that he [Renwick] was going to set about revising his plan and reducing the thing to the sum proposed." Renwick's revised plan showed a somewhat less ornate, two-story building.

Rhees, *Journals*, pp. 7–21; *Henry Papers*, 6:607n; Kenneth Hafertepe, *America's Castle: The Evolution of the Smithsonian Building and Its Institution, 1840–1878* (Washington, 1984), pp. 18–21, 27–38, 47–57, 62–65 (quotation on p. 55); Cynthia R. Field, introduction to Robert Dale Owen, *Hints on Public Architecture* (1849; New York, 1978).

5. Henry's estimate of $200,000 was close to the amount stipulated for the Smithsonian Building, $205,050, under the contract which the building committee signed on March 20, 1847. Cost overruns put the actual expenditure at $313,753 as of 1855, the year in which the building was considered "finished." Rhees, *Journals*, pp. 626–627, 711.

6. This was the second Grace Episcopal Church, Renwick's first major commission. Begun in 1843, it was consecrated in March 1846. While some observers commented unfavorably upon the church's interior and steeple, most shared Henry's opinion. Hafertepe, pp. 32–34; William Rhinelander Stewart, *Grace Church and Old New York* (New York, 1924), pp. 156–165, 422, 426–427.

7. William C. Redfield, a New York City transportation engineer, was a pioneer in the development of American meteorology. *Henry Papers*, 2:456.

8. Elias Loomis, professor of mathematics and natural philosophy at New York University, was influential in the development not only of American meteorology, but also of American astronomy. *Henry Papers*, 3:362–363.

9. Loomis did not submit a memoir for the Smithsonian Contributions to Knowledge until the late 1850s. He did prepare a "Report on the Meteorology of the United States," which appeared in the *Smithsonian Report for 1847*, pp. 193–207 (see Doc. 41).

10. Swiss-born Abraham Alfonse Albert Gallatin (1761–1849) was near the end of a distinguished career that included service as a United States senator and representative from Pennsylvania, as secretary of the treasury under Thomas Jefferson, as minister to Russia, France, and England, and as president of the National Bank of New York. Gallatin's interest in ethnography led him, in the 1820s, to begin work on a theory to explain the differential development of Native American civilizations. His "Synopsis of the Indian Tribes of North America" appeared in the American Antiquarian Society *Transactions*, 1832, 2:1–422. In 1842 he helped found the American Ethnological Society and became its first president, holding the office until his death.

Gallatin was among the individuals in New York whom Henry called on to discuss his plans for the Smithsonian. As Henry later recalled, Gallatin endorsed his plans, terming them "the best he had heard," agreeing that the Smithsonian fund should not be expended "on books collections and other objects of a merely local tendancy." According to Henry, Gallatin

> also promised if his health would permit to prepare an article for the first no of the Transactions on the subject of the application of the Languages of some of the Indian tribes east and west of our continent.

Gallatin planned to edit and republish part of the report of Horatio Hale (1817–1896, *DAB*), an ethnologist on the United States Exploring Expedition, which dealt with the languages of Pacific Northwest tribes. His essay never became a Smithsonian Contribution, instead appearing as "Hale's Indians of North-West America, and Vocabularies of North America with an Introduction by Albert Gallatin," American Ethnological Society *Transactions*, 1848, 2:xxiii–clxxxviii, 1–130.

DAB; Robert E. Bieder, *Science Encounters the Indian, 1820–1880: The Early Years of American Ethnology* (Norman, Oklahoma, 1986), pp. 16–54; Jacob W. Gruber, "Horatio Hale and the Development of American Anthropology," APS *Proceedings*, 1967, 111:5–37, especially pp. 9–10; quotation from Henry, "By the advice of my friend Bache," cited above.

11. James Waddel Alexander, a Presbyterian clergyman and close friend of Henry's, since 1844 had served as pastor of the Duane Street Church in New York City. *Henry Papers*, 2:177; 6:337.

12. Possibly William P. Furniss (d. 1871), a Wall Street real-estate broker and one of the city's wealthiest residents. He may have been the father of Robert L. P. Furniss of New York City, who boarded with the Henrys during his freshman year at Princeton. *New York City Directory*, 1845; Moses Y. Beach, *Wealth and Biography of the Wealthy Citizens of New York City . . .*, 6th ed. (New York, 1845), p. 11; *Catalogue of the Officers and Students of the College of New Jersey, 1845–1846* (Princeton, 1846), p. 16.

13. Stewart & Bussing, a confectionery, made "steam refined loaf sugar candies of superior quality." *New York City Directory*, 1849–1850.

14. Henry returned to Princeton on January 7 or 8, leaving for Washington on January 9. Henry to Eben N. Horsford, January 8, 1847, Henry Papers, Smithsonian Archives.

4. TO HARRIET HENRY

[January 16–17, 1847][A]
Washington Saturday night
½ past 9 o'clock

My dear H.

I have just got settled in a very suny room in the St Charles Hotel[1] and before I go to bed I must devote a few moments to you. After due consultation it was concluded that it was best for me for the present to take lodgings at a Hotel rather ↑than↓ at ↑a↓ private house on account of the Persons I would be obliged to see until after the meeting of the board of Regents. The room I now occupy is much plasanter than the one I had at the other Hotel on my former visit.[2] I dined this afternoon at Mr. Bache's with Mr. Owen[3] and Mr Ingersol.[4] We had quite a pleasant[B] party and after dinner I remained with Bache until within a few mintes. I have very little news I have been so much engaged in lectioneering for the Smithsonian and with Mr. Owen in the preparation of his report to the Regents[5] that I have heard or seen but little. The Regents meet on Wednesday next when the important affair of the building will be descided. Such are the conditions of things that I fear it will be impossible for me to prevent a large expenditure in the way of a building. This must be the case unless the Smithsonian affair be returned to congress and there the fear of its friends is that instead of an amendment the whole matter will be thrown over board on account of the war.[6] The Regents are all, who are on the ground, in favour of my plans but they think themselves tied up relative to the building and hope that they will be able to get farther assistance from Congress since the act of this body obliges them to put up the building.

I have been so much occcupied that I have not had time before this evening to be home sick but I now feel that I would be much gratifed to have you and our little ones around me; not that your company would not have been a source of comfort and pleasure to me continually since we parted but I feel just now particularly in want of you.

I have been at Bache's continually since I came to Washington and have been treated by Mr and Mrs B with their usual hospitality and kindness. Also I have been treated by marked attention by almost every person with whom I have come into communication since I came to washington.

I am very anxious to hear from home it appears instead of five days since we parted[7] almost as many weeks— How did you get home and how did you find all the little ons and Poor Aunt Louisa.[8] Perhaps your letter has miscarried so that in your second you must recapitulate what you said in your first. The passage over the chesapeak has been stopped up with ice so that for several mails there has been no intelligence from the north an[d][C] to this I have attributed the long delay of y[our][C] letter. I have nothing new—you can lea[rn][C] more about Washington by looking at the papers than by residing in the city. I found to day in passing through the rotunda that the new picture of Vanderlin—the landing of Columbus had been put up in its pannel.[D] It is a very beautiful picture and leaves but one pannel of the rotunday unfilled.[9] It is I think one of the best of the group and with the exception of the landing of the pilgrims[10] the best. Among the many letters I have received lately is one from our old acquaintance Prof Jager dated Eatown[E] N.J. asking from me no less a favour than that of procuring for him the situation of a Foreign charge defair—the one to France on the whole he would prefer but if this cannot be had he will take the one to Belgium or some other place[11] very I am a man of much more consequence than I though of.[F]

Sunday evening 9 o'clock your letter of Friday[12] the first I have received has just come to hand. It has given me a melancholy pleasure. I am happy to learn that you had so pleasant a time in getting home— the faces of Mrs & Mr Green[13] must have given you pleasure indeed. Poor Louisa & Stephen how sad is their condition and yet their is much in their case to be thankful for. I am glad to learn that the children are all well. Tell Will that he must write to me and I will answer his letter.[14] Tell Mary that I would like to receive a communication from her new desk if for nothing else to see how well she can write from it. Let the letter contain a piece of paper with something on it from Helen and also from Puss.[15] I have attended Dr Smiths church[16] to day. I[G] went with Mr & Mrs Stansbury[17] who are my next door nabours their room and mine is only seperated by a partition. Mrs Stansbury is a very pleasant and apparently good woman and I sat in her room for some time after church to day. This letter will start early in the morning—I did not get it into the mail last night & hence it has remained until to night.

I shall go to bed very soon after taking this down to the letter bag but not until I have commended you and our dear little ones to the protection of that kind providence which has been so bountiful to us—which has caused us to rejoice while others have mourned. Adieu my dear little Wife and be assured that while life remains you & our dear little[H] ones will be the first & last objects of my affection.[1]

J–H–.

Family Correspondence, Henry Papers, Smithsonian Archives.

1. Located near the Capitol, this hotel was popular among members of the Senate and southern visitors. James Goode, *Capital Losses: A Cultural History of Washington's Destroyed Buildings* (Washington, 1979), pp. 164–165.

2. The National Hotel. *Henry Papers, 3:*134; *6:*591.

3. Robert Dale Owen.

4. Most likely Joseph Reed Ingersoll, representative from Pennsylvania from 1841 to 1849, and a trustee of the University of Pennsylvania. His brother, Charles Jared Ingersoll, was also a representative from Pennsylvania during the same period. *Henry Papers, 6:*19.

5. Owen's "Report of the Organization Committee of the Smithsonian Institution" was presented to the Board of Regents on January 25, 1847. This was a heavily revised version of the original report, presented to the regents on December 1, 1846, which, along with several resolutions introduced at the meeting of December 4, had been referred back to the committee of organization on December 21 (see *Henry Papers, 6:*557n–558n). While the revised report still appeared under Owen's name, it bore Henry's extensive input, similar in form to comments he had previously expressed in letters to Alexander Dallas Bache, Gideon Hawley, and James Henry Coffin, among others (for which see *Henry Papers, 6:*493–500, 610–615, and 623–624).

In contrast to the original, which dealt almost entirely with how the Smithsonian could diffuse knowledge, the revised report, reflecting Henry's strong convictions, made clear that the institution's mission was a *dual* one:

"For the increase and diffusion of knowledge among men" were the words of Smithson's will—words used by a man accustomed to the strict nomenclature of exact science. They inform us, that a plan of organization, to carry into effect the intention of the testa-

tor, must embrace two objects; one, the calling forth of new knowledge by original research; and the other, the dissemination of knowledge already in existence.

The revised report struck much more of a balance between these two objects than did the original, fully describing how the Smithsonian should support research. Three resolutions embodied Henry's ideas for increasing and diffusing knowledge: premiums for publications and the Smithsonian Contributions to Knowledge; appropriations for original research; and periodic reports on the progress of knowledge in various branches. Two other resolutions appended to the report embraced elements from resolutions which had been introduced but not adopted on December 4; they called for popular lectures and the publication of tracts of general interest.

Adopted by the board on January 26, the revised report constituted the working plan of organization for the institution. (The regents adopted two additional resolutions at this meeting and another at the meeting of the twenty-eighth, relating to the "great compromise" between advocates of a large library and supporters of Henry's research-oriented programs; see below, Doc. 10.) It formed the basis for Henry's "Programme of Organization," adopted in December 1847.

Report of the Organization Committee of the Smithsonian Institution (Washington, 1847), reprinted in Rhees, *Documents* (1879), pp. 930–943 (quotation on pp. 930–931); Rhees, *Journals,* pp. 12–14, 19, 24–26.

6. At the regents' meeting of December 5, 1846, Bache moved that Smithsonian chancellor George M. Dallas should appoint a committee of three members "to procure the introduction, if they deem it expedient, of a bill amendatory of the act establishing this institution" (Rhees, *Journals,* p. 15). The motion car-

ried; Robert Dale Owen, William Jervis Hough (*Henry Papers*, 6:470), and George Evans (*Henry Papers*, 6:470) were named to this committee. (Hough was a representative from New York; Evans was a senator from Maine.) From Bache's (and Henry's) standpoint, the possibility that the act which had established the institution might be amended had much to recommend it. At the very least, Congress could specify a ceiling on the amount to be expended on a Smithsonian building or buildings. (On the provision for a building, see *Henry Papers*, 6:467–468.) Other possibilities presented themselves: Congress might relieve the Smithsonian of the burden of taking custody of the government's collections; it might agree to bear the cost of erecting the building, thereby reserving all of the accrued interest on the Smithson bequest for the actual operations of the institution; or it might replace the programs specified in the charter (a library, a museum, a chemical laboratory, an art gallery, and lectures), with measures closer to Henry's ideas for increasing knowledge.

On the other hand, recommitting the act was also fraught with risks. The bill had cleared the House of Representatives in April 1846 by a narrow margin (85 yeas, 76 nays), and a reservoir of distrust lingered against the institution. Among its most vociferous opponents was Andrew Johnson of Tennessee, who attacked the "legal fiction" of a loan by the institution to the government at six percent interest. In fact, the federal government had invested the Smithsonian fund in state bonds on which the states had then defaulted and the government was spending the money out of its general revenues. Johnson saw this as egregious at a time when the nation was at war with Mexico. Indeed, on January 2, 1847, he had offered a resolution calling on the secretary of the treasury to report "as to the propriety of suspending" the act which established the Smithsonian "for the present, or during the existing war with the republic of Mexico, and thereby avoid borrowing, or taxing coffee and tea the sum of $242,129"; the resolution did not carry. Andrew Johnson, "Resolution on Appropriations for the Smithsonian Institution," January 2, 1847, in *The Papers of Andrew Johnson*, ed. Leroy P. Graf and Ralph W. Hoskins (Knoxville, Tennessee, 1967), 1:349.

As members of Congress, Owen, Hough, and Evans were doubtless familiar with the hostile views of Johnson and others. Rather than try to have the original act itself amended, they drafted a bill which would have enabled the institution to purchase, for $35,000, the lot and unfinished building housing Washington's City Hall. Under this plan, the institution could either complete the building or tear it down and erect a new one (presumably with monies appropriated by Congress). Evans presented the bill to the Senate on February 15, 1847, and it was referred to the Committee on the District of Columbia. A week later, however, the Washington Common Council overwhelmingly rejected the plan. The regents' committee thereupon dropped its efforts to pass the bill in Congress and, so far as can be determined from the minutes, abandoned any further attempts to amend the original legislation. Rhees, *Journals*, pp. 15, 36–38; Rhees, *Documents* (1901), 1:438–439.

7. That is, in Philadelphia, to which point Harriet Henry had accompanied her husband on his return to Washington. See below, Doc. 6.

8. Louisa Meads Alexander, the wife of Stephen Alexander, was near death after a long illness. *Henry Papers*, 2:15n; 6:591.

9. John Vanderlyn's *Landing of Columbus at the Island of Guanahani, West Indies, October 12, 1492*, was hung in the Capitol rotunda on January 15, 1847, the seventh painting so installed. *Art in the United States Capitol* (Washington, 1976), pp. 134, 140.

10. Robert W. Weir's *Embarkation of the Pilgrims at Delft Haven, Holland, 22 July 1620*, installed in 1843. Henry first saw this painting when he visited Washington in July 1846. *Henry Papers*, 6:447–448; *Art in the United States Capitol*, p. 136.

11. Benedict Jaeger, an entomologist and former professor of modern languages and lecturer on natural history at Princeton, was now apparently connected with an academy in Eatontown, New Jersey. His letter of December 27, 1846, is in the Henry Papers, Smithsonian Archives. He never received the diplomatic posts he sought. *Henry Papers*, 2:55n–56n; J. Thomas and T. Baldwin, eds., *A Complete Pronouncing Gazetteer, or Geographical Dictionary of the World*, 2 vols. (Philadelphia, 1858), s.v. "Eatontown."

12. Not found.

13. Presumably James Sproat Green, a Princeton trustee and its professor of jurisprudence, and his wife, the former Isabella McCulloch, who were old family friends. *Henry Papers*, 1:440; Hageman, *Princeton*, 1:318.

14. See below, Doc. 12.

15. "Puss" was the Henrys' nickname for their youngest daughter, Caroline. The letter Henry requested has not been found, but see his replies to Helen Henry, January 30, 1847, and to Mary Henry, January 31, 1847, Family Correspondence, Henry Papers, Smithsonian Archives.

16. John Cross Smith (1803–1878), who attended Princeton Theological Seminary during the mid-1820s, in 1839 became pastor of the Fourth Presbyterian Church in Washington. Edward Howell Roberts, *Biographical Catalogue of the Princeton Theological Seminary, 1815–1932* (Princeton, 1933), p. 46; Washington City Directory, 1843.

17. Arthur Joseph Stansbury, formerly a trustee of the Albany Academy and pastor of the First Presbyterian Church of Albany, now worked as a congressional reporter and illustrator for the *National Intelligencer.* In 1803 he married Susanna Brown (1784–1852), a descendant of a founder of Providence Plantation. *Henry Papers, 1:*40; 2:443–444; Andrew J. Cosentino and Henry H. Glassie, *The Capital Image: Painters in Washington, 1800–1915* (Washington, 1983), p. 273; Frederick Howard Wines, comp., *The Descendants of John Stansbury of Leominster* (Springfield, Illinois, 1895), pp. 10–11.

5. TO HARRIET HENRY

[January 18, 1847][A]
Washington Monday
night ½ past 9 o'clock

My dear H

I have been very busy all day in the affairs of the Smithsonian. Governor Cass[B] was this day appointed to fill the vacancy occasioned by the death of Judge Pennebacker.[1] I called this[C] evening to pay my respects to the new Regent and to induct him into my views. He was however not at home and I am to call again tomorrow morning. All things at present look pretty fair for the Smithsonian but I cannot say how matters will go the only thing in the way is the great building. I am to dine tomorrow with Mr Ingersol of Phil[d] Mr Joseph Ingersol who takes a lively interest in my plans[2] and will advocate them to the extent of his abilities in the house and am to meet at[D] his table Mr Rush one of the Regents whom I have not yet seen.[3] Mr Ingersol has agreed to induct Mr Rush into my views previous to our meeting.[4] Bache has been quite sick to day and yesterday; confined to his room with ↑a↓ severe toothache. He had two teeth extracted this evening and is now better. This is a wonderful place for bustle the city is full of strangers—the Hotels are overflowing—among the crowd I caught sight of an old acquaintance whom I have not seen before for 20 years or nearly that time. I allude to George Clinton[E] son of Governor Clinton.[5] I saw him ↑but↓ for a moment and did not speak to him.

I have just been interrupted by by Mr Owen who has called to show me the plan of the building as cut down by Young Renwick it is certainly beautiful but will cost in its present state 202 thousand dollars. I hope however to see the wings cut off and then it will probably cost 150 thousand. Among the articles of Smithson in the patent office is a bronse medal of himself which I propose to have engraved as the embellishment of the transactions. I do not recollect to have informed you that there is a large case of articles which constitute the Personal Effects of Smithson— His knives forks spoons plate &c.[6] If the Regents do not go beyond 150 thousand in the building the Institution will get along very well with the remainder of the surplus of interest.[7]

This has been a very disagreeable drizzly day almost every person is complaining of colds—I have not got entirely rid of my cough but it is better than it was when I left Phil<u>d</u> I am quite snugly situated in a very cheerful and comfortable room and were you and our little ones with me I should be quite happy. I fear however you would scarsly enjoy yourself away from Louisa and Stephen at this time.

I shall expect a letter from you by the mail of tomorrow. I hoped to receive one to night but was disappointed. I do not recollect to have mentioned that among the members of the House I find William Campbell[8] the nephew of Dr Campbell[9] the biographer of Mrs^F Dr Grant[10,G] he is quite attentive and polite to me on account of his old uncle. I wish I could look in[H] upon you this evening an see that you are all well— that I could cover Hellen and see that Mary & Will.[I] are well tucked in. I must however be content with doing this in magination. Kiss the children for me and receive the assurance that I am and always shall be during life only yours.

PP Tell Will. that I expect now that I am away that he will take charge of the affairs of the family as much as possible and that he will be very industrious in the prosecution of his studies every month at this period of his life is of great value to him if properly improved. He must now lay in a store of learning which may serve to make him a man of importance in future life. He will soon be grown up and I hope he will realize the wishes of his father and mother inregard to him. Mary I have no doubt will endeavour to add to the happiness of her mother by doing in all cases what is right and proper and in helping to take charge of the little one[11] who is about to be deprived of her[J] mother and to experience a loss which ↑she↓ will never be able fully to realize. Helen and Carry will also I am sure be good children and continue to be as they have ever been a source of happiness and comfort to their parents.

I hope Sam[12] is attentive and steady— He must not be allowed to be out at nights now that I am away. I would say more but that my paper is full love to Grandmother[13] Stephen Louisa and Charlotte.[14]

Family Correspondence, Henry Papers, Smithsonian Archives.

1. Lewis Cass (1782–1866), former governor of Michigan, secretary of war, and minister to France, in 1844 was elected to the Senate. He was appointed a Smithsonian regent in place of Isaac Samuels Pennybacker (*Henry Papers, 6:470*), senator from Virginia, who died on January 12, 1847. Under section 3 of the act establishing the Smithsonian Institution, any vacancy created by the death or resignation of a regent who was a member of Congress was to be filled in the same manner as a vacancy in a congressional committee, namely, by election of the whole House or Senate or by appointment of the presiding officer. Acting in his capacity as president of the Senate, Vice-President George M. Dallas appointed Cass a regent. He served a single term. *DAB;* Goode, *Smithsonian,* p. 85; Rhees, *Documents* (1901), pp. 430, 436–437.

2. Remarks which Ingersoll made in April 1846 during the House debates over the Smithson bequest indicate why he may have been receptive to Henry's plans. He firmly believed that the bequest should not be used to establish a great national library in Washington, but rather, in keeping with Smithson's intent, to "cover general ground, in which all objects of science (if possible) should be included." (At the same time, he also shared Robert Dale Owen's hope that at least part of the bequest might be used for a normal school and a lecture series.) Rhees, *Documents* (1901), pp. 352–353 (quotation on p. 353).

3. Richard Rush, former attorney general, secretary of state, minister to England, and secretary of the treasury, had, as a special commissioner, secured the Smithson bequest for the United States. He missed the regents' meetings of December 21 and 23, 1846, the first which Henry attended as Smithsonian secretary. *Henry Papers, 6:470*; Rhees, *Journals,* pp. 18, 19.

4. In 1838, asked to give his opinion on the application of Smithson's bequest, Rush had suggested that it be used to sponsor lectures on government and law; that the Smithsonian should have its own press; and that it should publish international scientific communications. By 1844, however, he had shifted his views, urging that the bequest be used to revitalize the National Institute for the Promotion of Science; along that line, he supported the candidacy of Francis Markoe, Jr. (*Henry Papers, 6:482n*), the institute's corresponding secretary, for the Smithsonian secretaryship. Rhees, *Documents* (1879), pp. 849–856; Rush, "Smithson Bequest," *Third Bulletin of the Proceedings of the National Institute for the Promotion of Science, Washington, D.C., February, 1842, to February,* 1845; Also, *Proceedings of the Meeting of April, 1844* (Washington, 1845), pp. 455–460; *Henry Papers, 6:482–485, 551–552, 554.*

5. George W. Clinton, the son of former New York governor DeWitt Clinton (*Henry Papers, 1:9n*), in 1826 had accompanied Henry on a boating tour of the recently opened Erie Canal. *Henry Papers, 1:74n.*

6. Some of Smithson's personal effects—including papers and manuscripts, clothing, several boxes of kitchenware and crockery, mineral collections, and philosophical apparatus—had been turned over to Rush, who shipped them to New York in 1838. They remained at the New York Customs House until 1841, when they were transferred to the National Institute in Washington at its request. With the exception of the clothing, which was donated to an orphan asylum, Smithson's effects were displayed with the National Institute's collections in the "National Gallery" of the Patent Office Building until they were moved to the Smithsonian Building in 1858. Although the 1865 fire in the building destroyed much of the collection, some manuscripts and books escaped the fire and survive today in the James Smithson Collection in the Smithsonian Archives and in the Special Collections Department of the Smithsonian Institution Libraries.

The bronze medallion to which Henry referred became the source for the institution's official seal, as well as for an engraving of Smithson "to be printed on the title page of the books published by the Smithsonian," and is in the National Numismatic Collection of the National Museum of American History.

William J. Rhees, *James Smithson and His Bequest,* 1880, Smithsonian Miscellaneous Collections, vol. 21 (Washington, 1881), pp. 13–17; *Smithsonian Report for 1865,* pp. 16–17; Rhees, *Journals,* p. 462 (quotation).

7. The act had authorized the regents to spend up to $242,129—the accrued simple interest on the fund—on the building. Any amount not spent on construction could be applied to other Smithsonian activities.

8. William W. Campbell (1806–1881), a lawyer who graduated from Union College, in 1844 was elected to a single term as a representative from New York. *DAB; BDAC.*

9. William Campbell (d. 1844), a New York surgeon, state government official, and regent of the state university, had been a long-time acquaintance of Henry's. *Henry Papers, 1:100n.*

10. Judith S. Lathrop Campbell, William Campbell's adopted daughter, was the second

wife of Asahel Grant (*Henry Papers,* 3:50n), a physician and missionary. Henry referred to William W. Campbell's biography, *A Memoir of Mrs. Judith S. Grant, Late Missionary to Persia* (New York, 1844).

11. Presumably Charlotte Meads Alexander, the youngest daughter of Stephen and Louisa Alexander. *Henry Papers,* 5:377n.

12. Sam Parker, Henry's domestic worker and former laboratory assistant. *Henry Papers,* 4:452.

13. Maria Alexander, Henry's mother-in-law. *Henry Papers,* 1:230n.

14. Charlotte Meads, Louisa Alexander's sister. *Henry Papers,* 2:15n.

6. TO HARRIET HENRY

[January 19, 1847][A]
Washington Tuesday
night 20 minutes past
9 oclock

My Dear H

I have just returned from dining with Mr Joseph Ingersol and as I am in duty and affection bound I commence to pay my willing nighly tribute to you. We had a most plesant little party consisting of Mr Seaton the mayor of Washington,[1] Mr Rush Mr Bache Mr Ingersol and myself. Mr Rush is an admirable talker full of anecdotes[B] and remenisences of characters and things in England and this country. Mr Seaton has long lived in Washington and is familiar with the history of all political men in the country— The object of the party was to make me more intimately acquainted with the two gentlemen I have named and to enable Mr Ingersol to impress them with my plans or to give me an opportunity of presenting them with the scheme myself. General Cass has been elected to fill the vacancy occassioned by the death of Judge Pennybacker. I have seen him and am to meet him tomorrow moring inorder to impress him with my views of the plan of organization. Mr Rush has fully adopted my plan and will I have no doubt second all my movements. Tomorrow is the begining of the session of the smithson Board and the results of this meeting will I am sure be of great importance to the future usefulness of the Institution. I expect should my plans be carried that some attacks will be made ~~from~~ ↑by↓ those who wish to make a library on the one hand and by those who wish to use the money for the war on the other. I called at the Vice Presidents to go with him to the Presidents but was a little behind my appointment he had already gone[2]—the appointment was not definite and he will take me tomorrow evening on the occasion of the public Lavee.[3] The Vice President said that he though it propper that I should have a seperate and private

Introduction.[c] You will see by my letter that I am full of business but you must not think that amidst all this bustle and stir I forget those who are at home. The last hours of the day are spent in spirit with you and our dear children after finishing this letter I shall go to bed and after my prayers my last thoughts will be of you— Just before I began to wite I stepped into Mr Stansburrys[4] room he I found busily engaged in making up his reports—he is a man of great talents after spending the day in the house[5] from eleven oclock until four he comes home[D] and writes out the reports for the next day's paper which occupies him frequently until one or two o'clock in the morning. I expected to receive a letter to day but have been again disappointed. It is a week to day since we parted in Phil[d] but it appears a month and I have had but one letter[6] in that time. I suppose that you are much engaged with Louisa and the children— I am glad to learn that you have engaged the Miliner[7] or rather the [?Meuilanner] to put your person in good condition for though I love you independently of all outward adorments yet I am well pleased to see you properly dressed. I meet every day with a great number of our old graduates—they are all well pleased apparently to see me and I am much gratified with their attention. The library of congress is the place to see most of the strangers of literary taste and also the ladies of the city. It is almost constantly thronged with visitors and loungers.[8] It contains about 40 thousand vol. many of which are good works but among the number are not a few of questionable character in the novel line.

Remember me to Grandmother Uncle Stephen Louisa Will Marrie Helen Puss, Sam & all the other members of the family. I beg my dear little wife that you will be careful of your health though you give poor Louisa all the comfort you can in the way of attendance and I suppose she will want you much there do not attempt to do too much— Your sick headaches with you being obliged so frequently to take medicine alarms me when I think of it. I fear your health will give way and I have frequently accused myself of late and particularly of thinking more of my own health than of yours. Adue good night Dearest.

Family Correspondence, Henry Papers, Smithsonian Archives.

1. William Winston Seaton, who, by virtue of his office, was a Smithsonian regent, was also a prominent newspaper publisher. *Henry Papers,* 6:470.

2. President James K. Polk and his family customarily held an informal gathering at the White House on Tuesday evenings, to which visitors were welcome to come without an invitation. Vice-President Dallas and Richard Rush were among those who attended on the nineteenth. Milo Milton Quaife, ed., *The Diary of James K. Polk during His Presidency, 1845 to 1849,* 4 vols. (Chicago, 1910), 2:342; Charles G. Sellers, *James K. Polk: Continentalist, 1843–1846* (Princeton, 1966), p. 307.

3. The presidential bi-weekly Wednesday

evening "levees" (public receptions) were among "the capital's principal occasions for political gossip." Polk described the reception of January 20 in his diary:

Public notice having been previously given, my drawing room was open. All the parlours were brilliantly lighted up. The Marine Band were stationed in the large Hall. About 8 O'Clock P.M. the company began to assemble. All the parlours including the East Room were filled with ladies & gentlemen. The Foreign Corps, members of the Cabinet, of the Supreme Court of the U.S., members of Congress, citizens, & strangers were present. Though the snow was falling & it was a cold night it was a numerous and brilliant assembly. The Company retired between 11 and 12 O'Clock.

Sellers, pp. 307–308 (quotation on p. 308); Quaife, 2:344.

4. Arthur Joseph Stansbury.
5. That is, the House of Representatives.
6. Not found.
7. Identified as a "Miss Skillman." See Doc. 171.
8. Opened in 1818, the room in the Capitol which housed the Library of Congress became a gathering place whose "books and pictures [provided] an excuse for the meeting there of persons of both sexes." Relocated to more spacious quarters in the Capitol in 1824, the library remained a popular meeting place, as Henry's remark indicates. Wilhelmus Bogart Bryan, *A History of the National Capital*, 2 vols. (New York, 1914–1916), 2:41–42 (quotation on p. 42). See also *Henry Papers, 6:447*.

7. TO HARRIET HENRY

Washington Jany 20th[–21] 1847

My dear H

I write this evening with very little to communicate except the old story which I hope and trust you will not soon get tired of—Love and constancy— We have made but little progess in organization of the smithsonian to day though the Regents met for that purpose. The attendance[A] though good was not complete several of the Board were absent Mr Choat the great Library man[1] whom I have not yet seen and Mr Hawley[2] who has not yet got on and I think will probably not be here.[3] There is quite a tempest among the Architects and various[B] articles have appeared in the papers relative to the choise of the plan for the building. The Board agreed to suffer each architect to be heard tomorrow in succession and I presume we shall then have quite a series of lectures on the esthetic.[4] I can say with Mr[C] Lyle though I am an admirer of good bulding yet I do not choose to be its victim.[5]

There will probably be considerable[D] warm discussion on the subject of the bulding to morrow. I think I informed you that Gen Cass had been chosen in the place of Judge Pennebacker. I called this morning on the General and presented to him my views with which I appeared[E] much impressed and expressed himself strongly against a great expenditure for a library or a building[F] but more particularly against the building.

Judge Breese[6] (the cousin of Mrs Robey of Albany[7] whom you may recollect) goes[G] strongly against the building and will probably be pitted against Mr Seaton the mayor of the city so that the probability is that the building though large and expensive will be less by nearly a half than that at first contemplated. There is a great gathering at the Presidents this evening and during the day I though of going but the weather is so stormy with a fall of snow that I concluded not to venture out.

Another day has passed and still no letter has come you must begin to think that I am so filled with the affairs of the Smithsonian that I can have no room in my attention to receive the contents of a short letter from you or one of the children—Where is the letter which I have been expecting from a new desk the christmas present desk of a young lady who is said very much to resemble[H] in face at least her Father. Shurely it must have been detained by the way perhaps blocked up with the ice in the chesapeak[I]—and also where lingers the epistle which is to inform me of all the tricks of the little old horse push and his sable attendant Sam.

I wish I could look in upon you if but for a few minutes just now the hand of the watch points to ¼ past eleven and I suppose all the inmates of our house are buried in slumbers with perhaps one exception—one a little woman revolving in her mind the past the present and the future is too much occupied with anxiety, fears, perhaps sorrow for the condition of poor Louisa and the distress of Stephen.

Thursday Evening

My dear H

It was so late last night before I finished my letter that I did not take it down to be put into the office—your letter of no date[8] on note paper informing me of the low state of Louisa was receivd to day. It is the second I have had since I left home. I suppose you are so much occupied with attendance on Louisa that your time is all absorbed. I wish I could be with you but I fear I shall be unable to leave Washington for some days to come. The Board met again to day but without doing any thing more than ↑to↓ give a hearing to the architects. Poor Louisa I hope she will receive strength to support her through the brief span of time she has to remain. How uncertain are all things of Earth we live amoung the dying and yet do not realize as we should do that we are mortal—that as Louisa now is inreference to her hold on life so we must shurely and shortly be. The auful change awaits us all. Let the fact be constantly before our minds not to lessen our interest in the affairs of this life but to render us less anxious as to the events of this world whether they turn out for our advantage or not or how long we may be permitted to remain on Earth. Let us put our trust more fully than ever in Him[J] who will order all things for the best who put full reliance on Him.

Poor Stephen I fear the blow will fall heavily on him but he is not one who will mourn without hope and I trust the event when it comes will not be unexpected nor the effect such as he will not be able to be sustained under. I beg you my dear little Wife that you will in this trying season be careful of your health. Though I know you will be anxious to do all you can to mitigate the pain of Louisa[K] and to comfort Stephen. I fear you will[L] not be moderate or have a proper regard for your self— I beg my Dear H. that you will be mindful of your duty to your children and that you have a husband to whom life would be worthless were you to be taken from him. I have been anxious about you sinc I left you in Phil[d] Kiss the children for me. Give my Love and kind regards to Louisa. Tell her she has my most erenest praye for fath to sustain her in the hours of tryal[M] and that she must throw herself entirely on the merits of her saviour put full reliance on him. The saints are impure in the sight of the Righteous Judge[N] before whom all must appear ~~and~~ and none can plead their own goodness. They can only be saved through the merits of a Saviour. Adieu.

From as ever only yours.

Family Correspondence, Henry Papers, Smithsonian Archives.

1. Rufus Choate, former Whig senator from Massachusetts and one of six citizen members of the Smithsonian Board of Regents, led its "library faction," which advocated using Smithson's bequest to build a national library at Washington. *Henry Papers,* 6:465, 565n, 566.

2. Gideon Hawley, superintendent for public instruction for New York and another citizen member of the Board of Regents, had known Henry since his Albany days. *Henry Papers,* 1:50; 6:470.

3. Regents who were present at the January 20 meeting included Vice-President George M. Dallas, chancellor of the Smithsonian; Alexander Dallas Bache; William W. Seaton; Robert Dale Owen; Richard Rush; Lewis Cass; George Evans; William J. Hough; Sidney Breese (*Henry Papers,* 6:470), Democratic senator from Illinois; and Henry Washington Hilliard (*Henry Papers,* 6:470), Whig representative from Alabama. In addition to those named by Henry, regents who did not attend included Roger B. Taney (*Henry Papers,* 6:470), chief justice of the Supreme Court, and two citizen regents: Joseph Gilbert Totten (*Henry Papers,* 4:320), chief

of the Army Corps of Engineers, and William Campbell Preston (*Henry Papers,* 6:470), former senator from South Carolina and now president of South Carolina College. Rhees, *Journals,* p. 20.

4. Architects ostensibly had been given until December 25, 1846, to submit proposals for the Smithsonian Building to the Board of Regents; however, word spread that the building committee had, on November 30, endorsed James Renwick's two designs. A storm of protest ensued, with some architects charging that the competition was rigged from the start. To stem the controversy, at the January 20 meeting the regents approved a resolution offered by William Seaton, that the board would meet at ten the next morning to hear comments or receive more information from any architects who had submitted plans. These presentations occupied the board for several days.

Rhees, *Journals,* pp. 20–24; Kenneth Hafertepe, *America's Castle: The Evolution of the Smithsonian Building and Its Institution, 1840–1878* (Washington, 1984), pp. 37–61; Cynthia R. Field, introduction to Robert Dale Owen, *Hints* on *Public Architecture* (1849; New York, 1978), pp. [5]–[6].

5. Henry was paraphrasing criticisms made by the renowned British geologist, Sir Charles Lyell (*Henry Papers*, 2:135n), over the costly ornamentation of buildings for Philadelphia's Girard College and London's University College. If the trustees of these institutions instead had expended funds for learning, Lyell wrote,

> None would then grudge the fluted column, the swelling dome, and the stately portico; and literature and science would continue to be the patrons of architecture, without being its victims.

Lyell contrasted these institutions with the Lowell Institute, whose benefactor, John Lowell, Jr., had insisted that "not a single dollar

should be spent in brick and mortar." Henry was deeply impressed by Lyell's comments; he often paraphrased them in support of his argument that the Smithson bequest should not be used to erect an ornate Smithsonian building. Lyell, *Travels in North America, in the Years 1841–2*, 2 vols. (New York, 1845), 1:89–92 (quotations on pp. 89, 91); *Henry Papers*, 6:586, 608.

6. Sidney Breese had been a judge of the Illinois Supreme Court prior to his election to the Senate. *BDAC*.

7. Margaret Breese (1803 or 1804–1832), the daughter of Samuel Sidney Breese of Skenandoa (or Sconandoa), near Albany, New York, was the wife of Joseph Roby, Jr., an Albany hardware merchant. *Daily Albany Argus*, April 3, 1832; *Henry Papers*, 2:151n.

8. Not found.

8. TO HARRIET HENRY

Washington Saturday
night Jany [23] 1847[A]

My Dear H

I was much gratified to day in receiving a package of little letters[1] from the little girls. I was agreably surprised to find one from Helen and another from Harriet.[2] Tell the young ladies that they gave me much pleasure and that when I get a little more time I will answer ↑the↓ letters. This will not take very much trouble provided my letter to each[3] resembles those I received for though the chirography was some what various yet the news contained in each was remarkable the same. The letter from[B] Puss was fortunately accompanied by a translation which enabled me make out its meaning. Will's letter was not containd in the package but I presume it will be fourth comming.[4] I am quite anxious to hear something about Louisa but nothing was mentioned relative to her in the letters. I presume from this that she is about the same— I am still very busy about the Smithsonian the Regents have met every day since wednesday but they have been constantly engaged in examing plans of buildings and on monday will probably decide on a plan the feaver was high to day for a large building but the consideration of the subject was posponed until tomorrow I should say monday. I am not very certain as to the result. I found on my[C] return that there was so much feeling on the subject of a building that with Bache I concluded reluctantly that it was best on the whole to give way a little and

22

suffer an appropriation of 150 thousand if we could not get less; on this consideration I ceased to make any farther effort against the building and the consequence was that to day the indication seamed to be that the sum appropriated would be 200 thousand.

I have therefore been engaged this afternoon in renewing my efforts to allay the feever and I think with some effect. I felt at first some what depressed but after some conversation with Judge Breeze and Judge^D Tawney (Judge of the supreme court of the US) who are warmly with me I felt quite cheered. I have not suffered any of the affairs to perplex or annoy^E me. I have resolved to first study carefully what is my duty and then to do it fearlessly relying on a conscience void^F of offense for justification of my acts leaving the result to the direction of a kind providence.

I wish very much I could be with you if it were only until tomorrow morning. My cough has almost entirely left me the weather has been plesant to day and I think there is a prospect of its being^G considerably warmer. I left Bache this afternoon quite down in the mouth about the smithsonian.[5] I do not feel myself ver[y]^H much troubled. If after having done all in our power to direct the affair in the proper channel I leave the result to Providen beleving that the failure is for the best in the long run or it would not be permitted to take place.

Give my love to Louisa if she be still in the world to Stephen Grandmother all the children ↑&↓ Charlotte Meads and receive for yourself the assurance that I am as ever most sincerely your own—

H–

Family Correspondence, Henry Papers, Smithsonian Archives.

1. Not found.
2. Henry meant to write "Mary."
3. Henry to Helen Henry, January 30, 1847, and to Mary Henry, January 31, 1847, Family Correspondence, Henry Papers, Smithsonian Archives.

4. William Henry to Joseph Henry, [January 29, 1847] (dated "Friday," with a file note of "February 1847"), Family Correspondence, Henry Papers, Smithsonian Archives.
5. Perhaps a pun: Bache had two teeth pulled a few days earlier.

9. FROM GEORGE WASHINGTON SMITH[1]

Philadelphia Jany 26th 1847

My Dear friend

A Committee of the Am— Philosophical Society has been appointed to enquire in to the circumstances of the destruction of the Thomas P.

Cope—a packet of this port destroyed by lightning at sea,[2] having no conductor up at the time, the captain fearing to use one—apprehending that it might attract the stroke.[3] We have to enquire into the expediency of conductors their proper form &c As chairman of the Committee (Patterson[4] Peale[5] and myself) I hope to have your advice on the whole subject—and specially as respects ⟨illustration⟩ the lateral discharge—if danger is to be apprehended there- ⟨illustration⟩ from.[6] What is your opinion of Snow Harris' plan? do you ⟨illustration⟩ think the enormous[A] sise of the copper plat[e] on the lower mast necessary?[7] What do you think of the plan used in the French ships (iron or copper wire ropes as backstays[)?][8] I have the report and documents from t[he] British Admiralty.[9] Will you if perfec[tly] convenient ascertain from our Navy Department if they have any facts from our navy officers, or others, shewing the utility or otherwise of conductors—if any ship with a good conductor has ever been injured or saved by the conductors[10]— pray excuse my lame hand and believe me as ever

> Your friend
> Geo. W. Smith
> N° 3 Dugan's Row
> Spruce Street
> Philad[a]

P.S. I rejoice—but with fear and trembling at your appointment—but I regard you as Daniel in the den of lions to say nothing of meaner beasts.
Prof. Henry

Henry Papers, Smithsonian Archives.
First page torn on right edge. In original, illustration is in left margin.

1. A Princeton graduate (1822) and now a Philadelphia merchant. *Henry Papers*, 5:303.

2. Lightning struck the mainmast of the packet ship *Thomas P. Cope* on November 29, 1846, setting afire her cargo of hemp and tallow. On January 1, 1847, the American Philosophical Society appointed a committee to investigate the circumstances of the accident. Eliza Cope Harrison, ed., *Philadelphia Merchant: The Diary of Thomas P. Cope, 1800–1851* (South Bend, Indiana, 1978), pp. 518–519; APS *Proceedings, 1843–1847*, 4:300–301.

3. The *Cope*, like most merchant ships, carried a removable conductor. Typically, these consisted of an iron or copper chain hung from the mainmast, with the lower end in the sea. William Snow Harris, *On the Nature of Thunderstorms; and On the Means of Protecting Buildings and Shipping against the Destructive Effects of Lightning* (London, 1843), pp. 130–140; A. M. Griffiths et al., "[Abridged] Report of the Committee Appointed by the Admiralty to Examine the Plans of Lightning Conductors, of W. Snow Harris, Esq. F.R.S. and Others," *Annals of Electricity, Magnetism, and Chemistry*, 1840, 5:1–20, especially pp. 4–6.

4. Robert Maskell Patterson, director of the United States Mint and a trustee of the University of Pennsylvania. *Henry Papers*, 2:413n.

5. Franklin Peale, chief coiner of the United States Mint. *Henry Papers*, 4:177.

6. Opinions differed as to whether lateral discharges posed a danger to ships fitted with lightning conductors. Some authorities believed that flying sparks could ignite a ship's cargo or, on naval vessels, a powder magazine. Others disagreed, however, stating that little danger existed if the conductors used were of

sufficient capacity and continuous throughout their length. Such differing views about lateral discharges were part of a broader ongoing debate about the reality of the phenomenon. Griffiths, pp. 7–10, 19–20; *Henry Papers*, 3:53n–54n; 4:263; and 5:439n–440n.

Convinced that the threat posed by lateral discharges was real, Henry urged caution in the arrangement and use of lightning conductors on ships. As he observed in 1859,

> It is true, the quantity which tends to fly off laterally from the rod is small, yet we have shown by direct experiment that it is sufficient even when produced by the electricity of a small machine, to set fire to combustible materials; and therefore it cannot be entirely free from danger in a ship, loaded for example with cotton. ["Atmospheric Electricity," Part V of "Meteorology in Its Connection with Agriculture," *Report of the Commissioner of Patents for 1859: Agriculture* (Washington, 1860), p. 482.]

7. The plan devised by William Snow Harris, a Plymouth physician and author of several papers on electricity, was intended to afford ships permanent lightning protection. His conductor was a band of copper plates. Each link in the band consisted of two plates riveted together, each "about four feet long, from six inches to one and a half broad; the thickness of the under layer being one eighth, and of the upper layer one sixteenth, of an inch." The band was nailed in place in a continuous line along the ship's projecting points and beneath

the lower decks, terminating in the hull. In 1839, a British Admiralty committee stated that smaller plates could be used without detriment. Griffiths, pp. 5, 6–15, 16–17; *Encyclopaedia Britannica*, 8th ed., s.v. "Electricity," p. 610 (quotation); *Henry Papers*, 3:173n.

We have not found any comment by Henry on the size of Harris's plates. In 1859, he termed the plan an "admirable arrangement" whose only drawback was that it conducted lightning through the hull. "Atmospheric Electricity," p. 482; see also *Henry Papers*, 3:514–515; 4:263n.

8. French naval vessels carried removable conductors made of copper or iron wire rope, which, when installed, ran from the mainmast, down the backstays, and into the water. Such conductors had limited utility, since their capacity was insufficient and they were lost altogether if the mast fell during a storm. Griffiths, pp. 4–6; Harris, pp. 134–136.

9. A. M. Griffiths et al., *Copy of the Report and Evidence from the Commission Appointed to Inquire into the Plan of* William Snow Harris, *Esq. F.R.S. Relating to the Protection of Ships from the Effects of Lightning*, United Kingdom, Parliament, January 18–August 11, 1840, House of Commons Sessional Papers, No. 63, pp. 1–96. The report contained letters, descriptions of Harris's and other plans, and accounts of ships struck by lightning.

10. We do not know if Henry contacted the Navy Department regarding the information which the APS committee desired.

The committee never presented a report; its final disposition is not known.

10. TO HARRIET HENRY

[January 26, 1847][A]
Washington Tuesday
evening

My dear H.

I have heard nothing from you for several days and am begining to be quite anxious about home. Mr Duffield[1] met me in the Rotunday yesterday and called at my room in the evening. I had however but a short conversation with him he promised to call this evening previous to his leaving for Princeton that I might send a letter[B] by him. I have however been obliged to be out since dark and have therefore missed

him. How are you getting on?—almost becoming used to be without
me. I am very much engaged during the day but long for home at
night. The kind of life I am leading here makes me value home the
more. The board of Regents meets daily. They determined on the plan
of organization to day and adopted my plans in full so far as one half
of the income was concerened—the other half they were obliged to give
to the Library—the museum and other collections[2] with the hope that
if[C] the Institution does well congress will assist them by paying for the
keeping of the museum. They could not get rid of the museum unless
they went back with the institution to Congress and it was concluded
that this would be a hasardous plan and could not be thought of this
session. I shall have 15 thousand dollars at my desposal annually for
scientific purposes and the publication of reports [?unincombered] and
with this well expended something may be done though much less than
what could be effected with the whole sum. I fear however that they
will expend a large sum[D] on a building—the very salvation of the integrity of the union of the states is thought to be connected with a large
building at Washington— Bache has brought forward a plan of adopting the project of a large building and erecting[E] it out of the interest of
the fund set apart for the building namely[F] out of the 242 thouzand
dollars which have accrued in interest up to this time. I fear however
that it will not carry and nothing but a large building immediately
erected will satisfy the Washingtonians— Well let the affair go as it may
I have endeavoured to do my duty and have exerted all my talents and
influeence to prevent the expenditure. I have on my side all the best
men and those uninterested namely The vice President[G] Bache Chief
Justice Tawney Judge Breese and I think General Cass. The other side
however is the stronger now that Mr Rush is away. Unfortunately Owen
is struck with an architectural mania and were it not for this the builders
would be in the minority.

I have given you all the news about the Smithsonian and nothing
about Washington. Indeed I am so much occupied with the former that
I give but little attention to the latter. Last night was a great ball at which
nearly all the fashion of the city was assembled old and young.[3] To night
is the Lavee of the President at which no doubt there is a great gathering. I have not yet been in the White house though I have twice made
an engagement to go their. I was at Mr Walker's[4] this evening and saw
there Miss Cook[5] from Princeton. She has not heard from Princeton for
more than a week. She expects her Father in Washington in the course
of next week and will return with him. Last evening I spent with Senators Clayton[6,H] and Crittenden[7,I] or at least two hours or more of it they

amused meᴶ with an account of their experience as lawyers and each gave two remarkable stories of Murder trials in which had been engaged ~~in~~ professionally.[8,K]

Give my love to all our dear children to aunt Louisa Uncle Stephen Grandmother & Sam. Receive for yourself the old assurance that I am as ever only yourᴸ

Joseph H

Family Correspondence, Henry Papers, Smithsonian Archives.

1. John Thomas Duffield (1823–1901), an 1841 Princeton graduate, attended Princeton Theological Seminary from 1844 to 1848. Appointed Princeton's tutor of Greek in 1845, he became its adjunct professor of mathematics in 1847. *The Biblical Repertory and Princeton Review: Index Volume from 1825 to 1868* (Philadelphia, 1871), p. 156; *Princeton Catalogue*, p. 160.

2. The regents' actions—referred to thereafter as "the compromise"—were embodied in two resolutions which were appended to the revised report of the committee of organization. The first of these (numbered 6 in the minutes) declared that Congress had followed Smithson's wishes when, in chartering the Smithsonian, it defined as one of the institution's primary objectives the accumulation of art and natural history collections and the gradual formation of a library. The second resolution (number 7) provided for the permanent appropriation of the annual income between the "two great divisions of the plan of the institution" once the building was completed: $15,000 for the library and collections, and the balance (currently $15,910) for research, publications, and lectures. Salaries and other expenses were to be split evenly between both divisions. Rhees, *Journals*, p. 26.

3. The second Washington Assembly, held at Jackson Hall, was reportedly attended by a "numerous and fashionable company." *National Intelligencer*, January 27, 1847.

4. Robert J. Walker, former Democratic senator from Mississippi and now secretary of the treasury, was a brother-in-law of Alexander Dallas Bache. *Henry Papers*, 5:450n.

5. Leslie (or Lettie) Cook was presumably the daughter of Martha Elizabeth Duncan Walker Cook (1806–1874, *DAB*). Her mother, an author and a humanitarian, was Robert J. Walker's sister and the wife of William Cook, chief engineer of the Philadelphia & Trenton Railroad.

6. John Middleton Clayton (1796–1856), Whig senator from Delaware. *DAB*.

7. John Jordan Crittenden (1787–1863), Whig senator from Kentucky. *DAB*.

8. Clayton handled several murder cases as a lawyer in Delaware during the 1820s and 1830s, but none received special notice in his biographies. As a lawyer in Kentucky during the same period, Crittenden was involved in some notable murder trials; see Albert D. Kirwan, *John J. Crittenden: The Struggle for the Union* (Lexington, Kentucky, 1962), pp. 58–61.

11. TO HARRIET HENRY

Washington, Cap. Room of the Vice Pres.
January 27th, 1847

My dear H.— The Board of Regents have appointed a meeting this evening, to agree on a plan of a building and thus complete the business of the session, and before they arrive, being alone, I drop you a line. This morning I was quite dispirited and had resolved that if things took the turn they appeared to be likely to take, I would tender my resignation. Bache was also much depressed, but providentially the whole matter settled down into a very harmonious and satisfactory arrangement and, the probability is now, that we shall all separate well pleased with the transactions. The only difficulty which remained yesterday, was that of the erection of a large and beautiful building. Bache and myself were exerting ourselves to defeat the building scheme, while all the Washington influence was against us. This was the state of things when Bache devised a scheme to harmonize each party with each other, which consisted in proposing to defer the completion of the building for five years, and to expend in the process of erection the interest which would accrue from the money the other party proposed to devote immediately to the building. By this plan a large surplus will be saved from the annual funds of the Institution. He proposed this plan yesterday, but no attention was given to it until this morning, and not then, until Bache had introduced a proposition restricting the sum to be expended for building to one hundred thousand dollars. The other plan was then taken up explained, discussed, and in all probability, will this evening be adopted.[1] I have kept myself quite cool and, though difficulties innumerable have beset my path, yet all things have gone as well as I could have hoped. I have told the men of Washington that I intend to adopt a new line of policy—that of straightforwardness and honesty. I have pressed my points with vigor but not officiously. There was an indication of a squall this morning, which however passed over very well. Mr. Choate and his friends stated that they had concurred in my appointment, with the understanding that the plan of a library, though not a large one, would not be entirely abandoned, and that Prof. Jewett would be appointed as my assistant. He further stated that he had been informed that I was not anxious to assume the responsibility of nominating the [assistant][A] secretary, and he hoped that the Board would recommend to me Prof. Jewett—whereupon the Board or a majority of them recommended the above named gentleman, and in compliment with the recommendation I nominated him. On the minutes of the proceedings, I saw this morning, that the fact of the board having requested me to nominate the gentleman, had been omitted. I then requested that the minutes should be amended in this particular, which gave rise to quite a discussion; I have insisted that the facts should be stated just as they occurred and finally the whole was adjusted to my satisfaction.[2]

8 PM— The Board has just adjourned, but inasmuch as Mr. Choate, who thought of leaving tomorrow, has concluded to stop until another day—the Board adjourned until tomorrow without doing any business.

If nothing occurs to mar the proceedings which are now in a very favorable train we shall adjourn in harmony, and with a fair prospect of the Institution going into successful operation.

I am quite anxious to hear from you and Louisa. I have not heard from Princeton since the arrival of the package of letters from the little girls. The time seems so long, that the interval of a day or two appears like a week. I hope to get away next week, and be at home at the opening of the college.[3] The present is the longest vacation I have ever spent. It seems six months since my appointment to the Smithsonian took place.

The messenger is waiting to close this room, and therefore I must stop with the assurance that I am as ever

only yours
J.H.

Mary Henry Copy, Family Correspondence, Henry Papers, Smithsonian Archives.
Mary Henry Copy: Two variant copies in same location.

1. Bache's plan followed upon a resolution presented by Chancellor Dallas at the January 26 meeting, which stated that to preserve funds for Smithsonian programs, no more than $100,000 should be spent on its building; the resolution was tabled. The next day, Bache offered a similar resolution, limiting spending from the building fund principal ($242,129) to $100,000; it also was tabled. The regents then reconsidered Dallas's resolution, whereupon Bache offered as an amendment to it that "a plan of finance and construction can be adopted" (p. 28) under which no more than $100,000 of the building fund principal would be spent. After debate, the board decided to reconvene that evening.

A memorandum of understanding, dated January 27 and read to the board on January 28, outlined Bache's plan. It stated four principles. First, insofar as possible, the principal of the building fund was to be preserved. Second, the building's construction was to be spread out, with its wings completed in two years and the whole in five, at an average annual expenditure of one-fifth of the total cost (estimated at $202,000 to $217,000). Third, at least $15,000 per year was to be loaned, during the first two years, from the annual income of the Smithsonian fund and added to the interest on the building fund. Fourth, $252,000 was to be drawn from the treasury and set aside as a separate building fund. After five years, assuming an annual expenditure of $43,000 (from the new building fund, its annual interest, and the

$30,000 to be borrowed from the Smithsonian fund), a balance of $129,384 would remain, to be added to the Smithsonian fund's principal.

The memorandum was never entered into the minutes, nor is there any record of its official adoption. As Robert Dale Owen noted, however, the "prospective plan of finance and scale of expenditure, throughout the years in which the building shall be in progress, . . . did, in fact, receive the sanction of the Board" (p. 448). Its details formed the basis for the method of financing the construction which appeared in the contract signed by the building committee on March 20, 1847. And, though they slightly modified its particulars, the executive committee adopted the plan in December 1847 as a "scale of expenditures for the next four years" (p. 447).

Rhees, *Journals,* pp. 25, 28, 447-455, 627-628. Four copies of the memorandum are found in the Smithsonian Archives: three (one in Bache's hand) in Box 5 of the Bache Papers, and the fourth in Box 30 of the Henry Papers.

2. The board considered Jewett's appointment after first approving three resolutions offered by Henry W. Hilliard. The first set the salary of the assistant secretary acting as librarian at $2,000; the second requested the secretary "to nominate to the Board an assistant, who shall be the librarian," and whose salary would begin when the building could accommodate a library; and the third allowed compensation to the librarian for any services rendered for the institution in the interim. After

the resolutions were adopted, Henry was recorded as remarking that "understanding Professor Charles C. Jewett, of Brown University, to be the preference of a majority of the Board," he therefore nominated him as assistant secretary acting as the librarian. George Evans then called on the board to approve Jewett's nomination "and consent to his employment"; his resolution carried. Rhees, *Journals*, p. 27.

The minutes thus left it unclear who actually appointed Jewett: Henry, acting with the regents' consent, or the regents, by confirming Henry's nomination? As Henry's comments to Harriet indicate, however, his immediate concern was simply to insure that the minutes reflected that he had nominated Jewett only after being requested to do so by the board.

3. Princeton's second term commenced on February 4. *Catalogue of the Officers and Students of the College of New Jersey, 1845–1846* (Princeton, 1846), p. 22.

12. TO WILLIAM ALEXANDER HENRY

Washington Jany 27th 1847

My Dear Son

I have been expecting for some time past to receive a letter from you but as yet I have been disappointed. I suppose however that it will come in good time.[1] I was much pleased with the letters from the little girls[2] and shall expect some further communications from the same quarter. Washington is a city of great bustle during the session of congress but when the two houses have adjourned it is said to be quite dull. It* is a remarkable place for meeting persons whom you have not seen for a long time or have long forgotten. A man called on me a few nights ago who lived in Albany when he was a boy and knew me at the time. He called to my recollection several facts which I had entirely forgotten particularly one inreference to my having be caught by a man while throwing stones down a hill and being nearly put into the watch house. I was not however at the time doing wrong intentionally but carelessly; I was throwing stones with several other boys down a hill in the evening without thinking that they might hurt some person when several persons came running afer us and as I was the last to move I was caught. One of the stones had struck a man or came near striking him. It is not enought that we intend to do no harm but we must in all cases take heed to the effects of our actions and be assured that our carelessness or ignorance does[B] not injure others. For if we are not careful in these particulars we are very culpable though we had no intention of doing wrong. On this point you may recollect one of the stories of Gough the temperance lecturer[3] who relates that a man fired a canon from a hill into a [---] town and killed several persons when he was informed ~~that~~

*Ask Mother to explain to you the meaning of this sentence about the Houses.[A]

30

of what he had done he said oh! I [?diid]ᶜ ↑did↓ not intend to hurt any body I was only firing for sport. But to return to the man I had not seen him before since I was a boy and indeed he had gone entirely out of my recollection though he was still in my memory (What is the difference between recollection and memory) and as he might have become in the mean time a very unworthy person perhaps a very bad man I told him that until I knew more of his character I could not admit him to the intimacy of a friend though we had been companions in early life. I treated him however very civilly and after some time he left me. He had been an officer in Texas and though he had very respectable connections his breath smelt of rum and I was not sorrey when he left me except that he though give such evidence of not being a very good man— I met another old acquaintance George Clinton sone of the late Governor Clinton the author of the canal policy of the state of New York[4]—but I have mentioned the facts of this meeting I think in one of my letters to your Mother.[5] I have also met a great number of students—the young man that stopped at our house at the begining of last session and occupied for a week and more your little room, I have forgotten his name, I see frequently. Also there are many of the old graduates of Princeton in Washington some and not a few live here and others [ar]eᶜ on from the south and west. Washington is at present very much crowded with strangers. Several hundred young men are here applying at the war office for commissions in the army. It does not speak very well I think for the character of a young man to be anxious to get into the army, by an appointmnt without having passed through the academy at West Point. When the war is over they will be thrown out of employment not being in the regular army—they will be exposed to great hardships be liable to be killed and should they live through the war will be broken down in health and will have contracted such bad habits as will render them very unworthy citizens. War is a dreadful curse and I hope the time will soon come when nations shall go to war no more. [---] When you come to Washington as I think it probableᴰ you will next summer you will be pleased with ↑the↓ capital. It is an immense building I presume the largest in the united states. It stands on the brow of a hill and while you enter on the east side by a high flightᴱ of steps into the building on the first floor on the opposite side there are several flights and these introduce you into a lower story. In the middle of the building, is an immensely large circular room called the rotunda surmountedᶠ with a dome and a sky light ~~called the rotunda~~ and surrounddᴳ on all sides with large pictures each about 20 feet long by about 10 or 12 high. These pictures are placed in pannels or intentations in the circular wall. All the pannels are now filled except one—a new picture has lately been put up—the landing of columbus by Vanderlin. It is a very fine picture which the artist has spent several years in painting— Each picture cost if I am not mistaken 9 thousand dollars.[6] The sketch in the margin will give you some idea of the relative

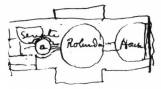 positions of the room of the House of Representatives and the senate chamber. The latter is much smaller than the former and the two are situated on opposite sides of the rotunda.

Adieu

To W A Henry From his affectionate Father[H]
a is a small rotunda for ventillation[1]

Family Correspondence, Henry Papers, Smithsonian Archives.

1. William wrote his father two days later: [January 29, 1847] (dated as "Friday," with a file note of "February 1847"), Family Correspondence, Henry Papers, Smithsonian Archives.

2. Not found.

3. John Bartholomew Gough, who in 1845 had lectured in Princeton on temperance. *Henry Papers,* 6:275–276.

4. Henry may have been referring to *The Canal Policy of the State of New-York: Delineated in a Letter to Robert Troup, Esquire* (Albany, 1821), by "Tacitus." A list by Henry named it as one of sixteen "Clinton Pamphlets" (by or about De-Witt Clinton) in his library.

5. Doc. 5.

6. Vanderlyn and the three other artists who in 1837 received commissions to execute four historical paintings for the Capitol Rotunda each were paid $10,000 for their work. Vivien Green Fryd, *Art & Empire: The Politics of Ethnicity in the United States Capitol, 1815–1860* (New Haven, 1992), p. 46.

13. TO HARRIET HENRY

Washington Thursday Jany 28[A][–29][th] 1847

My dearest

Your letter[1] giving me an account of the death of our dear Louisa[2] was received this afternoon on my return from the capital. Though the intelligence was not unexpected it shocked me very much and I have since been very melancholly and I may say home sick. I am deeply impressed this eveing with the uncertainty of Life and the unsubstantial nature of all earthly affairs— What a change in the course of two short months has been made in our little circle unbroken for ten years— Well all things are ordered by a Power which controlls events and over rules them for good to those who put their trust in Him. I fear you are extremely lonely and dispirited and I wish that I could transport myself in a moment to you. The Board met to day and settled the principal business of the pressent session but they meet again on saturday to finish a little business left unadjusted. The meeting has terminated[B] very harmoniously & ~~though~~ though the organisation is not precisely such as I could wish yet it is all I could reasonably expect form the several acts of congress which we were obliged to comply with. Baches plan of putting up the building has carried—the wings are to be erected first and the body completed in five years so that the cost of building will be drawn from the interest of the money which would otherwise have been expended immediately.

↑Friday↓[C] I shall not be able to leave Washington until the latter part of next week. The Board will adjourn on saturday and will not probably meet again until next December though according to law they are required to meet in Feb[y] next at this time those in Washington will meet and adjourn without doing business.[3] I have been all the forenoon busily[D] engaged with a clerk in the official duties of my office—in arranging the minutes and adjusting the ~~duties~~[E] business of the board. I have found the occupation plesant and by no means difficult. A little common sense will stand a man in place of much ~~practical~~[F] knowledge of a merely technical kind.

I am finishing this letter at Bache's in the Office[4] he has a dinner party of his relatives of the younger kind among whom is Miss Lesley Cook from Princeton. This young lady appears to be quite as great as favourite in Washington as in Princeton.

I have felt quite depressed all day Louisa has scarcely been out of my head for a minute the weather is gloomy and were it not that [I] ↑had↓ considerably to occupy me I should have been quite home sick. It appears a very very long time since I left home and I am wondering how you will all appear when I return. I hope you have been careful of your health and now that Louisa requires no more attendance you will rest yourself—send for a sewing woman and have the cloths of the children put in order without fatigue to yourself— Take some rest after all the exertions you have made—endeavour to cultivate a cheerful state of mind—put trust in Providence—amuse yourself with books and look if possible on the bright side of the passing changing scenes of Life. I am to visit Mr Webster[5] this evening though I do not feel very much inclined to talk. I am rather inclined to think I shall be very dull and not suceed in being even a good listner which next to the character of a good speaker is highly esteemed[G] particularly by good talkers.

I spent a short time this morning in the room of the Supreme Court of the US. The Judges of this court with their Gowns are the most dignifed asembly of men to be found in our Country. They hold office for life and consequently are above the temtation of being influenced by party considerations and since they owe their office to the integrity of the Union they will always be a check on the dendancies to its dismemberment. The House yesterday spent 9 hours in attempting to settle whether <u>yesterday</u> was to <u>morrow</u> or the day before. A resolution had been proposed two days ago that a debate on a bill should be terminated "tomorrow" the resolution however was not acted upon until the day after it was proposed and the question then was whether the "tomorrow" was the day after the bill had been proposed or the day after the bill passed. The House adjourned without I believe settling the question[6]— Adieu as ever your H.

Family Correspondence, Henry Papers, Smithsonian Archives.

1. Not found.

2. Louisa Alexander died on January 24, 1847. William Henry to Joseph Henry, [January 29, 1847] (dated "Friday," with a file note of "February 1847"), Family Correspondence, Henry Papers, Smithsonian Archives.

3. The board adjourned on January 30 and reconvened on February 5, when it adjourned *sine die*. In keeping with a resolution adopted September 9, 1846, fixing the times of their two regular annual meetings, the regents reconvened for the first such meeting on February 17, the third Wednesday in February. The second annual meeting took place on December 8, the second Wednesday in December. Rhees, *Journals*, pp. 4, 31, 32, 39.

4. That is, the office of the Coast Survey. See *Henry Papers*, 6:444n.

5. Daniel Webster (1782–1852), orator, statesman, and Whig senator from Massachusetts. *DAB*.

6. On January 26 a resolution was introduced in the House of Representatives to terminate debate on a naval appropriations bill "at one o'clock to-morrow," but it was not approved until January 28. Debate resumed after the vote. At the appointed hour, a member asked that the debate be ended, but the chair denied the request, stating that since the resolution only took effect upon its adoption, debate could continue until the afternoon of the following day, January 29. Numerous roll-call votes ensued on motions—all defeated—to suspend the debate or to adjourn, and proceedings dragged on for hours. Near the end, representative Reuben Chapman asked the chair "whether this was to-day or to-morrow? If the House could make to-morrow part of to-day, could it not make as well to-day into to-morrow?" The session finally ended at 10:30 P.M., after the chair cast a tie-breaking vote on a motion to adjourn; the issue of what was "to-morrow" was left for another day. *Congressional Globe*, 29th Congress, 2d Session, 1846–1847, *16*:280–283 (quotation on p. 283).

14. TO HARRIET HENRY

Washington Satur[d]—
Jany 30th 1847

My dear H.

The Board met again this morning but did not finish all the business. ~~they~~ They will I fear keep me until the latter part of next week. All the plans of the building and the operations for the future year (or I should say the present year) have been arranged. I am getting quite home sick and sometimes wish almost that congress would stop the whole affair and suffer me to return to Princeton.

I again take courage and resolve to persevere with a stout heart believing that all would be well were my wife and children around me— I have been engaged most of the day since the adjournment of the Board with the architect in arranging the plans of the different parts of the building. It will be a most magnificent affair when finished but if the whole fund necessary to ~~finish~~ ↑complete↓ the structure is derived from the accruing interest I think it will be more than five years in completion. I have just received a note of invitation from Mrs Marcy to dine with the secretary of war[1] on Tuesday next. I called last evening with Dr Lindly[2] to see Mr Webster but found him engaged in a political meeting with some of friends of the same side. Dr Lindly I think I have mentioned before; he is a Brother of Dr Lindly once a professor in Princeton.[3] His Wife is a relative of Daniel Webster[4] and was an acquaintance of Mrs Taylor.[5] She became acquainted with Mrs T. I think she said in New-ark. Finding Mr Webster engaged I called at General Dix's[6] and there spent the evening very pleasantly with the General—I never was intimately acquainted with Mr Dix I found him very kind and gentlemanly though he did not ~~much~~ impress me very much with his talents. I meet a great many persons every day that I have not seen before for some time. Yesterday I was acosted ~~with~~ ↑by↓ two persons from Albany and to day ↑by↓ others from the south. Mr Dix informed my that Horatio Potter[7] had come on from Albany to perform the marriage cerimony between an officer I think of the Navy and the eldest daughter of Mr Ferguson.[8]

Mr Espy and his wife are here staying at a boarding house.[9] I have not yet call on them though I have promised to do so. My time has been so much occupied with the meetings of the Board that I have been unable to make any calls except in the evening and then but seldom.

I wish I were with you and the children this evening— All the excitement of pressing my plans on the Board is now passed and I am left ↑at↓ this time in a state some what approaching a collapse and feel that nothing would give me more pleasure than a cheerful fire—a good easy chair with my wife and children around me. I sent a letter enclose with one to you to Will yesterday.[10] I mentioned in this that the cost of the of the pictures in the rotunday was 5 thousand dollars apiece. I am correctly informed to day that the cost was 10 thousand Dollars each. The only pannel yet unfilled is that which was assigned to Inman. He received before he died[A] 6 thousand dollars in advance but did little or nothing to the picture. It is not probable this pannel will be filled until the mexican war is finished. When this will be[B] the case is now not known—the prospect is darker rather than otherwise.[11]

I am writing this in the room of the vice President and it has become so dark that I can scarcely see the point of my pen. I must therefore close with the assurance that I am as ever

your H

Family Correspondence, Henry Papers, Smithsonian Archives.

1. William Learned Marcy, an acquaintance of Henry's from his Albany days, was appointed secretary of war in 1845. *Henry Papers,* 2:34n; 6:253n. His wife, the former Cornelia Knower, was the daughter of Benjamin Knower, a prominent Democrat and another of Henry's New York acquaintances. *Henry Papers,* 2:156n–157n.

2. Harvey Lindsley or Lindsly (1804–1889), a graduate of Princeton (1820), was a Washington physician. *Princeton Catalogue,* p. 133; John M. Lindly, *The History of the Lindley-Lindsley-Linsley Families in America, 1639–1930* (Winfield, Iowa, 1930), pp. 430–431.

3. Philip Lindsley (1786–1855), another Princeton graduate (1804), was its professor of languages from 1813 to 1824 and acting college president in 1823. He became president of Cumberland College (the University of Nashville) in 1824. *DAB.*

4. Harvey Lindsley's wife, Emeline C. Webster (1808–1892), was a cousin of Daniel Webster's. Lindly, p. 431; Charles M. Wiltse, ed., *Guide and Index to the Microfilm of the Papers of Daniel Webster* (Ann Arbor, 1971), p. 36.

5. Perhaps Julia Taylor, a family friend. *Henry Papers,* 5:379n.

6. John A. Dix, formerly New York's adjutant-general and later its secretary of state, was currently a Democratic senator from that state. *Henry Papers,* 3:37n; *BDAC.*

7. An Episcopalian minister, Horatio Potter was rector of St. Peter's Church in Albany. *Henry Papers,* 6:289n.

8. Robert A. Lacey and Blanche Ferguson were married on January 27, 1847. Her father, James Ferguson (*Henry Papers,* 2:15n–16n), another of Henry's Albany associates, was a first assistant on the Coast Survey. Old Marriage Records A-K (1811–1858), District of Columbia Marriage Bureau, Washington, D.C.

9. Since 1842, James Pollard Espy had been employed by the Surgeon General's Office of the War Department to coordinate its meteorological observations. He met his wife, the former Margaret Pollard (d. 1850), in 1812 while he was principal of, and she a teacher at, the Cumberland Academy in Maryland. After their marriage, he adopted her maiden name as his middle name. *Henry Papers,* 2:195n–196n; 6:574n; *DAB.*

10. Docs. 11 and 12.

11. Henry Inman had died the year previous just as he was beginning work on a painting of Daniel Boone's Kentucky cabin, the first in a series he had been commissioned to complete for the Capitol. William H. Powell (1823–1879, *DAB*), a former student of Inman's, received the balance of his commission in 1847. His painting, *Discovery of the Mississippi by De Soto A.D. 1541,* was installed in 1855. *Henry Papers,* 6:390; Vivien Green Fryd, *Art & Empire: The Politics of Ethnicity in the United States Capitol, 1815–1860* (New Haven, 1992), pp. 46, 57.

15. TO HARRIET HENRY

Washington Feby 3rd 1847

My dear H

The board of Regents meet for the last time during their pressent session on Friday morning[1] and after the meeting at 4 o'clock PM I intend to start for the north and hope to be with you at [?least] on saturday night.

This is a blustering day at Washington but quite warm. The wind is very high and has been so all night— I have been much engaged in superintending the affairs of the Institution and looking after the effects of Smithson. There is in the Patent office a number of boxes contaning many of his articles and a cupboard filled with manuscript papers belonging to him.[2]

Among the articles is a bronze metalion likeness of Smithson which is to be engraved for the frontis piece of the transactions. We are now looking out for a room which may serve as an office and depository for the books which are constantly coming in from the different publishers who according to law are required to send a copy to the Library of the smithsonian.[3]

I hope the children have received the package of letters I sent and that they were amused with the contents.[4]

I am beginning to feel a little more used to Washington and were we once settled here with the children around us I think I should be well pleased.

I have seen a number of students starting on their return to Princeton and have requested some of them to say that I would be on towards the latter part of the week.

Charles Abert[5] took me in his little waggon to see Mr Stone[6] who lives about 2 miles from the capital. He has a very beautiful situation and is now devoting himself to the art of sculpture and is suceeding most admirably. He was working on a bust of Prof. Dod[7] and has succeeded admirably. It is incomparably better than the one[8] made in Phil[d] I did not see his wife and daughter they were out at the time. On my return from Mr Stones I spent the remainder of the evening at Mrs Green's[9] brothers[10] and was much pleased with my visit. Mr Mc Culloh is a very intelligent man and is highly esteemed by all parties in Washington. He thinks that after the Institution is once organized it will go on without molestation and that I will have pretty much my own way in the management. I have been variously affected with the prospect of the success of the establishment. I have sometimes high hopes of its usefulness and then again the future is dark but every think in life is uncertain, and when we think we are standing on the firmest earth the hiden fire may be burning beneath us. The sailor boy on the bending mast often lives through the storm while the [?secure] landsman in fancied security is crushd with his falling house.

When you come to washington you will not want for the new books of the day they all come for the library of the Institution.[11]

Though I am in the focus of Political events I know but little of what is going on—my head quarters for the present during^A the day is in the vice Presidents Room in the Capital. It is a beautiful room finely carpeted, with armed chairs damask curtains &c. &c. With a servant in attendance.

The city is full to overflowing with strangers—hundreds of young men are flocking to Washington to get commissions. Young Webster the clergyman's son has been appointed comissary—with which I am well pleased.[12]

Your H–

Family Correspondence, Henry Papers, Smithsonian Archives.

1. February 5.

2. The previous day, Henry had visited the Patent Office Building and met with John Varden, whose duties as custodian of the collections housed in the "National Gallery" included caring for Smithson's personal effects. Entry for February 2, 1847, in William Q. Force, "Extracts from a Diary Kept by John Varden, at the U.S. Patent Office Building, and Placed by Him in My Hands," n.d., Folder "Telegraph Notes, Etc., 1846–1881," Box 23, Henry Papers, Smithsonian Archives; Douglas E. Evelyn, "The National Galley at the Patent Office," in *Magnificent Voyagers: The U.S. Exploring Expedition, 1838–1842*, ed. Herman J. Viola and Carolyn Margolis (Washington, 1985), pp. 226–241, especially pp. 236, 237.

3. Section 10 of the act establishing the Smithsonian Institution designated its library as a copyright depository; see *Henry Papers*, 6:466, 594.

4. Henry to Helen Henry, January 30, 1847; Henry to Mary Henry, January 31, 1847, Family Correspondence, Henry Papers, Smithsonian Archives. According to Harriet, Henry's letters produced "delight" and a "burst of laughter." Harriet Henry to Henry, February 2, 1847, in same location.

5. A Princeton graduate (1842), Abert was a brother-in-law of Alexander Dallas Bache.

Henry Papers, 4:220n. His father, John J. Abert (*Henry Papers*, 3:69n), was chief of the Army's Topographical Bureau.

6. Horatio Stone (1808–1875), a New York physician, had moved recently to Washington and taken up sculpture. His work included busts of several American statesmen. *DAB*.

7. Albert Baldwin Dod, professor of mathematics at Princeton, had died on November 20, 1845. *Henry Papers*, 1:434; 6:337n.

8. In 1846, Henry had arranged with Augustus Lenci, a Philadelphia sculptor, to make a portrait bust of Dod. Lenci also furnished twenty-five plaster casts for subscription sale to Dod's friends and Princeton alumni. Donald Drew Egbert, *Princeton Portraits* (Princeton, 1947), p. 99. Philadelphia City Directory, 1846; Lenci's bill to Henry, April 6, 1846, College Finances, 1840–1849, John Maclean Papers, Princeton University Archives, Seeley G. Mudd Manuscript Library, Princeton University; Samuel H. Pennington to Henry, December 30, 1846, Henry Papers, Smithsonian Archives.

9. Isabella McCulloch Green; see Doc. 4.

10. James W. B. F. McCulloch, the first comptroller of the treasury, whom Henry first met at Washington in December 1846, was the son of John McCulloch by his first wife, Anne Todd (d. 1789). Isabella Green was John McCulloch's daughter by his second wife, Eliza-

beth McBlair. *Henry Papers, 6:*593, 599; Alice
Norris Parran, *Series II of "Register of Maryland's
Heraldic Families": Tercentenary of the Founding of
Maryland* (Baltimore, 1938), p. 238.

11. On the contrary, Charles C. Jewett in
1850 complained that because of the cost of
shipping books to the Smithsonian for copyright deposit, "few publishers complied with
the requirement of the act of Congress." *Smithsonian Report for 1849,* p. 35.

12. Charles R. Webster, a Princeton graduate (1840), on January 18 was appointed an
assistant quartermaster. Webster had sought
Henry's recommendation, but it is not known

if he provided one. *Princeton Catalogue,* p. 160;
Charles K. Gardner, *A Dictionary of . . . the Army
of the United States,* 2d ed. (New York, 1860), p.
475; Webster to Henry, December 4, 1846,
Henry Papers, Smithsonian Archives.

Webster's father, Charles Webster, was pastor
of the Presbyterian Church of Monmouth
County, New Jersey; his grandfather, long a
prominent Albany publisher, had been a
trustee of the Albany Academy when Henry
was hired in 1826. George Rogers Howell and
Jonathan Tenney, eds., *History of the County of
Albany, N.Y., from 1609 to 1886* (New York,
1886), p. 371; *Henry Papers, 1:*27n, 132–133.

16. TO HARRIET HENRY

Washington
Thursday Ev.
[February 4, 1847][A]
11 O'clock

My Dear H

I have just returned from a very plesant dinner party at Secretary
Marcy's. The party was small but in good style and very agreeable. The
Secretary and his Lady were very attentive and polite to me—among
the guests were Governor Fairfield of Maine[1] and Governor Somebody
I have forgotten whom from Connecticut.[2]

After the dinner which commenced at about 7 o'clock I went to Mr
Walkers[3] to meet Bache. Where I have remaind until just now. This
morning I made my first appearance in the white House.[4] I had called
before and left my card but did not see the President. I was admitted
though a number of Gentlemen were wating audience.[5]

The man in the great position received me with much politeness and
afibility made enquiries as to me[B] and requested that I would call frequently particularly after the adjournment of congress.

The room of audience for business is on the second floor and is
though not very large quite plesant the President sits at a large table on
one side of the fire place and his visitors arrange themselves on the
other side fasing him.

The office though one of much honor is certainly not one of much
leisure— All day long strangers are arriving ~~or~~ and all at certain hours
are admitted.[6] We found alone with the President a roudy looking fellow with a monsterous [...] talking loud and urging the appointement
of himself or a friend to some office. The manners of the great man are

affible but considerably dignified not as much so as those of General Jackson but more than those of Mr Van Buren.[7]

This has been a very windy day and for Washington quite cold. I have been making many inquiries about the health of the city[8] and find various accounts. The general testimony is that the inhabitants in the months of aug. and sept and perhaps a part of nov are liable to chills and fever provided they expose themselves to the air at night by sitting in the open air or to the fog in the morning shortely after sun rise.

I also learn that the most health part of the city is on the mall where the Smithsonian Hall is to be erected.[9] It appears from the accounts of several with whom I have conversed that those who live on the out-skirts of the city are more exposed to chills than the inhabitants of the centre and more thickly settled parts.[c] This is the case with Charleston and other cities at the south while the middle of the city is perfectly healthy the country around is impregnated after sundown with malaria. The effect is probably due to the decomposition of the vegetable matter around the city and the impregnated air is purified by the smoke of the chimnies or is prevented by the houses reaching the centre of the city.[10]

I think when you are once settled here you will be pleased with the place you may go into society or not as you may think fit and as there is always somethg going on during the session of congress there is no want of excitement.

I had an invitation to a party this evening at the vice Presidents but as there was to be a great rout with dancing there I concluded not to go. I have been quite cheerful for two days past and begin to feel quite confident in the success of the Smithsonian though clouds and darkness have settled hereto-fore upon its prospect. I intend starting for home tomorrow evening but perhaps I shall stop at Baltimore to avoid riding during the night. I am living on the anticipation of the pleasure I hope to enjoy in meeting you and our dear little ones. I have been from you long enough to feel how much I need your company sympathy direction love and all that has rendered you a part of myself for the last 16 years and I feel most forceably the truth of your remark that life is too short to spend much of it in seperation.

Your H–

Family Correspondence, Henry Papers, Smithsonian Archives.

1. John Fairfield (1797–1847) was governor of Maine from 1839 to 1843, when he was elected to the United States Senate. *BDAC*.

2. Clark Bissell (1782–1857) was governor of Connecticut from 1847 to 1848. Thomas William Herringshaw, *Encyclopedia of American Biography of the Nineteenth Century* (Chicago, 1905).

3. Robert J. Walker.

4. That is, his first audience with President Polk. Henry had visited the White House before, in 1836. *Henry Papers, 3:*135.

5. Polk did not mention Henry's visit in his diary, noting only that he spent the morning in "the usual scene of receiving visitors. . . . Many of them as usual were seeking office and especially military appointments." Milo Milton Quaife, ed., *The Diary of James K. Polk during His Presidency, 1845 to 1849,* 4 vols. (Chicago, 1910), 2:366.

6. Polk's availability to the public was a hallmark of his administration. Except for days when Polk met with his cabinet, he "felt obliged by the doctrine of republican accessibility to interrupt his labors for several hours to receive anyone who wished to call on him." Charles G. Sellers, *James K. Polk, Continentalist, 1843–1846* (Princeton, 1966), p. 302.

7. For Henry's impressions of President Andrew Jackson and President-elect Martin Van Buren, see *Henry Papers, 2:*81–82 and *3:*135.

8. No doubt to reassure Harriet as much as himself. Washington's climate, swampy areas, and poor sanitation led many residents and travelers to consider it insalubrious. Charles Dickens's view was typical: "It is very unhealthy. Few people would live in Washington, I take it, who were not obliged to reside there." Dickens, *American Notes for General Circulation,* 2d ed., 2 vols. (London, 1842), *1:*283; Constance M.

Green, *Washington: A History of the Capital, 1800–1950,* 2 vols. in 1 (Princeton, 1976), *1:*12–13, 93–94, 134–135, 211–212. For a more positive description of the city, see Joseph B. Varnum, Jr., *The Seat of Government of the United States,* 2d ed. (Washington, 1854), pp. 62–63.

9. Henry was misinformed: the south side of the Mall, where the Smithsonian Building was to be erected, was considered one of the city's most unhealthy areas, situated as it was along a canal linking the Potomac and Anacostia Rivers. As early as the 1820s, the swampy stretches of land along the canal were recognized as health hazards. Green, *1:*134–135.

10. Henry's was an expression of the miasmic theory of disease, which held that decomposing vegetation in low-lying marshes produced poisons that caused fevers and illnesses. It was only after mid-century that this theory would give way to those which regarded microscopic organisms as agents of disease propagation. Morrill Wyman, *A Practical Treatise on Ventilation* (Boston and London, 1846), pp. 88–89; John K. Mitchell, *On the Cryptogamous Origin of Malarious and Epidemic Fevers* (Philadelphia, 1849), pp. 13–33; Phyllis Allen, "Etiological Theory in America Prior to the Civil War," *Journal of the History of Medicine and Allied Sciences,* 1947, 2:489–520, especially pp. 492, 494, 504–516.

17. FROM JONATHAN HOMER LANE[1]

Castleton Seminary Feb 8th 1847

Prof Henry

Dear Sir On reading your paper in the Jan number of Sillimans Journal I was particularly interested with the views you express in the last paragraph of page 27 in regard to the nature of common electric discharges as that of the Leyden jar.[2] I have entertained the same idea myself for a year or two without supposing it had ever occurred to anyone else. It was first suggested to me in reading Faraday's experiments and observations on the peculiar decomposing action of electric discharges[3] and I soon saw that it was no more than a reasonable inference from the known law of induction of currents for such is the comparatively small quantity and high intensity of a charge that up to the maximum rapidity of current in discharge we may reasonably believe that the resistance to conduction in a good conductor is very small com-

41

pared with the force of induction which like inertia in a ponderable body opposes either[A] increase or diminution of motion. If so we could not avoid the conclusion that the current once generated for instance in the discharge of a jar would rush on after an equilibrium was attained until it charged the inner coating nearly as highly positive as it was before negative when of course it would return and I have thought the vibrations might even amount to hundreds or thousands all in the time of a single shock or spark the penetrated interval of air offering it is probable during the time but small resistance. The number of vibrations would of course depend on the difference between the force of induction and the resistance to conduction just as the number of vibrations a pendulum will make before coming to a state of rest depends on the difference between the force of its inertia and the resistance of the air. In the case of a very long discharging wire in which it is thought that time is required for the spark to pass the length of the wire time if my impression is correct which is a considerable part at least of the duration of the spark we must perhaps modify the above view by supposing as you would have done a succession of waves along the wire. I would not however speak with confidence on that point because I have not read fully Wheatstone's experiments.[4]

I was waiting for a favorable opportunity to make some experiments with the design of publishing my views on the above subject[5] if they appeared to be sustained hoping to subject the phenomena of decomposition by common electricity to the laws of decomposition by voltaic electricity but from the tenor of the paragraph referred to I suppose you have before published similar views though I do not recollect to have met with them. My object then in troubling you with this communication is to inquire where I may find them. There is nothing at this time I should read with higher interest.

Very respectfully Yours
J. H. Lane

Please address J. H. Lane Castleton Vt.

Henry Papers, Smithsonian Archives.
Enclosed in Doc. 18. Reply: Doc. 42.

1. A schoolteacher and graduate of Yale (1846), Lane (1819–1880) received an appointment with the Coast Survey in 1847. He was later employed by the Patent Office (1848–1857) and the Office of Weights and Measures (1869–1880). In 1848, Henry described two of Lane's publications "on physico mathematical subjects" as exhibiting "much originality of thought, fertility of invention and a profound knowledge of the subject." Henry concluded "that with a suitable opportunity of developing his talents Mr Lane would become one of the first in the line of original physical research in our country." Henry to A. M. Clayton, June 1, 1848, Box 1, Scientific and Personal Papers of Jonathan Homer Lane, 1836–78, Records of the Bureau of Standards, RG 167, National Archives; *DSB*.

2. "On the Induction of Atmospheric Electricity on the Wires of the Electrical Telegraph," *Silliman's Journal*, 1847, 2d ser. *3*:25–32. Lane's specific reference was to Henry's theory of the oscillatory discharge of a Leyden jar.

3. Presumably a reference to Michael Faraday's *Experimental Researches in Electricity*, Twelfth Series, "On Induction (continued)," *Phil. Trans.*, 1838, pp. 83–123, containing Faraday's theory of electrical discharge.

4. Charles Wheatstone, professor of experimental physics at King's College, London, had measured the velocity of electricity in a long wire: "An Account of Some Experiments to Measure the Velocity of Electricity and the Duration of Electric Light," *Phil. Trans.*, 1834, pp. 583–591. Henry had worried repeatedly about this experiment while developing his theoretical ideas about electricity. *Henry Papers*, 2:290–292, 491–493; 5:14–15, 406, 411; 6:172–173.

5. Lane summarized many of his thoughts on electricity in "On the Law of the Induction of an Electric Current upon Itself When Developed in a Straight Prismatic Conductor, and of Discharges of Machine Electricity through Straight Wires," *Silliman's Journal*, 1851, 2d ser. *11*:17–35.

18. FROM JOHN FOSTER[1]

Union College Feb. 18 1847

My Dear Sir

I received a few days since the enclosed letter[2] directed as you will perceive to you & to my care. I was utterly at a loss what to make of the circumstance—thought it possible the writer might have learned that you were to visit our Dutch City about this time—had in short a great variety of unplausible explanations. At length after waiting sometime seeing something about electricity by the advice of a legal gentleman I opened it & found it abounding in a commodity of which I presume many of your letters are full—queres. How it should come to be directed to my care I can only explain in one way. A member of our Senior Class who takes great interest in Electricity resides in Castleton.[3] He had probably been conversing on the subject & so mingled the names of the originator & reporter of your discoveries that the brain of Mr Lane became confused & he supposed that the two individuals must be essentially one & the same. I hope you will bea[r][A] with becoming meekness the honor thus imposed on you—an honor entirely unsought & attributable to no active agency of yours.

Though often sorely tempted I have not written you before because I supposed the increase of your correspondence since your appointment to Washington must be excessively burdensome. Few have made greater sacrifices than myself in consenting to your acceptance. Nothing but a sense of duty to the scientific interests of the country could have induced me to allow[B] your removal to such a fearful distance that I may not be able to see you again in years. Bache & Henry both gone is a

43

thought to sigh over. I should much like to know whether there is a good degree of certainty that the Smithsonian is to be a Royal Institute or Royal Society[4] instead of an Agricultural school where lectures without number shall be yearly given to empty benches. I have watched with interest the efforts to give the Institution a right direction & sincerely hope they will meet with success even in this democratic & utilitarian country.

I was greatly rejoiced to receive the Bulletin containing your report on the Telegraph wires.[5] It came just in time for me to give the Seniors the substance of it at the close of my lectures last term. It ↑is↓ marked with all that transparency which characterizes your other papers & which I can never sufficiently admire.

My Oersted's app. for comp. water is out of order. A bubble of air has found its way into the glass bottle & divides the column of water. As yours[6] has most probably met the same accident often I should like to know what method you find best for expelling the intruder.

We all deeply sympathize with Prof. Alexander in the loss of his excellent wife. His house must be left desolate indeed.

If you can without too much trouble give me a few lines I should feel much obliged—not otherwise. I received Bache's report a few days since.[7] We are all pretty well—Jackson at work on the Optics & very dyspeptic.[c]

Yours as ever
John Foster

Prof. Joseph Henry LLD
PS. I stop the press for a moment to announce that I have just received from Mr Gurley[8] (Troy) a fine vertical & horizontal monochord.[9] The wires (two sets), I had before received from Paris.

My best regards to Mrs Henry

JF–

Henry Papers, Smithsonian Archives.

1. Foster was teaching mathematics and natural philosophy at Union College. *Henry Papers,* 6:78n.

2. Doc. 17.

3. Selah G. Perkins. *A General Catalogue of the Officers, Graduates and Students of Union College, from 1795 to 1868* (Albany, 1868), p. 74.

4. References to the Royal Institution and the Royal Society of London, respectively.

5. Either Henry's presentation in the APS *Proceedings,* 1843–1847, 4:260–268, or its reprinting as "On the Induction of Atmospheric Electricity on the Wires of the Electrical Telegraph," *Silliman's Journal,* 1847, 2d ser. 3:25–32.

6. Purchased in Paris. Henry used his Oersted apparatus for the compression of liquids both for classroom demonstrations and research. *Henry Papers,* 3:541; 5:28, 179.

7. Probably U.S. House, 29th Congress, 2d Session, *Report of the Superintendent of the Coast Survey, Showing the Progress of That Work,* House Documents, No. 6 (1846).

8. William Gurley (1821–1887) had been trained as a civil engineer at Rensselaer Polytechnic Institute. He was a partner in the firm

of Phelps and Gurley, makers of mathematical and philosophical instruments. Charles E. Smart, *The Makers of Surveying Instruments in America since 1700* (Troy, 1962), pp. 60–62.

9. An instrument for measuring and exhibiting the mathematical relations of musical tones.

19. FROM ISAAC W. JACKSON[1]

Febry 18th 1847 Schen

My dear Henry

Your letter[2] was duly recd;—but as I supposed you too much busied with matters of moment to spend time in an amateur correspondence even with a friend, I refrained from writing you in return, though especially tempted to do so. Before I say a word, let me beseech you to remember that you & I are on such terms that any question I may ask you or any request I may make may be treated precisely as a suggestion springing up in your own mind, entertained & thrown aside at your pleasure.— This being admitted,—I proceed— A change in politics has again had an unfavorable influence upon fortunes of our frnd Patterson,[3]—reduced him as he says to "Shoemaker's wages"— He is anxious to "quit a busines which has now become an unrequited drudgery & almost odious" to him— Such is his language— He is negotiating with a gentlemn relative to the sale of his books, in order he says "to enable him to pursue his studies" etc— — All this shows that he is reduced almost to the verge of despair,—for you know he idolizes his books— Besides the plan I think is a very unwise one & may exercise a most unhappy effect upon his future life— I have therefore determd to consult with his frnds & see if we cannot propose something better, than his project of parting with what he holds so dear, & abandoning all employment but study with its inevitably bad consequences— — I start for Alby in a few minutes for the very purpose,—tho I have little hopes of effecting any thing—

I write you to enquire if there is any probability of your being able ultimately to give him a place in the Institute.[4] It has occerd to me that if you should determ to publish a journal ↑etc↓, his services would be invaluable,—from his <u>perfect</u> acquaintance with his business—as a^ general directer in all matters relating to your printing, proof reading etc no trifling affair where mathematical symbols are concernd—for not one math. work in twenty publihd in the country is printed with even tolerable accuracy— — A very modest salary would I presume satisfy

45

him,—barely enough to support his family,—provd the position would be such as to give him a reasonable degree of leisure—

You mentnd the place of Calculater in the Coast Survey,—I have said[B] nothing to him about it,—as I was entirly ignorant of its dutie's, emolumt perid of its continuance etc— —

Is there no place at Washington under the governt that ↑would↓ answer for him, & which could be procured if a powerful influence were exerted in his favor— — If you are not too busy will you give the subject some consideration & write me soon.— But as I said at first, we must not be troublesome to you,—Patterson himself is wonderfuly averse to troubling any one with his matters— I presume he would object to my writing to you.— If you could afford the time,[C] I should like to hear a little about the Institute,—your plans etc all strictly <u>entr nous</u>— —

I am now attempting to prepare something on Physical Optic's[5]— I have nearly completed the generl exposition of the theory,—the principle of interference & its application ~~to~~ to reflection & ordinary refraction,—& the colors of thin plates & diffraction— I am so prodigeously afraid that I may make some egregious blunder, that I shall scarcely dare publish it unless I can get some one ~~to~~ well acquainted with the subject to read it over,—to give it a rapid reading at least— As there is not much reference to figures, it would require but little time. If you could borrow the time requisite,—it would gratify me,— but dont say that you can, if it will prove any serious inconvenience,—it may be out of the question, in which case dont hesitate to say no at once,— If I did not feel confidence in your frendship I should not make this request,—reciprocate it by saying <u>nay</u>,—if there is any thing in the way of granting it— We are all tolerly well— Myself suffering from dyspepsia as usual, when I confine myself to the study,—if I had a vacation of a week I would make you a visit— Mrs J[6] recd Mrs Henrys kind invitation by Miss Rily[7]— It would give her great plasure[D] to visit Princeton, & as she owes our frnds in Philadelph a visit it may be effected—

Poor Alexander, What an affliction has he been visited with, from the little I know of his character & habits I shoulod think he would feel it most deeply— — With the kindest remembrance of Mrs J & myself to yourself & Mrs Henry

your frn
I,W,J,

Henry Papers, Smithsonian Archives.
Reply: Draft, August 2, 1847, Henry Papers, Smithsonian Archives.

1. Professor of mathematics and natural philosophy at Union College. *Henry Papers*, *1*:254n.

2. Not found, but probably a response to Jackson's letter to Henry of November 30, 1846 (*Henry Papers*, *6*:542.)

3. John Paterson, a mathematician and printer for whom Jackson repeatedly tried to find employment. *Henry Papers*, *4*:14n.

4. No position was found. In his response, Henry excused the delay by claiming that Jackson's letter

was received at a time when I was . . . in the midst of the bustle of electioneering for the

carrying of my plans of the smithsonian I could not say what would be the results and whether there would be any place for a person of the character of Patterson.

5. We have found no evidence that Jackson ever completed this.

6. Elizabeth Pomeroy Jackson. *Proceedings of the Sesqui-Centennial Gathering of the Descendants of Isaac and Ann Jackson* . . . (Philadelphia, 1878), p. 128.

7. Jane Ryley was an old family friend. *Henry Papers*, *1*:445.

20. FROM FREDERICK SIDNEY GIGER[1]

Balt Feb. 20th 1847.[A]

My dear Sir.

I have not heretofore had [the][B] opportunity of congratulating you on yr appointment, though I can scarcely perceive much room for it, as the giver has received more than the recipient. But to my business; & it is of serious importance, or I would not have had the assurance to trouble you whilst so completely engaged with the arduous duties you have assumed.

The reports of the case I have cut from the Balt Sun from which you can gather the histo[r]y of the assault & also what is expected of me.[2] With the exception of an excess of fluid about the parts of generation there was no evidence to my mind sufficient to prove the actual commission of rape. Now the whole point hinges upon an answer to this question. Was that fluid spermatic or not? The microscope must determine this.[3] If spermatozoa can be found in it, I am free to swear that it is spermatic fluid & that rape was committed. I have placed the fluid under a capital microscope but have not had sufficient Sun light to make an examination which is satisfactory to me. Now the object of this letter is to ascertain wether, if, I should send on part of the linen upon which I have placed a portion of the fluid you would do me the kindness to make an examination of it by the Solar. & Eye. microscopes[4] I am very anxious that this should be done as the life of a human being may probably depend upon it. It will also be another illustration of the powerful application of science & another nut for the anti-cui bono philosphers, to crack—

I would write more, but I do not wish to occupy too much of your valuable time.

> With sentiments of respect
> & affection I remain your
> Disciple
> F. S. Giger

PS. The trial will take place on the 2ᵈ of May next, although the examinations should be made next week—

FSG

Henry Papers, Smithsonian Archives.

1. A former student of Henry's, Giger was practicing medicine in Baltimore. *Henry Papers,* 6:441n.

2. Giger was the attending physician in a case in which an African-American male, Horace Wright, was accused of raping Sarah Jane Allen, a teenaged white girl. On February 12, the badly beaten Allen was brought to Giger's office for treatment. Two days later, Wright was arrested. Initially, Wright was charged with assault and attempted rape, but on February 27 the latter charge was changed to rape, presumably on the evidence presented by Giger. On May 28, Wright was released from prison, having been found not guilty. There is no documentation of Henry becoming involved in the case. *Baltimore Sun,* February 15, 16, 17, March 1, 1847; Case Number 1108, Baltimore City and County Jail, City Criminal Docket, 1832–1853, Maryland State Archives.

3. Utilizing a microscope to identify spermatic stains on clothes was a relatively recent innovation. Alfred S. Taylor, *Medical Jurisprudence,* 4th American from 5th English ed. (Philadelphia, 1856), pp. 511–513.

4. A solar microscope projected a magnified image upon a white screen, using sunlight. *Encyclopaedia Britannica,* 8th ed., s.v. "Microscopes," p. 789. By "Eye. microscope," Giger was probably referring to observing the specimen directly rather than projecting an image.

21. FROM [SPENCER FULLERTON BAIRD][1]

Carlisle Feb. 25 1847.

Prof. J. Henry,
Sir

I wrote to you some weeks ago,[2] stating that having heard that the situation of Curator to the Smithsonian Institute was to be filled shortly, and being advised thereto by some of my friends, I wished to become a candidate. I also mentioned my intention of sending on letters from different individuals as soon as I could procure them. I accordingly take the liberty of sending the accompanying, ~~which I have received~~ ↑from Dr. Morton,[3] J. J. Audubon,[4] John Cassin,[5] J. D. Dana, &c.[6] Dr. Gray has kindly offered to write personally to you on the subject↓.[7] Some I retain on account of the too partial terms in which I am mentioned, and of those forwarded to you, many contain opinions to which my utmost self conceit will not allow me to subscribe.

I have been told by my friends to mention in my application to yourself,[A] such places and passages[B] of Scientific works as refer to my name ↑and any ↑scientific↓ publication I myself have made↓. The number of these is limited, Mr. Audubon, Dr. Gray and a few others are all who have put my name in print. My own publications are few. Various catalogues of the Plants and Animals of this region some of which I enclosed to you a few weeks ago constitute[C] the principal,[8] except various descriptions of new species of North American birds in Silliman's Journal, Journal of the Academy of Nat. Sciences[9] Supplement to Audubon's Birds of North America,[10] &c.

~~My constant labor on One[D] or two works have[E] confined my attention for a number of years. The principal[F] of which is a complete~~ ↑My labors for several years past have been directed principally to the collection[G] of materials for ~~two works, a~~ a work on the↓ Synonymies[H] of the Birds of North America. To do this in the most complete manner I have spared no pains. Every work to[I] be found by me in the Public and Private libraries of Boston, New-York, Philadelphia New Haven and Washington has been carefully examined. The result of this is that many[J] discoveries, have been made as to the correct nomenclature of our Species.[K] The whole occupies several hundred foolscap pages and is nearly ready for publication.[11] I am only waiting ~~the arrival of~~ ↑until I can consult↓ several Swedish[L] and German works to publish the results of my labors~~, the corrected list~~ ↑of our birds↓ ~~at least, if not all the Synonymies~~— All my ornithological friends at home and abroad have kindly urged the speedy[M] completion of this ~~labor~~ ↑work↓ as a very great desideratum, among them Hugh E. Strickland of Oxford,[12] Charles Bonaparte,[13] H. Schlegel[14] Curator of the Museum at Leyden, and others. (Bibliography

Should I go to Washington[N] my[O] collections would[P] of course accompany me. The principal of these are Specimens of North American Birds, Quadrupeds, Reptiles, and Fishes. ↑Complete skeletons & Crania of numerous vertebrata, and Forest tres↓ My ornithological collection is probably the richest in N. American species of any in the world containing with very few exceptions all those figured and described by Audubon, with many others ↑unknown to him↓. I possess numerous new species which I intend to publish in monographs of Families or genera. They are all in skins, about three thousand in number, properly labelled & well preserved. Especial care has been taken to procure every variety of age and♀ sex. I have besides a good series of European birds and eggs obtained from various correspondants in that country.[15]

~~In addition to the skins and bodies of animals I have a good collection of American Forest trees and shrubs Photographed some years ago—Complete skeletons of numerous vertebrata, beside various crania &c.~~

A principal object also of my studies has been the preparation of a Bibliography of Ornithology and of American Natural History in general.[16] With this view I have consulted all the Catalogues great and small of England France, Germany, Holland &c ↑which I could find.↓. I have had the honor of being called on to assist in perfecting the great Bibliographia Zoologia of Prof. Agassiz,[17] and to furnish various lists of desirable books in different branches of Zoology ↑& Nat. History↓ to different persons and Societies.

You will I hope pardon me for having said so much about myself and for repeating what I wrote to you before. May I hope for a speedy information as to what are the possibilities of sucess,[R] and whether any election has been decided on to take place shortly. I have the permission of the writers of the accompanying letters, Dr.[S] Morton, Mr. Cassin, J. J. Audubon, James D. Dana and of others as Dr. Gray, Major Le Conte,[18] &c. to use their names as references.

Draft, Folder "Copies of Correspondence Regarding Position for Curator of the Smithsonian Institution, 1847," Box 40, Baird Papers, Smithsonian Archives.
Reply: Doc. 22.

1. Professor of natural history at Dickinson College, Baird (1823–1887) specialized in ornithology. In 1850 he became assistant secretary at the Smithsonian, responsible for natural history collections, the foreign exchanges, and publications. *DSB; Smithsonian Report for 1850*, p. 10.

2. Draft, February 6, 1847, same location as present letter.

3. Samuel George Morton was one of America's leading physical anthropologists and paleontologists. *Henry Papers*, 1:461n; *DSB*.

4. John James Audubon, the artist and naturalist. *Henry Papers*, 2:58n.

5. The leading American ornithologist of the day, John Cassin (1813–1869) was curator of the Academy of Natural Sciences of Philadelphia. Elliott, *Dictionary*.

6. Copies of letters from Morton, February 13, 1847; Audubon, February 11, 1847; and Dana, February 7, 1847; same location as present letter.

7. Not found, but according to Gray's letter to Baird of February 23, 1847 (Baird Papers, Smithsonian Archives), written that day.

8. Three catalogues were published in the *Literary Record and Journal of the Linnaean Association of Pennsylvania College*. George Brown Goode, *The Published Writings of Spencer Fullerton Baird, 1843–1882*, Bulletin of the United States National Museum, No. 20 (Washington, 1883), pp. 1–3.

9. Two articles in *Silliman's Journal* and one in the *Journal of the Academy of Natural Sciences of Philadelphia* were co-authored with his brother, William M. Baird (1817–1872). Goode, *Published Writings*, p. 1.

10. *Birds of North America*, 7 vols. (New York, 1840–1844), 7:359.

11. Not published.

12. Hugh Edwin Strickland (1811–1853) had drawn up the authoritative rules for zoological nomenclature. *DNB*.

13. Lucien Jules Laurent Bonaparte (1803–1857), Napoleon's nephew and a former resident of Philadelphia, was an expert in both ornithology and ichthyology. *DSB*.

14. The ornithologist Hermann Schlegel (1804–1884) was on the staff of the Leiden Museum. Erwin Stresemann, *Ornithology: From Aris-*

totle to the Present (Cambridge, Massachusetts, 1975), pp. 192–219.

15. For a summary of Baird's collections, which he brought with him to the Smithsonian in 1850, see *Smithsonian Report for 1850*, pp. 42–43.

16. Not published.

17. *Bibliographia zoologiae et geologiae*, 4 vols. (London, 1848–1854).

18. A former army topographical engineer, John Eatton LeConte, Jr. (1784–1860), was best known for his work on North American Lepidoptera. Elliott, *Dictionary*.

22. TO SPENCER FULLERTON BAIRD

Washington March 3rd 1847

Prof S. F Baird

Dear Sir

Your letters and testimonials relative to the office of curator of the Smithsonian Institution[1] have been received and put on file to be considered when the time arrives for the appointment to be made. The Board of Regents I think will not appoint a Curator until the building is in a proper condition to receive the specimens of Natural History and this will probably not be the case under five years. With much respect

I am yours &—

Joseph Henry

P.S. I hope you will pardon the delay of this answer to your letter as well as its brevity. I am so much occupied with the organization and so overwhelmed with letters that without an assistant I cannot keep up with my correspondence. I send you with this a copy of the Report and Resolutions relative to the organization.

J–H–

Baird Papers, Smithsonian Archives.

1. See Doc. 21.

23. TO HARRIET HENRY[1]

Saturday night [March 13, 1847][A]

My Dear H.

I wrote to you by the afternoon mail and I fear my letter[2] was rather gloomy. Since writing I have seen Mr Owen[3] the vice President Bache and others and the prospect is rather brighter. The committee on the building[4] I think will pause and I am certain they will very much reduce their plans of expenditure.

Mr Owen will stop if he is not pushed on by the others. Mr Preston[5] I found did not leave the city and is still at Gadsby's[6] his convictions of the necessity of having the whole matter reconsidered is strengthened.

Bache has come more warmly into my views—the boldness of the measure took him by surprise and alarmed his prudence but he is now fully impress with the importance of staying proceedings[7] and I think there is but little doubt that things will yet[B] go right. I am now in much better sperits than when you left. Before the break of day is the darkest time— Honest intention with industry properly applied will I am sure make head way against any thing of personal interest or local object. It is quite chilly to night the large room is not very chearful in the way of fire and Miss Frost[8] has allowed me but one candle. I regret this because it does not look quite as liberal as we had though her. I suppose hower that it is the custom and therefore I must submit.

I wrote to John Ludlow[9] and prepared a note for Mary giving her in a few words the contents of your letter and telling her that on account of your having suddenly concluded to start for home you had left a letter to her unfinished every other consideration but that of seeing your children having for the moment been driven out of your head.

This must be in the mail to night or it will not start in the morning so I must close with the assurance that I am more than ever your own H.

Family Correspondence, Henry Papers, Smithsonian Archives.

1. Harriet had been visiting Henry in Washington from February 22 until the date of this letter. Henry to James Henry, February 22, 1847, and Henry to Harriet Henry, March 13, 1847, Family Correspondence, Henry Papers, Smithsonian Archives.

2. Family Correspondence, Henry Papers, Smithsonian Archives.

3. Robert Dale Owen, chair of the building committee of the Board of Regents.

4. In addition to Owen, the members of the building committee were William W. Seaton and Joseph G. Totten. William J. Hough sat on the committee during Colonel Totten's absence from Washington to participate in the Mexican War. Rhees, *Journals*, p. 33.

5. Preston had attended the meeting of the Board of Regents on March 1, 1847. It was the only meeting he ever attended. Rhees, *Journals*, pp. 39, 747.

6. Also known as the National Hotel, Gadsby's was one of Washington's leading hotels and a favorite with politicians. *Henry Papers, 3*:134; James Goode, *Capital Losses: A Cultural History of Washington's Destroyed Buildings* (Washington, 1979), pp. 168–170.

7. If Henry was to influence the issuing of the building contract, he had to act quickly. On February 17, the building committee had ordered Renwick's specifications printed for the use of contractors, with a deadline of March 10 (later extended to March 15) for receiving construction bids. Rhees, *Journals*, pp. 597, 599.

8. John T. Frost ran a boarding house on Capitol Hill. Washington City Directory, 1846.

9. One of Henry's acquaintances from Albany and provost of the University of Pennsylvania. *Henry Papers, 1*:106n. The letter has not been found.

24. TO HARRIET HENRY

Washington monday [March 15, 1847]ᴬ

My dear H

I expect to hear from you by the mail of this evening though I may not get your letter until the morning. I have just returned from attending the funeral of Mrs Allen.[1] She was burried in the congressional burrial ground[2] and placed I think temporarily in a vault. It is customary in this place to expose the face of the corps to all who choose to look at it. It struck me this morning for the first time that the custom is not an agreeable or proper one. We would in preference perfer to remain in the recollection of our friends and acquaintances as we were in health and life rather than in the condition of incipient decay.

I have met the building committee ~~and~~ this morning and I find them much modified in their views of the building. They do not intend to close the contract as soon as they intended and have promised to make no move without consulting me. I think they will consent to the calling of a new meeting of the board to reconsider the whole matter this meeting will probably take place in July.[3] The resolve which I made with your advise on thursday night or rather on friday morning has or will be of good effect. Mr Walker as Bache immagined has taken holed of the affair with great vigour and declairs that if they do not consider well their contracts he will withdraw the funds and stop the whole affair of the building.[4] Indeed he is desposed to proceeed at once to coercive measures. I think however that all will be arranged without violent action.

Mr Owen is now I think quite willing to give up his fantasy of the building provided there is any danger of any thing like a blow up. I wish you would not say much about the affair in Princeton for I think all will be as I wish.

I am now going to see Mr Walker to report progress to him as well as to restrainᴮ him from going to rapidly ahead.

I shall drop this into the office as I come back.

As ever yours
H.

Family Correspondence, Henry Papers, Smithsonian Archives.

1. The funeral of Effie McArthur Allen (1806 or 1807–1847), the wife of Senator William Allen of Ohio. *National Intelligencer,* March 15, 1847.

2. Although it has no direct connection with Congress, the Congressional Cemetery, a few kilometers east of the Capitol, is the site of hundreds of cenotaphs erected by Congress in

memory of its members. Eleanor M. V. Cook, *Guide to the Records of Your District of Columbia Ancestors* (Silver Spring, Maryland, 1987), p. 37.

3. No regents' meeting was held until December 8. Rhees, *Journals*, p. 39.

4. As secretary of the treasury, Robert J. Walker oversaw the actual disbursing of the Smithsonian's funds. Rhees, *Documents* (1901), 1:431, 432.

25. TO HARRIET HENRY

Washington Saturday
Night March 20th 1847[A]

Dearest

I am this evening very home sick or at least have been so but feel relieved by commencing this letter to you. I hoped to get off this morning so as to be with you this evening but was disappointed. The week which is just about comming to a close has been a very anxious one though all things appear now to be as I could wish or rather as well as I had any reason to expect. You know that I made a resolution with your concurrence to attempt to arrest proceedings as to the building or to put the affair in such a state that the Board of Regents at a future meeting might have the power of controoling the building and of reversing if they thought fit their action.

After much difficulty and many efforts I succeeded in getting a clause inserted into the contract which gives the Board the power of stopping the building after the wings are finished and of modifying the plan in any way they may deem proper.[1] But I will give you an account of the whole when I return. Suffice[B] it to say that I have had much trouble and have been obliged to use some coerrsive measures.

I hope to be with you on monday eveng and until then my Dearest farewell

H

Family Correspondence, Henry Papers, Smithsonian Archives.

1. The construction contract between the Smithsonian and the contractors, James Dixon and Gilbert Cameron, was supposed to be signed at the building committee's evening meeting on March 19. Henry attended that meeting and persuaded the committee to refrain from signing the contract until Bache—who was ill—had had an opportunity to examine it. At the first of two meetings on March 20, Robert Dale Owen, the chairman of the committee, at the suggestion of Henry and Bache, submitted an addendum to the contract giving the Board of Regents the right "to make important alterations in the plan of the building, or in the time of its execution," in exchange for proper compensation for the contractors. The contract, with the addendum, was signed on the evening of March 20. Rhees, *Journals*, p. 627.

26. TO CHARLES COFFIN JEWETT

Princeton, March 23th[A] 1847

My dear Sir. Your letter[1] was received a few days ago, while I was in Washington, but at that time I was so much engaged in matters of the highest importance to the institution, with which we are connected, that I could not find a moment of time in which to answer it. I am very desirous of having a long and free talk with you on the subject of the Smithsonian Institution; we have embarked together on a perilous voyage and unless the ship is managed with caution and the officers are of the same mind and determined to pull together we shall be in danger of shipwreck.

I was much pleased to receive your proposition of meeting and if you can make it convenient, you will oblige me very much by coming to Princeton. I have returned to this place to remain some time in order to finish my course to the present senior class and with the exception of a short occasional visit to Washington I shall remain here until June. . . .[2]

I was also much pleased to have had an interview with you at Washington,[3] because though I nominated you as the preference of the majority of the Board of Regents, yet as to you personally I had no objection and indeed you were the only candidate with whom I had any acquaintance.

> With much respect I remain truly yours
> Joseph Henry.

Professor Jewett.

Mary Henry Copy, Henry Papers, Smithsonian Archives.
Reply: April 12, 1847, General Manuscripts Collection, Department of Special Collections, University of Pennsylvania Libraries.

1. Of March 16, 1847, General Manuscripts Collection, Department of Special Collections, University of Pennsylvania Libraries. In it, Jewett expressed his surprise at being elected and the hope that Henry "will not have reason to regret the nomination," promised his "cordial cooperation," and suggested a meeting in New York to discuss "topics, connected with the duties of my office."

2. In his reply, Jewett wrote that he would be in Princeton on April 15. There is no documentation of a meeting. However, Henry was in Princeton on that date, having returned to Princeton from Washington on the fourteenth. Henry to James Henry, April 15, 1847, Family Correspondence, Henry Papers, Smithsonian Archives.

3. *Henry Papers,* 6:617, 618n.

27. TO CLEMENT RUSH DE LA NOUTANE[1,A]

Princeton march 24th 1847

~~Dear~~ Sir

The plan ~~plan~~ of publication of articles presented to the Smithsonian Institution has not been fully settled it will however most probably be as follows. The memoir presented for publication will be referred[B] to a commission of men of character and reputation and learned in the branch of knowledge to which the memoir pertains the name of the author being concealed until the decision has been given. Or the author may withdraw his memoir if the decision is unfavourable without making himself known.

If the commission decide that the memoir is an addition to the sum of human knowledge resting on original experiments observations, or researches, the article will be received for publication in the transactions and paid for out of the funds of the Institution.

It has been considered necssary to restrict the memoirs to be accepted to those which rest on original investigation particularly in the Physical sciences and to exclude all merely hypothetical or speculative articles because if this rule be not observed the Institution would be overwhelmed with the number of articles of the latter kind. Indeed we have already received a suficient quantity of material of the purely hypothetical kind to make quite a large volume.

Though this rule may exclude ~~the admission of~~ some articles of value yet its importance is so apparent to the Regents and councellors of the Institution that I doubt not it will be ridgidly adhered to.

The lecturers who[C] will be engaged are those to be called to Washington to deliver short courses during the session of congress. This however is one of the points not yet settled.

Accompayning this I send you a copy of the report on the organization of the Institution[2] by which you will see that many plans are proposed for carrying out the intention of the Donor but it must be recollected that the income is very limited and insufficeent to accomplish a tenth part of what is proposed.

with much Respect
Your's &c
Joseph Henry

~~P.S.~~ I do not think it forms any part of the present plan of the Regents to publish school books. ~~JH~~ ↑~~Accompanying the letter I send you a copy of the Report on the organization of the Institution.~~↓

56

P.S. This letter was witten several weeks ago but ~~as the~~ ↑but was not sent at the time because↓ the place of your residence was not ~~give~~ ↑mentioned↓ in your ~~letter~~ ↑commu[nic]ations↓ ~~I cound not send~~ I have howev ↑since↓ learnd that your[D] letters were from Virginia.[3]

Draft, Henry Papers, Smithsonian Archives.

1. Unidentified.

2. *Report of the Organization Committee of the Smithsonian Institution* (Washington, 1847).

3. According to the outside address, Henry had originally addressed his letter to Diana Mills, Maryland. Diana Mills, Virginia, was a post-village approximately 120 kilometers (75 miles) west of Richmond. J. Thomas and T. Baldwin, eds., *A Complete Pronouncing Gazetteer, or Geographical Dictionary of the World*, 2 vols. (Philadelphia, 1858).

28. FROM EPHRAIM GEORGE SQUIER[1]

Chillicothe, Ohio, March 24, 1847—

My Dear Sir:

I address you at the suggestion of a mutual friend, Prof. Marsh[2] of Burlington Vt., who takes as you well know, a lively interest in all investigations promising to add to the general stock of knowledge. I presume he has informed you, and you have probably observed intimations of the fact, in the public press, that in conjunction with Dr. E. H. Davis[3] of this place, I have been pretty actively engaged, for the past two years, in investigating the ancient remains of the West, but more particularly of the Ohio Valley. Before coming to this State, (two years since,) I had had my attention directed to the innteresting subject of our antiquities, and had read, with much Interest though with little satisfaction, the brief and detached notices which had been published relating to them. I found much speculation, ~~and~~ but few facts, and instead of being illuminated found myself involved ↑in↓ deeper darkness. Atwater's paper in the Archelogia American,[4] I found, in[A] common I presume with every person who has read it, to be a congeries of hearsays, many of them improbable and few wellattested—[B]presented rather with a view to excite the marvelousness of the public than to throw any clear and certian light upon our monuments, whereby we might solve the grand ethnological problem which they involve.[5] Upon coming to the State, located as I found my self in one of the centres of ancient population, I was not long in gratifying my curiosity respecting them. The second day after my arrival, found ↑me↓ ten miles in the country, on an expedition to visit the wonderful wells, of which I had read, dug in the solid rock, in the bed of Paint Creek. (<u>Arch. Am. p.[...]</u>)[6] I found them, and would you believe it?—they were—<u>hugh Septaria</u>[7] and their casts!—abundance of which occur in the Slate Strata of this region! A promising begining truly! This circumstance impressed me still more ~~of the~~ with the uncertain nature of our information on the subject of our remains, and contributed materially in inducing[c] me to conceive a Systematic plan of investigations, in respect to them. I soon found an associate, and from that day to this all my leisure has been occupied in pursuing it. It was not intended at the start to publish, and we should not probably think of doing so now, had it not been for the solicitation of our friends at the East, who feel interested in our researches. Upon visiting New York last summer, I took on with me a few relics and a number of plans, sketches &c, for the purpose of laying them before the Ethnological Society of that city with which we had been for some time in correspondence.[8] Mr. <u>Gallatin</u>, the venerable president, became so much interested that he volunteered to advance the funds for bringing out a sketch of the results of our inquiries, in the regular proceedings of the Society. It was at first proposed to publish a paper of 100 or 200 pages, ~~but the interest which has been exhibited as preliminary to a more~~ extended and imposing work, which should embrace in its scope a thorough ~~investigate~~ examination of the whole field. The original design was afterwards extended, (though without abanding the purpose of making a systematic and thorough investigation from the Lakes to the Gulf,) so as to include ~~an ample account of~~ all the facts which our labours have developed. In the ↑[?arrageing] these↓ preperation of these I am now busiley engaged: hoping that their publish~~ing enab~~ even if ~~they~~ ↑it↓ does not enable ↑lead↓ ~~me~~ to complete ~~my c~~ the cherished purpose of ↑a↓ systematic ~~exa~~ investigation of our antiquites, over the whole field of their occurnce, will serve to throw some ~~positive↓~~ clear and certain light upon them. The sole purpose of the publicatn is to[D] present facts; ~~leaving speculation out of to others leaving~~ without indulging in speculations; ~~if When~~ believing that it will be quite time enough to ~~draw gene~~ make ~~the~~ genrl &c[9]

Draft, Squier Papers, Library of Congress.
Reply: Doc. 38.

1. Born in upstate New York, Squier (1821–1888) attended the Troy Conference Academy in Vermont. He taught, considered a career as an engineer, and then turned to journalism. After working in New York State and Connecticut, he settled in Chillicothe in 1845 to edit a weekly newspaper. There he met E. H. Davis and began collaborative research on the ancient mounds in the area. An ardent Whig, he was elected clerk of the Ohio House of Representatives in 1846. His subsequent career included an appointment as chargé d'affaires to Guatemala (1849–1850), archaeological studies in Central America and Peru, the promotion of

railroads in Honduras, and journalism. Squier was aggressive, paranoid, emotionally unstable, quarrelsome, and unable to accept criticism well. He suffered increasingly from mental illness. Thomas G. Tax, "E. George Squier and the Mounds, 1845–1860," in *Towards a Science of Man: Essays in the History of Anthropology*, ed. Timothy H. H. Thoresen (The Hague, 1975), pp. 101–102, 109, 117–120; Robert E. Bieder, "The American Indian and the Development of Anthropological Thought in the United States, 1780–1851" (Ph.D. diss., University of Minnesota, 1972), pp. 307–308.

2. George Perkins Marsh, a representative from Vermont who had been a strong supporter of the Smithsonian as a national library during the congressional debate over the legislation, would become a regent later in 1847. *Henry Papers, 6:*465.

In a letter of February 23, 1847 (Squier Papers, Library of Congress), Marsh told Squier that "it has been suggested that you would do well to offer the results of your investigations to that body [the Smithsonian] for publication." Squier replied in a letter (not found) which Marsh showed Henry. On March 6 (Squier Papers, Library of Congress), Marsh wrote Squier that Henry "desires me to say to you that the Smithsonian Institution will publish your essay in the best style both of letter press and of illustration."

3. Edwin Hamilton Davis (1811–1888) was educated at Kenyon College and the Cincinnati Medical College. A long-time resident of Chillicothe, he was very familiar with the mounds. In 1850 he became a professor at the New York Medical College, which he left in 1860 to practice medicine. His later anthropological work centered on an ethnological map of the United States. Tax, pp. 102–103; *DAB*.

4. Caleb Atwater, "Description of the Antiquities Discovered in the State of Ohio and Other Western States," *Archaeologia Americana. Transactions and Collections of the American Antiquarian Society*, 1820, *1:*105–307. The first systematic investigation of the earth mounds of the Ohio and Mississippi River valleys, Atwater's publication hypothesized that the mounds were built by the ancestors of the cultures of Mesoamerica. The mound builders were not, in his view, the ancestors of modern Indians. Atwater, a lawyer living in Ohio, had personally surveyed some of the mounds, but relied heavily on the fieldwork of others. Thomas G. Tax, "The Development of American Archaeology, 1800–1879" (Ph.D. diss., University of Chicago, 1973), pp. 130–132; Curtis M. Hinsley, Jr., *Savages and Scientists: The Smithsonian Institution and the Development of American An-*

thropology, 1846–1910 (Washington, 1981), p. 23; *DAB*.

5. The problem was the nature of American Indians. Prior to the work of Squier and Davis, the accepted paradigm was that the mounds were built by a non-Indian civilization which fell victim to the Indians, migrants from Asia and a much more savage people than the Moundbuilders. There was no consensus regarding the origins of the Moundbuilders. The ancestors of the Moundbuilders were sometimes identified with Asian civilizations, sometimes with the Mesoamericans, sometimes with Europeans (for example, the Welsh), sometimes with the ancient Israelites. Even mythical people were sometimes credited with building the mounds. There was general agreement, however, that the ancestors of the Indian tribes were incapable of building the mounds and represented a decline in the level of civilization from their predecessors in North America, a decline further evident in the contemporary tribes. Tax, "The Development of American Archaeology," pp. 63–96.

6. On pages 150–151, Atwater classified these "wells" not as natural objects but as manmade, resembling "those described to us in the patriarchal ages."

7. Limestone nodules whose cracks were filled with crystallized carbonate of lime, septaria were a source of cement. Edward Hitchcock, *Elementary Geology* (Amherst, 1840), pp. 15–16.

8. In addition to the American Ethnological Society, Squier had sought patronage from the American Antiquarian Society and the American Academy of Arts and Sciences. Tax, "Squier and the Mounds," pp. 104–107.

9. Thus began the process which culminated in the publication of Squier and Davis, *Ancient Monuments of the Mississippi Valley: Comprising the Results of Extensive Original Surveys and Explorations*, 1848, SI Contributions, vol. 1 (Washington, 1848). This landmark publication was the catalyst in the transformation of American archaeology. Thanks to Henry's editorial control over the publication, "solid evidence replaced conjecture as the dominant archaeological method." Tax, "Squier and the Mounds," p. 99.

Subsequent letters in this volume will document the steps in the path from this letter to finished publication. Five themes dominate those letters. First, Henry was determined that the first Smithsonian Contribution to Knowledge would establish proper precedents, especially the procedure for refereeing submissions, even if it meant manipulating the correspondence and falsifying the record. Second, Henry felt it important that the first Smithsonian publication not be in the physical sciences, but rather in a field he was not identified with personally, to demonstrate the breadth of the institution's interests. (Henry had argued both privately and publicly that the Smithsonian should support a wide range of disciplines. In support, he cited the breadth of Smithson's own research. *Henry Papers, 6:*499; *Smithsonian Report for 1847,* pp. 178–179.) Third, Henry would come to consider Squier rash and untrustworthy. Fourth, and conversely, Squier would feel himself ill-used by the Smithsonian, both financially and intellectually. Last—but for the history of archaeology, most important—Henry was determined to purge as much speculation as possible from the Squier and Davis manuscript.

In the end, *Ancient Monuments* refrained from gross speculation. It offered no explanation for either the origin of the Moundbuilders or their subsequent disappearance. In a footnote, Squier and Davis did suggest that the native civilizations of Central and South America may have originated in a migration of Moundbuilders from North America. There was also speculation, attributed by historians to Squier, about the importance of comparative religious studies. *Squier and Davis,* pp. 302–303; Bieder, pp. 325–326.

29. "RECORD OF EXPERIMENTS"

March 25th 1847

It is mentioned by count Rumford in the Journal of the Royal Institution that the Introduction of balls of fine clay into a coal fire increases the heat though the clay cannot enter[A] into combustion and thus increase the heat.[1] The idea at first struck me as rediculous but on reflection I found that there was a clear physical analogy to support the probability of the truth of the fact namely the increase of light which is producd when a solid substance is intoduced into the feebly luminous flame of a sperit lamp.

To test conclusively[B] the truth of the proposition I put the thermo electrical apparatus in order and deflected the needle of the galvanometer by the[C] heat of a sperit lamp to the amount of 15 degrees the end of a platinum wire of about six inches in length was then coiled into the form of a spiral and plunged into the flame of the lamp the luminosity was of course considerably increased while at the same time the needle of the galvanometer moved from 15 to 27 degrees. The truth of the proposition is therefore conclusively proved by this experiment.

But was is the[D] cause of the phenomenon? is it due to the fact of the increase of the combination of the oxygen and hydrogen by the action of the platinum on the principle of the action of the flameless lamp[2] or is it the result of the conversion of heat of less radiating power into heat of greater.[3]

For a notice of Davy's new viws of flame see Brand Vol 2 page 126 1817. The heat[E] of flame may be diminished by increasing the light.[4]

Henry Papers, Smithsonian Archives.
The final paragraph is at the bottom of the page following a blank space and may be a later addition.

1. Benjamin Thompson, Count Rumford, "Observations Relative to the Means of Increasing the Quantities of Heat Obtained in the Combustion of Fuel," *Journals of the Royal Institution of Great Britain,* 1802, 1:28–33. A copy of this volume survives in the Henry Library, with an annotation (p. 29) to Rumford's remark that there were no good quantitative data regarding the amount of heat thrown off by different substances when raised to the same temperature.

2. The flameless lamp was an alcohol lamp with a fine platinum wire coiled around the wick. Once the lamp was lit, the wire would continue to glow red hot even after the flame was extinguished. The theory of the flameless lamp was that the platinum wire retained enough heat to continue the combustion of the alcohol at a level sufficient to maintain the temperature of the wire but insufficient to reignite the alcohol. J. L. Comstock, "Description of the Aphlogistic Lamp," *Silliman's Journal,* 1822, 4:328–331.

3. Henry summarized his thoughts regarding Rumford's assertion in the first two pages of a four-page memorandum, "Speculations on Light and heat," tipped into the "Record of Experiments" between the March 25 and 26 entries. He made a preliminary report on his experiments proving the truth of Rumford's assertion to the American Philosophical Society in 1849, and a fuller account to the American Association for the Advancement of Science in 1855. APS *Proceedings,* 1848–1853, 5:108; "On the Effect of Mingling Radiating Substances with Combustible Materials," AAAS *Proceedings,* 1855, 9:112–116.

In "Speculations on Light and heat," Henry first hypothesized that the cause of the increase of the heat was an increase in combustion. He laid out a number of experiments "for settling the question." The first, using thermoelectric apparatus, was conducted on this date. We have not been able to document the others, which are comparisons of the amount of fuel burnt in given time periods with or without the platinum wire.

In the second half of the memorandum, however, Henry suggested a different explanation. Spurred by the memory of a remark by Bache in Washington "a few days ago," Henry speculated that introducing the solid matter shortened the wavelength of the radiant heat, increasing its heating power. His 1855 paper presented this explanation, relying upon experiments utilizing a spirit lamp, documented in the March 1847 "Record of Experiments" entries, and those using a hydrogen jet, for which we have not found documentation.

4. Humphry Davy, "Notice of Some Experiments and New Views Respecting Flame," *Quarterly Journal of Science, Literature, and Arts,* 1817, 2:124–127. Henry is paraphrasing a supposition on page 127, one of six corollaries Davy drew from his belief that the brilliancy of flame was due to the production and ignition of solid matter within the flame.

30. TO ROBERT DALE OWEN

Princeton march 25th 1847

My dear Sir

Enclosed I send you the letter of introduction for Mr Stabler[1] and I have to acknowledge the receipt of several packages of letters of which I have made the proper disposition.

I intended to mention to you if I did not do so the fact that I had authorized the Rev Mr Russel[2] the brotherinlaw of Mr French[3] to receive and acknowledge the receipt of all books prints &c sent to the Institution, in my absence, from Publishers. Should any article of this kind come into your possession you will oblige me by delivering it to this Genleman.

I have made arrangements with Mr French to ↑have↓ the Journal of Proceedings of the Board of Regents copied into the large book by the same person[4] who copied the first part of the Journal. I thought it best to employ this Person ~~first~~ because by doing so we would have the supervision of Mr French and ~~secondly~~ ↑also↓ because this clerk had been paid ↑in advance↓ at ~~the last time he was employed in part~~ ↑leas in part~~ at least↓ for ~~this~~ ↑a part of the↓ work.

On reflection I think the engraving of the head of Smithson to accompany the memoir of the chancellor[5] should be considerably larger than the medallion—say about the size of one of the portraits in[A] the Democratic Review[6] perhaps a little larger. We shall require three different engravings of the head one for the seal another for the memoir and the third for the title page of our publications. The last should be a copy of the seal on wood or type metal so that it may be set up with the ~~tye~~ ↑letter press↓ of the page and struck off at the same time.

~~I have sent Daniel's letter[7] to Mr Mills[8] and requested him to attend to sending off the drawings.[9] I have also written to Daniel[10] returning the money enclosed in his letter and informing him that his drawings will be forward to him free of expense.~~

I have found to day a notice by Davies Gilbert[11] late president of the Royal Society of Smithson in an annaversary address to the society.[12] Gilbert and Smithson were at Oxford together and members of the same College.[B] I would write immediately to Gilbert for farther information as to the character of Smithson but I am under the impression that the former died a year or two ago.[13] This fact however I can ascertain by going over the volumes for the last few years of the Philosophic Magazine.

~~Also by asertaining to what college Gilbert belonged we shall have the one of which Smithson was a Member and by writing to Oxford something additional may be procured inreference to our patron Saint.~~

I arrived safely at home on Monday evening[14] and am now enjoying the quiet of myown family the pleasure of which is much enhanced by the contrast with the bustle and excitement to which I have been subjected for the last two months in Washington.

Please inform your Brother[15] that though I am almost overwhelmed with letters and lectures I have found time to verify the fact that an incombustible substance introduced into a flame increases in a very remarkable degree the amount of radient heat.

> With much Respect I remain
> Truly yours &—
> Joseph Henry

Hon R. D Owen

Draft, Henry Papers, Smithsonian Archives.

1. Edward Stabler (1794–1883) was the post-master of Sandy Spring, Maryland, president of the Mutual Fire Insurance Company of Montgomery County, and a noted engraver of seals and stamps. On March 15, 1847, the executive committee commissioned Stabler to prepare a seal for the Smithsonian. Roger Brooke Farquhar, *Historic Montgomery County, Maryland, Old Homes and History* (Silver Spring, Maryland, 1952), pp. 182–183; Rhees, *Journals,* p. 445; Stabler's tools, the screw press he made for the Smithsonian, the plaster cast of the seal, and other artifacts are in the National Numismatic Collection, National Museum of American History.

The letter of introduction has not been found.

2. Before being employed by the Smithsonian, Charles P. Russell had been a clergyman in New Hampshire and had briefly worked as a messenger in the House of Representatives. He remained with the Smithsonian, assisting in the library and handling the copyright correspondence, until 1850, when he became a clerk in the Post Office. Benjamin Brown French, *Witness to the Young Republic: A Yankee's Journal, 1828–1870,* ed. Donald B. Cole and John J. McDonough (Hanover, New Hampshire, 1989), pp. 92, 189, 271; Rhees, *Journals,* p. 477; Desk Diary, [July 7], 1850.

3. Clerk of the House of Representatives, Benjamin B. French had been assistant secretary, recording clerk, and librarian pro tem of the Smithsonian during the early months of its existence. French's wife and Russell's wife were sisters. *Henry Papers,* 6:555n; French, p. 4.

4. Adam J. Glossbrenner, a clerk in the House of Representatives. Rhees, *Journals,* p. 10. The original "large book" was destroyed in the Smithsonian Building fire in 1865.

5. A reference to the biographical memoir of Smithson, never published, projected for the first volume of Smithsonian Contributions to Knowledge. See Doc. 46.

6. These portraits were 12.2 centimeters high by 9.4 centimeters wide. *The United States Magazine and Democratic Review* was a general monthly magazine.

7. Not found. Howard Daniels was a Cincinnati architect who had submitted the only non-medieval entry for the Smithsonian Building. Kenneth Hafertepe, *America's Castle: The Evolution of the Smithsonian Building and Its Institution, 1840–1878* (Washington, 1984), pp. 29, 47.

8. Robert Mills (1781–1855) was the Architect of Public Buildings. In 1840 he had produced plans for a proposed Smithsonian/National Institute Building, selecting a medieval style. The building committee hired him as superintendent of the construction of the Smithsonian Building. *DAB*; Hafertepe, pp. 6–8; Rhees, *Journals,* p. 597.

9. Letter to Mills not found.

10. Draft, March 19, 1847, Henry Papers, Smithsonian Archives.

11. Promoter of the cause of science in Britain. *Henry Papers,* 3:300n.

12. *Proceedings of the Royal Society,* 1830–1831, *1:*8–9.

13. He died in 1839.

14. March 22.

15. David Dale Owen (1807–1860), former Indiana state geologist, had been appointed to survey the Chippewa Land District in Wisconsin. At the request of his brother, in 1845 he had drawn up a plan for the Smithsonian Building. *DSB;* Hafertepe, pp. 18–21.

31. TO PETER BULLIONS[1]

Princeton March 26th 1847

My dear Sir

That All the screws of the Smithsonian Institution have not as yet been ~~put in proper place and~~ ↑[f]ully tightened is most true but↓ this ↑need↓ not surprise you when it is recollected that the plan of the ↑great↓ edifice itself has not been fully settled. I am however some what surprised to learn that you have not received the certificate of deposit of the books you sent to the Library of the Institution.[2] I saw them ~~more than a month ago~~ ↑several weeks ago↓ in the office of Mr French and I think it not improbabl that he has sent the certificate to your printer instead of yourself. Inorder however to avoid delay I enclose a certificate which you may fill up with the titles of the books for I beleive I may trust to your honesty thus far.

We are all well— ↑~~poor fellow~~↓ Stephen ↑poor fellow↓ has met with a sad loss and feels it very ~~deeply~~ ↑much↓— ↑He is a man of few words.↓ Motherin law has gone to live with him and appears quite contented with the change— Mrs Henry made me a visit of a bout two weeks duration during my stay in Washington. She could scarcely bear a longer seperation from her children. Should she live however until they are grown up and have become active members of society she will be obliged to make a sacrifice of feeling in this respect particularly if we may judge of the destiny of our ofspring by that of yours.[3]

I have been at Washington nearly all winter and have now returned to Princeton for the purpose of completing my course of lectures ~~with~~ ↑to↓ the Senior class. I have not as yet intirely severed my connection with ~~Princeton~~ ↑this Institution↓ and may perhaps give a short course of lectures ↑there↓ next year ~~in college~~ but of this I am not certain. It[A] will depend on the action of the Trustees of ↑the↓ college at their next meeting. My[B] object in thus retaining my connection with Princeton was twofold first that I might not too suddenly leave the Institution in the midst of a ~~year before my~~ course of lectures ~~was completed~~ and secondly that in case the affairs of the Smithsonian were not very ~~inviting~~ ↑promising↓ I might return to ~~Princeton~~ my former position.[4]

My plans inreference to the Smithsonian Institution have ~~not~~ been adopted ↑perhaps↓ as fully as I could have ~~wished~~ ↑expected though↓ we were obliged to make a compromise inorder to harmonize the conflicting opinion. ~~As a~~ ↑And a↓ calm review of ↑however↓ all the proceedings ↑thus far↓ ~~of the Regents I see nothing~~ ↑at present to↓ to ~~prevent my going on for if my plans~~ ↑views↓ ~~have not been fully adopted I shall have less responsibility and the failure should it happen cannot intirely be attributed to me.~~ The whole affair is at present quite new and all are anxious to be active in the management but I think the Regents will soon be tired of it and then betwen ourselves I hop to have more of my own way. Indeed were it not for two persons who had particular objects ↑to↓ attain I should have had all the arrangements to my own mind before the adjournment of the Board.[C]

~~I am so much engaged just now that I cannot give you a full account~~

~~of the proceedings at Washington but I hope to see you during the summer and then to have a long crack with you.~~

I send you with this a copy of the Report of the committee of organization[5] and I have marked in the margin the several suggestions which form the parts of the plan proposed by myself. They were adopted by the committee and incorporated in their Report.

> With much Respect
> I remain as ever[D]
> Truly your Frend
> Joseph Henry

William coming to Princeton
Rev Dr Bullions

Draft, Henry Papers, Smithsonian Archives.

1. Professor of Latin and Greek at the Albany Academy and Henry's former colleague there. *Henry Papers*, *1:*129n.

2. Approximately two weeks earlier Bullions had submitted copies of his books to the Library of Congress and Smithsonian library as part of the copyright deposit procedure. The Library of Congress had already acknowledged receipt of his package. *Henry Papers*, *6:*594; Bullions to Henry, March 24, 1847, Henry Papers, Smithsonian Archives.

3. In his letter of the twenty-fourth, Bullions mentioned that four of his children no longer lived at home.

4. For Henry's relationship to Princeton while secretary, see Henry Papers, *6:*557, 559, 597–598.

5. *Report of the Organization Committee of the Smithsonian Institution* (Washington, 1847).

32. "RECORD OF EXPERIMENTS"

March 26th 1847

Placed a spiral of platinum wire in the lower part of the flame found the light much less intense than in the upper part also apparently the radiant heat.

The glalvanometer without the platina stood at 19° with the platina in the upper part of the flame it stood at about 25 with[A] the platina in the lower part a little less elevated.

This experiment must be repeated. I could not manage being alone to hold the wire in the flame and note the degrees of the galvanometer.

When a thin plate of mica ¾ of an inch in breadth was held in the flame the needle immediately passed from 15° to nearly 30° the mica exhibited a very beautiful appearance such[B] as I never before noticed.

It became white hot along the line of section of the outside of the flame and the mica while it remained dark in the middle. Showing in a vertical section the hollowness of flame.

It would appear from the experimts of to day that the increased amount of radiation is due to the greater rapidity of the combination of the elements of the flame and the oxygen of the air though the question is by no means settled.

Tried other substances— Flat plate of platina foil ½ inch wide effect grat needle of galvanometer passed from 11 to 30 degres— Nex carbonat of lime effect same—also pice of glass not all of the same intensity. Tried sulpate of lime effect not as grat as with platinum still an increase of temperature was indicated.

*This experiment shows the parts of the flame most intensly heated very distinctly and gives us a new analysis of the flame relative to its temperature in different parts.

Henry Papers, Smithsonian Archives.

33. "RECORD OF EXPERIMENTS"

March 27th 1847
Flame—Coloured circles around a candle—

Davy suggests that the greatest intensity of heat possible may be produced by the combination of the effect of the voltaic arc and the jet of the compound blow pipe[1]— This would merely produce a greater quantity of heat without increasing the intensity.

Dr Ure says the light of a flame may be increased while its heat is diminished.[2]

I was very much struck last night in going to bed to observe the candle in my hand surrounded with a series of perfectly distinct coloured circles—the perfect representation of Newtons rings.[3] My eyes were slightly inflamed and particularly the one with which the coulered rings were most distinctly seen. The inner &[A] more distinctly exhibited ring was about 4 inches in diameter the candle being about 15 inches from the eye. The order of colour was yellow Red blue Yellow Red Blue &c. The diameter of the rings increased as the candle was removed from the eye. The plane of the rings was perpendicular to the line joining the eye and the candle and continued to be so when the candle was moved. I have often seen colours around the candle when I have got up from bed in the night before washing my eyes but never so distinctly have the rings been exhibited as on the present occasion.

The effect is probably due to a film of mucus spread over the surface of the eye and may perhaps be imitated by dipping the finger into a Solution of sugar and applying this to the eye.

The order of succession is that of the transmitted light of Newtons rin[g]s.

Henry Papers, Smithsonian Archives.

1. Humphry Davy, "Some Researches on Flame," *Phil. Trans.*, 1817, p. 74.

2. Andrew Ure (1778–1857) was a consulting chemist in London. *DNB*. We have not identified the source.

3. A reference to Sir Isaac Newton's discovery that various spectra in the form of circular rings are produced when light is either reflected from or transmitted through a thin film of varying thickness. The order of the colors from reflected light differs from that due to transmitted light. David Brewster, *A Treatise on Optics* (London, 1831), pp. 102–103. See also *Henry Papers, 3:390; 6:60.*

34. "RECORD OF EXPERIMENTS"

March 29th 1847
Flame

Introduced into the lower part of a flame a piece of mica in the form of a slip of about a tenth of an inch in width[A] this became heated to whitness but when a piece of fine platinum wire was held in the same flame above the mica which was placed edgewise so as not to intercept the ascending flame the heat of the wire was less than when the slip of mica was withdrawn. This experiment was repeated a sufficient number of times to convince me of the truth of the fact. The flame became shorter when the mica was introduced evidently showing from all the results that the effect of the mica was to cool the flame and this was probably due to the increase of radiation.

The principal action of the solid introduced into a flame is to absorbe the heat of the luminous gas which is a bad radiator and an then radiate if freely into space the process is therefore a cooling one to the flame while it heats surrounding bodies.

I am informed within a few days that an account has been going the rounds of the newspapers of a method of saving fuel by mixing clay with the coal. The effect would be produced by the solid radiating into space a part of the heat which would find its way into the chimney.

Flame according to Count Rumford if I recollect aright is a bad conductor of heat[1] and now for the first time in many years a fact arises in my mind which was shown me by a Gentleman in Albany namely when a stove is burning briskly if the damper be shut the pipe around the valve will become red hot in this case the heated air is made to impinge against the side of the tube and thus to impart the heat which would otherwise pass up the chimney.

Make experiments on the heat of different flames.

Henry Papers, Smithsonian Archives.

1. Actually Rumford asserted that flame was "*a non-conductor of Heat*" (italics in original), a claim that was very controversial. Benjamin Thompson, Count Rumford, "Of the Management of Fire, and the Economy of Fuel," *Essays, Political, Economical, and Philosophical,* 3 vols. (1st American from 3d London ed.; Boston, 1798–1804), 2:65; Sanborn C. Brown, *Benjamin Thompson, Count Rumford* (Cambridge, Massachusetts, 1979), p. 149.

35. TO JOHN VARDEN[1]

Princeton March 29th 1847.

Dear Sir,

Your favour of the 24th instant[2] informing me of your disposition of the papers, books &c of the late James Smithson has just been received. I am much obliged to you for the care of the articles and will pay you when I come next to Washington. You will do me a favour if you will collect any articles belonging to the Smithsonian bequest which may come to your knowledge. In the library under the table were a number of boxes containing chemicals and other materials which I should like to have preserved for though they are of little intrinsic value yet they are interesting as being part of the effects of Smithson. Also, if you can procure any of the articles of clothing which were given away and preserve them by means of arsenic or otherwise you will be doing a service to the institution.

With much Respect
I remain truly Yours &c
Joseph Henry.

John Varden, Esq.

RH 411, Rhees Collection, Huntington Library.
In Harriet Henry's hand.

1. John Varden (d. 1865) opened a museum in Washington, D.C., in 1829. In 1841 he moved his specimens to the Patent Office Building, where he also oversaw the collections of the National Institute, the specimens of the Wilkes Expedition, and other government collections, in the "National Gallery." When the government collections were transferred to the Smithsonian Institution in 1858, Varden went with them. He remained with the Smithsonian until his death. Douglas E. Evelyn, "The National Gallery at the Patent Office," in *Magnificent Voyagers: The U.S. Exploring Expedition, 1838–1842*, ed. Herman J. Viola and Carolyn Margolis (Washington, 1985), pp. 230, 233, 236–241; Daybook of Washington City Museum, Varden Papers, Smithsonian Archives; Desk Diary, February 12, 1865.

2. Not found.

36. "RECORD OF EXPERIMENTS"

March 30th 1847
Flame Transparency of

According to the view I have taken of the cause of the phenomenon of the increased radiation of flame by the introduction of a solid body balls of clay introduced into the fire would not increase the rapidity with which water would be boiled but only the quantity of heat radiated into the room heated by coal.

The quantity of heat thrown on a dutch[A] oven would be increased so that the roasting of the meat would be facilitated while the boiling process going on over the fire would be retarded.

Count Rumform to prove that flame is transparent held a candle betwen his eye and the sun and thus eliminated the case which renderes the flame opaque namely the comparatively greater illumination of the flame than the body you attempt to view through it.[1]

A much simpler and better method is to hold the flame in the cone of diverging rays of light thrown on a screen in a dark room through a hole in the window shutter and a lens.[B]

In Flanders and in several parts of Germany and particularly in the Du[ch]ies[C] of Juliers and Bergen where coals are used as fuel the coals are always prepared before they are used by pounding them to a powder and mixing them up with an equal weight of clay and a sufficient quantity of water to form the whole into a mass which is kneaded together and formed into cakes; which are afterwards well dried and kept in a dry place for use. And it has been found by long experience that the expense attending the preparation is amply paid by the improvement of^D the fuel. The coals thus mixed with clay not only burn longer but give much more heat than when they are burned in the crude state.

Count Rumford[2]

Make^E experiments on the invisible heat of a lamp.

Henry Papers, Smithsonian Archives.

1. Benjamin Thompson, Count Rumford, "An Account of a Method of Measuring the Comparative Intensities of Light Emitted by Luminous Bodies," *Phil. Trans.*, 1794, p. 105.
2. We have not been able to locate an account by Rumford corresponding exactly to Henry's discussion. However, in "Observations Relative to the Means of Increasing the Quantities of Heat Obtained in the Combustion of Fuel," *Journals of the Royal Institution of Great Britain*, 1802, 1:28–33, Rumford discussed the practice in the Netherlands of mixing wet clay and coal (p. 32).

37. TO ALEXANDER DALLAS BACHE

Princeton March 31st 1847

My dear Bache

I would have reported myself before this time had I not since my return from Washington been afflicted with something like an opthalmia which has obliged me to use my eyes as little as possible though I have been under the necessity inorder to keep down my correspondence to write a number of letters daily. I arrived safely at home the next evening after I left you found all well and happy to see me.

Since my return I have taken entire charge of the Senior class and am now getting on quite rapidly with my lectures. I am again with the exception of my eyes in my normal condition and can look back if not with complacency at least with resignation on the erection of the norman cenotaph over one half the buried^A funds of the Smithsonian legacy and I have concluded that after making a reasonable effort to prevent this improper application of the trust I will take your advice and if the Regents will act in the matter without much pressing I shall in this respect let things take their course. Besides this the idea has lately impressed itself on me that since we are to form a large collection of articles of Foreign and curious research which may serve to excite the love of learning a collection of Physical instruments ~~instruments~~ should form an essential part of this and be of such a character as to induce a pilgrimage^B to Washington of all the quid nunc professors in our country to enlighten themselves as to the progress of science and to witness the new phenomena.[1] In accordance with this view I have sent out an order by the steamer of the 1ˢᵗ to Soleil[2] for a complete set of articles for the polarization diffraction and interference of light; also to Ruhmkorff for a complete collection of Melloni's apparatus with all the latest improvements.[3] I have ordered with this two extra galvanometers with wires of different lengths which will be useful in a variety of researches on electricity and heat. To these orders I have added another to Morloye for a set of the more interesting instruments on sound[4] and I have concluded to set some of the instrument makers in Boston at work on such articles as may be manufactured of a good quality in this country.

Since my return to Princeton though I have been much annoyed with my eyes and much driven with teaching and Smithsonian correspondence yet I have had by snatches quite an interesting time of experimenting. Science as if to make amends for the disquietude I have suffered for her sake during the last few days of my residence in Washington has opened her pirean[c] spring[5] and given me a few exhilerating sips which have completely restored my self-complacency and satisfaction with the world. I can now look back on the annoyances at Washington as a thing to be laughed at with the exception of the trouble and anxiety I gave you and your good wife. These are real sources of regret which no altered condition of my own mind can efface. I know that you were overwhelmed with business relative to the coast survey and preparations for your journey to the south and I deeply regret with feelings of mortification the large and perhaps uncalled for demands I made on your time as well as the uneasiness I gave you as to the fate of the Smithsonian. Still I think the stir which was made did good and were it not on your account I cannot wish that a move of the kind had not taken place.

I have written to a number of persons relative to the 'Contributions' and as an additional inducement for the working men of science in our country to publish in our transactions I have thought that the annual report of the secretary to the Board of Regents of the State of the Institution should contain a popular analysis of all the papers accepted for the transactions, and as this Report would be presented to congress and published as a public document a more wide diffusion would be given of the discoveres than in any other way.[6] I have also set one of my young men at work to explore all the scientific Journals accessible at Princeton for notices of Smithson and his labours and I have in this way procured an obituary notice of our Saint by Davies Gilbert who speaks of him in terms of affection and respect. They were college mates at Oxford and were drawn to each other by a kindred love of science. Smithson was considered the best chemest at Oxford and particularly excelled in the analysis of minute quantities. The story of the analysis of a tear which the chemest caught trickling down the cheek of a Lady is told. I am under the impression that Davies Gilbert died a short time ago or I would write to him for further particulars.

The subject of my experiments has been the radiation of heat from flame; the same we conversed on in Washington. I have conclusively established the fact that an increase of radient heat does take place when an incombustible solid is introduced in to a flame. So far as I have worked out the problem the facts are as follows the solid substance absorbs the combined but not latent heat of the flame and afterwards radiates it into the surrounding space or in other words flame is an exceedingly bad radiator of heat what ever may be the degree of its temperature and the effect of the solid is to increase this power. By introducing a solid into a flame of hydrogen or alcohol the quantity of water evaporated from a vessel placed over it will be diminished while the amount of heat radiated into surrounding space will be increased.

As far as economy is concerned in some cases the introduction of the solid will have the effect of robbing Peter to pay Paul the boiling ham over the fire will lose[D] what the roasting turkey gains but when the object is to heat an appartment by a blazing fire the solid introduced will increase the econom effect. I find in looking over all the books that the radient power of flame for heat has never been investigated—when the heat of flame is mentioned a reference is made to the power of heating a body by contact and in several of the standard works it is stated on the authority of Davy that the luminosity of flame is inversely as the heat.[7] If the radiant heat be understood the assertion is not true the two are proportional or very nearly so in all cases.

Though my eyes have been a source of considerable trouble for a week or more yet they have enabled me to make rather an interesting observation on the halo which is sometimes seen around a candle when we are suddenly roused from sleep. One of my eyes a few nights ago exhibited so distinct and beautiful ↑an↓ appearance of this kind that I was induced to observe it with care, and to determine the orders of succession of colours. These I found to be the same as those of the rings by transmitted light of thin plates. This fact gave the cause of the phenomenon and suggested to me a new method of exhibiting the rings of Newton[E] (do not smile) by means of a thin film of mucilage spread over the eye.

I should have mentioned while speaking of flame that I have hit on a very simple and perfect method of measuring the relative transparency of flame by placing the candle in a cone of light from a convex lens in a hole in a window shutter and receiving the image on a white screen. Two flames may thus be very readily compared, the refraction of light through the heated air exhibits very distinctly the out line and also all the motions of the rarified air around.

I have also been giving some thought[F] to the Cavendish experiment and think one cause of error in the performance of the expermt was the want of homogeneity in the parts of the metal of the large ball. It is possible to cast so large a piece of metal without having the lower half more dense than the upper? To obviate this cause of error the ball should be so supported as to be movable in all directions so as to present each side in succession to the attracted ball. If the experiment be made in the capitol the apparatus should be so placed that nearly an equal quantity of attractive matter would[G] be found on each side in the line joining the centres of the large and small ball. If however a position of this kind cannot be obtained the effect of unequal attraction may be elimenated by turning the whole apparatus through an arc of 180[H] degrees and repeating the observations in this position. I am not quite sure as to the effect of magnetic action; according to Faraday's late discovery all unferuginous matter becomes magnetic in a direction at right angles to the magnetic meridian. An effect of this kind could hower be elimenated by observing in the meridian and at right angles to the same.[8]

I have never seen the fact noticed but I am certain the electrical currents induced in the swinging pendulum ought to have some effect on the time.

You will readily infer from this letter that my mind is in a much more pleasant state than when I left Washington. The return to scientific investigations has given a relief to the feeling of doing nothing which oppressed ↑me↓ while dancing attendance on the Regents and Building committee. I am clearly of the opinion that could we once get the Smithsonian under head way your pleasure and comfort would be much enhanced, and perhaps your life prolonged by joining me in a series of physical researches.

Do you not intend to couple with the coast survey observations on the pendulum at different points and will not some observations of this kind be necessary to correct the results of the Cavendish determination.[9]

I hope you will put the article on the gulf[I] stream in process of preparation for the Smithsonian and also the observations on the magnetism of vessels.[10]

Please give our kind regards to Mrs. B—she has laid us under an unextinguishable debt which we can only acknowledge without the hope of being able to discharge. Mrs H. joins hartily in this sentiment. She request me to ask the colours determined on for a projected scarf.

You will oblige me by informing your sister that her package came safely to hand under the accomodating frank of Mr. Owen and that it has been sent to the Lady to whom it was addressed.

Were you not surprised by the anouncement of the results obtained by Pierce; I fear he has been too hasty.[11] Mauray I see by the papers attempts to give Walker a slight tap by stating that the orbit of the new planet determined[J] from the observations made since its reappearance does not pass through the missing star.[12]

I shall expect a note from you informing me when you intend starting for the south and in the mean time I shall remain as ever

most sincerely yours
Joseph Henry

[?Dr] A. D. Bache

P.S. My eyes were so bad last night that I could not finish this letter which was begun the day before. Mrs H. will act as my amanuensis in answering the letters of the Smithsonian. I have had a number of notes from Mr Owen[13] enclosing letters &— and I have written to him once[14] but I have heard nothing of[K] the movements of the building committee or when the ground is to be broken.

J.H

Did you see by the number of the comptes Rendus for 11th Jany that Arago has honored me by an analysis of my report on the electricity of the telegraph.[15]

Bache Papers, Smithsonian Archives.
Copies: Two partial drafts, March 30, 1847, in same location. Mary Henry Copy of one of the drafts, misdated March 20, 1847, in Henry Papers, Smithsonian Archives.

1. As early as December 4, 1846, the regents had approved a resolution accompanying the report of the Owen committee to appropriate $4,000 for the purchase of philosophical and chemical apparatus. On January 28, 1847, a resolution was approved authorizing Henry to contract for apparatus. The total amount spent in 1847 for scientific apparatus (exclusive of that for meteorology and expeditions) was $1,571.47. Henry described it as

> of importance, not only in the way of original research, but also in illustrating some of the most interesting and recent phenomena of physical science, as well as serving as samples for imitation to the artists of this country.

Rhees, *Journals*, pp. 14, 29, 452, 481; *Smithsonian Report for 1847*, p. 189 (quotation).

2. Jean-Baptiste-François Soleil, the premier optical instrument maker in Paris. *Henry Papers*, 3:382n. None of the orders mentioned in this paragraph have been found.

3. Heinrich Daniel Rühmkorff was a German instrument maker who worked in Paris and was known for his electrical apparatus. Henry had ordered a set of Macedonio Melloni's thermoelectric apparatus from him in 1841. *Henry Papers*, 5:125, 135, 156, 161–162, 236, 327.

4. An invoice, bearing a file date of August 1847, for approximately $350 worth of acoustical apparatus ordered by Henry from Chez

Marloye of Paris is in the Henry Papers, Smithsonian Archives. Marloye's 1840 and 1845 catalogs are in the Henry Library.

5. The Pierian spring was the fountain of the Muses and hence a source of inspiration.

6. Section 3 of the act establishing the Smithsonian required the Board of Regents to present to each session of Congress "a report of the operations, expenditures, and condition, of the Institution." Published as congressional documents, the annual reports included a report by the secretary to the Board of Regents. Henry did, in fact, comment on proposed publications.

7. We have been unable to find such a statement specifically attributed to Davy. In Henry's later article on his experiments, he qualified the assertion and eliminated any reference to Davy: "It is frequently stated, in works on chemistry, that the heating power of the flame of the compound blowpipe is very great, while its illuminating power is quite small." "On the Effect of Mingling Radiating Substances with Combustible Materials," AAAS *Proceedings*, 1855, *9*:112–116 (quotation on p. 116).

8. Henry had long been interested in Henry Cavendish's experiments to determine the density of the earth (see *Henry Papers*, *6*:255n). Here he suggested how Bache could modify his vacuum apparatus to eliminate the anomalies that Francis Baily had encountered in his extensive repetition of the experiments from 1838 to 1842. In his investigation of diamagnetism in 1845, Faraday had shown that all matter was affected by magnetic fields (*Experimental Researches in Electricity*, Twentieth and Twenty-First Series, especially paragraph 2420). Thus the earth's magnetic field would have an effect on the balls of the apparatus even if they were non-ferrous. George Whitehead Hearn of the Royal Military College, Sandhurst, had recently addressed this problem in "On the Cause of the Discrepancies Observed by Mr. Baily with the Cavendish Apparatus for Determining the Mean Density of the Earth," *Phil. Trans.*, 1847, pp. 217–229, which was read to the Royal Society of London on March 11, 1847. Hearn proposed to use iron balls whose obvious magnetism could be measured and corrected for. Henry presumably did not know of Hearn's work.

9. Pendulum observations such as Henry suggested would indicate changes in gravity on the earth's surface which were indicative of changes in the shape of the earth. The Coast Survey did not pursue such observations systematically until 1872 when Benjamin Peirce, Bache's successor, put his son, Charles Sanders Peirce, in charge of pendulum-swinging obser-

vations. Thomas G. Manning, *U.S. Coast Survey vs. Naval Hydrographic Office: A 19th-Century Rivalry in Science and Politics* (Tuscaloosa, 1988), pp. 5–6, 8–9, 74–77; Hugh Richard Slotten, "Patronage, Politics, and Practice in Nineteenth-Century American Science: Alexander Dallas Bache and the United States Coast Survey" (Ph.D. diss., University of Wisconsin-Madison, 1991), pp. 246, 248, 328.

Henry and others sympathetic to the Coast Survey cited the problem of the determination of the figure of the earth as one of the contributions that it could make to basic research as a natural outgrowth of, and without detriment to, its surveying work. See, for example, Joseph Henry, "[The Coast Survey]," *Biblical Repertory and Princeton Review*, 1845, *17*:342–343; *Proceedings of the American Academy of Arts and Sciences*, 1848–1852, *2*:127–128; Charles Henry Davis, "The United States Coast Survey," *The World of Science, Arts, and Industry Illustrated from Examples in the New-York Exhibition, 1853–54*, ed. B. Silliman, Jr., and C. R. Goodrich (New York, 1854), p. 40.

10. Neither was ever published by the Smithsonian, although Henry announced in the *Smithsonian Report for 1848* (p. 16) that the first was forthcoming. Bache commented on his late brother George M. Bache's work on the distribution of temperature in the Gulf Stream at the 1849 meeting of the American Association for the Advancement of Science and referred to it again at the 1854 meeting. Bache, "On the Distribution of Temperature in and near the Gulf Stream, off the Coast of the United States, from Observations Made in the Coast Survey," *Silliman's Journal*, 1856, 2d ser. *21*:29–37. We are unaware of any Bache publication on the magnetism of vessels.

11. A reference to Benjamin Peirce's part in the disputes following the discovery of Neptune in September 1846 by J. G. Galle, of the Berlin Observatory, who found it following French astronomer U. J. J. Le Verrier's theoretical prediction of its location. Working independently, Le Verrier and English astronomer John Couch Adams had hypothesized an undiscovered eighth planet to account for anomalies in the orbit of Uranus.

At the Naval Observatory in Washington, Sears Cook Walker (*Henry Papers*, *3*:369) searched old star catalogs and concluded that a supposedly fixed star observed by J.-J. L. de Lalande in 1795, but later missing from that location, was in fact Neptune. Combining Lalande's observation with recent ones, Walker computed new elements and found a much smaller and less eccentric orbit than Le Verrier and Adams had hypothesized. Peirce examined and verified Walker's work and announced to the American Academy of Arts and Sciences on March 16, 1847,

> THAT THE PLANET NEPTUNE IS NOT THE PLANET TO WHICH GEOMETRI-CAL ANALYSIS HAD DIRECTED THE TELESCOPE [emphasis in original] . . . and that its discovery by Galle must be regarded as a happy accident. [Hubbell and Smith, p. 270.]

Peirce thus discredited one of the most exciting scientific predictions of the century. His challenge to the theoretical discovery of Neptune by Le Verrier and Adams was instantly controversial not only in Europe, where Le Verrier defended himself by attacking Peirce, but also in the United States, where not even Walker initially agreed with him. Benjamin Apthorp Gould and James Dwight Dana represented two poles in the American reaction: Gould praised Peirce's "candor and moral courage" (Hubbell and Smith, p. 281), while Dana condemned him for presuming to act as "a critic upon European astronomy" (Hubbell and Smith, p. 284). For the episode and an analysis of what it meant about the American scientific community, see John G. Hubbell and Robert W. Smith, "Neptune in America: Negotiating a Discovery," *Journal for the History of Astronomy,* 1992, 23:261–291, which concludes:

> Peirce's own research, as well as his championing of Walker's studies, certainly had the effect of demonstrating the talents and abilities of American scientists in an extremely demanding branch of what was widely regarded as *the* science, astronomy. [p. 284.]

Henry Papers, 6:526n–527n; Philip S. Shoemaker, "Stellar Impact: Ormsby Macknight Mitchel and Astronomy in Antebellum America" (Ph.D. diss., University of Wisconsin-Madison, 1991), pp. 145–164; Morton Grosser, *The Discovery of Neptune* (Cambridge, Massachusetts, 1962), pp. 138–141.

12. In a letter to Secretary of the Navy John Y. Mason, Matthew Fontaine Maury (*Henry Papers,* 3:23n–24n), superintendent of the United States Naval Observatory, reported a recent observation of Neptune's position by Joseph Stillman Hubbard. Hubbard's observed position differed from that predicted by Walker, whose calculated orbit was based on the identity of Neptune with Lalande's "missing star." Maury wrote that this might "lessen the hypothesis as to identity." Walker had resigned from the Naval Observatory under duress in early March. Maury to Mason, March 26, 1847, in *Newark Daily Advertiser,* March 30, 1847 (quotation); Francis Leigh Williams, *Matthew Fontaine Maury: Scientist of the Sea* (New Brunswick, 1963), pp. 168, 526.

13. Only one such note or letter has been found. Owen wrote Henry on March 17 (Joseph Henry Papers, Duke University Library), introducing Judge Stryker, who was about to begin a periodical to which Owen thought the Smithsonian should subscribe. This is probably James Stryker, who began the *American Quarterly Register and Magazine* in 1848. Frank Luther Mott, *A History of American Magazines, 1741–1850* (New York, 1930), pp. 368–369.

14. Doc. 30.

15. The *Comptes rendus* for January 11, 1847 (p. 43), merely noted in three lines that Arago had presented a verbal analysis of Henry's report, originally delivered to the American Philosophical Society in June 1846 and published in the APS *Proceedings,* 1843–1847, 4:260–268. *Henry Papers,* 6:432.

---

38. TO EPHRAIM GEORGE SQUIER

Princeton April 3ᵈ 1847.

My dear Sir,

Your communication of the 24th of March[1] was received the day before yesterday via Washington and I hasten to answer it, at my first leisure moment.

I have heard of your interesting researches in Ethnology and it would give me much pleasure to publish an account of them in the first number of the Smithsonian Contributions to Knowledge.

I was authorized by the Board of Regents at their last session, to publish during the present year, a number of the Contributions to be printed in a quarto form and the matter to consist of such original memoirs as might be presented for publication and found on examination by competent judges to be actual and interesting additions, to the sum of human knowledge.[2]

It is not the present intention of the Institution to publish any memoirs in the form of seperate volumes; a plan of that[A] kind would lead to endless difficulties. The author however in all cases after a short time will be allowed to republish his materials in any form he may think proper and in order to assist him in so doing the free use will be given him of the engravings and other illustrations belonging to the Institution.

I hope after due reflection, you will agree with me in opinion that the best method of publishing the results of your labours will be in the way prescribed through the pages of the Smithsonian Contributions. The appearance of your researches in the transactions of a respectable Institution will immediately give them a character and make them favourably known to all engaged in the same persuit throughout the civilized world and thus establish on sure grounds the foundation of a lasting reputation.

The plan proposed is the one usually adopted by men of science abroad, particularly in publishing the results of their first labours and is the course which science has established to guard herself against the practices of those who would enjoy her honors without the industry or genius to merit them. The publication of a scientific memoir, in a seperate volume on the responsibility of the author, is an appeal to the public generally for that commendation which it is the privilige of only the learned few to grant and scarcly ever fails to produce a prejudice against the work in the minds of those who are best qualified to appreciate its merits and on whose judgement its character must ultimately depend.

I forgot to mention that a sufficient numbers[B] of extra copies will be struck off before the type is distributed to enable the author to furnish all his friends with the article and perhaps if you have no objection to the appearance of your work in a quarto form a whole edition may be worked off for your own use, not however to to be published until the numbers of the Contributions are distributed.

There are several points which I should like to discuss with you and if you intend to visit the east you will oblige me by coming to Princeton and I shall be happy to receive you at my house.

Excuse the freedom of my remarks, they are dictated by a desire to promote the best interests of science.

> I am with much Respect
> Yours truly
> Joseph Henry.

E. Geo. Squier. Esq

Squier Papers, Library of Congress.
In Harriet Henry's hand. Reply: See Doc. 46.

1. Doc. 28.
2. At its January 26, 1847, meeting, the Board of Regents authorized the publication of the Smithsonian Contributions to Knowledge and appropriated $1,000 from 1847 funds for the series. Rhees, *Journals*, p. 26.

39. TO HARRIET HENRY

> Washington Tuesday
> April 13th 1847

My dear H

I expect to start for home tomorrow and be with you the next day. The weather since I left home has been delightful and I have been quite well. In comming down the Bay on saturday night I was a little sea sick and the disturbance of my stomache did not entirely leave me all day sunday.

I informed you in my letter of yesterday[1] which I was obliged to stop short by the closing of the mail that I came on to Washington with a Dr Blake who brough letters for me from England.[2] He and his new wife are going to Texas to settle in matrimonial quiet—a strange determination of which I think he and she will repent but they are at present quite sanguine inreference to the pleasure they are to enjoy in the wilderness. I say they though I should say he because I have not met the lady. He left in the cars last night to return to Phil[d] and thence to proceed by the way of Cincinati to the west.

I have taken up my lodgings at Gadsbys and find this the most plesant house I have yet been in at Washington. The vice President is here and I am near my business— The affairs at Washington appear at this time in a more plesant condition than at any previous period. Col Totten who is on both the executive and Building committee has returned and under his direction things will go on properly. He looks remarkably well and appears highly pleased with the result of the attack of Vera

Cruse you will see by the papers that he was one of those who agreed on the terms capitulative.[3]

I have had three interviews with Mr Walker who at my suggestion has appended to the geological surveys which have been ordered by government ~~magnetic~~ observations on the dip and intensity of the magnetic forces— One set of instruments I am to purchase from the funds of the Smithsonian Institution and ~~the~~ ↑an↓ other to be paid for by Government. All the expense of the observations will be paid out of the public Treasury and the results will be given to the Smithsonian for publication.[4]

The Commissioner of the Land officce[5] with whom I had an interview will also instruct the public surveyors or those engaged in surveying the lands of the Government to make observations on the variation of the compass so that without expending but little of the funds of the Smithsonian I find I can here do a good deal for the cause of american science.[6]

Mr Owen is about starting for home[7] his brother has been appointed to make a geological survey of Wisconsin territory and will thus be employed for some years independent of the Smithsonian.[8]

I have to day drawn 500 dollars and can at any time get what I wish on my salary[9] so that with what I have done yesterday and to day in the way of science and the receipt of the money has made me feel more than any thing which has happened since I became connected with the affair. Having the money in my pocket makes me feel that I am really the Secretary of the Smithsonian Institution and come what will I shall not be without a small pecuniary compensation for my trouble.

I have not as yet seen the Frost family although I intend to call on them. Bache had left before I got on— He received however my letter[10] and appears to have reported that my mind is full of the subject of extending knowledge.

I feel considerable encouraged to think that my situation in Washington after I am once fairly settled will be one in which I shall be able to do considerable good— They will I think be inclined to put confidence in my suggestions and knowing that I have no other interests to serve than those of truth and science I think my influence will be of some importance to the country. The readiness with which my suggestions were complied with in the cases I have mentioned has given me this encouragement.— McPeak is very anxious to be employed and the committee have concluded to retain him at the rate of one dollar per day[11]—

Tell Mr Mclean[12] that I shall be home on Thursday and ready to take the class or classes next week and also the latter part of the present week— Tell Carry that Tom Thumb is on a visit to Washington.[13] His carriage has been driving about the streets with an immense crowd of boys around it. The General himself was not in. The carriage is about the size of the fireboard of the dining room and is drawn by two ponies which together would not weght as much as Push. They are just about the size of Alfred Woodhulls[14] dog or the one he used to have. The ponies[A] are driven by a boy of about the size of Carry dressed in the style of the old English drivers with a great profusion of lace a three cocked hat and silk breeches with knee buckles. On behind is a footman dressed in the same costume the whole affair making one of the most curious little equipages which can be immagined. As I went up to the War department I saw the little carriage drive up to the Presidents House. The General was making a call on the great man of the White House.[15]

Perhap I will call to see the little General this evening he holds his court at 7 o'clock and then I can give the children a full account of the little gentleman when I return or in my next letter.

As ever your

H

Family Correspondence, Henry Papers, Smithsonian Archives.

1. Family Correspondence, Henry Papers, Smithsonian Archives.

2. Possibly James Blake, who received an M.D. from the University of London in 1846. In his letter of April 12, Henry wrote that Blake gave him a letter of introduction from Thomas Graham, professor of chemistry there. *University of London: The Historical Record (1836–1926)*, 2d issue (London, 1926), p. 323.

3. Joseph Gilbert Totten was chief of the Army Corps of Engineers and a Smithsonian regent. He had returned the day before from Mexico where he helped plan the siege of Veracruz, Mexico's chief port and a gateway to Mexico City, to force an end to the war. He also negotiated the terms of surrender, which occurred on March 29, and carried General Winfield Scott's official announcement of the capitulation to the United States. *Henry Papers*, 4:320; K. Jack Bauer, *The Mexican War, 1846–1848* (New York, 1974), chapter 13.

4. Public land policies dating from 1785 required that land in the public domain be surveyed before settlement and classified as to whether or not it contained minerals. The mineral lands were to be reserved by the federal government, the non-mineral lands sold. In March 1847, Congress transferred authority over the reserved mineral lands from the War Department to the Treasury Department, established a Lake Superior Land District (Michigan) and a Chippewa Land District (Wisconsin Territory), and authorized the sale of the mineral lands to the public. Prior to sale, the federal government was to conduct surveys to distinguish areas rich in mineral resources from agricultural areas. Treasury Secretary Robert J. Walker chose Charles Thomas Jackson (*Henry Papers*, 3:60n–61n; *DAB; DSB*) to conduct the Lake Superior survey and David Dale Owen to survey the Chippewa region. Walker's instructions to Jackson and Owen, written three days after this letter, incorporated Henry's suggestion:

it is highly important that a series of observations be made on the dip and intensity of the needle, as intimately connected with the geological and mineralogical character of that region of country, and as likely to lead to results interesting to the cause of general science. [U.S. House, 30th Congress, 1st Session, *Letter from the Secretary of the Treasury, Transmitting His Annual Report on the State of the*

Finances, House Executive Documents, No. 6 (1847), pp. 8, 9, 131–139 (quotation on both pp. 132 and 136.)]

Combined with magnetic variation (declination) data produced by the routine land surveys, dip and intensity readings would constitute a full measurement of the earth's magnetic field. Jackson's magnetic instruments were to be provided by the Treasury Department, Owen's by the Smithsonian.

Jackson chose John Locke (*Henry Papers, 3:*420n), a veteran of several magnetic surveys, to make magnetic observations in addition to his duties as an assistant geologist. After a change of administration and a decision that Locke's work was government property, his observations were published in Jackson's *Report on the Geological and Mineralogical Survey of the Mineral Lands of the United States in the State of Michigan . . .* (U.S. Senate, 31st Congress, 1st Session, Senate Executive Documents, No. 1, Part 3 [1849], pp. 588–603). The tables were printed improperly, however, and Locke republished the data, along with earlier 1845 and 1846 observations, in *Observations on Terrestrial Magnetism,* 1852, SI Contributions, vol. 3 (Washington, 1852). The report on Owen's survey did not include any data on terrestrial magnetism although Locke was advised by Walker at one point to make observations in Owen's district also and Locke was interested in doing so (Jackson, p. 440; see Docs. 129 and 145).

Mary C. Rabbitt, *Minerals, Lands, and Geology for the Common Defence and General Welfare,* 3 vols. (Washington, 1979–), *1:*83–85; Dupree, *Science in the Federal Government,* pp. 91–92; *Smithsonian Report for 1847,* pp. 189–190; Jackson, especially pp. 371, 394, 563–572; D. D. Owen, *Report of a Geological Reconnoissance of the Chippewa Land District of Wisconsin,* U.S. Senate, 30th Congress, 1st Session, House Executive Documents, No. 57 (1848). For the dependence of geomagnetics on other disciplines and the Smithsonian's role as a catalyst in lending instruments to surveyors, see Gregory A. Good, "Geomagnetics and Scientific Institutions in 19th Century America," *Eos,* 1985, *66:*521–526.

5. Richard Montgomery Young (1798–1861), a lawyer and former senator from Illinois (1837–1843), was commissioner of the General Land Office from 1847 to 1849. *BDAC.*

6. Henry was referring here to the routine surveying of the public lands. The surveyors used a solar compass to determine true north-south lines by measuring the sun's position. Invented by surveyor William A. Burt, it was especially useful in areas where iron deposits caused erratic readings from a standard surveyor's compass and gave readings of magnetic variation within a quarter of a degree. As the readings were numerous, Henry thought lines of declination could be drawn from the data with reasonable confidence. Charles Whittlesey later summarized variation observations in the Michigan and Wisconsin area in J. W. Foster and J. D. Whitney, *Report on the Lake Superior Land District. Part II. The Iron Region Together with the General Geology,* U.S. Senate, 32d Congress, Special Session, Senate Executive Documents, No. 4 (1851), chapter 20; *Smithsonian Report for 1848,* p. 16; William A. Burt, *Description of the Solar Compass, Together with Directions for Its Adjustment and Use* (Detroit, 1844); a copy is in the Henry Library.

7. Robert Dale Owen attended building committee meetings through April 20 and then returned to Indiana to campaign for his reelection. Rhees, *Journals,* pp. 674–679.

8. David Dale Owen had advised the Smithsonian without charge on plans and materials for the building. Henry may have feared, as others did at the time, that his goal was to get a Smithsonian position, presumably as assistant secretary in charge of the natural history collections, through the influence of his brother. See, for example, G. P. Marsh to Mary Baird, February 10, 1847, Baird Papers, Smithsonian Archives; James Hall to E. N. Horsford, March 27, 1847, Horsford Papers, Rensselaer Polytechnic Institute Archives; J. B. Rogers to W. B. Rogers, April 5, 1847, W. B. Rogers Papers, Archives, Massachusetts Institute of Technology. Rhees, *Journals,* pp. 3–4, 5, 6, 604–610, 612–614, 664–667.

9. Although Henry's salary was $3,500 a year, he drew only $1,750 from the Smithsonian in 1847 as he was still receiving a salary from Princeton for teaching there. *Smithsonian Report for 1847,* p. 156.

10. Doc. 37.

11. On April 14, 1847, the building committee rehired William McPeake as a messenger, a function he had performed earlier. A native of Ireland, McPeake (ca. 1792–1862) remained at the Smithsonian as a messenger, doorkeeper, and janitor until his death. Sometimes referred to as "McFuss," McPeake was described by Caspar Wistar Hodge as "the most exalted dignitary" connected with the Smithsonian and "a character worthy of a novel." *Smithsonian Report for 1847,* pp. 122, 123; Eighth Census of the United States, 1860, District of Columbia (NARA microfilm M653, reel 104, frame [935]); *Washington Evening Star,* December 1, 1862; C. W. Hodge to Charles Hodge, November 11, 1848, Charles Hodge Papers, Manuscripts Di-

vision, Department of Rare Books and Special Collections, Princeton University Libraries.

12. John Maclean, vice-president of Princeton. *Henry Papers,* 1:433n.

13. Charles Sherwood Stratton (1838–1883), better known as "General Tom Thumb," was a midget under the artistic management of P. T. Barnum. At nine years of age, Stratton was only the size of a small toddler but was already a veteran of a three-year European tour during which he performed for the crowned heads of Europe. Stratton's visit to Washington consisted

of three days of public appearances at Jackson Hall. *DAB; National Intelligencer,* April 14, 1847. Neil Harris, *Humbug: The Art of P. T. Barnum* (Boston, 1973), pp. 50–52, 99–102, 215.

14. Alfred Alexander Woodhull (1837–1921), a young Princeton resident. *DAB.*

15. In his diary, Polk mentioned adjourning a cabinet meeting to meet Tom Thumb, "a most remarkable person." Allan Nevins, ed., *Polk: The Diary of a President, 1845–1849* (New York, 1968), pp. 216–217.

40. FROM EBEN N. HORSFORD[1]

Cambridge, Apr. 14,/47—[A]

[...] on the very da[y ...]ther.

I am at a loss to account for the glass not reaching you. It was enclosed within two or three pamphlets and prepaid. It grieves me indeed—as I know Prof— Faraday thought to please you, particularly.[2] I beg you will tell him this circumstance when you write him—

[...] the fact [?with] [...] the increase of radiant [...] the introduction of an incombustible body into flame is certainly most interesting.[3] Is the increase so very considerable that you might mark the differences, between the effects of Baryta, Strontia, Lime, and Magnesia compounds— say hydrates of the first three & carbonates of all?[4] I think I mentioned to you[5] having found the conducting powers, and [ge]neral chemical properties to be [...] the degree of their intensity, in [th]e order of their atomic weights. [I] have just been through with the entire chemical history of all the compounds of these earths & find the law true with two or three exceptions— If you would like to make the experiment, & have not the substances I will try and prepare them for you—though as yet I have no laboratory.

I am very Respectfully
and truly yours,
Eben N. Horsford

Prof Joseph Henry. LLD.

Henry Papers, Smithsonian Archives.
The top half of the first sheet and one side of the second sheet are missing; the ellipses indicate where one or two words are missing, except at the first and third instances, which indicate where the first sheet is torn in half.

1. The newly elected Rumford Professor on the Application of Science to the Useful Arts at Harvard. *Henry Papers*, 6:51.

2. Faraday had given Horsford some glass for reproducing the Faraday effect which Horsford had dutifully forwarded along with a letter of December 31, 1846. Henry wrote on January 8 that the glass had not arrived with the letter. Evidently Henry's letter had not reached Horsford by March 2, when Horsford wrote to ask for Henry's advice on his new position and to inquire whether Henry had received the glass. On March 24, Horsford wrote James Hall to complain that Henry had never responded to his three letters from Europe, written at Henry's suggestion and with the assurance of a response, or to his March 2 letter. Horsford attributed Henry's lack of response to "a negligence arising from an immense pressure of duties" or to some unintentional offense on Horsford's part. *Henry Papers*, 6:621; Mary

Henry Copy, Henry to Horsford, January 8, 1847, and Horsford to Henry, March 2, 1847, Henry Papers, Smithsonian Archives; Horsford to Hall, March 24, 1847, State Geologists' and Paleontologists' Correspondence File, Series B0561, New York State Archives.

3. Henry had evidently described to Horsford his experiments of late March on the increased radiation of heat from a flame due to the introduction of an incombustible solid.

4. In his later paper on these experiments, Henry mentioned trying "glass, carbonate of lime, sulphate of lime, stone coal, fire clay, &c." but being unable to determine relative effects without specimens of equal diameter. "On the Effect of Mingling Radiating Substances with Combustible Materials," AAAS *Proceedings*, 1855, 9:112–116.

5. In his letter of December 31, 1846 (*Henry Papers*, 6:622).

41. TO ELIAS LOOMIS

Princeton April 22nd 1847

My dear sir

Your favour of April 12th came to Princeton while I was in Washington[1] and I now begin this answer at almost the first moment ↑of↓ leisure I have had at my command since my return. I have nothing at present to suggest with reference to the plan of the memoir so far as you have given it in your letter it fully meets my views.[2] I can give you no information until I see or hear from Mr Espy as to the number and character of the observations made at the military posts.[3] Mr Espys salary was struck from the appropriation bill at the last session of congress and in consequence of this he intends to leave Washington next July.

I do not ↑think↓ that he can have any cause to be displeased with our proceedings you will of course give him due credit for his labours and he will be invited to furnish for publication in the Smithsonian Contributions to Knowledge the results of any researches he may have as yet not given to the world.[4] I would however be glad if it were in my power to do something in the way of attempting to restore him to his former position. I consider him a man of most excellent character who has laboured industriously and sucessfully in the cause of science and who in a country of so much wealth as ours should not thus be deprived of

the pittance ↑to↓ which a few months before he was thought entitled
t̶o̶. He has continued to receive the reports from the several government stations but has not published any results that I have heard of
since 1843.[5]

The secretary of the Treasury at my suggestion appended to his order
for a geological survey of the new Territories directions for a set of magnetic observations on the dip & the intensity. The condition was that I
should give the instructions and purchase the instruments the results
to be given to the smithsonian for publication.

I found by enquiry at the land office that all the surveys of the public
lands are now made with an instrument called a solar compass which
gives the meridian by means of an image[A] of the sun, the declination[6]
being known, to within about a quarter of a degree and perhaps less.
Also the surveyor has been directed in all[B] cases, on each line to note
the deviation of the magnetic needle and in this way considerable material has been furnished for perfecting the variation chart of our country.
Would not the plan of procuring a good map plate of the united states
and having a number of copies made of it by the electrotype process be
of interest? on one of the plates the magnetic lines being delineated on
anothe the thermal on a third the geology &c and thus in time forming
the elements of a physical atlas of our country.[7]

I think of visiting New York in the course of a week or two and I
will then give you a full account of all the proceedings relative to the
smithsonian. In the meantime I beg to assure you that I remain as ever

Truly yours
Joseph Henry

Prof. Loomis

Loomis Papers, Beinecke Rare Book and Manuscript Library, Yale University.
Draft: Henry Papers, Smithsonian Archives (differs in wording and order of material and has
an additional paragraph on Smithsonian affairs, specifically the funding compromise). Previously
printed in Nathan Reingold, ed., *Science in Nineteenth-Century America: A Documentary History* (New
York, 1964), pp. 155–156.

1. Letter not found.

2. Loomis's "Report on the Meteorology of
the United States" reviewed the progress of the
field and presented a plan under which the
Smithsonian would organize and direct "a
grand meteorological campaign" to collect systematic observations of phenomena. It appeared as an appendix to the *Smithsonian Report
for 1847*, pp. 193–207 (quotation on p. 206).

3. Loomis reported around sixty military
posts which recorded meteorological data. Observations were made four times a day on ba-

rometers and thermometers, the direction and
force of the wind, and the direction, velocity,
and amount of clouds. The amount and times
of rainfall were also noted. Loomis, pp. 195,
205.

4. Loomis devoted three pages to Espy's
"generalizations, given in his own words."
Henry published a brief extract from an undated letter on meteorology by Espy immediately following Loomis's report. Loomis, pp.
197–199 (quotation on p. 197); *Smithsonian Report for 1847*, pp. 207–208.

5. Espy's first report on meteorology was dated 1843 but issued in 1845. A two-page "report" to Surgeon General Thomas Lawson in 1845 restated the generalizations of the first report and added two new ones. Espy's second report on meteorology was not published until 1849. Fleming, *Meteorology,* pp. 70–72, 97; David M. Ludlum, *Early American Tornadoes, 1586–1870* (Boston, 1970), pp. 171–174.

6. That is, astronomical declination.

7. Under annual research grants in Henry's "Programme of Organization," he had included:

Explorations in descriptive natural history, and geological, magnetical, and topographical surveys, to collect material for the formation of a Physical Atlas of the United States.

The physical atlas suggestion was not pursued at this time. In a letter of May 4, 1865, to Henry, George Gibbs revived the idea. He proposed preparing skeleton maps and distributing them to government surveys and expeditions, members of learned societies, and individual scientists. As far as we can determine, the first actual product of the sort Henry envisioned appeared in a Census Office publication: Francis A. Walker, comp., *Statistical Atlas of the United States Based upon the Results of the Ninth Census 1870* ([New York], 1874). Part I, "Physical Features of the United States," included maps of river systems, woodlands, annual rainfall, storm centers, annual mean temperature and extreme temperatures, isobars, hypsometric (elevation) data, coal strata, and geological formations. The data on rainfall and annual mean temperature were provided by the Smithsonian. *Smithsonian Report for 1847,* p. 175; George Gibbs, "A Physical Atlas of North America," *Smithsonian Report for 1866,* pp. 368–369.

42. TO [JONATHAN HOMER LANE][A]

Princeton College of New-Jersey
April 22nd 1847

Dear Sir

Your communication of the 8th of Feb[y] on the subject of electro dynamic Induction[1] was received through the favour of my friend Professor Foster of Union College. It came to however at a time when I was so much occupied with the duties of the organization of the smithsonian Institution that I could give attention to no other subject.

I have made a long series of expermnts on the branch of electricity known by the name of Dynam Induction the results of which have been presented from time to time to the American Philosophical Society and published in the transactions or the proceedings of this Institution. Accounts or rather notices of my late experiments on this subject are to be found in the later volumes of the proceedings not the transactions of the Society. Also a brief notice of of my researches in general on the subjects of electricity and magnetism is[B] given in the suplmentary volume of the Encyclopedia Americana just published in Philadelphia under the direction of Professor Vethake.[2]

I intend publishing in the first no of the Smithsonian contributions to knowledge a memoir giving the full developement of all my later ~~experimnts~~ expimts on electricty.[3]

The phenomenon of the evolution of both oxygen and hydrogen from each wire of the decomposing apparatus with a discharge of ordinary electricty is I think readily explined on the prinples of the series of oscillations which precedes the restoration of the equilium in the discharge of a Leyden jar.[C]

Draft, Henry Papers, Smithsonian Archives.

1. Doc. 17.

2. Joseph Henry, "Magnetism," *Encyclopaedia Americana: Supplementary Volume* (Philadelphia, 1847), *14*:412–426.

3. Henry's own work was never published in the Smithsonian Contributions to Knowledge but appeared instead in appendices to the annual reports of the Smithsonian.

43. TO JOHN STUART SKINNER[1]

Princeton april 22nd 1847

My dear Sir

I hope you will pardon me for so long delaying to acknowledge the receipt of your letters[2] and the ↑interesting↓ volumes on agriculture you were so good as to send me. The truth is I have been so ~~overwhelmed~~ ↑much pressed↓ with busness since my appointment that I have ~~not been able~~ ↑found it impossible↓ to keep up with my correspondence particularly as I have ↑had↓ no assistance.[A]

I consider the Farmers Library a valuable publication[3] and on my own responsibility I ~~take the liberty of~~ ↑have concluded to↓ subscribe[B] for it on behalf of the Smithsonian Institution[4] you will therefore please to send the numbers to me directed for the present to Princeton.

Agriculture is one of the branches of knowledge which in my opinion should ↑especially↓ receive the ~~special~~ encouragement of the Smithsonian establishment and I think the plan of organization which I presented to the Board of Regents would as effectually ensure this end as the limited income of the bequest and the number of objects claming ↑its↓ assistance will permit. The pamphlet which I send you with this letter will give you the several propositions of this plan ↑as expressed↓ in the ~~form of the~~ Resolutions marked in ink with the numerals 1, 2, 3, 4 & 5.[5] ↑The ~~two~~ first ↑two↓ are intended to promote the increase of knowleged and the remainder to effect ~~the~~ its diffusion.↓ No. 1 offers inducements for undertaking new researches and the ~~discovery of new phenomena~~ ↑production of original memoirs↓. No 2 provides for special experiments ~~the~~ ↑at the↓ expenses ~~of which are to be defrayed by~~

the funds of the Institution. For example the Board of Regents may direct ~~that~~ a series of ~~experiments be made~~ on the analysises of particular plants to determine what substances should be ~~found in~~ ↑added to↓ the soil inorder to their better production. No 3⁶ provides for the publication of a series of periodical Reports on ↑the progress of↓ all branches of the three great divisions of human knowledge namely Physical science moral and political science critisim and the fine arts—these Reports[C] to be prepared by Collaborators eminent in there respective lines who are to be furnished with all the journals of the world[D] necssary for selecting ~~the~~ ↑proper↓ material. Under ~~the head of~~ ↑the head of Reports on↓ Physical science a small volume on agriculture would be annually published containing in a condensed form an account of all the positive additions which may have been made during[E] the year to this branch of knowledge.

This plan was adopted provisionally by the Board but unfortunately the law of Congress establishing the Institution requires so large an expenditure of the funds in providing for a Library ~~and a collection of specimens~~ ↑a museum & a gallery of art↓ that the scheme I have mentioned ~~for increasing and diffusing knowledge among men~~ cannot be carried out as effectually as I could wish.

The income of the smithsonian Institution is so small that little of general interest can be effected by collections Lectures and ~~agricultural~~ normal schools these plans can only produce local and partial results. The only means by which ~~kn~~ the Smithsonian bequest can be made available in increasing and diffusing knowledge ↑generally↓ among men ~~generally~~ is ↑princpally↓ by stimulating ~~original~~ ↑the labours of all in our country who are capable of enlarging the bounds of truth by↓ research in all parts of the ~~country~~ ↑and the world↓ and diffusing ↑valuable↓ information of ~~a valuable kind~~ as widely ↑and as cheaply↓ as possible through the press.

Plese accept my thanks for your kind offer of the use of the pages of your ↑valuable↓ journal journal. I shall perhaps avail myself of the ~~privilege~~ privelege at some futur time. I am very

~~I am Very~~ Respect fully
~~Truly~~ Yours
Joseph Henry

Draft, Henry Papers, Smithsonian Archives.
Drafts: Two partial drafts in same location.

1. Skinner (1788–1851) was editor of the *Farmer's Library and Monthly Journal of Agriculture* from 1845 to 1848. From 1819 to 1830, he had published the *American Farmer,* the "first continuous, successful agricultural periodical in the United States." *DAB.*

2. Not found.

3. Skinner was hired to edit the journal by Horace Greeley and Thomas McElrath of the *New York Tribune*. Each issue included a reprint of a major work on agriculture as well as practical information on farming and notices of experiments, machinery, and inventions. *DAB*, s.v. "Skinner, John Stuart."

4. At an August 10, 1848, executive committee meeting, Henry presented Skinner's request that the Smithsonian buy three volumes of the *Farmer's Library*. The committee approved the purchase. The first three volumes (1846–1847) are listed in *Catalogue of Publications and of Periodical Works Belonging to the Smithsonian Institution, January 1, 1866* (Washington, 1866), p. 540. Rhees, *Journals*, p. 464.

5. *Report of the Organization Committee of the Smithsonian Institution* (Washington, 1847), specifically the resolutions at the bottom of page 19 and the top of page 20.

6. Henry meant number 4.

44. TO JOHN KEARSLEY MITCHELL[1]

Princeton april 23rd 1847

My dear Dr

I happened a few evening ago to have a conversation with Mr Walker secretary of the Treasury on the subject of the yellow fever and his remarkes struck me as being characterized with ↑so much↓ philosophical discrimination that knowing your interest in this matter I am induced to note them down for your inspection.

The following as far as I can recollect are ↑the conclusions↓ he has arrived at from his own observations of the phenomena as they have been exhibited for several years at Natchis and New Orleans.

1 Yellow fever occurs spontaneously in certain places under the predisposing causes of heat filth and moisture.

2 Yellow fever is sometimes ↑produced↓ from the pent up air brought in the hold of vessels from a distance and thence spreads by propogation, provided the necessary conditions are present.

3 The cause of the disease is destroyed by a single exposure of the air to a white frost. A case to illustrate this fell under Mr Walkers notice in which a house was closed at the time the fever was raging and not opened until after a frost; when three persons died who attempted^{A} to live in it though there was no feave in any other part of the city at the time.

4 The cause of the yellow fever appears to require the presence of of collections of human beaings for its propagation; no instance has been known of the disease breaking out or spreading on an insulated plantation not in the vicinity of a city.

5 Yellow fever after having made its appearance from year to year in a certain place has entirely disappeared after the land has been drained, vegetabl and animal matter in a state of putrescence removed, and a more general attention ↑given↓ to the clenliness of the ~~place~~ grounds & buildings.

I do not suppose that any of these conclusions are new to you though they may serve to fortify some of your points and I doubt not that Mr Walker would readily communicate to you the details of facts on which he has founded his inductions.[2]

> With my best wishes for your
> continued success in
> all that renders life
> plesant and profitable
> I remn yours truly
> Joseph Henry

Dr J. K. Mitchell

Draft, Henry Papers, Smithsonian Archives.

1. Mitchell was professor of medicine at Jefferson Medical College in Philadelphia. *Henry Papers,* 3:325n.

2. The cause of yellow fever was unknown. The dominant view in the medical profession was that it was caused by miasma, or poisons in the air produced by marshes. Others blamed atmospheric conditions, while a minority believed the disease was caused by tiny animal or vegetable creatures usually termed animalculae. Doctors also divided into contagionists, who believed the disease was spread by people or animals, and non-contagionists, who believed it could arise spontaneously and be spread by infected air. As with other fevers, disease theorists tried to determine the cause by a process of induction from everything known about the disease. Henry was undoubtedly aware of Mitchell's lectures on fevers, six of which from the 1846–1847 academic year became *On the Cryptogamous Origin of Malarious and Epidemic Fevers* (Philadelphia, 1849). Having hesitated to publish because he feared controversy and felt he lacked conclusive proof, Mitchell joined the organic theorists by proposing a "fungous theory of fevers," in which yellow fever was caused by fungus (pp. iv, 106). Although Mitchell did not mention Walker's observations, he did discuss some of the same phenomena Walker noticed (pp. 102–107). The true cause of yellow fever, a virus carried by mosquitoes, was not discovered until the turn of the century. Phyllis Allen, "Etiological Theory in America Prior to the Civil War," *Journal of the History of Medicine and Allied Sciences,* 1947, 2:489–520.

45. FROM JOHN MACLEAN

College of New Jersey
Princeton. April 28. 1847.

My dear Sir

As it is desirable for all concerned, that there should be matured, before the next meeting of our Trustees, some plan which will secure to our students, as far as practicable, a course of instruction in Natural Philosophy, like to that which they now enjoy;—permit me to submit for your consideration the following propositions. If either of them should meet your views, I will do all I can to carry it into effect. If neither should be acceptable, I will thank you to suggest some one more agreeable to your own views and feelings.

In case you are not committed to a contrary course, I would propose, that you should give notice to the Regents of the Smithsonian Institution, that at the expiration of twelve months from the 1st of July next, you will resign your post of Secretary; and resume your former relation to the College: and that you should agree to do so on the following conditions,

1. That from the 1st of July 1848, your salary shall be $2.000 year.

2. That for the ensuing year, your salary shall remain as it now is;[1] with the understanding, that you are to make adequate provision for the instruction of the students in the studies of your department,—by instructing them youself alone, or with the aid of some competent teacher to be employed by you, with the approval of the Faculty.

If the above proposition cannot be acceded to, I would then propose, That you should make a permanent arrangement with the Regents of the Smithsonian Institution which will enable you to spend two months in a year in Princeton; and that you should also engage to deliver here, year by year, a course of thirty lectures on Physics:[2]—and that as a compensation, you should retain for the use of your family, should you deem it desirable, the house now occupied by you; and receive a salary of $500. a year, or $700. a year without a house.[3]

In this case it would be requisite to appoint another Professor, who might be styled Professor of Mechanical Philosophy; and whose duty it should be to teach, with the exception of Physics, the branches now taught by you, and also to lecture on Architecture.[4] For one, I would greatly prefer the first of these, propositions; and I mention the other simply because I deem it much better for the College than to lose your services altogether.

You need feel no delicacy about receiving a larger salary than your colleagues. With the exception of Dr Torrey, who ~~only~~ devotes only a part of his time to the College, and of myself, you have been much longer a Professor than any of your colleagues, and on that account you are fairly entitled to a larger compensation; to say nothing of the greater value of your services:—and I can assure you, that no one of us will feel himself undervalued, because of any addition to your salary, ours remaining as they are.

With the most sincere respect
& esteem,
Your friend & colleague,
John Maclean

Professor Henry.

Henry Papers, Smithsonian Archives.
Copy: Maclean Papers, Princeton University Archives, Seeley G. Mudd Manuscript Library, Princeton University.

1. Henry probably received his full salary ($1,500 and a house) from Princeton for the 1846–1847 academic year, during which he continued to reside in Princeton but traveled to Washington periodically.

2. The course Henry had been teaching was much longer. The previous year, for example, he delivered eighty-nine lectures. *Henry Papers,* 6:412n.

3. At a meeting on June 30, 1847, Princeton's Board of Trustees agreed to retain Henry as professor of natural philosophy, with a salary of $500 and the use of his current house, and specified that he could be assisted by other faculty members. The board promoted John T. Duffield to assistant professor of mathematics

so that Stephen Alexander could assume part of Henry's duties in natural philosophy. Trustees' Minutes, June 30, 1847, vol. 3, p. 480, Princeton University Archives, Seeley G. Mudd Manuscript Library, Princeton University; John Maclean, *History of the College of New Jersey, 1746–1854,* 2 vols. in 1 (1877; New York, 1969), 2:320.

4. George Musgrave Giger (*Henry Papers,* 6:338n), adjunct professor of Greek, took over the lectures on architecture, which had been given by Henry from 1833 to 1838 and then by A. B. Dod until his death in 1845. *Catalogue of the Officers and Students of the College of New Jersey for 1847–'48* (Princeton, 1848), p. 20; *Henry Papers,* 6:431n.

46. TO [EPHRAIM GEORGE SQUIER][A]

Princeton April 28th 1847

My dear Sir

Your letter of April 22nd has just been received[1] and I hasten to suggest the plan of publishing your memoir in parts in the sucessive nos of the Smithsonian Contributions. I should myself prefer this plan if the memoir ~~will be~~ ↑is to be↓ long and the plates difficult of execution. By adopting it you will be less hurried the publication of the first no. of the contributions will be less delayed and corrections and additions which may suggest themselves in the course of the preparation of the article can be more readily made.[2]

It is intended to refer your memoir to the Ethnological Society of New-York for approval and from this tribunal I presume you need fear neither delay nor hesitation as to an opinion of the character of your labours.

I wish if possible to get the first no. of the contributions published about the time of meeting of Congress[3] and should you conclude to publish in parts, say in the first and second nos. I would be pleased to receive the 1ˢᵗ part as soon as convenient.

The Introduction to the 1ˢᵗ No. will consist of a biographical memoir of Smithson by the chancellor of the Institution the Hon Mr Dallas. The no. will also contain a paper on the gulf stream the result of the re-searches of the late Lieut. Bache[4] who lost his live in completing ~~in com-pleting~~ this work. It will embrace a paper probably from Professor Pierce of Cambridge and another from myself as these papers are all on subjects of Physical science I should prefer ~~an article~~ ↑memoir↓ like yours for the first ~~no~~ article ~~of the no.~~

Draft, Henry Papers, Smithsonian Archives.

1. Not found.
2. The first volume consisted of the Squier and Davis memoir in its entirety and nothing other than that memoir.
3. Congress convened on December 6, 1847.
4. George M. Bache.

47. TO HARRIET HENRY

Washington Saturday
½ past 3 oclock
Mayᴬ 1 1847

My dearest

I arrived here this morning a little past 8 o'clock after quite a plesant passage. I found a place provided for me in the prossession and that if I had not come on there would have been some dissatisfaction. The vice President expected me of course. The order of proceedings were published in the papers and it was expected that I would see them and the plase assigned me the celebration.[1] The whole affair has just closed and I have returned to my room at Gadsbys covered with dust and while the servant is brushing my coat I devote the minutes which are to elapse before dinner to you. The procession formed at the city Hall[2] then marched through the streets to the Presidents House where the President and the heads of departments were received. It then returned passed down 11 st to the site of the building on the mall.

On the cround near the corner of the new building was erected a stage decorated with evergreens on which the principal personages connected with the Institution were assembled. In front of this the masons went through the ceremony of Laying the corner stone—after which an address was delivered by the vice President[3] and then the whole adjurned. I should have mentioned that before the corner Stone was laid a very impressive and eloquent prayer was offered by the Rev Mr Evans of the methodist Church.[4]

The number of persons assembled was very great perhaps 10[B] thousand with a considerable proportion of Ladies.[5] All the masons for miles around were assembled together with the military— At the conclusion of the ceremony ~~the~~ a salute from canon was fired.

The speach of Mr Dalass was very well but had I seen him a litler sooner I think I could have given him a few hints which might have modified some parts.[6] Speaches and celebrations of this kind are however the mere flourish of the moment and produce no lasting effect. They are the relics of the ages before the invention of the art of printing when ~~wh~~ men could only act on men through the medium of the senses when pagentry and oratory were invoked to captivate the eye and ear of those whoes intellects were dormant. But in these tims exhibitions of this kind are not as necessary and I hope the time may come when oratory and all the employed to lead the judgement astray through the impressions on the imagination will be do away with. If all the discussions in congress were divested of oratory the truth would sooner be settle on.

I have just returned from dinner where I enjoyed myself very much not in very voracious eating but in rather nice tasting of many articles of savery character.

I have not as yet heard through the telegraph of your being worse and as no news is good news I shall cherish the idea though with some anxiety that you are better. I left home with considerable misgiving but in the cars I found the Rev Mr Burns of Schenectady who kept me in pretty close conversation until we reached Phil[d] I did not have time to go to D[r] Ludlows but was obliged to leave one boat for the other and had only an opportunity of getting a "hasty plate of soup" of oysters. On board of the steam I found a young midshipman who had just returned from Vera Cruse and gave me a goodly number of long yarns as to the War.

We arrived at about eleven O'clock at Baltimore ~~and~~. I put up at the Eutor House[7] which I found a very plesant establishment. We started from Baltimore at ½ part 6 oclock and travelled over the distance to Washington in about one hour[c] and a half.

I found Mc Peak in great business in the way of attending to all the affairs of the ceremony. He expressed great pleasure at my appearan and has since been very attentive to my wants at the Hotel.

The weather has been quite plesant though rather cold to day— I was pleased with this for had the day been hot I would not have daird to walk as far in the sun as I have done to day. I had however an umberrella one belonging to Col. Totten withwhom I walked at the head of the civil part of the procession. The col. was very attentive to me and gave me some very minute and interesting accounts of the siege from which has lately returned. I was thrown a little into a state of mortification this morning when I arrived, covered with dust and one of the "pipes" of my nether garment dirtied with pitch, and expecting to be called upon in a ~~few~~ short time to join the procession or to go to the city Hall preparatory to joining to find on opening my trunk my clothes apparently missing. I afterwards recollected that you had informed me that the articles were put in the upper part. I was destined however to experience a little disappointment for when I came to put on my pants I found a wrong par had been put into the trunk namely a thin summer par instead of my new cloth ones. I put on the thin ones but found the weather so cool that I was obliged to take them off again not however until the cloath articles had been well brushed. I was alittle anoyed at first but the conclusion the occurrance fixed on my mind was the importance of the attention of my wife to all my affairs.

Without her I should be a lost man the world would be sad and life insupportable. The bell is ringing and I must close

Adieu my dearest

Family Correspondence, Henry Papers, Smithsonian Archives.

1. The *National Intelligencer* of April 30, 1847, published a notice of the upcoming ceremony of the laying of the cornerstone of the Smithsonian Building. In the mile-long procession, Henry was paired with Vice-President Dallas, chancellor of the Smithsonian, immedi- ately following President Polk and his cabinet and preceding the regents. The issue of May 3 reported the procession and ceremony at the site in detail.

Alfred Vail alleged in a letter to Samuel F. B. Morse that the building committee, irritated with Henry over his desire to contain building costs, insulted him intentionally by not inviting him:

> Henry was not even invited by Building Committee to be present at the laying of the Corner Stone—and came on and witnessed it, in the capacity of a "loafer" as one of his friends terms it.

The minutes of the building committee, which organized the event, mention specific invitations only to the president and vice-president. In the same letter, Vail claimed that Henry refused to let Vail's *American Electro Magnetic Telegraph* (Philadelphia, 1845) be put into the cornerstone. Vail to Morse, May 17, 1847, Morse Papers, Library of Congress. Rhees, *Journals*, p. 674.

2. At the foot of Judiciary Square (Four-and-a-half St. and Louisiana Avenue, NW).

3. Dallas's address appeared in the *National Intelligencer* and was also separately published in *Address Delivered on Occasion of Laying the Corner Stone of the Smithsonian Institution, May 1, 1847* (Washington, 1847).

4. The *National Intelligencer* reported that the lengthy prayer was actually delivered by Brother McJilton, grand chaplain of the Grand Lodge of Maryland. The Reverend F. S. Evans, of Ryland Chapel near the site of the Smithsonian, delivered the benediction. Washington City Directory, 1846.

5. According to the *National Intelligencer*, six or seven thousand people witnessed the procession and ceremony.

6. Dallas reviewed the origins of the Smithsonian and described the design of the building. In one section, he noted that certain functions of the Smithsonian, such as a museum, were dictated by the provisions of the act relative to the building: "Congress have stamped this character upon it, by prescribing and appropriating its vast interior compartments, and by other positive expressions of their will." In the same section, he explained:

> It is the first duty of the Regents to obey the unequivocal behests of Congress—to carry them out faithfully, on the scale and in the spirit they obviously import; and to let their measures flow, not from their own discretion, but from the provisions of the law which they are empowered to execute.

7. That is, the Eutaw House.

48. TO HARRIET HENRY

Washington May 2nd 1847

My Dearest

The cars leave at 6 o'clock tomorrow morning and therefore unless I write this evening I shall not have an other opportunity of sending a letter until tomorrow night.

This has been a dark and cloudy day of rather plesant temperature with rain in the morning the first which has fallen in this place for about four weeks. Though I have been some what lonely and a littl anxious about you I have spent the day rather plesantly and I hope some what profitably. I have been twice at Church with Dr Lindsly and in the morning heard a very interesting discourse from a gentleman from Boston whoes name I have forgotten. His subject was the Mysteries of Revelation and for clearness of exposition soundness of doctrine and aptness of illustration I have heard nothing to surpass it for a long time.

There must always be mystery however elevated our intellectual powers we are the finite contemplating the operations of the Infinite. The traveller who assends the gentle acclevity of a mountain beholds at each step new objects breaking in upon his vew but still his prospect is bounded and perhaps interrupted by obstructions at a little distance. As he assends higher these no longer obscure the vew but beyond is the bounding[A] circle of earth and heaven—even this expands in dimensions as his progress continues upward but to what ever mountain height he may clime his vision can ↑never↓ encompass the arth and his vew must still be terminated on all sides by the misty mingling of ocean and sky.

This afternon the church went in at half past four on account of the funeral of one of the elders and instead of a sermond a short address was given with the administration of the sacrament.

I hope my dearest you have recovered from the attack and that I will find you enjoying much better health than when I left home or indeed than you have done for several months past.

You have been to careless of your health and while you have been anxious about the children and myself my[B] better half yourself has not been thought of. You know I cannot do without you scarcely for a single day for though I may be from home for several days in sucession yet you make the arrangements—you facilitate my starting and highten the pleasure of return by the long anticipated kiss and the fond embrace.

I have found this house Gadsby's a very plesant stopping place. The room is comfortable and the servants attentive. Mr Gadsby[1] is quit obliging but the expense is rather heavy.

Washington is very beautiful at this season the trees are in full foliage & the fields around covered with a righ carpet of green.

I called last evening at Mr Frosts the old gentleman[C] was apparently much gratified with my call. Charlot made many enquiries about you the tall maden Lady Miss Frost was as calm and prim as ever.

I have been quite well since I left home the pill I took a few days ago have done me much good. I was however very greatly fatigued last night and could scarcely get asleep with the pain of my feet and leags after walking so far in the Procession and about the Town.

It is now half past ten and after commending you our dear little ones and myself to the Father of all merces I will retire to rest. I am writing this in my room on a little table at the foot of my bead after it is folded I will carry it downstairs and put it in a bag that hangs against the wall and which will be taken before I am up to the cars. That you may be preserved through the darkness of night and from the evils of the day that you may continue to be blessed in this world for many years and when you leave it have a full assurance of greate blessing in the world to come is the sincere prayer my dear Wife of your affectionate Husband. It is necssary almost to a proper appreciation of those we love that they should occasionally be placed in unusual positions with reference to us. That sickness or absence or some other circumstance should break the monotony ordinary existence inorder that we should know the state of our own feelins— The fact that I am from home and that I left you sick calls fourth my warmest feelings and at this moment I can think of nothing which would give me greate pleasure than to clasp you in my arms.

Do you know Dearest[D] that yesterday was our wedding day[2] and that we are getting to be an old couple. Good night

Darest[E]

Please kiss all the children for me.

Family Correspondence, Henry Papers, Smithsonian Archives.

1. Presumably a relative of the original proprietor, John Gadsby, who had died in 1844. He had a son named John Gadsby, Jr., who managed the hotel at one time. The 1846 Washington City Directory lists a William Gadsby at the hotel's address. Dorothy H. Kabler, *The Story of Gadsby's Tavern* (Alexandria, 1952), pp. 23, 51; James Goode, *Capital Losses: A Cultural History of Washington's Destroyed Buildings* (Washington, 1979), pp. 168–169.

2. The Henrys were actually married on May 3, 1830. *Henry Papers*, 1:274n; 6:443n.

49. TO HARRIET HENRY

Washington monday
morning 7 o'clock
May 3rd 1847

My Dearest

I have just got out of bed and with my wrapper on, seeing the writing materials so conveniently before me and missing your accustomed presence at this hour I cannot refrain from scribbeling a few lines to you though I have nothing to say. I am reminded however by the dating of the letter that this is the 3rd of May and that 17 years ago we were together in a little room in a tavern at New Haven just commencing the journey together of wedded ↑life↓. The beginning though perhaps as sunny as journeys of the kind usually are was yet not quite as bright as immagination could have painted it. I found you different in some respects from what I ↑had↓ immagined ~~you to be~~ and not knowing my peculiarities and faults of character until they were revaeld by more intimate communion you were perhaps shocked and disappointed. I have certainly great cause for thankfulness that you consented to be

97

mine, and that our love should have increased with our years. We know not what is in↓ store for us but of this we may be assured that we cannot escape the general lot of humanity—that difficulties and tryals await us but the anticipation of these should not prevent us from enjoying the goods which providence has bestowed on us at the present and when the evil day may come we can live over the past, in memory, and draw a lasting supply of plesant reflections from this source. The prospect of usefulness at Washington appears brighter than it did and I think there will be little difficulty in making arrangements by which I shall for some years to come be able to spend two or three months of the warmest weather in Princeton. I had much conversation with Col. Totten on Saturday and though he is a gentleman of not many words yet he entered very fully into my vews which was the more plesant since at first he was in favour of a library and voted I think for an other Person.[1] Bache told me that when we became acquainted with each other we would draw together. Now that he is on the ground every thing will go on well in reference to the building.[2] My views I find are becoming known and better appreciated and on the whole I am well pleased that I came on to. The^ celebration was authorized by the building Committee and consequently it was my duty to be in attendance the notice given in the paper of the order of proceeding which, however I did not see until I reached Baltimore, was con[si]dered a sufficent invitation both to myself and the Vice President.

In comming to Washington I may not consult my own ease but on the most mature reflection I think it my duty to continue my connection with the Institution and when this thought is presented to my mind I feel perfectly easy as to the result. If we act conscientiously and faithfully, endeavouring before God to do our duty, the result in the long run cannot be otherwise than good. I can truly say that my appointment has not been to me a source of self congratulation for though on some occasions and at some moments I may have felt a little proud of my advancement yet you can bear me witness that the prevailing feeling has been one of deep solicitude as to the responsibility I have assumed and of distrust of my ability to carry out the view of the Donor. I say of distrust ↑but↓ I do not intend by this that I have had any misgivings as to the success of the Institution could I have it entirely under my own controll, but ↑I speak↓ of my ability to induce the Regents to adopt the best measures and to keep the establishment free from the influence of designing individuals. In this undertaking fraught with important consequences to the country, the world, and to our family I must look to you for support—for sympathy—for assistance—for councel—we must set aside our sensitiveness—cherish the true pride of character which is not ready to notice the slightest want of attention;—which, conscious of merit in itself requires but little from the acknowledgement of the world— I think a residence in Washington where every one does as he chooses will not have a bad influence on your character—your position will if you chose give you standing and the constant changes in the ~~society~~ ↑inhabitants↓ will enable you to choose to mingle or not in society.

I am certain our children will be better off in this Place than in Princeton unless the society of the latter ~~place~~ changes very much we can have a governess in the family and in the course of a year or two our daughters will be companions for you—ready on all occasions to assist and support their mother; and in Washington not subjected to the mortification which I fear they will be liable to in Princeton. We shall if our lives ↑and theirs↓ be spared, have two grown up daughters in the course of 5 years and if we can procure for them good instruction we may hope to receve as much pleasure from their society as women, as we have done from them as children. Will. bids fair to be a good and useful man and his personal appearance as well as that of the girls ~~are~~ is such that a mother, even as fond as you are, and as proud as fond, need not be ashamd of. The gong has proclaimed the breakfast— I have been scribling near an hour and can scarcely recollet without an effort what I have written. I can however assure you that my pen has only served to give expression to the genuine feelins of my heart though[B] as you ↑know↓ my fingers are not adequate to the task of expressing ~~the~~ as much as I feel.

Eight o'clock P.M.

I have just come from supper and will now finish my letter. I have been all day engaged in writing out the plan of the Smithsonian and having the article copied[3]— I wish to show it to Col. Totten but the copiest has not yet finished the task so that I am not ready to go with it to night as I expected.

This has been quite a beautiful day. The Sun bright but not very warm. You will probably see the address of the vice President in the news paper. I do not think it is quite correct in some particulars though it is very prettily done so far as the expression goes. The articles the English embassador were sold be[fore][C] I arrived they went quite high some of the articles were sold to Persons in New York there was quite a rage to get a pece of furniture which had been imported from Europe for the English embassador.[4]

I hope you have intirely recovered and since [I ha]ve received no intelligence through the telegraph [or oth]erwise I presume you are better though I should [...] pleased to see you and judge for myself [...]ing— Kiss all the children for me [...] you get about again be careful [...] would give this advise from motives [...] love for we cannot spare you [... c]leaning or work is to be done let others [... lit]tle rest if it be possible for you to do [...] your own—H.

Family Correspondence, Henry Papers, Smithsonian Archives.
The lower left corner of the last page is torn off, causing missing material increasing from two letters at the beginning of the last paragraph to several words at the end.

1. Henry had written his wife in December that Totten had voted for Francis Markoe. *Henry Papers*, 6:600.

2. Totten was one of three members of the building committee. During his absence in Mexico, Robert Dale Owen and William W. Seaton, both proponents of a large Smithsonian building, had conducted the committee's business with the help of William J. Hough, who took Totten's place. Rhees, *Journals*, p. 33.

3. This was a draft of Henry's "Programme of Organization" (Doc. 130).

4. Following a period of difficult relations between the United States and Great Britain, the British ambassador, Richard Pakenham (1797–1868), left Washington on a leave of absence in May 1847 and retired rather than return to Washington. The auction notice called attention to "his very superior Furniture, &c., all of which is of the best kind, and most of it made in England." *DNB; National Intelligencer*, April 29, 1847.

50. TO HARRIET HENRY

Washing Tuesday morning
May 4th 1847

My Dearest

Yesterday as I informed you I was engaged nearly all day in writing out my programe of the organization of the Smithsonian Institution and in getting it copied to day I shall devote in part to the Smithsonian papers and tomorrow if nothing prevents I shall start for home. I do not think however that you need expect me before Friday.[A] I will write a line to day to Mrs Ludlow[1] telling her that I shall be in the city on Thursday and that she is expected to go to Princeton with me on Friday.

I went to bed last night a little after nine slept well and now feel in good condition for the duties of the day. I am writing this while the servant is brushing my clothes.

I have just finished a letter to Mrs L[2] and have informed her that you had been quite unwell and that unless she made her appearance in Princeton with me I should possibly be received very coldly and that you would be in danger of a relapse. I have informed her that she must

100

be ready with her family to start on Friday at the fartherest. I do not
know who are to accompany her and therefore I used the expression
"you and your's." Will. I suppose will have his establishment in good
condition and I think it will be well to get the addition to the seat I
suggested made as soon as possible. It should be small not more than
eight inches across just sufficient for the person
who[B] drives to sit on and made with a toung a
litle less in width to shove into two cleats on the
under side of the present seat. To make the fastening stronger a strap of iron may be screwed
across the under side of the front of the seat as a
b in the Figer which represents the under side of the seat turned upwards. Perhaps the whole may be most easily fixed by three straps of
iron see Fig 2nd screwed upon the lower side of the seat and

into which the toung
of the drivers seat may
be ~~thrusted~~ slid.

3 o'clock I have just re-
turned considerably tired from the Mall—the house I though of hireing
and the patent Office. The foundation of the building is commenced
but little progress has yet been made the workmen are waiting for the
supply of water through the pipe which is about being put down. I went
from the grounds to the house but could not get entrance. I found
however my way into the garden which is very beautifully laid out and
all things around appears in good condition. From the house I went to
the Patent office to look after some of the effects of Smithson sent up to
the Cost Survey Office. Among the articles which was found was the
grat coat of Smithson—a queer looking article.

12 o'clock at night—I have returned from Col Tottens. I call this evening first at Mr Walkers found him apparently well but unable to speak
or rather the physican had forbidden him to use his voice. He was apparently pleased to see me and read with apparent interest my schedule
of the organization of the Smithsonian Institution.

From Mr Walkers I went to Col. Tottens had a long talk with him
on the subject of the Smithsonian and gave him a copy of my plan of
organization with which he was well pleased and entered warmly for
him into the ~~plan~~ items of the scheme— All the house apparently have
gone to bed but I could not resign myself to sleep until I had devoted
a few minutes to you— I recollect that in my letter of yesterday or the
day before I spoke of needing your sympathy your support & assistance
but do you not require mine—have you no duties as the mistress of a

Family as the mother of my children which ~~do not~~ require my assistance. You have many—many cares—many days of suffering—many days of hard labour and many moments of vexation from bad servants—from the thousand ills of house keeping and yet you are on all occasions to be at the bidding of Husband and children and nothing can be done without mother—verily you are a pet but my feelings tell me the pet is sometimes sadly abused. You know however bad as we use you that we do love you and that though no excuse on our part will I know go a great ways towards reconciling you to the Lot of Woman.

From yours as ever

Family Correspondence, Henry Papers, Smithsonian Archives.

1. Anna Ludlow and her husband, John, were old friends of the Henrys from their Albany days. *Henry Papers*, 2:338n.

2. Not found.

51. TO HARRIET HENRY

Washington wednesday
morning 7 o'clock 1847
May 5

My Dearest

I have written to you every day since my arrival and therefore this is my fourth epistle I hope you will receive the whole number though they contain nothing of importance. I say nothing of importance meaning thereby of interest to any Person but yourself for I am happy in beleiving that every thing however, trifling which relates to me, is of <u>high</u> importance to you. And though it is impossible that I should appear in your physical eyes quite as great and as faultless a man as I may in the mental vision of those who have only heard of me from a distance yet I feel assured and rejoice in the assurance that I ↑am↓ very dear to you and that you are even more tenderly and anxiously attached to me on account of the faults of character which must be glaringly exhibitid to one in as close communion with me as you are. I was in my early life exposed to many temptations and I can never be sufficiently thankful that I have been preserved as I have been. "You may love me for the dangers that I have escaped and I will love you for pitying them."

I think the transfer to Washington when once it is made will be much less disagreeable than you immagine. You^A as well as myself will be roused to greater effort— Your time and thoughts have been for several years past engrossed necssisarily with the ↑whole↓ care of the Family the physical and moral developement of our children, but as they grow older their intellectual faculties wil require more attention. You will be called on to devote with them considerable time to reading and mental operations which will rouse your energies in the direction in which ~~they~~ ↑you↓ are well qualified to excell. Mary will soon be old enough to take an interest in works of ↑a↓ higher order than those which now occupy her attention— She wll read to you while you are sewing and your comments will as they do now but in a higher degree expand her mind. We must endeavour to get for our little Girls a Governess in the Family—if possible a Lady of good education, accomplished maners and of a good heart and temper. Mary requires a good deal of attention as to her carriage & her personal habits as to ease of action—Helen will require less of this and Carry least of all; she is a Lady born. The ~~substratum~~ ↑foundation↓ and the material of the character of each is admirable and they only require a little attention as to the embellishment. Will. I presume will be much pleased with the expected visit of Richard.[1] I must take him more under my charge and perhaps I can do this more effectually by carrying him with me when I travel we will then be more thrown together and a ↑more↓ free communication established.

I am now going to the Treasury office and shall not return until 3 O'clock[B] when I may perhaps scribble a few more lines. I start for home this evening or in the early train tomorrow. I expect to be in Princeton on Friday but should I not arrive until saturday do not be uneasy— For a time adieu—

Just through dinner—was quite hungry spent the morning in the west part of the city visited J. Q. Adams[2] in his 80th year remarkable memory related several interesting annecdotes of history— Exhibited to him my plans of the Smithsonian Institution with which he was pleased.[3] I promised to furnish him with a copy— I shall not be able to get off until tomorrow morning.

The day has been warm but plesant the spring is quite late for this place though vegetation is much ↑perhaps I should say considerably↓ farther advanced than in Princeton. I [...][C] my letter to Mrs Ludlow yesterday so that she will be prepared for my arrival tomorrow.

I hope to find you very much better on my return and shall be much disappointed if I do not receive the accustomed greeting in[D] the entry when I enter the door. Give my kind regards to Mary Ann LaGrange[4,E] and thank her for the use of her watch it has done me good service. I was however obliged to purchase a key for the article.

Kiss all the children for me and ↑receive↓ the unnecessary assurance that I am as ever

Your—H.

Family Correspondence, Henry Papers, Smithsonian Archives.

1. Presumably a son of Anna and John Ludlow.

2. John Quincy Adams, representative from Massachusetts and former president of the United States. Henry had first met him in 1836. Adams played a major role in debates over the Smithson bequest, which he thought should be used to fund a national observatory. *DAB; Henry Papers, 3:*135; *6:*464n.

3. In his diary, Adams noted a visit from Henry, "who h[ad] a long conversation with me on the management of the Institution—very edifying." In his more formal diary, Adams noted that Henry "conversed in a very edifying

manner upon the proposed management of that Establishment" but then continued: "Sunk as I have always apprehended it would be, into a nest of jobs for literary and Political adventurers." Diary entries for May 5, 1847, from "Rubbish IV" and Adams's formal diary, respectively, Adams Family Papers, Massachusetts Historical Society; both are quoted in Wilcomb E. Washburn, ed., *The Great Design: Two Lectures on the Smithson Bequest by John Quincy Adams* (Washington, 1965), p. 30.

4. An old friend from Albany. *Henry Papers,* 2:43n.

52. FROM WILLIAM FRANCIS CHANNING[1]

Boston, May 17. 1847—

Dear Sir,

I am at this time engaged in preparing an account of the electro magnetic telegraph for Davis Manual of Magnetism, an enlarged edition.[2] I have examined an article of yours in Silliman's Journal of Jan 1831 in which you refer to the electromagnetic telegraph & to some previous suggestions of Barlow which I have been unable to find[3]— I wish to do justice to all who had any share in suggesting the telegraph in its various forms, especially the electromagnetic telegraph— I should be greatly obliged if you would refer me to any paper of Barlow's on the subject or to any other notice of the telegraph by yourself— ↑Soemmering↓ Ampere, Babinet, & Davy seem to have been the first suggesters of the telegraph according to my information— Schilling & Gauss appear to have been the first who actually made a telegraph & Wheatstone the first who applied it to a practical purpose— Morse's telegraph is of course superior to all others, but ↑it↓ does not deserve the reputation of priority in most of its details which it has obtained[4]— I am very desirous to know to whom the plan of marking ↑or recording↓ of Morse & Steinheil[5] is due—also by whom the use of posts for supporting[A] the wires through the air was first invented[6]— Should any information on any of these points occur to you which you could communicate to me in a few words I should very thankfully receive it—

Mr. Davis has a form of telegraph on the principle of Page's axial motion, which I think is more prompt & sensitive than Morses,[B] & it is not an <u>electro-magnetic</u> motion but a <u>deflective</u> motion & is not therefore included in Morse's specification.[7]

I expect to leave the city in a few days & should therefore be glad to receive a few lines from you, if it is perfectly convenient, before that time[8]—

Truly & Respectfully Yrs
Wm. F. Channing.

Henry Papers, Smithsonian Archives.

1. The son of William Ellery Channing, the younger Channing (1820–1901) was an electrical inventor. *DAB*.

2. Daniel Davis, Jr., *A Manual of Magnetism*, 2d ed. (Boston, 1848). To improve on the first edition of 1842, Davis wanted "to adapt it better to the purposes of a text-book for Colleges and High Schools, and also as a companion to the apparatus." He credited much of both editions' work to Channing and to chemist John Bacon, Jr. Davis, 2d ed., p. vi; *Henry Papers*, 4:444.

3. "On the Application of the Principle of the Galvanic Multiplier to Electro-Magnetic Apparatus, and Also to the Developement of Great Magnetic Power in Soft Iron, with a Small Galvanic Element," *Silliman's Journal*, 1831, *19*:400–408. On page 404, Henry stated

the fact, that the magnetic action of a current from a trough is, *at least*, not sensibly diminished by passing through a long wire, is directly applicable to Mr. Barlow's project of forming an electromagnetic telegraph.

In 1857, Henry made this comment on that statement:

not being familiar with the history of the attempts made in regard to this invention, I called it "Barlow's project," while I ought to have stated that Mr. Barlow's investigation merely tended to disprove the possibility of a telegraph. [*Smithsonian Report for 1857*, p. 104.]

In 1825 Peter Barlow (1776–1862), a British mathematician interested in magnetism and in the strength of materials, attempted to construct an electromagnetic telegraph based on conducting wires and compasses. However, he abandoned the effort as impractical, because of the marked decrease of the signal over as little as sixty meters (two hundred feet). *DSB*; King, *Electrical Technology*, p. 281.

4. Except for Davy, all these scientists appear in the account of the electromagnetic telegraph in Davis, 2d ed., pp. 193–195. For further details, see King, *Electrical Technology*, pp. 275–295. Channing referred to Samuel Thomas Soemmering (1755–1836), German anatomist and anthropologist and member of the Bavarian Academy of Sciences; André-Marie Ampère (1775–1836), eminent French physicist of electricity and magnetism; Jacques Babinet (1794–1872), French physicist of optics and meteorology, and theoretical investigator of optical instruments; Edward Davy (1806–1885), British chemist and electrical investigator; Pavel Lvovich Schilling von Canstadt (1786–1837), Russian military officer and honorary member of the St. Petersburg Imperial Academy of Sciences; Carl Friedrich Gauss (1775–1855), distinguished German mathematician and physicist; Charles Wheatstone; and Samuel F. B. Morse. All except Davy and Schilling are in the *DSB*; for Davy, see *DNB*; for Schilling, *Poggendorff.*

5. Karl August Steinheil, German physicist and organizer of the Austrian telegraph system. *Henry Papers*, 5:151n.

Both Morse and Steinheil used the motion of a receiver to make marks on a piece of paper. Steinheil produced his system by 1836. Based on two independently operated styluses, it could produce two-dimensional symbols that stood for letters. By 1838, Morse, using only one receiver, generated long and short marks that soon became the familiar Morse code. King, *Electrical Technology*, pp. 284–285, 298.

6. The Wheatstone-Cooke telegraph line along the Great Western Railway, started in 1838, was moved out of insulated iron tubes to poles by 1842. In February 1844 Morse decided to resort to poles after buried cables proved permeable to moisture. King, *Electrical Technology*, p. 290. *Henry Papers*, 6:21–22.

7. See Davis, 2d ed., pp. 202–203, for the "axial telegraph." In Morse's key, an electromagnet with an iron core for greater strength attracted a lever which then produced a signal. Davis's "deflective" telegraph was "galvanic" rather than "electromagnetic" because the U-shaped iron core itself moved in and out of the solenoid to give the signal.

For further discussion of the appearance of the ideas and devices of American inventor Charles Grafton Page in Davis's works, see Roger Sherman, "Charles Page, Daniel Davis, and Their Electromagnetic Apparatus," *Rittenhouse*, 1987, 2:34–47.

8. We suspect that Henry did not respond, as Channing's discussion in the *Manual* did not resolve the issues he raised here. On page 195, he did, however, credit Henry both with the invention of the strong electromagnet that made the telegraph possible and with suggesting its application to telegraphy (the reference being to the paper cited in note 3).

53. FROM ROBERT M. PATTERSON

Philadelphia.
May 24, 1847.

My dear Sir,

You know, of course, that Dr. Hare has resigned his professorship.[1]

I have been gratified by the desire, expressed to me personally by four members of the medical Faculty, (Chapman, Gibson, Horner, & Wood,)[2] that I would allow my name to be used for the successorship. I have meditated upon the matter anxiously, and have very nearly come to the conclusion that I would not accept the place, if offered to me; and certainly that I will not ask for it.

Now I know that you would not allow yourself to be considered one among whom a choice may be made, if you thought that you might stand in my way; and I will not ~~allow~~ let any thing which you may say to me have any such effect. With this understanding, I ask you to let me know whether you could be induced to accept the professorship. I have reason to believe that you would have the voice of the Faculty in your favor, and I think that there would be no difficulty in the Board of Trustees.

You know that the office is not, like that which you now hold, subject to the influences of political changes, and legislative whims. Although the price of the ticket will be reduced from 25 to 15 dollars, the income would probably exceed that of the Secretariate of the Smithsonian Institute. &c &c.

I write in haste, but with great anxiety for your answer.

Frazer[3] will not be a candidate against either you or myself. In fact, if neither of us be an <u>eligible</u>, the lot will, in all probability, fall upon James Rogers;[4] and I do not think him at all calculated to give strength to the school.

Ever truly your friend
R. M. Patterson

Prof. Henry.

Henry Papers, Smithsonian Archives.

1. Robert Hare, the distinguished chemist and professor of that subject at the University of Pennsylvania School of Medicine, resigned his chair May 10, 1847. Edgar Fahs Smith, *The Life of Robert Hare* (Philadelphia, 1917), pp. 438–440; *Henry Papers,* 1:462n.

2. Nathaniel Chapman, professor of the practice of physic and clinical medicine (*Henry Papers,* 2:109n); William Gibson (1788–1868), professor of surgery, practicing in Baltimore; William Edmonds Horner (1793–1853), professor of anatomy; George Bacon Wood (1797–1879), chemist and professor of materia medica and pharmacy. Charles Wells Mouton, ed., *A Biographical Cyclopedia of Medical History* (New York, 1906); *Catalogue of the Trustees, Officers, and*

Students of the University of Pennsylvania (Philadelphia, 1843).

3. John Fries Frazer, Bache's successor in 1844 as professor of chemistry and natural philosophy at the University of Pennsylvania. *Henry Papers,* 5:478n.

4. James Blythe Rogers, a medical doctor and chemist and the ultimately successful candidate. He was then professor of chemistry at the Franklin Institute. During his short tenure at Pennsylvania, his research continued in analytical chemistry, while "as a clear and interesting lecturer on scientific subjects he had few superiors in his day." *Henry Papers,* 2:194n; *DAB* (quotation).

54. TO [GEORGE C. SCHAEFFER][1,A]

Princeton May 27th 1847.

My dear Sir

Your letter[2] informing me of the receipt of the letter of Dr Young[3] has just arrived and has given me much pleasure. I think you will find the situation a pleasant one and that it will be rendered more desirable in the course[B] of time or it will be a stepping stone to a better. You will find it much easier to get a clall from one Professorship to another than from a private position to a professorship.

High as the Dr thinks the house rent it appears to me an indication of the cheapness of living in the place.[4] The 500 dollars will fit you out very finely and with a few good articles shuch as an air pump and an electrical machine you will be able to shew much that will astonish the natives.[5]

Dr T[6] will be pleased to learn that your prospect is so good—with his characteristic goodness of heart he take a lively interest in the welfare of all his friends and deserves to pass through life with their best wishes for his continued prosperity.

The affair of the Smithsonian Institution is apparently in a prosperous condition. I was directed by the Board of Regents to publish the first no. of a volume of the Smithsonian contributions to knowledge. I wish to make this rather experimental and to present it as a sample of what I think the Institution ought to produce. I have already engaged a valuable memoir on Ethnology from two Gentlemen of Ohio which has been recommended by the Ethnological Society of New-York—also two papers on the new planet—a paper from Bache giving the results of his Brothers[7] investigations in the gulph Stream. I have also started through the agency of the secretary of the Treasury a magnetic survey of of Wisconsin and also another of the country around Lake Michigan. These surveys will cost the smithsonian nothing more than the printing and preparation for publication with the exception of the purchase of one of the sets of instruments which will afterwards be the property of the Institution. I have found that there is considerable valuable matter in the offices at Washington which by proper publication would be of importance to the cause of science and this I intend to work up at my leisure. I am however in a position in which I am liable to be assailed by every sciolist in the country and unless I can have the sympathy of the true lovers of truth and science in our country the situation will be a very disagreeable one. If I can carry out my plans the Institution will call forth[C] the original talent of the country and put those who are capable of increasing the sum of human knowledge in bold relief.[D]

Draft, Henry Papers, Smithsonian Archives.

1. A chemist and professor of natural philosophy, chemistry, and geology at Centre College, Danville, Kentucky, between 1847 and 1851. *Henry Papers, 6:*397n.

2. May 26, 1847, Henry Papers, Smithsonian Archives.

3. John Clarke Young (1803–1857), a prominent Presbyterian minister. Assuming the presidency of Centre College in 1830, he built the institution up to regional prominence during his life tenure. *DAB.*

According to Schaeffer's letter of May 26, Young's letter to Schaeffer had just been received and offered the professorship. Prior to

April 18, 1847, Henry had written Young a recommendation for Schaeffer; Young's acknowledgement of that date is in the Henry Papers, Smithsonian Archives. Schaeffer's letter to Henry stated Young's conditions of the professorship: salary of $900 and instructional duties of three hours per day until the college could hire another professor, when the teaching load would drop to two hours.

4. According to Schaeffer's letter to Henry, Young's letter to Schaeffer stated that the house rent was disproportionately high at $100 to $150 per annum.

5. Young had written that the college had es-

tablished a library and apparatus fund, and that Schaeffer would be authorized to spend $500 for apparatus when he arrived. Young to Henry (cited above).

6. John Torrey.
7. George M. Bache.

55. TO HARRIET HENRY

[May 29, 1847][A]
Washington[B] Saturday
One o'clock

Dearest

I have not as yet seen D[r] Patterson. I have called but did not find him in. It is possible that should I not be able to find him before the leaving of the boat I shall be obliged to remain until monday morning I therefore pen this letter in the Office of the mint while I am wating for the Dr. inorder to send it to relieve your anxiety in case I should not be able to get away. I cannot as yet give you any thing very definite as to the Professorship. Dr Ludlow supposed that I was so established in the Smithsonian that would not think of leaving though he had regretted in his own[C] mind that the resignation of Dr. H[D] had not taken place a year ago.

He is not quite clear as to the propriety of my giving up the Smithsonian unless I have reason to think it will not be permanent. Dr. Patter[son] I am informed has concluded to withdraw his application and from what I can learn is very anxious that I should be a candidate.

Frazier[E] also whom I met a few momets since is very urgent for me to stand inorder that Rogers may not be elected.

The election will not be made until July and in the mean time ma[n]y changes may take place probably Bache will return and shall have a good cause to resign the Smithsonn. I cannot however give up the Smithsonian unless I find it my duty all things considered to do so— and I know that you are of the same mind. If it is the design of Providence that I should be a candidate some way will be opened for me to retire with honor from the Smithsonian if not I must then do the best I can with the position in which I have been placed no doubt for wise purposes since the position is one not of my own seaking.

The shirt of Dr Ludlow was forgotten in the hurry of my departure. If I am obliged to remain I shall also regret that I left my collar behind.

This is the warmest day we have had this year and I have considered it proper to be cautious as to exposing myself to the sun.

Mrs Ludlow made many inquiries relative to the clothes whether you were pleased with them. She informed me that you were in her debt to the amount of ten dollars. The articles cost more by that sum than the money you gave her amounted to. I was sorry that I had not brought the means of paying her, with me but I promised to send the money in a letter on my return— So do not forget to remind me of this or to execute the promise yourself.

Livingston's wife starts with her sister and Father for Owego on monday.[1] She looks rather thinner than when she was in Princeton and perhaps a little paler.

I called at Mr Dalass'[F] this morning but did not find him at home. I shall call again as soon as I can find D[r] Patterson. Kiss the children for me and receive for yourself the assurance of what needs no assurance that I am

as ever yours

Family Correspondence, Henry Papers, Smithsonian Archives.

1. Mary A. L. Rozet Ludlow, the wife of John Livingston Ludlow, John and Anna's son and a Philadelphia physician; Mary's father, John Rozet, a merchant of Philadelphia; and her sister, unidentified. *Henry Papers,* 2:338n; *The National Cyclopaedia of American Biography,* 3:499–500.

56. NOTES ON OPTICS

Phil[d] May 29th 1847

I visited this evening Mr Thompson of Phil[d] to inspect his microsope. The article is one of great power. The frame work is of the French construction and the object glass from England. It is furnished with polarizing appparatus and the idea occcurred to me to try if cotton a quantity of which was on the table would depolarize light. ~~This~~ I found that it exhibited a beautiful appearance under the polarizing apparatus indicating the depolarizing effect. Mr Tompson informed me that he had tried the same experiment with gun cotton[1] and found that the same effect was not produced. This is a fact of considerable interest and one which I do not think has been noticed before. The precise statement of the case is as follows. I asked Mr Tompson to let me try if cotton would depolarize light he said that he had tried it but found that it would not producee this effect. I howev made the experimt found the result. Mr T then said that gun cotton was the substance he tried. The fact that ordinary cotton produces this effect and that gun cotton does not shows that though the latter presents to the eye and probably to the microscope all the external appearances of ordinary cotton yet it has under gone an entire[A] change in its interior structure.

I also made with the same microscope an experiment which I tried several years ago with D[r] Becks glass viz the depolarization of light by means of the capillarity of water.[2] For this purpose I made a film of soap suds in a ring of wire and when this was passed through the dark field of the polarizing apparatus a ring of light was clearly disernable around the metal where the water adhered to the ring. The same effect was not found to be produced when when the ring was passed through with out the soap water. This result was obtained several times still before publishing it I should like to try it again in day light— The result is of much importance because it serves to verifey the hypothesis of Poisson that the liquid is changed in density by the capilliary force.[3]

Box 8, Henry Papers, Smithsonian Archives.
File note: "Mr Furniss articles—Write."

1. Cellulose nitrate, an explosive material impermeable to moisture. Christian Frederick Schoenbein of the University of Basel prepared the first sample of this material in late 1845 and early 1846. News of its existence rapidly spread; later in 1846 Alfred Mordecai experimented on it at the Washington Arsenal. Arthur Pine Van Gelder and Hugo Schlatter, *History of the Explosives Industry in America* (1927; New York, 1972), pp. 768–770, 785–786.

2. For Henry's experiments of April 24, 1843, with Philadelphia physician Charles F. Beck's microscope, see *Henry Papers*, 5:324–326.

3. See *Henry Papers*, 5:300–301.

57. FROM ROBERT M. PATTERSON

Philadelphia. June 1, 1847.
Tuesday night. 10 o'cl.

My dear Sir,

I have just come up to the Mint, from a meeting of the Trustees of the University; and I have had the satisfaction of putting you on nomination for the vacant professorship of Chemistry in the Medical Department. I had the pleasure of stating to the Board, and of now repeating to you, that you have the choice of in your favor of every member of the Medical Faculty. I feel equally confident that you would unite the votes of the Board.

Mr. Kane[1] promised me that he would write to you this eving. I will therefore leave it to him to present to you his views and those of Mr. Dallas as to your scruples touching the question of good faith to the Smithsonian Institution.[2] You will find that they neither of them consider you bound in honor to retain your office there; and Mr. Dallas said, (as I understand,) that while he would deplore your loss in the new Institution, he could not, if consulted by you as a friend, do otherwise than advise your changing the office in Washington for that in Philadelphia.

I hope that you will come to a decision as soon as possible, and put it in my power to say that you would be willing to accept the vacant chair. It would not be necessary for you to resign the Secretaryship before the commencement of the Medical Courses here.

I beg you to present my regards to Mrs. Henry, and to tell her that I count upon her influence being exerted in favor of Philadelphia.

Very truly your friend,
R. M. Patterson.

Dr. Joseph Henry.

Henry Papers, Smithsonian Archives.

1. John Kintzing Kane, a Philadelphia jurist. Though not a trustee of the University of Pennsylvania, as a long-standing secretary of the American Philosophical Society Kane took a strong interest in science in Philadelphia. *Henry Papers, 1:*159n.

2. Kane's letter is Doc. 60.

58. FROM ROBERT HARE

[Early June 1847][A]

My dear Friend

I was sorry that you did not call upon me in your way to Washington. I find you are likely to be nominated as my successor. I should have liked to make you acquainted with the present features of the place. When you return call upon me. Should your present appointment be vacated by your resignation it might be worthy of consideration whether I should or could become your successor. I am affraid it would involve more trouble than would suit me.

You can think of the matter.

My successor ought preferably to be a physiological Chemist rather than one of your stamp but you are young enough to give a new direction to your talents. One motive for my resignation is that I have no taste for experimental physiology.

Do you think your voice strong enough to make yourself heard throughout my laboratory?

I am yours truly
Rob[t] Hare

Prof. Henry

Henry Papers, Smithsonian Archives.
Reply: Doc. 59.

59. TO [ROBERT HARE][A]

Princeton June 5th. 1847.
My dear Sir: Your letter, without date, has just reached me at Princeton.[1] I was very much surprised to hear that you had resigned. . . .

Were I not connected with the Smithsonian Institution and I were to be elected to the chair in the University, I would not hesitate to accept the office, for I am sure the situation would be on many accounts much more agreeable to myself and my family, than the one I now hold. I know from the experience I have already had, that I shall be very much annoyed by the efforts of interested persons, to pervert the funds of the Institution to their own uses, and that I shall be able to carry out but partially the plans which I think best calculated to promote the objects of the Smithsonian bequest. The idea of a residence in Washington is by no means pleasant to me or to my family; the situation is not as yet entirely certain as to permanency, and I shall be liable to the criticism and attack of all the friends of science in the country. But notwithstanding all the objections to the place, and although I can not carry out all my plans, yet now I am in it, I do not relish the idea of giving up; my pride of consistency is aroused, and I am not sure that I can honorably separate myself from the Institution in its present state. Not that the Board of Regents would greatly lament my withdrawal, for some of them differ widely from me in opinion on the subject of the expenditure of so large a portion of the funds upon a building. I do not at present see my way clearly as to resigning, even were I elected to the

Philadelphia position. I am now engaged in preparing for the publication of a volume of the Transactions of the Institution, which I wish to present as a sample of my plan; I have ordered a quantity of apparatus from France, which will be out in the course of a few weeks; I have set on foot, through the agency of the government, without drawing on the funds of the Smithsonian Institution, a magnetic survey of Wisconsin, and another of the country around Lake Michigan. Now, unless I am allowed by the University to retain my connection with the Smithsonian until I can settle up what I have begun, I do not see how in honor I can give up my present situation. I have labored to establish an honest reputation for moral as well as for scientific qualities, and I fear, even at the expense of future comfort, to do anything wrong. I would prefer the situation in Philadelphia to that at Washington, but I doubt the propriety of the change. I was elected principally through the influence of Prof. Bache and I do not think I would be doing him justice, were I to resign without consulting him. Unfortunately he is now in Alabama, and may not return under two or three weeks.[2] The affair may however present itself in a new phase in the course of a few weeks, should the election not take place before that time.

Mary Henry Copy, Henry Papers, Smithsonian Archives.

1. Doc. 58.
2. Bache supervised the Coast Survey's measurement of the base line on Dauphin Island in Mobile Bay from April 30 to June 12. *Coast Survey Report for 1847*, pp. 38–42.

60. FROM JOHN K. KANE

Phil[a], 8 June, 1847.[A]

My dear Sir,

I have been prevented by a train of interfering circumstances from writing to you till now on the subject of the Chemical Professorship. I have thought of it a good deal however, and have a fully formed opinion regarding it.

I presume from all I can hear, that the chair will be offered to you if it is understood that it will be acceptable to you. Dr. Rogers is understood to be the only available opponent, and he will avail but little.— The only doubt that I have seriously entertained has been of the propriety of your leaving the Smithsonians; and this rather because in the case of a friend's action, I am apt to be <u>jealous</u> of the proprieties, than be-cause I have had any better reason.

On this point I have taken occasion to gather the opinion of Mr. Dal-las, whose position and feeling and excellent judgment all suggest for his counsel great consideration.

I said to him, I understand an effort is making to rob you of your Secretary. Yes, he answered, I hear so, and I do not know what the Institution is to do without him: it will be a staggering blow to it. Per-haps then, said I, Prof. Henry may not feel himself at liberty to leave you: there has been I suppose some understanding between ↑you↓ as to his seeing the Institution started; and, whether it has ever been ex-pressed or not, I know Henry well enough to feel certain that he will religiously carry out under all circumstances every engagement he has entered into. Oh, he replied, I cannot say that we have any such hold of him: I should feel marvellously embarassed if I were called on to advise him as a personal friend, by the conflict between my wishes for the Institution and my sense of what may be his real policy. It is cer-tainly a great temptation; he added, for the place in the University is probably the most desirable one in the country that a scientific man can occupy.—

I think therefore that Mr. Dallas agrees with me, that you are at lib-erty as an honourable man to consult your interests and wishes; and; so thinking, I am anxious that you should accept the chair. I am anxious too that your purpose on the subject should be made up as soon as may be; for I am satisfied that your vote will in such case be larger than if your views are undecided or unknown to the Board.—

I am writing in Court, a confused letter I fear,—my mind forced astray every other minute by the exaggerating emphasis of a gentleman who is talking at me what he thinks an argument. You can probably gather my opinion: it coincides with my wishes.

Faithfully & truly
Your friend,
J. K. Kane

Prof. Henry.[B]

Henry Papers, Smithsonian Archives.

61. FROM ALBERT GALLATIN

New York 16th June 1847

Dear Sir

I have the honour to enclose a copy of the proceedings and resolutions of the N.Y. Ethnological Society on the intended publication of Mess[rs] Squier's & Daviss' work.[1] A copy of M[r] Morton's letter is also enclosed.[2] M[r] Marsh passed through this city yesterday and said that he would confer with you on the subject.[3]

I approve entirely the resolutions and recommendation of the Society. Correct descriptions of some detached works have been published. M[r] Caleb Atwater's publication in the first volume of the Transactions of the American Antiquarian Society of Worcester,[4] which appeared twenty years ago, is as yet, so far as I know, the only general account of the antiquarian remains of the Valley of the Ohio, which as far as it goes, is entitled to any credit: yet some mistakes have been discovered in it; and it is very incomplete, and in no degree to be compared to the extensive researches of Mess[rs] Squiers & Davis. What has particularly recommended them to me is their love of truth.

Such are the combined effects of the fondness for the marvellous, of the illusions of imaginative minds, of the thirst of notoriety, of credulity, and of the want of discrimination, that, in many specific statements and in almost all the general accounts of our western antiquities which I have seen, the most vague and fabulous reports (independent of most groundless theories) and even flagrant impostures are so mixed with true accounts as to render it almost impossible even for the American reader to make the proper discrimination. In Europe, the late M[r] Warden,[5] a most industrious man and a very useful collector of books, had resided but a very short time in America; and his knowledge of the United States and specially of the Indians was exclusively derived from his extensive reading. He has inserted, in a splendid French work on Mexican Antiquities, a statement of those of the Ohio valley, which is but a transcript of one of those undiscriminating American accounts to which I have alluded.[6]

Whatever may be the intrinsic value of the remains of former times which are found in the United States, it is necessary that they should at least be correctly described, and that gross errors should be removed: and I repeat my conviction that, though ardent, Mess[rs] Squire & Davis are animated by that thorough love of truth which renders their researches worthy of entire confidence.

The late Ethnological researches have thrown such light on the History of Man that it is unnecessary to dwell on their general utility. With respect to those which relate to the Indians of the United States, I am ready to acknowledge that the field is comparatively barren, and the results obtained neither satisfactory or refreshing. Still with proper caution, important information may be acquired on what man insulated, and almost without aid from intercourse with other Nations, can do by his solitary efforts. In order however to obtain true results, considerations foreign to the immediate object of this letter are required, which may ↑hereafter↓ be the subject of another communication.

> I have the honour to be
> with great respect
> Your most obedient Servant
> Albert Gallatin

Professor H. Al
Secretary of the Smithsonian Institute
Princeton
N. Jersey

Retained Copy, Gallatin Papers, New-York Historical Society.
Copy: June 18, 1847, Ephraim George Squier Papers, Library of Congress; published, under date of June 12 and highly abridged, in *Smithsonian Report for 1847*, p. 186.

1. Report of the Committee of the American Ethnological Society (fragmentary and lacking appended resolutions, n.d.), Squier Papers, Library of Congress; amended copy, June 12, 1847, in same location; latter published under date of June 1847, over names of committee members Edward Robinson, John R. Bartlett, and W. W. Turner, in *Smithsonian Report for 1847*, pp. 186–187.

The report was highly commendatory. It recounted the history of Squier and Davis's relationship with the society and reported that such a publication was beyond the society's means. The two resolutions stated that the research was of great importance and was worthy of publication by the Smithsonian.

2. Committee member Samuel George Morton showed his support in a letter to John R. Bartlett, June 8, 1847; copy in Squier Papers, Library of Congress; published in *Smithsonian Report for 1847*, p. 188.

3. Also a member of the American Ethnological Society's committee, George Perkins Marsh similarly provided a letter of support. A copy, dated June 19, 1847, is in the Squier Papers, Library of Congress; it is published, under date of June 9, 1847, in *Smithsonian Report for 1847*, pp. 187–188.

4. That is, the *Archaeologia Americana*.

5. David Bailie Warden, an American diplomat who had lived in Paris as an unofficial "cultural ambassador" until his death in 1845. *Henry Papers, 3:*387n.

6. *Recherches sur les antiquités de l'Amérique du Nord et de l'Amérique du Sud, et sur la population primitive de ces deux continents* (Paris, 1834), the second division of the second volume of Jean-Henri Baradère, ed., *Antiquités mexicaines*, 2 vols. (Paris, 1834). Pages 20 to 49 generally discuss the Ohio mounds, but we could not further specify Gallatin's reference.

62. FROM JOSEPH BRADLEY VARNUM, JR.[1]

21 Washington square
New York June 16. 1847

Joseph Henry Esq
  Dear Sir

Since I had the very agreeable conversation with you, a week or two since, I have been in daily expectation of receiving copies of the papers you so kindly promised to forward. I know it is imposing somewhat upon your goodnature to insist upon a too literal fulfilment of the promises you happen to make in a short conversation, and with one who is such a comparative stranger as myself; but I trust you will not find it inconsistent with your other occupations, and what must be a somewhat extensive correspondence, to ~~drop~~ ↑pen↓ me a few lines ↑at such times↓ as may be convenient. I feel an intense interest in the success of the Smithsonian; not merely on account of the interest I have in the City of Washington; but from a real desire to see the number of croakers who have ~~pronounced it~~ ↑prophecied↓ a failure, disappointed in their expectations, and to see some nucleus formed around which our Universities of learning may concentrate, as it were, and which shall in course of time become a Department of a great national establishment for the encouragement of practical science—which shall, at all events supply in some measure that deficiency which the Hon Abbott Lawrence has so well described in his letter presenting a donation of $50.000 to Harvard University[2]— It is proper that I should say to you that, while I have enjoyed all the advantages of an education at Yale College, and Foreign travel, and while appreciating to the fullest extent the importance of practical Science I possess little knowledge on those subjects, and do not pretend therefore to speak by the book in any remarks I make on this ~~sub~~ syllabus of yours;[3] but simply offer my suggestions, with deference to your superior learning and experience.

Shortly after my conversation with you I had occasion to write to a gentleman in Washington who has been long a citizen there is a member of the councils, and may therefore be supposed to be somewhat familiar with the views of the people. In his letter, received to day he expresses himself as follows

"The account you give of your conversation with Secretary Henry is full of interest. There would of course be objections to any plan, and it is by no means surprising that a variety of views prevail on a subject before the public mind so long, and of such importance. What an opportunity

to immortalize himself in the creation, and execution of a plan to sub-
serve results so glorious and lasting!— It is a better fulchrum than even
Archimedes desired. If equal to the task he can mould and shape his
bequest at will, and leave the impress of his genius as imperishable as
the Institution itself— Is he aware of his position and power?— The
responsibility is in a very great measure on him, and I hope earnestly
he will prove equal to this almost unparalleled opportunity. That he will
be tampered with by the Regents, or the public in the event of his pursuing an elevated course, or that he has, or will encounter a factious or
personal opposition here or ↑even↓ elsewhere, I do not for an instant
believe. On the contrary there is a disposition to indulgence and courtesy towards him, and the course to be pursued, an evident desire to
harmonize and aid in making this ~~whole~~ ↑noble↓ bequest, in its results
a blessing and honor to the age. There is a desire here to secure as
much power to the ~~Regent~~ ↑Secretary↓ as possible, in order to remove
from it the reproach of being a political affair; to keep it for the present
out of Congress, in order that it may acquire a name and position which
will place it beyond all danger of becoming a bone of contention— I
believe this feeling prevails amongst the Regents, as it certainly does
amongst the intelligent ranks in Congress— This influence of the Secretary is to be obtained by silent and gradual advances, and the first
step is of course of vast importance. Members of Congress are for the
most part mainly controlled in their views by what strikes the eye, and
therefore it appears to me that, in the beginning, the acquisition of actual material for study at the head-quarters of the establishment is of
more importance than from what you state, he appears to regard it.
After a ~~little~~ while he can draw from the funds to a larger extent for
the other department— If in the first instance too much money is appropriated for increase of knowledge by ~~composition~~ discovery, and
diffusion by publication, the time which will elapse before substantial
advantages are seen, and the plan fully appreciated, ~~that, while there~~
will seem to ~~be~~ ↑give↓ some ground for re-iterating the ~~charges~~ ↑opin-
ions↓ which at first prevailed; but are now in some measure corrected
that his purpose is to 'narrow it down to science <u>falsely</u> called, that is,
to little experiments in electricity galvanism etc, and a Congress of lilliputian ~~philosophers~~ Savans on these and kindred subjects, with buncombe[4] little pamphlets to publish and disseminate, and philosophizing
itinerants to lecture perapatetics.' But I am confidant that he will see
this himself as he develops his scheme.— Do what you can to encourage
him in pursuing a moderate course, and we will support him manfully,
and what is of infinitely more importance, he will deserve well of the

cause of letters, humanity and religion— I hope he will hold on it would be a real calamity to have such a man as Markoe officiating."

I have thought this quotation from the letter of an intelligent and reflecting man might prove more interesting to you than any thing I could at present say— You will perceive that he has obtained from my letter rather an imperfect idea of your syllabus. There are a number of questions which had occurred to me in connection with that paper; but I reserve them until I have an opportunity of looking it over more carefully.

As soon as my professional engagements will permit I propose to prepare my pamphlet for the press, and I should therefore like to obtain all possible information at an early day[5]—

Please direct your letter to No 51 Liberty Street—and when you next visit the City let me have the pleasure of seeing you at my house.

Yours very respectfully
Joseph B Varnum J[r]

Henry Papers, Smithsonian Archives.
Reply: Doc. 63.

1. A New York City lawyer, Varnum (1818–1874) was a Washington native and a graduate of Yale. A Whig and later a Republican, he served in New York's state assembly in the 1840s and 1850s, once as its speaker. Varnum was active in the cultural affairs of New York City as a member of the New-York Historical Society and the American Geographical Society. He maintained a continued interest in Washington as well, strengthened by his extensive real estate holdings there and exhibited by his two books on the capital: *The Seat of Government of the United States* (New York, 1848), 2d ed. (Washington, 1854); and, anonymously, *The Washington Sketch Book* (New York, 1864). *Obituary Record of Graduates of Yale College Deceased from June, 1870, to June, 1880* (New Haven, 1880), pp. 181–182.

2. In February 1847 Lawrence endowed the new scientific school at Harvard, afterwards named after him, for the purposes of advanced education in the sciences. His letter of endowment, June 7, 1847, to Harvard treasurer Sam-

uel A. Eliot, was published in the *Boston Courier;* this or a subsequent reprinting in a New York paper likely prompted Varnum's comment. *Henry Papers,* 6:369n; for the text of Lawrence's letter, see *Silliman's Journal,* 1848, 2d ser. 4:294–297.

3. That is, an early version of the "Programme of Organization."

4. That is, appealing only to Henry's fellow scientists. The word refers to a county in North Carolina. During the closing debates on the Missouri Compromise, its representative felt himself bound to speak at great length, ostensibly on the question, but more particularly with an eye to his home constituency. *Oxford English Dictionary.*

In his reply (Doc. 63), Henry twisted the meaning around, and used the word as a synonym for the American public.

5. For Varnum's plan of this article, see Doc. 105. It eventually appeared only in the fifth chapter of his *Seat of Government of the United States.*

63. TO JOSEPH BRADLEY VARNUM, JR.

Princeton June 22nd 1847

My dear Sir

Your letter of the 16th inst.[1] was received on Friday;[2] it found me in bed, and I am still too feeble to communicate with you except by means of an Amanuensis.

The promise I made you in reference to the copy of my programme was in good earnest, but I have since been so much occupied with duties, besides being obliged to make a visit to Washington, that I have been unable, as I intended to revise the article and have a number of copies of it made. As soon as I am sufficiently recovered to attend to business, I will send You the promised copy.

I have been somewhat amused with the remarks, of your friend, in reference to the "Congress of Lilliputian Savans" and Buncombe publications. You may inform him for me that although I prefer the Aristotelian to the Platonic philosophy, yet the Peripatetic scheme for the Smithsonian has never for a moment found favor with me,[3] and I am equally averse to penny publications for the diffusion, among the many, of science falsely so called. The most prominent idea in my mind is that of stimulating the talent of our country to original research,—in which it has been most lamentably difficient—to pour fresh material on the apex of the pyramid of science, and thus to enlarge its base. In order however to carry out this idea, and to harmonise different views, I feel that it will be necessary that a collection should be formed, and if in the course of time, this collection could be converted into a National Gallery, the whole would then form an harmonious arrangement.

The people of Washington have looked entirely to the expenditure of the money in buildings and collections while the Country at large expects something of more general and less local interest. Under the circumstances an intermediate course will be the proper one. The danger however still is that all the funds will be absorbed in the building and in a heterogeneous objects of mere curiosity and therefore the terms of the compromise should be strictly adhered to.

Though I have the highest respect for schools of practical Science, yet my ideas of the Smithsonian transcend even these— Practical Science will always meet with encouragement in a Country like ours. It is the higher principles—those, from which proper practice naturally flows that require to be increased and diffused. But since it will probably be found necessary to make a few oblations to Buncombe, practical science must have a share.

A quarto volume of 500 pages of interesting additions to human knowledge will probably be published in the course of a year, which cannot fail to make the Smithsonian Institution favorably known in[A] every part of the civilized world.

A great gathering takes place at Princeton on the occasion of the centennial celebration of the College and it would give me much pleasure to see you among the number on Tuesday and Wednesday next.

Very respectfully
Yours

The new law building[4] will be dedicated at 12. O'clock on Tuesday after the arrival of the cars; at 4 O'clock the ~~Rev. James W. Alexandr will read~~ a history of the college will be read by the Rev. James W. Alexander of New York; the next day will be occupied with the usual ~~college exercises~~ ↑commencement exercises↓ &c.[5]

Very respectfully
Yours &c.

Mr. Varnum[B]

Retained Copy, Henry Papers, Smithsonian Archives.
In Harriet Henry's hand, except as noted. The last paragraph and closing are an appended draft.
Reply: Possibly Doc. 105.

1. Doc. 62.

2. June 18.

3. That is, though Henry preferred empirical studies to idealistic schemes, he did not favor a literal following of Aristotle's epithet as the walking philosopher: Henry opposed the Smithsonian's support of itinerant lecturing.

4. Located on Mercer Street, designed by Philadelphia architect John Notman, and later known as Ivy Hall. Richard S. Field, judge and professor of law, erected the building at his own expense for the inauguration of the law school in 1847. V. Lansing Collins, *Princeton: Past and Present*, revised ed. (Princeton, 1945), item 97.

5. The centennial celebration ran from Sunday, June 27, through Wednesday the thirtieth. In addition to Alexander's address on the history of the institution, Henry W. Green, chief justice of the New Jersey Supreme Court, presented the other major speech, on the common law, in honor of the new law school. The social highlight of the celebration was the Wednesday evening dinner, at which James S. Green, professor of law, proposed a toast to the Smithsonian Institution, in response to which George M. Dallas offered one to Henry, whose illness kept him from the dinner. Enthusiasm for Henry extended to the end of the evening, when it was proposed: "As long as the Telegraph Wires shall extend from Maine to Louisiana may the name of Henry ever be prominent!" John Maclean, *History of the College of New Jersey*, 2 vols. in 1 (1877; New York, 1969), 2:323, 365, 368, 374–378 (quotation on p. 378).

64. TO EPHRAIM GEORGE SQUIER

Princeton June 23ʳᵈ 1847

My dear Sir

The Report of the ethnological society with accompanying letters from Messrˢ Gallatin and Bartlett reached me on Friday.[1] I was however in bed at the time and have since been so unwell as to be unable to attend to business.

I have no objection to the publication of the Report, of the Society, as proposed by Mr. Bartlett; provided the few corrections are made in it which I have designated in my letter to Mr. B. but it will not do to publish the Resolutions without some explanation as to the cause of their being offered and unless an essential change be made in the second one.[2] On the whole I think it will be the safest course to publish merely the Report leaving the Public for the present in the dark as to the manner in which the arrangement for publication in the Smithsonian has been made.

You know that I am obliged to be very cautious in conducting the first business of the Institution inorder that I may not establish precedents which may embarrass my future operations. The publication of the Report and Resolution as they stand I am afraid ↑would↓ serve to mislead, ~~the~~ and I should be overwhelmed with communications, under the sanction of Societies over the whole country. The conclusion drawn from the publication would be, that the Committee of the ethnological society had voluntarily offered the Resolution relative to the publication in the Smithsonian Transactions. It is of the highest importance that the public should understand that no memoir can be accepted for publication by the Institution until it receives the sanction of a committee of competent Judges to be chosen by the directors of the Institution and not by the author ↑or his friends.↓

In reference to your memoir the facts of the case so far as they are published should stand thus 1 The memoir has been presented to the Smithsonian for publication. 2 I have referred it to the Ethnological society for the purpose of receiving an answer to the question—Is[A] the memoir an interesting addition to knowledge resting on original research. 3 The committee of the society answer this question in the affirmative. 4 The memoir is then accepted for publication.

The committee I presume would have answered my question more explicitly had I placed the true state of the case before them, in writing, as I intended to do had I not been prevented by the want of the true title of your paper.[3] I presume however[B] the whole matter may still be arranged by a little management on the part of Mr Bartlett and yourself; provided the other members of the committee are not disposed to stand too much on etiquette and consider me as dictating to them.

My intention is, if the Resolutions of the committee are in accordance with the ~~Rules~~ ↑Requirements↓ of the Institution to publish them at the head of the article; but it must be recollected that the Bequest comes from a foreigner[C] and I should be unwilling to publish, as a peculiar merit of your paper, and a ground[D] for its publication by the Smithsonian that it is an American production. Though the Smithsonian Bequest will principally tend to benefit our country yet it must not be forgotten that the object of the Donor was to increase and diffuse knowledge among men. Should a paper of merit be presented by an Englishman for publication were it[E] found of the proper kind it would be accepted.

The committee have fallen into the prevalent error of supposing the Smithsonian Institution the establishment of the general government instead of the establishment of an Individual.

I am too feeble to exert myself farther to day— I believe however that you understand my feelings and I must beg that you will arrange ↑with↓ the matter with Mr Bartlett. I still think the safest course will be to publish merely the Report.

With much esteem
truly yours
Joseph Henry

P.S.[F] I think it important that the second resolution should be altered according to my suggestion provided it can be done without too much difficulty.

Squier Papers, Library of Congress.
Draft: Henry Papers, Smithsonian Archives. Reply: Doc. 67.

1. Doc. 61 and not found, respectively. Friday was June 18.

John Russell Bartlett (1805–1886), a Rhode Island antiquarian, at this time was the partner of Charles Welford in the New York City bookselling trade. Through his position as corresponding secretary of the New-York Historical Society, Bartlett became acquainted with Albert Gallatin and was a co-founder of the American Ethnological Society. *DAB*.

2. Henry to Bartlett, June 23, 1847, Squier Papers, Library of Congress. Henry specifically recommended that the words "favorable auspices" be substituted for "national auspices."

My reason for this change is, that the Ethnological Society may not increase the prevalence of the idea of the Smithsonian Institution being a National Establishment; it is the establishment of an individual and the more widely it is seperated from the Goverment the brighter will be its prospects.

Henry also insisted that the originality of the memoir and its research be stressed. To that effect he drafted a new second resolution. Henry's changes were accepted in the printed versions of the report and its two resolutions.

3. Henry had written Squier on June 4, asking for a precise title so that the authors would be unknown to the society. On the contrary, the report was quite specific in its praise of Squier and Davis. Squier Papers, Library of Congress.

65. FROM ROBERT M. PATTERSON

Philadelphia.
June 24, 1847.

My dear Sir,

I received your note[1] this morning; and, instead of complying with your injunction to consider your communication confined, in confidence, to Judge Kane and myself, I immediately took it down to Mr. Jos. R. Ingersoll, as the best answer I could give to the note which I send enclosed.

He agrees with me entirely, (and authorises me to say so,) that your retaining the nominal Secretaryship of the Smithsonian Institution, could not be considered an objection to your appointment as Professor of Chemistry in the University. We think it a question with which we have no direct concern, and one that ought not to be communicated to the Board. Those of us who know you, know that you will perform your duties, in the Chair, fully and faithfully; and if you can also make yourself useful elsewhere, we ought to be glad of it.

It is very important for all concerned that the election should take place at our next stated meeting, which will be on Tuesday the 6th of July. Before this, there must be a Special meeting to pass a resolution fixing the time of election,—such being the course required by our laws. You see, then, that it is very desirable that you make your dicision without further delay; as we only wait for it, in order to sign a call for the preliminary meeting. Let me hear from you, if possible, by return of mail. Do not think of waiting for Bache. You know what he will say. It will be, that he must regret your loss to one institution, while he will rejoice in your gain to another. He is not the man to stand in the way of his friend's true interest.

I can assure you, (though in confidence,) that all the Medical fees will be $15.

I beg you to present my regards to Mrs. Henry, whom we hope to bid welcome to Philadelphia.

Ever your friend,
R. M. Patterson.

Prof. Henry.

Henry Papers, Smithsonian Archives.

1. Not found.

66. TO ALEXANDER DALLAS BACHE

Princeton June 25ᵗʰ 1847.

My dear Bache,

Your interesting letter[1] from the South reached me in due time and I have since had the additional pleasure of hearing through your friends at Washington of the success of your topographical operations in that quarter.

The affairs of the Smithsonian Institution, so far as they have been under my care, are apparently as prosperous as I could have expected. I have made three visits to Washington since you left. At the first I happened to be present while Mr Walker was settling the preliminaries of the geological surveys of Wisconsin and the district around Lake Michigan, and with his usual liberality of views, and promptness of action he immediately yielded to my request to add a magnetic, to each geological, survey provided the Smithsonian Institution would furnish one set of the Instruments.* I have also made an agreement with Mr. Wilson[4] of the Land Office to collect all the materials relative to the[A] variation of the Compass which have been returned to the Government by all the surveyors who have used the Solar Compass. I am informed that the variation obtained in this way is certain within the fourth of a degree of the truth.

Prof. Loomis has completed his essay on a plan of an organization for meteorological observations. Mr. Walker has been eminently successful in his labours on the new planet. I have forwarded under the name of the Secretary of the Smithsonian Institution a synopsis of his results, furnished by himself, to Prof Schumaker for publication.[5]

I have commenced operations in reference to the first number of the Smithsonian contributions to knowledge and have accepted for publication a very important memoir on the aboriginal ethnological remains of the Valley of the Ohio by Messrs Davis and Squire. This paper was recommended to me by the Hon. George P. Marsh and also by Mr. Gallatin. I have referred it to a committee of the Ethnological Society of New York who have pronounced it the most interesting article on the subject which has ever been produced and eminently worthy a place in the Smithsonian Transactions. On the committee are Dr Morton of Philadelphia and the Hon Mr. Marsh. The memoir was presented for publication to the Ethnological Society but was found to be too expensive for the limited means of that Institution and the work could not

---

*One of the geological surveys has been intrusted to Dr. Owen[2] and the other to Dr. Jackson of Boston. Our friend Dr Locke has found a situation as the magnetician under the latter.[3]

have been published had it not been taken up by the Smithsonian Institution it therefore affords an admirable illustration of the utility of the plan of organization we have adopted for the increase of knowledge. The cost however of the publication will be considerable probably not less than 3500 dollars though the estimate falls somewhat short of that sum. The amount however which can be expended on the work before the next meeting of the board will not exceed the[B] thousand dollars which was appropriated at the last meeting of the Board. The illustrations will consist of about 200 wood cuts and 62 lithographic plates. The letter press will occupy about 400 quarto pages, and will appear of course in seperate numbers of the Transactions. I think the publication of this memoir will be a fortunate affair for the Smithsonian Institution first; on account of the ge[ne]ral interest that is felt on the subject; second, the intrinsic merit of the work as an example of cautious inductive research; third, the fact that it could not be otherwise published; and fourth, it will tend to dissipate the idea that our aim is confined to the increase alone of physical science.

As a reward to the authors I have agreed that after a proper time has elapsed they shall have the use of the wood cuts and engravings to strike off for themselves a popular edition.

My friend Durand[6] the celebrated historical painter and engraver has taken charge of one of the plaster casts of the medallion of Smithson and will superintend the execution of an enlarged portrait of Steel of the same. The work is to be executed by a protige of the artist, who engages in it as an object of ambition; Durand will see that it is well done and will himself give it the finishing touches.[7]

I have lately received a letter[8] from France stating that a majority of the articles that I have ordered were to be shipped in May.

I hope from all these facts to be able at the next meeting of the Board to make a report exhibiting a very respectable ↑progress↓ for the first year of the existence of the Institution.

I must now speak to[C] you on another subject which has cost me much trouble and solicitude. I allude to the vacant chair in the University of Pennsylvania and the connection of my name with the same. When I first heard of the resignation of Dr. Hare a regret passed my mind that it had not taken place before my connection with the Smithsonian, but I dismissed the thought as unpleasant without supposing that I should be obliged again to recall it. I understood that Dr. Patterson, Prof. Frazier, Mr. James Rogers and several others were candidates; about ten days afterwards I received a letter from Dr. Patterson[9] informing me that he had concluded not to run; that the next most prominent candidate was Rogers and that the only hope of the friends of the University of preventing his election was that I might be induced to say that I would accept the office if elected in that case there would be a unanamous agreement among ↑the members↓ of the Board on me. ~~and~~ All^D my friends whose feelings are not enlisted in the prosperity of the Smithsonian have urged me without exception to accept the position in Philadelphia.

The annoyances, the difficulties and the uncertainties of the position at Washington have all been forcibly exhibited.^E Also, I ~~am now~~ ↑have been↓ repeatedly informed that I have mistaken entirely the peculiarity of my talents in supposing myself the proper person to carry out the plan of the Smithsonian Institution. ↑These ↑remarks↓ have made some impression on me↓ for, though it does frequently happen that a man has more strength and versatility than his acquaintances give him credit for, yet it must also be acknowledged that it is more frequently the case that the talents of an individual are better appreciated by his friends than by himself. ~~As Harriet greatly prefers Philadelphia to Washington~~ [---]^F ~~while a home in Philadelphia would be pleasurable^G in the highest degree.~~ Were I to consult only my own ease, the dictates of prudence ~~& my own partiality~~ and pecuniary welfare I would not hesitate for an instant to accept the position in Philadelphia. I feel that the advantages to my family and myself are ~~all~~ on this side but I must be influenced by other and higher views. I have been placed in my position in the Smithsonian by much personal exertion on the part of a few and the country generally have approved of the selection and expect much from me— [---] The organization and the building, though not such as I think they ought to be, are such as I have tacitly acquiesed in and the progress of the Institution since the adjournment of the board is as favourable as I could have expected. Were I to resign immediately I fear the Institution would be thrown into inextricable confusion and much that is achieved might be lost. On the other hand I perceive great difficulties in my course. ↑_____↓

I have drawn up a programe of the details of the organization which I will submit to you for correction and revision but which I am resolved shall not be interfered with by the ulterior objects of any individual of the board. I foresee therefore difficulties at the next meeting which may cause me to resign and could I calculate the moral future, under given circumstances, with as much precision as the physical, I could more easily determine my course in reference to the position^H in Philadelphia.

I visited Washington about ten days ago for the purpose of conversing with Mr. Walker,[10] Col Seaton and Col Totten on the subject. Unfortunately on account of having been overworked before I started the fatigue of the journey brought on an attack of illness from which I am now slowly recovering. I had one conversation with Mr. Walker on the subject and promised him to call again the next evening but on my way to his house I felt myself so unwell that I was obliged to return to my lodgings and for fear of being taken down at the Hotel was induced to start for home in the early train the next day.[11]

After my conversation with Mr Walker I concluded to think no farther of the University but in a conversation the next day with Col Seaton he proposed as a compromise that I should accept the Professorship and retain the mental direction of the Smithsonian with a salary merely sufficient to pay expenses and that all the business should be transacted by others.

If an arrangement of this kind would meet ~~your views~~ the approbation of Mr. Walker, Col Totten and yourself I should be inclined to adopt it. Money though of much importance to my present circumstances is a secondary consideration and with an adequate income from another source I would willingly give my services to the Smithsonian without pecuniary reward.

But there may be ~~some~~ ↑and probably are↓ difficulty in regard to this plan ~~which~~ [---]¹ and I leave the whole matter for ↑deliberation &↓ decision with Mr. Walker, Col Totten and yourself. Col Seaton has already expressed his opinion, but ~~those~~ ↑the others↓ I have named are my confidential advisers. I leave my fate in your hands and will abide by whatever you think right⁰ both as regards myself and the smithsonian. Should I accept the chair in the university on the plan proposed by Mr Seaton would the Regents at the next meeting insist on my full resignation and would all that has been accomplished inreference to the increase of knowledge be lost? If so I cannot think of accepting the chair. If on the contrary one of the assistant secretaries could be called into active service at the beginning of the next year and I be allowed to carry out my plans I would accept. Please send me the result of your deliberation as soon as possible. I must give a definite answer to Dr Patterson by the last of next week.ᴷ I am in the condition as to feeling somewhat like the ass between two bundles of hay. The moral equipoise is almost perfect. I care personally litle which side may preponderate. I wish most heartily at this moment that Dr H had retained his chair.

Yours as ever

Joseph Henry

Mrs H. joins me in kind regards to Mrs B.— When will you be on at the north?

Though nearly well I am still to feeble to write much and herefore have employed an amanuensis which will account for some of the irregularity of some parts of this letter.

Bache Papers, Smithsonian Archives.
In Harriet Henry's hand, except for additions and end of letter. Partial draft in Harriet Henry's hand in same location. Reply: Doc. 69.

1. Not found.

2. David Dale Owen.

3. Locke's April application to Henry for assistance in his researches in terrestrial magnetism probably helped him secure this position. On June 18, 1847, Locke wrote to Henry from Detroit, waiting for funding to start the survey. Locke to Henry, April 19 and June 18, 1847, Henry Papers, Smithsonian Archives.

4. John Wilson, chief clerk of surveys in the Land Office. *American Almanac and Repository of Useful Knowledge for 1848* (Boston, 1847), p. 99.

5. Heinrich Christian Schumacher (1780–1850), an astronomer and geodesist associated with the observatory at Altona, then under Danish jurisdiction but now in Germany. From 1823 he had edited the *Astronomische Nachrichten. DSB.*

Henry's letter of transmittal, May 29, 1847, prefaced the article in the *Astronomische Nachrichten*, 1847, 26:cols. 65–78. Sears C. Walker's abstract (untitled, in the form of a letter to Henry, May 25, 1847) proposed to demonstrate that a star observed in 1795 by the director of the Paris Observatory, Joseph Lalande, and recorded in his 1802 catalogue of stars, but since then missing from the skies, was the planet Neptune. On the basis of this recognition, Walker computed an ephemeris. But neither the abstract nor Henry's letter indicated that Walker's early February discovery had been followed by his early March resignation from the United States Naval Observatory.

That the paper, based on observatory data and on work done by one of its employees, had gone out over Henry's signature and unbeknownst to observatory director Matthew Fontaine Maury became a source of great friction between the latter two. Frances Leigh Williams, *Matthew Fontaine Maury: Scientist of the Sea* (New Brunswick, 1963), pp. 167–169.

6. Asher Brown Durand (1796–1886), the eminent American artist based in New York City. *DAB.*

7. The protégé was John Wesley Paradise (1809–1862), an engraver and painter, who practiced in New York City from 1828 until his death. Henry wrote to Durand to indicate as a model the medallion of James Watt in the second volume of Thomas Tredgold, *The Steam Engine: Its Progress and Improvement*, 2 vols. (London, 1838). William J. Rhees, *James Smithson and His Bequest*, 1880, Smithsonian Miscellaneous Collections, vol. 21 (Washington, 1881), p. 16; George C. Groce and David H. Wallace, *The New-York Historical Society's Dictionary of Artists in America, 1564–1860* (New Haven, 1957); Henry to Durand, June 4, 1847, Durand Papers, New York Public Library.

8. Not found.

9. Doc. 53.

10. Presumably Robert J. Walker.

11. Henry arrived in Washington on Monday, June 14, and departed on Wednesday, June 16.

67. FROM EPHRAIM GEORGE SQUIER

Judson's Hotel,
New York, June 26, 1847.

My Dear Sir:—

Your acceptable letter of the 23d.[1] was received yesterday. I am gratified to learn that you are recovering from your recent indisposition.

I entirely concur in your remarks respecting the report of the Committee of the Ethnological Society. I felt, upon hearing it read before the meeting at Mr. Gallatin's, that it was not the thing you wanted, and that its form was objectionable,[A] but said nothing[B] lest I should expose myself to remark. Had you written a formal letter, as I believe it was expected you would have done, the terms would have suggested the character of the reply. Dr. Robinson,[2] the Chairman of the Committee, and author[C] of the report, did not seem to have any very clear notion of the plans of the Institution, or of what was desired, on your part, from[D] the Ethnological Society. That is sufficiently clear from his report.

If you will permit me to make a suggestion, I think the whole matter can be put in right form at once.

I hewith enclose you a letter, under date of the 20th. of May,[3] submitting to you as Sect. of the Smithsonian Institute, the embodied results of the Explorations &c. of Dr. Davis and myself, for your acceptance, under the conditions of the organisation of the Institution. You reply,[4] that you have recd. the Mss, & have submitted it to the ↑Am.↓ Ethnological Soc. for their decision upon its merits.

Our correspondence ceases, then, for the time[E] being, and you address a formal letter to the Ethng. Soc.,[5] ~~which can be placed in the hands requesting them to examine the same and MSS. and~~ submitting the MSS to their examination, and requesting them to say whether in their opinion it is a valuable contribution &c. To these specific inquiries their report can be made to reply specifically, and ~~the remainder can be made~~ throughout be made to conform to the tenor of your commication. This letter can be sent to Dr. Robinson and the committee can make the necessary alterations at once, leaving out the Resolutions if deemed expedient. By this means the whole thing would come out in proper form—a ~~right~~ correct precedent established and all confusion and difficulty avoided. You can then in another note to me, announce the result of the affair, and formally accept the MSS. ~~In the event of~~ The ↑simple↓ publication of the correspondence will ↑then↓ obviate all necessity for explanation or introduction, ~~and~~ in the proposed volume—

I make this suggestion, for I feel, with yourself, anxious that the ~~affair~~ matter shall ~~be~~ take a proper ~~and regular~~ form. "Nothing like System" as Eaton used to say.

Draft, Squier Papers, Library of Congress.
Reply: See Doc. 72.

1. Doc. 64.

2. Edward Robinson, professor of Biblical literature at Union Theological Seminary, New York City, and "one of the foremost geographers and Biblical scholars of his time." *Henry Papers*, 5:85n; *DAB* (quotation).

3. Not found, but printed (under date of May 15, 1847) in the *Smithsonian Report for 1847*, p. 185.

4. No such formal reply has been found.

5. Such a letter was prepared: Henry to Albert Gallatin, June 10, 1847, a copy of which is in the Squier Papers, Library of Congress. It was printed (under date of June 2, 1847) in the *Smithsonian Report for 1847*, p. 185.

68. TO WILLIAM WINSTON SEATON

Princeton June 28th/47

My dear Sir

Accompanying this note I send you the requisition for the draft on the Smithsonian fund. It came to Princeton by the last mail on saturday[1] and therefore I have been obliged to retain it until this morning. No mail having left this place since the arrival of the article.

I also enclose you a letter relative to the drawings of one of the architects which you will oblige me if you will deliver to Mr Mills[2] with a request for him to make enquiry about the missing articles at the express office.

I regret that I had not an opportunity of seeing you again before I left the city. I found myself quite unwell on Tuesday evening and for fear of being taken down at the ~~Tavern~~ ↑Hotel↓ I started for home in the early train on Wednesday—reached Princeton the same evening and have ever since until yesterday been confined to my bed.

In the mean time I have been much perplexed with the manner in which my Friends in Philadelphia have urged me to accept the chair in the University. I have written to my friend Dr Bache on the subject and have mentioned to him your proposition. If an arrangement of this kind can be effected with the Regents of the Smithsonian and the interests of the Institution not unfavorably affected by it I would be inclined to accept the chair. If however my leaving the Smithsonian at this time would tend to jeopardise the prosperity of the Institution I shall not think of leaving though I feel that ~~that~~ the position in the University would be more congenial to my taste and the health and comfort of my family.

The position in the Smithsonian is one in which I could perhaps do more good but it would be extreme egotism in me to say that no person can be found who would not do as well in this office as myself.

Mr Bache will probably reach Washington to day and will probably call on you relative to this subject.

My answer must be given to one of the Trustees of the University[3] this week.

With much
Respect I remain
truly yours
Joseph Henry

Hon W. W. Seaton

Draft, Henry Papers, Smithsonian Archives.

1. June 26.
2. Robert Mills.

3. Robert M. Patterson.

69. FROM ALEXANDER DALLAS BACHE

Washington. June 29, 1847.

My dear friend.

In reply to yours I beg that you will not think of looking back, now that you have set your hand to the plough. In point of usefulness the two positions do not compare with each other. Having said all that man could say as to your capability of carrying out the Smithsonian Inst. and believing that you are looked to by the country to guide it safely into port I cannot think with patience of your deserting the helm. I saw Mr Walker ↑(R. J)↓ about it last evening & he is of opinion that you should not think of abandoning this position for any other. Dr. Patterson's call to you to rescue the University from James Rogers is strange enough— if J. R. is fit for the place & the place for him you are not the man for it nor^A it the place for you. Turn not from the rising to the setting sun. Go not into an old institution to be shorn of emolument & uncertain from its connexion with those whom you cannot control, when you can be a new institution—ready to grow to your station. I will see Col. Totten to night & report to you to-morrow. At present the independent voices of two of your Committee say NAY.

Mrs Bache says nay. So I will venture to say will the science of the country if you consult those not prejudiced.

Yours ever truly A.D.B.

Professor Henry.

If not too[B] late, say what is civil—kind—to the Whig Soc. who invited me to their celebration.[1] Their invitation followed me to Dauphin I[d]

General Manuscripts Collection, Department of Special Collections, University of Pennsylvania Libraries.
Reply: See Doc. 70.

1. The America Whig Society, one of Princeton's two student literary societies, had evidently invited Bache to the college's centennial events.

70. TO ALEXANDER DALLAS BACHE

Princeton July 1st
1847

My dear Bache

After a short conversation with the Vise President[1] last evening I have concluded to give up all thoughts of the university. The only condition on which I could think of accepting was that of retaining direction of the Smithsonian without salary but this I find cannot be.

I expect to hear from you by the mail of to day or tomorrow but you need not advise I have made up my mind. Inclination points one way but duty urges stronger the other.

As ever yours
Joseph Henry

Bache Papers, Smithsonian Archives.
Reply: July 7, 1847, General Manuscripts Collection, Department of Special Collections, University of Pennsylvania Libraries.

1. George Mifflin Dallas.

71. TO [GIDEON HAWLEY][A]

Princeton July 1st 1847

My dear Sir

I beg you will pardon me for not before having sent you any written communication as to the affairs of the Smithsonian. I ~~sent~~ ↑I forwarded↓ to you at the close of the session of the Board 10 copies of the report of the committee of organization with the Will of Smithson and the Resolutions of the Board all in the same pamphlet.[1]

Shortly after the meeting of the Board which took place subsequently to my election I prepared a communication to be sent to you of which the enclosed[2] is a copy giving my views of the organization of the Institution. The letter however was delayed on some account and as I expected to see you in a few weeks in Washington I finally concluded amid my many engagements not to send it. I was much disappointed in not seeing you at the meeting for I counted on your support and cooperation in carrying out my plans ~~though~~ I was ↑however↓ afterwards informed ↑though I could scarcely credit it↓ that your preference was for a Library exclusively.

On my first visit to Washington after my election I pressed my views with much ardor and supposed at first that I would be able to carry out all my plans but in this I was mistaken. The inhabitants of the city of Washington who supposed that the money was bequeathed especially to them took the alarm and commenced a counter action which aided by the magnificent plans produced by the architects nearly turned the current of opinion against me. I however rallied ↑again↓ and was again ~~on the point of carrying my plans~~ ↑and was making considerable headway↓ when Mr Choat arrived and inorder to harmonise different views proposed as a compromise that one half of the annual income of the Institution should be expended on collections of objects of nature and art and the other half on the plans of increasing and diffusing knowledge proposed by myself.

To this proposition I agreed and the organization adopted is based upon[B] it. The next thing to be settled was the kind of building. I contended that an Edifice which would cost 50 or 60 thousand dollars would be sufficient and that the remainder of the 240 thousand dollars which had acrued in interest should be added to the principal inorder to make up in power in ↑the↓ future for the loss of time in the past. Several of the Board however were resolved on a large building and though a majority ~~of the Board~~ were of a contrary opinion ~~they~~ ↑the minority↓ would have carried their point had I not informed one of them[3] that I would ~~immediately~~ ask to be relieved from any further connection with the Institution ~~provided~~ ↑immediately after the adoption of↓ the Resolution ~~passed~~ appropriating 240 thousand dollars to the to the erection of a Building. To harmonise these discordant vews Professor Bache proposed the following plan—↑which was carried namely↓ that the 240 thousand dollars should be drawn from the treasury in Treasury notes bearing 6 per cent interest and that the Building instead of being erected immediately should be put up slowly—one wing the first year another the second the main body to be commenced the year after and so on ↑until↓ the whole to be finished in five years; the money during the ~~whole~~ time to be drawing interest. ↑On this plan↓ The longer the building is delayed the more interest will be saved and the longer the annual expense will be defered of taking charge of the museum of the exploring expedition. Indeed I hope before the building is finished to see ↑generally acknowledged↓ the gross injustice of putting the support of the museum of the government of the united states on a small fund the bequest of a foreigner for ~~a special~~ ↑another↓ object.

Draft, Henry Papers, Smithsonian Archives.

1. *Report of the Organization Committee of the Smithsonian Institution: With the Resolutions Accompanying the Same, and Adopted by the Board of Regents; Also, The Will of the Testator, The Act Accepting the Bequest, and The Act Organizing the Institution* (Washington, 1847).

2. December 28, 1846; draft in Henry Papers, Smithsonian Archives, printed in *Henry Papers*, 6:610–615.

3. Probably Robert Dale Owen.

72. TO EPHRAIM GEORGE SQUIER

Princeton July 3ʳᵈ 1847

My dear Sir

I presume on account of the articles in the news papers relative to my resignation from the Smithsonian you are somewhat anxious to here from me. Though I have been much tempted to accept the chair in Philᵈ particularly as a proposition was made by one of the Regents of the Smithsonian and agreed to by the leading members of the Trustees of the University, that I might retain the direction of the Institution, until it got fairly under way, the work being attendedᴬ to by others, and accept the chair of Chemestry. I found however this plan "impractical" and therefore resolved <u>sink</u> or <u>swim</u> <u>live</u> or <u>die</u> I would hold on to the Smithsonian.

I consider that I have made a sacrifise for the cause of American science and though I may not succeed in rendering the Institution what it ought to be yet I shall at least deserve some credit for the attempt.

The letter for the Ethnological society I will send by the next mail.[1] I have not been able to attend to business for some time past and my letters have so acccumulated that I am now much pressed.

I will visit new ↑york↓ in the course of a few days to settle the matters you mention.[2] Perhaps it may be better for me to delay my visit until after you have visited your relatives—drop me a line on this point. I have received two letters from Professor Marsh which speak in high terms of your memoir.[3] I think that he is a convert to the scheme of publications &— and that he will be[c]ome a valuable co adjutor in carrying out the plan.

> In haste
> Yours as ever
> Joseph Henry

E. G. Squire

Squier Papers, Library of Congress.

1. See Doc. 67, note 5.
2. Henry traveled to New York on July 13 or 14, staying in the city until the sixteenth. Henry Pocket Notebook [13279], p. [126].
   In another of Henry's notebooks is an undated entry summarizing various points relating to Squier and Davis's memoir, which Henry may have discussed with Squier during his trip to New York. According to the notes, Squier agreed to the deletion of his name from the second resolution of the committee of the American Ethnological Society; insisted that his name precede Davis's on the memoir's title page; promised to deposit woodcuts with Bartlett as they were finished, and to send Henry a copy of each cut; and stated his need for up to $200 worth of books, to be procured from Bartlett,

for completing the memoir. After Squier was done with the books, he was to return them to Bartlett, "to sell or keep for the Institution." Henry Pocket Notebook [13272], pp. 7, 8 of first enumeration (quotation on p. 8).

3. For Marsh's letter to Henry of June 19, 1847, see Doc. 61, note 3. In a letter of June 26 (copy in Squier Papers, Library of Congress), Marsh reiterated his belief in the value of Squier and Davis's research and expressed hope that the Smithsonian would support it. He also urged Henry to make arrangements to complete and publish the work expeditiously, among them assisting Squier to remain in New York, since "his personal supervision will be required at every step."

73. FROM BENJAMIN WOOD RICHARDS[1]

Philad[a] July 3. 1847

My dear Sir,

Your note of yesterday[2] gave me great regret & will be a source of disapointment to many of your friends, who have cordially desired you to occupy a Proffesorship in all respects so eligible and promising so much, through you, for Science & for our social intercourse here, as well as for the University. Our board would have speedily made the election with great, I believe, with entire unanimity. I have felt myself constrained however to mention the decided terms in which you have written to me & the election to fill the chair of D[r] Hare will probably be postponed until September. I can scarcely hope that any thing will occur to remove the obstacles you refer to but 1 cannot refrain from renewed expressions of regret that I shall not have the gratification of seeing you fill a Chair so attractive from its emoluments and distinction, and so well adapted to the prosecution and advancement of your favourite pursuits. I am

Dear Sir
very truly yours
B. W. Richards

To/
Prof^r Jos. Henry
Princeton

Henry Papers, Smithsonian Archives.

1. A Princeton graduate (1815), Richards was a trustee of the University of Pennsylvania. *Henry Papers*, 5:470n.

2. Not found.

74. TO EPHRAIM GEORGE SQUIER

Princeton July 5th/47

My dear Sir

Accompanying this note I send you the letter for Mr Gallatin[1] which you will make use of for the purpose of putting the matter of the aceptance of the memoir on a proper footing. I have purposely omitted your name in the letter because as a general rule I wish the memoirs to be examined without the name of the author being known.

I intend to visit New-York as soon as the condition of my family will allow me to leave home. We have been and are quite afflicted—I have just recovered from a fit of sickness and our three little Girls are now ill with the Scarlet fever. The youngest is considered in a dangerous state and I feel quite anxious about her.

I am not authorized to purchase any books but if our friend Mr. Bartlett will order those you mention I will endeavour to persuade the Regents at the next meeting to purchase them. I have no doubt that ↑they↓ will agree to the proposition. I intend to draw on the funds of the Institution and shall be able to make an advance on the work in the course of a week or two. I have mislaid your letter[2] and as the mail is about closing I have no time to look for it and therefore may not have answered all your enquiries.

Yours as ever
Joseph Henry

E. George Squire

Squier Papers, Library of Congress.

1. See Doc. 67, note 5.

2. Presumably the one Squier wrote on June 26 (Doc. 67).

75. FROM CHARLES G. PAGE[1]

Patent Office
July 6. 1847

My dear Sir

I have just rec[d] yrs of 3d inst.[2] and am much delighted to hear of your decision to adhere to the Smith. Inst. I was over yesterday to look at the work, which appears to be going on well and rapidly. The appearance[A] of the stone is fine and will I am satisfied prove a most popular and valuable selection.[3]

In regard to the Prof[hp] in Harvard[4] I think it would suit me and on the whole be pleasant, and shall be greatly obliged if you will be on the lookout to serve me there.

The report in the papers concerning yr resignation commenced in the Baltimore Sun.[5] Some letter writer[B] in this City wanting material furnished a garbled communication as food for busy bodies. The same article spoke of the "vacancy in the Pen. Univ. occasioned by the death of Prof Hare."

I have looked at subject of Rotations a[c] little further and find experimentally that the magnet must revolve under the conditions I stated to you.[6] That the revolving force is greatest when[D] contact is made at (a) and that it diminishes on either side of (a); xx is of course constant and when xa and ab are in oposition to each other xx is still left. So far as I can find, the operation of the terminated current xx has not been considered in this connexion. Placed any where between the two[E] poles the terminated current (c)

N revolves[F] in one direction by the conjoint action of the two[E] poles. Roget makes out in paragraph (274) of his treatise the rotation of a magnet on its own axis; but I think it is all[G] wrong, and incompatible with Amperes theory.[7] Of this however I will explain more when I see you. Mean time I am preparing a Communication on the subject.[8] Would you like it for the Smith Inst?

In much haste
Yrs truly
Chas. G. Page

Henry Papers, Smithsonian Archives.
Addressed to Henry in Princeton. Reply: Doc. 78.

1. Charles Grafton Page, a physician interested in chemistry and electrical science, had been an examiner at the Patent Office since 1842, and, simultaneously since 1844, professor of chemistry and pharmacy in the medical department of Columbian College. *Henry Papers,* 4:34n; Elliott, *Dictionary.*

2. Not found.

3. Page's interest in the stone used in the Smithsonian Building was more than casual: he had served as a consultant to the regents' committee on the buildings. In keeping with its charge to recommend the best materials for the Smithsonian Building, this committee ordered a series of experiments on the durability of different types of building materials. It turned to "a gentleman of this city, experienced in chemistry, and having a laboratory at his command," namely, Page, to conduct these tests.

Page tested twenty-two samples of brick, granite, marble, sandstone, and limestone from quarries and public buildings in the northeast and mid-Atlantic regions. In his report of March 5 to the building committee (which had succeeded the committee on the buildings), Page offered no firm conclusions. However, his data indicated that the finer a sample's texture, the better it would tolerate weathering.

Rhees, *Journals,* pp. 5–6, 590, 600–601 (quotation on p. 590).

4. That is, one of the three Harvard professorships (engineering, mining and metallurgy, and the invention and manufacture of machinery) endowed by Abbott Lawrence. "Science and the Arts at Harvard," *Silliman's Journal,* 1848, 2d. ser. *4*:146; see also Doc. 62, note 2.

5. Not found.

6. Page had recently written an article on this topic: "Revolution of a Magnet on Its Own Axis without the Use of Mercurial Conductors, and Also without Visible Support," *Silliman's Journal,* 1847, 2d ser. *3*:252–254.

7. P. M. Roget, *Treatises on Electricity, Galvanism, and Electro-Magnetism* (London, 1832), "Electro-Magnetism," pp. 84–85. Roget's work was predicated upon his acceptance of Ampère's electrodynamic theory. For his part, Henry considered Roget's explanation of rotary motion to be wanting, though not necessarily in error; see *Henry Papers,* 3:327–328.

8. No such article was published.

76. FROM ROBERT M. PATTERSON

Philadelphia.
July 6, 1847.

My dear Sir,

I was absent from the city when your letter of the 2d[1] came here, and I did not get it 'till yesterday. I need not tell you how much I was disappointed and distressed at learning the conclusion to which you had been led. It is an important step that you have taken; and I wish it may prove to be a right one. I confess, however, that I have serious doubts with regard to it. I have little confidence in literary and scientific institutions placed under the control of political bodies. Our friend Bache had mortifying evidence of this in the Girard College;[2] and even in the letter before me you show the foreshadowing of one of the movements to be anticipated with regard to the Smithsonian Institution. You say that "already, as you learn, plans are laid to lower the salary, and to put into the Secretaryship an inferior man." What assurance have you that such a movement will be long arrested by your retaining the office?

Our Board of Trustees met this evening. I stated, to the regret of all, the conclusion to which you had come, but I did not withdraw you from nomination. I could not abandon the hope that you might, before the election, change your mind, and exchange Washington for Philadelphia; and an office under political surveillance, to a permanent, independent, and honorable chair in our University.

I placed Dr. Torrey[A] in nomination; and he is on a list of not less than twenty. The Board would have united on you, but they are now thrown into confusion, and no man can tell who will receive the choice. We adjourned without naming the day of election, and I now think it will not take place before September.

Very truly your friend &c
R. M. Patterson.

Prof. Henry.

Henry Papers, Smithsonian Archives.

1. Not found.

2. Patterson referred to the campaign which the Philadelphia city councils had waged against the Girard College trustees and against Bache during his tenure as college president. The councils not only frequently challenged Bache and the trustees over the administration of Stephen Girard's will, but also questioned Bache's character and authority. In 1841, the councils abolished both the presidency and the board. See *Henry Papers*, 4:156n; 5:128–130.

77. FROM CHARLES G. PAGE

Washington
July 7, 1847.

My dear Sir

As I promised you some time since an article upon Electro-Magnetic power, I thought it right to inform you that I am at present preparing a short communication for a London journal (Walker's) upon the subject,[1] more by way of reclammation than anything else, and which will in no way interfere with the promised paper. I am desirous of publishing a few facts in the History of Electro-Mechanics and of bringing them out abroad as some peculiar circumstances in the case seem to require this course. By Electro-Mechanics, (which seems to be an appropriate term and draws a clear line through Electro-Magnetism) I mean such[A] mechanical applications of the power as we find in the Electro-Mag. Engine—Telegraph, Clocks etc. In the two first I have given your claims that preeminence to which they seem to me to be entitled. I have also a disclaimer to make on my own account.

While trying the experiments a few days since on rotations, I tried two which were of considerable interest in connexion with[B] a subject upon which we conversed lately. It occurred to me that a ↑mutual↓ repulsion of particles of a circuit in line should be manifested when an amalgamated wire is raised from the surface of mercury, that is, the portion of mercury raised above the surface by adhesion to the wire should be less, or drop sooner when a current was passing than when not. To my surprise I found no difference. Perhaps my battery was not strong enough to manifest the difference which should take place if the principle is correct. I had 5 pairs Groves, platinums 4 inches square, in feeble action. The second experiment is novel and interesting. Some pure mercury was placed upon a glass plate and covered with dilute[C] sulp acid and the poles inserted in the acid in imitation, of the induction experiment of Draper.[2] I expected to see the mercury contract in the line joining the poles and expand or spread out transversely.[D] But the result was very different. The globule[E] of mercury moved immediately towards the negative pole and so strong was this tendency that it would move through the distance of ½ inch and even up an inclined plane. This seems to be important in a theoretical point of view, but will need further experiment. ~~The~~

Dr & Mrs L[3] and Mrs P.[4] send their kind regards and are much gratified with your decision and the prospect of your company.

Yrs truly Chas. G. Page

Henry Papers, Smithsonian Archives.

1. No communication of Page's appeared in Walker's *Electrical Magazine*.

2. Page referred to the experiment described and illustrated on pages 28–29 of John W. Draper's article, "Of the Tidal Motions of Conductors, Free to Move," *Journal of the Frank-* *lin Institute*, 1836, n.s. *17*:27–33. For Henry's earlier comment on Draper's experiment, see *Henry Papers, 3*:35.

3. Harvey Lindsly and Emeline Webster Lindsly.

4. Priscilla Sewall Webster (1823 or 1824–

1899), the younger sister of Emeline Webster Lindsly and a cousin of Daniel Webster's, married Page in 1844. Robert C. Post, *Physics, Pat-* *ents and Politics: A Biography of Charles Grafton Page* (New York, 1976), pp. 63–64, 180; Elliott, *Dictionary*.

78. TO CHARLES G. PAGE

Princeton July 8th
1847[A]

My dear Sir

Your letter[1] of the 6th was received yesterday and this morning I have given a hasty glance at article 274 of Roget's Treatise; but I do not find the error you mention— The radiating current through the mercury is a true cause of motion though not the only one. The radiation through the magnet from the axis is another and also the current from the top of the bar down to its middle, if it happen to be excentric, is a third.

The current from the top to to the middle must in all cases be excentric for according to the law of galvanic conduction the current must pervade the whole bar and consequently but a very small portion of it will pass along the axis.

There may however be some points which I do not see ↑but↓ which would be presented in a conversation with you. I shall therefore be pleased to converse with you on the subject when we next meet.

with much
Respect
yours truly
Joseph Henry

Dr. Page.

Retained Copy, Henry Papers, Smithsonian Archives.

1. Doc. 75.

79. TO NATHAN APPLETON[1] AND JEFFRIES WYMAN[2]

Princeton July 8, 1847

Gentlemen

I accept with much pleasure your invitation[3] to attend the eighth meeting of the Association of American Geologists and Naturalists to be held in the City of Boston on Monday the 20th of next September.[4]

If it will be agreeable to the Association I shall gladly avail myself of the opportunity offered by this meeting to submit to the Naturalists of our Country an account of the Smithsonian Institution and of the plans proposed for carrying out the design of its founder, namely the increase and diffusion of knowledge among men.[5] Also if my engagements will permit I will endeavour to prepare a paper on some branch of physical science for presentation to the Association.[6]

> I am very respectfully
> Gentlemen your ob.^{t} Ser^{v}
> (signed) Joseph Henry

Nathan Appleton. Esq
Chairman Local Com.
J. Wyman Secretary,

Retained Copy, Henry Papers, Smithsonian Archives.
In Charles P. Russell's hand.

1. A textile industry magnate who founded the manufacturing centers of Lowell and Lawrence in Massachusetts and Manchester in New Hampshire, Appleton (1779–1861) was also a patron of learned culture in Boston. He helped organize the Boston Athenaeum and in 1842 underwrote the publication of the proceedings of the Association of American Geologists and Naturalists. *DAB;* Kohlstedt, *AAAS,* pp. 69–70.

2. Formerly curator of the Lowell Institute, Wyman had recently been appointed Hersey Professor of Anatomy at Harvard. *Henry Papers,* 5:306n; *DSB.*

3. Not found.

4. This marked Henry's first attendance at a meeting of the Association of American Geologists and Naturalists. The 1847 meeting was to be its last as such. Reflecting an interest in broadening the association's scope to include all sciences, and also a desire to transform it into a truly national scientific organization, at that meeting the members resolved to reorganize it as "The American Association for the Promotion of Science." (The name was soon changed to "the American Association for the *Advancement* of Science.") Despite earlier misgivings about "the propriety of forming an association which should embrace every department of science," Henry supported the reorganization. Kohlstedt, *AAAS,* pp. 76–80; *Henry Papers,* 5:121 (quotation).

5. Henry read his paper, "On the Organization and Objects of the Smithsonian Institution," on September 25; it was the final presentation of the meeting. "Eighth Annual Meeting of the Association of American Geologists and Naturalists," *Silliman's Journal,* 1847, 2d ser. 4:429.

6. In his paper "On Heat," presented on September 24, Henry reported the results of his experiments with a Melloni thermopile to demonstrate the interference of radiant heat, to measure the heat of sunspots, and to determine the nature of the moon's heat. "Eighth Annual Meeting," pp. 428–429; "On Heat," *Silliman's Journal,* 1848, 2d ser. 5:113–114; *Henry Papers,* 6:64n–65n, 536n.

80. TO EPHRAIM GEORGE SQUIER

Princeton July 8th/47[A]

My dear Sir

I am not very desirous that the name of the author should not appear in the Report of the committee it is enough that I do not mention it in my letter. I propose in all cases to conceal the name of the author so far as it is practical; but in many cases it will be impossible for me to do so— The judges may discover the author from data unknown to me. I have written to Washington for a draft[1] and shall in the couse of next week or perhaps the latter part of this be able to advance, say, 200 dollars to the engravers.[2]

I will meet you in new-york at the time you mentioned if I receive the money and my family are in such a condition that I can leave home—though I think perhaps it will be safer to say monday following. I am much obliged to you for the notic you published.[3] In haste

yours truly

Joseph Henry

E. G. Squire Esq.

P.S. On reflection I think I shall be obliged to go to N.Y. on Tuesday[4] that I may get a draft on Paris[5] to send by the steamer of the 15th

J–H–

Squier Papers, Library of Congress.

1. Letter not found.
2. Nathaniel Orr & Company.
3. Not found.
4. July 13.

5. On July 15, Henry sent a draft for $1200 to John McMullen in Paris for apparatus. Henry Pocket Notebook [13279], p. [126].

81. TO JAMES HENRY

Princeton July 10th 1847

My dear James

I have not written to you in so long a time[1] that I am now almost ashamed to address you. Before the college adjourned I was so overwhelmed with teaching and attention to the affairs of the Smithsonian that I had scarcely time to breathe. Indeed I have been over worked, and on my return from Washington the last time, I was attacked with a derangement of my stomach and bowels[A] which confined me upwards of a week and though I have nearly recovered I am still in rather ↑a↓ feeble condition. During the time of my illness I was called upon to decide as to my leaving the Smithsonian and accepting the chair of chemestry in the university of Pennsylvania, vacated by the resignation of Dr. Hare. This is a situation I have long looked forward to as the most desirable in our country for a scientific man and had the offer been made me before I became engaged in the Smithsonian I would not have hesitated about accepting it or had I my free choice betwen the two[B] positions I would[C] have chosen the one in Philadelphia but I considered my self in honor bound to hold on to the Smithsonian so long as there is a reasonable prospect of my being able to direct the funds to some useful purpose. The friends of the Institution considered that my resignation at this time would be most disasterous to the Establishment—that it would dwindle down into a mere hospital for Invalids and an omnium gatherum of all kind of trash. Though I was induced to look at the position in Philadelphia and to pause for a time as to the propriety of accepting it I finally came to the conclusion that I was too deeply involved in the affairs of the smithsonian to be able honorably to withdraw myself from it. Though all my views have not been adopted and some measures have been carried to which I was opposed still the prospects of usefulness of the Institution are much more favourable than the Public would seem to think they are.

Harriet and myself have concluded to defer our visit to Albany until September when the heat of the weather will have abated and I can make my visit conducive to the transaction of my business. I intend to be present at the Meeting of Geologists which takes place in Boston on the 20th of September. I met Dr Wing[2] in Philadelphia and we dined together at Dr Hare's. I intended to see him again before I left town but was obliged to start the same afternoon and as the Dr. left the table before I knew it I missed the opportunity of biding him good by. Please give my kind regards to him with the assurance that whether my days be bright or dark many or few I intend to hold on to him as one of my long tried and early friends.

Lucinda[3],[D] is still with us and appears to be enjoying herself in a quiet way very much she will probably accompany us to the sea shore.[4] Stephen has informed you I presume of all the news relative to the children. They are now on the mending hand. Mary & Helen go about and Carry sits up though she cannot walk.[E]

Family Correspondence, Henry Papers, Smithsonian Archives.

1. A letter of April 15, 1847 (Family Correspondence, Henry Papers, Smithsonian Archives), is the last we have found.

2. Joel A. Wing, an Albany physician, was an old family friend. *Henry Papers, 1:*50n.

3. Lucinda McMullen (b. 1814), of New

York City, was also a family friend. *Henry Papers,* 2:6n–7n. Ramsay MacMullen, private communication.

4. The Henrys spent two weeks at the Jersey

shore "for the benefit of sea bathing." Henry to Isaac W. Jackson, August 2, 1847, Henry Papers, Smithsonian Archives.

82. TO EPHRAIM GEORGE SQUIER

Princeton July 19th 1847

My dear Sir

This letter will be handed to you by my friend Mr J. T. Robinson[1] of Princeton whom I have deputized to confer with you and settle on the kind of paper for the Smithsonian Contributions and also to advise with you as to the best means of purchasing the same. Mr. R. has had considerable experience in book printing and may be able to give some suggestions of value. He is a Gentleman[A] of great moral worth in whom you may repose full confidence.

There must I think be an error in the calculation you give in your note[2] of the 17th as to the cost of the paper. In your estimate of June 9th the cost of the same article is put down at 540 dollars instead of $840.[3] Mr Robinson suggests that you have made the mistake of estimating ↑for↓ double the quantity required.

I have spoken with three of the Regents on the subject of the publication of your memoir and though they think the cost of the publication is considerable they are in favour of incurring the expense. I am very anxious that the cost of the work should not exceed the estimate you have given and which I have mentioned to the Regents and indeed it will be better if it can be executed for less than this.

I have examined the paper of Harpers bible[4] and think that one a little less costly would answer our purpose.

No periodical in our country is published on paper of a quality equal to this. The Transactions of the American Phil. Society are[B] printed on paper which can be purchased for 14 cts per lb and is much lighter than that to which you refer— Also the paper of the Memoirs of the American Aca[dy] is much less expensive. The paper mentioned by Mr Owen weighs from 30 to 35 lbs per ream instead of 40 lbs.[5] While I wish the work to be well got up I do not wish ↑it↓ to be extravagant.

The paper ordered should be sufficient for a volume of about 550 or 600 pages since several other papers will be included in the same volume with your memoir though your article will form an entire no.

Mr R. will also confer with you on the bill for printing and will make some suggestions which may be of use.

I will write you my decision as to the paper as soon as I get the report of the result of the conference of Mr R and yourself.[6]

Enclosed with this note I send you the draft for $50[7] which you will please to acknowledge.

Yours truly
Joseph Henry

E. G. Squier.

Squier Papers, Library of Congress.

1. John T. Robinson was a printer and the editor and publisher of the *Princeton Whig.* *Henry Papers,* 5:138n.

An entry in one of Henry's pocket notebooks noted that Robinson received $10 "for agency in purchasing paper engraving printing &c" for Squier and Davis's memoir. Henry Pocket Notebook [13279], p. [126].

2. Not found.

3. Squier's estimate has not been found.

4. *The Illuminated Bible,* published in 1846 by Harper & Brothers of New York.

5. Henry was presumably referring to the paper which Robert Dale Owen, in the contract entered into between the building committee and Wiley & Putnam of New York in April

1847, had stipulated was to be used in *Hints on Public Architecture.* The contract called for long quarto letterpress paper, weighing no less than forty pounds (eighteen kilograms) per ream. Rhees, *Journals,* pp. 668–669.

6. Neither Squier's report nor Henry's response to it has been found. Although undated, one of Henry's pocket notebooks contains several pages of notes on paper reams, dimensions, and costs for printing and composition, all presumably referring to Squier and Davis's memoir. Henry Pocket Notebook [13279], pp. [32], 33, [36], [40], 41, and [48].

7. This was a draft for Squier's "superintendance" of the memoir in New York. Henry Pocket Notebook [13279], p. [126].

83. FROM ROBERT WILSON GIBBES[1]

Columbia S.C. July 19th 18[47][A]

My Dear Sir,

I have just returned from an [ex]cursion at the North, and had promised [my]self the pleasure of seeing you. Letters from home communicating the intelligence of the illness of one of my most esteemed friends, whose physician I have been for twelve years required my immediate return and shortened my visit.

While in N. York I was fortunate in seeing the collection of M[r] Squier from the western mounds, and much pleased to find him preparing his publication for the first number of the Smithsonian Journal. It will be a work of much interest abroad and at[B] home.

Will you allow me to ask your attention, in selecting matter for a future number, to the researches of Prof. Bailey of West Point on Infusoria, recent and fossil. He has accumulated a mass of facts and illustrations which are important to geologists and [...]^C of great scientific value.[2] He can[not] [aff]ord to publish them at his own ex[pe]nse, as the subject is new and the public [no]t sufficiently interested in it to render [the] sale profitable. Prof. Agassiz lately informed [me] that he had lost $16.000 by the publi[catio]n of his "Poissons fossiles,"[3] and all^D scientific works with numerous plates are usually published with loss. These are the works, when on^E new subjects which should merit the attention of the Regents of the Smithsonian Institute.[4] I have always felt a deep interest in the N. Institute[5] which I suppose will be superseded by the S.I.,[6]— and beg you will excuse my calling your attention to this matter. I write at the suggestion of our friend Col. Preston, and enclose you his letter,[7] which he kindly gave me.—

With respect
Yr obdt serv^t
Robert. W. Gibbes M.D.

Prof. Joseph Henry.
Princeton.

Henry Papers, Smithsonian Archives.
Paper mutilated along top right edge and lower left corner of front side, and top left edge of reverse. Reply: Doc. 84.

1. An 1827 graduate of South Carolina College (where he was now assistant professor of chemistry, geology, and mineralogy), Gibbes (1809–1866) was a physician with an active interest in paleontology. He may have been a candidate for the Smithsonian secretaryship in 1846. *DAB; Henry Papers, 6:*549.

2. Jacob Whitman Bailey was professor of chemistry, mineralogy, and geology at the United States Military Academy. The country's leading authority on fossil microorganisms, he had already written some half-dozen articles on American infusoria and diatoms. *Henry Papers,* 4:227n, 290, 326.

3. *Recherches sur les poissons fossiles,* 5 vols. (Neuchâtel, 1833–1844). Agassiz referred to this work and others he published during his Neuchâtel years as his "unhappy books, which never pay their way because they do not meet the wants of the world." That he incurred heavy financial losses from the *Poissons fossiles,* however, was due not only to the work's poor sales, but also to the funds Agassiz expended in publishing it. Dissatisfied with the quality and pace of publication of the early volumes,

Agassiz in 1836 established his own publishing house and employed several assistants to prepare his scientific monographs. Though initially profitable, the publishing house went bankrupt in 1845. Agassiz's indebtedness was one reason he came to the United States, where he hoped to earn money delivering lectures. Edward Lurie, *Louis Agassiz: A Life in Science* (1960; Chicago, 1966), pp. 91–92, 107–114, 128–129 (Agassiz quotation on p. 114).

4. The Smithsonian subsequently published three of Bailey's memoirs on microorganisms in SI Contributions: two in volume 2 (1851), and one in volume 7 (1854).

5. Gibbes had been a corresponding member of the National Institute since July 1841. "List of Members, 1841–1842," p. 101, Box 15, Records of the National Institute, RU 7058, Smithsonian Archives.

6. The act establishing the Smithsonian Institution had come as a blow to the National Institute's backers, who hoped that Congress would place Smithson's bequest under their care. By 1847, the institute had become all but moribund, having suspended its meetings and

cut back its publications. "Notice to the Members of the National Institute," *Fourth Bulletin of the National Institute for the Promotion of Science* (Washington, 1846), pp. 1–2; *Henry Papers,* 6:62n, 77n–78n, 464, 495n.

7. Not found.

84. TO ROBERT WILSON GIBBES

Princeton August 3ᵈ 1847

My dear Sir

I have just returned to Princeton after an absence of about two weeks, and find your very acceptable letter,[1] of the 19ᵗʰ on my table. I regret very much that your engagements did not permit you to visit this place. It would have given me much pleasure to become personally acquainted with, and to have had a full conversation on the affairs and organization of the Smithsonian Institution.

I am pleased to learn that you approve of the memoir of Messrs Squire and Davis, and I must thank you for the facts you mention in reference to the loss of Agassiz in his scientific publications, it will be of importance to me in illustrating the value of the plan we have adopted in expending a part of the income of the Smithsonian bequest.[2]

I am glad to learn that Professor Bailey thinks of preparing an extended article on his researches. I shall visit him, in the course of next month, on my way to the meeting of the American Geologists in Boston, and confer with him on the subject.[3]

With reference to the National Institution I can assure you that nothing on my part shall be wanting to harmonise and concentrate[A] the efforts of the lovers of science in Washington. During my soujourn however in Washington last Winter I heard nothing of the National Institution and I know nothing of the present condition of the Society.

Please give my kind regards to Col.[B] Preston and my thanks for the note of introduction of yourself. I have lately learned that he is in feeble health, and I hope his friends around him induce him to use every precaution necessary to the preservation of his valuable life. Our Country has but few such men and cannot afford to lose them. He is one of the master minds of the Smithsonian, and the person I most rely on to give it, at the next meeting, its proper direction.

With much respect
I am truly yours
Joseph Henry

Dʳ Robert W. Gibbes[C]

Retained Copy, Henry Papers, Smithsonian Archives.
In Charles P. Russell's hand.

1. Doc. 83.

2. Though Henry did not refer specifically to Agassiz, in his explanation of the "Programme of Organization" he did cite examples of scientists who had incurred pecuniary losses in publishing their work. He termed "perhaps the most important effect" of the "Programme" that of "giving to the world many valuable memoirs, which, on account of the expense of the illustrations, could not be otherwise published." *Smithsonian Report for 1847*, pp. 22–23 (quotation on p. 22).

3. Henry wrote Bailey on August 5, stating his intention to travel to Boston, expressing hopes that they could meet, and discussing his plans for the Smithsonian, particularly the SI Contributions. He urged Bailey to submit a memoir, since "from the first I have looked to you for an elaborate paper embodying all your discoveries, furnished with all the necessary illustrations irrespective of cost." Mary Henry Copy, Memoir, Henry Papers, Smithsonian Archives.

85. FROM RICHARD STOCKTON FIELD[1]

August 4, 1847[A]

Dear Sir

I have examined with much interest the paper you were so good as to hand me in reference to the Smithsonian Institution.[2] So far as I am capable of judging the plan seems to be well considered and judiciously arranged. I trust sincerely both for your own sake, and for the cause of Science that you may be able to carry it into full effect. And yet I confess I have always been apprehensive that in your Connexion with this Institution you might meet with obstacles that you would find it difficult to overcome; obstacles to which you were not accustomed, the force of which could not be calculated, and which were not to be surmounted by patience or research or intellect or science. I was afraid you would find the materials with which you had to work more intractable than those you were in the habit of dealing with. Thus far your Success has been signal, and should it continue, so as to enable you to mould this Institution into such a form and to put it on such a footing as you may desire, it will be a triumph of which you may well be proud.[3]

There is on the first page 4 an expression as to the propriety of which I am inclined to hint of[B] doubt. It is "the discovery of new knowledge." Is this strictly a correct expression? you may make discoveries in Science or knowledge—you may discover new facts or new truths which are the objects of knowledge; but can you discover new knowledge? At all events is it a happy expression?

Would this be any improvement?

"The first and most important is to increase the stock of existing knowledge; the[C] second to diffuse it among men. Most of the plans heretofore proposed for the organization of the Institution have reference rather[D] to the diffusion than the increase of knowledge".[4]

This is a very small matter and I am almost ashamed to have made so minute a criticism. But it may convince you that I have read with care what you have written, and that I feel a deep interest in whatever pertains to the Smithsonian Institution, and if so I shall be satisfied.

> I am my dear Sir
> Very respectfully & truly yours
> R. S. Field

Professer Joseph Henry

Henry Papers, Smithsonian Archives.
Reply: August 5, 1847, Mary Henry Copy, Memoir, Henry Papers, Smithsonian Archives.

1. An 1821 Princeton graduate, Field had recently been appointed its professor of constitutional law and jurisprudence. *Henry Papers,* 2:364n; *Princeton Catalogue,* pp. 31, 133.
2. That is, a draft of Henry's "Programme of Organization."
3. In his reply, Henry told Field that the difficulties to which he alluded "are to be expected," since "The Gods have placed a price on every thing valuable, and nothing of importance can be attained without effort." He reassured Field that his commitment to the institution remained firm, however, terming it "a duty I owe to the cause of knowledge to persevere in the attempt" to preserve Smithson's bequest.
4. Henry incorporated Field's suggestion in subsequent revisions of the "Programme." See item 5, page 1, of the facsimile printed in this volume.

86. ROBERT DALE OWEN TO ALEXANDER DALLAS BACHE

> New Harmony, Indiana
> August 5, 1847.

My dear Sir:

On my return, two days since, from a long, laborious, and (as you have undoubtedly heard ere this can reach you) an unsuccessful Congressional canvass,[1] I found a letter from our friend Seaton, regarding our Institution, a portion of which gave me considerable uneasiness. It regarded the possible resignation of Henry.

I am not surprised that he wishes to resign & shall never blame him if he does. Such a situation as that vacated by Professor Hare is a more desirable one, for a man of Henry's temperament, than the Secretaryship; its remuneration, I suppose, is fifty per cent higher;[2] & a residence in Philadelphia is preferable to one in Washington. Add to all this, that, as Professor, he would be occupied but during four winter months; &

it is evident, that Henry cannot but be a great gainer, in every sense, by the exchange.

If he still remain with us, the Institution ought to consider itself, while he lives, as deeply his debtor. But if he decide to resign, the question is, what are we to do?

This question causes me to write to you, at the risk of encroaching on the time of one, who has already far too much to do on his hands.

Seaton writes me:

"Could not Henry give his name (even if he accept the Philadelphia professorship) and all requisite scientific service to the Institution; relieving him of all but scientific pursuits, & reduce his salary proportionably, saving enough therefrom to pay a competent clerk & accountant; or else, call Mr Jewett into active duty. I tell Mr Henry, that I conceive such an arrangement practicable; & the plan is quite agreeable to him."

——————

My opinion is, that neither of these plans will do at all. We must, to push matters successfully & energetically, have the full, undivided heart & soul of such a man as Henry; or, if he must leave us, of the best substitute we can find for him. Jewett, in my opinion, is a man if not without soul, at least without anything like warm-hearted, generous devotion to a cause: and, besides, he is far too exclusively literary to be made head of an Institution such as ours should be. All Choate's ideas would be fully carried out by him.

Then there is the chance of Marcoe's claims being again pressed.[3]

I write all this, because on you I chiefly depend, in this exigency, if Henry really decides to leave us, which I still earnestly hope he may not do. You found us Henry. If we lose him, cannot you find[A] some other, who, if not his equal—that we cannot expect—shall yet fill, with honor to himself & credit to the Institution, his place? I pray you to think of this, & to write me the result of your thoughts.

I am wanted in Washington, on the building committee in September; & shall do my best, to get away from this place, so as to reach the city from the 20th to the 30th of that month.[4] Shall you be then at Washington? or where? I wish I could see you, so that we might talk over this matter, some time in advance of the meeting of the Board. There must surely be, among y^r scientific friends, some man of eminence, who would accept such a situation, & could fulfil its duties.

If Henry can only make up his mind to remain with us, permanently, & to devote his undivided energies to the Institution, I cannot doubt its prosperity. If not you may want the aid of my vote to elect his successor. I sh^d be sorry to go out, (as you know I do, in December)[5] &

think, after all the successful struggles we had to bring the vessel into safe haven, she was out, at the mercy of the waves, once more.

I am, my dear Sir
faithfully Y^{rs}
Robert Dale Owen

Bache Papers, Smithsonian Archives.
File note: "Thompsons/Recd Aug. 18th."

1. Since April, Owen had been campaigning in Indiana for reelection to his House seat. He faced a spirited challenge from Elisha Embree (*BDAC*), a Whig lawyer and former circuit court judge, who portrayed himself as a non-partisan to attract disaffected Democrats. Embree attacked Owen's voting record, exposed his free-thinking ideas, and tarred him with allegations of corruption. He also made an issue of Owen's interest in "a useless Smithsonian Institution" (p. 237). In "the most stunning political upset of the decade in Indiana" (p. 239), Embree won by 391 votes. Richard W. Leopold, *Robert Dale Owen: A Biography* (1940; New York, 1969), pp. 236–241.

2. Owen likely was not privy to direct information about Hare's chair, but, assuming certain factors held true, his estimate about its remuneration was a good guess. Like other Medical School faculty, Hare did not earn a fixed salary, but rather was compensated by the purchase of tickets to attend his lectures. Students were required to attend two courses in chemistry as part of their degree requirements. In any given academic year, the total number of matriculants averaged over four hundred students; roughly three-fourths were in either their first or second year, attending courses rather than doing a residency. Assuming an attendance of three hundred students per chem-

istry course, the professor of chemistry would receive $7,500 (at $25 per ticket, the fee set for Hare's lectures). Even given the university's plan to reduce the lecture fee to $15 for Hare's successor (see Doc. 53), the incumbent could still earn $4,500 per course, well above Henry's salary ($3,500).
Catalogue of the Trustees, Officers, & Students of the University of Pennsylvania (Philadelphia, 1843), pp. 14–23, 28–29; Joseph Carson, *A History of the Medical Department of the University of Pennsylvania* (Philadelphia, 1869), p. 171, 219–220.

3. Owen alluded to Francis Markoe's possible claim to the Smithsonian secretaryship should Henry resign; Markoe had finished second in the balloting. *Henry Papers*, 6:554.

4. Owen did not arrive back in Washington until October 16; the building committee met two days later. Rhees, *Journals*, pp. 689, 690.

5. Under section 3 of the act establishing the Smithsonian, Owen—as one of three regents appointed by the speaker of the House of Representatives—was to serve a term expiring on the fourth Wednesday of the second December after the act's passage, namely, December 22, 1847. The same applied for the other House appointees, William J. Hough and Henry W. Hilliard. Rhees, *Documents* (1901), pp. 430, 463.

87. FROM GEORGE MIFFLIN DALLAS

Winchester, 6. Aug. '47^A

My Dear Sir,

You may probably have noticed that, in carrying into execution a plan for lighting the Capitol & grounds at Washington approved by Congress, the contractor, Mr Crutchett, proposes to erect a mast through the Dome about 80 feet high and to place on it a lantern six feet in diameter.[1] Some of his rival workmen have tried to awaken public apprehension as to the dangers of his design; and among other allegations, it is asserted that the mast and lantern will attract the lightning. I directed M[r]. Crutchett to report his project in sufficient detail on this point to enable me to ask you, on reading it, to express an opinion as to the alleged risk. I enclose you the copy sent to me by M[r] Dickens,[2] and hope that it will be enough to authorize you to releive my mind. If there be the slightest increase of danger to the Capitol, I will, of course, have that part of the work suspended. You will much oblige me by letting me hear from you at your earliest convenience, and by addressing your answer to me at Philadelphia.

> Ever truly & respt. y[rs].
> G. M. Dallas.

Professor Henry.

Henry Papers, Smithsonian Archives.
Replies: Docs. 89, 90.

1. About 1846, James Crutchett (ca. 1816–1889), a native of England who had been promoting gaslighting in several midwestern cities since the early 1840s, bought a house near the Capitol in Washington, and built a small plant to light it with "solar gas" (carburetted hydrogen). Crutchett's were the first gaslights in Washington, and they attracted considerable attention, including that of Congress. He proposed to illuminate the Capitol, stating that a system based on his plan would furnish the equivalent of seventy thousand candles inside the building, and thirty thousand around its grounds. In March 1847, Congress appropriated $17,500 for his system, to consist of a gas plant, gasholder, a lantern and mast atop the Capitol dome, exterior burners, and interior fixtures. Construction began in June; the mast and lantern were erected in August, and the interior lights were installed in November. The interior gaslights were a success; as for the lantern, one member of Congress wrote that it "affords a tolerable light immediately about the Capitol, but the light is not extended as far as has been anticipated." Crutchett also proved inept at running his system as a business; in 1848, a group headed by Benjamin B. French organized the "Washington Gas Light Company" and bought him out.

National Intelligencer, March 3; June 4, 1847; [Washington] *Saturday Evening News,* August 28; November 20, 1847; Robert Mills, *Guide to the Capitol and National Executive Offices of the United States* (Washington, 1847–1848), pp. 36–37; Robert R. Hershman and Edward T. Stafford, *Growing with Washington: The Story of Our First Hundred Years* (Washington, 1948), pp. 19–23 (quotation on p. 23); William Worthington, Division of Engineering and Industry, National Museum of American History, private communication.

2. Asbury Dickens (1773–1861), secretary of the Senate. Charles Lanman, *Biographical Annals of the Civil Government of the United States,* 2d ed. (New York, 1887), p. 139.

Dickens's letter to Dallas of August 4, transmitting Crutchett's memorandum (not found), is in the Henry Papers, Smithsonian Archives.

88. TO [ROBERT DALE OWEN]ᴬ

Princeton Aug 7ᵗʰ 1847

My dear sir

Enclosed with this letter I send you a copy of the article from the Annales de Chemie on the method of testing building stones.¹ I would have forwarded it before but I found some difficulty in getting the article copied in Princeton. I presume however that the delay has been of little consequence since your Brother must have been so much occupied with his survey as not to be able to attend to the experiments on building materials.²

I have ordered two sets of magnetic instruments which will probably arrive before the commencement of operations in the Spring. It is proposed to give both sets to your Brother that he may make up for the time lossed on account of the want of the articles this season. The magnetic survey under Dr Jackson is in charge of Dr Locke who is useing his own instruments.

All the affairs of the Smithsonian appear in as favourable a train as could reasonably be expected. The building is going up with sufficient rapidity and the scheme of investing the money for its erection, in Treasuryᴮ ~~bank~~ notes has proved a very successful operation. The notes have been 7 or 8 per cent above par and moreᶜ of them have been disposed of for paying the contractors the money for this purpose has been drawn from the current interest of the original capital. But of these facts you have probbabby been informed by Mr Seaton.

I have commenced operations with respect to the publication of the first vol. of the "contributions" and find no want of materials.

The first article is an extensive memoir on the remains of the mound builders "in the valley of the Mississiphi by two gentlemen of Ohio. It has been accepted for publication on the responsibility of a committee of the ethnological society of New York. The Hon Galatin,ᴰ Hon. Mr Marsh and Dr Morton are among the vouchers for its importance, in the way of an addition to human knowledge and its fitness for publication in the Smithsonian contributions. The sum required for the publication of the article will however be considerably greater than the appropriation made at the last meeting of the board. It will require 60 quarto plates and 200 woodcuts for its illustrations; while the letter press will occupy 430ᴱ pages.

This memoir could not have been published in this country except by means of the Smithsonian funds and it will therefore serve to illustrate the value of the plans adopted by the Regents of the institution.

The subject of the paper will also prove that our object is not exclusively the promotion of physical knowledge but that we intend to offer every branch of human thought susceptible of increase proper incourage-ment.

On the whole I think the present condition of the scientific part of the scheme of organization presents a very incouraging aspect and I am more than ever confirmed in the opinion that this plan of desposing of the funds will receive the full approbation of a great majority of the intelligence of the country as soon as it is fully understood and its work-ing in practice properly exibitd. I have still however my fears that when the building is completed so much of the income will be absolved in its erection &c and the support of the establishment necessaraly connected with it that ~~that~~ the scientific operations will be materially interfered with. If however you can induce congress to pay for the main building or even to bear the expence of keeping the great museum all will be well and you will deserve a statue in one of the nitches of the Smith-sonian edifice.

You may perhaps have seen a paragraph going the rounds of the papers stating that I was about to resign my office in the Smithsonian for the chair of chemistry occupied by Dr Hare of Phil[a] It is true I had the offer of this situation and that I did hesitate for a moment as to the course I should take but though I prefered the situation in Phil[a] to the one in Washington yet I soon concluded that I was too much involved in the affairs of the Smithsonian to leave it with honor under such an inducement and at this period of its history. I consider however, that I have now made a sacrifice[F] for what I think the good of the Smithsonian and I shall be more disposed than ever to insist[G] on[H] ~~the~~ carrying out the scientific plans of the institution. If these plans cannot be carried out the sooner I leave the Instituti[on][I] the better for myself and for the Smithsonian and I must say to you in candor that I think the fate of the Institution at present depends very much on an harmoneous coopera-tion between you and myself and I most sincerely hope that we may agree on a course which shall be for the best interest for the cause of knowledge. Professor Bache has gone to his station near Boston we are to meet at the reunion ↑of the↓ geological association in Boston on the 20th of Sept. I shall go on with my[J] family to Washingto[n][I] about the first of nov. I hope you will come to Princeton shoul[d][I] you visit the east preavous nov. Please give my kind[K] regard[s][I] to your Brother and receive for yourself the assurance that I remain your friend

Joseph Henry

Retained Copy, Henry Papers, Smithsonian Archives.
In Harriet Henry's hand. Variant copy: In same hand, same location.

1. "Sur le procédé proposé par M. Brard pour reconnaître immédiatement les pierres qui ne peuvent pas résister à la gelée, et que l'on désigne ordinairement par les noms de *pierres gelives* ou *pierres gelisses*," *Annales de chimie et de physique*, 1828, *38*:160–192.

2. Henry presumably meant the "series of more extensive experiments, to determine both the strength and the durability of the principal building materials throughout the United States," which the regents had authorized on February 27, and for which purpose they appropriated up to $500 two days later. These experiments were never made. Rhees, *Journals*, pp. 38, 39 (quotation on p. 38).

89. TO GEORGE MIFFLIN DALLAS

Princeton August 12th. 1847

The Hon: George M Dallas.
Vice President of the United States.
Sir

Your letter of the 6th inst,[1] relative to the danger from Lightning to the Capitol on account of the fixtures about to be erected on the dome, was received yesterday, and after due consideration of the subject I submit the following answer.

I gather from your letter, and the account furnished by Mr Crutchett, that it is proposed to erect a mast of 80 feet in height[2] on the top of the dome of the Capitol; and through the axis of this mast to pass an iron pipe to be placed in metallic connection with the earth below and with a large lantern, in part at least constructed of metal, above.

The question proposed—is, will this fixture attract the lightning from the clouds, and thus endanger the safety of the building?

This question may be considered under two heads 1st will this fixture increase the tendency of lightning to fall on the area occupied by the Capitol? 2nd Will the metallic conductors transmit the discharge which may fall on the lantern Silently to the earth so as not to endanger the building?

From well known principles of electrical action I do not hesitate to answer the first part of the question in the affirmative.

The effect of an ordinary lightning rod in attracting the electricity of the clouds must be exceedingly small and in most cases inappreciable. The value of the article consists in the protection it affords, in case the lightning begins to descend, and when in its course to the earth it would fall on the house, the rod will then within certain limits attract the descending discharge to itself and transmit it to the earth. The conditions are however very different with reference to the fixture, proposed to be erected on the Capitol; The height of the dome above the base of the edefice according to the account of Mr Mills[3] is 145 feet; if to this 80 feet be added for the mast, we shall have an elevation of 225 feet exclusive of the height of the top of the lantern. Besides this the capitol is situated on the edge of an elevated plane above the average level of the surrounding surface. The whole height of the lantern will therefore bear a considerable ratio to the ordinary elevation of a thunder cloud, and since both the intensity and quantity of action, of a conductor, depend on its elevation above the earth, we have reason to conclude, particularly, when we also take into the account the surface of metal of the lantern, that the proposed fixture, will produce a direct action on the cloud sufficient to cause ~~the~~ ↑a↓ discharge to fall on the space occupied by the Capitol when without such influence no discharge would take place. There is also another condition highly favourable to the production of a discharge connected with the lantern, I allude to the heated air which ascends from the flame. It is well known to practical electricians, that one of the best instruments, for collecting atmospherical electricity, consists of a wire elevated by means of a fishing rod out of an upper window with a small lighted lantern attached to the upper end. The proposed arrangement furnishes a collecting apparatus of this kind on a magnificent scale.

From these considerations I do not hesitate to say that the tendency of the lightning to fall on the Capitol will be increased by the action of the proposed fixture.

The other part of the question namely,—will the metalic conductors transmit the discharge silently to the earth so as not to endanger the building, does not admit of as definite an answer as the first. The degree of safety will depend principally on the perfection and arrangement of the several conductors.

An uninterrupted course of metallic conductors should extend from the top of the lantern to the water basin at the foot of the building; and it is proposed to effect this by means of the vertical gas pipe, the copper roof, and the water spouts connected at their lower ends with the ground.

I see no objections to this plan, with reference to the line of conductors proposed, provided it is rendered perfectly continuous; and the metallic connection be carried to the water of the basin. But to the proposition of passing the vertical pipe through the whole extent of the axis of the mast, I do see an objection. With this arrangement in case of a powerful discharge the mast would be liable to be split into pieces and the whole structure, lantern and all, would be in danger of falling on the dome. During the passage of a discharge through a conductor the electricity on account of its self repulsion tends to pass at the surface, and to produce, on the matter surrounding the conductor, a pressure, which might in some cases be sufficient to cause the result I have mentioned.[4] The safest plan would be to support the tube on the outside of the mast by means of loops and bands passing around each.

I am not informed whether the prolongation of the gas-pipe from the foot of the mast, is to pass over the convex surface of the dome, and thence, down the outside of the building to the tank below; or whether it is proposed to carry it directly down through the interior of the edefice, and out through the cellar. If the latter plan be the one contemplated, I should object to the arrangement. If the copper sheathing which covers the roof were extended on all sides to the ground, so as perfectly to encase the building, the electricity which arrived at the foot of the mast would pass along the metallic[A] surface to the earth, and in this case there would be little objection to the plan in question; but in the actual condition of things, the descending tube would divide the discharge with the water pipes, and a considerable part of the electricity would be transmitted through the interior of the building. Though a discharge might in some cases be transmitted through the interior of an edefice without producing danger; yet I do not consider the experiment a safe one. During the passage of electricity through the most perfect conductor sparks may be drawn from every part of it by the approach of another conductor.[5]

From these remarks I would wish it to be understood, as my opinion, that though the proposed fixture will have the effect of increasing the tendency of the lightning[B] to fall upon the Capitol; yet if proper precautions be taken the probability of danger, to the building, will be but little increased. I say but little because, strictly speaking, no protection against the effects of lightning can be so perfect as to render the building, as safe, as one, in which there is no increased tendency whatever of the electricity to fall.

A[C] small amount of increase of danger such as I have mentioned may however in some cases be reasonably incurred provided an important object is to be attained but with reference to the importance of this fixture I am not called upon to express an opinion.

> I have the honor to be very respectfully
> Your obedient Servant
> Joseph Henry

To the Hon: George M Dallas.
Vice President of the USA.

Retained Copy, Henry Papers, Smithsonian Archives.
In an unknown hand, with Henry's signature. Enclosed in Doc. 90. Draft: August 11, 1847, in same location. Reply: See Doc. 95.

1. Doc. 87.
2. Other accounts—including one by Henry—gave the height as 90 or 100 feet. Henry, "On the Forms of Lightning-Rods," AAAS *Proceedings*, 1850, *4*:40; Robert Mills, *Guide to the Capitol and National Executive Offices of the United States* (Washington, 1847–1848), p. 36.
3. Mills, p. 36.

4. Henry referred to a phenomenon associated with lightning, the lateral explosion. See *Henry Papers*, *5*:66–72, 73–74, 251–253; *6*:352–353, 583–584.
5. A reference to another lightning phenomenon, the lateral discharge. For Henry's earlier remarks on protecting buildings against it, see *Henry Papers*, *5*:439, 440n, 441.

90. TO GEORGE MIFFLIN DALLAS

Princeton Aug 12th 1847

My Dear Sir

Your letter[1] relative to the fixture proposed to be erected on the top of the Capitol, was received on Tuesday,[2] but my engagements were such that I was unable to give the subject due consideration until yesterday after noon. I now send you a formal answer,[3] involving opinions which I am prepared to support. If any part of my letter is not sufficiently explicit I shall be pleased to make my views plainer.

I am not called on by the terms of your communication to express an opinion as to the value and probable success of the scheme. I may however say to you in confidence that without an examination of the plans my impressions are not very favorable with reference to the whole project of thus lighting the grounds of the capitol and that I do not think the mast will long be allowed to disfigure the dome of this imposing edifice.[4]

As to the value of the Scheme Congress has given an opinion in the act of authorizing the construction of the work and it might therefore be unpleasant[A] to stop the ~~work~~ ↑erection↓ at this stage of its progress on account of the small increase of danger to the building I have mentioned.

There is howev an other point which in the end may have some effect on the question of the continuance of the mast on the top of the dome. I allude to the influence which the knowledge of the fact of the greater tendancy of the lightning to fall on the Capitol on account of the lantern may have on the minds of the members of congress. Will they be disposed to put ful confidence in the deductions of science and to rest in security on the means of protection provided by the best arrangement of conductors.

> With much respect
> I rem your obt servt.
> Joseph Henry

Hon George M Dallas
vice President U.S.A

Retained Copy, Henry Papers, Smithsonian Archives.
Draft: Same location. Reply: See Doc. 95.

1. Doc. 87.
2. August 10.
3. Doc. 89.
4. In a later discussion, Henry termed Crutchett's mast a "gigantic apparatus" which was "erected in defiance of all the principles of architecture and illumination." "Atmospheric Electricity," Part V of "Meteorology in Its Connection with Agriculture," *Report of the Commissioner of Patents for 1859: Agriculture* (Washington, 1860), p. 508.

91. TO EDWARD SABINE[1]

> Princeton Colledge of NJ
> Aug 13th 1847

My dear sir

I beg leave to tresspass on your kindness with a request for your assistance in a scientific matter and I am the more free to ask this favor since it pertains to the advance of terrestrial magnetism a branch of science which owes more to your labor than to that of any other living person.

The government of the United States has instituted for the sake of a better knowledge of its mineral resources a geological explanation of the terotory of Wisconsin and of the region around lake Michigan and Mr Walker the liberal secretary of the Treasury has consented to add to these explorative magnetic surveys of the same districts provided the Smithsonian Institution will take the direction of the operations. Now the favor we wish to request of you is the aid of your knowledge and position in selecting and procuring instruments for these surveys. In order to expedite the completion of this work as well as for the more efficient prosecution of other operations of a similar kind[A] which will probably be hereafter undertaken under the direction of the same Institution we shall require two sets of instruments. These will each consist according to the guggestions of Dr Bache of the following articles.

1 From Jones[2]

A potable magnetoneter for declination ↑&↓ absolute horizontan intensity with theodolite and stands complete.[3]

2 From[B] Barrows[4]

A dip circle.[5]

The money for the payment of these instruments is at my command and will be forwarde in the form of a bill of exchange on London, Albany, time you may direct. We should be pleased to receive the instruments as early as possible inorder that observers may be trained in the use of them previous to the time of begining operations in the spring.

The survey in the region[C] around lake Michigan has already been commenced under the care of Dr John Locke with his own instruments.

You will probably be interested in the history and object of the Smithsonian institution before mentioned and I therefore give you the following account of it. It was founded by the munificent bequest of your countryman the late James Smithson the illegitmate son of the Duke of Northumberland and a chemist in his day of some celebrity. He was a frequent contributor to the transactions of the Royal Socienty and to the Philosophical magazine. He died in 1829 at Genoa leaving all his property in case of the death of his nephew to found an establishment at Washington under the name of the Smithsonian Institution (such are his words) for the increase and Diffusion of knowledge among men.

The money (500000 dollars) came into the Treasury of the US about eight years ago but congress was unable to fix upon a plan for carrying out the dsign of the testator ↑until last year when an act was past giving some general derections and placing the institution under the care of a board of trustees called Regents. At the second meeting of this board I was elected the active executive officer of the ~~Ins↓~~ Institution under the name of Secretary. I was not an applicant for the office my name was brought before the Board through the influence of my friend Bache who is one of the Regents without my knowledge and though I dislike the noteriety of the position and the executive duties which it involves I was induced to accept with the hope of being able to direct at least a part of the income of the funds to some useful purpose. Indeed our friend Bache urged upon me the acceptance as a matter of duty; I being the only scientific candidate on whom the Board would agree. What the result may be I am unable to say. Unfortunately, the Institution has too much connection with Government and is liable to be affected by party influence still there[D] ↑is a↓ prospect of much good resulting from the bequest provided the plan of organization which has been adopted is rigerously carried out. Of this plan I send you a programme[6] and beg that you will examine it at your leisure and give me an opinion of its importance with any suggestions which may occur to you as to its improvement. This plan as a whole is by no means the best which might have been adopted. It gives in the opinion of Dr. Bache and myself too much of the income to collections which though interesting in themselves are but very indirect means of increasing and diffusing knowledge among men. But we were obliged by the Law of Congress (of which you will find a copy in the printed pages accompanying this letter)[7] to make a compromise between the two leading views of the method of employing the income in carrying out the design of the testator. It is a remarkable fact that few persons in our country placed any importance on the words increase of knowledge which occur in the will of Smithson and hence[E] all the provisions of the acts of Congress had reference to the diffusion of knowledge by means of a Library, a museum and Lectures.

In accordance with that part of the plan of organization (see programme) which contemplates the increase of knowledge by means of original researches, I have requested Professor Loomis to furnish a report on a plan of meteorological observations with reference particularly to the nature of American storms. The plan he has submitted is substantially the same as that ↑which↓ he described to you in his letter of the 28th of Feb. 1845 and published in the proceedings of the conference held at Cambridge in June of the same year.[8] It consists in the organization of corps of observers principally furnished with instruments from the funds of the Smithsonian Institution and to be distributed over the whole country at the rate of one observer for every area of 100 square miles.

May I ask your opinion of this plan and of the probability of the cooperation of your government in extending the same observations into your Canadian possessions.

Your opinion on the points I have mentioned would have much influence on the Board of Regents of the Smithsonian Institution and assist Dr. Bache and myself in carrying out our plans for the increase of knowledge.

I beg leave to acknowledge the receipt of two volumes of the Reports of the British association those for 1844 and 5.[9]

Please address your communication to me at this [pl]ace[F] if it be sent before the first of October but to Washington if after this date. I must also thank you for a copy of your memo[i]r[F] Terrestrial magnetism Nos 7 & 8.[10] Your name will by these contributions be for ever connected with the history of the magnetism of our country— You have given full credit to the labours of American observers and thus rendered their observations more valuable as authentic data of science[11]—

> With much respet I rem
> truly yours
> Joseph Henry

Lieut. Col. Edward[G] Sabine FR.S.
& &c &c.

Retained Copy, Henry Papers, Smithsonian Archives.
In Harriet Henry's hand, except for interlineations. Reply: Doc. 100.

1. The general secretary of the British Association for the Advancement of Science, foreign secretary of the Royal Society, army officer, and physicist, Edward Sabine had met Henry in England in 1837. *Henry Papers, 3:*296.

2. Thomas Jones (1775–1852) was a London instrument maker. *DNB.*

3. The portable magnetometer could be used for both magnetic measurements (finding the angle between magnetic and geographic north, as well as the strength of the earth's magnetism) and astronomical observations (locating geographic north). Robert P. Multhauf and Gregory Good, *A Brief History of Geomagnetism and a Catalog of the Collections of the National Museum of American History* (Washington, 1987), p. 4.
Bache and Henry were probably guided in their selection of instruments and instrument makers by C. J. B. Riddell, *Magnetical Instructions for the Use of Portable Instruments Adapted for Magnetical Surveys and Portable Observatories* (London, 1844), which Henry owned. Riddell provided descriptions of magnetical instruments, recommendations, instructions, and price lists. His book was "among the more generally useful and practically important publications relating to this science." It provided instructions for the instruments "of universal or nearly universal employment," whether in use in fixed observatories or by surveys. "Sixth Report of the Committee, Consisting of Sir J. Herschel, . . . Dr. Lloyd and Colonel Sabine, Appointed to Conduct the Co-operation of the British Association in the System of Simultaneous Magnetical and Meteorological Observations," *British Association Report for 1844,* p. 149.
According to Riddell, *Supplement to the Magnetical Instructions* (London, 1846), p. 14, Jones charged from £30 to £40 for a theodolite magnetometer and stand according to size.

4. Henry Barrow (1790–1870) was an En-

glish instrument maker. Multhauf and Good, p. 73.

5. Used to measure the downward inclination of a needle from the plane of the horizon, a Barrow dip circle would cost from £15 to £25 according to size. Multhauf and Good, p. 4; Riddell, p. 99.

6. Found in BJ3/49, Letters to Sabine from Renwick and Henry, 1845–1853, Sabine Papers, Records of Kew Observatory, Public Record Office, London. This was a manuscript copy of Henry's first draft of his "Programme of Organization." It is apparently the only surviving copy of that draft and is discussed below, Doc. 130.

7. *Report of the Organization Committee of the Smithsonian Institution; With the Resolutions Accompanying the Same, and Adopted by the Board of Regents; Also, the Will of the Testator, the Act Accepting the Bequest, and the Act Organizing the Institution* (Washington, 1847).

8. *British Association Report for 1845,* pp. 20–22. Loomis's letter was in response to the December 1844 circular of the British Association concerning international cooperation in magnetic and meteorological observations. It supported the continuance of international cooperation and called for "a chain of meteorological posts extending indefinitely northward from the great lakes across the British possessions" (p. 21).

9. Copies of these survive in the Henry Library.

10. Edward Sabine, "Contributions to Terrestrial Magnetism. Nos. VII and VIII," *Phil. Trans.,* 1846, pp. 237–432. An offprint is in the Henry Library.

11. Among the scientists whose observations Sabine acknowledged on pages 241 to 243 are Bache, James D. Graham, Locke, Loomis, and James Renwick.

92. TO EPHRAIM GEORGE SQUIER

Princeton Aug 16th/47

My dear Sir

Your letter[1] and the accompanying account of Mr Orr[2] were[A] received some days ago but I have been so much engaged with a Report I have been called on to make—the preparation of a number of communications for Europe and the meeting of my class at the opening of college that I have been unable to attend to your affairs until to day. The Report of the Ethnological is now completely satisfactory and I will send you the copies of the articles as soon as I can get them prepared.

I know nothing of the announcement you mention with reference to the publication of the Smithsonian Contributions ~~which you mention~~. Should you learn any thing concerning the matter you will oblige me by letting me know it.

I will send the draft to Mr. Orr[3,B] by the mail of tomorrow evening and I shall require of him a more detailed account of the work finished by him the number of wood cuts finished and the number afixed to each cut for the purpose of refering to it in the letter press— My object in requesting this is that I may be able to present a more definite account of my expenditures to the executive committee— You will also oblige me by sending a receipt for the money advanced to you stating that the payment was for services rendered in superintending the preparation of wood cuts and plates for the illustration of the Smithsonian Contributions.

I intend to visit Boston to be present at the meeting of american Geologists on the 20th of September and shall place before this body a programme of the plan of organization of the Smithsonian.

I am overwhelmed with letters on all kinds of fancied discoveries and requests for aid in publishing all kinds of works which in the opinion of the authors are of the highest importance in the way of increasing and diffusing knowledge among men.

Yours Respectfully
Joseph Henry

E George Squire

Squier Papers, Library of Congress.
Draft: August 10, 1847, Henry Papers, Smithsonian Archives.

1. Not found. Dated August 8, according to Henry's draft.

2. Nathaniel Orr of New York City was a leading wood engraver. George C. Groce and David H. Wallace, *The New-York Historical Society's Dictionary of Artists in America, 1564–1860* (New Haven, 1957).

3. Henry to Orr & Co., August 18, 1847, Orr Family Papers, Rare Books and Manuscripts Department, University of Florida Library.

93. FROM RICHARD ALBERT TILGHMAN[1]

London. Aug 19th 1847

My dear Sir

I should long since have written to thank you for the kind reception which your letters[2] secured[A] for me among your English friends, and I have only deferred doing so in hopes that I might be able at the same time to send some scientific news that might be interesting— Obliged at last to abandon this idea, I must content myself with speaking of your friends whom I have seen since my arrival— Dr Faraday was then quite unwell and unable to see any one; his general health and a stiffness of one knee joints confined him to his room; he is now quite well I believe but obliged to use a cane in walking.[3] I attended several Friday evening lectures[4] by him at the Royal Inst[n.] and also [a] course of lectures on Physico Chemical Philosophy which he gave this spring[5] [at] the same place; as a lecturer and experimenter I do not think I ever saw his [e]qual; his experiments are most ingeniously contrived and always successful but at the same time so very numerous that it seemed to me that a large portion of his audience were content to be steadily amused by them without using their ears or brains to attend to his explanations of their object— The general subject of his course was the consideration of the various natural forces, Gravity, Heat, Light, Electric[y] & chemical Affinity, showing the intimate connection and convertibility of all but the first. His conclusion was that Gravity was the only power nonconformable to those general rules which govern all the rest to a greater or less extent. Its principle irregularities were—that it affected all matter alike without reference to state or properties; that while it acted between two atoms to draw them together yet their union produced neither increase nor diminution in their attraction for all other ↑existing↓ matter, thus forming a force ever acting but never neutralized; it was also incapable [o]f conversion into any other form of force & could not be communicated from one body to another. He mentioned that the present subject of his own researches was the investigation of this apparently anomalous force to ascertain its real connection with the others. Although I could not agree with all the instances ~~of~~ he quoted as illustrating the non conformity of gravity, yet the general view he took of this force was to me I confess both new and interesting[6]—

From Prof. Solly[7] I have received the greatest kindness and attention—ever since my arrival he has been unremitting in his endeavors not only to make my visit an agreeable one by procuring me admission to the various Societies &c but also to assist me by his advice and information in the more important business matters I have been engaged upon. He has a very thorough knowledge of Chemistry and seems to be equally familiar with many other branches of Science with which I am not acquainted. I hope that he will soon ᵽ be placed[B] in some more prominent professorship than that he now holds in the East India College,[C] so that the talents and information whic[h] he really possesses may be fully appreciated[8]— He frequently enquires af[ter] you & the prospect there may be of your making a second European visit a possibility which he looked forward to with much pleasure—

Prof. Graham[9] I did not call upon till quite lately; I found him a very pleasant gentlemanly person, but one whose calm reserve and Scotch caution in every thing, formed quite a contrast with the unhesitating frankness and straight forward manners of Prof. Solly. So far as one can judge from half a dozen interviews I should not suppose him to be a man of bold or comprehensive genius but rather owing his celebrity to a minute and [care]ful accuracy in all he attempts.

Now that I have given all that I know of interest to you on [this] side the Atlantic I must pass to some thing that interests me very much, that [is] to take place at home. You may possibly recollect that when I last saw you at Princeton, while we were speaking of the Secretaryship of the Smithsonian; (a ma[tter] at that time undecided) I mentioned to you the hope I had long entertained of seing you located in Philadelphia as Dr Hare's successor in the University, although untill his chair became vacant I thought no more desirable post coul[d] be presented than that in the Smithsonian Inst[n.] It gave me therefore great pleasure shortly after my arrival here, to learn that you had been elected to the latter office, inasmuch as I had but little hope that Dr Hare woul[d] eve[r] resign untill he became Physically unable to read his lectures. After my frien[ds] in Phil[a] had sent me the surprising news of his resignation, being well aware of my hopes as to his successor, they continued by every steamer to inform me of the increasing probabilities that these would be fulfilled. Judge then of my disappointment on the arrival of my last letters, at the same time that I received almost official account of the absolute certainty of your election by a most flattering Majority of the Trustees, I was also informed that the election had been postponed in consequence of doubts of your acceptance of the Professorship.

If your hesitation arose from any private objection I would not, of course venture to allude to it; but as the reports sent me all agree in attributing it entirely to an over sensitiveness on your part to the imagined claim of the Smithsonian Inst[n.] I cannot lose this opportunity of expressing my conviction how inadequate a cause (even if it did exist) this would be for abandoning all the advantages both to Science and the Public which w[ill] follow your acceptance of this chair. Do not think that I undervalue the importance of such an institution as the smithsonian when in proper hands and in a proper sphere of action; but I believe that <u>both</u> these are essential to extended utility and the desert of Washington seems to be the last place in which such a sphere could be obtained. If it had been placed in Philadelphia the case would be very different as a Public as well as a public Taste for Science both exist there already and would not have to be created. I believe that a single man of scientific reputation, holding as prominent a post as Dr Hare has done but who was not only actively engaged in researches himself, but would also <u>wish and encour[age]</u> others to do ↑so↓ likewise, would be able in a short time to stimulate the [p]ublic taste for such matters in Phil<u>ª</u> to a degree practicable in few other places. This desideratum the tenure of important scientific [p]osts by persons who really desire the promotion of science even by the labors of others as well as their own is I^D am sorry to say rarely to be met with. [S]o far as I can learn the state of things here ↑is↓ as bad or worse in this respect, than with us; Those who have crept into office by mere favoritism oppose bitterly every aspirant to scientific eminence, as their own imbecility is thus made more & more prominently conspicuous; the few scientific men who have [ear]ned their way by mere merit, seem to regard every new discovery by another [as] lowering their own reputation & oppose it accordingly. Real, prac[t]ical encouragement is therefore rarely to be met with.

The importance of impressing upon so large a class of Physicians as those [in] our Univers^y [an] intimate knowledge of an agent which has been so lo[ng th]e subject of y[our o]wn researches, which has so intimate a connectio[n w]ith its representative the nervous influence in the animal system, c[ould I] think hardly be overestimated. The great and radical improvements [in] medicine will more probably arise from this combination of study than [any] other.[10] Did time or space allow, a hundred other reasons could be urged upon you in favor of this Chair; the opportunity and time afforded for your own investigations should alone be sufficient to decide the matter. As to the Smithson[i]an, what possible wish, can an institution, formed only for the diffusion of useful knowledge, have to prevent your accepting a post in which you could far more effectually promote its real objects than if you remained at its head? As ↑to↓ your being under any obligations to it on account of your election thereto, I must beg of you not to trouble yourself ↑in the least↓ with any such idea. The benefit was on their side; they chose you because you were the best person they could find, and would not have done so had it been otherwise.— Prof. Solly continually expresses the greatest interest in the result of this matter, and could hardly understand that there could be hesitation on so slight grounds—

And now my dear Sir I must ask your pardon for having [dared] to express myself so freely on this subject, but you must rememb[er that] this has been a long entertained project with me and that be[cause] as a Philadelphian I have a most direct interest in your dec[ision.]

With great Respect I remain very truly your[s]
R. A. Tilghma[n]

Prof. Joseph Henry—

P.S.ᴱ Being too late for the mail of the last steamer I am oblige to wait for this—Sep 3ᵈ

Henry Papers, Smithsonian Archives.
Paper torn on edges, and holes in paper.

1. A Philadelphian, graduate of the University of Pennsylvania, and acquaintance of Henry's from the American Philosophical Society, Tilghman was studying industrial chemistry in Europe. *Henry Papers*, 6:507n.

2. According to Henry's address book, page [2] (Box 17, Henry Papers, Smithsonian Archives), Henry "gave letters to Stilghman" for Michael Faraday, Edward Solly, Jr., Thomas Graham, and "Terrell" [Alfred Tyrrell]. None of these letters have been found.

3. For Faraday's health during this period, see L. Pearce Williams, ed., *The Selected Correspondence of Michael Faraday*, 2 vols. (Cambridge, 1971), *1*:500, 507–510.

4. For the Friday evening popular lectures of the Royal Institution, see *Henry Papers*, 3:241.

5. A reference to eight lectures given between April 17 and June 12. Alan E. Jeffreys, *Michael Faraday: A List of His Lectures and Published Writings* (New York, 1961), p. 47.

6. In 1849, Faraday would attempt, and fail, to convert gravitational into electromagnetic force. L. Pearce Williams, *Michael Faraday* (New York, 1965), pp. 466–470.

7. Henry met Edward Solly, Jr., in England in 1837. *Henry Papers*, 3:249–250.

8. Solly quit scientific research about 1849 to become a director of the Gresham Life Assurance Society. *DNB*.

9. Thomas Graham was professor of chemistry at University College, London. He, too, had met Henry during the latter's visit to England in 1837. *Henry Papers*, 3:324n.

10. During the middle third of the nineteenth century, electricity became an accepted agent in medical therapy, diagnosis, and experimental physiology, with German and French physicians taking the lead. The surge of interest in the application of electricity for medical purposes during this period was fueled by the availability of reliable sources of electric currents, thanks to the magneto-electric and electromagnetic machines which appeared in the wake of the work of Henry, Faraday, and others. Electrotherapy did not became popular among American physicians until the 1860s. Margaret Rowbottom and Charles Susskind, *Electricity and Medicine: History of Their Interaction* (San Francisco, 1984), pp. 55–113.

For Henry's long-continuing interest in electro-physiology, see *Henry Papers*, 2:90–96.

94. FROM ROBERT M. PATTERSON

Philadelphia.
Aug. 25, 1847.

My dear Sir,

A Church in Kensington has lately been destroyed by lightning, though armed with a lightning-rod.[1] The fire is ascribed to the circumstance that the rod passed in its course, particularly at the upper part, through wood. This explanation is consistent with the laws of dynamic induction, as illustrated by your own experiments, and is probably the true one; though there must have been some other reason why the rod did not perform its appropriate function, and suffered itself to be struck at all.

Now the occurrence in question has given great uneasiness to our City authorities, because the rod in the steeple of the venerable old State-house[2] passes through wood for a considerable part of its course. The upper part is attached to a bar of iron, enclosed in, and supporting, the uppermost member of the steeple; and the rod, in its course down, is often surrounded by wood.

I have been consulted on the subject; and this morning, Mr. Peale,[3] Mr. McCulloh,[4] and myself, made an examination into the circumstances of the case. I have already mentioned those immediately connected with the rod. I have now to state that there is a large gas-pipe rising nearly to the top of the steeple, and (of course) connected, at the earth, with all the great leading pipes in the city.

Now there are three courses which may be taken.

1st. To retain the present rod, and to attach to it, at the top of the wood-work, and outside of it, another rod to be carried down 'till it can be connected with the gas-pipes, which light the clock-faces at night. There would thus be two rods connected with the point, and one of them, at least, would have a perfect connexion with the earth. Might we not, in this case, depend upon the electricity being carried quietly away, and the rods never being struck.

2. The same course as above might be taken, but the present rod to be interrupted wherever it is practicable, by removing its accessible parts. There would then be virtually but one rod, principally of gas pipes, which, however, are, in several places, surrounded or nearly surrounded by wood.

3. The old rod to be interrupted as above, and a new rod to be carried

171

all the way down to the earth, on the outside of the steeple. This would be very difficult, and very expensive.

Be so kind as to let me know your views on this subject. The destruction of Independence Hall would be an evil felt by the whole American Nation, and forever to be regretted.[5]

When will you visit Philadelphia?

Your sincere friend,
R. M. Patterson.

Prof. Henry.

I have no news to give you regarding the Professorship of Chemistry. As at present advised, I shall vote for your friend;[6] but there will be many to prefer Dr. Rogers because he has the reputation of being a more eloquent lecturer. It has been asserted that Dr. T. is wanting in the copia verborum, and it has even been said that he has to read the explanations of his own experiments. This I know to be untrue; and I have also been assured that he is happy in his mode of lecturing, while Dr. R. is theatrical.

Henry Papers, Smithsonian Archives.

1. St. Paul's Lutheran Church was struck on July 25, 1847. *Philadelphia Public Ledger,* July 26, 1847; *Pennsylvania Inquirer and National Gazette,* July 26, 1847.

2. Independence Hall.

3. Franklin Peale.

4. A former student of Henry's, Richard Sears McCulloh was melter and refiner at the United States Mint in Philadelphia. *Henry Papers,* 3:83n–84n.

5. During the summer of 1847 the lightning rod on Independence Hall was adjusted, but there is no direct evidence of Henry having provided expert advice. *Philadelphia Daily News,* August 28, 1847.

6. John Torrey.

95. TO GEORGE MIFFLIN DALLAS

Princeton August 27th, 1847.

The Hon: George M Dallas
Vice President of the United States.
Sir,

Since the date of my letter[1] to you on the subject of the fixture proposed to be erected on the top of the Capitol, Mr Crutchett has visited me, for the purpose of giving a more definite account of his plans.[2] He informs me, that the gas pipe does not pass through the axis of the mast, as I was led to suppose from the previous accounts, but along a groove in the outside; and also, that he has concluded to change the intended ~~deviation~~ ↑direction↓ of the same pipe in its course from the lower part of the mast to the ground; carrying it down on the outside of the building, instead of conducting it through the interior, as was first proposed.

With these arrangements, provided the iron braces of the mast are in metallic contact with the tube, and the groove be open on the outside to the air, I ~~see but little~~ ↑see no↓ objection to the proposed means of protection. (I think it proper, however, to again express the opinion, that no protection which human foresight can suggest, will render the building as safe as one on which there is no increased tendency of the electricity to descend.^A

It may also be proper for me to say, that though my impressions of the propriety, and value of the plan proposed by Mr Crutchett for lighting the grounds of the Capitol are not very favourable, and though I would have discouraged the appropriation of money for the purpose had my advice been asked, yet now that the apparatus is completed, I would not say that it should not be, at least temporarily, put up, in order that the effect as to appearance, lighting, &c. may be seen, and the data thus furnished for ascertaining whether the value of the results more than balance the objections to the fixture. In deciding how this question, the mechanical effect of this experiment on the stability of the dome, should be considered.[3]

I have the honor to be
With much respect
Your Obt. Servant

~~Hon George M Dallas~~
~~Vice President of U.S.A.~~

Draft, Henry Papers, Smithsonian Archives.
In unknown hand with second interlineation by Henry. Variant draft in same hand, signed by Henry, in same location, has different wording for the last sentence of second paragraph and lacks the final paragraph.

1. Doc. 89.
2. Henry also had another visitor in regard to Crutchett's system: Benjamin B. French, who saw him in Princeton on August 24 "about the aptitude of lightning to strike our mast & stave the Capitol all to atoms & kill Congress at a lick." Showing Henry "all our plans, drawings &c," French persuaded him that "he was all out in his calculations, & now the mast will go up." French to Henry Flagg French, August 26, 1847, B. B. French Papers, Library of Congress.
3. After receiving Henry's letter, Dallas apparently approved the installation of the mast

and lantern atop the Capitol dome, with the modifications Henry recommended. Henry's prediction that the mast would attract lightning was soon borne out, however, as within a month after the erection of the mast, a bolt struck and perforated a copper-gilt ball atop the lantern, though without injuring the dome itself. According to Benjamin B. French, the exterior iron pipe conveying gas from the holder to the burners worked as Henry said it would, safely directing away the charge.

Henry, "On the Forms of Lightning-Rods," AAAS *Proceedings*, 1850, 4:40; Henry, "Atmospheric Lightning," Part V of "Meteorology in

Its Connection with Agriculture," *Report of the Commissioner of Patents for 1859: Agriculture* (Washington, 1860), p. 508; French to Clement L. West, December 9, 1863, typescript copy,

File "Lighting-Gas, Crutchett's Lantern 1847–1848," Art and Reference Library, Office of the Architect of the United States Capitol.

96. FROM HENRY O'REILLY[1]

Cincinnati, Sept. 2. 1847.

Professor Henry, Princeton:

Dear Sir—The freedom with which you conversed on Telegraphic subjects when I was favored with your remarks on a visit to the Telegraph office in Philadelphia, as well as the nature of the subject involved, induces me to forward to you a copy of a Circular[2] which is wrung from me by the wrongs & outrages to which I have been subjected by the controllers of Morse's Patent—Mesrs F. O. J. Smith[3] & Amos Kendall.[4] Your remarks to Prof. House,[5] & to the Superintendant of the New York & Wash. Telegraph (Mr Zook)[6] who lately conversed with you & asked your opinion, as well as what was understood respecting your opinions when you reported along with Mr Welsh,[7] seemed to justify an allusion to your opinions;[8] and I trust that I have not mentioned your name in any way that can be unpleasant to a friend of truth & Science. Professor House is now here; & we hope to work his Telegraph to Pittsburg to-night—370 miles; which will show whether it will work on a long line or not; & the first despatch shall be sent by me to you, if all works as we believe it will. Hoping you will excuse this freedom,

yours truly,
Henry O'Rielly

Henry Papers, Smithsonian Archives.

1. A newspaper editor, O'Reilly (or O'Rielly, 1806–1886) became a contractor for the Morse telegraph in 1845, agreeing to establish service between the East Coast and the Mississippi River Valley and the Great Lakes. O'Reilly organized the Atlantic, Lake & Mississippi Telegraph Company later that year. In November 1846, the Morse patentees declared the contract with O'Reilly void. Litigation followed, in which O'Reilly was victorious. In addition, in the fall of 1847, O'Reilly proposed building a telegraph line from Louisville to New Orleans, a line not covered by his Morse contract, using the Columbian telegraph. When Morse forces

subsequently sued, claiming that the Columbian telegraph infringed upon the Morse patent, O'Reilly called upon Henry for a deposition on the history of the telegraph. *DAB; Smithsonian Report for 1857*, pp. 90, 107–117; Robert Luther Thompson, *Wiring a Continent: The History of the Telegraph Industry in the United States, 1832–1866* (1947; New York, 1972), pp. 70–93, 146–161; Doc. 332.

2. Presentation copy of Henry O'Rielly, "Progress and Results of Electric Discovery, with Special Reference to Telegraphing," September 1, 1847, in same location as this letter. O'Reilly's circular attacked Morse's efforts to

monopolize the telegraph industry in the United States. It offered a prize of $300 for the best essay on the topic of the "Progress of Electric Discovery, with Reference to the Telegraphic System." It was reprinted in the *American Railroad Journal*, 1847, 2d ser. *3*:659.

3. Francis O. J. Smith was one of Morse's partners. *Henry Papers, 4*:181n.

4. Amos Kendall (1789–1869), a journalist and member of Andrew Jackson's "Kitchen Cabinet," became Morse's business agent in 1845. *DAB*.

5. Royal Earl House was the inventor of a printing telegraph. In 1850 Henry provided a deposition on behalf of House against charges of infringement of the Morse patent. *Henry Papers, 6*:326n.

6. Samuel K. Zook (1822–1863) was co-inventor of the Columbian telegraph; Thompson describes the inventors as "telegraphic handy-men." *National Cyclopaedia of American Biography, 12*:256; Thompson, p. 154.

7. Ashbel Welch, a former student of Henry's, was an engineer who may have assisted Henry in experiments on the House telegraph. *Henry Papers, 4*:332n; *6*:327n.

8. In his circular O'Reilly wrote that

> it is but justice to say that some of the most competent judges in the Union, (such as Professor Henry.) familiar with House's as well as Morse's Telegraphs, declare that House's system does not infringe on Morse's.

97. FROM CHARLES G. PAGE

Washington DC.
Sept 7, 1847.

My dear Sir

I noticed yesterday a statement in the N.Y. Observer that the chairs of Engineering and Geology were to be filled as soon as possible, and that Prof. Horfords school was already open.[1] Have you ascertained what salaries they will pay?[2]

They will have an interesting time in Boston on the 22[d] The Geological Association, Inventors convention,[3] which I trust you will be enabled to attend and the Mechanics fair[4] are all to be held at once.

Some malicious person has attacked the S. Institution and I am glad to see the Editor of the Union[5] coming to the rescue.[6] I send the paper.

I understood a few days since that hopes were entertained that Mr Owen would again be in the Regency in Mr Rush's place. I hope not. How much better to select such a man as Mr Marsh—

Our regards to Mrs Henry and believe us

to be yours sincerely
Chas G. Page

Henry Papers, Smithsonian Archives.

1. Newspaper not found.

2. Page's biographer has argued that Page did not vigorously pursue the possibility of a position at the Lawrence Scientific School of

Harvard University. Robert C. Post, *Physics, Patents, and Politics: A Biography of Charles Grafton Page* (New York, 1976), p. 80.

3. A reference to the Third Annual Conven-

tion of Inventors, which convened on September 22. The group, which had met in previous years in New York and Philadelphia, was lobbying for amendments to the patent laws which would streamline the patent system and make it more efficient. *Boston Courier,* September 20, 1847; Steven Lubar, "The Transformation of Antebellum Patent Law," *Technology and Culture,* 1991, *32:*950.

4. A mechanics' fair, with nine thousand items on display, opened in Faneuil Hall on September 21. *Boston Courier,* September 21, 1847.

5. Thomas Ritchie (1778–1854), editor of the *Washington Union* from 1845 through 1851. The newspaper had been established as an organ of the Polk administration. *DAB.*

6. The issue of the paper Page refers to has not been found, but the article in question was reprinted in the *Washington Weekly Union,* September 11, 1847. The *Union* had reprinted an article from the *Rochester Daily American* of September 1, entitled "Abuse of the Smithson Gift," which accused the Smithsonian of a "perversion of a trust" by wasting the Smithson legacy. According to the Rochester newspaper, the Smithsonian Building would cost half a million dollars, with the remainder of the funds being spent on old books. For evidence, it cited a London newspaper which claimed that the Smithsonian had just purchased an old Bible for five hundred dollars.

Below the reprint of the Rochester article, the *Union* defended the Smithsonian. It rejected the story of the Bible purchase, relying upon information supplied by "a distinguished member of the Smithsonian Institute." The paper also pointed out that the building would cost less than half the sum mentioned by the *Daily American* and would be paid for out of the interest, not the principal.

98. TO JOHN TORREY

Princeton Sept 8th 1847

My Dear friend

I am sorry to be the bearer of bad news. Rogers is elected.[1] The scale was turned by the action of the faculty; all the members of which except Dr. Hodges[2] went strongly for him. Dr Wood with Dr. Horner[3] went around as I am informed, with Rogers to the members of the Board advocating his claims. Rogers operated through the younger members of the Profession. His poverty in opposition to your reputed wealth was also turned to his advantage.

I had strong hopes that the election would be postponed until a letter from Dr. Skinner[4] of New-York might be made to operate on the board through Dr. Barnes[5] who was out of town.

Dr. Potter[6] was not in the city yesterday but arrived shortly before the meeting of the Board. I saw him at about 5 O'clock and left him believing that he would vote for you. I found however that a strong effort had been made to engage him for Rogers.

The truth of the case is that while your claims have rested on your merits as a man of science and character those of Rogers have been pressed by means more efficient than just. I allude to the statement as to your manner of lecturing. I hope my dear friend that this decision unrighteous as it is may be over ruled for good and that it will redound to your final benefit. I am sure it will meet with the reprobation of all the men of true science in our country.

Most sincerely and
affectionately
I remain your
Friend
J.H.

1. J. B. Rogers was selected for Hare's professorship in the University of Pennsylvania Medical School.

2. Hugh L. Hodge, a Princeton graduate, was professor of obstetrics at the University of Pennsylvania. *Henry Papers*, 2:241n.

3. William E. Horner.

4. Thomas Harvey Skinner (1791–1871) was a New School Presbyterian clergyman. *DAB*.

5. A trustee of the University of Pennsylvania, Albert Barnes (1798–1870) was a prominent New School Presbyterian theologian. *DAB; Catalogue of the Trustees, Officers, & Students of the University of Pennsylvania, Session 1846–47* (Philadelphia, 1847).

6. Alonzo Potter, bishop of Pennsylvania for the Episcopal Church and an acquaintance of both Henry's and Bache's, was a trustee of the University of Pennsylvania. *Henry Papers*, 5:353n; 6:322n, 539; *Catalogue . . . of the University of Pennsylvania, Session 1846–47*.

99. FROM HENRY M. ALEXANDER[1]

New York, September 11. 1847
11 Nassau Street.

My dear Sir,

In this country, and especially in our city where every body seems to be looking about, to see where they can make money, the thought has often struck me that a silent connexion with a well established and respectable newspaper could be made not only profitable but agreeable and useful. Not that I would think for an instant of giving up my profession for such work; but simply to use the facilities thrown in my way to increase my receipts, by work done at leisure moments. I should never think of connecting myself with a paper as a political writer, and I do not consider my talents and acquirements suited to the part of a literary contributor. But in looking at the papers of the day, it has struck me that a person, if he would prepare himself by a course of study and general reading upon the subject of Internal Improvements, using that term in its widest sense as embracing the advances made in the Mechanical Arts, the examination[A] of new inventions with their relations to scientific discovery &c, he could occupy a place in our <u>daily</u> journals now entirely unoccupied— I am constantly surprised, (and if I am how much more men of real scientific knowledge,) with the ignorance displayed, whenever such discussions are attempted by our Editors, who upon their usual "beats" exhibit much talent and acquirement— I have been so much impressed with this idea—the money-making first, and after that the improvement to myself and, I flatter myself, improvement to the public, that I have been induced to trouble you upon the subject to ask your advice and opinion in reference to it.

In this City where the division of labour is becoming every day more & more apparent; (as for example the division professional men make in the different branches of their own profession, and down to the division made by Shoemakers into Ladies Shoemaker & Gentlemens Shoemaker—) we find the different parts of an Editors duty devolving on different men. This is eminently the case in our great papers. Now do you not suppose that such a branch as I have mentioned could be made of much interest and somewhat useful if conducted properly and knowingly? And if so, may I venture to trouble you to give me your views on the subject. I could not ask advice & counsel of a person who knows so well as yourself how little qualified I am for such a task. You know that excepting a little general information, which I owe solely to yourself, my qualifications are o. But I feel that with some study, which my inclination prompts me to undertake without a pecuniary stimulus, I could at least do better, than the grossly ignorant attempts which we now see.[2]

Will you then, if your engagements permit, write to me not only on the probable success such matters would have in interesting readers generally; but also, in case your opinion should be favourable what course one should pursue to enable him to be successful— I do not intend that a set article, one following another like an essay, should be published, but that when called out by constantly occurring facts, whatever is said should be said knowingly. I have an article, which I will show you, which I cut from a New York paper which says "that Prof Morses discovery of the new style of electrical machine does him no more credit than the apparatus for writing, the ideas conveyed by the wires"— This is a gross case, but it stands for a class of the articles I have referred to. If I was prepared I do not think it would be difficult for me to get employment.

I wished to see you when I was in Princeton but was prevented by the illness of my sister,[3] and left before I could call. I trust you will pardon the trouble I give you— I do not for a moment believe that you ~~could~~ ↑will↓ think science could be advanced in the minutest degree by such work & such an agent; it is that I believe you feel some interest in me as a friend and pupil, although in the latter relation doing you so little credit, ~~& this it is~~ which emboldens me to trouble you

> I am with much respect & affection
> H. M. Alexander.

It may be ~~necessary~~ ↑proper↓ to say that I am succeeding in my profession beyond my expectations. I look at this matter as additional. And if you consider it impracticable I beg that you will have no hesitation in plainly saying so. The subject of Political Economy has been suggested to me. I do not fancy the study and I have dry work enough in my professional studies without occupying my leisure in this way: At your suggestion I have been studying Hitchcoks Geology,[4] although from the necessity of learning, out of the book, the immense number of incomprehensible terms, the work has been uphill, though far from unpleasant. I now feel in its full force the loss of the time I wasted in College— Had I but half improved my advantages I should be in possession of a respectable education. Until I came under your direction I cannot recollect of ever having possessed an idea— This is no exaggeration, but my serious opinion— I mean that I had never once thought for myself on any one subject— I speak thus freely to you, as you have always advised with me on the subject, and I trust not without effect.

Henry Papers, Smithsonian Archives.

1. A former student of Henry's, Alexander was a lawyer in New York City. *Henry Papers,* 6:337n.

2. Nineteenth-century newspaper accounts of science generally fell into three categories: long articles (including the texts of public lectures), news accounts, and fillers of miscellaneous information. Medicine, meteorology, and astronomy were the favorite topics. The quality of newspaper reporting of science declined in the late nineteenth and early twentieth centuries, reaching its nadir around World War I. At least part of the cause of the low quality was the ignorance of journalists about the topic. It was not until the 1920s that Alexander's vision of science journalists became a widespread reality. John C. Burnham, *How Superstition Won and Science Lost: Popularizing Science and Health in the United States* (New Brunswick, 1987), pp. 37, 41, 139–141, 153–155, 172–175.

3. Janetta Alexander. Hageman, *Princeton,* 2:347–348.

4. Edward Hitchcock, *Elementary Geology* (Amherst, 1840). This was the principal geology textbook in antebellum American colleges. Stanley M. Guralnick, *Science and the Ante-Bellum American College* (Philadelphia, 1975), p. 109.

100. FROM EDWARD SABINE

Spa in Belgium September 11th 1847

My dear Sir

I am most happy to learn that your sphere of usefulness has been extended, and in the prospect which presents itself to me of more frequent and intimate communication with you.[1] I will most readily undertake the superintendence of the provision of instruments which will be required for the magnetic surveys. The Dip Circle is a straight forward matter, and I write to order it at once; it should be of the improved construction, of which one has been sent to Professor Heily[2] of Waterville College, and furnished with a pair of needles for observations of the (relative) total force upon the statical method of D[r] Lloyd, which is particularly suited to surveys, such as you propose where the dip is considerable, and the Country tobe surveyed does not include consider-able differences of force.[3] In respect to the other instruments, i e that for absolute Horizontal intensity and Declination, I prefer to wait until my return to England before I order it; and indeed I should be glad to hear from you before I decide on the size of the Theodolite. If as I at present understand from your letter the survey is tobe magnetical and geological, such astronomical determinations as will be required, viz, for the regulation of the Chronometers, and for the determination of the true meridian, will I suppose fall on the magnetic observer; in which case it will be desirable to substitute for a Theodolite, an altitude and Azimuth Instrument of the necessary dimensions, or what I should myself greatly prefer, an universal Instrument,[4] such a[s is] made in Germany, and is desc[ribed both in dim]ensio[n and price in Ertels cata-logue[5] in the Astron. Nach[n] of Schumacher (the most convenient] and portable size costs about £45.) The process of determining the latitude and time, and of fixing the true azimuth of some distant point in the horizon with this Instrument is extremely simple, and may be carried to any degree of accuracy; it is also quite competent to the determina-tions of the longitude by the Moon culminating stars,[6] a method easily acquired, and requiring no tedious previous or subsequent calculation, and would refer to Washington Observatory, where no doubt the transit of the moon and accompanying stars are regularly observed.[7] With such an instrument I should prefer a delicate azimuth compass[8] to a Decli-nometer: placing its stand in the alignment of the distant object, and observing its magnetic bearing at the hours of the day when the diurnal variation passes through its mean, and either correcting or rejecting altogether observations on days known by the records of either the

Washington or the Toronto Observatory[9] tobe those of considerable magnetic disturbance. The stand of the Azimuth compass should be sufficiently distant from the Theodolite or Universal Instrument tobe free from its disturbing influence, and is known tobe in the alignment by being seen at the centre wire of the telescope. The Instruments thus described determine the magnetic elements, the latitude, and occasionally the longitude, in a single day, and by a single Observer without much effort: but I should strongly recommend, that in addition to the statical observations of the total force, the time of vibration of the magnets of the absolute Horizontal force Instrument should also be observed on the same stand that the dip circle is used, and in an apparatus similar to that of Hansteen's.[10] The magnetic moment of these magnets should be well determined (by experiments of vibration and deflection combined) at a base station before and after a journey, also if the journey is tobe of long continuance and to include halts of long duration, the deflecting apparatus may itself be carried, and the magnetic moment re-examined on such occasions; otherwise ↑by↓ taking three such magnets, and vibrating one two or three (as time may suit) at each station, they will prove a valuable accompaniment[A] to the statical needles, but without overcharging the observer, or employing him when travelling in determinations which are better made at a fixed station. Having thus submitted to you the scheme of Observation which appears to me most likely to suit, and the Instruments which it will require, I shall be glad to learn from you what variations may be suggested by your better knowledge of the persons likely tobe employed, and the opportunities they are likely to have—also whether you will require one or two such equipments; I apprehend the cost of each will be certainly under £150. If you write soon after the receipt of this letter, I shall hope tobe able to send you all the instruments in the course of the winter, so that there may be proper time to practice with them before the spring operations ↑commence.↓

The investigation of the phenomena of the great American storms is, without doubt, an undertaking most worthy ↑of the↓ Smithsonian Institution and the execution of the plan suggested by Mr Loomis can scarcely fail to lead to a discovery of their laws— But in order to give full efficacy to that plan you should have the co operation of British observers in Canada and the Provinces to the north and west of Canada: Mr Loomis's investigations have already shewn that such concurrence is essential to a complete investigation. You will have it readily if you will ask for it.

After your own plan is formed, an application may be made through

M[r] Bancroft[11] from your Government to ours, stating that such a plan has been organised in the united States for the investigation of the laws of those great American storms of which the cause may be briefly noticed, that to render the investigation complete and successful the cooperation of the Government of Great Britain is necessary in causing similar Observations tobe made in the British provinces to the north of the united states—and that the Government of the United states has the more readily permitted itself to make this application, from the example which has been so recently given by the Government of Great Britain in requesting the cooperation of other Countries in magnetical and meteorological researches with which request the Government of the United States had great pleasure in complying.[12] I have thus roughly sketched the form of application which we have found successful both in obtaining the good offices of our Government and of others through it. If you can accomplish such an application on your part, I have no doubt of its success with us;[13] nor of our being able to organise an extensive and sufficiently numerous co-operation East of the Rocky mountains and north of the latitude of 45°.

> I remain, my dear Sir
> Very sincerely yours
> Edward Sabine

Professor Joseph Henry
Princeton
New Jersey

Retained Copy, BJ3/30, Copies of Correspondence to and from Magnetic Dept. re Domestic and Foreign Observatories, 1841–59, Sabine Papers, Records of Kew Observatory, Public Record Office, London.

In unknown hand. Bottom of first sheet torn; supplied material taken from partial copy in an unknown hand with a file notation of September 1847, Henry Papers, Smithsonian Archives. A complete copy in the same hand, which varies from Sabine's retained copy, is in the Bache Papers, Smithsonian Archives. A partial copy is in Letters Received, Records of the Smithsonian Meteorological Project, Records of the Weather Bureau, RG 27, National Archives. Reply: Doc. 161.

1. Sabine is responding to Doc. 91.

2. George Washington Keely (d. 1878), professor of mathematics and natural philosophy at Waterville College (now Colby College). *Third General Catalogue of Colby College, Waterville, Maine* (Waterville, 1909), p. 12.

3. Ten years earlier, in another context, Sabine had recommended Humphrey Lloyd's method to Henry "as being more easily used and in high altitudes more correct." *Henry Papers*, 3:313. For a description of Lloyd's method, see *Henry Papers*, 3:275–276.

Lloyd was a senior fellow at Trinity College, Dublin, where he ran a terrestrial magnetic observatory which served as a model for other observers. *Henry Papers*, 3:239n.

4. Altitude and azimuth instruments allowed the observer to measure both the altitude and azimuth of a star at the moment of transit. Portable versions of such instruments were called "universal instruments." Although too inexact for serious astronomical research, these instruments were quite adequate for the purposes described by Sabine. William Chauvenet, *A Manual of Spherical and Practical Astronomy*, 2 vols. (Philadelphia, 1863), 2:315, 319.

5. We have not been able to identify the catalog referred to by Sabine. However, a contem-

porary catalog of T. Ertel and Sons lists five universal instruments of differing dimensions and price. *Catalogue des instruments d'astronomie et de mathématique de T. Ertel & Fils à Munich* (Munich, 1843).

6. The observer times the crossing of the meridian by both the moon's limb and a star in the same telescopic field of view. The difference in time between the two crossings is noted and compared to the same observations at another site. From that comparison, the difference in longitude of the two observing sites can be calculated. This was a widely practiced and fairly accurate method. W. T. Brande, ed., *A Dictionary of Science, Literature, and Art* (New York, 1843), pp. 687–688.

7. Although lunar and stellar transits were observed at the Naval Observatory, the usefulness of these observations was questionable. The 1847 observations were not published until 1853; those of 1848 in 1856.

8. The azimuth compass was simply a compass fitted with sights. According to Riddell, azimuth compasses were recommended for magnetical observations at sea and in situations where portability was important. Peter Barlow, *A New Mathematical and Philosophical Dictionary* . . . (London, 1814), s.v. "Compass"; C. J. B. Riddell, *Magnetical Instructions for the Use of Portable Instruments Adapted for Magnetical Surveys and Portable Observatories* (London, 1844), pp. 7–8.

9. The magnetic observatory at Toronto, built in 1840, was part of Sabine's effort to measure global magnetic forces (the Magnetic Crusade). Edward Sabine, "Introduction," *Observations Made at the Magnetical and Meteorological Observatory at Toronto in Canada*, 3 vols. (London, 1845–1857), *1*:9–19. For the background of, discussions of American contributions to, and Henry's involvement in the Magnetic Crusade, see *Henry Papers*, *3*:303, 304n; *4*:243–244, 315–320.

10. Christopher Hansteen's intensity apparatus, which Henry had used in 1830. *Henry Papers*, *1*:290.

11. George Bancroft (1800–1891) was the American minister to Great Britain. *DAB*.

12. A reference to requests issued to foreign governments in 1845 by the British government for assistance in Sabine's Magnetic Crusade. Roderick Impey Murchison, "Address," *British Association Report for 1846*, p. xxviii.

13. The Sabine-Henry correspondence is full of references to possible official American-British cooperation for meteorological observations on the North American continent. However, Henry kept putting off the request. As Henry noted in a letter of July 4, 1852: "We have not abandoned the idea of applying to your government for cooperation in our meteorological labours but we have delayed doing so until we could offer some definite inducement for urging the request." American participation in international meteorological cooperation also became entangled in the power struggle between Henry and Bache, on one side, and Matthew Fontaine Maury, on the other, for control of American meteorology, and particularly over who would represent the United States in international science. Henry to Sabine, March 22, 1851, *British Association Report for 1851*, pp. 320–325; Sabine to Henry, September 26, 1851, Sabine Papers, BJ3/30, Copies of Correspondence to and from Magnetic Dept. re Domestic and Foreign Observatories, 1841–59, Records of Kew Observatory, Public Record Office, London; Henry to Sabine, July 4, 1852, Sabine Papers, BJ3/49, Letters to Sabine from Renwick and Henry, 1845–1853, Records of Kew Observatory, Public Record Office, London; Fleming, *Meteorology*, pp. 106–110.

101. TO EDMUND BURKE[1]

Princeton September 11th 1847.

To Edmund Burke Esq.
Commissioner of Patents
Sir.

Your communication[2] asking my opinion as to the novelty of the discovery claimed by L B Swan[3] of Rochester with reference to an improvement of the galvanic battery was received several days ago but absence from home and unavoidable engagements have prevented my giving any attention to the subject until this evening.

I do not consider the use of the solution of Sulphate of Soda in sulphuric acid as an exciting liquid for the galvanic battery a novelty; all the more common sulphates dissolved in sulphuric acid have been used for this purpose; but that this solution possesses the property of producing a more continuous action of the battery than the other compounds in use is a new fact to me, and if true, is one which may be of considerable importance in the practical application of the galvanic apparatus.[4]

The question however of the right to the exclusive use of this solution, on account of this discovery is in my opinion one of law rather than of science. It appears to me perfectly analogous to the following case. Several modern chemists have discovered the fact that certain vegetables in common use are better adapted to fattening cattle than others;[5] now on account of this discovery would these chemists be entitled by law to the exclusive use of the more valuable articles for the purposes mentioned. This is purely a question of law which from your attainments in legal knowledge you are much better qualified to answer than I am.[6]

> With much respect I have the
> honor to be your very
> Obt. Servant.

Retained Copy, Henry Papers, Smithsonian Archives.
In an unknown hand.

1. A former Democratic congressman, Burke (1809–1882) was appointed commissioner of patents in 1846. *BDAC.*

2. Not found, but dated August 23, 1847. Identical letters were sent to Robert Hare and Benjamin Silliman, Sr. U.S. House, 30th Congress, 1st Session, *Edmund Burke, on the Complaint of Thomas G. Clinton,* House Reports, No. 839 (1848), p. 79.

3. Lansing B. Swan was a druggist. He had received a patent in 1838 for a soda fountain. Rochester City Directory, 1847–1848; Edmund Burke, comp., *List of Patents for Inventions and Designs Issued by the United States from 1790–1847* . . . (Washington, 1847), p. 212.

4. Swan placed crystals of Glauber's salt (sodium sulfate) in the sulfuric acid of a Grove cell and discovered that the sodium sulfate preserved the mercury amalgam on the zinc cylinder. Instead of requiring daily restoration of the amalgam, batteries could be used for weeks at a time without additional mercury. There was an important technological application for this discovery: Grove batteries were used by the American telegraph industry, and the Rochester telegraph office quickly adopted Swan's innovation.

Even Swan's supporters conceded that he was not the first to add Glauber's salt to the sulfuric acid in a battery. His patent application was based on a different claim of priority: his discovery of the fact that the introduction of sodium into the solution led to the creation of sodium nitrate instead of mercuric nitrate, thus preserving the mercury.

Thomas P. Jones to Henry, September 10, 1847; Chester Dewey to Henry, October 1, 1847, both in Henry Papers, Smithsonian Archives; George B. Prescott, *Electricity and the Electric Telegraph* (New York, 1877), pp. 64–66; *Edmund Burke,* pp. 79–93; for a description of a Grove cell, see *Henry Papers,* 4:323–324.

5. This is probably a reference to the work of Jean Baptiste Boussingault and Eben N. Horsford on the nutritional value of different grains used as animal feed. Margaret W. Rossiter, *The Emergence of Agricultural Science: Justus Liebig and the Americans, 1840–1880* (New Haven, 1975), pp. 63–65.

6. Charles G. Page, in his role as patent examiner, twice rejected Swan's application. He denied both the novelty of the solution, citing Henry's letter among other evidence, and the chemical explanation of the process supplied by Chester Dewey on Swan's behalf. Burke, acting on the generally accepted principle that the applicant should be given the benefit of the doubt, overruled Page. A patent, limited to ap-

plications in telegraphy, was issued in December 1847. *Edmund Burke*, pp. 14–15, 79, 82–93.

In the case of the chemists and the nutritional value of certain plants, the information was not patented. Instead, chemists disseminated the knowledge through the scientific literature and educational systems. For example, the comparative nutritional values of different animal feeds was one of the topics covered in the lectures of John P. Norton at the Yale Analytical Laboratory. Rossiter, pp. 64, 112.

For a detailed discussion of Henry's views toward patent law and the relationship between the discovery of scientific principles and patents, see *Henry Papers, 1:*367–372.

102. "RECORD OF EXPERIMENTS"

September 16th 1847
Heat of the moon & heat
reflected from ice

Melloni with a large convex lens[A] has been able to exhibit the effects of heat from the moon by means of the thermo electrical apparatus see his account of the experiment in the compt Rendus for 1846.[1] The results of this experiment does not appear to me perfectly satisfactory the heat obtained in the experiment was not that of the moon—but the reflected heat of high[B] intensity which accompanies the light of the sun in its reflection from the surface of the moon. The object of the inquiry is the proper heat of the moon and is analogous to the question of the self luminosity of the moon. To determ whether the temperature of the moon is greater than that of the surrounding celestial space we must observe with the most delicate instrument the dark part of the moon and even in case an indication of temperature were obtained we could not be certain that it was not in part at least from the sun hence reflected once from the earth and again from the moon.

That the moon may be covered with ice at the temperature of celestial space and still reflect the heat of the sun is evident from the following experiment which I devised nearly or quite a year ago but which I made only to day with the assistance of Dr Schenck.[2] A piece of solid ice was smoothed on one surface—so as to form a plane mirror. On[C] this a beam of light from the sun was thrown so that it might be reflected into the end of a thermo pile. The temperature of ↑the↓ ice without the reflection was indicated by the needle and noted—the beam of light

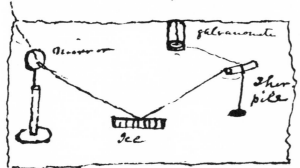

from the sun was then thrown on and the temperature again noted. The glalvanometer indicated a very considerable increase of temperature showing that ice is a reflector of heat as well as of light. If therefore the moon were cooled down below the freezing point it would still reflect the heat of the sun and the thermo electrical apparatus exposed to the light of the full moon would exhibit an elevation of temperature over that of the surrounding space.

The moon from analogy and the appearance of its surface is in my opinion a cooled body.[D] Smaller than the earth and plunged in the same medium or space the temperature of which is much below that of freezing the moon should be colder than the earth.

The kind of heat reflected from the moon is that called white heat and approximates light in its properties. We may suppose it to differ from black heat or that given off from no luminous bodies in the length or intensity of the vibrations of the ethereal medium on which the phenomena of heat are supposed to depend. In the foregoing experiment the heat reflected from the ice was that from the sun. It would be an interesting enquiry whether black heat can be reflected from ice.

The Thermo electrical telescope is susceptible of great improvement and of of great extension. The mirrors do not require the same degree of perfection of form as in the case of the light telescope because the rays are not converged to a point but to a surface of some extent namely the surface of the end of the pile.[3]

Henry Papers, Smithsonian Archives.

1. "Sur la puissance calorifique de la lumière de la lune. Extrait d'un lettre de M. Melloni à M. Arago," *Comptes rendus*, 22:541–544. For Henry's earlier thoughts on Melloni's experiment and this line of research, see *Henry Papers*, 6:536, 537n.

2. The curator of the zoological museum and lecturer on zoology, anatomy, and physiology at Princeton, John Stillwell Schanck (d.

1898) had graduated from Princeton in 1840 and the medical school of the University of Pennsylvania in 1843. *Princeton Catalogue*, p. 159.

3. Henry presented his results to the 1847 meeting of the Association of American Geologists and Naturalists. The only published version is an abstract: "On Heat," *Silliman's Journal*, 1848, 2d ser. 5:113–114.

103. TO HARRIET HENRY

Tremont House
Boston Monday
Sept 20th[–22] 1847

Dearest

I have safely arrived at this place in the midst of soucing rain. I have stopped for the night at the Tremont with the intention of going to Dr Gray's tomorrow. I arrived at stonington on board the splendid new steam boat the Vanderbildt^A at about 12 o'clock on Friday evening. Most of the passangers went on immediately to Providence but I concluded sleep on board of the boat until morning. The experiment however did not prove a very successful one. The engineer set about reparing his engine, the servants were constantly walking about and on two occasions when I was just falling asleep, I was shook by a water to know if I were not gowing on to Stonington. I was so provoked with the second shake, for I had just sunk into forgetfulness, that I caused the fellow to jump almost across the cabin by the emphatical exclamation^B of No. I passed on the whole an uncomfortable night and found in the morning that I had taken cold in my bowels and was somewhat unwell. I started in the accomodation train for Providence at about 7 o'clock and arrived in the city of Roger Williams about half past 9. After getting a poor breakfast at the Franklin House, to which I had been recommended, I started for the college to find Professor Jewett but was unsuccessful. It was concluded by some who appeared to know that the gentleman had gone to a place about 20 miles off on a courting expidition. It was certain he had done such a thing before and from the principle of the Universality of causation or that like effects are produced by like causes it was reasonable to conluded that this was the true explanation of his absence. I then called on Dr Wayland[1] the President who received me with great kindness insisted on my stopping with him and said that he had much desired to have a conversation with me particularly on account of our mutual friend Dr. Potter.[2]

I remain with him all the morning until about 3 o'clock;^C was introduced to his wife[3] a Boston lady of very pleasant manners who brought him a large fortune and enables him to live in good style and to endulge his benevolent propensities. I took dinner with him ~~after~~ and after discussing on various subjects of Science returned to my lodgings with the promise that I would return in the morng to go with the Dr. to hear him preach. While in New York Mr Bartlett of the ethnological society promised to give me a letter of introduction to Mr. Allen[4] of Providence a celebrated manufacturer and a very intelligent[D] ↑man↓. The letter however was not prepared and I promised to introduce myself. I accordingly called on the gentleman found him at home we soon became well acquainted. He had been studing all my papers on electrity and I was astonished to find in him the first person who had gone over some of the same principles of mechancs with myself— He would not hear of my returning to the Tavern but sent for my lugage and <u>nolens volens</u> kept me at his house until monday morning. I found his wife and two daughters very interesting ladies. Mrs Allen[5] is a collector of autographs a correspondent and acquaintance of Dr Sprague.[6] They over whelmed me with kind attention and on the whole I was much pleased to find myself in such good quarters; for in the middle of the night I was taken quite ill with a pain in my bowells and but for a water closit in the hall[E] adjoining my room I should have been in a bad condition. The next morning I was better but concluded to keep my bed and did not rise until about one in ↑the↓ afternoon. Dr Wayland sent me word that he was too unwell to go out and I therefore remained in the house all day lived on gruel and this morning felt quite well. I have never been more kindly entertained than by Mr. Allen and his family. He is a man of wealth and influence[F] but entirely unassuming. His daughter said she was much surprised to find her Father unusually excited and wondered who the stranger could be that thus drew him out. In the evening several persons called on me and among the number the new senator from the state.[7] Also Mr Wheaton our former minister to Germany.[8] Mr Jewett returned this morning called immediately to see me— Appears anxious to join in the business of the Smithsonian wishes to marry[9]— Dr Wayland was much taken with my plans of the smithsonian and has promised me a backing in the way of carrying ~~it~~ ↑them↓ out. Also Mr Allen approved of it entirely. Indeed I have not exhibited it to an intelligent Gentleman out of Washington who has not given it his approbation. I met Governor Marcy in New York who said that Dr Beck[10] and the people in Albany ↑were↓ very anxious to learn ↑from him↓ something of my doings but he was unable to give them any account of me.

I feel quite well this evening but as the rain a "deluge pours"[11] I have concluded not to go out ~~this~~ until tomorrow and inorder to amuse myself and get ready for the meeting I shall arrange my papers and make some notes of my communication to the association of geologists. What a contrast there is in the intilligence of the people in this part of our country and about Princeton and farther South. I was much amused on

Saturday[G] morning while riding in the ~~stage~~ cars to listen to a discussion betwen two persons on the subject of Religious progress. The whole company took an interest in the debate and amoung the number thre females put in their words while several others with exclamation and expression of countenance approved or disappoved the sentiments advanced. One of the disputants frequently illustrated his position with regard to progress by reference to Websters spellingbooks. The progression was like going from <u>ab</u> to <u>baker</u> and from the latter to [?<u>ail</u>] to be troubled.

Wednesday morning

I was all day yesterday engaged in the meetings of the association and did not get out to cambridge. Dr Gray was not at home he arrived last evening and I am to take lodgings with him for the remainder of my stay. Bache has not yet come on and I have heard nothing of him. Thus far my visit to Boston has been highly gratifying. I am engaged to dine for several days a head and this eving to take tea at Mr Lawrenc's.[12] The next evening at Dr Warrens[13] &c. Capt Wilkes[14] is here and disposed to be very attentive to me.

I am quite well this morning and I think entirely recovered from the attack of the bowell complaint of which I complained in the first part of this letter.

I dined yesterday at a gentlemans table where I met William and Dr Rogers[15] the successful candidate for the chair in the University. We were on very good terms though I had not an opportunity of telling him what I intend to do, that Dr Torrey would have withdrawn his name from the list of candidates had he known that he (Rogers) was the choise of the Faculty. Peter Lesley[16] was also at the Table and desired to be kindly remembered to you. He is about to be settled within a few miles of Boston. Professor Silliman[17] sent his kind regards to you and expressed the hope that you would be well pleased with a residence in Washington.

The association will probably continue to meet for a week and therefore I cannot say when I shall be on. I saw Dr Gray last night he had been on a visit to his Lady Love;[18] this information did not however come from him. I was yesterday introduced to Mr Hosford's wife and called the scarlet into the face and neck of the Lady by asking if she had not been a pupil of ↑the↓ Albany Female[H] academy and saying that Mr H. had been a successful lecturer on ↑an↓ other subject than that of chemestry.[19]

Kiss all the children for me. Tell will to mind the stick in his mouth[I]

189

to act the dear to you. Mary must take care of Cary and Helen of mother and mother of all.

Kind regards to Uncle James Family Nancy & all.

Family Correspondence, Henry Papers, Smithsonian Archives.

1. A Baptist minister, Francis Wayland (1796–1865) had become president of Brown in 1827. *DAB.*

2. Horatio Potter.

3. Hepsy S. Howard Sage Wayland, his second wife. *DAB,* s.v. "Wayland, Francis."

4. Zachariah Allen (1795–1882), a graduate of Brown, was a lawyer by training and an inventor and technologist by inclination. He made contributions to the textile industry, steam-engine safety, and fire insurance underwriting, and was interested in water power and its transmission. *DAB.*

5. Eliza Harriet Arnold Allen. *DAB,* s.v. "Allen, Zachariah."

6. A Presbyterian clergyman, biographer, and autograph collector, William Buell Sprague was a friend of Henry's from Albany. *Henry Papers,* 1:464n.

7. John Hopkins Clarke (1789–1870), a Whig, was a graduate of Brown. *BDAC.*

8. Another graduate of Brown, Henry Wheaton (1785–1848) was minister to Prussia from 1837 to 1846. *DAB.*

9. Jewett married Rebecca Green Haskins on April 5, 1848. *DAB.*

10. T. Romeyn Beck, principal of the Albany Academy. *Henry Papers,* 1:4n–5n, 2:54n.

11. Perhaps Henry had in mind the line from John Gay's poem (1720), "Of the Implements for Walking the Streets, and Signs of the Weather": "And when the bursting clouds a deluge pours."

12. Presumably Abbott Lawrence.

13. John Collins Warren, professor emeritus of anatomy and surgery at Harvard University. *Henry Papers,* 4:114n.

14. Commander Charles Wilkes, United States Navy, had been the commander of the United States Exploring Expedition from 1838 to 1842. In 1843, he was placed in charge of the expedition's collections and publications. *Henry Papers,* 2:87n, 5:285–286; Joye Leonhart, "Charles Wilkes: A Biography," in *Magnificent Voyagers: The U.S. Exploring Expedition, 1838–1842,* ed. Herman J. Viola and Carolyn Margolis (Washington, 1985), pp. 197–198.

15. William Barton Rogers and his brother James Blythe Rogers. The former was professor of natural philosophy and geology at the University of Virginia. He served as chairman of the Association of American Geologists and Naturalists at the 1847 meeting. *Henry Papers,* 2:194n.

16. A Presbyterian minister and geological assistant to Henry Darwin Rogers, J. Peter Lesley had attended Princeton Theological Seminary from 1841 to 1844. *Henry Papers,* 5:130.

17. Benjamin Silliman, Sr., professor of chemistry at Yale and editor of the *American Journal of Science. Henry Papers,* 1:120n–121n.

18. In May 1847, Gray became engaged to Jane L. Loring, the daughter of a member of the Harvard Corporation. They married a year later. Dupree, *Gray,* pp. 177–182.

19. Mary L. Gardiner and Horsford had married in the summer of 1847. As Henry indicated, she was a former student of Horsford's. Margaret W. Rossiter, *The Emergence of Agricultural Science: Justus Liebig and the Americans, 1840–1880* (New Haven, 1975), pp. 53–54, 73.

104. FROM MATTHEW FONTAINE MAURY

National Obsy. Wash[n] Sept[r] 20[h]/47

Sir

I beg leave to call your attention to a communication dated Washington, 1847, May 29th purporting to be from the Secy. of the Smithsonian Institution, & addressed to the Editor of the Astronomische Nachrichten. It is published under your name, Aug. 2ᵈ 1847, in Nᵒ 605, of that popular Journal. Said communication relates to a discovery made at this Obsy. with regard to the planet Neptune, in which also both my-self & office are concerned. Wherefore I request of you the favor to state whether that communciation be genuine, & if it be genuine, whether the "abstract of ↑the↓ researches" transmitted by you ↑were↓ furnished by Mʳ Walker of his own free will & accord, or at your invitation as therein stated.

Be pleased to reply at your earliest convenience & oblige

Yours &c

(signed) M. F Maury

Profʳ Joseph Henry
Secy. of Smithsonian
Institution
Princeton N.J.

Retained Copy, Letters Sent by the Naval Observatory, Records of the Naval Observatory, RG 78, National Archives.
In an unknown hand. In left margin: "Sent Duplicate Oct. 6ʰ 1847, to Washington DC." Reply: Doc. 107.

105. FROM JOSEPH BRADLEY VARNUM, JR.

New York October 2ᵈ 1847

Prof Henry
My dear Sir

I left this City some five weeks ago on an excursion to the White mountains. We were detained a long time on the way by the severe illness of my mother-in law— Scarcely had we congratulated ourselves on her recovery, and resumed our journey, before intelligence arrived of the illness of my mother, at Washington, to which place I immediately hurried; but arrived two-days after her remains had been carried to the grave. A few days after I received intelligence from this City that a dear and lovely cousin who lived under the same roof, and was to me as a sister, was dangerously ill— We hurried on but arrived too late, and we only had the satisfaction of seeing her body committed to the tomb.

Amid these severe afflictions, of course my mind has been diverted from every thing else, and my plans for publication have been deferred as to their execution— I must however say a word or two in reply to your very civil note[1] which I find upon my table— I have been apprehensive that I should put you to more inconvenience than[A] was called for by the object I had in view which was to make a brief outline of the plans which had been decided upon for the organization of the Institution. I proposed first to set-forth what had been decided upon in order to comply[B] ~~the~~ with what the Act of Congress expressly or impliedly called for—and upon this point I had taken what the Committee in their report[2] say relative to the library the museum, the chemical laboratory and the gallery of art, as containing what I supposed to be the general views on the subject—intending however to accompany it with some remarks upon the impropriety of placing a national collection, purchased with public money under the name of Smithson, and the meanness of calling upon individual funds to sustain it; with the hope that before many years an appropriation by Congress in payment of the cost of that portion of the edefice intended for the museum, and an annual appropriation, as heretofore, for its support, would justify the calling of that portion of the ~~edefice~~ ↑building↓ "the National gallery" ~~and~~ as distinctive from the "Smithsonian Institute" so that the whole might be christened "National gallery and Smithsonian Institute."

This much for the requirements of the Act— I then proposed to set forth the plan for carrying into effect the power vested in the Regents, of appropriating the rest of the funds in such manner as they should deem best calculated to fulfil the object of the testator[3]— I do not use the very words of the act; but you will know to what I allude— And here the report of the Committee was most too indefinite to furnish the information I required— Your syllabus as I understood it, first referred to the Increase of knowledge—and secondly to the Diffusion of knowledge—

Under these heads I wished to state concisely your plans, referring to such ~~portions~~ of the express requirements of the act as came under ↑one↓ or the other, and then setting forth the scheme for publication of transactions, reports and particular works.

The great apprehension which seems to be felt as to the execution of your scheme, is that the Institution will publish many things which might, without its aid, have been published by private enterprise. I wish to state, with as much particularity as possible, what guards will be resorted to against such unnecessary expenditures— During the two or three days that I spent in Washington I heard some of these difficulties enlarged upon; especially, the great danger of the Secretary and Regents' being imposed upon by experimenters in different parts of the Country, men who think they have made valuable inventions, and whose demand for means to illustrate them knows no limit— Perhaps this is more observed at Washington, where so many of these characters resort to ~~lay~~ ↑lay↓ their plans before Congress or the Patent office— I thought you misunderstood an allusion I made in my last letter[4] to the advantage of extending practical knowledge— I was thinking of the subject treated of in Mr Lawrence's letter to the University of Cambridge—the absence of knowledge by mechanics and artisans of "what has been done in their ~~various~~ ↑respective↓ departments" so that they are constantly "trying to invent what has already been invented or proved impracticable."[5] The Committee of Organization hint at something of the kind where they suggest, in connection with the museum, "complete series of models illustrating each great invention" so far as the Patent office does not already supply them.

I have informed all whom I have seen that you only want your plan to have a fair trial; and are ready to mould and modify it as experience, and the reception it meets with from the public shall suggest.

It would afford me great pleasure to see you in New York, and to advance your objects by any means in my power—

I have the honor to be
Yours very truly
J B Varnum J[r]

P S—I should be glad of any suggestions as to the best plan for presenting this whole subject in a short space.[c]

Mrs Lindsley tells me that you are in great apprehension that your health will suffer in Washington, the Princeton people having got the idea that it is "very unhealthy" an idea without the slightest foundation in fact. There have been as few deaths there in proportion to population as in any City of the Union.[6]

Henry Papers, Smithsonian Archives.

1. Possibly Doc. 63.
2. The report of Robert Dale Owen's committee of organization (*Henry Papers*, 6:557n–558n).
3. A reference to the "elastic clause" of the act. *Henry Papers*, 6:469.
4. Doc. 62.
5. Lawrence actually wrote:

Inventive men laboriously reinvent what has been produced before. Ignorant men fight against the laws of nature with a vain energy, and purchase their experience at great cost. Why should not all these start where their predecessors ended, and not where they began?

He proposed a school for young men who intended to be engineers, chemists, or men of science, "where they may learn what has been done at other times and in other countries." *Silliman's Journal*, 1847, 2d ser. 4:294–297 (quotations on pp. 294 and 295).

6. Varnum made the same claim in *The Seat of Government of the United States*, 2d ed. (Washington, 1854), p. 62, where he cited the death rate as averaging "no more than two per day in a population of twenty to twenty-five thou-

sand," which works out to a rate of 29.2 to 36.5 per thousand. Vital statistics was in its infancy in this period. Census data for 1850 yield a rate of 17.62 deaths per thousand for Washington and an average rate of just under 14 per thousand for all the states and territories listed. The author, however, considered the data highly unreliable:

> Upon the subject of the Deaths no one can be deceived by the figures of the Census, since any attempt to reason from them would demonstrate a degree of vitality and health-

fulness in the United States unparalleled in the annals of mankind, would overthrow the best established principles of statisticians, and, in coming down to details as well as in the aggregates, contradict all science and experience. The truth is, but a part of the deaths have been recorded, varying for sections from a very small to a very large part of the whole.

The Seventh Census of the United States: 1850 (Washington, 1853), pp. xl, xli (quotation on p. xl).

106. FROM SAMUEL TYLER[1]

Frederick, Marylan[d]
The 7[th] Oct. 18[47][A]

My dear Sir.

In the last number of the North British R[eview] in an Article on Photography, I find the following remark [...] "The electro-magnetic power, which speeds over the globe the te[le]graphic message, will carry the name of Wheatstone to its most distant terminus whether in space or time."[2] I have seen the same remark uttered again and again by European writers. Now, I have always thought that the discovery here attributed to Wheatstone, should be credited to you on the scroll of fame. Will you be so good, as to inform me how the fact is? I wish justice done to you, and scientific history vindicated, in this matter of the discovery of the principles and their applications, on which the magnetic telegraph is f[ixed.][B] I will therefore esteem it a great favour, if you will tell me what are your claims. &c.

I read with much interest in a late number of Silliman's Journal of Science and the Arts, your paper on the meteorological disturbances of the magnetic telegraph.[3] I had seen views of the subject very different from yours, ascribed to Prof: Olmstead of New Haven, which struck me as so absurd, that I remarked to a friend, that if such were really Prof: O's views, ~~then~~ he should no longer be considered a competent interpreter of nature. Since then, I have seen that Prof: O. den[ied] that he is the author of the article con[taining] that [...].[4]

I am glad to see that your have begun the pub[licatio]n of the Smithsonian papers. I allude to the researches [on] the antiquities of our western country. It is an excellent plan you are employing, to refer matters for publication, to societies or individuals distinguished for a knowledge of the subjects, before you accept them for publication. This plan [?brings] into your aid the whole science and literature of the [cou]ntry and is therefore much more efficient and capa[ble] than a mere standing committee of examination connected immediately with the Smithsonian Institution. And besides, it gives a diffusiveness to the operations of the Institution, which comports with its great design. The plan therefore seems to me, to be founded upon a very enlightened expediency.

I have been grieved, to see it stated at various times in the public prints, that you were about to resign your place in the Smithsonian Institution. I should [view]ᴮ such a result as a great calamity to the scientific world. I do believe, that in your hands <u>unfettered by conceited sciolism</u>, the Institution will fulfil the high behests of its founder. And I do further believe, that in the hands of no other man in our country, can the Institution maintain the scientific honor of the nation. I do [h]ope therefore, that you may not be compelled to resign the reins into the hands of some Phaeton of science.[5] I feel a patriotic pride in the science and letters of my country. And I am often mortified at the miserable charlantantry of many of our publications. The American publishers often disgrace the country by employing men to [ed]it and a[nnota]teᴮ European works, who show by almost every note that they are the merest tyros in knowledge. [...] really seen some books intended by their authors for the [g]eneral reader, filled with such gross ignorance by the American editors, as to be fit only to light a fire. I will give as an example one of Prof: Nicol's astronomical works, republished by some one in New York.[6] I looked over it a year or two ago, and would have thr[own] it into the fire, though it was not mine, if every [...] of the American edition could have been thereby distroyed. Could your Institution take any step to have this enormous evil corrected? Our booksellers are absolutely sowing error in physical science broadcast over the land.

I was in Washington City for two weeks in July last, and hoped to have met you there. When will you take up your residence there? I should have been at Printon at the Semi-centenial celebration, if it had been practicable. I have remembered with much pleasure our meeting in Phil'a, and as I value above all things whatever enlarges the sphere of the heart, I hope to renew and consolidate by future meetings, an acquaintance that has filled me with such friendly regards.

In all truth I am sincerely yours &c
Sam<u>l</u> Tyler

Prof: J. Henry
P.S. Please remember me to Prof: Hodge.[7]

Henry Papers, Smithsonian Archives.
The letter is torn at its outer edge at the top, at two places in the middle, and at the bottom.

1. A lawyer and author of philosophical works, treatises on law, and biographies. *Henry Papers*, 6:560n.

2. *North British Review*, 1847, 7:454–504, quotation on p. 466. The anonymous essay, authored by David Brewster according to Walter E. Houghton, ed., *The Wellesley Index to Victorian Periodicals, 1824–1900*, 3 vols. (Toronto, 1966–1979), 1:670, reviewed eight works on photography and light. The quotation is from the introductory paragraphs, in which Brewster wrote that while many inventions and discoveries emerge gradually from the contributions of several individuals and thus have obscure origins, others are indelibly associated with one particular name, such as the laws of planetary motion with Kepler, universal gravitation with Newton, and the telegraph with Wheatstone.

3. "On the Induction of Atmospheric Electricity on the Wires of the Electrical Telegraph," *Silliman's Journal*, 1847, 2d ser. 3:25–32, which was taken from the APS *Proceedings*, 1843–1847, 4:260–268.

4. We have not identified the article, which was presumably anonymous as Tyler says the views were "ascribed" to Olmsted and that

Olmsted denied authorship. Denison Olmsted (*Henry Papers*, 1:274n) was professor of natural philosophy and astronomy at Yale. In 1846, Ebenezer Meriam wrote Henry that Olmsted "expressed the opinion that the Magnetic Wire during thunderstorms are dangerous." *Henry Papers*, 6:437.

5. The son of Helios, Phaeton drove his father's chariot recklessly and set heaven and earth on fire. Used allusively, Phaeton refers to "a rash or adventurous charioteer." *Oxford English Dictionary*.

6. Possibly Scottish astronomer John Pringle Nichol's *Views of the Architecture of the Heavens* (Edinburgh, 1837), which was published in New York in 1840 and 1842 by H. A. Chapin & Company. Although no editor is named, the American publisher added notes and a glossary. Tyler may have had philosophical differences with the editor, whose notes reveal him to be a catastrophist. Nichol himself was a progressivist.

7. Charles Hodge, Presbyterian theologian, professor at the Princeton Theological Seminary, and editor of the *Biblical Repertory and Princeton Review*. *Henry Papers*, 2:240n–241n.

107. TO MATTHEW FONTAINE MAURY

Princeton Oct 11th 1847

Dear Sir

I have just returned to Princeton after an absence of three weeks and find your letter of the 20[th] of September[1] on my table.

The no. of the periodical containing the articles you refer to has not yet been received in Princeton, and I am therefore at present unable to give you a definite answer, as to the genui[ne]ness[A] of the letter you mention. I presume however it is a copy of one which I sent to Professor Schumaker accompanying an abstract of researches on the planet neptune furnished by Mr Walker.

Several[B] months ago a memoir was deposited with me, as Secretary, of the Smithsonian Institution, by Mr Walker relative to his researches on the planet neptune and I have since received a number of communications from the same gentleman giving accounts of farther researches in the same line. All of these I have provisionally accepted, as parts of a memoir, not yet completed, to be published in the Smithsonian Contributions to Knowledge, provid[ed] a commission of Scientific Gentle-[men] chosen to examine the article shall find it worthy a place in the publications of the Institu[tion].[2]

As the publication of the entire memoir would be necessarily[C] delayed for a considerable time and as Mr Walker was desirous that his researches should be known abroad as early as possib[le] I agreed to transmit to Professor Schumaker an abstract of all the results obtained up to the time, provided, as is usual in such cases the abstract were prepared by Mr Walker himself.[D]

I see no cause of controversy between us and I regret that you have considered it necessary to adopt in your letter an unpleasant categorical form, unusual in scientific correspondance and I think uncalled for by any thing in our previous intercourse. I have not a copy of Mr Walkers abstract and am unacquainted with the grounds of your complaint. If you will be so good as to state them explicitly, and if I find I have been instrumental in doing wrong to you or your office my own sense of justice will be sufficient to prompt me to make the proper reparation. I remain very respectfully

> Your obt. serv.
> Joseph Henry

Lieut M F Maury[E]
Director of the Observatory
Washington

Box 3, Incoming Correspondence, Superintendent's Office Correspondence, Records of the United States Naval Observatory, Library of Congress.
Right margin of second page cropped. Reply: October 20, 1847, Letters Sent by the Naval Observatory, volume 2, pages 349–353, Records of the Naval Observatory, RG 78, National Archives.

1. Doc. 104.
2. Henry eventually published Walker's work on Neptune in *Researches Relative to the Planet Neptune,* [1850], SI Contributions, vol. 2 (Washington, 1851); the same volume included ephemerides for 1795 and 1846 to 1851 in appendices. The referees were James D. Graham (1799–1865, *DAB*), of the Corps of Topographical Engineers, and Stephen Alexander.

108. FROM FRANCIS LIEBER[1]

Columbia S.C.
12th October 1847

My dear Sir,

You recollect that I told you of a paper of mine on the Vocal Sounds of Laura Bridgman the Blind-Surd at Boston, as possibly fitting for the first volume of the Smithsonian Transactions.[2] Do you want it? I trust that, short as our ↑personal↓ acquaintance has been, you will have seen that the frankest and shortest way is the most agreable to me, and, as I cannot know the precise character of your Transactions or Contributions I cannot judge for myself whether the paper has its proper place there or not. On the other hand, the subject is truly American, has attracted much notice in Europe and would be proper in a first number of an American publication of comprehensive character, if, as I said before, the peculiar character of the ~~publicatio~~ Contributions admits of it. I think it does; but I may be mistaken. That I should be glad to appear in the first number, if otherwise perfectly proper, ~~need not be mentioned~~ ↑I willingly admit↓, for, it is on the one hand a matter of course, and ↑my admission↓ on the other ~~has~~ ↑hand↓ can have no weight regarding its ~~admission~~ ↑publication↓. Had I more time I would send you a copy at once, but I am very busy at present, and would not rewrite the paper unless I knew something of the probability of its admission. You will oblige me by sending me an answer as soon as possible.[3]

I have seen the building of the Smithsonian Inst. so far as completed. I hope I am mistaken, but so far the style appears to me most inappropriate. Massive turrets and battlements, taken from a time when all faught with all and each with each, seem[A] to me droll for a fabric destined for those who have buckled on the armour of Knowledge and are eminently missionaries of peace. It looked to me almost as if a community rearing a church of Christ were sapiently to select of all architectural models, that of a mosque with minarets. However, the deed is done.

When I was at Philadelphia, Mr Hodge, a gentleman who showed the most obliging kindness to me, told me that he had shown a piece of poetry of mine to his nephew, the Rev. Mr Hodge[4] of your place. Now, the poem, as I showed it ↑to↓ the elder Mr Hodge was little more than the first ~~drau~~ putting down of the thing, and on the principle that a man prefers appearing before others decently dressed and shaved, I send a copy of the rhymes ~~to~~ that you may show it to the Rev. Mr

Hodge. Donot think I set a great value on it—though I own its value has vastly increased, since Mr John L Hodge attempted to read it to me, but was repeatedly interrupted by "the rising lump in his throat"— but I merely send it because it was shown in an imperfect state. After the Rev Mr Hodge has read it, it may be destroyed and rest in peace.

The Railway Company has very promptly paid all I asked for the loss of my trunk, and I acknowledge the promptness and readiness.

Mr Preston is and looks better than I have seen him for a long time. He has happily doffed his uncouth wig and looks ten times better in his natural and white hair and with his baldness. He will not be able, he says, to attend the Smithsonian winter meeting. He sends his best regards and was delighted with the account of the impression our 12 hours' meeting had made upon me.[5]

Is it true that the Daguerotype is using in Europe for important astronomic purposes?[6]

I hartily wish government could be persuaded to make some important scientific enquiries in Mexico—enquiries which require power and means we may now possess. It would shed the lustre of Knowledge upon our gallant blades and set a stamp of civilisation, or an additional one, upon the rude work of war. You or Beach[7] ought to devise something. Is there no problem connected with light or sound, in those rarified regions, that could be solved with the help of our soldiers and only with the assistance of many men?[8] The savans of ~~the~~ Napoleon's expedition in Egypt will grace that campaign for ever.[9]

My best regards to Mrs Henry.— I have not had a copy of your sketch of the organization of the Sm I.

Most truly Yours

F. Lieber

You said something of my plan of a Statitical Board—that I ought to write to you upon it. What is it you want, and for what purpose?[10]

FL

I ought to have acknowledged the Rev. Mr Alexander's lines to me; I found them on my return here.[B]

A word in private. I thank you for your letter.[11] I would have shown my suggestions to Mr Preston, who by the way is not very well, did I not know from experience that it is very difficult to obtain papers once given to him back again, which in this case might have left to a detention beyond the time for which you want ~~it~~ the paper.

I was told—how true I donot know—that Mr Reid has little chance and that the two candidates between whom the presidency of G. College lies are Mr Hart and myself.[12] He collects testimonials![13] Is this not somewhat beyond the line? I wish to hurt no one, but I could wish that if should be apparent that Mr Ried cannot be elected and perhaps withdraw, Mr Beach would then consider whether it would or would not be conducive to the interests of the College to have me there or not.[14] So soon as I shall ascertain anything more definite regarding Mr Reid's expectation, I shall candidly write to Mr Sergeant[15] who told me that it was only on account of his obligation to vote for Mr Reid, whom he considers of course fully competent, that he does not exert himself for me. This was the import of his conversation.

You will see that this whole note is a confidential one.

I believe you may consider it certain that Mr Preston will <u>not</u> visit Washington this winter.

Once more
Very truly
F. Lieber

Henry Papers, Smithsonian Archives.
Reply: Doc. 119.

1. A German émigré, Lieber was professor of history and political economy at South Carolina College. He became a highly regarded political scientist and educator in the United States. *Henry Papers*, 2:437n.

2. Laura Dewey Bridgman (1829–1889) was the Helen Keller of the mid-nineteenth century. Left blind and deaf by scarlet fever, in 1837 she came under the guidance of Samuel Gridley Howe (*Henry Papers*, 6:371n), a pioneer educator of the blind. Bridgman became Howe's student at the Perkins Institution in Boston, where she spent the rest of her life. Confuting the conventional wisdom that such doubly deprived individuals were idiots, Laura Bridgman became "the first blind, deaf, mute in whose case systematic education had been at all successful." Howe's descriptions of her education in the reports of the Perkins Institution were picked up by magazines and newspapers here and abroad. *DAB* (quotation); Harold Schwartz, *Samuel Gridley Howe: Social Reformer, 1801–1876* (Cambridge, Massachusetts, 1956), pp. 67–90.

3. Lieber's paper appeared in the second volume of the series: *On the Vocal Sounds of Laura Bridgman*, 1850, SI Contributions, vol. 2 (Washington, 1851). He had written a book on her in 1841 but was unable to find a publisher. Schwartz, p. 88.

4. Charles Hodge.

5. In a letter of September 18, 1847, Lieber wrote his wife:

I passed one of the happiest days of my life with Professor Henry, the Secretary of the Smithsonian, at Princeton. He is one of the rarest men in the United States, a deep thinker, liberal, genial[,] candid, thirsting to learn more, and therefore inspiriting and bringing out others. We soon stood not only face to face together, but mind to mind, and even soul to soul. He treated me, I mean, my views and opinions, with great consideration, submitted his plans, adopted my amendments and wishes me in Washington. He coincides wholly with another plan of my heart—a statistical bureau and will do all he can to promote it. This is far more important than I can make it appear this moment. [Memorandum of letter (filed with September 1847 letters but sent by Mrs. Lieber to Harriet Henry sometime after Henry's death), Henry Papers, Smithsonian Archives.]

6. Lieber's comment is too vague to be able to identify what caught his interest. The possibilities photography offered to astronomy had been obvious to scientists since Arago's announcement of Daguerre's process in 1839. By 1847, a number of scientists in Europe and the United States had taken daguerreotypes of celestial bodies and events. For what had been accomplished to date, see Daniel Norman, "The Development of Astronomical Photography," *Osiris*, 1938, 5:560–594; Dorrit Hoffleit, *Some Firsts in Astronomical Photography* (Cambridge,

Massachusetts, 1950); and Deborah Jean Warner, "The American Photographical Society and the Early History of Astronomical Photography in America," *Photographic Science and Engineering*, 1967, *11*:342–347, especially p. 346.

7. Bache.

8. Henry copied Lieber's suggestions into one of his pocket notebooks (Henry Pocket Notebook [13272], pp. 15–16 of first pagination). Although the military included scientifically trained officers from the Coast Survey, the Naval Observatory, and the Topographical Engineers, we are unaware of any organized work of the kind Lieber suggested. Working in cooperation with private and institutional collectors, individual soldiers collected what they could and shipped the specimens, largely botanical, zoological, and geological, back East. Some civilian collectors, such as Augustus Fendler, a young German backed by the botanists George Engelmann and Asa Gray, accompanied Army detachments. Following the end of the war in 1848, the Mexican Boundary Survey produced a great deal of scientific data and inaugurated the "Great Reconnaissance," a series of government expeditions to explore the trans-Mississippi West. Bruce, *American Science*, pp. 202–205.

9. A group of French scientists, engineers, and artists accompanied Napoleon's 1798 expedition to Egypt. Led by Claude Louis Berthollet and Gaspard Monge, the commission founded the Institut d'Égypte and eventually published the multi-volume *Description de l'Égypte par la commission des sciences* (1808–1841). Charles C. Gillispie, ed., *L'Expédition d'Égypte: 1798–1801* (Paris, 1989), pp. 371–396; Gillispie and Michel Dewachter, eds., *Monuments of Egypt: The Napoleonic Edition . . .*, 2 vols. (Princeton, 1987), *1*:1–29.

10. See Doc. 116.

11. Not found.

12. After a delay of several years while its buildings were being completed, the Girard College for Orphans in Philadelphia was finally preparing to begin operations on January 1, 1848. "Reid" was probably Henry Hope Reed (*Henry Papers*, *4*:224n), professor of rhetoric and English literature at the University of Pennsylvania. "Hart" referred to John Seely Hart (*Henry Papers*, *2*:172n), a former tutor at Princeton who was presently principal of Philadelphia's Central High School. In 1839, Lieber had written a lengthy report for the Girard trustees which discussed European precedents and proposed an educational plan, rules, and regulations for the school. The trustees passed over these three candidates and elected Joel Jones (1795–1860, *DAB*), a Philadelphia judge and founder of Lafayette College, who resigned after only eighteen months in office. Cheesman A. Herrick, *History of Girard College* (Philadelphia, 1927), pp. 7–8, 139–140; *Henry Papers*, *4*:156n.

13. Hart solicited a testimonial from Henry in a letter of November 19 (Henry Papers, Smithsonian Archives).

14. Bache had recommended Reed. Merle M. Odgers, *Alexander Dallas Bache, Scientist and Educator, 1806–1867* (Philadelphia, 1947), p. 139.

15. John Sergeant (*Henry Papers*, *3*:535n–536n) was a leader of the Philadelphia bar, a former member of Congress, and counsel of the Commissioners of the Girard Estate. He was also Reed's uncle. It was Sergeant's legal interpretation of the Girard will that kept the institution from opening until all the buildings were completed. *DAB*, s.v. "Reed, Henry Hope"; Ernest Cunningham, *Memories of Girard College* (Philadelphia, 1942), p. 17.

109. TO JOHN QUINCY ADAMS

Princeton Oct 13ᵗʰ 1847

Hon John Quincy Adams
    Dear Sir

    Accompanying this note I send a copy of the Programme of organization of the Smithsonian Institution which I promised when I had the honor of an interview with you in Washington.[1]

You were so kind as to consent to look over the article and to give me any suggestions which might occur to you in the course of reading.[2]

I have delayed sending the article because I intended to present it to you in person; but on my visit to the north I was unexpectedly obliged to leave Boston without getting out to your residence. I regret this because some parts of the programme may require explanation and also because it would have given me much pleasure to pay my respects to you.

> I have the honor to be
> very respectfully yours
> &— — &—
> Joseph Henry
> Sec. Smith Inst.

Adams Family Papers, Massachusetts Historical Society.

1. Henry enclosed a copy of the preliminary printed version of his "Programme of Organization," promised to Adams during an interview on May 5 (Doc. 51). The copy in the Adams Papers is the only extant version of this printed draft of which we are aware. A line at the top of the first page reads *"This article is printed for a special purpose, but is not intended in its present style* [hand altered to "state"] *for the public."* A facsimile is printed as an appendix to Wilcomb E. Washburn, ed., *The Great Design: Two Lectures on the Smithson Bequest by John Quincy Adams* (Washington, 1965).

2. In a rough diary entry of October 18, Adams noted that the draft began with "General considerations which should serve as a guide in adopting a plan of organization" and then sarcastically commented that although Henry called on him last spring, "it appears however that the Institution is still to be organized." In his formal diary, he wrote:

> I suppose the Institution is already organized by an Act of Congress under which this Mr Joseph Henry has been appointed the Secretary—but he has a different plan of organization which is evidently sliding into a job.

Diary entries for October 18, 1847, from "Rubbish IV" and Adams's formal diary respectively, Adams Family Papers, Massachusetts Historical Society; both are quoted in Washburn, pp. 31–32.

110. TO FRANCIS LIEBER

Princeton Oct 14th 1847

My dear Sir

I have just returned from the north and find your letters of the 16th & 22nd of September[1] on my table. I am happy however to learn from Mr Green the Lawyer of the Rail-Way company[2] that your claims on account of the loss of ↑your↓ trunk have been allowed and that the whole affair has been amicably settled. I need not therefore write to Mr Ingersoll[3] though I could do so without trouble for I distinctly remember seeing the check handed to you and the trunk put into the baggage cars. An affair of this kind is one of the most vexatious occurrences of life. The contents of a mans trunk are in some sense a part of himself particularly when they include his letters and papers.

I have had a very pleasant time in Boston and found that that the plan of organization of the Smithsonian set forth in the Programme took well with all the gentlemen of literature and science to whom it was shown.

Accompanying this note I send you two copies of the Programme one to keep and the other to be sent back with any corrections and additions which may suggest themselves to you in the course of your reflection.

The great difficulty in the way of carrying out the plan is the want of funds. We can do but little unless the Government take the keeping and providing for of the great museum off our shoulders.

I will send a copy of the syllabus to Col. Preston and I wish you would urge him to come on. He can do more than any one else to put things in proper order as to the Smithsonian. I believe that he approves of all the views given on the first page and indeed I have used some of his own expressions in setting them forth.

The plan of offering premiums for the best publications and treatises on particular subjects is I think a good one. The term tract does not strike me very pleasantly. It is a favourit project of Mr Owen to publish Tracts prepared by persons employed for the purpose by the Institution on given subjects. This I am not in favour of; it is liable to abuse and would subject us to the charge of favouritism.[4]

Do not fail to give me any hints you may think important. I will note them down if not for present at least for future use. I shall not fail to speak with Mr. Walker[5] on the subject of the statistical bureau. You were to give me some remarks on the statistical report which is mentioned in the Programme.[6]

I received a letter from Mr. Hart yesterday[7] requesting me to furnish him with an expression of my opinon as to his character. I must give him a general expression for he was a Tutor in our college for several years and has considerable talents particularly in the executive line. The person alluded to in the letter of Professor Bache to you was Professor Reed of Phil[d] I shall[A]

I shall visit Philadelphia in a few days on my way to Washington and shall not fail to speak in warm terms of your character and acquirements. Your chance of success is I think less than either of the other two candidates for though I consider them inferior to you in reputation learning and talents yet they are on the ground and know, particularly

Mr Hart, how to "manage" the affair to best advance their interest. Mrs. H joins me in kind regards

I remain truly yours & Joseph Henry

Dr Lieber

LI 1624, Lieber Papers, Huntington Library.
Reply: Doc. 116.

1. Not found.
2. James Sproat Green was a director of the Camden and Amboy Railroad Company. Hageman, *Princeton, 1:*319.
3. Possibly Joseph R. Ingersoll.
4. In his proposed legislation for the Smithsonian in 1846, Owen envisioned the Smithsonian publishing "essays, pamphlets, magazines, or other brief works or productions for the dissemination of information among the people, especially works in popular form . . . and generally tracts illustrative of objects of elementary science and the rudiments of history, chemistry, astronomy, or any other department of useful knowledge" (Rhees, *Documents* [1901], *1:*326). Tracts are also mentioned in the original Owen committee report of December 1846, in a section presumably written by Owen: "Knowledge in these branches [physical sciences, useful arts, and public education] can be most effectually diffused by free lectures, and by brief tracts or periodicals, issued either without charge or at the lowest cost price" (*[First] Report of the Organi-*

zation Committee of the Smithsonian Institution [Washington, (1846)], p. 2). In the revised Owen committee report of January 1847, similar popular publications are mentioned but the word tract is used only in a reference to the publications of the British Society for the Diffusion of Useful Knowledge (Rhees, *Documents* [1879], p. 936). Henry may have been uncomfortable with the association of the word with religious or political propaganda.
5. Robert J. Walker.
6. In the printed draft "Programme of Organization," as an example of subjects for which research grants would be considered, Henry listed "Institution of statistical enquiries with reference to Physical, Moral, and Political Subjects" (p. 2). Under diffusion of knowledge, reports on different branches of knowledge were to include "Statistics and Political Science" (p. 3).
7. Not found. Hart wrote again on November 19 (Henry Papers, Smithsonian Archives) to renew the request.

111. TO [WILLIAM CAMPBELL PRESTON][A]

Princeton Oct. 14th. 1847.

My dear Sir: Accompanying this letter I send you a programme, which I have prepared for the Smithsonian Institution, setting forth in detail the plans which were personally adopted at the last meeting of the Board of Regents. On the first page I have given the will of Smithson, with a series of inductions from it, most of which, if not the whole, I think will meet your approbation, for some of them you will find expressed nearly in your own language.

The plan of organization, relative to the increase and diffusion of knowledge by means of publications and researches which is given in the second and third pages of the programme, has met the approbation of all the men of literature and science, to whom I have shown it, and

I have found out of Washington but one opinion, among the disinterested and intelligent, as to the impropriety of spending so large a sum on the building, and the injustice of putting the keeping of the National Museum on the Smithsonian bequest. The only difficulty in carrying out the first plan will be, the smallness of the sum which can be devoted to it, under the present arrangement. One half of the thirty thousand dollars is to be devoted to the collection and preservation of objects of nature and art, and the other half, deducting certain expenses, to the plan above mentioned. This sum will not exceed ten or eleven thousand dollars. The income ought to be at least forty thousand dollars annually, and three fourths of this sum, for the present, expended in testing the literary plan.

We can spend with great advantage to the country and the world, at least five thousand dollars annually in the publication of original experiments and memoirs. The geologists, naturalists and ethnologists of the United States cannot give to the world many of their labors, because the expense of the illustrations is too great to be encountered by any bookseller, or by ordinary scientific journals, and cannot be borne by the individuals themselves. I have already materials engaged for a quarto volume of 650 pages, of original matter, which will do honor to our country and is such I am sure Smithson himself would have approved. The first and most expensive article, is on the labors of the mound builders in the valley of the Mississippi, by two gentlemen of Ohio, who have been engaged in the exploration of the ancient remains of this part of our country, for a number of years. The cost of publication will be upwards of three thousand dollars; it is illustrated with two hundred woodcuts, and sixty quarto plates. It was referred to a committee of the Ethnological Society, of which Mr. Gallatin is President.

Mr. Smith informed you of the final agreement of the building committee, namely to introduce a clause in the contract, allowing the regents, if they think fit, to abolish the main building, or to defer the time of its erection, provided the contractor is paid reasonable damages, to be assessed by persons chosen by the Board. This clause was introduced and the situation of affairs is such that the Regents can, if on second sober thoughts, they were to do so, abolish the main building or they can put off its erection until Congress sees fit to erect it for the accommodation of the National Museum. The two wings joined together by a screen would form a symmetrical arrangement, and would be sufficient to answer our purpose for several years to come. I had a world of trouble after you left, and would gladly have abandoned the course, could I have done so with propriety. I hope you will not fail to attend the next meeting of the Board, which takes place in December. Though it may not be possible to strike out the main building entirely, yet it may be so delayed in the erection that the cost will in a great part be derived out of the interest of the two hundred and forty thousand dollars.

I am much indebted to you for the introduction to Dr. Lieber. I spent with him one of the most intellectual and pleasant days of my life, and received from him many valuable hints, with reference to the organization of the Smithsonian. I also am obliged to you for the introduction to Dr. Gibbes;[1] although I did not see him I received from him an interesting communication.

With the highest respect I remain yours.
Joseph Henry.

Mary Henry Copy, Henry Papers, Smithsonian Archives.
File note: "Draft of letter to Col. Preston."

1. Robert Wilson Gibbes. See Doc. 83.

112. TO GEORGE MIFFLIN DALLAS

Priceton Oct 16th 1847

My Dear Sir

Your letter of yesterday[1] was received last night and I hasten to answer it by the return mail.

You will probably recollect that in accordance with the plan of finance proposed by Prof Bache all the interest which had accrud up to the time of the last meeting of the board was drawn from the Treasury and invested in Treasury notes payable to your order. The money thus invested is no longer in the Treasury of the United states and cannot be drawn by a requisition as in the case of the other Smithsonian funds and hence Mr Seaton calls on you for a power of atorney.[2] I am surprised however to be informed that you have lately been called on to sign a requisition for 45 thousand dollars. I think there is a mistake in this no such requisition has been signed by me. About[A] two weeks ago you sent a requisition to me to sign for 7,500 dollars, the same sum for which you are now called upon to furnish a power of atorney. The executive committee have found out their mistake; they though I presume that the interest on the Treasury notes could be drawn in the same way ~~way~~ as the money from the treasury. Please drope me a on this point. I ~~intend to go to Washington as soon as I can get money~~

↑am myself much pressed for money to ~~pay the demands against~~ me↓ to discharge the demands against me at ~~new-york~~ ↑the north↓. I have written to Mr Seaton[3] to send me on a thousand dollars to pay the duty on apparatus now in the Custom House ↑in new york↓ and the engravers for the memoir on ethnology.

Besides my salary I am authorized by the Resolutions of the Board to draw 4000 dollars for apparatus and 1000 for the first no. of the transactions. The whole sum ↑however↓ I have ~~I have~~ thus far received is 2500 dollars the greater part of which I have expended in a bill on Paris for apparatus and in paying for the wood cuts to illustrate the publication.

I shall be obliged to remain a few weeks longer at the north before going with my family to Washington in order to attend to the engravings in new-york.

I fully agree with you in opinion as to the propriety of understanding fully the state of the accounts.[4]

The proceedings of the centennial celebration have not yet been published a copy will be sent you as soon as they are printed.[5]

Mr Walker[6] spent last evening in Princeton and I had the pleasure of inviting the faculties of the college and Theological semenary to meet him at my house. I was glad to see him looking in good health.

I have the honor to be
very respectfully
yours &c
Joseph Henry

George. M. Dallas
Vice President
USA[B]

I think of going on for a few days next week ~~or as soon as~~ to see what is ~~doing~~ going on with refer to the building &c.

Draft, Henry Papers, Smithsonian Archives.
Reply: October 19, 1847, Henry Papers, Manuscript Department, Duke University Library.

1. Joseph Henry Collection, Manuscripts Division, Department of Rare Books and Special Collections, Princeton University Libraries. Dallas wrote that he had received a request from W. W. Seaton that he give a power of attorney for the sale of treasury notes worth $7,500.

2. At its January 28, 1847, meeting the Board of Regents authorized the withdrawal from the United States Treasury of the $250,000 interest that had accrued on the principal of the Smithsonian fund. This amount, previously unproductive, was invested in treasury notes bearing six percent interest, payable semi-annually. To sell the notes required a check or warrant signed by Dallas, Henry, and Seaton, the chairman of the executive committee. Rhees, *Journals*, p. 448.

3. Henry to Seaton, May 11, 1847, General Manuscripts Collection, Department of Special Collections, University of Pennsylvania Libraries.

4. Dallas wrote on October 15 that he had asked Seaton "to let me know the state of the funds and expenditures." Expressing frustration with Seaton, he continued: "I do not exactly understand this short mode of asking for more money:—nor, altho' my action is essentially one of form, do I like being kept in the dark, when such amounts are dealing with." In his reply, he expressed satisfaction with explanations offered by Owen and Seaton.

5. *Centennial Anniversary of the College of New Jersey* (Princeton, 1848). Dallas was a Princeton graduate and had attended the celebration.

6. Robert J. Walker.

113. "RECORD OF EXPERIMENTS"

Oct 18th 1847[A]

Received to day a letter[1] from A S Williams[2] teacher Orange[B] Co N.J. an account of the windows of a house broken by a powerful discharge of lightning which must have passed at a distance for no signes of splintering or other effects to show the passage of the discharge along the building were observed.

The roofs of the dormitories at[C] the University of Virginia are covered with metal. Dr Patterson informs me that they have been repeatedly struck. The Dr himself once saw a discharge fall on a row of Dormitories and pass to the ground.

Don[3]

Henry Papers, Smithsonian Archives.

1. October 14, 1847, Henry Papers, Smithsonian Archives.

2. Alfred Smith Williams (d. 1849) graduated from Princeton in 1844. *Princeton Catalogue*, p. 167.

3. This was the last "Record of Experiments" entry until August 1, 1851.

114. TO ALEXANDER DALLAS BACHE

Princeton Oct. 19th 1847

My dear Bache

Accompanying this note I send you a copy of a letter from Col. Sabine.[1] He advises the purchase of a new instrument and I beg you will give me your opinion on the subject as soon as possible that I may write to him by the next steamer. The following is the part of my letter to him[2] which related to the instruments—namely

We shal require two sets of instruments each consisting of

October 19, 1847

1ˢᵗ From Jones

A portable magnetometer for declination and absolute horizontal intensity with theodolite and stands complete.

2ⁿᵈ From Barrows

A dip circle.

I arrived safely in Boston at 8 o'clock of the evening on the day I left you but in decending Agamenticus I bcame much heated and was afterwards chilled in the waagon and took a violent cold which has only just now left me.

When we returned to Princeton we found your Sister Mrs Walker[3] at the Hotel. She had been in this place about two weeks her children having had the hooping coughh prevented her from staying at General ↑(late (Col)↓ Cooks.[4] She remained but a few days after our return and left on Thursday ↑last↓[5] for Philᵈ Mr Walker arrived the same day in Princeton having passed his family on the way he spent a night in our village and I had the pleasure of inviting the Professors of the college and Theological seminary to meet him at my house. He appeared in excellent health and spirits and ~~appeard~~ ↑I think↓ was pleased with his visit. I regret that Drs Miller & Alexander could not come out in the evening.[6]

On my return I found a large pile of letters ~~fro~~ relative to the Smithson which I have lesened very much in altitude but which has not yet been entirely demolished. Among the ~~number~~ letters was one of a belligerent character from Maurey[7] relative to an ~~abstract~~ of a letter seen in Schumakers Journal accomping an abstract of Walkers results. ~~To his letter I gave him a temperate reply[8] and after^ closed with telling him that I could see no necssity of a contrversly betwn us and that I regretted that he had seen fit to addresse such a letter to me.~~

This letter and my answer I will shew you when we meet. I shall ~~at~~ endeavour to avoid a newspaper controversy.

I shall start for Washington the beginning of next week. I intended to go ~~on this this~~ on monday last but I have been detained on account of a draft from the smithson.

Draft, Bache Papers, Smithsonian Archives.
Mary Henry Copy: Variant copy in Folder 6, "Typed Copies of Correspondence," Box 50, Henry Papers, Smithsonian Archives, with two significant passages either not in this version or very different here. The first reads:

When I arrived in Cambridge, I found our friend Peirce not well pleased with a conversation he had with me previous to my visit to you. The difficulty, which arose from a mistake on his part was however adjusted to our mutual satisfaction . . . When I arrived in Princeton I found a letter from Dr. Davis, complaining that the committee of the ethnological society had done him injustice in placing Mr. Squier above him and lastly I received quite a belligerent letter from

Lieut. Maury, with reference to a letter of mine addressed to Professor Schumacher, accompanying an abstract of Mr. Walker's researches. So many storms made me almost call for my boots, but I believe I shall be able to stand my ground, and live through them all, and that too without much disquietude. I am resolved not to allow Maury to draw me into a newspaper controversy, and accordingly gave him a civil answer, with a small flourish towards the end, in the way of hands off. I have heard nothing from him since, though my letter was mailed more than a week ago.

The second:

My visit to Albany was quite a pleasant one, Mr.Hawley appeared quite pleased with the plans and prospects of the Smithsonian. Also Dr. Beck gave the programme his approbation and is particularly in favor of the publication of memoirs and the formation of a library, of the transactions of all the learned societies of the world.

Reply: Doc. 117.

1. This copy is in the Bache Papers, Smithsonian Archives; the retained copy is Doc. 100.

2. Doc. 91.

3. Mary Blechynden Bache Walker (1808–1873), Bache's closest sibling in age, was the wife of Secretary of the Treasury Robert J. Walker and had at least two children by this time. Leonard W. Labaree, ed., *The Papers of Benjamin Franklin* (New Haven, 1959), *1*:lxv; James Dallas, *The History of the Family of Dallas* (Edinburgh, 1921), p. 514.

4. William Cook (ca. 1801–1865) was the chief engineer of both the Camden and Amboy Railroad and the Philadelphia and Trenton Railroad. A graduate of the United States Military Academy, Cook was at this time an officer in the New Jersey militia. His wife was Robert J. Walker's sister. George W. Cullum, *Biographical Register of the Officers and Graduates of the U.S. Military Academy*, 3d ed. revised and extended (Boston, 1891), *1*:280; *DAB*, s.v. "Cook, Martha Elizabeth Duncan Walker."

5. October 14.

6. Samuel Miller (*Henry Papers*, 2:438n) and Archibald Alexander (*Henry Papers*, 2:437n–438n) of the Princeton Theological Seminary were both in their seventies.

7. Doc. 104.

8. Doc. 107.

115. TO SAMUEL FOSTER HAVEN[1]

Princeton Oct 19th 1847

My Dear Sir

In a conversation which I have just had with a gentleman who is well acquainted with Worcester, I am informed that after having visited the mounds, figured and described by Messrs. Davis and Squire, you were not well pleased with the execution of their work and that in your opinion these gentlemen have not been as thorough or as accurate in their investigations as they ought to have been.[2] If there be any truth in this statement I beg that you will give me some information on the subject. Our object is the advance of positive knowledge, and not to add to the existing stock of error. If there be any imperfections or errors in the drawings or descriptions they should be corrected and amended before the memoir is published.

The committee of the ethnological society have spoken highly of the work but I must confess that I am a little startled by what I have heard

and am very anxious to hear from your ↑self↓ withreference to the matter. We are comparatively strangers to each other so far as personal
intercourse is necessary to an acquaintance but from what I saw of you
in New York and from what I have since heard of your character I am
disposed to put full confidence in your judgement and candor.

In reference to subjects of physical Science I should have little difficulty in judging myself of the truthfulness of an article but inregard to
the character of a Memoir on Antiquities I must trust entirely to others.

Enclosed with this note I send you a printed copy of the Programme
of ↑the↓ plan of organization of the Smithsonian Institution and I beg
leave through you to present it to the ↑A.A.↓ society and to ask if it be
compatible with your rules to give me an expression of opinion as to
the character of the plan; particularly with reference to that part of it
which relates to the increase and diffusion of knowledge by means of
publications and researches and which is given on the 2$^{\underline{nd}}$ and 3rd pages
of the programme. It should be the object of the Smithsonian Institu-
tion to co-operate with other Institutions and not to interfere with them
and ↑we↓ would therefore be pleased to receive any suggestions from
your society which might serve to direct us as to any future expenditures in the cause of American Antiquities.

I made a visit a short time since to Boston and started from home
with the intention of calling to see you but I was prevented by some
engagements from doing so. I regret this because we might have discussed matters much more effectually by conversation than by writing.

I find the plan of expending a part of the funds of the Smithsonian
bequest in the publication of original memoirs takes well with the Geologists[A] and naturalists. The illustrations of their labours frequently cost
more than they can afford to expend on them and on this account many
valuable articles never see the light.

The plan which I have given of the organization of the Smithsonian
Institution can be modified or adopted in part to suit the income or the
experience which time will afford. Please let me hear from you at your
earliest convenience and,

> Permit me to assure you that
> I am with much Respect
> very truly yours &
> Joseph Henry

Samuel F Haven Esq
Librarian of the A A Society
Worcester.

Miscellaneous Collections, American Antiquarian Society.
Reply: See Doc. 118.

1. Haven (1806–1881) was librarian of the American Antiquarian Society in Worcester, Massachusetts, from 1838 until his death. Essentially an executive director, Haven also functioned as manuscript curator and librarian and was known for his intelligent assistance to scholars. His own research interests included archeology. *Dictionary of American Library Biography* (Littleton, Colorado, 1978).

2. Haven had visited Chillicothe, Ohio, in 1845 and become familiar with Squier and Davis's work. He described their contributions in his *Archaeology of the United States*, 1856, SI Contributions, vol. 8 (Washington, 1856), pp. 117–123.

116. FROM [FRANCIS LIEBER][A]

Oct. 22. 1847.

To Professor Henry of the Smithsonian Institute

. . . As to the Board of Statistics on which you desire my views in consequence of our conversation at Princeton[1] they are briefly these: Statistics, rightly understood, become in the same degree more important as civilisation advances, because man's activity becomes intenser and more expanded and he presses more and more natural agents into service, while one of the blessed effects of civilisation is, that the various parts of society become more dependent upon one another. This is felt everywhere and a proportionate attention is paid to statistics; but, owing to our peculiar circumstances resulting from our federal character, the extensiveness of our territories, and the earnestness with which we are naturally yet engaged in subduing the land, and in a general point of view in mastering the material world, there is no country which stands more in need of correct and comprehensive statistics, and in which it is as difficult to collect them. No private means can accomplish it. Besides the Census, a constitutional periodical duty of our Government, leads to the desire of seeing a Board established, which may be expected to furnish substantial plans for undertaking it properly and experienced men to digest the materials correctly and judiciously.[2] Our Census is near ↑at hand↓ and the last one has been stigmatized as very incorrect.[3] I have written therefore to several of my friends in Congress that they ought to prepare in time for it. I intended to have taken the liberty of conversing with our very able Secretary of the Treasury who seems to me of a peculiarly quick perception for every thing substantially good, on this important subject, when I passed the last time through Washington, but several attempts on my part to see him failed, and the time had come to return to my college duties. . . . The subjects properly falling within the province of statistics, are all those which belong to human society or affect it, and the observation of whose repetition (a repetition of co-existence or succession) can be expressed numerically, so that their total gives an accurate statement of the status, an account of the actual state of a given society (We might undoubtedly speak of the Statistics of the heavens, and most interesting it would be, but, for our purpose we understand by statistics the account of ever changing human society, taken at a fixed period.— Unless government does something, nothing can be done; for, I ought to have added that one of the great difficulties in the way of collecting statistics in this country, is the absence of a searching police, nor do I by any means desire such a police, but I maintain that, since we are fortunately deprived of this means of collecting statistics, it becomes the more the duty of Congress to provide for a Board.— The Board would be obliged to correspond with proper persons in all States and the chief would be required to investigate personally. It would be no sinecure, but the good to be done, the promotion of substantial truth of the highest practical value to government and benefit to the community, in furnishing information for business-operations would be incalculable—most amply repaying all the expences to which the establishment of such a Board with the necessity of travel and a vast correspondence would unquestionably lead. . . .

Retained Copy, LI 1629, Lieber Papers, Huntington Library.
In an unknown hand, the copy is incomplete; the ellipses are from the original. Reply: Possibly Doc. 119.

1. Henry and Lieber had previously discussed a proposed Smithsonian statistical report and the establishment of a statistical bureau in the federal government (Docs. 108 and 110). This fragment evidently relates to the latter.

2. Although various European countries had national statistical bureaus by this time, the United States did not. The most prominent statistical activity in the federal government was the decennial census, which was mandated by the Constitution to determine each state's proportional representation in the House of Representatives. There was no permanent census office, however, to lend continuity to data gathering efforts, and Congress, often invoking states' rights arguments, had repeatedly resisted efforts to enlarge the scope of the census. Congress likewise resisted establishing and adequately funding a general statistical bureau outside of the census. In 1836, citing European models, Lieber had unsuccessfully memorialized Congress to set up a federal statistical bureau. A short-lived Bureau of Statistics in the Treasury Department in the mid-1840s dealt only with banking statistics. Sometime following his meeting and correspondence with Lieber in 1847, Henry noted that he discussed the statistical bureau idea with Secretary of the Treasury Robert J. Walker and that Walker promised to mention it in his next report. Although influential people both inside and outside various administrations agitated for a bureau for many years, Congress did not enact legislation creating a permanent Bureau of Statistics in the Treasury Department until 1866. Despite a theoretically broad mandate encompassing "any statistics of public utility" (Cummings, p. 586), it was chronically understaffed and underfunded and had to limit itself largely to statistics of foreign commerce and navigation. Reformers such as Lieber and fellow

members of the American Statistical Association, founded in 1839, had more success expanding the scope of the census and working toward its better organization and management. By the turn of the century, the enormous amount of data collected in the decennial census made inevitable the establishment of a permanent census office, one that shortly became "professionally and preëminently the statistical office of the United States government" (Cummings, p. 662).

Patricia Cline Cohen, *A Calculating People: The Spread of Numeracy in Early America* (Chicago, 1982), pp. 179–180, 197–198; Robert C. Davis, "The Beginnings of American Social Research," in *Nineteenth-Century American Science: A Reappraisal,* ed. George H. Daniels (Evanston, 1972), especially pp. 154–166, and 176–178; Frank Freidel, *Francis Lieber, Nineteenth-Century Liberal* (Baton Rouge, 1947), pp. 171–174; Henry Pocket Notebook [13272], pp. 1, 23 (first pagination); John Cummings, "Statistical Work of the Federal Government of the United States," in *The History of Statistics: Their Development and Progress in Many Countries,* ed. John Koren (1918; New York, 1970), pp. 585–587, 589, 597–601, 661–682.

3. Echoing Lieber's judgment, Patricia Cohen has called the 1840 census "a complete fiasco" (p. 177). Lieber had recommended in 1838 that Congress authorize new schedules, including some for manufacturing data, and entrust the work to trained census commissioners rather than United States marshals. Congress had responded to such suggestions by more or less duplicating the 1830 enumeration act, with minor changes in the population schedules. It also, however, authorized "statistical tables" with "all such information in relation to mines, agriculture, commerce, manufactures, and schools, as will exhibit a full view of the pursuits, industry, education, and resources of the country" (as quoted in Cohen, p. 183). This sweeping authorization was "breathtaking in its ambitiousness, naiveté, and vagueness" (Cohen, p. 184). Secretary of State John Forsyth of Georgia chose William A. Weaver, an undistinguished former civil servant, to conduct the census. Shortcomings included the format of the forms, which led to recording and aggregating errors, confusing manufacturing schedules, and printing problems. Mishandling of the 1840 census gave reformers the ammunition they needed and led directly to the landmark 1850 census, "the first modern census run according to rational principles and conducted by efficient experts" (Cohen, p. 259). Cohen, chapter 6; Cummings, pp. 673–676; Freidel, pp. 173–174.

117. FROM ALEXANDER DALLAS BACHE

Agamenticus Oct 25, 1847

My dear friend.

Your letter relating chiefly to the Mag^c Surv is received,[1] & as Col. Sabine's advice is so different from mine I must wait to answer until I have a conversation with Mr Fauntleroy[2] who is to be here every day, & who will probably direct Mr Owen's operations:[3] he is now fresh from using the mag^c instruments[4] & has been obliged in some cases to determine his own azimuths. Col. Sabine does not know that the land surveys give more accurate determinations than could be reached by rough astr^l means, does not know the difficulties of transporting instruments. Besides he comes back to the old fashion almost precisely & that in some of its worst forms, azimuth compass! Hansteen!![5] It is more important that you should do right than be prompt so I ask you to wait for Fauntleroy's coming here when I will at once write again.

The movements of Ferguson & Eakin[6] prefigure an onslaught.[7] I am disposed to send my last report & that of M[r]. Hassler[8] in 1843 (his last) to the Colleges say to a confidential person at each where I know one, explaining that in my official course it has been necessary to get rid of one person for cooking, & to vex others by proportioning their pay to their doings & abilities[9] & that an attack is designed, & asking for a general expression of opinion in regard to the conduct & progress of the Coast Survey since it has been under my direction. If not satisfied with any parts to suggest what is desired. Mrs. B. says no but she undervalues public opinion & overvalues me & my reputation. Think it over for a day or two at intervals & then give me your opinion, do not delay more than a few days. Such storms as howl about these high places! I promised Walker[10] to write to you about the Lieut:[11] but your action anticipated the [?Aud]. I had no doubt you would decline the combat as I did. He must think we are a pusillanimous pair. Life is too short & there is too much of the positive to do to waste it in broils: what amount of civilization did the Highlanders reach while they were always in feud? Fight yes if assaulted—friend thou hast no business here said the quaker as he lifted the pirate over the taffrail & let him fall into the Sea!

Kindest regards from all here to you & yours. My man begs to be allowed to set off early this morning as it has rained all night & the streams are full. So good bye

Yours ever truly
A.D.B.

Professor Henry.
A call was made on Gen. Disb. Ag. Coast Survey[12] the other day by one of the malcontents to know how much Prof. Henry had rec[d]. fr. C.S.!!! Answer x = o. Some men can only conceive of purchased friendship! Their hearts are as large as their heads!!!

General Manuscripts Collection, Department of Special Collections, University of Pennsylvania Libraries.

1. Doc. 114.

2. Robert Henry Fauntleroy (d. 1849) was an assistant on the Coast Survey. His wife was Jane Dale Owen, the sister of Robert Dale and David Dale Owen. U.S. Senate, 31st Congress, 2d Session, *Report of the Superintendent of the Coast Survey, Showing the Progress of the Work for the Year Ending November, 1850,* Senate Executive Documents, No. 7 (1850), pp. 47, 116–117; Richard William Leopold, *Robert Dale Owen: A Biography* (1940; New York, 1969), pp. 129, 234, 254.

3. David Dale Owen had written Bache on April 30, 1847 (Bache Papers, Smithsonian Archives), requesting permission to borrow Fauntleroy from the Coast Survey for six months so that he could make the terrestrial magnetism observations for Owen's survey of the Chippewa Land District in Wisconsin. Fauntleroy is not mentioned in Owen's report, and we do not know whether he joined Owen's survey.

4. In 1847 Fauntleroy made magnetic observations on Long Island Sound and on Mobile

Bay and the Mississippi Sound. *Coast Survey Report for 1847*, pp. 18–19, 43.

5. Bache wrote Sabine two days later asking him directly why he recommended "the old magnetic instruments" when the new ones were superior. BJ3/25, Letters from Americans re magnetic observatory in U.S., 1839–1854, Sabine Papers, Records of Kew Observatory, Public Record Office, London.

6. Constant M. Eakin (ca. 1794–1869), an 1817 graduate of the United States Military Academy, was an assistant on the Coast Survey from 1834 until 1850. G. W. Cullum, *Biographical Register of the Officers and Graduates of the United States Military Academy, at West Point, New York*, rev. ed., 2 vols. (New York, 1879), *1:*167–168; F. B. Hough, *American Biographical Notes* (Albany, 1875).

7. James Ferguson had been dismissed from the Coast Survey in March 1847 and was probably beginning to assemble ammunition to attack Bache. By December, one of Bache's assistants reported that Ferguson was trying to create problems for Bache in Congress. Although Eakin was not forced out until 1850, he wrote to Treasury Secretary Walker as early as August 1847 to defend himself against Bache's complaints about his data-gathering methods. Hugh Richard Slotten, "Patronage, Politics, and Practice in Nineteenth-Century American Science: Alexander Dallas Bache and the United States Coast Survey," (Ph.D. diss., University of Wisconsin-Madison, 1991), pp. 163–182, especially pp. 167–169. For the circumstances of Ferguson's dismissal from the Coast Survey and his eventual attack on Bache in *Hunt's Merchants' Magazine*, see *Henry Papers*, 6:437n–438n, and Doc. 311.

8. Ferdinand Rudolph Hassler, Bache's predecessor as superintendent of the Coast Survey. *Henry Papers*, 1:297n.

9. Eakin's pay, for example, dropped from $3,500 to $2,000 between 1846 and 1847. *Register of All Officers and Agents, Civil, Military, and Naval, in the Service of the United States* (Washington, 1847), p. 266; *The Washington Directory and National Register, for 1846* (Washington, 1846), p. 38.

10. Sears C. Walker.

11. Matthew F. Maury.

12. Samuel Hine was the Coast Survey's disbursing officer. *Register of All Officers and Agents*, p. 266.

118. TO EPHRAIM GEORGE SQUIER

Princeton Nov^A 4th 1847

My dear Sir

I leave Princeton for Washington to remain during the winter, in the course of two or three weeks. The Board of Regents meet on the 8th of next month and before that time I wish to have a full set, so far as they are finished, of all the woodcuts and plates of your memoir for exhibition to the Board.

I wish each wood cut pasted on the middle of a sheet of coloured paper so as to form together a quarto scrap book which will exhibit the drawings to the best advantage.

I have received a very satisfactory letter from Mr Haven[1] relative to the fidelity of your delineations. He expresses however the hope that you will be careful in giving due credit to your predecessors in the same investigationes and speaks of the importance[B] of the labours of Atwater though his work may contain some errors which your examination of the same objects may serve to correct.

I have written to Mr Bartlett on the subject of an expression of opinion from the Ethnological Society and from Mr Galletan as to the plan of organization of the Smithsonian Institution set forth in the Programme a copy of which I left with Mr Bartlett to be presented to the society.[2] I wish you would see that this matter is brought before the society. I am not sure that my time before the meeting of the Board of Regents will permit me to be present at any of the meetings of the society. I would have attended the last meeting were it not that I was in Washington at the time it took place.

I remain truly
Yours &c &c
Joseph Henry

E. G. Squire Esq

Squier Papers, Library of Congress.

1. Letter not found, but in response to Doc. 115.
2. Henry's letter to John Russell Bartlett, November 4, 1847, is in the Bartlett Papers, John Carter Brown Library at Brown University. Henry solicited a report from the society that would provide

an expression of opinion particularly with reference to the plan of devoting a considerable part of the income of the Institution to the publication of original memoirs—the institution of original research—and to the preparation of Reports on the different branches of knowledge.

No report has been found, and likely there was not time to produce one, as Henry suggested that an "extra meeting" of the society be called, so that the report would reach him before the regents' meeting.

119. TO FRANCIS LIEBER

Princeton Nov 5th/47

My Dear Sir

On my way through Phi^d I called on Mr Dallas but did not find him at home. I then called on one of the Directors, of the Girard College, with whom I am ↑on↓ terms of intimacy. This gentleman, Mr Wegand,[1] informed me that from present appearances the casting vote between Hart and Reid would rest with himself. He thought your ~~choice~~ ↑chance↓ was small unless the Directors could not agree on one of the above mentioned candidates.

I think it probable that Hart will be elected though great effort will be made in favour of Reed.

Enclosed I send you an expression of my opinion of your character which has the merit of being true.

I am just now so much pressed with engagements that I cannot give an answer to your several interesting communications.[2] I can say however that I am much indebted to you for the corrections and suggestions you wrote on the margin of the programme of organization. I intend to have the article reprinted and shall adopt most of the alterations you have suggested.[3] I have time also to inform you that I think a memoir relative to Laura Bridgeman such as you mention would be highly interesting and very proper for insertion in the Smithsonn Contributions, provided the facts on which your conclusions ↑are founded↓ have not before been published as a whole.

Cannot you prepare a more extended memoir on this subject giving a full account of the case from materials furnished by Dr. Howe. It is highly important that all the facts relative to the mental phenomena exhibited by this Individual[A] should be described and recorded in some permanent work easily accessible to the learned world. The memoir might be illustrated ~~by a~~ and embellished by an engraved likeness of Laura and by wood cuts to assist in giving a better idea of the implements, if there be any thing peculiar in them, which were used in her instruction.

Your memoir must hower pass the ordeal of a reference to a commission of Judges. It cannot appear in the first vol. of the Contributions because sufficient matter has already been accepted to complete it.

I go to Washington to remain for the Winter in the course of about three weeks and until after the meeting of the Board which takes place on the 8ᵗʰ of December I shall be overwhelmed with business. I regret very much to learn that Col. Preston will probably not come on to the meeting. I beg that should he talk of resigning you will dissuade[B] him from such a course.

With much Respect
I remain truly [ys][C]
Joseph Henry

Dr Lieber

LI 1625, Lieber Papers, Huntington Library.
Abstract in Henry's hand: Henry Papers, Smithsonian Archives.

1. John Wiegand, a cashier at the Philadelphia Gas Works and a manager of the Franklin Institute. In 1844, he had served with Henry on a Franklin Institute committee investigating the explosion of the "Peacemaker." *First Annual Report of Board of Directors of the Girard College* (Philadelphia, 1848); *Henry Papers, 6*:67n, 105n, and 142.

2. Docs. 108 and 116.

3. Lieber's annotated copy of the draft "Programme of Organization" has not been found.

120. TO ASA GRAY

Princeton Nov 5th 1847

My dear Dr.

In consequence of repeated journeyings between this place, New-York, and Washington ↑since↓ my visit at the north, my unanswered letters have so accumulated that I have only been able to clear them off atfer several days of constant labor. Your letter,[1] though not the least interesting of the lot, has accidentally been left among the last to receive attention.

I am much gratified with the appointment of so respectable and influential a committee and I am confident their opinion will have great weight with the members of the Smithsonian Board.[2]

I have no suggestions of importance to make in addition to those we discussed when I was in Cambridge. Should the Natural history society of Boston see fit to give an expression of opinion on the same subject it might perhaps be well for them to state that though they approve of the establishment of a national museum yet they think it highly improper to put the support of it on the Smithsonian bequest, the income of which can be much more efficiently applied in the way of advancing natural history by the publication of expensive original memoirs on this subject.[3]

The next meeting of the Regents takes place on the 8th of December and it is highly important that I have the report of the Acad^y in my possession before that time.

I rejoice to learn that our friend Aggasiz is producing an admirable effect in New-York which cannot but redound to the good of American Science and the advantage of your new School at Cambridge.[4]

Wilkes and myself when I return to Washington are to make an attempt to get up an audience for him in that city. The project originated with Wilkes but I shall give it ~~my~~ ↑a↓ cordial and industrious support.

It was my intention to propose to the Board to engage Aggasiz to open the Smithsonian Institution with a course of lectures as soon as the first wing of the edifice is fit for occupation which will be in the course of next summer probably about may and should the present plan not succeed the other will be carried out as soon as the engagements of the Professor at Cambridge will permit him to deliver the course. I am sure he will be of much service to Bache and myself in carrying out our plans for rendering the Smithsonian Institution of use to our country and the world.[5]

Please give my kind regards to your fellow Professors particularly to

Peirce Felton[6] and Dr. Walker.[7] I regret that I had not an opportunity of seeing more of these gentlemen as well as of the other members of your faculty.

I was highly gratified with my visit to cambridge it forms a bright spot in the events of my life ↑and↓ will always be conspicuous in my memory. I hope to have an opportunity of discharging a part of the debt in which you have involved me by attention to you and yours at some future time in Washington.

I learn from Walker[8] that Pierce is very busily engaged on the investigation of the mass of neptune from the motion of his satellite.[9] How much interest this subject continues to excite! and how much on this account has it added to the rational and intellectual pleasure of the world!

> I remain as ever
> truly your friend
> Joseph Henry

Dr A Gray
Professor &c

↑P.S.↓ Perhaps in the report of the committee it will not be advisable to give me the credit of the plan of the Smithsonian developed on the programme. It is indeed eclectic. I have taken parts from all quarters and put these together.

> J.H.

Historic Letters, Archives, Gray Herbarium Library, Harvard University.
Variant retained copy: Henry Papers, Smithsonian Archives. Reply: December 8, 1847, RH 3181, Rhees Collection, Huntington Library.

1. Not found.

2. Henry solicited comments from the American Academy of Arts and Sciences on his printed draft "Programme of Organization." The academy appointed a committee composed of Edward Everett (chairman), president of Harvard (*Henry Papers*, 6:374n); Jared Sparks (1789–1866), biographer, editor, and McLean Professor of History at Harvard (*DAB*); Benjamin Peirce; Henry Wadsworth Longfellow; Louis Agassiz (who did not participate because of his lecturing engagement in Charleston, South Carolina); and Gray. Its report, dated December 4, is in the *Proceedings of the American Academy of Arts and Sciences*, 1846–1848, *1*:185–194, and is reprinted in Rhees, *Documents* (1879), pp. 964–970. For further details, see Doc. 130.

3. No expression of opinion has been found from the Boston Society of Natural History.

The amateur society, founded in 1830, became an important organization of scientific popularization in New England, with its museum, public lecture hall, and library. Sally Gregory Kohlstedt, "The Nineteenth-Century Amateur Tradition: The Case of the Boston Society of Natural History," in *Science and Its Public: The Changing Relationship*, ed. Gerald Holton and William A. Blanpied (Dordrecht, Holland, 1976), pp. 173–190.

4. After Agassiz delivered successful lectures on natural history in Boston, the New York College of Physicians and Surgeons asked him to deliver a course of twelve lectures in their hall. The series started in mid-October and was extremely popular, drawing heavily from the intelligentsia of the city. The lectures reached a popular audience as well; the *New-York Daily Tribune* reprinted them, as did the *Weekly Tribune*, and they came out in book form as *An*

Introduction to the Study of Natural History (New York, 1847), under the auspices of Horace Greeley, the *Tribune*'s publisher.

Edward Lurie, *Louis Agassiz: A Life in Science* (Chicago, 1960), pp. 142–143; Jules Marcou, *Life, Letters, and Works of Louis Agassiz*, 2 vols. (New York, 1895), *1*:288–293; *2*:2–3; *New-York Weekly Tribune*, October 23 and 30; November 6, 13, 20, and 27; and December 4 and 11, 1847.

5. No evidence exists of Agassiz lecturing in Washington before 1850, when he gave a series of lectures sponsored by the Smithsonian. *Smithsonian Report for 1850*, p. 26.

6. Cornelius Conway Felton (1807–1862), professor of Greek. *DAB*.

7. James Walker (1794–1874), Alford Professor of Natural Religion. *DAB*.

8. Sears Cook Walker.

9. In October and November 1847, William Cranch Bond made extensive observations of Neptune's satellite, Triton, which English astronomer William Lassell first saw on October 10, 1846, and observed again in July 1847. Bond presented his observations to the American Academy of Arts and Sciences on November 2. On November 10 and December 7, Benjamin Peirce presented his computation of the mass of Neptune from the orbital elements of its satellite, based on both Lassell's and Bond's observations. He used this material to show that Neptune's mass was far less than that assumed by either John Couch Adams or U. J. J. Le Verrier, and thus bolstered his claim that the planet discovered was different from the one predicted.

Proceedings of the American Academy of Arts and Sciences, 1846–1848, *1*:184, 185, 295; Elias Loomis, "Historical Notice of the Discovery of the Planet Neptune," *Silliman's Journal*, 1848, 2d ser. *5*:187–205, especially pp. 202–203.

121. TO MATTHEW FONTAINE MAURY

Princeton Nov. ↑9th↓ 1847.

Dear Sir,

I trust you will pardon the long delay of this answer to your letter of the 20th ult.[1] when I assure you that it has been caused by unavoidable circumstances. I have been so overwhelmed by engagements and so much called from home since it was received that I have not found leisure, before to day, to give your communication the attention which it required. And besides these causes of delay I was unwilling to write to you until I should have an opportunity of procuring[A] a copy of the publication which has led to this correspondence.

The No. 605 of the Astronomische Nachrichten containing the article has been received and I have now before me, for the first time, the facts necessary to enable me to form an opinion as to the ground of your complaints and my duty with reference to them.

The facts of the case, as they appear to me stripped of all extraneous considerations, are as follows.

(1).[B] As Secretary of the Smithsonian Institution I have agreed to accept, provisionally, from Mr Walker, a memoir on the planet Neptune for publication in the Smithsonian contributions to knowledge.

(2.) I have written to Professor Schumaker a letter[2] in which I have stated in substance that a full account of Mr Walker's investigations will be published in the transactions of the Smithsonian Institution.

(3.) With this letter I have sent an abstract, of Mr Walker's researches, prepared by himself, for insertion in the Astronomische Nachrichten.

Let us now consider the facts in the order in which they are stated.[C] 1. With reference to the acceptance of Mr. Walker's memoir.— By a resolution of the Board of Regents of the Smithsonian Institution, rewards are offered, for original memoirs on all branches of knowledge. All persons are invited to present such memoirs and it is my duty to accept, provisionally, all that may be presented; ~~to~~ refer them to a commission of competent judges for examination and to publish them in the Smithson contributions to knowledge, provided, they are found worthy, with reference to origin[ality] and importance, to appear in the Transactions of the Institution.

In accordance with this resolution I have received from Mr Walker sever[al] communications and have agreed to accept others in course of preparation, the whole[D] to form an original memoir, on the planet Neptune, presented by Mr W[alker] himself, for a premium, and ↑for↓ a place in the transactions. In thus accepting Mr Walker's memoir I have neither intentionally nor otherwise done wrong to you, or th[e] Observatory. The memoir of Mr Walker has not yet been published in the Smithson[ian] contributions and cannot be so published if it is found to contain matter belongi[ng] to the Observatory.

2. The letter in ↑no.↓ 605 ↑of the Astr. Nach.↓ was written by me, but I cannot admit that there is any real discrepancy between it, and my letter to you;[3] or, that the various inferences, me[n]tioned in your last communications,[E] can be legitimately drawn from it; thoug[h] from your relation to Mr Walker and from other circumstances it is perhaps not strange that such inferences should[F] suggest themselves to your mind.

The letter was necessarily brief, and gives no description of the plan of organiz[ation] of the Smithsonian institution and when I stated that a full account of the investigations would be published in the transactions of the Smithsonian In[sti]tution I merely wrote what I believed would take place; I knew that the paper Mr Walker was preparing would be an important one; I saw no reason to expect the possibility of its rejection by a commission; and at the time I did not dream that you would object to its publication; so far from this I had been informed by Mr Walker that you had given him permission to use the observations made at the Observatory for the purpose of continuing his investigations. Also the words "full account of the investigations" which occur in my letter refer principally, in my mind, to what Mr. Walker pr[o]posed yet to do in working out the series of investigations on which he was en- gag[ed.]

From these facts I presume you will do me the justice to admit that there is [no] real discrepancy between my letter to you and the one published in the Astronomische Nachrichten. The letter though (for obvious reasons) dated Washington was written at Princeton and at a time when I was so much occupied with my own arduous duties that I could give no attention to the difficulty existing between you and Mr Walker and up to this time I have not read the public controversy[4] which for the sake of the cause of American science I regret to learn was carried on between you.

As to the invitation mentioned by Mr Walker in his abstract it can only refer to the preparation of the article. The proposition to send an abstract to Prof Schumaker came from Mr Walker himself, the request that he would prepare it came from me; and my object in making this request was that the responsibility of errors of statement ↑&c↓ &c— if any, might rest with the author.

3. My reason for complying with the request, to send an abstract to Prof Schumaker, is given in my last letter, and in addition to this I may state that in thus forwarding the article for publication I was acting in accor- dance with the usages of the Secretaries of other scientific institutions. Indeed an abstract of the same researches had been given to the public by the Secretary of the American Philosophical Society through the Bul- letin of the proceedings of that institution for March 1847.[5]

With reference to the contents of the abstract though I consider Mr. Walker responsible for the statements it contains yet on reading the article I regret to find reference made to the Superintendent of the Observatory in terms which I highly disapprove.[6] In reference to this I can only say the article was received by me just before the sailing of the Steamer and when I was on the point of starting for New York I had therefore scarcely time to write my letter and placing full confidence in Mr Walker's sense of propriety in such matters I sent the abstract with but a slight examination.

In concluding the examination of this matter I have to charge myself with not having been sufficiently explicit in my letter to Prof. Schu- maker and in not examining more critically the abstract of Mr. Walker before sending it. To make amends for these inadvertencies on my part I propose to write to Professor Schumaker, to give him a more detailed account of the plan of the Institution—to state on what terms Mr. Walker's memoir was accepted and my disapproval of the remarks above mentioned.

↑Of this affair↓[G] I have given you a candid and as it appears to me a true exposition ~~of this affair~~[H] with which and the course my judgement and feelings[I] prompt me to take I presume you will be satisfied. My mission is one of peace and good will—the advance of American science; and in the coscientious discharge of my duty, nothing has been, or shall be, farther from my thoughts than the intentio[n] of arraying institutions or individuals against each other.

I remain very respectfully—
Your Obt. Servant.
Joseph Henry

Lieut. Maury.
Superintendent of the
Observatory. Washington.

Box 3, Incoming Correspondence, Superintendent's Office Correspondence, Records of the United States Naval Observatory, Library of Congress.

In an unknown hand, with Henry's signature, additions, and corrections, except as noted. Right margin cropped, second and fourth pages. Reply: November 15, 1847, Letters Sent by the Naval Observatory, vol. 2, pp. 372–378, Records of the Naval Observatory, RG 78, National Archives.

1. Letters Sent by the Naval Observatory, vol. 2, pp. 349–353, Records of the Naval Observatory, RG 78, National Archives. Significant portions are printed in Frances Leigh Williams, *Matthew Fontaine Maury: Scientist of the Sea* (New Brunswick, 1963), pp. 170–171.

Maury complained, in bitter language, of Henry's taking sides against the observatory. Henry, as head of one government institution (in Maury's estimation), was accused of supporting Walker, "who had just been compelled to leave, in Official disgrace, Another Institution under the same Government," and, moreover, of appropriating "the labors of the Observatory . . . without due Acknowledgement." Even more outrageous was that Henry had acted "without regarding the rules, and usages of Official intercourse or the Comity which obtains among men of science, but in derogation of all."

2. The letter to H. C. Schumacher, May 29, 1847, prefaced Walker's article in the *Astronomische Nachrichten*.

3. Doc. 107.

4. In letters to the editor of the *National Intelligencer*. Walker's of May 20, 1847, printed in the issue of May 22, was an abstract of his *Astro*-

nomische Nachrichten article. Maury responded rancorously in the issue of May 27, stating that Walker was trying to rob the Naval Observatory of credit. Walker in turn denied that any credit should go to the observatory. The debate quickly degenerated to charges of astronomical incompetency and personal deceit. *National Intelligencer*, May 22, 27, and 29; June 4, 17, 19, 26, and 28, 1847.

5. In the form of a letter from Walker to Robert M. Patterson, vice-president of the society, May 3, 1847. APS *Proceedings*, 1843–1847, 4:332–335.

6. Henry probably referred to Walker's statement that implied Maury's reluctance to act:

When *Leverrier's* prediction reached Washington in August last, I requested the Superintendent at once to put all the instruments upon the search for it. This advice was not complied with till the following October, when the news of the Berlin discovery Oct. 23. found the Superintendent, on the point of sweeping in its discovered place. [Walker untitled abstract, *Astronomische Nachrichten*, 1847, 26:cols. 65–66.]

122. FROM CHARLES COFFIN JEWETT

Providence Nov. 16 1847

My dear Sir,

I beg leave to call your attention to the accompanying letter,[1] which, at the suggestion of some of our friends, particularly Mr. Choate, I have written, respecting the Library of the Smithsonian Institution. I do not think it, as a general thing, either wise or dignified, to notice newspaper attacks; but the false reports concerning the Library are circulating so widely & are doing such injustice & injury both to the Institution & to ourselves, that an explicit & official denial seems to be demanded. I have taken advantage of the occasion to state some facts & considerations respecting the Library, which I have no doubt will meet your approval. If you see nothing in the paper to disapprove, will you be so kind as to forward it to the Editor of the Union at Washington, with the accompanying note.[2]

The next meeting of the Regents will be, I think, a very important one. I hope it may be harmonious & prosperous. As it approaches I suppose you are much occupied in laying out the business. I cannot think that you will encounter opposition to[A] your plans. I cannot sufficiently regret having seen so little of you while you were here. I was very desirous of talking over with you more fully, than I had opportunity for, the plans ~~& pros~~ which have been & which should be formed for my own department. I was very happy to find that you were desirous of beginning[B] immediately upon the Library & of securing for it, at first, as large an appropriation as possible from the half of the income, devoted to Collections. If we are to have a Library, atall, delay in commencing it is the worst possible economy. To lay properly the foundations of such an establishment is slow work. It is so much a matter of detail that much time is necessarily consumed in producing but small visible results. As I do not expect to have the pleasure of seeing[C] you again before the meeting of the Regents, I will, with your indulgence, refer to some of the principal matters which will require attention in commencing the Library. They would no doubt all occur to you, in their order, but I have though[t][D] you might find it convenient to have this part of the business ↑in some degree↓ prepared to your hand. A great deal of preparatory[E] work is to be gone through with before any books can be placed upon our shelves.

On the plan proposed for our Library, it seems to me that the first thing to be done, is to make arrangements for obtaining catalogues—printed or in manuscript—of the principal Libraries[F] of the United

States;^G to examine these Libraries^H as far as I can, personally, in order to know their general character, the statistics of their increase &c;—& to form such alliances with the Librarians^I as will be indispensable to us in making our Library a Supplemental one & a centre of bibliographical reference.[3] Some Libraries possess printed catalogues, complete nearly to the present time,^J others are several years behind hand. It will be necessary to procure MS. catalogues in continuation of those which have been printed & to make arrangements for receiving from month to month or from year to year, lists of all future accessions. These supplementary catalogues should all be prepared on a uniform plan. The titles should be written on cards of the same size, so that they^K may be placed together in one alphabet in order to facilitate research. A mark placed on the back of each card will designate the Library from which it came. Now, in every Library with which we are in correspondence some one must be employed to do this. It would be merely clerk's^L labor, where the catalogues are properly kept; & no doubt, the Librarian or assistant might in every case be induced to undertake it for a small compensation. It will not be necessary to include in this arrangement more than eight or ten libraries. All the smaller libraries of the country are but duplicates, for the most part, of a few larger ones.

~~A second~~ The next thing to be done, will be to make arrangements for procuring the books to which we are entitled by the 10th <u>Section</u> of our charter.[4] Unless something be done, this provision will scarcely bring us in twenty good books a year. The very enactment is perhaps merely directory & compliance with it not essential to the validity of a copyright. I have no doubt however that publishers, generally, would send their books, if the subject were properly presented to them & arrangements made by which they could transmit them to Washington, without subjecting the Institution or themselves to expenses altogether disproportioned to the value of the books. It has occurred to me that it might be well to appoint a number of agents, say one in each state & to pay them a small percentage upon all the books which they collect & forward. Some young booksellers might be found in every city who would gladly accept such an agency, or perhaps the several district-clerks might be induced to attend to the business. It is perhaps legally their duty to do so,[5] but I suppose it would be unsafe to rely upon their performing faithfully such an unexpected duty, unless they received for it some additional compensation. Besides this a circular might be printed & sent to publishers setting forth the advantages which would result directly to the cause of letters & indirectly to themselves, from compliance with this requirement. By these means I think we should obtain nearly all the publications of importance issued from the American press. The[M] Selection of books for the first purchase must be made. This will I suppose comprise three classes of works— 1. Those which may be immediately needed in the Scientific department. 2. Bibliographical works, & descriptions, histories & catalogues of similar Institutions— & 3. The general collection, which, as you suggested, might ↑for the first year or so↓ consist of the Memoirs, Transactions & Journals of the Learned Societies of Europe & America.[6] These three classes of books will form a Library quite unique & one of very great utility. The catalogue if it be made with fulness & accuracy will be a valuable publication. I think further that a somewhat extended list of books should be made out—for future purchases. These lists should be left with honest & faithful men in some of the principal book marts in Europe, with orders to buy the books whenever they can find them at say ½ the ordinary prices. In this way we should obtain at very low prices great numbers of the books which we should want. Of course the same list would not be left with different men. The length of time which would be occupied in making out these lists would of course depend upon the amount of money appropriated. The work should be done with care & by consultation with the best scholars in the country. It will be difficult to find the necessary bibliographical helps. The best collection of them in the country, is in the Library of Brown University, but this is very imperfect.

The first purchases are to be made & the arrangements for future purchases. These of course should not be commenced until the lists are so far completed as they can judiciously be in this country. It will I suppose be desirable for me to go to Europe, for these purposes. I am sure that I could do more with 10,000 dollars in buying the ~~buying~~ books myself than with 20,000 in procuring them through the ordinary channels of trade. My experience has taught me that if only 5,000 dollars are to be expended it is far better to go to Europe ↑to buy them↓, paying the expenses out of the sum, than to obtain the books by correspondence.

Another subject connected with the department of collections & which should, I think, receive immediate attention, is the procuring of copies of some of the most celebrated works of art.[7] It will probably be best, to confine ourselves, at first, principally to plaster casts of some of the finest specimens of ancient & modern statuary. These can be procured very cheap, & convey of course a perfect representation of the original. While in Europe, purchasing books, I might procure these. I have no doubt that for a public Institution, ~~we could~~ & one under national auspices, we could wherever we desire it obtain permission to take casts directly from the Statues. The expense of doing so would of course be somewhat greater than of buying such copies as we might find in the market—but the difference between 10 & 20 dolls—is not to be thought of in such a case & I presume that most which we should want would not cost more than 20 dolls apiece. It would further be desirable I think to procure models in cork of some of the houses, temples theatres, baths &c &c in Pompeii & Herculaneum. These can be procured at comparatively small prices. Models of every ↑interesting↓ part of Pompeii which has been excavated presenting in miniature a perfect view of nearly the whole ↑on the scale of 1 ft to 150↓— might be procured for about $2,000 ↑(It would require nearly two years of their work, as they affirm)↓—. I have in my possession an agreement entered into by the men who have the monopoly of this business at Naples by which they promise to furnish me all these at the aggregate price which I have mentioned. Of course they can only furnish at this low price all the buildings & streets ↑(either all together or separately)↓ which they have previously modelled. They charged the King of Bavaria[8] 5000 dolls for an original model of the house of Sallust[9] alone. It might also be well to procure a few Etruscan vases—also a few antique coins & medals, sufficient to convey some illustration of ~~the use~~ Numismatics as a subsidiary branch of History. The Trustees should of course decide what proportion of the appropriation for Collections should each year be expended for these purposes. I will merely remark that 1000 dolls or even 500, at the outset, prudently expended, would procure for us a very interesting collection.

I have thus stated, quite in detail, the work which must be done before the Library can be ready for use,] or rather <u>before any part of it can be placed upon the Shelves</u>, before it can be ready for use much more is to be done in arranging & cataloguing. I think it will be manifest that if one officer is to do this within a year, or even within two years it is time he were about it— The Regents seem to have supposed that I would prefer to do the preparatory work of making out lists &c whilst retaining my situation here. This I have found, however, utterly impossible. My duties here require <u>all</u> my time & strength I cannot be released of a part of them, without giving up the whole. The college have been cherishing all along the hope that I would not leave. They have not wished therefore to make any arrangements for my successor, which would preclude the possibility of my remaining— I have always told them however that I should probably leave about this time, as I had supposed ~~from~~ that it would be necessary for me to ↑begin to↓ devote all my time to the Smithsonian Institution as soon certainly as Jany 1. 1848. You will see therefore that I am placed in rather an embarrassing situation, & feel that I ought very soon to resign either my situation here or my appointment at Washington. I should not of course urge any personal considerations, were it not that the interests of the Institution manifestly require the same course, which would at present be best for me also, namely my commencing immediately upon the duties of my office.[10]

Since I saw you I have had an interview with Mr Choate. He seemed to be much interested in your plans. I think he would be very willing to join you with reference to the building, with the understanding that the Library should be provided with room as fast as it might be needed— He seemed very unwilling to devote any part of our funds to the custody of collections belonging to the government.

I do not know precisely when the meeting of the Regents will take place. If it is ~~between~~ later than the 10th of Decr I may be able to be in Washington at the time.[11] Will you be so kind as to inform me on this point.

I hope, my dear Sir, that this meeting, may pass off pleasantly & result in establishing the Institution upon a firm & enduring basis. There cannot fail to be differences of opinion with reference to the best possible plan of organization for such an Institution. But one who has the interests of ~~learning~~ "knowledge" really at heart can most cheerfully cooperate in plans, which though they may not in his opinion be the best possible are still excellent.

I fear I have wearied you with this long communication; but I am sure you will require from me no apology.

Will you be so kind ↑as↓ to favor me with a note in reply, as soon as you can conveniently, & please state particularly the time of the meeting of the Regents.

I am, my dear Sir,
with great respect
very truly
your friend & serv^t
C. C. Jewett

Prof. Henry &c &c

Henry Papers, Smithsonian Archives.

Extract printed in *Smithsonian Report for 1847*, pp. 191–193. Preparation of the extract produced numerous editorial marks by Henry and possibly by Jewett, in a similar ink and hand to the original. Additions and deletions reported are only those reasonably attributable to Jewett's original letter. Reply: Doc. 125.

1. Not found.

2. See Doc. 97.

3. The language here evokes that of the report of the committee of organization (Rhees, *Documents* [1879], p. 939). This was amplified in the drafts of Henry's "Programme of Organization." He listed, among the duties of the librarian:

> to form a Library, which at first shall consist of books necessary in carrying out the other parts of the plan; to procure catalogues of all the books in the different Libraries of the United States; to gradually form a supplementary Library; to collect all the information necessary for rendering the Institution a centre of Bibliographical knowledge, whence the student can be directed where any book, which may be required, can be found; to report on plans of Libraries. [Found in both the manuscript and printed drafts of the "Programme," as described in Doc. 130.]

See also Michael H. Harris, ed., *The Age of Jewett: Charles Coffin Jewett and American Librarianship, 1841–1868* (Littleton, Colorado, 1975), especially pp. 25–30 (including quotations from this letter), for the context of Jewett's ideas on librarianship.

4. The copyright deposit provision of the act establishing the Smithsonian Institution.

5. Under the system set up in 1831, clerks of the United States district courts served as agents to receive books and other works whose authors desired copyright protection. They forwarded annually to the secretary of state these copyright deposit works, along with lists of all such works they had received. John Y. Cole, "Of Copyright, Men, and a National Library," *The Quarterly Journal of the Library of Congress,* 1971, 28:114–143, especially p. 116.

6. Again, this description of the nature of the library matches that given in the report of the committee of organization. Rhees, *Documents* (1879), pp. 938, 939.

7. The art gallery was almost an afterthought—it was not even included in early drafts of the Smithsonian act—and the report of the committee of organization only stated that it should have "painting and sculpture, . . . engravings and architectural designs" (Rhees,

Documents [1879], p. 933). Jewett's concept of his responsibilities and the nature of the fledgling gallery reflected an understanding that is found in both of Henry's drafts of his "Programme." They contained language providing that the librarian was "to take charge of all collections of Art" and that "attempts should be made to procure for the Gallery of Arts, plaster casts of the most celebrated articles of ancient and modern sculpture."

(In the manuscript draft "Programme," Henry amplified this further: "Copies of the Elgin Marbles can probably be procured through our Minister at the Court of St James." In his rough notes on the "Programme" [Henry Pocket Notebook [13279], pp. 115–121], Henry repeated this statement and then recounted his earlier attempts, starting in 1837, to procure such copies for the United States. For these, see *Henry Papers, 3:*530–532.)

8. Ludwig or Louis I (1786–1868), who reigned from 1825 until his abdication in 1848, distinguished himself by his promotion of the fine arts. *Henry Papers, 5:*81n.

9. A house in Pompeii, "preserved with most of its original decorations." The dwelling apparently had belonged to a rich family, and was on one of the major thoroughfares of the ancient city. L. Richardson, Jr., *Pompeii: An Architectural History* (Baltimore, 1988), pp. 108–111 (quotation on p. 108).

10. Rufus Choate promoted Jewett's case for taking up more duties. However, on December 21, after Henry presented this letter, the board only agreed to have a full-time assistant secretary for the library from March 19, 1849. On December 27, the board determined that in the intervening fifteen months Jewett could prepare catalogs of books for the Smithsonian library, purchase books on bibliography, collect and arrange printed catalogues of American libraries, and obtain books through the copyright deposit provision. He was to receive no more than $1,000 for his services. Rhees, *Journals,* pp. 45–49.

11. Jewett did come to Washington. See Doc. 134 and Jewett to Henry, January 20, 1848, General Manuscripts Collection, Department of Special Collections, University of Pennsylvania Libraries.

November 18, 1847

123. FROM ZACHARIAH ALLEN

Providence November 18th 1847

Dear Sir

When I had the pleasure of a visit from you, a few weeks since, you expressed a wish to receive an account of the present state of the "Gas-Wells", as the salt makers on the borders of the Kenawha river, in Virginia, denominate their Artesian Wells; which send forth streams of carburetted hydrogen gas as well as of salt water.

Agreeably to my promise, I now forward to you a sketch of my observations of the truly wonderful phenomenon of the discharge, from the apertures of tubes sunk into the earth, of[A] commingled streams of salt water, and of inflammable air, in sufficient quantities to serve as fuel in furnaces for boiling the brine to make several thousand bushels of salt every week.[1]

These notes, although hastily taken during a tour to the Falls of St. Anthony,[2] probably contain more particulars of recent information, than may have yet reached you from other sources—

I remain yours with sincere regards
Z. Allen.

All my family join with me in kind recollections of your friendly and very agreeable visit, and hope that you will not fail to consider your home in Providence to be with us, whenever you have occasion to pass through the city.

It has occurred to me, that the scope of the Work, which I am about to publish, will admit of a detailed explanation of the discoveries you have made in Electro-dynamics, adapted to popular readers, who form a more extensive class than the scientific readers to whom you have communicated them in detached notices published in various Journals of Science. It may, perhaps, be in my power to do more ample justice to the merits of your original suggestions and discoveries, and in a manner that may have a better effect, than if attempted directly by yourself.

Should you feel disposed confidentially to furnish to me a brief outline of the facts most interesting, and references to the notices you have at different times published in various public Journals, with the dates, it is my desire to attempt to place ~~them~~ in a proper light before our Countrymen, the merits of your original discoveries and suggestions in advancing the science of Electro-Magnetism, and particularly that branch of it which relates to the Electro-Magnetic Telegraph.[3]

Henry Papers, Smithsonian Archives.
Note top right, first page: "Read Dec 3, 1847 R.D." in the hand of Robley Dunglison, a secretary

231

of the American Philosophical Society. Replies: February 1, 1848, Collection 5040, Reynolds Historical Library, The University of Alabama at Birmingham; and March 27, 1848, Joseph Henry Collection, Manuscripts Division, Department of Rare Books and Special Collections, Princeton University Libraries.

1. Henry presented Allen's sketch, entitled "An Account of the Inflammable Gas-Wells on the Banks of the Kanawha River, in Virginia, As They Appeared in June, 1847," to the American Philosophical Society on December 3, 1847. Robley Dunglison read the article, which was printed in the *Proceedings* (1843–1847, *4:*366–368). The river lies within the borders of the present state of West Virginia; the site is above Charleston. The artesian wells there date from 1807–1808. W. W. Mather, *Report on the State House Artesian Well, at Columbus, Ohio* (Columbus, 1859), pp. 26, 33.

2. At the head of steamboat navigation of the Mississippi River, at Minneapolis.

3. In his reply of March 27, Henry said that he would give Allen the requested outline of his researches after Congress had adjourned. However, he also directed Allen to his article "Magnetism," in the *Encyclopaedia Americana: Supplementary Volume* (Philadelphia, 1847), *14:*412–426. We have no other record of a scientific communication of this nature.

Allen's discussion of electromagnetism in his *Philosophy of the Mechanics of Nature, and the Source and Modes of Action of Natural Motive-Power* (New York, 1852) noted Henry's work on the electromagnet and on the distance over which electromagnetic effects could be produced (pp. 515–516).

124. TO [EPHRAIM GEORGE SQUIER][A]

Princeton Nov 24th 1847

My dear Sir

In my free though I trust you will believe friendly remarks to you yesterday I fear I may have said something to wound you and which may have had a tendancy to depress your feelings. I need not assure you that nothing of the kind was intended and thus I was actuated in all I said by a desire to promote your own best interest and the good of the Smithsonian Institution; the two for the present being identified; but least I should have produced an impression other that what I intended I have concluded to address you this morning though I can scarcly spare the time from my pressing engagements preparatory to the meeting of the Board of Regents.

I consider your present prospects superior to those of any other young man of my acquaintance and with proper caution—a prudent and labourious application of your talents in the line you have commenced in all probabilty will secure you a permanent and enviable reputation and lead you to fame if not to fortune. There is a great want of original talent in our country and when a man of this kind is found and does apply his genius to the production of interesting and important results he does meet with reward. You need be under no apprehension as to your future course if you can only exist at the present time and keep from starving until your book is published. I am sure the means will be furnished both for your maintance and the prosecution of your farther researches. I am myself acquainted with a number of wealthy gentlemen who would be pleased to join as patrons of a series of researches for exploring all the remains in our country but inorder to effect this your book must be published and receive the commendations of the learned abroad as well as in this country. As soon as the firt vol of the Contributions are out I will send a copy to Sir David Brewster through whose reccommendation I was elected to my present position[1] and have the work noticed in one of the english reviews. Your own course in the mean time must be one of labour and in some degree of sacrifice. You must as you have concluded to do fulfill all your contracts implied or otherwise with Dr Davis. I do not say that the publication of the article in the Ethnological transactions[2] should not have been given under your own name alone because I have not fully examined all the circumstances but as I now see the matter I should have preferred an other course. This however is now done and we can only act with caution in the future. Your true course in my opinion in this affair even were you to regard ↑only↓ your own interest is a generous one. Depend upon it you will loose nothing in the long run by not being too anxious to secure even as large a share of the honor as is your due. The ethnological society know that you are the writer of the article and if you go on with the Researches as I presume you will you will in due time secure all you desire and more.

"When I commenced my researches" said Dr Faraday to me, I was obliged to share the results of my labours with other and to see them accredited to persons who had no knowledge of them; but now that I have gained some reputation the world as if to make amends gives me more than my due.[3] You must go on with your researches the field is just opened and what will yet be accomplished by E. G. Squier will completely absorbe the labours of Messrs Squier and Davis; or in other words the latter will be merged in the former. I can speak from experience on this point I know how strongly you are tempted to swerve from your agreemnt particularly sinc your share of the labours have turned out to be much greater than you anticipated and[B] the fact that you are the writer of the article and apparently should not give your litterary ~~character~~ ↑labours↓ to ↑an↓ other; but there are higher considerations which should induce you ↑to↓ have a watch on yourself on this point and give no cause for a shade to settle on the fame you will hereafter acquire. I say you will[C]

Retained Copy, Henry Papers, Smithsonian Archives.
Partial draft in same location.

1. For Brewster's letter of recommendation, see *Henry Papers*, 6:527–528.

2. E. G. Squier, "Aboriginal Monuments of the Mississippi Valley," *Transactions of the American Ethnological Society*, 1848, 2:131–207. In late 1847 this publication appeared as an offprint of the *Transactions* under the title *Observations on the Aboriginal Monuments of the Mississippi Valley*, published in New York by Bartlett and Welford. *The Literary World*, December 4, 1847.

A footnote to the title page credits Davis with being Squier's associate and points to their joint forthcoming Smithsonian publication. Nonetheless Squier represented the article as based on his own observations, and, to justify separate publication, he contrasted its general and limited presentation with the larger, more detailed, and more finely produced Smithsonian memoir.

3. See, for example, Faraday's 1821 conflict with William Hyde Wollaston, who thought that Faraday had misappropriated his ideas on the rotational effects of galvanic currents. The London scientific society had initially thought Faraday guilty of plagiarism; the incident had darkened his early scientific career. L. Pearce Williams, *Michael Faraday* (New York, 1965), pp. 152–160.

125. TO CHARLES COFFIN JEWETT

Princeton Nov 25th/47

My dear Sir

Your interesting letter[1] with the accompanying communication for the Union came to hand just before I was about to start for New York and therefore I have had no opportunity of answering your inquiries before now.

I have read with much interest your communication intended for the Union and think the matter which it contains may ↑be↓ properly given to the Public with advantage to the Institution but I regret to be obliged to say, because I may wound your feelings by so doing, that I do not think it advisable both on your own account and that of the Institution to publish it at this time and in the manner you propose. It is highly important to the future well doing of the Institution that we should start fairly and do nothing which may tend to establish an improper precedent. The Board ~~as yet~~ have not as yet made any arrangement as to whom the duty shall fall of making communications to the public. I have myself published nothing except what I considered myself authorized to publish by a Resolution of the Board. If any officer be allowed to publish under his own name what he may think fit in reference to the Institution we shall be constantly liable to fall into difficulty on account of the precipitancy or error of judgement of many individuals. We must recollect that in starting we are not only working for ourselves but also for all who are to come after us.

The[A] subject of the publications ~~with reference to the Institution~~ has troubled me not a little. At[B] the last meeting of the Board a Resolution was passed authorizing ~~Mr Owen as chairman of the building~~ ↑the bulding↓ committee to publish a quarto volume givin an account of the plans of the building and containing hints on public architecture.[2] Now I very much regret the passage of this Resolution not on account of the ↑nature of the↓ publication ~~being prepared by Mr Owen~~ but because the precedent is a bad one. Though this work may ~~have~~ ↑contain↓ nothing objectionable yet some other may be published in the same way which would tend to diffuse error rather than ~~knowledge~~ ↑truth↓ among men and if one person is allowed to publish his views on any subject another in the same office may also claim the same privilege. You will perceive from these considerations ↑and your own good sense when you reflect on the subject↓ that it is highly important some rule should be established as to the organ of communication with the public and the ground of my objection just at this time to the publication of your article in the manner you propose. The plan I think best is that of p[r]esenting to the Board by the Secretary a general account of the doings of the Institution and appended to this the Report of the librarian &c and the whole submitted to Congress[C] for publication and distribution. If at any other time information is called for by the public and the officers of the Institution think it important that it should be given let the subject be discussed and the suitable statement be prepared and approved of by the executive officers and signed by the Chancellor and[D] the Secretary in the[E] official capacity. I have as yet refrained from publishing any thing in my own name directly; the various notices which have appeared in the papers relative to the publications of the Institution came from the Report of the Ethnological society as given in the proceedings of that society and published in the Literary world;[3] and also the advertisement of Mr Owens book by Wiley & Putnam.[4]

My own ~~feeling~~ ↑conviction↓ is that nothing should be published with any thing like an official sanction excet it has gone through a regular course of inspection and approval by competent judges.[5]

I know not what turn things may take at the next meeting of the Board. From what I can judge of the feeling of ~~a majority of~~ the ↑few↓ Regents[F] I ~~think~~ ↑have seen I should think that↓ they are convinced that an error of great magnitude has been committed with reference to the building; but I do not think[G] they will take the responsibility of undoing what they have done, and strike out the main building though I think it probable the building fund will be so arranged as not to absorb after this and the next year so large a portion of the income of the original fund.

The board meets on the 8th of Dec. the 2nd Wednesday in the month. I hope Mr Choat will not fail to be present and that I may have an opportunity of a conversation with him previous to the meeting with reference to your commencing operations.[6] My impression is, from the state of the funds so far as I have been able to gather any thing relative to them, that there will be an objection to your commencing full operation until the time specified in your appointment. I have drawn from the funds to carry on my operations including the purchase of apparatus about 2500 dollars the remainder of the yearly income will be absorbed in the payment of the installment to the building fund and other expenses.[7] You are acquainted with the fact that during this year and the next 15,000 dollars annually goes to the building fund to carry out the plan of finance agreed upon.

I am just now overwhelmed with engagements and am obliged to have my eyes open on all sides. Though I have as yet met withno insurmountable difficulty my whole thoughts are occupied in adjusting ~~difficulties and~~ ↑matters so as to a↓ avoiding obstacles.

> With much Respect
> I remain truly yours
> Joseph Henry

Professor Jewett

Draft, Henry Papers, Smithsonian Archives.

1. Doc. 122.

2. On February 5, 1847, the regents appropriated $1,000 to publish a thousand copies of *Hints on Public Architecture*. On March 6, the building committee assigned this task to Robert Dale Owen. The book was to explain the choice of design for the Smithsonian Institution Building and to present James Renwick's plans as well as any others that Owen might consider suitable. As published, the work was an elaborate defense of the Norman style of architecture of the building, on economic and aesthetic grounds, and was lavishly illustrated with Renwick's drawings and designs.

Rhees, *Journals*, pp. 32, 602; Cynthia R. Field, "About This Book and Its Author," in Robert Dale Owen, *Hints on Public Architecture* (1849; New York, 1978).

3. *The Literary World*, September 18, 1847, pp. 157–158.

4. No advertisements by Wiley & Putnam prior to the date of this letter have been found; the book appeared in 1849 under the auspices of George P. Putnam alone.

5. On December 15, 1847, the regents resolved, on A. D. Bache's motion, "That the Chancellor of the Smithsonian Institution be the organ of communication of the Smithsonian Institution with the public, and that the Secretary be the organ of communication between the officers of the institution and the Board." The last provision was perhaps prompted by Jewett's direct interaction with Choate. Rhees, *Journals*, p. 44.

6. Choate did not join the regents' meeting until December 21. Rhees, *Journals*, p. 45.

7. The report of the executive committee shows that, from the instigation of the institution, exclusive of his $1,750 for salary, Henry had spent approximately $1,500 on philosophical and chemical apparatus, about $200 on the SI Contributions, and about $1,300 on other objects: messengers, printing, postage, freight, and so forth. Almost all the rest of the some $40,000 spent was devoted directly or indirectly to the building. *Smithsonian Report for 1847*, p. 156.

126. FROM T. ROMEYN BECK

Albanyᴬ
Novʳ 29. 1847.ᴮ

Joseph Henry, LLD &c
Dear Sir,,

I have perused the copy of the "Proposed Organization" which you have been good enough to send me.[1]

I notice an omission, which may be either intentional or not. It is the exclusion of Medicine & Surgery from the Physical Class.[2] It appears to me that there are subjects belonging to them, which are legitimate subjects of philosophical research & therefore should be included. I instance, the Materia Medica, i:e the discovery of new Remedies orᶜ the improved application of oldᴰ ones; improvements in Surgery; Discoveries in Physiology; & lastly, the applications of one or moreᴱ to Medical Jurisprudence.

True, you are careful in your specifications, to leave room for this addition, but you must be aware that the Medical Profession embraces in this country a considerable portion of the talent & learning that might be roused into activity by the adoption of your plan & I submit whether the insertion of these subjects is not due to them.

There is another branch intimately connected with the above, which deserves every encouragement. It is the promotion of the Health of Communities or Hygiene as the French call it. No subject is less understood—none calls for public encouragement & attention more strongly than this dreadfully neglected matter.[3]

You will see that I refer in all this to the divisionᶠ of Reports. The "British Association" in directing ↑attention to↓ & popularising (if I may use the word) this plan of diffusing knowledge has done more good than most of the learned societies in the world.[4]

I prefer, with your permission, to give you my ideas in this way, instead of noting them on the programme.

I will in conclusion only hint at at a danger which unless early & constantly guarded against, may render your scheme unpopular & hence in a measure impair its usefullness. It is, the possibility of the selection of particular persons—orᴳ of associations of persons in different places, who may appear to assume the control in any particular department of Science—in other words, the formation of predominant cliques. These are the curse of most of our most distinguished Societies at home & abroad and in this country the danger is greater, from the fewness of men well grounded in Science & the disparity that exists between those, claiming to be adepts.

These views I give you, if I know my own heart, with a sincere desire that the Smithsonian Institution may attain the highest usefulness under your administration & that it may go on, "prospering & to prosper".

According to your wish, I direct to Princeton, as I mail on Monday.[5]

I remain with respectful remembrances to Mr Alexander & Mrs Henry.

Yours very truly
T. Romeyn Beck

I forgot to add, what indeed I expressed to you verbally, that your plan as a whole has my unqualified approbation.

RH 2719, Rhees Collection, Huntington Library.
Published, with slight editorial changes, in Rhees, *Documents* (1879), pp. 961–962.

1. Henry's printed draft "Programme of Organization."

2. The draft "Programme" provided for three classes of subjects for semi-popular reports: the physical class, the moral and political class, and the class of literature and the fine arts. The four divisions of the physical class—physical science, natural history, agriculture, and the application of science to arts—did not include the medical sciences per se; neither did these divisions change from the draft to the final "Programme."

3. The French were the primary innovators and leaders in public health in the nineteenth century. William Coleman, *Death is a Social Disease: Public Health and Political Economy in Early Industrial France* (Madison, Wisconsin, 1982). British sources brought the expanded sense of the word "hygiene" as *public* health from its French origins to American audiences. For example, the 1843 New York edition of W. T. Brande's *Dictionary of Science, Literature, and Art* defined hygiene as "that branch of medicine which relates to the means of preserving public health."

Beck's call for the encouragement of and attention to public health was timely. For example, at the first meeting of the American Medical Association, in May 1848 in Baltimore, the National Institute's committee on the sanitary condition of the United States called for the establishment of a permanent committee on hygiene, to promote educational and information-gathering efforts. "Communication on Hygiene, from the Medical Department of the National Institute," *Transactions of the American Medical Association*, 1848, 1:305–310.

4. For the British Association reports, see *Henry Papers*, 6:614n.

5. November 29.

127. FROM JOHN TORREY

New York, Decr 1st 1847.

My dear friend.

You are now quietly settled in what must be (for some years at least) your home, & I trust you will find it a pleasant one. By the papers I see that the building is quite up, & looks extremely well. The other wing, I suppose, will not be commenced till this one is finished.[1] At this moderate rate the fund will be properly economized.

We have been greatly delighted with the Lectures of Prof. Agassiz. He gave a popular course of 10 lectures to an audience of ladies & gentlemen[2]—& a short one (of 6 lectures) on Embryology. The latter a voluntary matter to our students, & such medical gentlemen as we might invite. He had a room for himself & artists, in our College, & spent some hours there every day so that I saw much of him, & learned how he works.

On Saturday last[3] he sailed for Charleston, where he is to deliver a course of lectures, & on the 1st of January he lectures before the Lowell Institute of Boston. Capt. Wilkes informed me lately that he meant to consult you about a course on Nat! History in Washington—& I think it would be an excellent plan—as it would make the subject popular, where there is either prejudice against it—or it is little known— Cannot you connect a course with your institution in some way?

We raised for Mr. Agassiz nearly $1300 clear of all expences—which is pretty good for New York.

Capt Wilkes has been very urgent of late that I should take the whole of the plants of the Exploring Exped^n—& I have agreed to do so conditionally[4]— If I could only get some place in the Smithsonian where my knowledge would be worth a moderate salary,—I would cut loose from the Med. College—(which is very uncertain—& turned out badly this year)—as well as from Princeton, & take up my quarters in Washington—

I wrote to you several weeks ago[5] about a young man, Thomas Evans,[6] for whom I was desirous of obtaining some occupation—but I suppose you were to busy to answer it. It has occurred to me that he could be very usefully employed in one of the Surveys—geological or topographical. Perhaps you would write a word—or speak a word in his favor, to Mr. Owen[7]— T.E. is a good chemist & mineralogist & would be willing to make himself useful in any way, in an exped^n & for moderate pay— Do remember him if you are not too much pressed for I feel much interested in the young man.

What is to be done in the Survey of the Dead Sea? Will the plants be collected?[8]—

Remember me most kindly to Mrs Henry, & believe me Cordially Yours

John Torrey

Henry Papers, Smithsonian Archives.

1. A short article on the Smithsonian in the *New York Daily Tribune,* November 5, 1847, stated in part: "The Smithsonian building is so far advanced as to attract much attention. The east wing is now nearly completed, as to its exterior, and it is a most impressive and attractive edifice."

2. Agassiz gave twelve lectures, not ten. See Doc. 120, note 4.

3. November 27.

4. That is, in addition to the plants of California and Oregon, which he had agreed to work up in April 1847, in the wake of William Rich's disastrous attempts at scientific description. However, other botanists, notably Asa Gray, wrote on the balance of the plant specimens. *Henry Papers, 6:*582.

5. October 17, 1847, Henry Papers, Smithsonian Archives.

6. Torrey's letter described Thomas Harley Evans (born in the United Kingdom, d. 1885) as being recommended by James Apjohn (*Henry Papers, 3:*325n), professor of chemistry at the College of Surgeon's School, Dublin, and by the professors of the Royal College of Surgeons there. He had worked in Apjohn's laboratory, had had experience in a terrestrial magnetic observatory, and had been Torrey's chemical assistant at Princeton. Evans himself wrote to Henry in the summer of 1848, seeking employment which he said that Henry had promised.

He failed to find work and went into the United States Army. Evans to Henry, July 14 and 22, and August 21, 1848, Henry Papers, Smithsonian Archives; F. B. Heitman, *Historical Register of the United States Army, from Its Organization, September 29, 1789, to September 29, 1889* (Washington, 1890).

7. Either Robert Dale Owen or David Dale Owen.

8. On November 26, 1847, a Navy expedition sailed from New York to the Holy Land. Under the command of Lieutenant William Francis Lynch, the expedition lasted approximately a year. Although Philadelphia naturalist Samuel Haldeman wished to accompany it, funds were insufficient and Lynch appointed his son, Francis E. Lynch, as the expedition's botanist. Upon its return, Robert Eglesfeld Griffith, a Philadelphia physician and naturalist, prepared a botanical catalogue of the plants collected. But no plates were prepared, "as the plants, although sufficiently well preserved for classification, were many of them too much mutilated to be *truly* represented by drawings." W. F. Lynch, *Official Report of the United States' Expedition to Explore the Dead Sea and the River Jordan* (Baltimore, 1852), pp. [5] (quotation), 10, 46, 59; John Dryden Kazar, Jr., "The United States Navy and Scientific Exploration, 1837–1860" (Ph.D. diss., University of Massachusetts, 1973), pp. 127–135, especially pp. 128, 131.

128. FROM BENJAMIN SILLIMAN, SR.

New Haven Dec[r] 4— 1847

My dear Sir

Your letter of Nov[r] 26,[1] with the programme of the Smithsonian Institution, was duly received, and I have endeavored to bestow upon it a degree of consideration proportionate to its importance.

Regarding the will of M[r] Smithson as the rule and the only rule which ought to govern, I have no hesitation in saying, that the views propounded in the Programme are sound & correct, and ought therefore to be sustained.

It is obvious, that M[r] Smithson intended that his fund should operate, intellectually, and no farther physically, than is necessary for the mental effects. Books, instruments and museums of objects of nature & art are necessary to that end and are therefore within the views & purpose of the donor; but splendid buildings of costly materials and construction, if erected at the expence of the Smithsonian fund would prove a perversion of the design and an abuse of the trust.[2]

The neglect in which the bequest was allowed for eight years to lie, created a claim both of honor and equity which ought to result in the enlargement of the fund by the appropriation of the accumulated interest to become a part of the productive capital. It would be a meritorious application of a portion of the national revenue if the buildings requisite for the accommodation of the Smithsonian Institution were to be furnished by the government in aid of the great design for the "increase and diffusion of knowledge among men."—

If however that course is impracticable, we may well enquire whether an appropriation of the income of a single year—say fifty thousand dollars[3]—might not afford sufficient funds for the requisite building constructed in a style of chaste and elegant simplicity without expensive ornament and adapted mainly to utility.

If this course were pursued the fund would be preserved inviolate and it would seem to be a wise forecaste to limit the annual expenditures ↑so↓ that an accumulating fund might be formed—which in a few years—with compound interest resulting from frequent investments of savings might augment the capital to a million of dollars.

If it is within the views of the government to bestow the National Museum upon the Smithsonian Institution the very bequest would seem to draw after it an obligation to furnish the requisite accommodations without taxing the Smithsonian funds; otherwise the gift might be detrimental instead of beneficial and ↑if↓ the government should retain the proprietorship of the National Museum but at the same time impose upon the Smithsonian Institution the burden of providing a building for its accommodation—not to say for its increase—this would obviously be an invasion of the rights of the Institution which could not be justified.—

Will not every purpose promotive of the object of Mʳ Smithson be accomplished by allowing the National Museum to remain in buildings furnished by the government and augmented from time to time as the exigencies of the collections may require.

It will then be equally accessible to all cultivators of any feild of knowledge demanding such illustrations and the Smithsonian Institution will be left a liberty to pursue its own objects in its own way. ~~and should~~

As regards the objects of research indicated in the Programme I would suggest that in addition to the law of storms* observations should be made on our various climates in relation to temperature—moisture & electricity and their effect upon agriculture and health.[4]

Under the head of Surveys it is desirable also to include our most important mineral resources in coal and metals and in permanent materials for architecture and for civil & military engineering.[5]

No mention is made of Natural History in extenso & Zoology & Botany are not named.[6]

The outline of subjects might perhaps be made more concise and still more comprehensive and it is desirable not to enact unnecessary limitations which might prove embarrassing.

As Mr Smithson object was all men—not merely Americans or Englishmen—it is desirable that every latitude should be allowed for cooperation with all cultivators of knowledge.[7]

I have had not opportunity to consult the Connecticut Academy but will lay the subject before them towards the close of the month.[8] I have the coinciding opinions of Mr Dana & my son[9] with the above & remain my

dear Sir truly yours
B Silliman

Prof Henry

*Not confined however to American storms.^A

RH 3841, Rhees Collection, Huntington Library.
Published, lacking salutation and close, in Rhees, *Documents* (1879), pp. 962–964.

1. Not found.

2. The tenth and eleventh of Henry's general points introducing the "Programme of Organization" addressed themselves to the building, urging economy and maintaining it should be a reflection of the objects of the institution and not the reverse.

3. Currently the institution realized $45,310 annually from its investments: $30,910 in interest on the original bequest of $515,169; and $14,400 in interest on treasury notes of $240,000, which was the bulk of the interest which had accrued on the bequest from its receipt in 1838 until the institution's organization in 1846. *Smithsonian Report for 1847,* p. 164.

4. Under the general head of the increase of knowledge, Henry's "Programme" provided for directed research. It listed many different examples throughout the natural and social sciences. His suggestion for a system of meteorological observations was directed to "solving the problem of American Storms."

5. Henry's suggestions encompassed "Geological, Magnetical, and Topographical surveys to collect materials for the formation of a physical atlas of the United States." Architecture and engineering only appeared under topics for reports—as means of diffusing knowledge, but not as subjects for directed research. The final "Programme" did not incorporate Silliman's suggestions.

6. Again, the draft "Programme" named botany and zoology only as possible subjects of reports. The final version added "exploration in descriptive natural history" to the language on research surveys, but did not specify this further.

7. Though the "Programme" specified that

"the bequest is for the benefit of mankind" and the institution was "not a national establishment," neither in draft nor final version did it specifically mention that researchers and report preparers could be of any nationality.

8. No response from the academy has been found.

9. Benjamin Silliman, Jr., professor of chemistry at Yale and co-editor of *Silliman's Journal*. *Henry Papers,* 4:100n.

129. FROM JOHN LOCKE

Cincinnati Dec 10 1847

My Dear Sir

I have been sometime returned fro[m][A] the Lakes, and am anxious to know how things are going on with my friends. I sent you from Detroit I believe some pretty heavy packages[1] subjecting you to a tax of postage which I shall refund. As Congress is now assembling[2] and I am anxious to obtain an appointment to the Magnetical Department of the two surveys[3] I venture tax your attention so far as to inform me, if convenient to you what is the prospect in reference to the magnetical communications which I have forwarded. If they cannot be published in the papers of the Smithsonian I am desirous of publishing them myself at this place to distribute amongst my friends.[4] I must rely on your friendship for such suggestions as your knowledge of affairs may enable you to make.

My expedition was in itself interesting but I found a corps of Boston[B] boys not very well suited to the the Woods service, and they were too well satisfied of their own superiour qualifications and accomplishments to be instructed or directed by me; at least this was true of part of them.[5] My magnetical in re researches have afforded a rich harvest. I found repeatedly poles of local attraction at which the Dipping needle stood vertical.[6]

I had prepared a newspaper article relative to the atitude assumed by the Washington folks in relation to yourself and the Smithsonian but I have so far withheld it, being doubtful of the expediency of publication. If it is not too much trouble please inform me of the present posture of affairs.

Your much obliged
Friend & Humble servt
John Locke

Henry Papers, Smithsonian Archives.

1. According to a previous letter, Locke sent his magnetic observations for the previous two years. Locke to Henry, June 28, 1847, Henry Papers, Smithsonian Archives.

2. Congress convened December 6. *BDAC*.

3. That is, to both the Jackson survey of the Lake Superior Land District of Michigan (in which Locke had just participated) and the Owen survey of the Chippewa Land District of Wisconsin. See Doc. 39.

4. Locke's communications comprised work from Ohio to Maine, done in 1845, and in the mid-Atlantic region, done under Coast Survey auspices in 1846. With his 1847 Michigan work, these were to form the eighth through the tenth of his series of observations. The government held back the last of these, and none appeared in the Smithsonian Contribu-

tions to Knowledge until 1852. See Doc. 39, note 4.

5. Of the fourteen members of the expedition, Jackson, subagent William F. Channing, and packman G. Dickenson were from Boston. Other Massachusetts natives were assistant Josiah Dwight Whitney, from Northampton; subagent Joseph Peabody, from Salem; assistant subagent George O. Barnes, from Plymouth; and subagent John W. Foster, from Petersham. Charles T. Jackson, *Report on the Geological and Mineralogical Survey of the Mineral Lands of the United States in the State of Michigan*, U.S. Senate, 31st Congress, 1st Session, Senate Executive Documents, No. 1, part 3 (1849), p. 394.

6. Most likely, indicative of deposits of iron ore.

130. "PROGRAMME OF ORGANIZATION OF THE SMITHSONIAN INSTITUTION"

December 13, 1847

Henry's program of organization of the Smithsonian Institution—presented with his report to the regents on December 10, 1847, and provisionally adopted three days later—became the most widely distributed and concise expression of the nature of the institution.

The development of the program was intimately tied to ongoing discussions over the direction of the institution. The act establishing the Smithsonian gave little guidance on its active programs, specifying little more than a building.[1] At the regents' meetings in December 1846 and January 1847, three groups emerged. The first, the populist faction, was represented by Robert Dale Owen and William Winston Seaton and was concerned with constructing a grand building, supporting a museum, and sponsoring an active program of popular lecturing and publishing. The second was the library faction, led by Rufus Choate and dedicated to the creation of a great national library. The final group was headed by Alexander Dallas Bache; dedicated to using the bequest primarily for the promotion of scientific research and publication, its views accorded with Henry's ideas.

These three groups contended for control in the early regents' meetings. Their uneasy compromises are marked by the final report of the committee of organization, adopted January 25, 1847, and the resolutions authorizing the building and dividing the income of the institution between collections—for a library and a museum—and programs of research, publication, and lecturing.

Out of these compromises came Henry's program. As the regents concluded their business, they charged the committee of organization with developing a plan to effect their resolutions. They also directed Henry to one, but only one part of this task: "to present to the Committee on Organization a plan for executing the resolutions relating to Smithsonian contributions, to annual reports and other publications, to premiums, and to original researches" and "to communicate with men eminent in science and literature, and to ask their advice . . . in regard to the subjects for which premiums shall be offered, and upon which reports and essays shall be prepared."[2] Excluded from Henry's charge was concern for the library, other collections, and popular lectures. By the time that Henry presented his program to the Board of Regents in December, however, it was a full plan of organization[3]—and in his report he had retrospectively expanded his directives from the board to account for that development as well.[4]

The program shows its origin as a document originally limited to the research and publication programs. Its focus is "Section I," which details his plan of offering premiums for "positive additions to human knowledge," of directing research, of establishing the Smithsonian Contributions to Knowledge series and the Smithsonian reports series, and of commissioning semi-popular "treatises on subjects of general interest." Henry made clear his distinction between plans for the increase and for the diffusion of knowledge and gave examples of subjects appropriate for scholarly research and for popular reports. He also gave a preliminary indication of the type of consultation and review that the institution would use to guide its research and publication program.

These plans are not startling on their face; they largely embody Henry's thinking about the institution since at least September 1846 and presumably were forcefully argued in regents' meetings in January 1847. What is striking is the way these ideas were presented. The subheading which Henry gave to this section was "Plan of organization of the institution, in accordance with the foregoing deductions from the will of Smithson." And indeed "Section I" was preceded by an "Introduction" presenting thirteen items giving the terms of Smithson's will and Henry's analysis of what that language implied.[5] Not surprisingly, these "deductions from the will of Smithson" stated that knowledge can be increased by "facilitating and promoting the discovery of new truths"— that is, by research—while it "can be most efficiently diffused among men by means of the press." These general considerations (as well as the limited funds of the institution) argued against a large building, "unnecessary expenditure on local objects," and a large permanent staff, that is, against a museum, library, and attendant activities. Smithson's will supported Henry and Bache, not Owen or Choate.

Thus, Henry rhetorically reversed the thrust of the *Report of the Organization Committee*.[6] Where that report had begun with the congressional act and discussed the museum building, and then worked around to research, publications, lectures, and, finally, to the library, Henry started with Smithson's will and presented his research and publication program as flowing from it. More importantly, he presented his program as the *only* one lying within the strictures of Smithson's will. All other activities lay outside it and were explicitly labeled so: "Section II," describing these activities, bore the subheading "Plan of organization, in accordance with the terms of the resolutions of the Board of Regents, providing for the two modes of increasing and diffusing knowledge."[7] These operations were authorized by the regents, working within the act establishing the institution.[8] But in a larger sense, they were illegitimate, as violating Smithson's intent. Henry maintained this position throughout his life; in 1877 he claimed that at his first meeting with the regents in 1846 he had argued against the museum and library, saying: "the resolutions of Congress may be changed, but the will of a dead man should be inviolable."[9]

Finally, despite Henry's strategy in presenting his ideas, the program shows Henry's essential pragmatism in dealing with the regents and their wishes. He was at pains to point out that the "two modes" were not incompatible and might in fact reinforce one another. A good library was essential to scientific research. Conversely, the publications of the institution might be exchanged for the corresponding ones of other institutions, and so build up the library.[10] Similarly, a carefully selected collection of natural history specimens, objects of art, and scientific instruments, could support both scientific research and especially demonstration. Henry looked for mutual support where he could find it, and insisted that the institution remain flexible: "the organization should also be such as can be adopted provisionally, can be easily reduced to practice, receive modifications, or be abandoned, in whole or in part, without a sacrifice of the funds."[11] In this way, Henry may have been realistic, in knowing the changes through which new organizations develop. Or he may have indicated his continued willingness to push for changes in the organization, as indeed he did after 1853, when he abandoned the compromises of 1847. It was in this same vein of flexibility, however, that the regents approved "Section I" and "Section II" of the program "provisionally" on December 13, 1847.[12]

Henry's program was widely distributed, and became the Smithsonian's public statement on the aim and nature of the institution. *Silliman's Journal* printed it as part of its review of the annual report of the institution.[13] In a slightly edited version it became the centerpiece of Henry's address to the American Association for the Advancement of Science in August of 1848. It was published as part of the proceedings of the association; moreover, Henry repeated his remarks almost verbatim to the New Jersey Historical Society the following week, and in this form the speech—and the program—were printed as an official publication of the Smithsonian and widely distributed.[14] The program appeared in virtually the same form at almost the same time as a preface to Squier and Davis's *Ancient Monuments of the Mississippi Valley*.[15] The program then led off every volume of the Smithsonian Contributions to Knowledge series throughout Henry's tenure as secretary. The program was also printed as a four-page pamphlet, and sent out with the circular on libraries[16] and on many other occasions.

The program had one other important function for Henry, to secure his own vision of the institution. Although reprinted in the 1848 annual report of the institution to Congress, it was thereafter absent until 1855. At that time, Henry was emerging from his ultimately successful battle for control of the institution's activities, during which he had had to abrogate the compromises and to fire Charles C. Jewett. He took this occasion to republish the program of organization. There were a few significant changes, however. In "Section II," instead of the descriptions of the duties of secretary and assistant secretary, was this language, derived from the Smithsonian act: "The Secretary, by the law of Congress, is alone responsible to the Regents. He shall take charge of the building and property, keep a record of proceedings, discharge the duties of librarian and keeper of the museum, and may, with the consent of the Regents, *employ assistants.*"[17] This was followed by the statement that the program, "which was at first adopted provisionally, has become the settled policy of the institution" (with the exception, of course, of those changes involved in repealing the compromises of 1847).[18] This version of the program, with its forceful language of Henry's control, formed the preface to every succeeding annual report of the institution through 1872.

The program of organization was thus a defining document for the institution. In the most prosaic sense, it provided the occasion for Henry to clarify not only his own thoughts, but also the disparate actions the regents had taken from the formation of the institution up through the meetings of early 1847. He was able to work out many of his ideas for supporting scientific research and publication, while fitting the demands for a museum, a library, and a popular lecture series into the organization as well, coordinated with what he saw as the main charge of the Smithsonian. But in a broader sense, this was a defining document by the way it allowed Henry to take the initiative. He was able to set the program: to make his favorite component of it the centerpiece, to clearly distinguish between his ideas and others', to define the terms of legitimation between Smithson's will and Congress's act, and to publicize the result. That he was able to get the regents' approval for the program is a credit to his persuasive powers. But that he was able to use the program as an effective tool to turn the mission of the Smithsonian increasingly to his own views shows Henry's vision and his persistence.

For the text as adopted by the Board of Regents, see the *Smithsonian Report for 1847*, pp. 173–177, with "Explanations and Illustrations of the Programme," pp. 177–184. The date is that of the provisional acceptance by the regents: Rhees, *Journals*, p. 41. The program, as it was printed for distribution, also forms one of the illustrations of this volume.

1. See *Henry Papers*, 6:463–471, for a discussion of the Smithsonian act.

2. On January 26, 1847. Rhees, *Journals*, pp. 26–27.

3. Henry drafted the program in May 1847, sharing it with friends, scientific colleagues, and other interested parties. He presented his ideas in public at the meeting of the Association of American Geologists and Naturalists in Boston in September 1847, and sent printed drafts to eminent American scientists, literary figures, and politicians, and American scientific and cultural organizations, in October and November, for comments and to gather support for the regents' meeting, which began December 8. In preparation for this meeting, Henry presented the program to the committee of organization for its consideration and approval.

There were at least four and perhaps five versions of the program previous to the one that was finally adopted. Of these, only two survive. Of Henry's earliest conception of the program—of May 1847—nothing is known as no copies have been found. (Henry's undated manuscript notes on the program are in Folder "Smithsonian Institution Notes and Papers [Misc.]," Box 30, Henry Papers, Smithsonian Archives, and in Henry's Pocket Notebook [13279]. Mostly these notes concern plans for the research and publication programs, with some disparaging remarks about the National Museum and the National Institute.) The earliest extant version is a handwritten one sent to Edward Sabine on August 13, 1847. By this time, the program had grown to cover all the proposed operations of the Smithsonian and possessed the same format as the final version. The only other extant draft is in printed form and was presented to John Quincy Adams in October. It is in the Adams Papers, Massachusetts Historical Society, and has been photographically reproduced in the appendix to Wilcomb E. Washburn, ed., *The Great Design: Two Lectures on Smithson's Bequest by John Quincy Adams* (Washington, 1965). There is some evidence that another printing of the program, possibly of a revised edition, took place in late November. Presumably this produced the version that was presented to the committee of organization. Finally, there were some "unimportant additions and corrections made by the committee of organization to whom the article had to be submitted" (Doc. 134), indicating one more set of changes before the final version.

4. "In accordance with my instructions, I consulted with men of eminence, in the different branches of literature and science, relative to the details of the plan of organization, and arranged the various suggestions offered, in the form of the accompanying programme." [*Smithsonian Report for 1847*, p. 172.]

5. Henry credited William Campbell Preston with much of the ideas and language of this first page (see Doc. 110). The fourteenth item, not pertaining to the will, was added between the printed draft given J. Q. Adams and the final version, and probably represents the wishes of the committee of organization.

6. Printed as a separate publication, Washington, 1847.

7. That the two modes are first, the "active program" of research and publication and, second, the program of collections and lectures, is clear from the subtitle in the printed draft in the Adams Papers, which reads "Plan of Organization, in accordance with the terms of the compromise between the two modes . . . ."

8. Again, see *Henry Papers*, 6:463–471, especially the discussions of the sections that specified a building, provided for a library through copyright deposit, and left the rest up to the regents through the "elastic clause."

9. Henry to J. P. Lesley, January 12, 1877, Henry Papers, Smithsonian Archives.

10. In the "Explanations and Illustrations of the Programme," *Smithsonian Report for 1847*, p. 183.

11. Introduction, item 9, *Smithsonian Report for 1847*, p. 173.

12. Accommodation had its limits, however. "Section II," item 17, of the program looked forward to the reception of the National Museum upon the completion of the building. Yet in the "Explanations and Illustrations of the Programme," Henry explicitly called for that museum to be supported in another manner. *Smithsonian Report for 1847*, pp. 177, 184.

13. *Silliman's Journal*, 1848, 2d ser. 6:289–305.

14. *Smithson's Bequest: Prof. Henry's Exposition, before the New Jersey Historical Society at Its Meeting in Princeton . . .* ([Washington, 1848]).

15. There were some minor editorial changes, and two major ones: the introductory material was not included, although Smithson's will was summarized; and in "Section II," items 14 and 15 were dropped, describing the duties of the secretary and assistant secretary.

16. Doc. 231.

17. *Smithsonian Report for 1855*, p. 12, emphasis in the original.

18. The regents' provisions repealing the compromises followed directly after the program.

PROGRAMME OF ORGANIZATION

OF THE

SMITHSONIAN INSTITUTION.

[Presented to the Board of Regents, Dec. 8, 1847.]

INTRODUCTION.

General considerations which should serve as a guide in adopting a plan of organization.

1. WILL OF SMITHSON.   The property is bequeathed to the United States of America, "to found at Washington, under the name of the Smithsonian Institution, an establishment for the increase and diffusion of knowledge among men."

2. The bequest is for the benefit of mankind.   The Government of the United States is merely a trustee to carry out the design of the testator.

3. The institution is not a national establishment, as is frequently supposed, but the establishment of an individual, and is to bear and perpetuate his name.

4. The objects of the institution are—1st, to increase, and 2d, to diffuse knowledge among men.

5. These two objects should not be confounded with one another.   The first is to increase the existing stock of knowledge by the addition of new truths; and the second, to disseminate knowledge, thus increased, among men.

6. The will makes no restriction in favor of any particular kind of knowledge; hence all branches are entitled to a share of attention.

7. Knowledge can be increased by different methods of facilitating and promoting the discovery of new truths; and can be most efficiently diffused among men by means of the press.

8. To effect the greatest amount of good, the organization should be such as to enable the institution to produce results, in the way of increasing and diffusing knowledge, which cannot be produced by the existing institutions in our country.

9. The organization should also be such as can be adopted provisionally, can be easily reduced to practice, receive modifications, or be abandoned, in whole or in part, without a sacrifice of the funds.

10. In order to make up for the loss of time occasioned by the delay of eight years in establishing the institution, a considerable portion of the interest which has accrued should be added to the principal.

11. In proportion to the wide field of knowledge to be cultivated, the funds are small.   Economy should therefore be consulted in the construction of the building; and not only the first cost of the edifice should be considered, but also the continual expense of keeping it in repair, and of the support of the establishment necessarily connected with it.   There should also be but few individuals permanently supported by the institution.

12. The plan and dimensions of the building should be determined by the plan of the organization, and not the converse.

13. It should be recollected that mankind in general are to be benefited by the bequest, and that, therefore, all unnecessary expenditure on local objects would be a perversion of the trust.

14. Besides the foregoing considerations, deduced immediately from the will of Smithson, regard must be had to certain requirements of the act of Congress establishing the institution.   These are, a library, a museum, and a gallery of art, with a building on a liberal scale to contain them.

Henry's "Programme of Organization of the Smithsonian Institution," as printed
for distribution. Courtesy of the Smithsonian Institution Archives.

SECTION I.

Plan of organization of the institution in accordance with the foregoing deductions from the will of Smithson.

To Increase Knowledge. It is proposed—

1. To stimulate men of talent to make original researches, by offering suitable rewards for memoirs containing new truths ; and,

2. To appropriate annually a portion of the income for particular researches, under the direction of suitable persons.

To Diffuse Knowledge. It is proposed—

1. To publish a series of periodical reports on the progress of the different branches of knowledge ; and,

2. To publish occasionally separate treatises on subjects of general interest.

DETAILS OF THE PLAN TO INCREASE KNOWLEDGE.

I. *By stimulating researches.*

1. Rewards, consisting of money, medals, &c., offered for original memoirs on all branches of knowledge.

2. The memoirs thus obtained to be published in a series of volumes, in a quarto form, and entitled Smithsonian Contributions to Knowledge.

3. No memoir, on subjects of physical science, to be accepted for publication, which does not furnish a positive addition to human knowledge, resting on original research ; and all unverified speculations to be rejected.

4. Each memoir presented to the institution to be submitted for examination to a commission of persons of reputation for learning in the branch to which the memoir pertains; and to be accepted for publication only in case the report of this commission is favorable.

5. The commission to be chosen by the officers of the institution, and the name of the author, as far as practicable, concealed unless a favorable decision be made.

6. The volumes of the memoirs to be exchanged for the Transactions of literary and scientific societies, and copies to be given to all the colleges, and principal libraries, in this country. One part of the remaining copies may be offered for sale ; and the other carefully preserved, to form complete sets of the work, to supply the demand from new institutions.

7. An abstract, or popular account, of the contents of these memoirs to be given to the public through the annual report of the Regents to Congress.

II. *By appropriating a portion of the income, annually, to special objects of research, under the direction of suitable persons.*

1. The objects, and the amount appropriated, to be recommended by counsellors of the institution.

2. Appropriations in different years to different objects ; so that in course of time, each branch of knowledge may receive a share.

3. The results obtained from these appropriations to be published, with the memoirs before mentioned, in the volumes of the Smithsonian Contributions to Knowledge.

4. Examples of objects for which appropriations may be made :

(1.) System of extended meteorological observations for solving the problem of American storms.

(2.) Explorations in descriptive natural history, and geological, magnetical, and topographical surveys, to collect materials for the formation of a Physical Atlas of the United States.

(3.) Solution of experimental problems, such as a new determination of the weight of the earth, of the velocity of electricity, and of light ; chemical analyses of soils and plants ; collection and publication of articles of science, accumulated in the offices of Government.

(4.) Institution of statistical inquiries with reference to physical, moral, and political subjects.

(5.) Historical researches, and accurate surveys of places celebrated in American history.

(6.) Ethnological researches, particularly with reference to the different races of men in North America ; also explorations, and accurate surveys, of the mounds and other remains of the ancient people of our country.

SECTION I.—CONTINUED.

DETAILS OF THE PLAN FOR DIFFUSING KNOWLEDGE.

I. *By the publication of a series of reports, giving an account of the new discoveries in science, and of the changes made from year to year in all branches of knowledge not strictly professional.*

1. These reports will diffuse a kind of knowledge generally interesting, but which, at present, is inaccessible to the public. Some of the reports may be published annually, others at longer intervals, as the income of the institution or the changes in the branches of knowledge may indicate.

2. The reports are to be prepared by collaborators, eminent in the different branches of knowledge.

3. Each collaborator to be furnished with the journals and publications, domestic and foreign, necessary to the compilation of his report ; to be paid a certain sum for his labors, and to be named on the title page of the report.

4. The reports to be published in separate parts, so that persons interested in a particular branch, can procure the parts relating to it without purchasing the whole.

5. These reports may be presented to Congress, for partial distribution, the remaining copies to be given to literary and scientific institutions, and sold to individuals for a moderate price.

The following are some of the subjects which may be embraced in the reports:

I. PHYSICAL CLASS.

1. Physics, including astronomy, natural philosophy, chemistry, and meteorology.
2. Natural history, including botany, zoology, geology, &c.
3. Agriculture.
4. Application of science to arts.

II. MORAL AND POLITICAL CLASS.

5. Ethnology, including particular history, comparative philology, antiquities, &c.
6. Statistics and political economy.
7. Mental and moral philosophy.
8. A survey of the political events of the world; penal reform, &c.

III. LITERATURE AND THE FINE ARTS.

9. Modern literature.
10. The fine arts, and their application to the useful arts.
11. Bibliography.
12. Obituary notices of distinguished individuals.

II. *By the publication of separate treatises on subjects of general interest.*

1. These treatises may occasionally consist of valuable memoirs translated from foreign languages, or of articles prepared under the direction of the institution, or procured by offering premiums for the best exposition of a given subject.

2. The treatises should, in all cases, be submitted to a commission of competent judges, previous to their publication.

3. As examples of these treatises, expositions may be obtained of the present state of the several branches of knowledge mentioned in the table of reports. Also of the following subjects suggested by the Committee on Organization, viz: The statistics of labor, the productive arts of life, public instruction, &c.

SECTION II.

Plan of organization, in accordance with the terms of the resolutions of the Board of Regents providing for the two modes of increasing and diffusing knowledge.

1. The act of Congress establishing the institution contemplated the formation of a library and a museum; and the Board of Regents, including these objects in the plan of organization, resolved to divide the income into two equal parts.

2. One part to be appropriated to increase and diffuse knowledge by means of publications and researches, agreeably to the scheme before given. The other part to be appropriated to the formation of a library and a collection of objects of nature and of art.

3. These two plans are not incompatible with one another.

4. To carry out the plan before described, a library will be required, consisting, 1st, of a complete collection of the transactions and proceedings of all the learned societies in the world; 2d, of the more important current periodical publications, and other works necessary in preparing the periodical reports.

5. The institution should make special collections, particularly of objects to verify its own publications.

6. Also a collection of instruments of research in all branches of experimental science.

7. With reference to the collection of books, other than those mentioned above, catalogues of all the different libraries in the United States should be procured, in order that the valuable books first purchased may be such as are not to be found in the United States.

8. Also catalogues of memoirs, and of books in foreign libraries, and other materials, should be collected for rendering the institution a centre of bibliographical knowledge, whence the student may be directed to any work which he may require.

9. It is believed that the collections in natural history will increase by donation as rapidly as the income of the institution can make provision for their reception, and, therefore, it will seldom be necessary to purchase any articles of this kind.

10. Attempts should be made to procure for the gallery of arts casts of the most celebrated articles of ancient and modern sculpture.

11. The arts may be encouraged by providing a room, free of expense, for the exhibition of the objects of the Art-Union and other similar societies.

12. A small appropriation should annually be made for models of antiquities, such as those of the remains of ancient temples, &c.

13. For the present, or until the building is fully completed, besides the Secretary, no permanent assistant will be required, except one, to act as librarian.

14. The duty of the Secretary will be the general superintendence, with the advice of the Chancellor and other members of the establishment, of the literary and scientific operations of the institution; to give to the Regents annually an account of all the transactions; of the memoirs which have been received for publication; of the researches which have been made; and to edit, with the assistance of the librarian, the publications of the institution.

15. The duty of the Assistant Secretary, acting as librarian, will be, for the present, to assist in taking charge of the collections, to select and purchase, under the direction of the Secretary and a committee of the board, books and catalogues, and to procure the information before mentioned; to give information on plans of libraries, and to assist the Secretary in editing the publications of the institution, and in the other duties of his office.

16. The Secretary and his assistants, during the session of Congress, will be required to illustrate new discoveries in science, and to exhibit new objects of art; distinguished individuals should also be invited to give lectures on subjects of general interest.

17. When the building is completed, and when, in accordance with the act of Congress, the charge of the National Museum is given to the Smithsonian Institution, other assistants will be required.

131. TO EPHRAIM GEORGE SQUIER

Washington Dec. 17[th][–25] 1847

My dear Sir

I have been so much engaged in the meetings of the Board that I have been unable to keep up with my correspondance and have only answered such letters as required immediate attention. The Board are still in daily session but will probably adjourn on Tuesday next.[1] All things appear to be taking a proper direction ~~and such an arrangement has been proposed and will probably be adopted as will increase the annual income from 30 to 40 thousand dollars at the time the building is finished.~~[2] There is a cloud in the House which portends something of a storm but ~~but~~ I do not at this time see much to fear as to the prosperity of the Institution provided there be no unforeseen difficulties in the way of carrying out the plan of Increase and Diffusion which I have been advocating[3]— And I beg leave to say to you that much odium and abuse will rest on the Secretary of the Institution if your memoir is not published in due[A] time and if when published it is not found to do justice to the subject or to previous explorers.

I regret on the whole for more reasons than one that your paper in the transactions of the ethnological society[4] was published just at this time and under your own name since it has given rise to considerable enquiry on the part of some of the members of the Board.

I beg that you will now devote all your time to the completion of the memoir. In order to give you all the facility possible in preparing your paper I suffered you to go on with the engravings before the memoir was finished. In future I shall make it a rule to have nothing to do with a paper until it is entirely finished—all the drawings completed and the article given up entirely into my hands. In your case I was desposed to furnish you with every facility in my power and am still inclined to give you any indulgence compatible with the good of the Institution but the memoir must be finished as soon as possible for there are other papers to be published.

I do not think it advisabl that you should extend your researches until the present memoir is finished and indeed I would be just as well pleased if this article were confined almost exclusively to an accurate account of the facts of your explorations.

I send with this letter a communication from Mr Whittlesy[5] which he requests me to forward to the Secretary of the ethnological society.[6,B]

Dec. 25th Board still in daily session—will probably adjourn on monday[7]— I will send a draft to Major[8] and an other to Orr as soon as the

Board adjourn— I shall visit New York as soon as I can get away from Washington. The Institution is threatened with some storms but I think it will weather them all.

Yours &—
Joseph Henry

E. G. Squire Esq

Squier Papers, Library of Congress.
Reply: Doc. 133.

1. December 21.

2. Henry referred to the calculations of the executive committee that, by taking advantage of the accruing interest on the building fund of $250,000, about $140,000 of it would be left when the building was scheduled for completion on March 19, 1852. At six percent interest, this would yield approximately $8,400 in annual income, to be added to the fixed yield of $30,910 from the bequest's principal. On December 21 the regents adopted the resolutions effecting this plan of expenditure. *Smithsonian Report for 1847*, pp. 160, 163–171 (figures from p. 168). See also Doc. 11, note 1.

3. On December 13, New York Representative Hugh White introduced a resolution to establish a House committee on the Smithsonian, to supervise the actions of the regents. Regent and Representative Henry Hilliard was able to forestall this, but not before Andrew Johnson of Tennessee took up the attack. Johnson considered the institution to be a drain on the treasury, and he thought it needed the constraint of congressional supervision, as "was needed in all Government establishments." He tried to introduce a bill on January 17, 1848, calling for such a standing committee, a suspension of Smithsonian operations because of the expense of the Mexican War, a reconsideration of the design of the building, and the conversion of the institution into a manual training school. The resolution died on procedural points, but, in the next session, in December 1848, Johnson again called for the standing supervisory committee. After heated debate, with Regent Hilliard again opposing the committee and Regent George Perkins Marsh favoring it, the proposal was defeated. Rhees, *Documents* (1901), pp. 443–463 (quotation on p. 450).

4. See Doc. 124, note 2.

5. Charles Whittlesey to Squier, December 6, 1847, Squier Papers, Library of Congress. This letter indicated that Henry also received a copy. A geologist and ethnologist, Whittlesey (1808–1886) had been undertaking a system-

atic survey of the Ohio mounds since 1837, when he was an assistant geologist on the Ohio State Geological Survey. He had not yet published, awaiting completion of his labors. Squier had nonetheless asked him for assistance and information, and Whittlesey had provided plans and descriptions of some eighteen of the mounds he had studied, expecting that he would be credited in publication. But when Squier sent him a copy of his *Transactions* article, Whittlesey wrote back this letter of complaint, stating "the reader is left to infer that you are the original & principal source of information." Whittlesey thought that not only he, but all earlier researchers had been slighted:

> A reader not otherwise acquainted with the fact would infer that before you there were none or none worthy of notice & that all the relics sketched & commented upon were found by either yourself or partner.

In a point that must have struck Henry quite hard (and probably prompted his directions in the paragraph immediately above), Whittlesey complained:

> If the institutions you represent intend nothing more than a theoretical & general work on the role of the mounds I have mistaken their object, my great desire having been for years to see a complete detailed description of the works in Ohio & should not wish to contribute even with due acknowledgement to a partial & speculative one—

Whittlesey would see his "factual" work in print, published by one of the institutions he thus criticized: *Description of Ancient Works in Ohio*, 1851, SI Contributions, vol. 3 (Washington, 1852). Elliott, *Dictionary*.

6. That is, John R. Bartlett.

7. December 27, the day the board did adjourn.

8. Henry B. Major (fl. 1844–1854), a lithographer, of the firm of Sarony and Major, 117 Fulton Street, New York, who prepared the

plates for Squier and Davis's publication. *Squier and Davis*, p. xxiii; George C. Groce and David H. Wallace, *The New-York Historical Society's Dictionary of Artists in America, 1564–1860* (New Haven, 1957).

132. TO TRYON EDWARDS[1]

Washington Dec 18th 1847

Rev. T. Edwards

Dear Sir

Your letter, of the 18th November last,[2] on account of some cause of delay, did not reach me until within a few days ago, and I now beg leave, in behalf of the Smithsonian Institution, to thank you for the suggestions which it contains.[3]

It is the intention, of the officers of the Smithsonian Institution, to organise a system of meteorological observations, with reference to the solution of the problem of American Storms.[4] The details of the plan have not yet been fully settled but it is intended to establish several observers in each State of the Union, and to ask the cooperation of the British Goverment, so that simultaneous observations may be made from the Gulf of Mexico, to the region of the Arctic Circle. We shall probably begin with a simple organization for determining the aspect of the Sky, the direction of the wind and the temperature of the Air, and gradually supply each observer with other instruments. It is thought that a sufficient number of persons may be found, in each State, who will be willing to cooperate, without charge, provided the instruments are furnished to them free of expense.

Attention should be turned to but few objects at the first, and could we get all the mechanical phenomena of a single storm passing over the surface of our Country the results would be of the highest importance to science. We may perhaps attempt to furnish one set of observers— the smallest number,—with Barometers, Rain-Gauges and Thermometers; another set with Thermometers and a third with directions to observe and register the face of the heavens. The cost of full sets of instruments, for all the observers required, would be too great for the funds of the Institution.

Should any suggestions occur to you on reflection, you will oblige us by sending an account of them.

With much respect
I am your ob[t] serv

Retained Copy, Letters Received, Records of the Smithsonian Meteorological Project, Records of the Weather Bureau, RG 27, National Archives. In Charles P. Russell's hand.

1. Edwards (1809–1894), of New London, Connecticut, was a grandson of Jonathan Edwards, a Congregational clergyman, and an author of religious and moral works. He was a meteorological observer for the Smithsonian from 1849 to 1858. Thomas William Herringshaw, *Encyclopedia of American Biography of the Nineteenth Century* (Chicago, 1905); *Smithsonian Report for 1869*, p. 70.

2. In same location.

3. Edwards encouraged Henry to use his position to organize a system for obtaining uniform meteorological data "for the comparison of climates." He also noted that he and others had considered presenting the matter to the Association of American Geologists and Naturalists, but decided to approach Henry instead.

4. On December 15, the regents had appropriated $1,000 for this project, organized along lines suggested by Elias Loomis in his report on meteorology. Rhees, *Journals*, pp. 42–43.

⁕{ 1848 }⁕

133. FROM EPHRAIM GEORGE SQUIER

Judson's Hotel,
New York Jan. 3, 1848

Sir:

Yours of the 17th. ult.; Postscript of 25th.,[1] and subsequent note of the 31st. with draft for $50.[2] was duly received—

Immediately upon the receipt of the above very singular communications I wrote a reply,[3] which however, I laid aside for the time, lest under the excitement of the moment I might have expressed myself improperly or decided rashly. Up to this time I have found no reason to change my resolutions and but little to alter my language.

From the day I came to this city up to this time, I have had constant occasion to regret that no more definite understanding was had with you, both before and after the acceptance of my MSS. for publication by the Smithsonian Inst. Had there been a clearer understanding of what was proposed to be done, the mode in which it was to be accomplished and of what was expected of me on the one part and of you on the other, I am sure much unpleasant feeling would have been avoided, and probably the necessity of your late communications as well as of this rejoinder, avoided. If I understood the parole[4] arrangement made with you it was as follows:—

1st.— The Inst. was to pay a certain sum for the MSS., the amount to be fixed by the Board of Regents at their annual meeting.

(This, you will remember was your substitute for the proposition to furnish the Author of the work[B] an edition of _____ copies; a proposition which you at first regarded with favor, but afterwards thought would be likely to establish a precedent fraught with difficulties.)

2d.— The Author of the work ↑in whom the copy right should be invested↓ was to be allowed to use the plates, engravings and if he chose the type of the Inst., to print an edition for himself, which however was not to be published until the Inst. had had time to circulate its own edition.

3d.— The edition of the Inst. was not to be sold; its circulation was to be confined to exchanges &c. with learned Societies and public libraries at home and abroad.

4th.— The Inst was to pay my necessary expenses while here, engaged in superintending the execcution of the engravings and the publication of the work.

This was the understanding at the time the work was accepted, and under it I entered upon my duties here. Since that time however, every one of the conditions seems to have been forgotten on your part, at least I infer so from the tenor of your letters and the non fulfillmt of the principal ~~conditions~~ stipulations.

1. The board of Regents has adjourned, and so far as I can learn not only[C] without making an appropriation for the work, but without having been asked to make one. Without some such aid— which I never expected would cover one fourth of the actual[D] cash expenditures made in the investigations upon which the Work was founded—I say, without some such aid the privilege of publishing an edition for sale, under all the ~~privileges of the second~~ advantages of the second ↑and third↓ ~~condi~~ stipulations, would be eminently a barren one, ~~and~~ —a mere mockery, of no practical benefit to me. Especially would it be so—as all the public Inst. and Libraries ~~in this country~~ in this country and in Europe, (which after all would constitute the principal purchasers of a work of this kind,) would be Supplied <u>gratis</u> by you. Consequently ~~reliance would~~ my reliance for muneration, would depend upon a doubtful sale amoung individuals. ~~Most of whom~~ Most of them interested in such matters reside in the vicinity of ~~librar~~ public libraries, and would find it more convenient and economiccal to consult the work there, than to spend 10 or 15 dollars in purchasing it. You may think I look upon the "cash returns" of this work with more ~~feeling~~ interest than upon the <u>honors</u> which it might possibly yield. Had I been influenced by such considerations the work would never have been undertaken. And al-

though I presume I have an ambition quite as ardent as any one else, yet my peace of mind imperatively demand that I shall never rest long under pecuniary obligations.)

I now am obliged to refer to a matter of much more delicacy; ~~The preparation superintendence arrangements &c of the illustrations of and~~ ↑one↓ which is connected with further stipulations ~~above~~ above quoted. You lay great stress upon the fact that you have advanced me the sum of $150.—which covers something less than half of ~~my~~ ↑the↓ necessary expenes ↑to which I have been subjected↓ while here. I have ↑all↓ along been deluding myself with the belief, that I was rend[er]ing an equivalent for this ↑liberality↓ in the laborious and [?harrowing] work of arranging and preparing the plates &c. for the proposed pub. of the Inst.—a task which you well know no one else ~~was comp~~ is competent to undertake, and which no one would undertake, except they were paid a salary beyond their expenses. (I volunteered my time and services, expecting to devote all [?interminate] time to a revision of my MSS, under the new facilities afforded by access to books.) I was foolish enough to suppose I was granting a favor instead of incurring one. ~~However since I was mistaken, so~~ [?was] ~~mistaken, and the~~ It seems however that this munificent advance was a simple act of charity—an instance of which the newspapers would perhaps term "prncely patronage." I shall therefore take the earliest possible opportunity of returning the amount to the Treasury of the Inst., for I fear I am not ~~properly~~ ↑sufficently↓ grateful for the alms thus bestowed.

There are several passages in your ~~last lett~~ letters just received to which I shall not ~~trust myself to reply now to~~ trust myself to reply. I allude ↑to↓ those portions ~~in~~ indicating "what you were disposed to do," the things which "you have suffered me to do" and "indulgences which you are still inclined to grant &c &c.^{E}

Nor shall I notice the insinuation conveyed in the "hope" which you express that I "will now devote all my time to the completion of the work"— ~~which~~ an insinuation equally unfounded and ungenerous.^{F} You express a regret also based upon more reasons than one, that my paper presented to the Ethng. Soc. was pub. just at this time, and over my name. Time? Pray what time better thn that which suited my convenience? And? Whose name if not my own?

One thing more, and I am done. ~~Circumstances,^{G} some of which I know you are acquainted with, have do~~ Circumstances, some of which are not unknown to you, have transpired^H which place me beyond any obligation to be generous in the matter of ~~the my work~~ the publication to which this letter refers. I am determined to be simply just, to myself as well as to others. My MSS. if published ~~be at all,~~ under any circumstances, must ~~sustain~~ ↑bear↓ the following title,[5] with a preface in which the part sustained by each person named will be distinctly and impartially set forth.[1]

I am indisposed to embarrass you or the Inst., but ~~I shall now require~~ as the work under notice is ↑wholly↓ mine in design and execution, and as I am anxious to have all responsibility properly placed, ↑~~Justice requires me to say that,~~↓ ~~I shall now require the fulfillment of the conditions parole arrangement entered into some months~~ ago, ~~or a new written agreement mutually satisfactory and shall hold myself reponsible to nothing in future which is not duly wr to I shall be glad to meet you in this city I cannot~~ cannot I think it would perhaps be ~~be~~ best to suspend ~~operations par~~ operations, until it suits your convenience to visit this city, where a complete understanding can be had; As the matter at present stands I cannot feel that the Inst. has fulfilled its obligations, and that our connection in a business point of view is, temporarily at least, at an end. I ~~need~~ hardly need assure you that my personal respect and esteem ~~is undiminished,~~ for your self is undiminished, although I must regret that you should ↑have↓ felt yourself called upon to write me in the tone that⌋ you have done. Please let me know how soon you may be expected here, so that I can make my arrangements accordingly.

Draft, Squier Papers, Library of Congress.

1. Doc. 131.

2. Henry's note was dated December 29, not 31. Henry wrote Squier that the $50 draft he was sending was "all I am able to do for you at this time"; stated that the $150 the institution had advanced Squier (including the $50 draft) was double the sum which Squier had estimated for his superintendence of the memoir; and declared his intention to visit New York soon "to settle the whole business of your memoir" once and for all. Squier Papers, Library of Congress.

3. An incomplete, four-page draft, dated December 31, 1847, with a note, "Reply to Henry's of Dec. 17," is in the Squier Papers, Library of Congress.

4. That is, a verbal pledge or word of honor.

5. Although Squier's draft did not specify a title, he presumably had in mind the working title which was given in the contract for the memoir's printing, signed by Edward O. Jenkins and Joseph Drayton (as Henry's agent for the Smithsonian Institution) on January 20, 1848: "Archological Researches, an Inquiry into the Origin and Purposes of the Aboriginal Monuments of the United States." Box 41, Subject Files, William J. Rhees Collection, Smithsonian Archives.

134. TO ASA GRAY

Confidential[A]

Washington Jany 10th 1848

My Dear Dr

I presume you have been expecting a letter from me for several weeks past, and I regret that I have not been able to give you any account of the prospects of the Institution before this time. Indeed I am still unable to say what a day may bring forth. The Board contined in daily session for three weeks and since their adjournment I have been much occupied in preparing the Reports and proceedings for publication.

The Report from the Amer. Aca[y] came in good time and served[B] a good purpose. I regret hower that it gave me the whole credit of the programme since it contained all the suggestions, so far as I thought them valuable,[C] of all the persons with whom I consulted on the subject; and ↑because↓ by giving me the credit for the whole offence would be given were the article published. The programme was provisionally adopted in full with a few unimportant additions and corrections made by the committee of organization to whom the article had to be submitted and I was charged with carrying ↑them↓ into operation so far as the appropriation of funds for the purpose would permit.

When I came on to Washington I found Owen[D] busily engaged in devising a plan to increase the income of the Institution so as to cover the odium of the expenditure on so large a building. For this purpose he proposed that the operations of the Institution should be limited to an expenditure of 15 thousand dollars annually instead of 30 thousand until the end of 4 years from next mar[c]h or until the building shall be completed; the other 15 thousand with its interest to be added indirectly to the principal and thus to make the annual income ever after 40 thousand dollars instead of 30.[1] I at first gave but little attention to this matter I was however surprised to find that Owen had brought over every member of the Board in Washington to his scheme and when I found that it met the approbation of Bache I was induced to look upon it with more favour and at length to desire its adoption at least in part, for I wished to encourage the spirit of economy which now appeared to actuate the measures of the Board and because I thought if Owen was once out of the Board the whole could afterwards be adjusted. There was however one stipulation which I made namely that Mr Choate should have an opportunity to be present and object to the Resolutions if he were so disposed—for this purpose I sent him two telegraphic messages and one to Mr Jewett. The latter gentleman came on and by means of another message induced Mr Choate to start for Washington.[2] Mr Jewett was very anxious to be immediately engaged in the duties of his office though by the terms of his appointment he was not to begin his services until the Building was in a fit state to receive the Books— Mr Choate at first objected to the Resolution and insisted that the purchase of books should be commenced immediately[3] he however I think came to regard the proposition more favourably, and on condition that Mr Jewett should be immediately employed in the way of preparing catalogues and making arrangements for the purchase of books at the proper time the Resolutions passed.[4] During the present year I shall have about 7000 dollars to expend in the way of memoirs, experimts apparatus,[5] &— and as I am not anxious to push the operations too rapidly, I am, for this year, content with this sum. If hower all things go on well we shall require a larger sum the next year which must be drawn from the interest and the desired result (the increase of the funds) be produced by an extension of the time of putting up the less essential parts of the building.

I had no idea at first that Mr Owen could have any chance of getting into the Board after his time expired, Mr Rush has signified a desire to remain a^E Regent during his absense and there was therefore apparently no vacancy.[6] I was however surprised by the proposition from one of Owens friends that Mr. R. should be made an honorary member and Mr O. elected in his place.[7] Finding that Owen would probably get in I had a free conversation with him and insisted that he should resign his positions in the executive and organizing committees and confine his ~~whole~~ attention to the building. To this he agreed.[8] The Board afterwars on motion of Gen. Hough recommended Mr O. as the sucessor of Mr Rush. His appointement however has not yet taken place.[9] He will probably be nomenated in the ~~house~~ ↑Senate↓ and the nomenation sent to the House for concurrence. I know not what will be the result.

At the begining of the session of the Board I presented my report which should have gone through the hands of the committee on organization in accordance with the resolution of the Board under which I acted. I showed it to Bache and Hilliard[10] and then presented it to the Board it was well receivd and ordered to be entered at large on the minutes. A resolution was adopted directing the secretary to report annually the condition and operations of the Institution[11] so that in future I shall not be controled by a committee.

The executive committee now consits of Seaton, Bache and Pierce,[12] and with the two latter to back me I think all things will go well during the present year. I hope to be able to receive Pierces paper[13] in the course of two months. The Ethnological memoir is not yet published— it could not be completed until after the meeting of the Board because I had but 1000 dollars to expend on the article.[14] I start tomorrow for New-York to make the final arrangements for the printing of the Memoir of Squire and Davis the wood cuts and plates are nearly all[F] finished.

The attention which Squire has received from some of the great men in Boston and New York has nearly turned his head and caused him to give me considerable trouble.

I will write to Pierce relative to his paper— What I have given you is confidential.

As ever your friend
Joseph Henry

Dr A Gray[G]
There is a proposition in the House to look into the affairs of the Smithsonian by the appointment of a committee. This I think will pass.

Historic Letters, Archives, Gray Herbarium Library, Harvard University.
Printed (with minor variations) in Nathan Reingold, ed., *Science in Nineteenth-Century America: A Documentary History* (1964; Chicago, 1985), pp. 156–159. A partial draft is in the Henry Papers, Smithsonian Archives.

1. Henry referred to Robert Dale Owen's "Proposed Scale of Expenditure, for Four Years from the 19th of March, 1848, Being the Remainder of the Term of the Contract for the Erection of the Institution Building," which the executive committee adopted on December 7, 1847, and the full board approved two weeks later. See Rhees, *Journals,* pp. 447–455, for Owen's plan and its accompanying resolutions, and Doc. 131, note 2.

2. None of these telegraph messages has been found.

3. That is, the sixth resolution appended to Owen's plan of finances, which construed the meaning of a regents' resolution of December 4, 1846, relating to expenditures for the library. That earlier resolution had authorized an expenditure of $20,000 for purchasing books and outfitting a library, beginning January 1, 1848. Owen's resolution construed it to mean that it authorized "for the present" only the purchase of such reference works as the secretary, the building committee, or the executive committee deemed necessary or appropriate. His resolution effectively disempowered the library committee and the assistant secretary acting as librarian, while at the same time it temporarily suspended general book purchases. Owen sought to assuage the library fac-

tion by reminding them that, assuming the division of income proposed under the compromise of January 1847 was adhered to, the increased annual income obtained after 1852 by following his plan would yield an additional $4,200 per year for book purchases. Rhees, *Journals,* pp. 451, 453 (quotation on p. 453).

4. See Doc. 122, note 10.

5. On December 15, the full board adopted a schedule of appropriations, prepared by the executive committee in keeping with Owen's plan of finance, for the year commencing March 19, 1848. Of the $15,000 budgeted for current expenses, $7,500 was to go for salaries, postage, and other contingencies, and $1,000 toward the purchase of books. The remaining $6,500 was to be allocated among various programs as follows: SI Contributions, $3,500; occultation computations, $250; magnetic instruments, $600; meteorology, $1,000; arranging apparatus in the building, $150; lectures, $500; and reports on the progress of science, $500. Rhees, *Journals,* pp. 42–43.

6. In March 1847, President Polk appointed Rush minister to France. There is no evidence to show that Rush—then one of six citizen regents—intended to give up his seat on the Smithsonian board; indeed, in a letter to Owen of May 20, Rush stated his intention to follow

the regents' proceedings from abroad with "constant interest" (quoted in Rhees, *Journals,* p. 689). *DAB,* s.v. Rush, Richard.

7. On December 17, the regents accepted William J. Hough's resolution declaring that Rush's seat on the Board of Regents was vacant, although no action was taken on Hough's subsequent resolution naming Owen as Rush's replacement. Bache offered a resolution on December 17 to elect Rush as an honorary member of the Smithsonian. Rhees, *Journals,* pp. 44–45.

8. On December 22, Owen asked to be excused from the executive committee, stating that if he were reelected to the board, his duties as chairman of the building committee, in particular overseeing the publication of *Hints on Public Architecture,* would make too many demands on his time. The board concurred, appointing Pearce to replace him. The regents' minutes do not mention any similar request by Owen to be excused from the committee of organization. Rhees, *Journals,* p. 47.

9. Hough's resolution to have Owen replace Rush actually preceded Bache's resolution to elect Rush as an honorary member and Owen's request to be excused from the executive committee. Rhees, *Journals,* pp. 44–45, 47.

10. Henry referred to a resolution offered by Bache and adopted by the board on January 26, 1847, which had directed him "to present to the Committee on Organization" a plan to implement the institution's scientific and publication programs; Bache and Hilliard served on this committee. Rhees, *Journals,* p. 26.

11. This was the third clause of a resolution introduced by Bache on December 13, 1847; the other clauses covered the provisional adoption of "Section I" and "Section II" of the "Programme of Organization" and charged Henry with its implementation. Rhees, *Journals,* p. 41.

12. James Alfred Pearce (1805–1862), a Princeton alumnus (1822) and former United States representative, was elected to the Senate in 1843 as a Whig from Maryland; he served until his death. Appointed a regent on February 22, 1847, to fill a vacancy occasioned by the resignation of George Evans, he attended his first board meeting on December 10. Pearce, who remained a lifelong regent, became an outspoken champion in Congress not only for the Smithsonian, but also for the broader issue of federal expenditures for science. *DAB;* Rhees, *Journals,* p. 40; Rhees, *Documents* (1901), *1:*437; *Smithsonian Report for 1862,* pp. 100–103.

13. Presumably a reference to Benjamin Peirce's proposed memoir on Neptune for SI Contributions.

14. On January 26, 1847, the regents had authorized an expenditure of $1,000 for SI Contributions, all of which had been spent on Squier and Davis's memoir. A resolution of December 15, 1847, authorized $3,500 for SI Contributions. Rhees, *Journals,* pp. 26, 43.

135. TO WILLIAM C. REDFIELD

Washington Jan 11th 1848.

My dear Sir,

The Board of Regents of the Smithsonian Institution at their session which has just closed appropriated one thousand dollars for the purpose of beginning a series of observations to solve, if possible, the problem of American storms. I beg leave to ask of you any hints or suggestions which may occur to you from reflection on this subject. Whatever you may offer will be appended to my report[1] so that you will receive full credit for it. This report will be published in about ~~thre~~ three weeks[2] and you will oblige me by forwarding your communication before that time.[3]

It is believed that when our plan of operation is fully organized the British Government will be induced to co-operate with us by establishing a series of corresponding observations in its North American possessions.

> I remain very respectfully and truly
> Your Obedient Servant
> Joseph Henry
> Secretary S.I.

W.C. Redfield Esqr.
P.S. I regret that I did not find you in NY.[4] If your suggestions cannot be forwarded in time they will be given in my next Report.

> J.H.

Redfield Papers, Beinecke Rare Book and Manuscript Library, Yale University.
In Harriet Henry's hand except for the signature, Henry's title, and the postscript. Reply: Doc. 215.

1. That is, the secretary's annual report to the regents.

2. The regents submitted the Smithsonian's annual report for 1847 to Congress on December 31, 1847. On January 6, 1848, the report was ordered to be printed. Henry was overly optimistic in his estimate of its publication, however, since the printing only commenced in May. *Smithsonian Report for 1847*, pp. 1, 3.

3. Henry apparently sent similar letters to Elias Loomis and James P. Espy, whose replies were printed (Espy's letter was excerpted) in *Smithsonian Report for 1847*, pp. 193–208.

4. Arriving in New York on January 14, Henry spent several days there transacting business for the institution. He called on Redfield on January 17, but found that he had just left for Albany. Henry to Harriet Henry, [January 17, 1848], Family Correspondence, Henry Papers, Smithsonian Archives.

136. TO BENJAMIN PEIRCE

Washington Jany 12th 1848

My dear Sir

I hope you will pardon me for the long delay of this answer to your letter of last month:[1] my excuse is that the Board of Regents continued in session almost continually until the end of the month and I have since been so much occupied in preparing the Reports and proceedings of the session for publication that I have not been able to keep up with my correspondence.

I start this afternoon for New-York to ascertain definitely ↑when↓ the ethnological memoir will be printed and as soon as this is settled I will write to inform you when your paper will be required— The scale of prices agreed on betwen us when I was in Cambridge will be adopted.

The Report of the Committee of the Aca^{dy} was received at the proper time and did good service; the Programme was adopted in full with some unimportant additions and alterations by the organizing committee.

An appropriation of 250 dollars was made for the computation of occultations. Downes has finished the calculations and they will be published in a few days.[2]

Also 1000 dollars was appropriated for the beginning of a series of meteorological observations for solving, if possible, the problem of American storms. We propose establishing observers in each state and when our plan is properly organized we have the assurance of Col. Sabine that the British Government will cooperate with us by establishing observers in its possessions on this continent.

We propose at first to furnish thermometers to the observers and afterwards barometers—our funds are not sufficient to enable us to furnish full sets of instruments to all the observers, but much important information relative to the nature of storms may be obtained by merely noting the face of the sky and the direction of the wind—these observations will determine the progress of the storm— It is expected that important assistance will be derived from the telegraph in giving notice of the progress of stormes.[3]

If you can give us any suggestions on this subject they will be thankfully received and properly acknowledged.

The Reports will be published in about a month and as soon as they are out I will send you a copy.

Bache is well and in good spirits. He has a more liberal committee to second his application for the coast survey appropriation than he had last session.[4]

> Very Respectfully and
> truly I remn your
> freind and servt
> Joseph Henry

Prof. Pierce

Peirce Papers, Houghton Library, Harvard University.

1. Not found, although Henry presumably referred to a letter of which an undated draft exists in the same location. In it, Peirce told Henry that he had nearly finished a memoir "upon the theory of the mutual ~~influence of~~ action of Uranus and Neptune," which he hoped to have published in SI Contributions; he stated that he was awaiting Sears C. Walker's refined computation of the elements of Neptune's orbit. Peirce described his and Walker's efforts to determine the elements of Neptune's orbit, and the results of his investigations into the planet's interaction with Uranus, in two communications to the American Academy of Arts and Sciences, the first on December 7, 1847, and the second on April 4, 1848. He apparently never submitted a memoir on Neptune for publication in SI Contributions. *Proceedings of the American Academy of Arts and Sciences, 1846–1848, 1:*285–295, 331–342.

2. On December 15, 1847, the regents had appropriated funds for computing occultations

of fixed stars by the moon; these data would be used to prepare tables to assist surveyors, explorers, and cartographers "in the accurate determination of the longitude of important places on the continent of North America." Henry assigned these computations to John Downes (1799–1882), a former commissioner of the Northeast boundary survey then living in Philadelphia, where he published an ephemeris, *The United States Almanac*. The Smithsonian published Downes's tables as a pamphlet, *Occultations Visible in the United States during the Year 1848* (Philadelphia, 1848). Copies were mailed "to all persons known to be interested in practical astronomy," with a request "that the observations which might be made in connexion with them might be sent to the Institution for computation," or to an astronomical journal for publication. *Smithsonian Report for 1848*, p. 14 (quotations); *Appleton's Cyclopaedia of American Biography* (New York, 1887–1900), s.v. "Downes, John."

3. Henry had made a similar remark in his report for 1847, telling the regents that the scattered locations of Americans throughout the south and west, together with "the extended lines of telegraph," would provide a means of alerting eastern and northern observers about impending storms. The idea of

applying the telegraph for such purposes originated the year before with William Redfield, who suggested it could be used to warn Atlantic ports of approaching inclement weather. Similarly, Elias Loomis, in his "Report on the Meteorology of the United States," asserted that the extension of lines to the Mississippi River Valley would render the telegraph "subservient to the protection of our commerce." News of a coming storm could be rapidly communicated to the eastern seaboard, he wrote, "in season to save a fleet of ships from putting to sea, to be engulphed in the bottomless deep." *Smithsonian Report for 1847*, pp. 190, 203 (quotations); Fleming, *Meteorology*, pp. 141–145.

4. The House Committee on Expenditures in the Treasury Department had jurisdiction over Coast Survey appropriation requests. In 1847, the committee approved an appropriation of $146,000, the full amount Bache had requested. The following year, he once again received all he sought—$165,000—or roughly a twelve percent increase over the previous appropriation. *Coast Survey Report for 1847*, p. 43; *Coast Survey Report for 1848*, p. 57; *U.S. Statutes at Large*, 9:162, 244; *Congressional Directory for the First Session of the Thirtieth Congress of the United States of America* (Washington, 1848), p. 38.

137. TO HARRIET HENRY

New York Saturday night
[January 15, 1848][A]

My Dear H

I arrived here this morning at about 10 o'clock and have been since so much engaged that I have been unable to write before now. I informed you by telegraph that I arrived safely in Phil[d] on Thursday night or rather[B] on Friday morning after a comfortable ride. I went immediately to bed and had a tolerably good nap until near[C] 10 o'clock—then took breakfast had an interview with Mr Downes relative to printing computation of occultations[D]—next went to Dr Ludlows— found Dr L.[1] Dr Cuyler[2] Mrs L.[3] and Jane Riley[4] in the parlor— Jane appeared much distressed looked old and hagard— Soon after I came in she went into the back room whence I followed and attempted to comfort her but was unsuccessful— She reverted[E] to the fact that she

was alone in the World and that her Father[5] had said several times before his death that Prof. Henry would see to her—this was said before
Mrs Ludlow and made me feel[F] rather awkward. I told her she was not
without friends and that it was not right for her to say she was alone[G]
in the world because she did injustice, by sodoing to those who loved
her,— Mrs Ludl[o]w appeared much distressed and I was releived
when Jane left the room in a paroxism of grief. Mrs H.[6] bid me ask you
to write to Jane and say all you could of a soothing nature to calm her.
On the subject of her father Jane appears to have a kind [of] Mono-
mania.[H] James[7] brought her down—he reached Schenectady on Friday
night the old gentleman died on saturday morning— The weather was
intensely cold the thermometer stood at 22 degress below Zero— I left
Phil. in the afternoon and came on to New Brunswick where I stopped
over night had a good sleep and have been quite well to day—at the
Princeton basin I was informed that Mr Stephen Alexander had gone
on to New York but I have as yet not been able to find him and have
concluded that he is not in the city. I dined with James Alexander and
in the evening attended a meeting of the ethnological society at Mr
Galletans.[8] Dr Davis is here and is settling his difficulty with squire the
last named gentleman has found his senses and now appears quite reasonable— I was prepared to put the screws on him but at the requst
of Dr Davis I have treated him[I] more civilly than he deserved.[9] He[J] is
apparently ashamed of the course he has taken and is not deserous that
I should show the letter he wrote me.[10] Indeed the course he proposed
to take whould have completely destroyed his character with men of
science and litterature in this country.

I hope you and our dear children are well and that the shade of home
sickness which passed over you when I came away is passed and that all
things now appear as bright as when I was with you with out the pros-
p[ect][K] of leaving— I am much disappointed in not finding Stephen I
think it probable that he has stopped at Elizabethtown. I know that he
wished to see Mr McGee[11] on business relative to the college and that
he will be here on Monday.[L] When I passed the Princeton Depot I could
not resist a feeling of[M] deep sadness which came over me. I though[t] it
scarcely right to pass without stopping and before I arrived I had concluded to spend the night with Grandmother but when I learned that
Stephen had gone on and that the road to the Village was very bad I
concluded to go on to New York. I found myself however quite fatigued
before I got to New Brunswick and concluded to stop there for the
night. I got supper soon after my arrival and after a good nights rest I

started ~~at~~ for New York at ½ past 7 o'clock. Good night and m[a]y[N] the father[O] of all mercies protect and direct you and our dear children.

Forever Yours til[P] death
J–H–

Family Correspondence, Henry Papers, Smithsonian Archives.

1. John Ludlow, provost of the University of Pennsylvania. *Henry Papers, 1:*106n.

2. Cornelius C. Cuyler, pastor of the Second Presbyterian Church of Philadelphia. *Henry Papers, 2:*267n.

3. Anna Ludlow.

4. Jane Ryley, Anna Ludlow's sister. *Henry Papers, 2:*173.

5. James Van Slyck Ryley, a Schenectady judge, had been an old family friend. *Henry Papers, 1:*444.

6. A slip of the pen for "Mrs. L."

7. James Ryley Ludlow, John and Anna Ludlow's son. *Henry Papers, 2:*338n.

8. Due to Albert Gallatin's poor health, the American Ethnological Society met regularly at his house. Robert E. Bieder and Thomas G. Tax, "From Ethnologists to Anthropologists: A Brief History of the American Ethnological Society," in *American Anthropology: The Early Years,* ed. John V. Murra (St. Paul, 1976), pp. 12–13.

9. In a letter to George P. Marsh, Squier offered a somewhat different view of his meeting with Henry, the result of which, he wrote, was that "a better, but far from a clear or satisfactory arrangement of our affairs, has been effected." Squier learned that the engravers had been paid and a contract had been awarded for printing the memoir. Moreover, he continued, Davis had "explained some portions of his conduct," and Squier was now willing "to recede somewhat from the position which I felt myself forced to take in respect to him." However, Squier still felt compelled to "insist upon a proper explanation in the preface" of each individual's contribution to the memoir.

As Squier made clear to Marsh, he still resented the manner in which Henry and the institution had treated him, especially Henry's unwillingness to pay him more money for superintending the memoir's completion. Regarding Henry's insistence that any copyright, if such be secured, must be vested in the institution, Squier responded: "Encouraging prospect truly! A man must needs be rich to endure such 'patronage!'" Squier opined that "if . . . all the circumstances were placed before the Board of Regents" (presumably by Marsh, who was appointed a regent on December 22, 1847), "they would take some action upon them, such as due both to the dignity and honor of the Institution."

Previously, Marsh had urged moderation on Squier's part, advising him that "I do not think you will find Prof. Henry disposed to be illiberal or unjust towards you," adding that he expected the regents to "fulfill your reasonable expectations in the matter of compensation."

Squier to Marsh, draft, January 28; Marsh to Squier, January 7, 1848, both in Squier Papers, Library of Congress.

10. Doc. 133.

11. David Magie (1795–1865), a graduate of Princeton (1817) and of Princeton Theological Seminary (1820), in 1821 became pastor of the Second Presbyterian Church of Elizabeth, New Jersey, a post he occupied until his death. He became a Princeton trustee in 1835. *Biographical Encyclopaedia of New Jersey of the Nineteenth Century* (Philadelphia, 1877), pp. 32–33; *Princeton Catalogue,* p. 129.

138. FROM ROBERT HARE

Philad[a] Jan[y] 31st 1848

My dear Sir

Your programme has reached me together with your letter.[1]

I approve it highly in general. Yet the following remarks appear to me to be justified.

In section 10 should not *time* be inserted after the word "last"?

In section 11 building is mention'd without due explanation. I recommend the insertion of these words which it has been decided should be erected.

Judging from my own experience there is nothing more useless than a *"medal"* a sum of money to be expended in books or apparatus were much preferable. A fine pair of scales and beam for a chemist a telescope for an astronomer books for a classical scholar or poet & C' &C.

You reject unverified speculations,[2] yet how can speculations be verified. ↑Those of↓ Stahl Black Lavoisier Newton Ampere Dufay[A] have all been considered as verified; and yet now all ↑more or less↓ called in question if not considered obsolete.[3]

I take it for granted that mine would be put under the ban.

Possibly it is meant that they should be supported by new experiments so that although mine are built upon those of Faraday, yourself and others, they are not as true as if I had my self made the same observations.

The words "weighing the Earth" last last paragraph 2nd page is ambiguous. Do[B] you mean to convey the idea of ascertaining the density of this terrestrial Globe? or wheighing a portion of the soil.

Consistently[C] in offering a premium for the best essay, you should add which does not consist of unverified speculations; but how is the line of demarcation to be drawn?

As you have not mention'd my essay[4] I presume you have been to busy with your programme to study it.—

With regard
Yours
Robt Hare

Prof Henry

Henry Papers, Smithsonian Archives.
Reply: Doc. 168.

1. Not found, but a draft, dated January 28, 1848, is in the Henry Papers, Smithsonian Archives. In it, Henry reiterated his support for an idea that he had expressed as early as September 1846, but had since decided was impractical, namely, applying a portion of Smithson's bequest to establish, in this country, a national institute modeled upon France's. Under this plan, "a limited number of members [would be] chosen from among the working men of science and allowed a small compensation." Henry acknowledged that the construction of the Smithsonian Building would drain off too much of the institution's income "to

carry such a plan into operation," but he still hoped that "by the aid of government it might be effected." (For his earlier thoughts along these lines, see *Henry Papers*, 6:495–497.) Henry's draft also asked Hare for suggestions on the Smithsonian's proposed meteorological research program.

2. Under Henry's "Programme of Organization," a memoir on physical science would be accepted only if it "form[ed] a positive addition to human knowledge resting on original research," while "all unverified speculations [were] to be rejected."

3. Taking in turn each of the individuals

Hare named and their rejected speculations, he referred to German physician Georg Ernst Stahl (1659 or 1660–1734, *DSB*), a proponent of the theory of vitalism in medicine and biology; Scottish chemist Joseph Black (1728–1799, *DSB*), who, like Stahl, adhered to the theory of phlogiston; Lavoisier and the caloric theory of heat; Newton and the emission theory of light; Ampère and his electrodynamic theory (for which see *Henry Papers*, 2:230n-232n); and the French chemist Charles François de Cisternai Dufay (1698–1739, *DSB*), who espoused a controversial doctrine of "two electricities" to explain electrostatic attraction and repulsion (a theory whose merits Henry and Hare had previously debated; see *Henry Papers*, 5:408–410, 414–416).

4. Hare referred to his "Objections to the Theories of Franklin, Dufay, or Ampere, with an Effort to Explain Electrical Phenomena by the Statical or Undulatory Polarization of Omnipresent, Ethereal, or Ethereo-Ponderable Matter," originally given as a lecture before the Philadelphia Academy of Natural Sciences, and later published in *The Medical Examiner, and Record of Medical Science*, 1847, 2d ser. *11*:715–736. As we noted in an earlier volume, Henry commented upon a manuscript of it which Hare sent him (*Henry Papers*, 6:615–616). Hare incorporated some, though not all, of Henry's comments in an "improved edition" of his essay, published as a pamphlet: *Objections to the Theories Severally of Franklin, Dufay and Ampere, with an Effort to Explain Electrical Phenomena, by Statical, or Undulatory, Polarization* (Philadelphia, 1848). The pamphlet subsequently was reprinted in several scientific journals, including the *Journal of the Franklin Institute, Silliman's Journal*, and the *Philosophical Magazine*, as well as in newspapers such as the *National Intelligencer*. On Hare's "highly speculative, elaborate and exhaustive" essay, see Edgar Fahs Smith, *The Life of Robert Hare: An American Chemist (1781–1858)* (Philadelphia and London, 1917), pp. 441–443 (quotation on page 441).

139. TO JEFFERSON DAVIS[1]

Washington Feby 2nd 1848

My Dear Sir

I beg that you will pardon me for not having paid my respects to you since your appointement as one of the Regents of the Smithsonian Institution.[2] I was called out of the city soon after your appointment and since my return I have been so much occupied with the duties of my office that I have been unable to command the time for making a number of visits.

Please inform me by the Bearer on what evening I may find you disengaged. I would be pleased to give you a full account of the plan of organization and of all the proceedings of the Institutions. I have made an engagement for this evening and also one for saturday evening[3]— Perhaps some evening next week would suit you and would be more convenient for me.[4]—

I remain very
Respectfully your[A]
Obt.[B] serv.
Joseph Henry

Hon Jefferson Davis
U.S. Senate

Retained Copy, Henry Papers, Smithsonian Archives.
Previously printed in James T. McIntosh, Lynda L. Crist, and Mary S. Dix, eds., *The Papers of Jefferson Davis* (Baton Rouge and London, 1981–), *3:*262–263. Reply: February 4, 1848, Henry Papers, Smithsonian Archives.

1. A Democratic representative from Mississippi from 1845 to 1846 (during which time he served on a House select committee on the Smithson bequest), and subsequently a hero in the Mexican War, Davis (1808–1889) in 1847 was appointed to the United States Senate. While this letter marks the first known contact between Henry and Davis, they probably were acquainted through their mutual friend, Alexander Dallas Bache. Davis had "formed a close attachment" with Bache in the mid–1820s, when both were students at the United States Military Academy; the Bache and Davis families often interacted socially during their residencies in Washington. Both during his years in Congress, and during his tenure as secretary of war from 1853 to 1857, Davis was an ardent supporter of the Smithsonian and the Coast Survey.

DAB; Rhees, *Documents* (1901), *1:*321; William C. Davis, *Jefferson Davis: The Man and His Hour* (New York, 1991), pp. 34, 124, 173, 186 (quotation [from Jefferson Davis's autobiography] on p. 34); Merle M. Odgers, *Alexander Dallas Bache: Scientist and Educator, 1806–1867* (Philadelphia, 1947), pp. 5, 102–103, 149, 152, 203–204.

2. On December 30, 1847, Davis was appointed a regent in place of Lewis Cass, who had resigned. Rhees, *Documents* (1901), *1:*463.

3. February 5.

4. In his reply, Davis suggested that he and Henry meet on Monday, February 7, expressing his desire "to learn thus easily and pleasantly the affairs" of the Smithsonian.

140. TO WILLIAM CAMPBELL PRESTON

Washington Feb 8th 1848

My dear Sir,

Your letter enclosing your communication[1] to the Board of Regents of the Smithsonian Institution was received just as I was about starting for the North, and since my return I have been so much pressed with correspondence that I have been obliged to postpone answering all letters not requiring immediate attention until[A] a season of more leisure.

I beg you will accept my sincere thanks for the kind and encouraging expressions; as well as for the wise counsel contained in your letter. I have been very much perplexed on several occasions during the past year and must expect to encounter many difficulties; but I am resolved not to desert the post which has been entrusted to me on account of slight annoyances or voluntarily resign my position while there is a reasonable prospect of carrying out at[B] least in part the plans which I deem the most consistent with the will of Smithson.

The building is going on as rapidly as could be expected and thus far it has not exceeded the amount of the contract. The building committee however now allow that including all the fixtures, the improvement of the grounds &c[C] the cost will not be less than $250,000 dollars but I think it probable judging from past experience that the whole cost of what may be called the "material" part of the establishment will not be less than 300 thousand dollars. It is true that this sum is not expended at once but is in part to come out of the interest of the 240 thousand dollars which accrued in interest on the original sum, let it come however from what source it may every dollar thus improp[er]ly^D spent on local objects is a fraud on the cause of the increase and^E diffusion of knowledge among men. It is now impossible to stop the building and all I can do is to restrain the tendency to farther extravagances. I live in hope however that Congress in due time will be made to see the injustice done the Smithsonian fund by putting upon it the support of the National Museum and that the main building will be paid for by the government. All things are just now going on smoothly and I am left for the present untrammled in making what progress I can in developing and reducing to practice the plans presented in my programme to the Board at thei[r] last meeting. There is however some feeling in the House relative to the Institution and it is thought not improbable that a committee of supervision will be appointed.

The letter tendering your resignation was received after the Board adjourned and as there will be no opportunity of placing it before the Regents until next December^2 I have kept it to myself and indeed I am somewhat desirous that it should not be known that you think of resigning and with your permission I will say nothing about it until the next meeting of the Board when if you continue of the same mind I will present your letter.^{F} Were it known that you wished to resign there would be an effort made to put in a person more favourably disposed to pressing the completion of the building than to carrying out my plans.^{3} Besides, this I wish your name as one of my friends to stand as a Regent in the first volume of the Smithsonian contributions to knowledge which will be published as soon as the printing can be completed.

My Report with a mass of matter relative to the building is in the hands of the printer as soon as it is out I will send you a copy.

Please give my kind regards to Mrs Preston^4 and receive for yourself the assurance that I remain most truly

and sincerely Yours—

Retained Copy, Henry Papers, Smithsonian Archives.
In Harriet Henry's hand.

1. Neither letter has been found.
2. The regents' next annual meeting was set for December 13. Rhees, *Journals,* p. 49.
3. Presumably an allusion to Robert Dale Owen.

4. Preston married Louise Penelope Davis, the daughter of a physician from Columbia, South Carolina, in 1831. *DAB,* s.v. "Preston, William Campbell."

141. TO JOHN YOUNG MASON[1]

Washington Feb[y] 12th. 1848.

To the Hon. John Y. Mason
Dear Sir,

I am informed that a proposition has been made to renew the Meteorological researches of Mr. Espy, under the charge of the Navy Department, and I beg leave to express my opinion in favour of these researches.[2] I have always considered them as tending to develope principles of the highest interest both in a practical and a scientific point of view,[A] and I am certain that the reinstatement of Mr. Espy into his former office would meet the approbation of all persons interested in the progress of science.

> I remain very respectfully
> Your Obedent Servant.
> Joseph Henry

Folder 2, HR 30A-D25.3 (Estimates from Navy Department, House Ways and Means Committee, Committee Reports and Papers, Legislative Proceedings, 30th Congress), Records of the United States House of Representatives, RG 233, National Archives.
In Harriet Henry's hand, with Henry's signature and correction as noted. Draft: Henry Papers, Smithsonian Archives.

1. A former Democratic representative from Virginia, Mason (1799–1859) had been secretary of the navy under President Tyler, and attorney general under President Polk until September 1846, when Polk reappointed him secretary of the navy. *BDAC.*

2. Espy's name had been stricken from the War Department appropriations bill for fiscal year 1848 (July 1, 1847–June 30, 1848); see Doc. 41. The effort to renew Espy's appropriation was led in Congress by a long-time friend, Democratic representative Charles Brown of Pennsylvania, who solicited letters of support in the hope that, as he wrote Mason, Espy might "be connected with your department in some way, so that he may go on to collect information & digest it properly." Alexander Dallas Bache, Charles Wilkes, Edmund Burke, and associate Supreme Court justice John Catron all provided letters. Mason sent the letters to House Ways and Means Committee chairman Samuel F. Vinton, promising that if Congress approved funding for Espy's meteorological work, the navy would provide "every facility in the power of this department."

Edmund Burke to John Y. Mason, February 10, 1848; Alexander Dallas Bache to Mason, February 17, 1848; Charles Brown to Mason, February 17, 1848; John Catron to Mason, February 22, 1848; Charles Wilkes to James P. Espy, February 20, 1848; Mason to Samuel F. Vinton, March 9, 1848, all in the same location as Henry's letter. See also Fleming, *Meteorology,* pp. 78–81, 97, 99–101.

142. TO EPHRAIM GEORGE SQUIER
AND EDWIN HAMILTON DAVIS

Washington Feb 16 ↑16↓th 1848.^A

Messrs Squier & Davis,
Gentlemen,

Mr. Drayton[1] has informed me that he has made all the arrangements for printing your memoir[2],[B] and that it may be put to press as soon as the manuscript is^C ready. The paper he thinks is finished by this time. I hope nothing will now delay the publication and that it will be given to the world ↑as↓ soon as it can pass through the press.

I exhibited the woodcuts to Dr. Morton and also to a practical engraver in Philadelphia. They both said the execution was equal to any thing they had seen done in this country; but they thought the price exhorbitant.

I have also conferred with Dr. Morton, Mr Marsh and Prof Bache and they all agree with me that it will be improper to admit into the memoir any theoretical matter except in a very subordinate degree. They think that you have already had too many engravings of other articles than those which are original and that the insertion of these will detract from the merits of your memoir as a positive contribution to existing knowledge. They are unanimously of the opinion that some of those already engraved should be rejected—e– g– the drawings of coins; of structures of doubtful authority such as that from Beck's book;[3] and sketches from works readily accessible.

The Memoir was presented to me for acceptance and publication subject to the prescribed rules of the Smith. Inst. These rules are the same as those which govern learned societies in this and other countries viz— the article is submitted to a commission^D of competent judges and if any part is found objectionable it is stricken out, or the memoir is rejected. Also, the Author is not allowed to make any additions to his paper after it has been examined unless with the consent of the Society. Of course the author may withdraw his paper if he does not choose to abide by the result of these rules; but he must do this before the society has incurred any expense in the way of engravings or in commencing the printing of his article.

When your memoir was presented to me, I was informed that the whole was finished, except the introduction, and the arrangement of the plates. And in order to give you every facility for bringing it out as perfectly and as speedily as possible I allowed you to retain the manuscript, and the wood cuts cuts to be ~~prepared~~ commenced before the whole was fully prepared. I had however no idea that any other engravings were to be made than those of an original character. I must therefore insist upon your striking out some of the engravings which have already been finished and also that no additions be made to the number of the character in question, I do this with the concurrence of those[E] influential members of the board of Regents who are intimately acquainted with the usages of learned societies and who are fully impressed with the importance of adhering to them in the publications of the Smithsonian Institution.

I hope you will not consider this injunction as prompted by a desire to promote the interests of the Smithsonian Institution at the expense of your reputation by abridging your memoir. It is the opinion of your friends, who are best qualified to judge in this matter that your first labours should be given to the world as free as possible from every thing of a speculative nature and that your positive addition to the sum of human knowledge ~~may~~ ↑should↓[F] stand in bold relief unmingled with the labours of others.

The better plan will be briefly to indicate the analogies to which you have arrived and to publish in a seperate memoir a full exposition of your theoretical views.[4] In order to facilitate a publication of this kind you can have the use of any of the engravings belonging to the Institution including those we may reject.

All the additions which have been made to the memoir since it was submitted to the Committee appointed to examine it must receive the approbation of the same committee before publication, otherwise they may disavow their testimony in favour of the work.

I hope Dr. Davis will remain in New York until the publication is finished, or at least until every thing relative to the memoir is definitely settled. And I beg to remind you that a copy is to be sent me of every new wood cut—and every lithographic plate as soon as it is finished.

Please give me an account of the progress of the work and when the printing will be commenced.

> I remain very respectfully
> Your obt serv
> Joseph Henry

Squier Papers, Library of Congress.
In Harriet Henry's hand, except for corrections as noted, the concluding paragraph, and the signature, which are in Henry's hand. Reply: Doc. 146.

1. Joseph Drayton (d. 1856), an engraver and painter, worked in Philadelphia until 1838, when Charles Wilkes retained him as an artist for the United States Exploring Expedition. He afterwards superintended the production of illustrations for the expedition's reports. Ac-

cording to Wilkes, Drayton "understood his profession as an artist in all that appertained to the execution and getting up" of engravings for publication. George C. Groce and David H. Wallace, *The New-York Historical Society's Dictionary of Artists in America, 1564–1860* (New Haven, 1957), pp. 188–189; William J. Morgan et al., eds., *Autobiography of Rear Admiral Charles Wilkes, U.S. Navy, 1798–1877* (Washington, 1978), pp. 382, 532–533, 542–543 (quotation on p. 542).

Henry knew Drayton through his son, Edward F. Drayton (d. 1894), an 1845 Princeton graduate. *Princeton Catalogue*, p. 167; Edward F. Drayton to Henry, November 2, 1845, Henry Papers, Smithsonian Archives.

2. Most, if not all, of these arrangements were specified in a contract which Drayton (acting in Henry's name, as an agent of the Smithsonian Institution), signed with Edward O. Jenkins, a New York City printer, on January 20, 1848. The contract gave Henry "or his agent" final say over the memoir's typography, allowable charges for corrections and alterations, "the spacing or margin of the make-up," and "the arrangement of all title matter." Box 41, Subject Files, William J. Rhees Collection, Smithsonian Archives.

3. Lewis C. Beck's *Gazetteer of the States of Illinois and Missouri* (Albany, 1823) described walls and other stone works found in Missouri, speculating that some represented the ruins of ancient towns. Noting that "nothing of this character has been observed elsewhere," Squier and Davis commented that "it is extremely probable that there is some mistake in the matter." Their published memoir did not reprint any illustrations from Beck's book. *Squier and Davis,* pp. 135–136 (quotation on p. 136).

4. Squier followed Henry's advice with respect to the memoir, which, in its final form, was all but devoid of theory, with speculations relegated to a brief final chapter. He surmised that the mounds were religious artifacts of considerable vintage; that their builders had been largely sedentary and agricultural; and that the monuments of the Mississippi Valley were all part of one system. Searching for commonalities among these monuments, the mounds of Central and South America, and the pyramids of the Nile Valley, Squier wrote that such a consideration would involve

a preliminary analysis of the religious belief of the various aboriginal American families, an examination of their mythologies and superstitious rites, and a comparison between them and those of the primitive nations of the old world.

Although he believed that such lines of inquiry deserved "a full and separate consideration," Squier wrote that they were "beyond the scope and design" of his present memoir. He never prepared a full exposition on the religious significance of ancient monuments. *Squier and Davis,* pp. 300–306 (quotations on p. 304). See also Thomas G. Tax, "E. George Squier and the Mounds, 1845–1850," in *Toward a Science of Man: Essays in the History of Anthropology,* ed. Timothy H. H. Thoresen (The Hague and Paris, 1973), pp. 99–124, especially pp. 114–115.

143. TO JOHN TORREY

Washington Feby 18th 1848

My Dear Dr.

Col Emory[1] has just informed me that a full account of his plants cannot be published in his Report to congress[2] and I hasten to suggest that you should prepare a memoir on the subject for the Smithsonian.[3] The plates can be prepared under your own direction and the memoir can be printed as soon as the manuscript is ready for the press. We are all well and in good sperits. The children are at school and with the exception of an occasional cloud on the smithsonian horizon a little too much business on my part and a touch of home sickness on that of Mrs.

H. we are getting ↑along as well↓ as can be expected in a world of as much care trial and wickedness as this we inhabit.

There is nothing going on in Washington of which you do not hear in new york and therefore I need not give you the news.

Dr Scoresby is here[4] and I have got up a lecture for him indirectly connected with the Smithsonian. The affair is to come off to night and I hope he will have a respetable audience.[5]

I have got into a small room in the patent office which I call my office and find myself very much occupied for several hours each day in attending to the correspondence and other business of the Institution.[6]

We have heard melancholy news from Princeton the death of Dr Foremans son and his own sickness[7]—

Mrs Henry request me to give her kind regards to Mrs T.[8] and ↑her↓ thanks for the cap which came safely to Washington and apparently gave much satisfaction.

I have as yet heard nothing from the maker of the miceroscope[9] since I received the letter[10] accepting the offer I made him. Do you know whether he is at work on the article and when it may be expected to be finished.

I have just published a set of tables of occultations computed by Downe's of Phil^d which appears to find favor with the Astronomers and which is intended to facilitate the determination of the Longitude of places on the American continent. It will be found of importance to our officers in Mexico. The Corps of Engineeres and Topographers have been supplied[A] with copies and I think we shall obtain a harvest of results which will be of importance to the geography of our country.

Give my regards to Mrs T & the girls[11] and receive for yourself the assurance that I remain as ever truly yours &—

Joseph Henry

Dr Torrey

Torrey Papers, Library, New York Botanical Garden.

1. William Hemsley Emory (1811–1887), an 1831 graduate of West Point, in 1838 was appointed to the Corps of Topographical Engineers. During the Mexican War he was chief topographical engineer and acting adjutant general for the Army of the West. His reconnaissance of the Southwest during late 1846 and early 1847 was among the most important surveys of this period. Emory's marriage to Matilda Wilkins Bache in 1838 made him the brother-in-law of Alexander Dallas Bache. Elliott, *Dictionary;* William H. Goetzmann, *Explo-*

ration and Empire: The Explorer and the Scientist in the Winning of the American West (1966; New York, 1972), pp. 253–257.

2. William H. Emory, *Notes of a Military Reconnaissance, from Fort Leavenworth, in Missouri, to San Diego, in California, Including Part of the Arkansas, Del Norte, and Gila Rivers,* U.S. House, 30th Congress, 1st Session, House Executive Documents, No. 41 (1848). Emory's report also appeared as Senate Executive Document No. 7 (1848).

3. Shortly after returning from his South-

west survey, Emory asked Torrey to examine and catalog the botanical specimens which he had gathered. Torrey's descriptive list of plants formed part of appendix 2 of Emory's report (pages 136–155), as did a list of cacti prepared by George Engelmann (pages 155–159). Torrey hoped to publish a fuller description of the plants, but never did so. Andrew Denny Rodgers III, *John Torrey: A Story of North American Botany* (1942; New York, 1965), pp. 186–193.

4. William Scoresby, an Anglican minister, Arctic explorer, and lecturer, was in the United States on his second speaking tour. Henry had met him in 1844 during his first American tour. *Henry Papers,* 6:114n–115n; Tom Stamp and Cordelia Stamp, *William Scoresby: Arctic Scientist* (Whitby, England, 1975), p. 145.

5. Scoresby's lecture discussed the work of the British astronomer William Parsons, Third Earl of Rosse (1800–1867), whose telescope, fitted with a 1.8 meter (6 foot) solid mirror, was the most powerful in the world. Rosse used it to observe nebulae and to take lunar photographs.

Held in Washington's Odd Fellows Hall, Scoresby's free lecture was aimed at "members of Congress and all interested in the subject," according to an invitation notice in the *National Intelligencer* on February 18, 1848. Scoresby had "feared a failure," he wrote Henry the day after the lecture; instead, he noted, a large audience had attended, including "many of the first class of intelligence & position."

As Henry wrote, the Smithsonian's involvement in Scoresby's lecture was only indirect; he, Dallas, Bache, George P. Marsh, and W. W. Seaton were among the ten individuals listed in the invitation (though not by their titles) as sponsors. The institution's own lecture program did not begin until 1849.

Stamp and Stamp, *William Scoresby,* pp. 145–146; *DSB,* s.v. "Parsons, William, Third Earl of Rosse"; Scoresby to Henry, [February 19, 1848], Henry Papers, Smithsonian Archives.

6. Since December 1847, Henry had sought space in the "National Gallery" (wherein was housed the United States Exploring Expedition collections) to use as an office and storeroom for the Smithsonian's books and scientific apparatus. What he got turned out to be little more than a cubbyhole filled with drawings and cases of plant specimens. The room was not completely cleared until June. John Varden diary entries for December 23, 1847; January 10 and 31; February 1, 3, 7, and 8; March 17; June 3 and 5, 1848, in William Q. Force, "Memoranda Respecting the Smithsonian Institution while Occupying Rooms in the Patent Office Building," Box 23, Henry Papers, Smithsonian Archives.

7. An 1848 typhoid outbreak in Princeton claimed the lives of Alexander Reed Forman, an 1842 graduate of the college, and his father, William Forman (ca. 1796–1848), a prominent local physician. Hageman, *Princeton,* 1:275–276.

8. Eliza R. Shaw Torrey. *Henry Papers,* 2:171n.

9. Charles Achilles Spencer (1813–1881), of Canastota, New York, in the mid-1840s became the first manufacturer of compound achromatic microscopes in the United States. In 1847, after he saw a favorable notice of Spencer's microscopes, Henry ordered one from him. It was not until 1854 that Spencer completed an instrument that met his own high expectations. Its performance, Henry asserted, "far exceeds that which was anticipated when the proposition was made." Oscar W. Richards, "Charles A. Spencer and His Microscopes," *Rittenhouse,* 1988, 2:70–81; *Smithsonian Report for 1847,* p. 189; *Smithsonian Report for 1854,* p. 26 (quotation).

10. Not found.

11. The Torreys had three daughters: Jane Robertson (1825–1912), Eliza Shaw (ca. 1827–1913), and Margaret Antoinette (1829–1904). Christine Chapman Robbins, "John Torrey (1796–1873): His Life and Times," *Bulletin of the Torrey Botanical Club,* 1968, 95:519–645, especially p. 645.

144. EXCERPT, DIARY OF ALFRED VAIL[1]

FRIDAY, February 18th. 1848[A]

[...] Prof Morse D[r] Gale[2] & Prof Walker[3] held an interview with Prof Henry today. Prof H now states that many years[B] since & before Prof

Morse invented his relay magnet that[C] he used a relay magnet on a line one half mile long and an electro magnet for the purpose of ringing a bell & so exhibited it before his class.[4]

The question now arises if this be so why did he not in 1841 & 42 and since state it to prof M with whom he had frequent conference & correspondence and know what Prof Morse's inventions were and the arrangement of his magnets?

Was it because he wished to wait[D] until Prof Morse had tried it and run the risque of all the obliquy of such a visionary thing as the public pronounced it; before he Prof H should claim it as his own?

Box 5, Vail Telegraph Collection, RU 7055, Smithsonian Archives.

1. Since 1837, Vail had been a partner of Samuel F. B. Morse's, providing him financial assistance and technical advice. *Henry Papers*, 6:326n.

2. Leonard Dunnell Gale, an old acquaintance of Henry's and another of Morse's technical advisors, was associate professor of chemistry at the National Medical College in Washington. *Henry Papers*, 2:94n.

3. Sears Cook Walker.

4. This marked Henry and Morse's first meeting since December 1846, when they spoke in Washington about Vail's failure, in his 1845 history of the telegraph, to discuss fully Henry's discoveries relating to electromagnetism and telegraphy (see *Henry Papers*, 6:451n). The February 1848 meeting proved to be their last direct contact.

Though they later differed over some key points, including its date, those present at the February 1848 meeting agreed in two respects: that it was occasioned by comments Walker made in part of a report he prepared for the Coast Survey on the use of the telegraph in determining longitude, and that the major item under discussion was who should be credited with proposing the use of the receiving magnet in the electromagnetic telegraph. The part of Walker's report in question (which we have not found) dealt with the theoretical aspects of Morse's telegraph. Walker credited Henry with the receiving magnet, a statement to which Morse (to whom Walker had sent a copy of his manuscript) objected.

Morse recalled that after reading Walker's manuscript, he wanted "to do justice, publicly, to Henry's discovery, bearing upon the telegraph," and thus asked Henry and Walker to meet with him to "learn definitely what [Henry] claims to have discovered" (*Shaffner's Telegraph Companion*, p. 82). He asserted that they, along with Gale, met in January 1848. Morse recalled that he had "questioned [Henry] closely and particularly" about whether he had conceived of the receiving magnet before visiting Europe in 1837, but found Henry's response equivocal. He stated that he left the meeting convinced of Henry's "not having conceived even the *idea*, much less invented the *thing*," a sentiment he recalled voicing to Gale (*Shaffner's Telegraph Companion*, p. 83). Soon after the meeting, Morse claimed, he wrote a lengthy letter to Walker, dated January 31, 1848, in which he traced the history of the electromagnetic telegraph. In his letter, Morse agreed that Henry was "unquestionably due the honor of the discovery of a principle which proves the practicability of exciting magnetism through a long coil, or at a distance." Morse maintained, however, that he himself was "*the first* to propose the use of *the electromagnet for telegraphic purposes*," as well as the first to build a telegraph on that basis. In a cover letter of February 1, Morse urged Walker to print the January 31 letter with his report, adding that Henry should "see it and approve of it, and criticize it before it is published." Walker sent both his report and Morse's January 31 letter to Bache, asking him to show them to Henry. On February 10, having not heard from Walker, Morse wrote him again, stating that he hoped soon "to have the decision in regard to the disposal of the note I addressed to you on the subject of Prof. Henry's discovery." However, Morse stated, he never heard anything more about the matter.

Both Henry and Walker testified that the meeting with Morse took place *after*, rather than before, Morse wrote his letter of January 31. (Vail's diary entry thus supports Henry and Walker's chronology.) Henry testified that Morse asserted he was unaware of Henry's article, "On the Application of the Principle of the

Galvanic Multiplier to Electro-Magnetic Apparatus, and Also to the Development of Great Magnetic Power in Soft Iron, with a Small Galvanic Element," *Silliman's Journal,* 1831, *19*:400–408, until he read it in 1847. (Morse later rebutted this statement, insisting that Henry had confused 1847 with *1837,* the year he claimed he first saw Henry's article.) Henry stated that after Morse had finished speaking, Henry asked Gale (with whom he had conferred before the meeting) to present *his* version of what had happened. Gale, according to Henry, related that in 1836, knowing of Morse's technical difficulties with the telegraph, he asked Morse if he had seen Henry's 1831 article; when Morse replied negatively, Gale told him he would find in it "the principles necessary to success" (French v. Rogers, *Respondents' Evidence,* p. 257). Gale noted that he and Morse then used Gale's apparatus to repeat what Henry had found. Morse, according to Henry, did not challenge Gale's comments during the February 18 meeting. Henry also related what he said Walker had been told by Morse after the meeting, namely, that Morse was prepared to relinquish his claims. Testifying in 1849, Walker recalled that he left the meeting convinced "that Prof. Henry was the sole discoverer of the law on which the intensity magnet depends for its power of sending the galvanic current through a long circuit," and that Morse had succeeded only after reading Henry's article (French v. Rogers, *Respondents' Evidence,* p. 199). (Gale, for his part, wrote Henry in 1853 that he could not recall either the meeting or its circumstances, but agreed that "as the facts are in themselves true, I can do no less than admit that they may have been stated by me at the time.")

Vail (who was not present at the meeting) related in his diary entry for February 17 that Henry had told Walker "that he Prof H had many years ago used the relay magnet for making signals. He [Henry] has just made this known." Despite the significance Vail attached to this news in this and in his diary entry for February 18, it apparently did not figure prominently in the meeting of that date. Regarding Henry and the electromagnetic relay, see *Henry Papers,* 3:219n–220n.

On Walker's 1847 report, see *Coast Survey Report for 1847,* p. 21. Morse's comments on the 1848 meeting appear in *Shaffner's Telegraph Companion,* 1855, 2:80, 82–83, 87–89, 110n–111n. His letters to Walker of January 31, February 1, and February 10, 1848, along with Walker's reply of February 11, are in the Morse Papers, Library of Congress; a copy of Morse's January 31 letter is also in the Henry Papers, Smithsonian Archives. The letters are reprinted, with slight variations, in *Shaffner's Telegraph Companion,* pp. 84–88 (our quotations are based on the originals of the letters). Henry testified on the 1848 meeting in an 1849 deposition, which was published in Circuit Court of the United States, Eastern District of Pennsylvania, Benjamin B. French, et al. versus Henry J. Rogers, et als., *Respondents' Evidence* (Philadelphia, 1851), pp. 256–257 (reprinted in *Shaffner's Telegraph Companion,* 1855, 2:109–110; see also his letter to Walker, December 17, 1851, Henry Papers, Smithsonian Archives (a copy of which is in the Bache Papers, Library of Congress), and his annotated copy of *Shaffner's Telegraph Companion,* in the Henry Library. Walker's deposition appeared in French v. Rogers, *Respondents' Evidence,* p. 199 (reprinted in *Smithsonian Report for 1857,* pp. 94–95). A copy of Gale's letter to Henry of July 5, 1853, is in the Bache Papers, Smithsonian Archives; see also his letter to Henry of April 7, 1856, Henry Papers, Smithsonian Archives (reprinted in *Smithsonian Report for 1857,* pp. 92–93).

145. FROM JOHN LOCKE

Cincinnati Feby 19. 1848[A]

Dear Sir

I am doubtful from what I learn whether Dr Jackson will again be sent into the field, and I have modified my proposition to Dr Owen to this: that I undertake the magnetical observations in his district under him but that I have the appointing of my own assistants and manage the affairs of my party within itself. This I communicated to Robert Dale Owen when he was lately here. But I have received no answer or communication on the subject. I am on the whole rather[B] discouraged. It would be desirable to me to pass down the river this spring to New Orleans and thence along the Tertiary portion of the Atlantic[1] to Washington making my magnetical observations by the way.[2] Can this be done; or is there nobody to care for Magnetical Observations much less for my making them?

There is some excitement here about our friend Squiers and his forth coming publication. I felt apprehensive that he would treat contemptuously the works of his predecessors. When he first called on me it was to show me some of his specimens and to present me with a few. In the interview he honoured me by remarking that he had come to me because I was a "smatterer" in these affairs. As he was an Editor from the East, the sapient East, and then only a yearling in the west[C] I was amused. I do not hold my self to be even a "smatterer" but what little I have done has I belive been well done. Again I was amused when I saw the amount of credit given me in reference to Fort. Ancient. "John Locke, surveyor."[3] Dr Davis is[D] probably not satisfied with the treatment he is receiving. Mr Squiers may nullify himself by pursuing the wrong course, and you have by this time become acquainted with his peculiarities. But I hope the Smithsonian will not undertake to back any thing which will be justly offensive to any one. I am just about closing my course of lectures in College[4] and feel somewhat exhausted and low spirited. I hope some change may occur to relieve me. Perhaps after being relieved a little from duty I shall be better. I hope your situation although or may be attended with less of the disagreeable than it was last year.

Very cordially Yours
John Locke

Henry Papers, Smithsonian Archives.
Reply: Doc. 148.

1. Strata dating from the Tertiary period (from seventy million to two million years ago) exist as deposits of clay, sand, and marl. In the United States, such strata occur within a band running south from Cape Cod along the Atlantic coast to the northern part of Florida, west to Texas, and north along the Mississippi River Valley to the Ohio River. The precise extent of this band was still being defined by American paleontologists, by comparing fossil shells found in the United States with those taken from known Tertiary deposits in Europe. John Finch, "Geological Essay on the Tertiary Formations in America," *Silliman's Journal*, 1824, 7:31–43; T. A. Conrad, "Observations on the Tertiary Strata of the Atlantic Coast," *Silliman's Journal*, 1835, 28:104–111, 280–282; Jules Marcou, *A Geological Map of the United States and the British Provinces of North America . . .* (Boston, 1853), especially pp. 12, 48–51. See also Leonard G. Wilson, "The Emergence of Geology as a Science in the United States," *Journal of World*

History, 1967, *10*:416–437, especially pp. 423–430.

2. Locke presumably hoped to make detailed observations of the magnetic variation, dip, and intensity of various points in the South, similar to the extensive surveys which had been made in the area east of the Mississippi River and north of the thirty-eighth parallel. Below that latitude, relatively few systematic data on terrestrial magnetism were available. A list prepared by Elias Loomis of 193 stations at which observations of magnetic variation had been made showed that only 46 were below the thirty-eighth parallel; detailed observations had been made at only a few of these southern stations.

Locke suspected that a connection existed between the magnetic variation and the geology of a given site. Localities with sub-surface igneous rocks, he believed, would show the greatest magnetic variation. His magnetic observations at coastal points between New York and Baltimore, where Tertiary deposits were known to overlay igneous rocks, showed "ascending and descending undulations, like the outlines of distant primitive mountains." He may have hoped to find similar data from southern localities characterized by Tertiary deposits. However, he apparently never made such southern observations.

Elias Loomis, "On the Dip and Variation of the Magnetic Needle in the United States," *Silliman's Journal,* 1842, *43*:93–116, especially pp. 112–113; John Locke, "Connection between Geology and Magnetism," in "Abstract of the Proceedings of the Fifth Session of the Association of American Geologists and Naturalists," *Silliman's Journal,* 1844, *47*:101–103 (quotation on p. 102); Locke, *Observations on Terrestrial Magnetism,* 1851, SI Contributions, vol. 3 (Washington, 1853), pp. 1–29, especially pp. 18–19.

3. Locke referred to four plates from the report that he had prepared for David Dale Owen's *Report of a Geological Exploration of Part of Iowa, Wisconsin, and Illinois . . . in the Autumn of the Year 1839,* U.S. Senate, 28th Congress, 1st Session, Senate Documents, No. 407 (1844). They depicted a group of fox-shaped earthworks near Madison, Wisconsin. (Locke discussed the site and other Wisconsin Territory antiquities on pages 167–171 of the report.) Modified versions of the plates appeared in Squier and Davis's *Ancient Monuments,* with Locke credited simply as a "surveyor."

4. That is, the Ohio Medical College in Cincinnati, where Locke taught chemistry and pharmacy. Elliott, *Dictionary.*

146. FROM EPHRAIM GEORGE SQUIER

New York, Feb. 21, 1848.

My Dear Sir:—

Your letter[1] formally addressed to "Messrs. Squier and Davis" but actually intended for my special edification, has been received. I have read it with no pleasure and have passed it over to Mr. D., to whom I have no doubt it will prove more acceptable.

No doubt Dr. Morton and Mr. Marsh are very good judges of what should be admitted into a work of the kind I have prepared: Mr. Bache I presume knows more of sand banks, reefs and clam-shells than of Archeology: but neither of the first-named gentlemen, much less the latter, know whether any, (what you choose very loosely to denominate) "theoretical matter" at all is embodied in the work. It will be quite time enough to get frightened and cry "wolf," when the wolf is seen. I certainly have no theory to support; whatever collateral matter I have introduced relates principally to the antiquities of this continent, and it is only so far as they serve mutually to illustrate each other, that remains^A not found in our own country are alluded to, at all. And here I beg to say that I consider myself quite as competent to judge of what is pertinent and proper as the Sect. of the Smithsonian Inst. or the Superintendent of the Coast Survey.—at

I know little of the "usages" of Learned Societies, of which you speak, and care less about them. If the "usages" of the Smithsonian, so far as developed, may be regarded as a fair specimen, I have only to pray that I may be safely kept from having to encounter them.[2]

In respect to the wood engravings which you feel yourself compelled to "insist on striking out," I beg you would designate them, for there may be some that I shall insist on keeping in. So far as the cuts of coins are concerned, or so far as the eng. from Beck is concerned, I am quite willing to omit them. They are perhaps the least essential of all that have been engraved. What others strike the learned critical^B conclave at Washington as objectionable?

I have the profoundest regard for the interests of the Institution (my own are eminently subordinate) and I have no doubt your various "injunctions" are, as you say, "prompted by a desire to promote them." As however these "injunctions" were all laid down with due ~~pomp and~~ emphasis at the time of your late visit, I can hardly perceive the necessity which now exists for their repetition. Perhaps however they are this time intended for Dr. D. who I hope will profit by them in the preparation of his part of the work!!!

With regard to the paper of which you speak, I know nothing. Mr. Drayton promised to inform me of what he might determine in the matter, but has not yet done so,—although I have written to him on the subject. Of course I shall not think of going on until our own paper is ready—and this cannot be arranged until it is ascertained where, when & how Mr. Drayton procures his. He also engaged to write to the printer about the type he had selected, but has not done so; I have therefore taken the liberty of directing Mr. Jenkins to procure a supply of the kind fixed upon, and get ready to go ahead. He tells me the type will be ready this week. I now see nothing except the lack of paper, to prevent comencing printing early in March.

There is much labor of one kind and another to be done, and for the past week, owing to a severe indisposition, under which I am still laboring, I have been able to do ~~nothing of muc~~ very little. I am now ~~laboring~~ ↑suffering↓ under a secondary attack of fever which permits me^C to sit up only at intervals.

Dr D. is here, for what object I know not. He has done nothing, will do nothing, <u>can</u> do nothing, and I cannot discover the value of the advice which you give that he shall remain here until the work is out.

Yours &c. E. Geo. Squier

Prof. J. Henry.

Draft, Squier Papers, Library of Congress.

1. Doc. 142.
2. The conflict between Henry and Squier was an example of an endemic problem. The Smithsonian was attempting both to promote scientific research and simultaneously establish criteria for evaluating the quality of research at a time when professional and disciplinary boundaries were still fluid. Individuals were provided unique opportunities, but at the same time exploited for the good of American science generally and the Smithsonian particularly. It is not surprising that an ambitious individual like Squier would clash with Henry. Curtis M. Hinsley, Jr., *Savages and Scientists: The Smithsonian Institution and the Development of American Anthropology, 1846–1910* (Washington, 1981), p. 76–77; Hinsley, private communication.

147. TO JOHN TORREY

Washington Feby 28<u>th</u> 1848

My Dear Sir

I wrote to you a few days ago[1] to say that I would expect to receive a paper from you giving an account of the new plants brought home by[A] Lieut Emory. I hope that you have received this letter and that you will prepare the paper as soon as your leisure will permit. I now write to ask that you will oblige me by procuring for our friend Bache a nine inch globe without a paper cover and which presents a smooth plaster surface in a condition to receive a pencil mark. Such articles can be procured at the globe makers provided one is to be found in New York. Bache wishes the article verry much and as soon as it can be procured for the purpose of illustrating to some of the powers under whom he serves a problem in his survey.

Enclosed with this note I send a communication[2] for Dr Davis which I wish you to oblige by giving into the hands of the Dr.

All things are just now going on as usual in reference to the Smithsonian. I know not however at what moment a storm may rise.[B] Little things do not annoy me as much in Washington as they did in Princeton and the motto I have adopted is "hope on hope ever."

Mrs Henry joins me in kind regards to Mrs Torrey and the young Ladies. Mrs H says Mrs T must show that she has not forgotten her by sending a letter. My report is still in the hands of the printer and I know not when it will appear.

Mrs H and myself have just returned from a visit to Bache and his Lady on the Hill. The finger of time points to the key stone of nights black arch and therfore I must close with the assurance that

I remain as ever
truly yours &
Joseph Henry

Dr John Torrey

If[C] Dr Davis has left New York you will much oblige me by informing me of the fact. In that case please burn the letter for it contains matter intended for his eyes alone.

J–H–

Torrey Papers, Library, New York Botanical Garden.
Reply: Doc. 149.

1. Doc. 143.   2. Not found.

148. TO JOHN LOCKE

Washington Feby 29th 1848[A]

My dear Sir

~~Your letter[1] of the 19th was received on saturday[2] night and I now answer it at my first moment of leisure of to day.~~ I am sorry to learn ↑by your letter of the 19th received on saturday night↓ that you are rather in a desponding mood and to cheer you up I make the following proposition namely make the tour you propose in your letter, give the results with all others you have not ↑before published↓ to the Smithsonian and backed by Bache I will advise that you be paid a sum for the same not exceeding 200 dollars.

Bache on whom I have called this evening with your letter will make you an offer of ~~a more advantageous kind~~ ↑~~relative to the~~ ↑d↓ ~~a surv↓~~ ↑an other kind [---]↓ and you will choose betwen them. I do not wish to meddle in the affairs of Dr. Owen and I think it proble he would rather keep the whole operation in his own hands than surrender any of these to another.

I have become preetty[B] well acquainted with Mr Squier.[C] He is a young man of considerable talent but with modesty be it spoken I do not think he has had quite as much experience in the practical ethics of science as we have. I shall endeavour to see that justice is done to all con[ce]rned[D] in the ethnological pa[per][D] so far as I am acquainted with the facts.

I noticed myself the manner in which[E] your name was given on the map and expressed to Mr Squier[C] my disapprobation of the same and directed that your name should be placed in large letters on the title of the ~~map~~ ↑plate↓. The publication of the pamphlet ↑you mention↓ did good service in the way of calling forth som pretty severe criticism and in convincing Mr S that he was on the wrong track.

My report for the doings of last year is still in the hands of the printer where it will remain I fear for several weeks to come.

~~Enclosed I send a letter for Dr. Davis which I wish you to deliver into his own hands and if you do not see him has left the city please inform me of the fact and put the letter into the fire. It contains matter~~ [in]-~~tended~~[3,D]

All things are now going on peacefully inregard to the Smithson but I know not how soon a storm my rise. I shall hower endeavour to do some good with the funds so far as they are under my direction. Unfortunately my means in this way will be much abridged by cause which I have before exp[r]essed to you.

> I remn truly
> Yours
> Joseph Henry

Write me as soon as convenient.

Draft, General Manuscripts Collection, Department of Special Collections, University of Pennsylvania Libraries.
A partial Mary Henry Copy, consisting of the final paragraph, is in the Henry Papers, Smithsonian Archives.

1. Doc. 145.
2. February 26.
3. Not found. This passage is from Henry's letter to Torrey of the day before (Doc. 147).

149. FROM JOHN TORREY

New York. March 3rd 1848

My dear friend—

Your letter of Feb[y]. 28th[1] reached me only this morning. I was in the midst of preparations for leaving the city that I might be in Princeton tomorrow. I gave two lectures to-day, & feel much <u>fagged</u>— The family left for home some days ago.

I went to town that I might look up a globe-maker—but have found none as yet. Tomorrow I will put Holton[2] on the search—but I fear there is not one in the city. There is a globe factory in Boston (in Cornhill), and another (if I mistake not) in Albany. The note for Dͬ Davis was delivered to him myself this afternoon. That man Squier I do not like—& you will find difficulty in keeping him in the traces.

As to the paper on Emory's plants, I cannot tell yet whether I can prepare one that will be what I should like to see in the Smithsonian Contributions. Will you allow me to get drawings made by <u>Sprague</u>[3]—& if so—how many?

I hope you will soon get matters arranged to your satisfaction in the Smithsonian—but the task is not an easy one. The materials to be harmonized are very discordant. As yet I have not heard the result of Mr. O's[4] exertions to be appointed a Regent— It would be well if he had no connection with the Institution—or any influence over its officers. I am glad to learn that you have grown somewhat <u>pachydermatous</u>—so that little things no longer annoy you. Living for some time in Washington is said to produce that happy change of the integuments. I must try a short residence there myself for my skin is entirely too thin for comfort.

A letter from Mrs. T. informs me that you & Mrs. H. purpose making a visit to Princeton ere long. I hope you will share it between your brother-in-law & us. We have plenty of room, & quite enough welcome for all of your family. Do you mean to give ↑up↓ your house? I learn that it is considered a <u>fixed fact</u>—that McCulloch is to be appointed:[5] Prof. Stephen[6] is decidedly opposed to the arrangement. I shall not remain long at P. if I can dispose advantageously of our place. Mrs. T. is quite anxious to remove. She feels that besides Mrs. Schanck there is scarcely a lady there she would regret leaving—now that your good wife is no longer with us.

↑Rev↓ Mr.ᴬ Schanck[7] has accepted the call to the Presbyⁿ Ch. & will commence his duties in five weeks.

What sad events have occured in Princeton lately— The deaths of Dͬ Foreman & his son have cast a gloom over the place.

Had I not been so excessively occupied for three weeks past I should have acknowledged the receipt of your former letter.[8] We have ~~been~~ just finished our examination—which occupied every evening during more than a fortnight, until about midnight. This was in addition to the ordinary duties of the lecture room & the laboratory.

I shall work hard at the Expl. Exped[n] plants on my return to Princeton. The undertaking is more difficult than I expected it would be—yet I hope to finish it satisfactorily. I have written to Capt. Wilkes that I do not wish to undertake any more work for the Exped[n] Exotic Botany is out of my line—& I could not describe the large collections that he wished to place in my hands—without a voyage to Europe & remaining there for nearly a year. Besides there is no library in this country that would furnish all the books that would be required, even after making copious notes in Europe. The utmost that I could undertake would be to superintend the work & ~~edit~~ act as editor— Some of the families I could elaborate, but much of the Material could ~~only~~ be properly digested ↑only↓ by the standard Monographers. This Capt. Wilkes does not like—but many of the plants must be described in this way if they ever see the light.[9]

I had a visit from Nuttall[10] this afternoon—the first time that I have seen him since he left the country to receive his large income in England. He can be absent a very little longer without risk—as the will requires his residence in the "Old Country" for nine months in every year![11]

Should you visit Princeton soon it will give us an opportunity for a good long talk— My very kind regards to Mrs. Henry. I shall tell Mrs. Torrey to write to her—

Yours cordially
John Torrey

Henry Papers, Smithsonian Archives.

1. Doc. 147.
2. Possibly Charles Alexander Holton. See Doc. 280.
3. Isaac Sprague (1811–1895) was a landscape painter of Cambridge, Massachusetts, who made the drawings for several of Asa Gray's botanical works and whose work was highly regarded by him. In 1843 he had accompanied John James Audubon on his Missouri River expedition. George C. Groce and David H. Wallace, *The New-York Historical Society's Dictionary of Artists in America, 1564–1860* (New Haven, 1957); Dupree, *Gray,* pp. 166–167, 168.
4. Robert Dale Owen.
5. Richard Sears McCulloh was the leading candidate to succeed Henry at Princeton but later withdrew to become a candidate for the equivalent chair at the University of Virginia.

See Doc. 193. William B. Rogers to Henry, June 9, 1848, Henry Papers, Smithsonian Archives.
6. Stephen Alexander.
7. William Edward Schenck (1819–1903), a former student of Henry's, left the Hammond Street Presbyterian Church in New York City to become pastor of the First Presbyterian Church of Princeton in May 1848. He remained until 1852. *Princeton Catalogue,* p. 155; Hageman, *Princeton,* 2:145, 151–152.
8. Doc. 143.
9. Gray eventually agreed to describe the specimens but only after getting Wilkes to agree to very favorable conditions, including a trip to Europe. Dupree, *Gray,* p. 187; Richard H. Eyde, "Expedition Botany: The Making of a New Profession," in *Magnificent Voyagers: The U.S. Exploring Expedition, 1838–1842,* ed. Her-

man J. Viola and Carolyn Margolis (Washington, 1985), p. 38.

10. Thomas Nuttall, an English-born botanist who had lived in the United States for thirty years. He had supplied Torrey with plant materials from the West and had contributed to Torrey and Gray's *Flora of North America. Henry Papers,* 2:351n–352n; *DSB.*

11. The terms of Nuttall's inheritance of an estate from his uncle required that he live there nine months of every year. This was the only time he returned to the United States, arriving in November and leaving in March. *DAB;* Jeannette E. Graustein, *Thomas Nuttall, Naturalist: Explorations in America, 1808–1841* (Cambridge, Massachusetts, 1967), pp. 372–376.

150. FROM BENJAMIN SILLIMAN, JR.

Office of the Amⁿ Journal of Science
New Haven March 6 1848.

Prof Jos Henry.
Washington D.C.
Dear Sir

Your communication and the letter[1] announcing it were both received in due season. It had been our purpose from the moment of reading Prof^r Baches last & very interesting report to ask some friend who was competent to the task to do the scientific public the favor of reviewing it. Indeed we had already made partial arrangements for this purpose with another person not an unworthy coadjutor of the Survey [?or] of science to undertake this agreeable duty, but I need not say how willingly the proposed Reviewer & ourselves yeilded this pleasure to yourself.[2]

With kind & respectful regards to Mr Bache. I remain Dear Sir
Yours truly
B Silliman Jr.
for Ed. Am. Jour Science

Henry Papers, Smithsonian Archives.

1. Not found.

2. The unsigned "Review of the Annual Report on the U.S. Coast Survey" appeared in the May 1848 issue of *Silliman's Journal* (2d ser. 5:307–318). In a letter to Bache of February 18, 1848, Henry referred to his promise to prepare such an article for *Silliman's Journal* and requested time with Bache to "get from you the more important points." He continued: "I presume it will be best to dewell on the points of greatest interest to science giving a briefer account of all the other operations" (General Correspondence of Alexander Dallas Bache,

1fcRecords of the Coast and Geodetic Survey, RG 23, National Archives). Three years earlier Henry had reviewed Bache's first annual report for the *Biblical Repertory and Princeton Review* (*Henry Papers,* 6:250–252), also in consultation with Bache. Henry's twelve-page account for *Silliman's Journal* gave, in fact, a better overview of the scientific operations than Bache's longer report, not only because he left out many non-scientific details, but because he organized the review by various scientific topics rather than by geographical sections as Bache did. Not surprisingly, Henry praised the Coast

Survey's accomplishments during the year as reflected in the report:

It exhibits an improvement in the quality of results, and an increase in quantity over that of the former plan, which may be estimated at double the amount for an increase of fifty per cent in the cost. [p. 308.]

151. TO LEWIS C. BECK[1]

Washington March 17th, 48

My dear Sir

Your letter of the 15th was received this morning[2] and I immediately called upon Mr Burk[3] of the Patent office relative to the contents. He is much pleased with your suggestion as to the investigation of the adulterations of bread stuffs and thinks he would prefer to begin with this immediately ↑provided the ~~cost will~~ ↑expense will↓ not be too much↓.[4] He requests me to ask of you an estimate of the probable cost of the investigation and whether you can furnish him with a report on the subject befor[e]^A the next meeting of Congress.

I shall probably pass through New Brunswick in the course of a week or two on my way to New York and I will endeavour to to arrange my movements as to be able to stop over night with you. We can then exchange ideas as to the analysis of plants &c.

I remain truly yours &c
Joseph Henry

Dr L. C. Beck.

P.S. Please give me an answer at your earliest convenience to the queries I have propounded.

J– H

Draft, Henry Papers, Smithsonian Archives.
Reply: Doc. 153.

1. Beck, an old friend of Henry's, was professor of chemistry and natural history at Rutgers and also professor of chemistry and pharmacy in the Albany Medical College. *Henry Papers*, 1:69n.

2. Letter not found.

3. Edmund Burke.

4. Under Burke's predecessor, Henry L. Ellsworth, the Patent Office had become involved in agricultural matters, particularly agricultural chemistry. Beck had impeccable credentials for the work, which was the first federally-funded chemical analysis of agricultural products in the United States. He had investigated the adulteration of potash for the State of New York in 1836 and had written a comprehensive report covering all the issues from manufacturing processes to proposed corrective legislation. Several years later he published *Adulterations of Various Substances Used in Medicine and the Arts, with the Means of Detecting Them* (New York, 1846), which discussed food, in addition to drug, adulteration. Dupree, *Science in the Federal Government*, pp. 110–113.

Beck eventually made two reports to the commissioner of patents on the breadstuffs of the United States. Although he initially intended to include rye, maize, and buckwheat, his actual analysis was confined to wheat and wheat flour, which he gathered from various states and foreign countries and tested for water, gluten, starch, and sugar content. He concluded that although some domestic grains were equal to the best in the world, a large proportion deteriorated during storage and transport within the country and abroad, both through poor packing and shipping practices and through intentional adulteration. Beck's recommendations included reducing moisture content through drying, shipping in barrels, and exposing fraud. His reports were published in the Patent Office annual reports for 1848 and 1849 (U.S. House, 30th Congress, 2d Session, House Executive Documents, No. 59 [1849], pp. 245–273; U.S. House, 31st Congress, 1st Session, House Executive Documents, No. 20, part 2 [1850], pp. 49–82). L. F. Kebler, "A Pioneer in Pure Food and Drugs: Lewis C. Beck, A.B., M.D.," *Industrial and Engineering Chemistry*, 1924, *16*:968–970 (Kebler does not point out that the idea for the investigation came from Beck and preceded the appropriation by several months).

152. TO CHARLES COFFIN JEWETT

Washington March [18]th 1848A

My dear Sir,

I presented to the executive committee of the Smithsonian Intsitution at their last regular meeting[1] your letter and the accompanying papers.[2] They were refered to Mr. Pearce to be placed before the Library committee of Congress and as soon as this committee has acted upon them I will inform you of the result.[3]

All things have gone on quietly during the last month. The building is advancing as rapidly as the terms of the contract require. The east wing will be ready to be occupied in the course of the summer and the west one at the end of the year dating from this time or at least this is the intention of the architect and from what has been done I presume it will be accomplished.

I have published a set of tabbls of occultation computed by Mr. Downes of Philadelphia for facilitating the determination of the longitude of important places in the United States. I [...] prepared. For fear of mistakes I had only a few copies struck off at first and these were sent to the colleges and to those persons who would be most likely to put them to immediate use. From the number of letters I have received commending the plan I infer that the publication has generally met the approbation of the Astronomers of our country. The publication was ordered at the last meeting of the Board.

A resolution has been introduced into the Senate to reappoint Mr Hawley and Mr Choate as Regents and Mr Owen in the place of Mr. Rush. I have informed the chairman of the Library committee to whom the matter was refered that the time of the two Regents above named has not yet expired and I think their names will be struck ~~off~~ out of the resolution before it is reported to the Senate.[4] I know not what will be the result. Of this however I am very much afraid, that the reappointment of Mr Owen should it take pl[ace will br]ing [...] opposition to him in the house but if he is appointed by the Senate as I think he will be it is probable the house will concur. I have refrained from taking any part in the movements which have been made in regard to this matter.

With much esteam
I remain truly Yours—
Joseph Henry.

Professor Jewett.

Retained Copy, Henry Papers, Smithsonian Archives.
In Harriet Henry's hand. The first two pages are torn at the bottom; we estimate the missing material to be two lines from each page. Reply: April 26, 1848, Archives Collection, Brown University Library.

1. March 14, 1848. Rhees, *Journals*, p. 462.

2. Not found.

3. Pearce was a member of the executive committee and also chairman of the Joint Committee on the Library. Jewett's letter and papers related to copyright deposit, according to the executive committee minutes, which characterized them as "recommending a plan for the collection of the books presented to the Institution, under the act of Congress establishing the Institution" (Rhecs, *Journals*, p. 462). Section 10 of the act establishing the Smithsonian required that one copy of each book or other copyrighted work be deposited in the Smithsonian Institution and one in the Library of Congress. One of the earliest advocates in the United States of copyright deposit as a means of building library collections, Jewett wanted stricter enforcement of this provision, which was often ignored.

In what may have been a related move, Senator John Davis of Massachusetts presented a resolution on May 8 that the library committee consider whether the provisions requiring copyright deposit in the Library of Congress needed amendment. (U.S. Senate, 30th Congress, 1st Session, Senate Journal, p. 322.) Although the resolution was agreed to, we have found no record of any action. John Y. Cole, "Of Copyright, Men & A National Library," *Quarterly Journal of the Library of Congress,* 1971, *28:*114–136; *Smithsonian Report for 1849,* pp. 34–36.

4. Jefferson Davis had introduced this joint resolution on March 4, 1848. It was referred to the Joint Committee on the Library, which concluded there was no vacancy. The terms of the citizen regents Hawley and Choate did not expire until December. At that time, Davis successfully introduced a resolution for their reappointment. Rhees, *Documents* (1901), *1:*463–464.

153. FROM LEWIS C. BECK

New Brunswick March 21st/48

My dear Sir

I received your letter of the 17th inst.[1] & embrace the first leisure moment to comply with your request for an early answer. I find, however, that in regard to the 'cost' of the proposed investigation, which seems to be the principal subject of enquiry, it is very difficult for me to give definite information. I may need some articles of apparatus more than I have, & then the analyses will require the employment of several reagents, some of which are expensive. But all these, I think will not involve an expenditure of more than $75— It may be more—it may be less— The investigation, however, if properly conducted, will require a good deal of labour on my part & if the ↑results↓ are, (as I think they will be), of public utility, I ought to receive a somewhat corresponding remuneration. I am not much in the habit of fixing prices, ↑but↓ by comparing the outline of the work, with what has been done in other cases, perhaps some estimate may be formed.

As the subject is not entirely new to me, I have arranged in my mind something like the following plan; & I have to say, that in regard to the more common & important grains, viz. wheat, rye, maize & buckwheat, the investigation, if commenced soon, may, I think, be completed by the first of January next.

The first ↑thing↓ then to be done is, to analyze these grains in their normal state, selecting samples from distant parts of the U.S. to determine, at least in a general way, what are the peculiarities fairly referable to climate & soil— As we have already many trustworthy analyses of these grains, this part of the work will not probably occupy much time. The next business is to analyze samples of these grains (& the flour) obtained from the principal cities or depots for export in the U.S.;— say Boston, New York, Philadelphia, Baltimore & New Orleans—in order to ascertain what injuries they sustain in the transport from the interior, & what frauds (if any) are practiced. The same investigation to be extended, if possible, to specimens obtained from Vera Cruz, Cuba, Liverpool & Havre. Thus, at least, to present the facts in regard to the deterioration or adulteration of these grains & to offer suggestions or propose processes for prevention or detection.

The principal difficulty which I apprehend is, the obtaining of authentic samples from the southern & foreign ports, which will of all things be most desirable, as the injuries arising from careless shipment & from the considerable & often sudden changes of climate, will form a most important part ↑of the plan.↓. I think, however, this may be effected, either through the agency of our Consuls, or by interesting some of the shipping merchants in New York engaged in this branch of business.

But I must stop— You can now form some judgment[A] in regard to my plan. I should engage in the work con amore, but I must candidly say, that this alone would not perhaps be sufficient to induce me to lay out my strength upon it, as I should feel it my duty to do, if I was under the responsibility of completing it at a certain fixed ↑time↓. I must leave the amount of remuneration to be determined by that of the appropriation & by Mr Burke's own ~~notions~~ ↑views↓ of the importance of the work & the amount of labour which it will impose upon me.

I shall be very happy to see you on your way to New York, & hope you will not fail to fulfil your promise.

Yours sincerely
Lewis C. Beck

Prof. J. Henry.

Henry Papers, Smithsonian Archives.
Reply: Doc. 154.

1. Doc. 151.

154. [TO LEWIS C. BECK][A]

Washington March 24th 1848

My dear Sir

Your letter[1] of the 21st was received this morning and I have since had an interview on the subject with Mr Burke. He thinks there will be no difficulty in getting a specific appropriation from Congress for the investigation proposed and he has concluded ~~fo~~ to ask for one of a thousand dollars for this year.[2] The ↑whole↓ investigation will probably last four or five years but he wishes a definite beginning before the ~~h~~ next session of congress and a report on what may be accomplished ↑in this time↓. I shall endeavour to be with you next week or the beginning of the week after and we will then settle on the part of the work to be finished this year.[3] Mr Burke will ~~then~~ ↑afterwards↓ give you an official letter embracing the instructions necssary for ↑authoralitively↓ establishing the investigation.

I think the field is one well suited to your talents and in which you will be able to add much to your reputation and something to your income. Mr Burke is disposed to allow a fair compensation while he is not disposed to be lavish of the funds intrusted to his care.

There will be no difficulty in ~~getting~~ ↑procuring authentic↓ samples of of grain and flour from any part of the Union you may designate. Mr B has agents and correspondents in all quarters of our country and the articles can be sent by mail. Also th[r]ough ~~amer Cons~~ the officers of our government in foreign countries samples of all the grains of ~~Europe~~ ↑the different quarts of the [globe]↓ can be readily obtained.

Inorder to render the smithsonian Inst. popular we shall be obliged to do something for the application of sience to the useful arts and I have been thinking of offering a premium for the best report on the present state of chemistry applied to agriculture or for an elementary scientific treatise on Agriculture containing simple directions for the analysis of soils &c. Before we meet I wish you would think of this subject and give me ~~some pra~~ any practical suggestions which may occur to you on the subject.

Draft, Henry Papers, Smithsonian Archives.
Reply: Possibly Doc. 162.

1. Doc. 153.
2. In a letter of April 25, 1848, Burke wrote Beck that he had applied for a $1,000 appropriation, but that if Congress did not fund the study, "the Smithsonian Institution will undertake it, and the results will be published in the proceedings of that institution." Congress appropriated the money in August. Scrap Book,

Box 1, Beck Papers, Special Collections and Archives, Rutgers University Libraries; *U.S. Statutes at Large*, 9:285.
3. Henry made a quick trip to New York City in early April and may have met with Beck then. Henry to Harriet Henry, April 4, 1848, Family Correspondence, Henry Papers, Smithsonian Archives.

155. FROM ELISHA WILSON[1]

Trenton March 24th/48

Prof— Henry
Dear Sir

Can you give me any information to aid in procuring a good compound Microscope. I have heard there was an American named Spencer I think who has produced Superior Instruments. If this is true please favour me with his address, as you are probably acquainted with him— I would not take this liberty to trespass upon your time & convenience, but I know no other way at present to obtain the desired information: I will feel very much indebted to you therefore if at your earliest convenience, you would write me: As I am a lover of Science I venture to improve this opportunity to learn a little.

I want to learn how those beautifull Wheels & Circles of ~~light~~ the primary rays of Light are produced. Moving in a hundred or[A] thousand different ways Concentric and excentric Wheels, Stars, and Figures, thrown on Canvess, as was Exhibited in the American Museum[2] about ten months since: I cannot now give the name by which they were called when announced in their Bills. The light was obtained from the Oxy-hydrogen blow pipe. But the manner of producing such an infinite & regular moving combination of the primary colours I do not under-stand.[3]

Will you please refer me (where) to some source where I should ↑be↓ enabled to make myself acquainted with this. I cannot bear that any thing connected with Science should remain a mystery if a knowledge of it is in my power:

Last June I proposed a plan of a Printing Teleg—by Changing the Poles of the receiving magnets, I produce two independant motions with a single current & one wire. By one motion I move around & select the desired Letter to be written, by the other, The Letter is printed. Confidentially I have proposed to the Board of the NY & Wash Teleg to take up my plan & offer means for carrying it into practice. —It was objected to on the ground that fixed Magnetism would be fatal to its success— I am convinced by actual experiment in my own mind that such is not the case:[4]

I should however esteem your opinion of much importance on this point:—Morse as a matter of Course veto's the whole thing, as a thing impossible since he has carried Telegraphing to the heightth of its per-fection: And if he has given it up as perfect, who should not?— Please excuse me, the liberty taken in trespassing thus upon you:—

I shall look for your reply with great pleasure.

Please consider that part of this communication referring to the Tele-graph as <u>Confidential</u>.

Very Respectfully yours
Elisha Wilson
Telegraph Office Trenton N.Jr.

To
Prof Henry
Princeton College
Princeton NJr

Henry Papers, Smithsonian Archives.

1. An 1877 letterhead for Wilson, otherwise unidentified, reads "Bonds, Notes, Loans, Col-lections," and gives a New York City address. In correspondence with Thomas A. Edison in 1877, he sold Edison an insurance policy but also referred to "the telephone topic" and "the etherial medium," suggesting he and Edison had mutual interests other than insurance. Wil-son to Edison, February 17, March 16 (quota-tions), March 26, and September 3, 1877, in Thomas E. Jeffrey et al., eds., *Thomas A. Edison Papers: A Selective Microfilm Edition, Part 1 (1850–1878)* (Frederick, Maryland, 1985), reel 14, frames 317, 318, 322, 896.

2. A Philadelphia institution. *Henry Papers,* 2:285n.

3. The exhibition was probably produced by projecting images formed by polarized light, by a kaleidoscope, or by sending polarized light through a kaleidoscope. For projection through a kaleidoscope, see David Brewster, *The Kaleidoscope: Its History, Theory, and Construction* (1819; Holyoke, 1987), pp. 118–119, 122–125, 131–133.

4. In response to a reply from Henry (not found), Wilson explained his system for three-and-a-half pages, assisted by a few small sketches, and then wrote: "I will not tire you with the plan of my Inst— It is the principle to which I solicit your attention. Can it succeed." The plan was, apparently, workable, the objection mentioned in the text presumably based on the assumption that the iron cores of the electromagnets would become permanently magnetized. Wilson was never granted a patent for this or any other device. Wilson to Henry, June 13, 1848, same location as this letter; Bernard S. Finn, Curator of Electricity, National Museum of American History, private communication.

156. TO BENJAMIN PEIRCE

Washington March 29th 48

My dear Sir

Professor Bache and myself have concluded to send one copy of your table to the American Phil. Society for publication in the bulletin[1] and another to Cincinnati for insertion in Mitchels Messenger.[2]

You are at liberty to connect the name of the Smithsonian with your article in any way which may seem agreeable to yourself.[3]

I am ready to receive your paper at any time you may present ↑it↓ and I would prefer that it should occupy the position of the first article in the 1st no. of the 2nd vol. of the Contributions. I shall be obliged to remain in Washington until the adjournment of congress and immediately^A after this I intend to drive the printing of the Contributions as rapidly as possible.

My report is still in the hands of the printer and all things move so slowly in this place that I know not whether it will be published in a month or more.

Give my kind regards to my friend Dr Gray and receive for yourself the assurance

That I remain
truly yours
Joseph Henry

Professor Pierce

Peirce Papers, Houghton Library, Harvard University.
Draft: Henry Papers, Smithsonian Archives.

1. Peirce had written either to Bache or to Henry on March 23 (not found) with data supporting his conclusion that Neptune alone was sufficient to account for anomalies in the per-

turbations of Uranus. Interested in providing Peirce's findings to the American Philosophical Society, Henry wrote him on March 30, enclosing an abstract for his approval or revisions, and stating that Bache would send it to the society and that John F. Frazer would be asked to provide a copy for the *National Intelligencer*. Frazer presented the abstract and the table, "Residual Differences between the Theoretical and Observed Longitudes of Uranus, from the Theories of Peirce, Leverrier and Adams," at the April 7 meeting (APS *Proceedings*, 1848–1853, 5:15–16). Bache to Peirce, March 29, 1848, and Henry to Peirce, March 30, 1848, both in same location as this letter; Peirce report, November 15, 1848, p. 20, volume 8, supplement 1 (1847–1848), Overseers' Reports, UAII 10.5, Harvard University Archives.

2. According to Bache's letter, Sears C. Walker prepared "a posting up of the question" for O. M. Mitchel's *Sidereal Messenger*. Walker's summary was not published, however. The last item relating to Neptune was an editorial note, based on a March 22 letter from Peirce, which immediately followed a Peirce letter of March 13 responding to Le Verrier's accusations. *Sidereal Messenger*, 1848, 2:70–71.

3. In his draft, Henry wrote: "You can publish the same in Silliman's Journal connected in any way you may think fit with the Smithsonian Institution." The table accompanied a letter to the editor by Elias Loomis of April 11, 1848: "The Relations of Neptune to Uranus," *Silliman's Journal*, 1848, 2d ser. 5:435–437. The Smithsonian was not mentioned.

157. TO ROBERT DALE OWEN

Washington march 30th 1848

My dear Sir

In accordance with your direction I have been shown your letter[1] containing remarks relative to your publications and candor as well as friendly feelings to you prompts me to give you a frank expression of my opinion on this subject. In doing so I must repeat what I have said to you on a former occasion namely that in my conversations relative to yourself with my friends at Princeton and elsewhere I have stated that I beleived your zeal in behalf of the Smithsonian Institution arose, at least in part, from your desire to establish in connection with the Institution a reputation which ~~you~~ would neutralize the effects of the publications of your earlier days—that I believed your objectional opinions had been changed on some points you were now a married man the father of a family and that you were sorry for having made the publications alluded to in your letter. To these remarks the answer was why does he not himself come out with a statement of this kind. To this I could make no very satisfactory reply and I am sorry from the false view you take of the tendancy of your book that you cannot make the recantation required. I am surprised that you should continue to defend the publication. It evidently teaches the means of enjoying ↑the pleasures of↓ illicit love without the fear of its penalties and in this light the one in which it is [vie]wed[A] by your political friends ~~and~~ ↑as well as↓ opponents it must be [...][B] by the moral sense of the pub[lic.][2,B]

There is much feeling in the House relative to your reappointment and I fear if it be pressed the consequences will be disasterous to yourself and the Institution. In this I may perhaps be under a mistake but where your case my own or where you my brother I would advise that the appointment be not pressed.

Excuse the freedom and frankness of these remarks which are prompted by no unkindness to you ↑but↓ ~~by~~ solely by a desire to discharge my duty inregard to yourself and the Institution with which I am connected.

I remain truly
yours &c
Joseph Henry

Hon Robt Dale Owen

Draft, Henry Papers, Smithsonian Archives.

1. Not found.
2. While editor of *The Free Enquirer,* the leading free thought journal in the United States, Owen had published a seventy-two page pamphlet entitled *Moral Physiology; Or, A Brief and Plain Treatise on the Population Question* (New York, 1830). Like Malthus, Owen was concerned about overpopulation. In his tract, he not only described several methods of birth control but also argued the benefits of contraception, which he saw as stronger marriages, an improvement in the position of women, a decrease in unnatural and unhealthy celibacy among unmarried adults, less prostitution, and fewer mouths to feed for the poor. Although one critic called it "a mean, disgusting, and obscene book" (quoted in Leopold, p. 81), the tract sold well, going through five editions in nine months. Owen's biographer characterized it as "the most temperate, refined, and readable

of the nineteenth century tracts on birth control" (Leopold, p. 84). It was, however, a liability in Owen's later political career and provided ready ammunition for his opponents. Despite this, Owen never repudiated his work, now considered the "first important American tract on birth control" (Reed, p. 7). Richard W. Leopold, *Robert Dale Owen: A Biography* (1940; New York, 1969), pp. 57–84; James Reed, *From Private Vice to Public Virtue: The Birth Control Movement and American Society since 1830* (New York, 1978), pp. 7, 11; Peter Gay, *Education of the Senses* (New York, 1984), pp. 260–262; Peter Fryer, *The Birth Controllers* (New York, 1966), pp. 70, 89–94, 168.

According to one of Henry's friends, he never read Owen's tract. T. R. Peale to J. F. Frazer, August 15, 1848, Frazer Papers, Library, American Philosophical Society.

158. TO ALEXANDER DALLAS BACHE

Washington march 31. 48
1 oclock A.M.^A

My dear B.

We had quite a pleasant time at Mrs Walkers[1] reception, and I was glad I went. I met several pleasant persons and the company quite refreshed me after somewhat of a fatiguing day. I am off at 6 o'clock and therefore shall not have a very long [?nap].

I write to say I called this morning on Mr Burk[2] relative to the nomination of Mr Peal.[3] I was informed that the papers in his favour would be duly considered and that the best man for the place would be seelected. Mr B said that he knew Mr P. and that provided he was as will qualified as any other person he would stand as good a chance as any one else. Mr B was determined to find the best man irrespective of any other considerations. This was about the amount of the information I obtained relative to the matter.

Enclosed I send you the memorandum of the proceedings of the Executive committee at the last meeting.[4]

Also a letter addressed to Mr Owen[5] which I submit to your judgement as to the propriety of sending it. It is an honest expression of my opinion and though it may not give him pleasure it will do him no harm. I will howev leave it to your judgement wether the letter should be sent if any doubt exists on your mind give the doubt the preference and retain the article[B] until I come back.

If any thing should occur requring my presence inform Mrs H. and she will send a telegraphic dispatch for me. I most sinerely hope that Mr O's nomenation may stop in the committee—

Yours J–H.

Bache Papers, Smithsonian Archives.

1. Presumably Bache's sister Mary, the wife of Secretary of the Treasury Robert J. Walker.

2. Edmund Burke, commissioner of patents.

3. Titian Ramsay Peale, the artist and naturalist. *Henry Papers*, 2:391n. A bill was pending which called for additional patent examiners.

Robert C. Post, *Physics, Patents, and Politics: A Biography of Charles Grafton Page* (New York, 1976), pp. 113–117.

4. Held on March 14, with Bache in attendance. Rhees, *Journals*, p. 462.

5. Doc. 157.

159. TO JOHN GORHAM PALFREY[1]

Washington March 31st [1848][A]

My dear Sir,

It is highly important, that the nomination,[2] of which we spoke, be stopped in the Library committee, the discussion of it, in the House, will produce effects disastrous to the Institution, in the angry excitement, which would ensue. If, it can not be stopped, endeavour to postpone, the consideration of it, until I return. Please not to mention, my name in connection with this; for, if it be necessary, for me to come out, I ought not to do so, without, previously having a confidential conversation, on the subject with Col. Davis.[3]

Mrs. Henry, will send to you, for information as to what has been done, in the meeting of to day. I start this moment for New York.

Respectfully Yours
J. Henry.

Hon. J. G. Palfrey.

bMs AM 1704 (432), Palfrey Collection, Houghton Library, Harvard University.
In Harriet Henry's hand, with Henry's signature. Retained Copy: Henry Papers, Smithsonian Archives.

1. Palfrey (1796–1881) was a Unitarian clergyman and writer who was serving as a Whig congressman from Massachusetts. He presumably became a member of the Joint Committee on the Library when John Quincy Adams died in February. *DAB*.

2. Of Robert Dale Owen to be reappointed to the Board of Regents, this time as a citizen regent.

3. Jefferson Davis.

160. GEORGE PERKINS MARSH TO JOHN RUSSELL BARTLETT

Confidential

Washington Mch 31 '48

Dear Sir

Professor Henry left for N.Y. last evening or this morning. I rec'd yesterday a letter from Mr Squier, which he desired me to deliver to Mr Henry, but as I knew that Mr H. had been for some days on the point of departure for your city, with a view of attending to the publication of Mr S's book, I thought it better not to deliver it, but to leave the matter to be settled in a personal interview between them. I have no doubt that Squier has been ill used. He is a little hasty perhaps, but from my observation of Mr Henry's manner of transacting business, I presume S. is in the right of the controversy. In all matters of business, Prof. H. is as imbecile a person as I ever met, & a man more utterly unfit for his place could hardly be found. Still the aid of the Institution is important to S. & I hope your influence with him may prevent an outbreak between him & Prof. H. I shall write him by this mail,[1] & refer him to you. It [---] was expressly understood between Prof. H. & me, that S. was to have 200 copies of the book, & such funds as were necessary in the progress of the work for his support &c, & I really don't know wherein the disagreement between them consists, though I can easily understand, that it must be very difficult for a person of common sense, & reasonable acquaintance with men, to agree with Prof. H. in anything.

Did you get anything for me at the Thompson sale?

yours truly
G P Marsh

Bartlett Papers, John Carter Brown Library at Brown University.

1. Marsh to Squier, March 31, 1848, Squier Papers, Library of Congress. Marsh promised "to do all in my power to see that justice is done you."

161. TO EDWARD SABINE

Washington, April 1st. 1848—

My Dear Sir,

You will probably be surprised that I have so long delayed answering your letter relative to procuring magnetic instruments.[1] Shortly after the receipt of your communication, a plan was agitated for introducing a more refined & accurate method of surveying the public lands of the U.S., & it was contemplated to connect with this plan a series of magnetic determinations. I think it probable that such a plan will finally be adopted; & if so, the results will be highly important with regard to the knowledge of the magnetism of our country. I must request however that you will not publish, for the present, any intimations that such a plan is in prospect.[2] Prof. Bache & myself at first concluded to defer the purchase of instruments with the funds of the Smithsonian Institution; for should the plan above mentioned go into operation, the expense of instruments would be borne by the government of the U.S. We have concluded however to order one complete set, & a duplicate of that part of the apparatus used for determining the absolute variation.

On the opposite page is a memorandum drawn up by Prof. Bache of the instruments required. I will send you a draft on London to pay for the articles, as soon as you may advise me that the money is required.

During the past summer Dr. John Lock has been engaged in the country around Lake Michigan, in making observations on the dip & intensity. He will also probably be employed during the present summer in observations of the same kind— It is for his use that we order the duplicate of the apparatus for determining the absolute variation. He has at present no means of accurately ascertaining this element.

I am gradually bringing the plans adopted by the board of regents of the Smithsonian Institution into practical operation, & I hope to be able in the course of the present summer to send you the first volume of the Smithsonian Contributions to Knowledge.

> I remain very respectfully
> Your ob[t] serv[t]
> Joseph Henry

Lieut.-Col. Edward Sabine. F.R.S. &c.

For magnetic observations—

> Two instruments, I. Declinometer—(with ~~the~~ ↑a↓
> theodolite.   II. Dip circle.
>   I. Jones. II. Barrow.
> The theodolite of I from Gambey[3] or Estel.[4]

Magnetic Declination.

1. A declinometer by Jones of the kind made in 1846 (Lloyd, Weber,[5] & Riddell,[6]) with suspension fibre &c, but without the small theodolite[7]— (not the most recent pattern of Jones' instrument). Collimator magnets & scale divided in focus of lens. Lamp &c. Stand &c.

2. A theodolite & portable stand. The theodolite by Gambey or Estel, with horizontal & vertical limb, each of about six inches, & divided to five or ten seconds; repeating both horizontal & vertical angles. The telescope arranged so as to give a siderial focus, & one for near objects. Axis pierced & reflector for illuminating cross hairs. Two vertical & one horizontal wire. The diaphragm should turn so as to adjust vertically or horizontally. Diagonal as well as direct eye piece. Riding level &c.

The stand of round sticks braced with turning braces as invented by Prof. Lloyd.[8]

Magnetic Intensity. (Absolute horizontal.)[A]

The declinometer above described, by Jones,[9] with deflecting magnets, scale &c; also with wooden box for vibrations; weights or ring for moment of inertia, &c.

Magnetic Dip.

Dip circle by Barrow of Gambey's or Robinson's pattern.[10] If of Gambey's, should be more study in making it pack in a small space. (Two extra needles.) Stand like the foregoing.[11]

BJ3/49, Letters to Sabine from Renwick and Henry, 1845–1853, Sabine Papers, Records of Kew Observatory, Public Record Office, London.
In Caspar W. Hodge's hand, with Henry's corrections and signature. Replies: May 12, 1848, not found, gloss in Sabine's hand at bottom of this letter; October 19, 1848 (retained copy), BJ3/30, Copies of Correspondence to and from Magnetic Dept. re Domestic and Foreign Observatories, 1841–1859, Sabine Papers, Records of Kew Observatory, Public Record Office, London.

1. Doc. 100.
2. Possibly this refers to a series of moves by the General Land Office to standardize and centralize surveying methods and to combine legal land surveying with topographical mapping. Prior to 1851, land surveying was undertaken by appointing a surveyor general for each territory, who then drew up instructions and hired deputy surveyors to do the field work. The methods of surveying and standards of supervision and control differed from place to place; dissatisfaction with fraudulent or inaccurate surveys was common. The acquisition of new western lands apparently gave some impetus for reform and central control. In 1851, just after the establishment of the Oregon survey, the General Land Office issued to the surveyor general of Oregon a *Manual of Surveying Instructions,* prepared by John M. Moore, principal clerk of surveys. It mandated methods for that survey, rather than leaving them to the surveyor general's discretion. The General Land Office afterward sent copies to the surveyors general of California, Louisiana, Arkansas, and Iowa, to provide for either initial surveying or re-surveying to correct errors. The manual contained the instruction to note the variation of the compass needle and the places where it changed, and perhaps it is to this that Henry referred. This was not the first instruction of its kind to note compass variation: at least as far back as 1833, instructions from territorial surveyors general to their deputies specify noting magnetic variation. But this was the first general, country-wide mandate to note and record variation as part of the land survey. (Indeed, Congress and the General Land Office had recently tried to link land surveying and mapping more closely. On the basis of an act of June 28, 1848, the United States Coast Survey was given responsibility for the land survey of the islands and keys of southern Florida, although they never produced good legal surveys. Similarly in the act setting up the survey of Oregon, Congress allowed for a "geodetic" method that, if carried through successfully—it wasn't— would have created topographic maps as well as land survey plats.) C. Albert White, *A History of the Rectangular Survey System* (Washington, [1983]), pp. 111, 114, 115, 300, 444.
3. Henri Prudence Gambey, a Parisian precision instrument maker, whom Henry met on his European trip in 1837. *Henry Papers,* 3:312n, 387–388.
4. That is, T. Ertel and Son of Munich.
5. Wilhelm Eduard Weber (1804–1891), professor of physics at the University of Leipzig, an early proponent of terrestrial magnetism studies, and an innovator in magnetic instrumentation. *DSB.*
6. Charles James Buchanan Riddell, a British military officer and, in 1839, the first director of the Toronto magnetical and meteorological observatory. *Henry Papers,* 4:419n.
Bache referred here to three publications that specified portable magnetic instruments and their use. The first was the Royal Society of London's *Report of the Committee of Physics, Including Meteorology, on the Objects of Scientific Inquiry in Those Sciences* (London, 1840; revised ed., London, 1842), prepared on request of the British government to guide scientific observations that the Ross Antarctic expedition might make. The first thirty-eight pages of the *Report* (1st ed.), its *Supplement* ([London, ca. 1840]), and the *Supplemental Instructions for the Use of Magnetic Observatories* (London, 1841) all considered terrestrial magnetism. (Riddell's *Magnetical Instructions,* considered below, attributed this work to Lloyd, a member of the Committee of Physics and Meteorology.) Weber's contribution was "On a Transportable Magnetometer," from the *Resultate aus den Beobachtungen des magnetischen Vereins im Jahre 1838,* published by Weber and Gauss, but available in English in Taylor's *Scientific Memoirs,* 1841, 2:565–600. The last reference was to Riddell's *Magnetical Instructions for the Use of Portable Instruments* (London, 1844, with supplement of 1846), which was based on these sources, among others. For it, see also Doc. 91, note 3.
7. This instrument was the one ordered in duplicate, with one intended for Locke. According to the terminology of Riddell's *Magnetical Instructions,* it was a "Portable Declinometer, to be used with a Theodolite, or Altitude and Azimuth Instrument, for determining the absolute declination [variation]." Riddell, pp. 6–9, 15–16 (quotation on p. 9); Robert P. Multhauf and Gregory Good, *A Brief History of Geomagnetism and a Catalogue of the Collections of the National Museum of American History* (Washington, 1987), pp. 22–23, 31.
8. Unknown. Bache probably saw this dur-

ing his visit to Lloyd's Dublin observatory, but the latter's own account of his observatory does not mention it. Riddell's *Magnetical Instructions* specifies a portable stand for the portable declinometer that provided for adjustments of the parts to one another and orientation of the whole to the azimuth. Alexander Dallas Bache, "Observations of the Magnetic Intensity at Twenty-One Stations in Europe," *Transactions of the American Philosophical Society*, 1841, 2d ser. 7:79–80; Riddell, p. 16; Humphrey Lloyd, *Account of the Magnetical Observatory of Dublin, and of the Instruments and Methods of Observations Employed There* (Dublin, 1842).

9. This instrument was what Riddell's *Magnetical Instructions* refers to as a "Portable Unifilar Magnetometer, for determining the absolute horizontal intensity." Riddell, pp. 6–9, 13–14 (quotation on p. 9).

10. Thomas Charles Robinson, whose instruments Henry had seen in London on his 1837 trip. *Henry Papers*, 3:275.

At this time, a specification of Gambey's or Robinson's dip circles meant a specification of size, the former having a dipping needle 22.9 centimeters (9 inches) long or more, the latter, 15.2 (6 inches). The smaller size was due to James D. Forbes's direction to Robinson to produce a more portable dip circle, in connection with Forbes's extensive European observations in 1837, which included many Alpine stations. He found Robinson's smaller instrument to give as good a performance as Gambey's larger one. Bache was probably introduced to Robinson's smaller circle when in Europe, for he employed it there during his trip of 1836 to 1838.

James D. Forbes, "Account of Some Additional Experiments on Terrestrial Magnetism, Made in Different Parts of Europe in 1837," *Transactions of the Royal Society of Edinburgh*, 1844, *15*:28; Lloyd, p. 23; Bache, pp. 75–76; Multhauf and Good, pp. 24–26, 30, 73; Gregory Good, Department of History, West Virginia University, private communication; Deborah Jean Warner, "Gambey's American Customers," *Rittenhouse*, 1990, *4*:65–78.

11. According to Sabine's replies, he directed Jones to send the portable declinometers directly to Henry, advised Henry to procure his own theodolites, and directed the other instruments and stands to Woolwich, for his testing prior to sending them on to the Smithsonian.

162. FROM LEWIS C. BECK

New Brunswick N.J. April 4/48

My dear Sir

Enclosed are the hints in regard to the Researches on Breadstuffs, from which, I suppose, definite[A] instructions may be concocted.[1] I have also drawn out a programme for the proposed "Report on Agricultural Chemistry", which, I think, I can fill up during the Summer, should you desire it.[2] Both these arrangements I should like to have definitely made as soon as circumstances will allow. If anything is to be done before the next session of Congress it is time that the work should be commenced in earnest—not a day should be lost— I shall probably go up to Albany next week in order to ascertain what facts & samples may be there obtained, & also to select the books which may be useful in the investigations. On my return I hope I shall be ready to go on— Still, I should like to have the "Instructions" in due form, so that I can work up to the plan. I ~~should~~ ↑like am anxious↓ to have as full details as possible, in regard to the mode of conducting the researches, collecting specimens, expenditures &c.

I now leave the matter in your hands, according to your suggestion.

Yours truly
Lewis C. Beck

Prof. Henry.

Henry Papers, Smithsonian Archives.

1. "Researches in Regard to the Vegetable Substances Used for the Food of Man, or Breadstuffs in the United States, under the Direction of the Hon. E. Burke, Commissioner of Patents," in the same location as this letter. The piece was a slightly expanded account of the program of research outlined in Doc. 153. Its major extension was Beck's desire to treat potatoes, peas, and beans in addition to cereal grains.

2. "Programme of a Report on Agricultural Chemistry for the Smithsonian Institution," in same location. With minor variations, the program is identical to that given in Doc. 190.

163. TO HARRIET HENRY

Princeton April 6th [1848][A] ½ past 10 oclock P.M.

My Dear H

I have been much disappointed to day not to hear from you. I expected certainly a letter from you this evening but none came. I however received three communications one from Squier & Davis relative to the memoir[1] another from James[2] informing me that he has 600 dollars to pay before the 13th inst and that he will have hard scratching to do it. And a third from Bache[3] informing me that he has appended my name to an invitation to Mitchel to lecture and requesting me to make provission of a room for the purpose. You will therefore direct Mc Peak to engage the room at the Odd fellows Hall[4] the same in which Dr Scoresby lectured in.[5] Also look amoung my papers and endeavour to find a copy of the note of invitation which send to Bache. If you cannot find one amoung my papers <u>Will</u> can find one in my room in the patent office in the cupboard of drawers. I put a package of them in (I think the upper drawer they look like a package of envolopes— I shall probably be home on friday morning next.[6] Do not fail to write I am very anxious about affairs in Washington and since my absence have receivd but one note from Will and one from yourself. It seems an age since I left home.

as ever your
H–

Family Correspondence, Henry Papers, Smithsonian Archives.

1. Letter not found, but Henry's response of April 6 (Squier Papers, Library of Congress) indicated that it concerned their proposal to retitle the work from *Aboriginal Monuments* to *Ancient Monuments,* with which Henry agreed, as the former term "appears . . . to express more than is known."

2. Not found.

3. Not found.

4. On Seventh Street between D and E Streets NW, the hall was dedicated in 1846; its second story provided an assembly hall for entertainment and educational events of all types. *Records of the Columbia Historical Society,* 1908, *11:*330; 1928, *29–30:*77.

5. Subsequent correspondence makes clear that Bache wrote about John Pringle Nichol (1804–1859), a Glasgow astronomer and popular lecturer, who undertook an astronomical lecture tour of the United States in 1848–1849. On April 17, he spoke in Washington on "Modern Views of the Structure of the Starry Universe." He was advertised to speak at the Odd Fellows' Hall on May 4, 6, and 8; on the first occasion he spoke on the discovery of Neptune. *DNB;* Simon Schaffer, "The Nebular Hypothesis and the Science of Progress," in *History, Humanity and Evolution: Essays for John C. Greene,* ed. James R. Moore (Cambridge, 1989), pp. 131–164, especially p. 150; *National Intelligencer,* April 17; May 3 and 6, 1848.

Henry probably thought that Bache referred to Ormsby MacKnight Mitchel (1809–1862), the director of the Cincinnati Observatory and editor of the *Sidereal Messenger.* In the early 1840s, Mitchel had given popular lectures on astronomy in Boston, New York, and elsewhere, to wide acclaim. F. A. Mitchel, *Ormsby MacKnight Mitchel, Astronomer and General: A Biographical Narrative* (Boston and New York, 1887), especially pp. 159–162; Elliott, *Dictionary.*

6. April 14.

164. TO ALEXANDER DALLAS BACHE

Princeton April 7th, 1848

My dear Bache . . . .

I am now working under high pressure, examining manuscripts, lecturing to students, devising plans for carrying out the several parts of the programme. I have the publication of the memoir of Squier and Davis in good train; the first part will be out before the adjournment of Congress,[1] and the remainder in rapid succession. Prof. Turner of New York[2] is responsible for the accuracy of the literary part, and also every proof is to pass through the hands of Mr. Marsh. I wish to keep up the responsibility of those who have vouched for the memoir. Prof. Turner is also the representative of the committee of the Ethnological Society, which is to sanction whatever he may suffer to pass.

With reference to the programme, I have thought of having prepared before the next meeting of the Board the following articles.

1st. A report on the present state of chemistry as applied to agriculture, with sample formula for the analysis of soils &c.

2nd. A report on the economical and ornamental uses of the forest trees of our country. (the report by Dr. Gray of Boston)[3]

3rd. A report on the late discoveries in astronomy. (from Peirce and others)[4]

4th. A more extended report on meteorology from Loomis.[5]

5th. A report by myself on the present state of our knowledge of the phenomena of lightning, with the means to be adopted to prevent accidents from this.[6]

I find that a short absence from the stultifying influence of Washington has given my mind an increase of elasticity.

In great haste, as ever yours— J– Henry—

Mary Henry Copy, Henry Papers, Smithsonian Archives.
Reply: April 8, 1848, Henry Papers, Smithsonian Archives.

1. Congress was scheduled to adjourn during the summer. *BDAC*.

2. William Wadden Turner (1811–1859), a linguist of ancient languages, was professor of oriental languages at Union Theological Seminary from 1842 to 1852. Curtis M. Hinsley, Jr., *Savages and Scientists: The Smithsonian Institution and the Development of American Anthropology, 1846–1910* (Washington, 1981), pp. 49–50; Carolyn H. Dall, *In Memoriam: Susan Wadden Turner, William Wadden Turner, Jane Wadden Turner* (n.p., [1898]).

3. Henry asked Gray to prepare this report in his letter of May 23 (Doc. 177). Although the report never appeared, some of the plates were published in Asa Gray, *Plates Prepared between the Years 1849 and 1859, to Accompany a Report on the Forest Trees of North America* (Washington, 1891).

4. By May 23, Henry had started to shift his attention to Elias Loomis as a possible contributor, and by the end of the year he was selected for the job.

5. That is, an elaboration of the report found in the *Smithsonian Report for 1847*, pp. 193–207; this never appeared.

6. This also never appeared, although the subject was treated in the semi-popular manner envisioned for the Smithsonian reports in Henry's "Meteorology in Its Connection with Agriculture: Part V. Atmospheric Electricity," *Report of the Commissioner of Patents for 1859: Agriculture* (Washington, 1860), pp. 461–524, especially pp. 494–524.

165. TO HARRIET HENRY

Princeton April [8–10]th 48[A]
Saturday night

My dear H

Enclosed with this you have Lucinda's note[1] giving an account of her purchases. The box containing the articles and my coat came safely this evening. Your letter[2] mentioning the death of Mr Black[3] arrived last night. I have been very busy this week and have given six lectures since I came to Princeton this afternoon ~~by~~ ↑being↓ that of saturday I have kept quiet on my back most of the time for the purpose of recruiting my exhausted energies. Last evening Grandmother Stephen & myself took

Ephraim George Squier (1821–1888), 1850, mezzotint by Philip M. Whelpley (active 1845–1852) from photograph by Bertha Whernet-Beckman (1815–1901). Courtesy of the Anthropology Branch Library, Smithsonian Institution Libraries.

Edwin Hamilton Davis (1811–1888), circa 1855, photograph from daguerreotype. Courtesy of the National Anthropological Archives, Smithsonian Institution.

William Winston Seaton (1785–1866), 1855, lithograph by Leopold Grozelier (1830–1865) from a painting by George Peter Alexander Healy (1813–1894). Courtesy of the National Portrait Gallery, Smithsonian Institution.

Joseph Gilbert Totten (1788–1864), circa 1850–1855, oil painting by Robert Walter Weir (1803–1889). Courtesy of the West Point Museum, United States Military Academy.

George Mifflin Dallas (1792–1864), n.d., oil painting by unidentified artist after Thomas Sully. Destroyed in a fire in 1969. Courtesy of Princeton University.

Robert J. Walker (1801–1869), circa 1850, photograph by Matthew Brady (1823–1896). Courtesy of the Prints and Photographs Division, Library of Congress.

Sears Cook Walker (1805–1853), n.d., engraving originally published in *Popular Science Monthly,* 1894, volume 46, No. 1. Courtesy of the Library of Congress.

John Locke (1792–1856), n.d., engraving originally published in *The Cincinnati Journal of Medicine,* 1937, volume 18, No. 5. Courtesy of the Academy of Medicine of Cincinnati.

George Perkins Marsh (1801–1882) with his wife, Caroline Crane Marsh, and an unidentified
woman (possibly Lucy Crane), circa 1843–1849, daguerreotype. Courtesy of the
Prints and Photographs Division, Library of Congress.

Spencer Fullerton Baird (1823–1887), circa 1850, daguerreotype. Courtesy of the Division of Photographic History, National Museum of American History, Smithsonian Institution.

Charles Coffin Jewett (1816–1868), circa early 1850s, copy photograph by Levin C. Handy (circa 1854–1932) after original daguerreotype. Courtesy of the Prints and Photographs Division, Library of Congress.

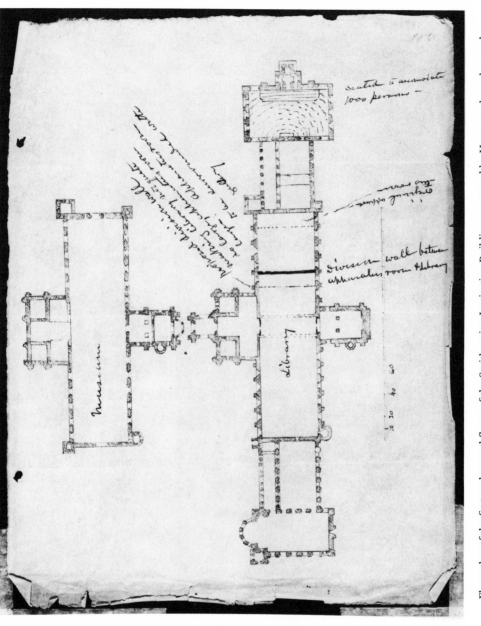

Floor plan of the first and second floors of the Smithsonian Institution Building annotated by Henry to show changes he considered in 1849 in the east wing lecture room and in the position of the wall separating the library and apparatus room (Doc. 308). Private Incoming Correspondence, Folder 25 "6/18–26/49." Box 4, Bache Papers, Smithsonian Archives.

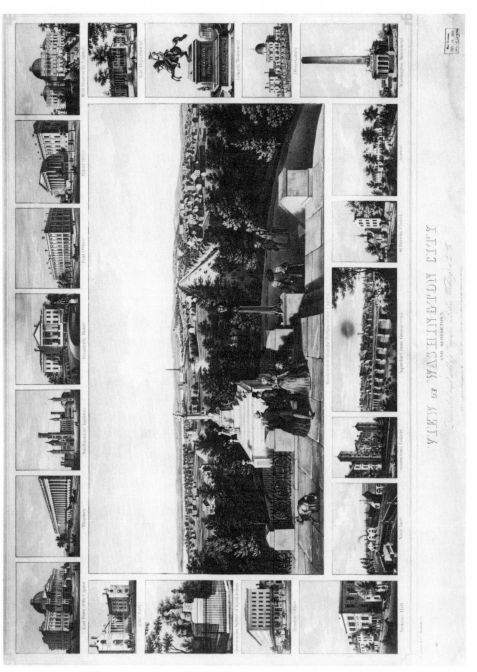

View of Washington City and Georgetown, 1849. Lithograph printed by E. Weber and Company and published by Casimir Bohn, 1849. Courtesy of the Prints and Photographs Division, Library of Congress.

tea at Dr Carnahans;[4] we met there Dr. and Mrs. Torrey with Dr & Mrs. Hope.[5] Mr. and Mrs. Forsyth had gown to Newbergh.[6]

I have nothing new to communicate all the stock has been exhausted in the previous letters. I saw Yankee Gibson[7] this afternoon he called upon me made many enquiries about you and the children. Said that Stephens Lectures had done him great credit and were universally admired.

I went though the upper rooms of the house this evening towards dark with grandmother found all things as we left them. I wished to get an old morning gown for I had felt much the want of some thing of the kind since I left home.[B] Sam was in the yard at the time. I was surprised to learn that he had the poney in the stable he said he had brought him home to doctor him; by long standing idle his feet had become lame. I fear Sam will neglect him and shall take care that he is not left in his care. We had quite a plesant visit at Dr Carnahan's; or I should say that the company generally had for I was myself so much exhausted with lecturing that I was unable scarcely to utter a single world. Schenck the preacher has come on with his family, and is to preach tomorrow. The families of the Professors now attend the new chapel[8] and the attendance is said to produce a very good effect on the conduct and dress of the students— Grandmother and Stephen both expect that we are to take up our abode with them when we come on and indeed I think it will be less troublesome and less expensive for us to do so. Mrs McDonald has commenced house keeping the Dr has purchased a house in which they are residing and which in due time I presume will be theirs.[9] I have as yet made no calls but at Dr Carnahan's and Dr Torrey's Stephen has promised neighbour Clark that I will call upon her before I leave—.

Monday morng

8 oclock Grace[10] has just returned from the Office bring with her your letter[11] of the 8th. I am much relieved by its contents. I have also by the same mail got a letter from Bache[12] stating that all the arrangemets for the lecture have been made. I mis read his former letter and thought the lecturer was Nitchel[C] instead of Nichol. I am glad all things remain quiet as to the Smithsonian. I have arranged all the matters in New York so that I think I shall have no farther difficulty.

I went to the chapel in the morng yesterday and to the church in the evening. The appearance of the chapel is quite imposing ~~imposing~~ the students occupy the main part of the area and the families of the Professors the more secluded parts namely the extremities of the transeps.

There is a small galery at the farther end which contains an organ. Yesterday Mrs Carnahan[13] Mary Maclean[14] [?Terry] Sallomans[15] Jane & Eleiza Torrey were there. In the evening Schenck preached in the church and gave an excellent discourse.

I had quite a fright last evening—Moses Hunter[16] asked me if I had had ↑heard↓ the news of the death of Mr Dallas in Washington. I thought little of it until I went to church where I met Mr Field[17] who informed me that it was certainly true for a telegraphic dispatch had arrived on sunday morning to that effect— Before I got into church however I met Ash Green[18] who said that he had seen the superintendent of the telegraph and that it was not Mr Dallas but Dallas Bache that was dead. I had seen in the paper the eveng before that Bache had lost his father and I concluded that the whole had arisen from this fact.[19] I cannot remain long enough this time in Princeton to finish my lectures though I shall be able to make quit an impression on them. I intend to return this week and shall leave in time to reach home on saturday. The weather sinc I left home has been delightful with the exception of the two first days.

I have been so actively engaged since I left home and so many ideas have passed through my brain that the time appears more than a month. Your letter of this morning and that of Bache's have been a great relief to me. I feel as if I ought not to be away from Washington and that something may go wrong during my absence. I also feel more and more a disinclination to be seperated from you and our dear little ones. I hope you will make yourself as comfortable as possible until I return.

Kiss all the children for me— Do not fail to go with all the House to the lecture[20] you are my representative while I am away— If I am inquired for say that I started for New York but will be back this week. Give my kind regards to Mr Schoolcraft & his[D] Lady[21] also to Miss Jane and Sarah[22] and receive for yourself the assurance that I am

as I ever shall be
only yours
H–

Family Correspondence, Henry Papers, Smithsonian Archives.

1. The letter from Lucinda McMullen is not found.

2. Not found.

3. Probably James Augustus Black (1793–1848), Democratic representative from South Carolina, who died in Washington on April 3. *BDAC.*

4. James Carnahan was president of Princeton. *Henry Papers,* 1:18n.

5. Matthew Boyd Hope was the professor of

belles lettres at Princeton; his wife was the daughter of merchant Matthew L. Bevan of Philadelphia. *Henry Papers, 4:*333n; Doc. 202, note 7.

6. John Forsyth, Jr. (1810–1886), professor of Latin and history at Princeton from 1847 to 1852. Prior to that, Forsyth was professor of Hebrew and Greek at the Theological Seminary of the Associate Reformed Church, Newburgh, New York. His wife was Ann D. Heyer. *DAB; Princeton Catalogue,* p. 430.

7. Perhaps Luther S. Gibson, of Winthrop, Maine, an 1845 graduate of the college who was attending the seminary. *Princeton Catalogue,* p. 168; *Catalogue of the Officers and Students of the College of New Jersey for 1844–1845* (Princeton, 1845), p. 5.

8. The Princeton Trustees authorized a new chapel in December 1846; it was constructed in the course of the following year. The chapel's cruciform shape and its inclusion of an organ (through the initiative of a student subscription) generated fierce protest on the part of some trustees, who associated the architecture and music with medievalism and Catholicism. Henry's comments below seem to indicate that the furor had died down. John Maclean, *History of the College of New Jersey, 1746–1854,* 2 vols. in 1 (1877; New York, 1969), 2:316–317; Thomas Jefferson Wertenbaker, *Princeton, 1746–1896* (Princeton, 1946), pp. 239–241.

9. Possibly a reference to Hannah McDonald, the wife of William King McDonald, a Newark lawyer, and the daughter of James Carnahan, who may have been providing a house for his daughter and son-in-law. *Henry Papers, 6:*394n; Maclean, 2:404–405.

10. Stephen Alexander's servant.

11. Not found.

12. April 8, 1848, Henry Papers, Smithsonian Archives.

13. James Carnahan's wife, Mary Van Dyke Carnahan (d. 1854). *Henry Papers, 2:*83n; Hageman, *Princeton, 2:*276.

14. The sister of John Maclean, Jr. *Henry Papers, 3:*82n.

15. An otherwise unidentified member of the prominent Salomans family of Princeton, and possibly the daughter of Susan Salomans, who was the daughter of former Princeton president Samuel Stanhope Smith. *Henry Papers, 2:*23n; Hageman, *Princeton, 1:*189, 235; 2:268.

16. Possibly Moses Hoge Hunter (1814–1899), who attended Princeton Theological Seminary from 1836 to 1838, although he was apparently employed as a school principal in Detroit at this time. Edward Howell Roberts, *Biographical Catalogue of Princeton Theological Seminary, 1815–1932* (Princeton, 1933), p. 101.

17. Probably Richard Stockton Field, professor of law.

18. Ashbel Green was at this time a student in the first class of Princeton's new law school. *Henry Papers, 6:*588n; *Catalogue of the Officers and Students of the College of New Jersey for 1847–'48* (Princeton, 1848), p. 5.

19. Richard Bache died March 17, 1848. *Henry Papers, 6:*456, 457n; Leonard W. Labaree et al., eds., *The Papers of Benjamin Franklin* (New Haven, 1959–), *1:*lxv.

20. Perhaps a reference to the Nichol lecture.

21. Henry Rowe Schoolcraft (1793–1864), an ethnologist of native Americans and former superintendent of Indian affairs in Michigan; and his second wife, Mary E. Howard (1812–1878) of South Carolina. The Henry family lodged with the Schoolcrafts. *DAB;* Chase S. Osborn and Stellanova Osborn, *Schoolcraft-Longfellow-Hiawatha* (Lancaster, Pennsylvania, 1942), pp. 542, 555–556, 623; Henry to James Henry, January 8, 1848, Family Correspondence, Henry Papers, Smithsonian Archives.

22. Probably Jane Susan Anne Schoolcraft (1827–1892), daughter by his first wife, Jane Johnston (1800–1842); and Sarah Rebecca Howard (1825–1902), a younger half-sister of his second wife. Osborn and Osborn, pp. 537, 548–550, 621–622.

166. NOTES ON ELECTRICITY

Princeton April 10th 1848

I gave a lecture this morng on the phenomena of atmospheric electricty and after the lecture I tride an ~~experi w~~ experment which I have long thought of[A] namely I sent shocks and sparks of electrity over the convex surface of the globe of glass on which an electrometer was suspended but I could perceive no effect the leaves remain immovable. This effect was due eather to the quickness of the operation or to the equality of the distribution.

To determ this send shock over plate of tinn foil on one one side of a ~~she~~ plate of glass and note the result.[B]

If card be placed[C] between the balls of the universal dischargier gold leave on each ball will[D] be carried in each direction and thrown upon

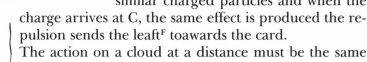

the card. The explantation is as follows as soon as the charge arrives at the ball a it[E] repells the gold leaf towards the paper on account of the repulsion of the similar charged particles and when the charge arrives at C, the same effect is produced the repulsion sends the leaft[F] toawards the card.

The action on a cloud at a distance must be the same on a ball as on a point sinc the attraction of the forme is the same as if all its force were consentrated in the centre the differe is in the action on the air.[1]

Folder "Non-Correspondence Pulled from JHPP," Box 50, Henry Papers, Smithsonian Archives.

1. Henry reiterated these conclusions in his comments on Elias Loomis's paper, "On the Proper Height of Lightning Rods," AAAS *Proceedings*, 1850, *4:*39–42.

167. TO HARRIET HENRY

Princeton Tuesday
morning April 11th 48

My dear H.

I lectured three times yesterday and at the end I was so much fatigued that I went immediately to bed. We have this morning the beginning of another delightful day the bell is just ringing for college prayers the sun is shining brightly and the temperature is of the most pleasant kind. Were it not that I am seperated from you and our children I would enjoy myself notwithstanding the labour I am obliged to under go.

April 11, 1848

Princeton has somewhat improved since we left; the house opposite^A the campus has been finished and is now occcupied with stores. Benjamin the tin smith has opened in one. A new house is beginning^B on the vacant lot near Uncles. The new methodist church is in quite a forward state[1] and with the new college chapel there is considerable advance. Mr Duffield last night said that Mr Topping is doing very well in Baltimore and will probably succeed in establishing a school of much celebrity.[2] He^C also informed me that Mr Lord is in a very feeble state of health not likely to live long does not expect himself to recover; is working industrious upon a poem which he wishes to publish before he dies. Poor fellow! he is really a man of genius and my sympathies are strongly excited towards him.[3]

Mr Forsyth has made a very favorable impression and bids fair to be a very important accession to the faculty. His instruction thus far has been well received and I should think it will be efficient.

All things appear to go on smoothly in this house. Grandmother is as active as ever. The children are about the same. The little one is very bright and makes occasionally some very striking remarks[4]— Old Mary is washing in the kitchen of the other house she was engaged there yesterday and has gone again this morng.

I presume you have seen by the news from Europe the wonderful spread of the revolutionary principles. We live in a time of great excitement and changes of the most vital importance are going on. The great truth is becomming more and more known that every human being ~~is~~ ↑has↓ an immortal rational ~~sole~~ soul— that the many are not made for the convenience of the few and that man has a right to self government as soon as he is prepared by moral and intellectual culture^D for so doing.

A remarkable feature in these movements is that they are attended with comparatively little violence they are not the revolutions of brutal passion but of enlightened reason.[5]

I will write more particularly relative to the apparatus of Mr Owen in my next. I have not as yet found time to make any researches on the subjct of books on magnetism.[6]

I remain as ever only
Yours

P.S I have finished my morning lecture and have returned to dinner—the day is almost oppressively warm and as there are fires in various part of the house^E I am rather hot. My lectures this time have been quite crowded and though I have been much pressed for time and have not been able to get at my notes Stephan having mislaid the key of my library yet I have lectured with much satisfaction to myself what ever may have been the reception of the descourses by my audience. This morning Dr Hodge Dr Hope Dr Carnahan & several other gentlemen whom I did not know were present.

> I remain as ever
> your own
> JH.

Family Correspondence, Henry Papers, Smithsonian Archives.

1. In 1847, the Methodist Episcopal Church constructed its first permanent structure, to accommodate a congregation which had grown considerably in size during a revival in 1845. Hageman, *Princeton*, 1:271; 2:195–196, 438.

2. In 1846, probably after a dispute with the college president over teaching methods, Evert Marsh Topping had left his position as adjunct professor of ancient languages to found a school in Baltimore. *Henry Papers*, 4:201n; Thomas Jefferson Wertenbaker, *Princeton, 1746–1896* (Princeton, 1946), pp. 234–235; Caspar W. Hodge to Charles Hodge, November 11, 1848, Charles Hodge Papers, Manuscripts Division, Department of Rare Books and Special Collections, Princeton University Libraries.

3. William Wilberforce Lord, a fellow of the college in 1845–1846, outlived this bout of bad health. *Henry Papers*, 6:387n.

4. Charlotte Meads Alexander.

5. The revolutions of 1848 started with the change of government in France. Rioting began on February 22; on the twenty-fourth, Louis Philippe abdicated and a provisional republican government formed. News of these events only appeared in American newspapers starting on March 20. The second great influx of news took place on March 29–30, and chronicled the spread of revolution earlier that month to Germany, Italy, and other European lands. On April 8 through 11, stories of the European revolutions again dominated the American press.

Henry's response was typical of many Americans:

> When the news of the overthrow of King Louis Philippe spread through the United States in late March and April of 1848, it set off frenzies of jubilation. Great mass meetings and torchlight processions acclaimed the final emancipation of Europe. . . . [T]he 're-generation of man by self-government' seemed assured.

For a democratic republic such as the United States, support for popular movements was seen as fitting. Indeed, with the overture of the American minister to France, Richard Rush, this country became the first to accord diplomatic recognition to the Second Republic. However, with notable exceptions for romantic nationalist revolutionaries such as Louis Kossuth, American interest in and enthusiasm for the revolutionary movements waned by late 1848. William L. Langer, *Political and Social Upheaval, 1832–1852* (New York, 1969), pp. 319–350; Priscilla Robertson, *Revolutions of 1848: A Social History* (Princeton, 1952), pp. 7–8, 51, 305–306; Guillaume de Bertier de Sauvigny, *La révolution parisienne de 1848: vue par les américaines* (Paris, 1984), pp. 9–11; John Higham, *From Boundlessness to Consolidation: The Transformation of American Culture, 1848–1860* (Ann Arbor, 1969), pp. 15–18 (quotation on p. 16).

6. This response related to a request conveyed through Harriet, the precise nature and purpose of which has eluded us. The "apparatus of Mr Owen" presumably refers to the terrestrial magnetic instruments ordered through Sabine (see Doc. 161) for, among other things, David Dale Owen's survey of Wisconsin. In his next letter to Harriet (April 11–12, 1848, Family Correspondence, Henry Papers, Smithsonian Archives), Henry mentioned that "Owen's instruments" had been ordered.

168. TO ROBERT HARE

Washington April 17th, 1848

My dear Sir: ~~I regretted much to learn on my arrival in Washington th you had left the same day.~~[1] ↑Prof. Bache informs me↓ that you are about preparing a paper on the explosion of saltpeter, and that you have some thoughts of giving it to the Smithsonian for publication. I hope that you will conclude to do so; a paper of this kind would be one of the very character for our volumes of Contributions to Knowledge. I should be pleased to see your name among our contributors, not only on account of the matter which would be connected with it, but also on account of the weight attached to it.[2]

I am much obliged to you for the criticism you gave me on my programme, and I shall be pleased to discuss the proposition with you when we meet relative to the admission of unverified speculations.[3] This is inserted for the purpose of relieving us from the annoyance of the many articles of a pseudo-scientific kind with which we are now deluged. I hold that every well conditioned hypothesis is capable of yielding fruit in the way of new phenomena, the discovery of which is due to the deductions from the hypotheses. Such fruit is the verification of the hypotheses but until it is produced by means of the hypotheses, the latter must be considered an unverified speculation.[4]

I remain very truly your obedient servant.
Joseph Henry.

Dr. Robert Hare.

Mary Henry Copy, Henry Papers, Smithsonian Archives.

1. Probably April 15. Henry to Squier, April 14, 1848, Squier Papers, Library of Congress.

2.. Hare had investigated the chemical cause of explosions that occurred during a tremendous fire which took place in New York City on July 19, 1845, and which destroyed about two hundred houses. The explosions were surprising, because although 135,000 kilograms (300,000 pounds) of potassium nitrate was kept in a store that had burnt, no other component of black powder was, and no explosion had been expected from a fire. Hare attributed the explosion to the superheating of the nitrate into a fluid, incandescent state, which could and did explode when it made contact with the fused sugar, shellac, molasses, wood, and other combustibles of the store. He presented his results in a short communication to the Franklin Institute on April 20, 1848, and later sent Henry a longer article, which was published in the SI Contributions. *Journal of the Franklin Institute*, 1848, 3d ser. *15:*390–392, 452–456; Robert Hare, *Memoir on the Explosiveness of Nitre, with a View to Elucidate Its Agency in the Tremendous Explosion of July, 1845, in New York*, 1850, SI Contributions, vol. 2 (Washington, 1851).

3. See Doc. 138.

4. In 1843 Henry and Hare had similarly discussed issues of the role of speculation and the verification of hypothesis. See *Henry Papers, 5:*414–416. This same concern with scientific method was an important part of Hare's celebrated dispute with Faraday over field theory, and would prompt him—for example, in a spiritualist pamphlet in 1854—to avow "positive scientific proof of a future state." *Henry Papers, 5:*409; Edgar Fahs Smith, *The Life of Robert Hare, An American Chemist (1781–1858)* (Philadelphia and London, 1917), pp. 480–483 (quotation on p. 481).

169. TO EPHRAIM GEORGE SQUIER

Washington April 18th 48

Dear Sir

Your note of the 15th, 48[1] and the accompanying proof came to hand last night after my communication to you[2] had been sent off.

The alteration you have made in the notes by taking out the middle line has considerably improved the appearance but still I do not like the appearance and must therefore request that you will make but one column.[3] I am responsible for the style of the work and were we publishing a single volume I would not be so anxious but as this is the beginning of a series of volumes each no of which must be on the same plan it is highly important that we start aright.

After we have settled upon the minutia of the first form all the others will follow of course and each proof may be returned[A] without delay.

Had I received the accompanying proof a few hours sooner or had you sent one to Mr Marsh[B] I could have returned the article th[e][C] same day.

Send us[D] a proof afte[r][C] all the revises have been made. It will be necssary for us to have one complete copy in Washington inorder to compare the different parts of the work.

I remain truly
Yours &—
Joseph Henry

E. G Squier

PS I have sent a line to the printer requesting that a revised proof be sent us of the first form and that two proof afterwards be sent to Washington.

One of these should be directed to Mr Marsh and the other to myself.

J–.H–

Squier Papers, Library of Congress.

1. Not found.
2. With date line of "Princeton Friday Morning" and assigned the date, from internal evidence, of April 14, 1848; Squier Papers, Library of Congress.
3. Henry's letter of April 14 also specified double columns and suggested lines to separate the text from the notes. He offered as a guide J. F. W. Herschel's *Results of Astronomical Observations . . . Made at the Cape of Good Hope, . . .* (London, 1847). The footnotes to Squier and Davis's work were set in full-width single columns, separated from the text by a full-measure rule.

April 19, 1848

170. TO WILLIAM CAMPBELL PRESTON

Confid[en]ti[al]ᴬ

Washington April 19ᵗʰ, 48

My dear Sir

On my return to this city after an absence of two weeks at the north I found your letter of the 8ᵗʰ of March[1] on my table. The letter however was received in Washington only a day or two before my return and I am at a loss to know the cause of its delay.

To procure a proper person for the position you mention[2] is by no means a very easy matter. Not only his learning, his ability to teach; and his power of governing are to be considered but also his moral character and the peculiarities of his family relations. I will carefully run over in my mind a list of my acquaintances in the line of chemistry and in the course of a few days will give you a candid expression of opinion as to the man I think ↑best↓ qualified for the office.[3]

In the mean time I beg ~~of you~~ ↑of you↓ as a friend of the Smithsonian Institution that you will not resign your office of Regent even though you should be requested to do so. Great efforts are now making by the friends of ↑Mr Owen &↓ General Hough (the gentlemenᴮ whom I was obliged to oppose in their contemplated expenditure on the building) for their election as members of the board; but the library committee of congress to whom the subject has been refered has concluded that there is no vacancy. General Hough has written to Mr Hawley informing him that it is the wish of the Regents in Washington that he (Mr Hawley) should resign inorder to make an opening for himself.[4] Your friend Capt Wilkes I am sorry to say is exerting himself for the election of Mr Owen, Renwick the Architect as you may recollect is the nephew of Wilkes and they are afraid unless Owenᶜ is in the Board to oppose me that the expenditures relative to the building will be curtailed. In the long run I think the character of young Renwick will be found safer ↑in my hands↓ than in those of Mr Owen.

I consider that the election of Mr Owen would be ↑a↓ disasterous affair to the Institution and should he be brought before the House his nomination will produce a very disagreeable controversy. There is in the public mind a deep and well founded prejudice against Mr Owen. He is the author of a book which he declares has done much good but of which the tendency ~~of which~~ is to teach young persons how to enjoy the pleasures of illicit love without the fear of its consequences. He has had unlimited control in the Board and has succeeded in carrying his measures.

313

You may recollect that there are two classes of Regents namely members of Congress and citizens at large.[5] I think it a very bad precedent to establish that of electing as a lay member of the board an ex member of Congress.

This is a confidential communication though there is nothing in it which I may not be obliged ↑here after↓ to publish to the world.

Me kind regard to Mrs Preston. I remain very truly your

obt serv.
Joseph Henry

Col Preston

Retained Copy, Henry Papers, Smithsonian Archives.
Reply: Doc. 173.

1. Not found.
2. At South Carolina College, where Preston was president.
3. Henry's following letter has not been found, but was received by Preston. See Doc. 173.
4. Hough had been a congressional regent. As he had not run for reelection to the House of Representatives for the Thirtieth Congress of 1847–1848, according to the Smithsonian act his term as regent expired on December 22,

1847. Like Owen, he was now attempting to return to the board as a citizen regent. Also according to the act, no two regents could come from the same state. Both Hawley and Hough were citizens of New York, so Hough was trying—unsuccessfully—to persuade Hawley to resign.
5. The Smithsonian act actually provided for a third class of regents, comprising the chief justice, the vice-president, and the mayor of Washington.

171. TO HARRIET HENRY

Princeton Wednesday
morning april 26th, 48

Me dearest

Your letter[1] acknowing the receipt of my first communication[2] reached me last night. I need not say that it gave me much pleasure. I regret that we are obliged to be so often separated in body[A] but I should much more regret were we separated in mind. You and our dear children are ever present with me unless I am for the moment engaged in some absorbing business.

I remained in New York until yesterday morning— I learned from Dr Forsyth that I could not get the class until Tuesday afternoon and therefore it was not necssary for me to leave the city before Tuesday morning. I was induced to stop inorder to inspect a new electrcal telegraph the invention of a young Scotch man ~~by~~ of the name of Bane the same person who invented the first printing telegraph.[3] I was well paid for [?remaining] the invention is a most important addition to the art of transmitting intelligence. Morse's telegraph at its utmost speed can send 70 or 80 ~~words~~ ↑letters↓ in a minute while this can transmit 5000 in the same time.[4] After visiting the telegraph with Dr Forsythe I went with him to his mothenlaws to tea—we here met Mrs F who on account of the illness of her mother has been staying in N.Y. for two weeks past. I next went to McMullens where I remained all night and had a long talk with John relative to the affairs of Europe.[5] He thinks England is in a very precarious state and the general opinion on the continent is that she must also undergo a change of government. The Queen by the last accounts has left Londondon though not yet recovered from her late confinement.[6] Lucinda regretted that you had not got the patern she sent you of a new form of dress. It looks very neat—is without seemes at the shoulders and is used in cases of morning dresses. The patern was cut out of muslin and basted. I will make inquiry for it of Grandmother and shall probably find it at Miss Skillman's.

I saw James Alexander his wife[7,B] is still feeble. I heard him preach on sunday morning and his Brother[8] in the afternoon. He is becoming if anything more popular in the city.

All things are going on well at Princeton there was some difficulty in regard to the senior class. One of its members bribed the printer's boy to give him a copy of the examination paper the evening before the examination. Stephen then concluded to set the examination aside and to have another this produced some commotion in the class but it was complied with—the examination took place yesterday morning and will lead to good results though S. thinks some of the new members of the faculty were rather inclined to show the white feather. Stephen's course was in this case marked with dis[c]ression and perfect fairness.

Granny Mary has gone to Mrs Schenck's. Mrs Voorhees is still in the kitchen. Sam continues to occupy the room under the dining room in the basement of the other house. Grace's sister is better and has gone until she recovers to reside with an Irish Friend.

If any thing ocures send me a telegraphic dispatch it will reach me in due time—the failure in the case of your message arose from giving the message to the wrong messenger—the same difficulty will probably not occur again. Write me relative to the information you get from Mrs Emory[9]—I will write to the printers in New York about the money for the paper.

I lecture this morning and must therefore close with the old assurance which needs not be assured that I remain my own dear wife as ever only

Your— H

Family Correspondence, Henry Papers, Smithsonian Archives.

1. Not found.

2. Henry wrote on April 22 after leaving Washington the previous day for New York. He wrote Harriet again on the twenty-fifth, after arriving back in Princeton. Family Correspondence, Henry Papers, Smithsonian Archives.

3. Alexander Bain, a Scottish clock-maker and telegraphic inventor. *Henry Papers, 6:*326n. Henry became aware of Bain's printing telegraph in 1845. We have previously—*Henry Papers, 6:*326—identified this apparatus with his electrochemical telegraph, described below, but should have instead referred to an electromagnetically based mechanical printing telegraph, for which see, for example, "Mr. Bain's Electric Printing Telegraph," *Journal of the Franklin Institute,* 1844, 3d ser. *8:*61–65.

4. "The Bain system, . . . is one of the simplest forms of telegraphy ever worked. No magnetism is used, and only the chemical effects of the electric current are necessary." The system worked by the reaction of iron—liberated from its elemental state by the electricity of the telegraph wire—with cyanide to form a distinctive blue compound. The system was remarkably effective over long distances, and, because it did not rely on a moving arm, it was very fast. It was further accelerated by Bain's invention of a paper tape system, with perforated dots and dashes on the sending end and a similar tape at the receiving end, set up for chemical reception. With this, Bain could achieve astounding rates of transmission for the time: approximately five thousand words per hour (not letters per minute, as Henry claimed), which was about three times as fast as Morse's system. Bain had obtained a patent for this system in the United Kingdom in 1846. He was now trying to extend it to the United States and had filed an application with the commissioner of patents on April 18, 1848. The Patent Office initially ruled against him, on the basis of infringement of Morse's patents. Eventually it granted the patent, but only a year later and after appeal to the United States District Court. George B. Prescott, *History, Theory, and Practice of the Electric Telegraph* (Boston, 1860), pp. 128–135 (quotation on p. 128); for Bain's English patent of 1846 and his attempts to secure an American patent, see Circuit Court of the United States, Eastern District of Pennsylvania, Benjamin B. French, et al., versus Henry J. Rogers, et als., *Respondents' Evidence* (Philadelphia, 1851), pp. 117–131, 158–167, and 496.

5. John McMullen (later MacMullen, 1818–1896), a graduate of Columbia (1837) and a teacher in New York City, had just returned from Europe. He had been in France during the revolutionary days of February 1848. *Henry Papers, 2:*6,7n; Henry to Harriet Henry, April 25, 1848, Family Correspondence, Henry Papers, Smithsonian Archives; Ramsay MacMullen, private communication.

6. Although Victoria had given birth to a daughter, Louise, on March 18, 1848, she left London for her estate at Osborne on April 8, to avoid the disturbances that her advisors thought might attend the Chartist rally set for April 10. Cecil Woodham-Smith, *Queen Victoria: From Her Birth to the Death of the Prince Consort* (New York, 1972), pp. 287–288.

7. Elizabeth C. Cabell (d. after 1879), daughter of George Cabell of Virginia. Hageman, *Princeton, 2:*370.

8. Two brothers of James's were in the ministry: Samuel Davies Alexander, ordained in 1847 and currently pastor of Richmond Church, Philadelphia; and Joseph Addison Alexander (1809–1860), professor of oriental and biblical literature at Princeton Theological Seminary. For the former: *Henry Papers, 4:*205n and William Edward Schenck, *Biography of the Class of 1838* (Philadelphia, 1889), pp. 29–32; for the latter: *DAB.*

9. Possibly Mrs. William H. Emory.

172. FROM ALEXANDER BAIN

New York
April 29th 1848

My Dear Sir

I duely recieved your kind Note[1] of the 28th I need not tell you how much pleasure it would have given me to have spent an Evening in your society and before long I hope to have that pleasure as I expect soon to return to this Country, But at present every momment of my time is taken up in preparations to leave for England. I will leave New York on Tuesday morning[2] for Boston to sail from thence for England. I expect to be again in America about the begining of Agust.[3] Permit me to thank you very kindly for the intrest you have taken in inventions, and if I can be of any service in procuring you any information Instruments &c—I will most gladly do so.

I have now no hopes of coming to an arrangment with Professor Morse & his Parties so that myself & Friends are to form a Company to work out the invention. I am to bring over a stack of Instruments from England with me, I have been occupied these two days ↑in↓ showing the invention to the gentlemen of the Press.

I will not forget to make the enquiries you mentioned respecting the Electrical Machines.

I am My Dear Sir
Yours very Truly
Alexander Bain

Henry Papers, Smithsonian Archives.
File note in Henry's hand: "Alexander Bain inventor of the printing telegraph."

1. Not found.
2. May 2.
3. Henry met Bain again in November 1848. Caspar W. Hodge to Charles Hodge, November 11, 1848, Charles Hodge Papers, Manuscripts Division, Department of Rare Books and Special Collections, Princeton University Libraries.

173. FROM WILLIAM CAMPBELL PRESTON

Columbia 30th [April 1848][A]

Dear Sir.

I am much obliged to you for your kind note & for y[r] previous[1] respecting a chemist for us. If a vacancy occur—it will not be filled until next December.[2] I had the pleasure of a visit from Capt Wilkes. He was aware of my resignation being in your hands—and I told him it was made subject to your discretion— We had some conversation concerning the Smithsonian in which he expressed himself favourable to the re-election of M[r] Owen,—and as I did not concur with him in this, the conversation was somewhat. The Capt left with me (in writing) a project[3] for the revival of the national institute, and a connection of it with the Gov[t] scientific property &c &c—in the general objects of which I concur but greatly doubt—the working powers of the machinery— We fully agreed that the Smithsonian should not be smothered by the fatal munificence of the Goverment in throwing upon it the proceeds of the Exploring Expedition.

I hope you have become acquainted with my Cousin M[r] Preston[4] on the Library committee. He is conected and liberal and may be able to serve you.

I am profou[ndly][B] grieved by the news from England. The tendency of the Chartists is to destroy that bulwark of European Civilization the only country on that side of the water—capable of reform without revolution.[5] Poor little Victoria and her baby it seems have run off from the Basiliphobia[6] of the times.

M[rs] Preston joins me in kind salutations.

Yr obt svt
W[m] C Preston

D[r] Henry.

Henry Papers, Smithsonian Archives.

1. Not found and Doc. 170, respectively.

2. William Henry Ellet was professor of chemistry, mineralogy, and geology at South Carolina College. He left for his native New York City at the end of 1848 and was replaced in January 1849 by Richard Trapier Brumby (1804–1875, *DAB*) of Alabama College, a South Carolinian, and former law partner of Preston's. *Henry Papers*, 1:337n; Francis Lieber to Joseph Henry, December 30, 1848, Henry Papers, Smithsonian Archives.

3. Not found. The plan was to combine the National Institute, the United States government collections, and the American Association for the Advancement of Science, all under the name of the National Institute. Wilkes presented his ideas at the June 10 meeting of the committee on the future of the National Institute, and they were discussed privately at the AAAS meeting in September, but they came to nought. "Meeting of Members of the National

Institute was held at the house of Col Force, May 27th 1848," Box 13, Records of the National Institute, RU 7058, Smithsonian Archives; Kohlstedt, *AAAS*, p. 88.

4. William Ballard Preston (1805–1862), a Whig representative from Virginia, and subsequently Zachary Taylor's secretary of the navy. *BDAC*.

5. Agitation for working-class political democracy—epitomized by the demand for a "Charter" guaranteeing universal suffrage, a secret ballot, annual elections, and salary for holding office in Parliament—rose up in the mid-1830s and seemed to have largely spent its energy by 1840. The revolutions of 1848 prompted one final mass effort, with a rally on Kennington Common and a march to the Houses of Parliament planned for April 10. The determined efforts of the authorities, who secured London militarily and mustered 150,000 special constables to counter 25,000

Chartists, led to peaceful dispersal and the general collapse of the movement. William L. Langer, *Political and Social Upheaval, 1832–1852* (New York, 1969), pp. 66–71.

6. An invented word whose Greek roots mean "fear of kings."

174. TO EPHRAIM GEORGE SQUIER

Washington May 13th 1848

My dear Sir

Both Mr Marsh and my self have been much surprised at the delay of the proofs. We have received none for more than a week past. I hope that nothing has occurred which will interfere with the rapid printing of the work. I wrote[A] to the printer[1] to ask the cause of the delay and to request him to forward me copies of all the forms which have been struck off with the exception of the two first of which I have copies.

I have received from the Brother of N. Orr[2] a letter[3] asking payment for an engraving of a large mouned of the existance of which no information was given me when I was last in New York. I cannot pay it as a seperate account and if ↑the engraving↓ is admitted as one of the illustrations of the memoir[B] it must be[C] presented in the account of Orr & Richardson[4] with whom ↑alone↓[D] I have made arrangements for furnishing the wood cuts. I will send tomorrow or rather on monday to Orr a draft in part payment for the remainder of his account and he must then let the rest stand until I can go to New York and have a critical examination of his charges.

I beg to remind you of the necessity of preparing the preface as soon as possible that there may be no delay in the apparance of the present no as soon as it is printed. After having agreed with Dr Davis on the form of the preface and the proper[E] credit to be given to those who have contributed information send the article to me by mail and I will add the part relative to the smithsonian Institution and submit the whole to the literary criticism of Mr Marsh.

I remain truly your friend
Joseph Henry

E. G. Squier Esq.

Squier Papers, Library of Congress.

1. Letter not found. The printer was Edward O. Jenkins.
2. John William Orr (1815–1887), formerly a partner with his brother, Nathaniel, was a wood engraver in New York City. His work was frequently used to illustrate books and maga-

zines. George C. Groce and David H. Wallace, *The New-York Historical Society's Dictionary of Artists in America, 1564–1860* (New Haven, 1957). He made some of the engravings for Squier and Davis's *Ancient Monuments;* see p. x.

3. Not found.
4. The partnership of Nathaniel Orr and James H. Richardson, which lasted only one year. Groce and Wallace. They engraved the remainder of the woodcuts for *Squier and Davis*.

175. TO ROBERT HARE

Washington May 14th 1848

My dear Sir

Your second letter[1] relative to the presentation of your apparatus to the Smithsonian Institution was received to day. I delayed answering the first letter[2] until after the meeting of the executive Committee which has been postponed on account of the illness of one of the members until Wednesday next.[3]

The chemical lecture ↑room↓[4] of the Institution is now in the course of preparation and will be finished in about three or four months. If you give your apparatus to the Institution I presume it will be displayed in the rooms adjoining the lecture room and though I cannot say that a seperate room will be exclusively devoted to it yet it will be kept as much as possible by itself in cases on which your name as the donor will be conspiciously painted and the whole so arranged as to present your gift to every visitor as a memento of your liberality.[5]

The regents of the Institution are chosen by a joint resolution of the two houses of congress[6] and though it would give me much pleasure to see you one of them[A] ~~board~~ yet I cannot say that you will be elected. Several persons have made great exertions lately to get in but the library committee to whom the nominations were refered have conclud that there is ↑at present↓ no vacancy. The board of Regents consits of three members from the House of Representatives, three from the Senate ~~and~~ the vice president the Chief Justice of the United States Court and six citizens at large.[7] The ~~latter~~ last mentioned members should be exclusively chosen from among the literary and scientific men of the country and should your apparatus be presented I ~~would~~[B] think you would be among the most conspicuous candidates. The members of congress are however very jealous of their prerogatives and have generally sensured the board of Regents for having nomenated a member,[8] whose term of service in congress had expired, for the situation of one of the citizens at large namely that of Dr Rush. The committee of the

Library as I have before mentioned have concluded that the position of Mr Rush is not vacant.

I am sure the executive committee will authorize the expense of repairing cleaning and packing the apparatus and that they will direct me to take charge of the articles as soon as they are ready for delivery. I wish you would address me a formal letter[9] on this subject as secretary of the Institution such as I can placed before the Committee and present to the Regents at their next meeting. State the terms on which you propose to present the apparatus and if possible let me have your letter before the meeting of the executive committee on Wednesday.

I remain as ever truly
Your friend
Joseph Henry

Dr Robert Hare

Draft, Henry Papers, Smithsonian Archives.

1. Not found.
2. Not found.
3. At the May 19 meeting of the executive committee, Henry presented Hare's proposal to donate his collection of physical and chemical apparatus to the Smithsonian. A subcommittee, consisting of Henry and Bache, was selected to determine the precise terms of the gift. Rhees, *Journals*, p. 463.
4. The lecture room projected for the east wing.
5. Although Henry announced the Hare donation with great pleasure, the apparatus proved to be a mixed blessing. Hints from Hare that Henry had taken too much from Hare's laboratory became demands for the return of certain pieces of equipment. In 1853 Hare complained at a meeting of the Smithsonian Establishment of the Smithsonian's delay in meeting the terms of the gift, specifically its agreement to repair the apparatus and place it on exhibit. Not until the following year were cases for the apparatus placed in the east room on the second floor of the main part of the Smithsonian Building, which became known as the "Apparatus Room." Most of Hare's donation was destroyed in the Smithsonian Building fire of 1865.
Smithsonian Report for 1848, pp. 21, 61; *Smith-*

sonian Report for 1865, p. 18; Rhees, *Journals*, pp. 237, 462–464, 472–473, 709, 773; Henry to Hare, October 21, 1851, and December 11, 1851; Hare to Henry, undated drafts, ca. 1852, all in Hare Papers, American Philosophical Society.
6. Only the citizen members are selected in this manner.
7. Henry left out the mayor of Washington.
8. Robert Dale Owen.
9. Not found, but probably similar to Hare's letter to the Regents of January 3, [1849], printed as an appendix to *Smithsonian Report for 1848*, pp. 60–61. In it, Hare explained that his successor at the University of Pennsylvania had brought his own apparatus. This led Hare to offer his collection to

> any institution for the promotion of science which would give it suitable apartments and cases, so as to have it kept in due order, and to render it available for the advancement of scientific knowledge. [p.61.]

In response to Henry's solicitation, Hare established the terms of the gift: he would donate the material if the Smithsonian would agree to pay all expenses for the transfer and restoration of the apparatus and to provide suitable space.

176. TO CHARLES COFFIN JEWETT

Washington May 19th/48[A]

My dear Sir

Your letter[1] relating to funds for the purchase of books &c for prosecution of your labours relative to the library came to Washington during my absence at the North and since my return I have delayed answering it with the hope of sending the money as soon as I could get a meeting executive committee. Owing to the illness of Mr Seaton and the absence of Mr Pearce this has been postponed from time to time until to day.[2]

Enclosed I send you a draft on the Merchants Bank of Boston for 100 dollars for which you will please to send me a receipt specifying the use to which the money is to be applied.[3] Any other funds you may want within the limit of the appropriation for your salary or otherwise I will forward to you as soon as possible after the receipt of your order. Your suggestions as to the copyright law[4] have been given to Mr Pearce[B] and by him presented to the committee of congress to whom the subject has been refered.

The report of the Smithsonian Institution to congress and the accompanying documents are at last in the process of printing and I presume will appear as soon as they can be put through the press. I will submit the proof of the suggestions from you relative to the library which are appended[C] to my report[5] to Mr Marsh for correction and alteration if any are required.

Mr Pearce will introduce a resolution into the Senate giving 500 copies of the records of the magnetic observations made at Girard College to the Smithsonian Institution for distribution.[6] These observations are printed in three quarto volumes and slightly bound for distribution.

I am still much oppressed with correspondance and am obliged to make large demands on the time of Mrs H for assistance in this line. Mr Russell takes charge of the books and occassionally does some copying for me. I hope in another year to be better situated both in regard to a location and assistance.

I am now in correspondance with Dr Hare of Phil[d] relative to the presentation of his large collection of apparatus to the Institution. The conditions of the gift have not yet been definitely settled but I have no doubt of the presentation being made. The gift will be of much value to us in the way of practial experiment and of service as establishing a precdent which I hope may often be observed. All things relative to the Smithsonian in Congress are just now very quiet and ~~I think the Institution is gaining in[D] the good feelings of the members~~ the prospect of usefulness and permanacy of the Institution I think ~~ever~~ becoming ↑every day↓ more favourable. The building is going on quite rapidly and will be ready for use according to the last account of the architect in about three months. ~~My time is still much employed~~ The printing of the memoir of Sequre ~~of~~ and Davis is still in progress though the press was stopped for a week on account of ~~the~~ ↑a↓ delay in the arrival of the pape. The printing of the volume in New York while I am in Washington continues to be found very inconvenient and I would gladly avail mysef of your offer of superintending the printing could I transfer the work to Boston. Would it not be possible for you to reside a part of the present summer in New York and take charge of the printing. An additional compensation would probably allowed you for this service. Write to me on this point and inform me when you will probably visit New York for possibly if the time you mention is not too early I may meet you there.

> I remain with kind[E]
> regard yours truly
> Joseph Henry

Profr
C. C. Jewett

Draft, Henry Papers, Smithsonian Archives
Inside address in Harriet Henry's hand. Reply: Doc. 180.

1. Of April 26, 1848, Archives Collection, Brown University Library.

2. The executive committee had not met since March 14.

3. Jewett had asked for $100 for the purchase of books and stationery, as well as for incidental expenses.

4. Jewett recommended that three copies of every book be deposited with the government to secure a valid copyright. One of those copies was to be placed in safe storage.

5. Jewett's suggestions (Doc. 122) were published in the *Smithsonian Report for 1847*, pp. 191–193.

6. A reference to *Observations at the Magnetic and Meteorological Observatory at the Girard College, Philadelphia,* 3 vols. (Washington, 1847). No evidence of such a resolution has been found.

177. TO ASA GRAY

Washington May 23rd 1848

My dear Dr

I presume that you are still somewhat interested in the affairs of the Smithsonian and desire to know what we are doing. I would[A] have written to you before this but I am so oppressed with correspondence that every letter [?counts] one. I may however write to you with less care than to others and consequently with less expense of time. All things relative to the Smithsonian Institution are now in a quiet state the attacks made upon it at the beginning of the present session of congress have ceased without any serious result and I think the prospect of the stability popularity and usefulness of the Institution is every day becoming[B] more & more favourable. The Library committee of Congress to whom the nomination of Mr Owen was refered have come to the conclusion that there is no vacancy and that the absence of Mr Rush is not a sufficient ground for his leaving the Board. Mr Owen is in the city and apparently acquiesses in the decision of the committee.

I hope in due time to get control of the affairs of the Institution the members who were in the Board at the time of my election are fast passing out[1] and those which remain are either my fast friends or take but little interest in the affair.

The memoir of Davis & Squire is still in the press but[C] will be out in the course of a few weeks. I think it will make one of the most beautiful books ever published in this country. It has however given me much trouble printing in New-York while I am in Washington is a very inconvenient arrangement. I hope however to establish a small printing office in connection with the Institution. In the publication of the memoir of Squire[D] and Davis I made one false step which has caused me much trouble namely I allowed Squier to superintend the engravings and the printing and he has I say this in confidence proved wholly unworthy of the trust. I hope however to get through with the volume without farther difficulty. The building is rapidly advancing and will be ready for use in one wing in the course of the present summer. I have concluded not to attempt to stop the erection but to endeavour to control the[E] expenditure. I hope in due time congress will be made to see the injustice of ~~the~~ putting[F] the keeping of the national museum on the Smithsonian fund and not only pay for its keeping but also in part refund a part of the expenditure on the building which has been erected to contain it.

Dr Hare offers under the condition that a suitable room be provided to give his apparatus to the smithsonian Institution. The gift will not only be of importance to the Institution in the way of research and illustration but also as serving to establish[G] a precedent which I hope may frequently bring us in other donations. It will also serve to increase the confidence of the public in the stability and character of[H] the Institution. I have received several papers for the second volume of the contributions and shall commence the printing of it as soon as the first volume is through the press. This will be I hope in september.

I have been considering the the subject of Reports and wish to consult you particularly on this point. All our operations thus far have been of a scientific kind intended to increase rather than to diffuse knowledge. I have thought of getting prepared before the end of the year if possible Reports on the following subjects

1 On the present state of chemestry as applied to ~~the~~ Agriculture with simple directions for the analysis of soils &c.

2 On[I] the economical and other uses of the forest treas of our country their mode of culture method of transfer &c &c with a popular description of them &c. &—.

3 One on astronomy giving[J] a sketch of the later discoveries and particularly what has been done during the last few years as well in our country as abroad. ~~4 these~~

4 One on the phenomena of lightning with directions for protection from the danger of meteor &—&.

These reports should be prepared on the plan of the Systeme du monde of Laplace sufficenly popular to interest the many while it will also instruct the few.[2] The first report will be prepared by Dr[K] Lewis Beck the Second by Dr A Gray of Cambridge[L] the third by Professor Pierce or Professor Loomis and the fourth by Professor Henry. What[M] say you to this arrangement? The report on asstronomy I should prefer to have prepared by Professor Pierce were it not that an account of his own labours would be included. How would it answer to give[N] the report of the discoveries made abroad to Pierce and those of our own country to Loomis?

As to the compensation for these reports I can say nothing very definitely the whole is as you know[O] very much a matter of experiment. The price should not be put so high as to make it much of an object to prepare these reports and yet sufficient to reward properly the labour of preparation. The Board appropriated 500 dollars for a begining of reports during the present year but something may be derived from the sale of the articles. Suppose we should say $~~1.00 per page~~ from one dollar to one dollar and fifty cents a page with an addition to be derived from the sale or the[P] writer to receive a certain number of copies to dispose of on his own account. What is the amount per page given by the North American Review?[3]

Beside the Report on the forest trees of our county much good might be done by giving a report on the foreign plants which may be advantageously introduced into our country the mode of culture to be adopted perhaps this might come in under the other report but I think the subject demands a seperate article which I think would be made the bases of an^Q action^R in Congress several members have spoken to me on the subject[4]— This report might be prepared for the next year. I depend upon you to take charge of the botanical branch of the reports unless Dr Torrey should wish to join in some of them. Do not attempt to decline the report on forest trees but give the subject your immediate attention. I would have written to you before on this subject but could not properly do so until I saw my way clearly. Write to me as soon as convenient and confer with Pierce on the contents of this letter.[5]

I remain as ever truly yours
Joseph Henry

Dr A Gray^S

Besides the Reports I have mentioned Professor Bailey of West Point has proposed to give me a report on the use of the microscope with descriptions of new test objects.[6]

P.S. The Smithsonian Reports ~~are y~~ to Congress still in the hands of the printer but are promised in the course of a week or two.

Historic Letters, Archives, Gray Herbarium Library, Harvard University.
Reply: June 2, 1848, Archives of the Hunt Institute for Botanical Documentation, Carnegie Mellon University.

1. Four members of the original Board of Regents were gone: three congressional regents, Evans, Hough, and Owen, were not re-elected; a fourth, Pennybacker, had died.

2. "One of the most successful popularizations of science ever composed," Pierre-Simon Laplace's *Exposition du système du monde,* 2 vols. (Paris, 1796), summarized late eighteenth-century knowledge of the motions of the planets, stars, satellites, and comets; the laws of motion; the theory of gravitation; and the history of astronomy. It concluded with a presentation of Laplace's explanation of the origin of the solar system in terms of natural law—the nebular hypothesis. *DSB* (quotation on *15:*342).

3. The *North American Review* paid $1 per printed page. Frank L. Mott, *A History of American Magazines, 1741–1850* (New York, 1930), p. 505.

4. Attempts had been made to introduce foreign plants into the American agricultural system since colonial times. One of the rationales for exploration during the antebellum period was the discovery of economically useful plants. During the 1840s and 1850s the Patent Office distributed seeds brought back from exploring expeditions, part of its larger program of distributing free seed to farmers. Brooke Hindle, *The Pursuit of Science in Revolutionary America* (1956; New York, 1974), pp. 197–204; Dupree, *Science in the Federal Government,* pp. 110–111.

5. Instead of Gray writing, he and Henry conferred in Washington. Gray to Henry, June 2, 1848, Archives of the Hunt Institute for Botanical Documentation, Carnegie Mellon University.

6. Never published by the Smithsonian.

178. FROM JACOB WHITMAN BAILEY

West Point. N.Y. May 27th. 1848

My dear Sir

I should have had the Notes on test objects done some time since, if I had not concluded to wait to obtain from Spencer his views as to the angle of aperture required and absolutely indispensable for ↑the resolution of↓ each of the tests.[1] When I get this, it will not take long to finish the manuscript. The figures however trouble me much. I fear no engraver can give the lines as they appear under the microscope unless he himself sees them by means of this instrument. I myself have not minuteness of touch enough to represent them in a drawing, and unless I employ a draughtsman here, or get the engraver to come here for detailed instructions I doubt whether the plate will be worth much, and yet this plate ought to constitute the chief value of the paper.

I have not drawn up this paper to comprehend any thing except new test objects. It is not a report on microscopes— If you wish one with regard to the instrument Spencer is making for you, that can be made a separate affair.

The microscopists in Philadelphia have recently been trying their skill and powers on one of these tests, the Navicula Spencerii[2] and after they had all failed, and some had expressed scepticism about the existence of the lines, Dr Beck[3] came on here to see the lines "if they were to be seen". He soon became satisfied of their existence, as I showed them to him not only with Spencer's objectives but also with his own, made by Powell of London.[4] This last which magnifies[A] rather more than Spencer's shows the lines even _more_ distinctly than Spencers, but the difference is due only to its greater magnifying power. In other respects it is not superior to our American artists. There is some mistake about this lens of Beck's—he calls it a $\frac{1}{12}$th of inch (compound focal distance) yet it magnifies more than Spencer's $\frac{1}{16}$th— With equal powers I still believe that Spencer is equal to _any_ foreign artist and much superior to all except Ross[5] and Powell of London.

Please write soon and let me know whether I had better employ a draughtsman (at an expense say of $10.) or whether it is best to send an engraver here for directions about the plate.

Yours with sincere regard
J. W. Bailey

Prof. J. Henry
Smithsonian Institute
Washington City

Henry Papers, Smithsonian Archives.

1. Bailey wrote in response to Henry's letter of May 23, 1847, Bailey Papers, Boston Science Museum, in which Henry asked that Bailey submit his "report on the use of the microscope with a description of test objects . . . before the next session of Congress."

2. A species of alga discovered by Bailey and named after Charles A. Spencer. Bailey considered detecting the transverse lines on the *N. spencerii* "the most difficult of all tests for high powers." "Spencer's Microscopes," *Silliman's Journal*, 1848, 2d ser. 5:285–286, 443 (quotation on p. 443).

Bailey's claim led to a controversy with the English scientist Warren De La Rue (1815–1889, *DSB*) over the use of *N. spencerii* as a test for the quality of a microscope. Ultimately, Bailey conceded De La Rue's contention that the difficulty of seeing the lines on the *N. spencerii* was overrated, but continued to defend the quality of Spencer's microscopes. John Quekett, *A Practical Treatise on the Use of the Microscope* (London, 1848), p. 440; J. W. Bailey, "Some Re-

marks on the Navicula Spencerii, and on a Still More Difficult Test Object," *Silliman's Journal*, 1849, 2d ser. 7:265–270; Warren De La Rue, "On the Navicula Spencerii," *Silliman's Journal*, 1850, 2d ser. 9:23–29; J. W. Bailey, "Reply to Mr. De La Rue's Remarks on the Navicula Spencerii Contained in the American Journal of Science, Vol. IX, p. 23; with a Notice of Two New Test-Objects," *Silliman's Journal*, 1851, 2d ser. 11:82–84.

3. Charles F. Beck.

4. Hugh Powell, whose microscopes were considered a standard of excellence. *Henry Papers*, 5:325n.

5. Andrew Ross (1798–1859), a London optician, has been credited, along with J. J. Lister, with transforming the microscope "from a toy to a scientific instrument of immense importance." Gerard L'E. Turner, *The Great Age of the Microscope: The Collection of the Royal Microscopical Society through 150 Years* (New York, 1989), p. 154.

179. TO [ALEXANDER DALLAS BACHE][A]

Washington May 27th 1848

My dear friend

I have intended to give you from time to time a bulletin of events but I have as yet little to communicate which you have not seen in the papers. The Whigs are in high hopes of success from the dissension in the ranks of the other party[1]— The House of Mauritania[2] has apparently turned its eyes from the bottom of the ocean[3] and again sought[B] glory in the heavens.[4] A new Comet is an auspicious star when it appears at the right time. The joke about the sinking of Nantucket[5] must have come from Capt Davis.[6] The day the article appeared in the intelligencer signed H̲ I was asked if I were not the author. The coincidence did not at first strike me.— I have visited the land office almost every day. I found Mr Young[7] at first not very favourably disposed towards magnetism but after some conversation he concluded that it might be promoted[C] by the employment of Dr Locke provided the appropriation ~~bill~~ passed and afterward agreed to set the Dr. at work immediately provided there was money sufficient of[D] the remaining appropriation. Unfortunately Mr Wilson[8] who has charge of this branch has been absent from the treasury building for several days past on account of sickness in his family and nothing more can be done until he returns which will be on monday. I have a copy of Dr Lockes Report. The blunders of the printer[9] are amusing and so is the Dr's acount of the pictured Rock.[10] I should myself doubt the propriety of introducing quite so much poetical description into a report intended for congress.

The printing of the ethnological memoir is again going on quite briskly I get a proof about[E] every other day & sometimes oftener.

McCulloch showed me his paper on the formula for specific gravity &. &c[11] which I think would make a good contribution for the Smithsonian. He goes to see you at camp.

I have written to Professor Silliman asking him to lecture now or in the autumn his expenses being paid.[12]

I spent yesterday with Renwick in the building and gave him the plan of cases for the philosophical apparatus. The Institution is not at present to be converted into a normal school and as we will want much more room for apparatus than we can obtain until the main building is finished I have suggested the propriety of devoting the room ~~just mentioned~~ ↑called the students working laboratory↓ to apparatus.[13] The small one next the main building will scarcely more than contain the articles which I have already procured. The stone floor however will be an objection to the room in which apparatus is placed on account of the deposition of moisture as in the case of an unfurred house. The stone floor can ↑however↓ be put down at any time if necssary and I shall suggest these alterations to the building committee and reccomend that other cases than those ordered shall be placed in the room mentioned— The perfection of Architecture the norman style has furnished a laboratory in the rear of the small lecture room which ~~will~~ ↑may↓ be sufficiently lighted with several gas burners in a cloudy day, I presume the obscurity of this room will be represented as a peculiar advantage because as it is well known many chemical articles deteriorate when exposed to too much light— I have suggested that glass windows be inserted ~~on~~ ↑in↓ each partition wall of this room so as to give it some more light from the adjoining rooms this will be done. Renwick is exceedingly obliging and is disposed to make any ~~any~~ change I may suggest but I do not wish to have the credit of spoiling ~~a~~ ↑the↓ plan of a laboratory which is to be pronounced the most convenient in the world. The second floor is cut up into cubbies, the partitions of which however may be easily removed. I shall visit the building daily as soon as Mr O. has given up the direction of it. It appears that the architect did not understand the plan of the small lecture room and has framed the timber for a gallery ~~all~~ round and across the windows the plan of Dr. Owen[F] is that of a gallery on either side and the gradual rising of the seats to the level of the gallery in the rear. This plan will be better for light but I am not yet sure of the esthetic effect. Utility however before beautely is my maxum.

I intend to be present hereafter at all the meetings of the building committee whether I am asked or not and to have an eye on all that is going on.[14] Mrs H and myself have been trying to get a lodging on the mall but have not as yet been successful.

I have just recived a note[15] inviting me to attend a meeting this evening (Saturday) at Mr Forces to take into consideration some measures for the formation of the National[G] Institute.[16] I shall be very cautious and no committall to any definite scheme until it is properly digested. In the first place I object to the name ↑National↓ Institute and would propose that of the National aca<u>d</u> with different departments.[H] In the second place the movement should not be alone made by persons in Washington. The more prominent men of science throughout the country should be allowed to participate. The programme of Mr Vattemere[17,I] is crude and mixes up the business of instruction with the operations of the Institute. He proposes that the begining of the Institution should be made by an election of the first members by the Senate.[18] I will give you an account of the proceedings ~~at~~ ↑in↓ the next bulletin.

I remain as ever your
J–H–

Bache Papers, Smithsonian Archives.
Reply: Doc. 181.

1. The Democratic National Convention had met in Baltimore from May 22 through May 26. New York was represented by two delegations, one radical, one conservative. When the party attempted a compromise by seating both delegations and splitting the vote between them, the radicals withdrew. Subsequently, the radical Democrats and the Liberty party united in support of Martin Van Buren as a Free Soil, third-party candidate. Although the Whigs won the presidential election, current historical analysis contends that the Free Soil party was not an important factor. James M. McPherson, *Battle Cry of Freedom: The Civil War Era* (New York, 1988) pp. 60–63; *The American Almanac and Repository of Useful Knowledge, for the Year 1849* (Boston, 1848), p. 351.

2. A punning reference to the Naval Observatory.

3. The *National Intelligencer* of May 17 had reprinted the unsigned (written by Henry) "Review of the Annual Report on the U.S. Coast Survey" from the May 1848 issue of *Silliman's Journal* (2d ser. 5:307–318). In that review, George M. Bache was credited with the idea of a geological map of the ocean floor. Three days later, the *National Intelligencer* carried a story signed "A.," claiming that Maury had proposed a map of the sea bottom in 1840, two years before Bache made his suggestion. On May 22, the same newspaper carried a paragraph signed "H.," claiming that the proposed maps of Bache and Maury had different objectives: Bache wanted to aid navigation by providing a more accurate and systematic description of the coastal ocean bottom, while Maury wanted to chart the relative distribution of sea fauna.

4. The May 25 issue of the *National Intelligencer* carried a May 23 letter from Maury, which quoted a French newspaper announce-

ment of the discovery of two stars, one of which was probably an asteroid.

5. Just below Maury's letter was an anecdote of a sea captain who navigated according to the sea bottom samplings brought up by soundings. When presented, as a joke, with a sampling of sand taken from a Nantucket beach, the captain concluded that the island had sunk and the ship was sailing over it.

6. The anecdote was signed "M." Henry may have been alluding to Charles Henry Davis, a naval lieutenant assigned to the Coast Survey. *Henry Papers*, 6:263n.

7. Robert M. Young.

8. John Wilson.

9. In U.S. Senate, 31st Congress, 1st Session, *Report on the Geological and Mineralogical Survey of the Mineral Lands of the United States in the State of Michigan* . . . , Senate Executive Documents, No. 1, part 3 (1849), pp. 588–603, the tables of John Locke's terrestrial magnetic observations were printed without explanatory headings.

10. Locke described the sandstone along the south shore of Lake Superior as

occasionally excavated into arches. . . . The partitions between two of these arches are often perforated, so as to leave a pillar supporting two arches. The effect of this is very picturesque. [*Report on the Geological and Mineralogical Survey*, p. 579.]

11. Perhaps Henry was referring to an extract from Richard S. McCulloh's *Report of Researches on Hydrometers and Spirituous Liquors, Made under the Superintendence of Professor A. D. Bache*, U.S. Senate, 30th Congress, 1st Session, Senate Executive Documents, No. 50 (1848), pp. 397–653. He reported on research conducted in Europe on the specific gravity of alcoholic liquids, as well as on his own research to verify the European results.

12. Henry to Silliman, May 23, 1848, Daniel C. Gilman Papers, Ms. 1, Milton S. Eisenhower Library, The Johns Hopkins University. According to Silliman's file note, he declined the invitation.

13. Robert Dale Owen had conceived of a chemistry laboratory for student experimentation modeled after that of Justus Liebig. [*First*]

Report of the Organization Committee of the Smithsonian Institution (Washington, [1846]), pp. 3–4. The published Owen-Renwick ground plan does not indicate which of the two laboratories was for students. Robert Dale Owen, *Hints on Public Architecture* (New York, 1849), between pp. 104 and 105.

14. The minutes of the building committee do not exist for this period.

15. Not found.

16. Peter Force, a printer and local politician, was very active in the National Institute. *Henry Papers*, 6:483n.

The topics of the special meeting were the causes of the National Institute's "embarrassments" and "the best means of restoring it to activity." To that end, at least four members had drawn up plans of reorganization. A committee of eleven, including Henry, was appointed to evaluate the different plans, "embody what was desirable in each, and submit the results of their deliberations to a future meeting." Journal of Meetings, No. 2 (1842–1849), May 27, 1848, Box 11, Records of the National Institute, RU 7058, Smithsonian Archives.

17. Nicolas Marie Alexandre Vattemare (1796–1864) was a French ventriloquist who had come to the United States in 1839 to perform. He became an advocate of the international exchange of books. *DAB*.

18. Vattemare's plan for the revival of the National Institute envisioned an international, professional learned society. Membership would be limited to one hundred members, eighty Americans and twenty foreigners, all of whom would receive a salary from the government. The first domestic members would be nominated by senators, with election by lot if the number of nominees exceeded the requisite eighty. Foreign members would be selected by the domestic members, subject to confirmation by the Senate. Science would be but one of five "academies" in the institute, each concerned with a different aspect of human knowledge and creativity. "Mons. Vattemare's Plan for a Nat. Institute," May 27, 1848, Box 13, Records of the National Institute, RU 7058, Smithsonian Archives.

180. FROM CHARLES COFFIN JEWETT

Boston, May 30th 1848.

My dear Sir,

I had the pleasure of receiving on Friday last,[1] your interesting letter of the 19th inst[2] & containing a draft for one hundred dollars. For the latter I send you a receipt, & will hereafter forward you the bills for all purchases. It will, as you have supposed, facilitate my labors very much, to be able to receive from time to time, the sums which I may need for stationery & books, & also in compensation for my services. I had supposed that the latter would have to stand till the end of the year, but as you have thoughtfully made other arrangements, I will call for some portion at least, before then.

I am very happy to learn that the condition & prospects of the Institution are so favorable. It is, I believe, constantly gaining in public favor & in the good opinion of the few. I see now no reason to apprehend opposition or even indifference. On the contrary I think we shall meet the hearty & active cooperation of men of science & learning throughout the country, so long as we act harmoniously upon the basis of organisation which has been adopted. The work of laying the foundations of such an establishment is indeed a^A vast & responsible one. It is hardly possible to escape all errors, or to adopt plans which may not demand modification. But a sincere & earnest desire to promote, in the highest degree possible, the cause of good letters & true science will prove the best safeguard against mistakes, & the strongest incentive to efficient & judicious action.

I am glad to learn that you are in treaty for the valuable apparatus of Dr Hare. I hope the negociation may fully succeed, & that this may be but the first of a long catalogue of munificent donations.

The result of the first experiment of lecturing[3] is certainly encouraging, & justifies the belief that lectures, if able, gratuitious & not too frequent, would be well attended in Washington, & would do much for the popularity of the Institution among the inhabitants of the city, as well as the members of Congress.

With regard to the printing, I should suppose the present arrangement would be found both inconvenient & expensive. Indeed I do not see how it can be properly executed until we have a press of our own. It will give me pleasure to render you every assistance in my power in superintending the publications. I am willing to take up my residence in New York ↑a part of the year↓ for that purpose, if you think it desirable. As to additional compensation, I should be content with sufficient to defray my extra expenses. I suppose you would not require my assistance till autumn. New York is not a desirable residence in Summer. I presume that while attending to the publications I should have time to pursue the work for the Library. I think it is desirable for me to spend some time in examining the public & private libraries of the city & in conferring with Dr Cogswell,[4] who has the charge of the Astor Library;[5] so that my residence there for a few weeks or months would be advantageous to both departments. For the last six weeks I have devoted six hours a day to the work assigned me by the Board. I have been gathering the Statistics of some 150 Libraries in the United States.[6] At present I am engaged upon my catalogue of bibliographical & other works of reference in my department.[7] I am making it very full, not of course with the expectation that they can be all purchased immediately, but rather to enable us to select with the better judgment. I hope to have the list ready to send to you before the adjournment of Congress. As Dr Bache & Mr Marsh are in Washington & Mr Choate here, it will hardly be possible to hold a meeting of the Committee.[8] I will send the list to you, however, first, & if it meets the approval of yourself & the other gentlemen I have no doubt but that Mr Choate will be satisfied with it. I should like very much to order some of the books by Mr Henry Stevens,[9] who will sail for Europe soon. He will go to France, Germany & England & will be able to get most of the books which I need ~~more immediately~~, much more expeditiously as well as at lower prices than we can obtain them by any other means. Mr Stevens informs me that he has formally offered to you his services as our agent for distributing & exchanging our publications in Europe.[10] He has established relations with seven of the largest libraries in England & on the continent & for the present at least, could, perhaps, serve us more promptly & suitably than any other person whom we could employ. It will be a long task to arrange properly our distribution & exchange list. I wish I were in Washington to assist you in the work. In order to prevent mistakes & omissions, it will be necessary I suppose to keep a Record-Book of Exchanges & Donations,[B] in which the time & manner of forwarding shall be noted— I suppose it will be necessary also to accompany the first packages sent to the more important Institutions, with letters stating briefly the history & general objects of ~~the~~ ↑our↓ Institution & proposing an interchange of publications & friendly offices. Mr Stevens suggests also, & I think very properly, that the copies sent to the principal Institutions in Europe should be enclosed in printed wrappers— If I can be of any assistance to you in these matters I beg you to call upon me. I regret extremely that our funds will not allow us to begin our purchases for the Library immediately. The late revolutions & financial troubles in Europe, are affording, it is said, the richest opportunity that has occurred since the first French revolution, for the collection of books & works of art. A person, acquainted with the languages of the continent could purchase now, with the cash in hand more for 1000 dollars than[C] at ordinary times for 4000[11]— This state of things may however continue for a year or two longer.

I sympathize with you, fully, respecting Mr Owen's book & building. To spend so much money in such a way (handsome as the edifice will be) while we need it so much for[D] the higher & nobler purposes of "increasing & diffusing knowledge" is but starving the soul to gratify the senses. It is surprising how prone we are in this country to commit & repeat this folly. Almost all our colleges & public Institutions furnish melancholy illustrations. It is profoundly to be regretted that instead of setting our faces as a flint against this absurd & wicked tendency, we shall present so conspicuous an example of it & do much to stimulate & sanction it by one of our earliest publications. The sad mistake seems now however irretrievable. I see by the papers that Congress are about purchasing another Collection of the Madison Manuscripts.[12] It has occurred to me that the safest & most appropriate place for preserving them would be the Smithsonian Library— Would it not be desirable to make some effort to procure them? I merely throw-out this suggestion, not knowing what the views of the government are, respecting them. Manuscripts & books in a climat[e][E] like that of Washington require I suppo[se][E] especial care & attention to prevent their being destroyed or injured by dampness, & insects— Besides, they ought to be so arranged & catalogued as to be most serviceable for reference— Of course I do not suppose it would be wise to commit these MSS to our care until our building is ready to receive them,[F] but I thought it might be desirable to introduce into the act of Congress providing for their purchase, a clause respecting their final place of deposite.

I am, my dear Sir,
very truly & respectfully
Yours &c
C. C. Jewett

Prof Henry—
Sec of the Smithsonian Instit, &c

Henry Papers, Smithsonian Archives.

1. May 26.
2. Doc. 176.

3. By William Scoresby.
4. Joseph Green Cogswell (1786–1871) had

been on the faculty of Harvard (and its assistant librarian) before becoming John Jacob Astor's advisor in 1839 in the planning of the Astor Library. In May 1848 he became the superintendent of the Astor Library. Henry M. Lydenberg, *History of the New York Public Library: Astor, Lenox and Tilden Foundations* (Boston, 1972), pp. 2–11; *DAB*.

5. John Jacob Astor, who had died on March 29, 1848, left $400,000 for the establishment of a public library for New York City. The first meeting of the trustees had been May 20. Lydenberg, pp. 6, 9.

6. Jewett incorporated these statistics, and those later gathered in response to a circular (Doc. 231), into a report published as an appendix to the *Smithsonian Report for 1849*, and as Jewett, *Notices of Public Libraries in the United States* (Washington, 1851).

7. Jewett's list included approximately three thousand volumes. *Smithsonian Report for 1848*, p. 43.

8. The committee of the Board of Regents appointed in December 1847 to oversee Jewett's activities until March 19, 1849. Rhees, *Journals*, p. 49.

9. Stevens (1819–1886), an 1843 graduate of Yale, was a book collector and bibliographer. *DAB*.

10. Letter not found. Stevens was given the responsibility for distributing Smithsonian publications in England and in turn receiving donations for the institution from that country. Henry was not pleased with his efforts, complaining that Stevens "sent in our boxes in an irregular manner, a number of books which might lead us into difficulty with the custom house." Henry to Asa Gray, June 7, 1850, Historic Letters, Archives, Gray Herbarium Library, Harvard University.

11. Cogswell went to Europe in November 1848 to purchase books for the Astor Library, using the same justification given by Jewett. According to Jewett, Cogswell acquired approximately twenty thousand volumes for a quarter to a half of what it would have cost in more stable times. Lydenberg, p. 12; Jewett, p. 92.

12. On May 31, 1848, Congress appropriated $25,000 to purchase all the manuscripts of James Madison in the possession of his widow. This was the second purchase of Madison papers; the first was in 1837. The material was delivered to the secretary of state. *U.S. Statutes at Large*, 5:271; 9:235.

181. FROM ALEXANDER DALLAS BACHE

Station Linstid. May 31, 1848.

My dear friend.

Your very acceptable bulletin[1] reached me last evening. We have much less vanity, more quiet, & better opportunities for work here than in Washington. The lines formerly cut from this point to others had so grown up that many required re-opening, & I have had one new line to open which is now completed.[2] The weather has been quite favorable for work in observing. Less so for study.

McCulloh left here yesterday after a sojourn of a couple of days to go over his new report on hydrometers with me. I prepared a sort of syllabus as an introduction to it.[3] It is quite able & digested with care.

I feel very curious to know the result of the Force meeting. It seems to me to found an American Institute under the leading of Vattemare would be to insure its failure at once. The eccolosion would never hatch it, after having been thus set upon.

The convention I suppose could not[A] have done better, & it is plain that the political struggle will be a fierce one. Its elements yet undeveloped. We of the neutral ground lookers on. When a provisional government is to be formed it will be time enough to begin to follow our illustrious perpetual Secs. lead! Did not the name of the President of the d. Convention[4] recall most ignoble & patriotic reminiscences[B] of Portland place![5] I remember— I remember— Faugh!

This is a beautiful spot. [...] Nature in all her luxuriance. Water & woods. Hills & valleys all spread out around us. Come & see us & try the Arab hospitality. You may play Rechabite.[6] We will give you & M[rs]. H. a whole tent to yourselves. Leaving Washington at 6 A.M. you breakfast at the Annapolis junction; leave there at 10 for Annapolis. There you will find my man Friday, George Whelden at the P.O., & he will bring you & the lady over two Ferries & eight miles of hills [?safle] up to Linstid, & with no less expenditure of time, or fatigue than it would cost to go to New York.

I was truly mortified on Sat.[7] to receive a letter[8] from Philad. saying that I had recommended Peale for Assist. examiner when he wanted to be examiner.[9] Now why could he not have said to you when he received my letter that I had made a mistake!? I supposed the new bill provided for Assists. only.[10] To go so round about to his friends in Philad. & to stir up such a mess was not worthy of him. If after urging him to come forward for the position he could not have confidence that I meant to do right, there must be a screw loose in his own mind. How I hate such things. If men of science may not trust each other, then alas for humanity.

Regards from Mrs. B. who is not yet wide awake to Mrs. H. & Co. I am not yet determined whether to come to W. on Sat. or not.

Yours ever truly A. D. B.

Professor Henry.

Henry Papers, Smithsonian Archives.

1. Doc. 179.

2. Bache was involved in verifying primary triangulation observations from a site on the Magothy River, near the Chesapeake Bay, in Maryland. *Coast Survey Report for 1848,* pp. 34, 71.

3. In his transmittal letter of May 29 to Robert Walker, Bache provided a three-page analysis of Richard S. McCulloh's *Report of Researches on Hydrometers and Spirituous Liquors, Made under the Superintendence of Professor A. D. Bache,* U.S. Senate, 30th Congress, 1st Session, Senate Executive Documents, No. 50 (1848), pp. 398–400.

4. Andrew Stevenson was the president of the 1848 Democratic Convention. Henry and Bache had met him in London in 1837 when he was American minister to Great Britain. *The American Almanac and Repository of Useful Knowledge, for the Year 1849* (Boston, 1848), p. 351; *Henry Papers, 3:*212, 262.

5. Stevenson had resided at 23 Portland Place while in London. Stevenson to Lord Palmerston, August 18, 1836, Stevenson Family Papers, Library of Congress.

6. That is, a tent dweller.

7. May 27.

8. Not found, but written in response to the

letter from Titian Ramsay Peale to John F. Frazer, May 21, 1848, Frazer Papers, American Philosophical Society.

9. Bache had written a letter of recommendation for Peale to Edmund Burke, the commissioner of patents, which he transmitted to Peale through Henry. In his letter to Frazer, Peale complained that the job of assistant examiner was "a mere clerkship,— without promotion, includes the hardest work and clerks pay." He wrote also that the letter from Bache "fell on me like an icy hand."

In a letter to Frazer of June 2, 1848 (Frazer Papers), Peale related that Bache sent him a second letter, to be transmitted to Burke, re-questing that Burke ignore the word assistant in the first letter as "an unintentional error."

10. In the spring of 1848, Congress passed legislation establishing two additional patent examiner and two assistant patent examiner positions. It also raised the pay of the examiners to $2,500. The two new examiners were Henry B. Renwick (1817–1895, *DAB*), the elder brother of the architect of the Smithsonian Building, and Leonard Gale. Peale received one of the assistant examiner positions. The other went to J. H. Lane. Robert C. Post, *Physics, Patents, and Politics: A Biography of Charles Grafton Page* (New York, 1976), pp. 113–118.

182. TO SAMUEL STEMAN HALDEMAN[1]

Washington May 31ˢᵗ 1848

My dear Sir

I would gladly assist Mr Baird in his researches by means of the funds of the Smithsonian Institution provided I can do so with a certainty of good results and in such a way as not to establish an improper precedent. I will appoint Dr Morton and yourself a commission to examine the researches of Mr Baird and if you will make me a formal report on the subject stating the character and importance of the researches I will advance the money required out of some funds at my disposal. In your report it may be well to mention that the researches cannot be properly prosecuted unless with the aid required from the Smithsonian Institution.[2]

I remain truly yours &c
Joseph Henry

Dr S. S. Haldeman

P.S. Accompanying this letter I send your official appointment as a commission.[3] If you think it advisable to appoint a third person as one of the commission please suggest the proper man. Business of this kind must be conducted cautiously and in accordance with established rules.

J.H.

Haldeman Papers, Library, The Academy of Natural Sciences of Philadelphia.
Reply: Not found; undated draft reply in Box 25, Baird Papers, Smithsonian Archives.

1. Active in the Academy of Natural Sciences of Philadelphia, Haldeman (1812–1880) had published extensively on mollusks and insects. Elliott, *Dictionary*.

337

2. In the draft reply, Haldeman and Morton characterized Baird's research as an attempt to clear up the confusion surrounding amphibia. Baird was attempting to clarify the distinctions between species and the variations within species. However, he lacked the services of an artist "to delineate and fix in colors the various peculiarities of structure & phases of development as they arise." The reviewers, responding to Henry's suggestion, stated that without Smithsonian support, the drawings "are not likely to be executed."

On July 6, 1848, Henry informed the executive committee of

his intention to advance sums of fifty dollars, from time to time, as might be necessary, to

Professor Spencer F. Baird, to enable him to have drawings made of researches in embryology of reptiles and fishes. [Rhees, *Journals*, p. 463.]

Two days later, Henry wrote Baird that he was prepared "to advance a small sum," and asked how much Baird needed. Baird Papers, Smithsonian Archives.

There is no evidence that Henry ever provided any funds for Baird.

3. Henry to Samuel G. Morton and S. S. Haldeman, May 31, 1848, Box 25, Baird Papers, Smithsonian Archives.

183. TO THOMAS T. KINNEY[1]

Washington May 31ˢᵗ 1848

My dear Sir,

I see by the Newark Daily[2] that the house No. 180 was struck on Friday last[3] with lightening and that the discharge made a hole in the leader which I suppose is the tin gutter leading the water from the roof to the ground. A hole pierced in a plate of metal by electricity involves some interesting theoretical considerations and if it be not too much trouble you will oblige me by examining the hole and giving me an account of your observations. Note if there be a burr on one side or both and if but one on which side— Also the path of the discharge before and after it reached the hole with any other facts or appearances unmingled with any conceptions as to the course or the mode of operations of the electricity.— I should be very glad to get possession of the part of the gutter which contains the hole, and would cheerfully pay any expenses which might attend the cutting of it out and the replacement of the part by a new piece of tin. If this can be done please send the article to me at Washington by the express line and I will pay all charges.

I do not hesitate to make this call upon your time & kind services knowing the interest you take in science and your feelings towards me.

I remain as ever truly yours
Joseph Henry.

Thomas Kinney Esq
P.S. Give my kind regards to your father[4] and please inform him that all things at present relative to the Smithsonian are going on smoothly[A]

and that I am much encouraged with the belief of rendering the Institution of great importance to our country.

J–H–

1. A former student of Henry's and resident of Newark, New Jersey. *Henry Papers*, 4:7n–8n.

2. Henry was referring to an article in the *Newark Daily Advertiser* of May 26, 1848.

3. May 26.

4. William Burnet Kinney, the editor of the *Newark Daily Advertiser* and a trustee of Princeton. *Henry Papers*, 4:81n.

184. DIARY OF JONATHAN HOMER LANE

Washington D.C.
Saturday[A] evening June 10th 1848

Had a fine visit with Prof Henry at his room—staid with him from about 8 o'clock till after 11. Showed him[B] a written description of my proposed experiments on the velocity of solar heat with drawings and held considerable conversation on the subject. He expressed his approbation of the plan in quite flattering terms and proposes if I remain in Washington to join with me in making those and some that he had himself devised on the subject of radiant heat:[1] it being his intention to procure some apparatus for the purpose at the expense of the Smithsonian Institution. Some of his experiments will be to determine the wave lengths of the calorific and of the chemical rays.[2]

He gave me an account of his experiments showing the interference of radiant heat.[3] They were conducted with a thermoelectric battery closed by a plate perforated with a fine slit running across it. These experiments might be subject to a possible but not probable fallacy that afterward ~~pre~~ occurred to me. If the slit were at some little distance from the battery the change of effect as the battery passed along ~~might~~ transversely might be imagined to have arisen from change in the point of incidence on the battery from parallax. But I do not suppose such fallacy did take place to any perceptible extent.

Also in the course of the evening he gave an interesting account of how he was anticipated by Faraday in the discovery of magneto-electric induction.[4] His apparatus had been prepared a year or more—consisting[C] if I remember correctly—of a wire coil around the keeper of a steel magnet—but he was prevented from making his experiment by interfering circumstances until he heard the indefinite report ~~of~~ that Faraday had produced electricity from magnetism. He immediately concluded it must be the very thing he had been after and at once set up his apparatus—brought the keeper up to the magnet and the galvanometer needle at once whirled round and in a few minutes he obtained the sparks.

Faradays later discovery also of the effect of magnetism on a ray of polarized light passing through certain media had also presented itself to Prof Henrys mind and he had made experiments <u>exactly</u> like that of Faraday using first however air and afterwards some other medium denser. He was going to repeat his experiments with stronger magnets but was again compelled to defer them on account of interruptions until the vague report of Faradays discovery reached him. He then went to work just as he had intended and produced the ~~af~~ effect.[5]

Many speculations of his were mentioned but I do not remember much of them having too long neglected to take notes of them. In relation to the undulations of radiant heat if they have a different velocity from light he thinks it not consistent with the simplicity of nature to suppose them undulations of a second ether interpenetrating the first. This idea of a second ether had occurred to myself and I afterwards saw it adverted to in Henry's Chemistry[6] but rejected as extravagant. It hardly seems so to me if it have only a moderate degree of proof particularly that of a materially different velocity.

He stated before that he had an idea that the ether was nothing more than electricity and then went on to mention the idea that I knew he had thrown out in the press that the discharge of a leyden jar consisted of several vibrations of the ether from one coating to the other.[7] He made many experiments in support of this idea conducted with small steel needles in helices through which the discharge of the jar was made. The idea of the experiments was that a discharge might be much more than sufficient at the first oscillation or rush to magnetise to saturation and then the return stroke would destroy the first imparted magnetism and magnetise in the opposite direction. A ↑With↓ a still stronger charge or a different coil or distance the third rebound might destroy the magnetism of the second and remagnetise in the first direction and so on.

Lane Papers, Records of the National Bureau of Standards, RG 167, National Archives.

1. There is no evidence that Lane and Henry experimented together.

2. No documentation exists for such experiments.

3. For a discussion, see *Henry Papers*, 6:64, 65n.

4. In the account that follows, Lane paraphrased Henry as claiming much less than

Henry's daughter and supporters later claimed for him. There is nothing in Lane's account about Henry discovering magnetoelectricity in 1829 or 1830, but failing to publish his discovery. Thomas Coulson, *Joseph Henry: His Life and Work* (Princeton, 1950), pp. 85–88; *Henry Papers*, 1:437–439.

5. Details are given in *Henry Papers*, 6:350–352, 353–358.

6. William Henry's *Elements of Experimental Chemistry*. There are numerous London and American editions. We have not located Lane's reference.

7. Joseph Henry, "Contributions to Electricity and Magnetism. No. V.—On Induction from Ordinary Electricity; and On the Oscillatory Discharge," APS *Proceedings*, 1841–1843, 2:194–195.

185. TO EDWARD HENRY COURTENAY[1]

Washington June 15th 48

My dear Sir

I have been informed[2] that my friend Richard McCullough is a candidate for the chair of Natural Philosophy in the University of Virginia[3] and I beg leave through you to express my opinion of his fitness for this position. He is a graduate of the College of New-Jersey and stood among the first of a large class. He was afterwards engaged as an assistant under Dr Bache in the magnetic observatory of Girard College— also an assistant in a geological survey—a pupil in analytical chemestry under Professor Booth[4] next professor of Mathematics and Natural philosophy in Jefferson College afterwards engaged in an elaborate examination of the sugars of the United States on optical principles and finaly the Occupanitt of a scientific position in the US mint. ~~What~~ In these various positions and employments Mr McCullough has exhibited unusual talents and has in every case discharged his duties with more than ordinary success. What ever he has undertaken to do ↑he↓ has ~~been~~ done well and among all the younger men in the line of Natural philosophy with whom I am acquainted I would in preference recommend ~~Mr~~ him to the vacant chair as the most promising. ~~B~~ He is well versed in analytic mathematics and is fully prepared for the investigation of any physico mathematical ~~problem~~ subject. I may mention in a letter to you ~~th~~ a fact of some importance connected with the choise of a professor that his wife[5] is an agreeable well educated and intelligent ~~young~~ Lady.

Hon ~~And. Stevenson~~[6]

Profr Courtenay

Draft, Henry Papers, Smithsonian Archives.
Inside address in Edward Foreman's hand.

1. Professor of mathematics at the University of Virginia. *Henry Papers,* 2:32.

2. In Richard S. McCulloh to Henry, March 31, 1848, Henry Papers, Smithsonian Archives.

3. This was the chair of William B. Rogers, who had recently resigned. *DAB.* See Doc. 193.

4. James Curtis Booth (1810–1888) was an analytical chemist in Philadelphia. From 1836 until his death he directed a teaching laboratory which was one of the centers of chemical instruction in the United States. Elliott, *Dictionary.*

5. Mary Stewart Vowell of Alexandria, Virginia, had married McCulloh in December 1845. Milton Halsey Thomas, "Professor McCulloh of Princeton, Columbia, and Points South," *The Princeton University Library Chronicle,* 1947, *9*:21.

6. A member of the Board of Visitors of the University of Virginia. *BDAC.*

186. TO JAMES MURRAY MASON[1]

Washington June 16th 1848

Dear Sir,

In compliance with your request that I would suggest the names ~~of any~~ ↑of↓ gentleman of my acquaintance competent to fill the chair of natural Philosophy in the University of Virginia I submit the following namely

> Dr A. D. Bache of of the US Coast Survey
> Professor Bartlett,[2] West Point
> Professor Loomis, New York University
> Professor Mc Cullough[3] U.S. Mint Phil^d^
> Professor Gibbes[4] South Carolina
> Professor Frazier University Penn^a^
> Professor Lovering[5] Harvard University Cambridge

The first two gentlemen mentioned could not I presume be induced to leave their present positions and the third though a man of much talent and reputation might not on some accounts be inclined to reside in the south. I would place Prof. Mc Cullough at the head of the list of the younger men and believe that all things considered he is the best available candidate of my acquaintance. ~~It must however be observed that~~ though ~~this opinon is the result of my~~ unbiased judgement, yet the communication ↑is of such a nature that I would prefer ~~that~~↓ is confidential to the Board of visitors. The situations of importance in this country which can be held out as inducements to high scientific attainment are so few that for the sake of the cause of knowledge in our country the selection to fill one of these positions should be made with great care

342

and it is in consideration of this that I have been induced to comply with your request in giving ↑confidentially↓ the foregoing list.

> I remain with considerations
> of the highest respect
> your obt servt
> Joseph Henry

Hon J M Mason
U.S. Senate

Draft, Henry Papers, Smithsonian Archives.

1. Mason (1798–1871), a member of the University of Virginia Board of Visitors from 1833 to 1851, entered the Senate in 1847 as a Democrat from Virginia. In 1849, he was appointed a Smithsonian regent. *BDAC;* Goode, *Smithsonian,* p. 102; Virginia Mason, *The Public Life and Diplomatic Correspondence of James M. Mason* (New York, 1906), p. 38.

2. William H. C. Bartlett was professor of natural and experimental philosophy at West Point. *Henry Papers,* 2:311n–313n.

3. Richard S. McCulloh.

4. Lewis Reeve Gibbes taught at the College of Charleston. *Henry Papers,* 3:536n.

5. Joseph Lovering was Hollis Professor of Natural Philosophy and Mathematics at Harvard. Henry held Lovering in low regard. *Henry Papers,* 6:460–461.

187. FROM SEARS C. WALKER

Cambridge Mass June 26/48

To Joseph Henry L.L.D.
Secretary of the S.I.
Dear Sir,

I have not yet received the copies 10 innumber of my article on Neptune.[1]

Will you do me the favour to direct 10 of the [?thin] paper copies to me at Cambridge Mass? franked. I wish to make special[A] distribution of them.

Mr Mitchell[2,B] has answered my letter, and says that Miss Maria Mitchell[3] is preparing the paper.[4]

What a munificent bequest is that of Edward Philips who died last week $100,000 to the Camb. Observatory, for salaries of astronomers and purchase of books, no portion to go for bricks or mortar![5]

It is understood that Abbot Lawrence has signified his intention of gradually enlarging his donation to the Scientific School to $150.000.[6]

Peirce proposes to engage in a 20 years work on the whole theory of Mechanics.[7] He will have his paper when you wish.

If you decide to print my paper, I must request to be notified of it so as to see proofs. I would be glad to submit the First Section to Prof. Peirce for his appobation. My regards to Mrs Henry.

Yours truly & Resp^y.
Sears C. Walker

Henry Papers, Smithsonian Archives.

1. *Ephemeris of the Planet Neptune for the Opposition of 1848* (Washington, 1848) was distributed in June. *Appendix I,* 1849, SI Contributions, vol.2 (Washington, 1851), p. 4.

2. William Mitchell (1791–1869), by profession a bank cashier, was an astronomer of some note. He served as a member of the visiting committee of Harvard College Observatory (1848–1865), chair of that committee (1855–1865), and an overseer of Harvard (1857–1865). *DAB.*

3. The librarian of the Nantucket Athenaeum, Maria Mitchell (1818–1889) had learned astronomy from her father. On October 1, 1847, she had discovered a telescopic comet, winning a gold medal from the King of Denmark and international recognition. A pioneer in American science, she was the first American woman to be a professional astronomer (computer for the *Nautical Almanac,* professor at Vassar), the first American woman elected to the American Academy of Arts and Sciences, and the first female member of the American Association for the Advancement of Science. *DAB;* Phebe Mitchell Kendall, comp., *Maria Mitchell: Life, Letters, and Journal* (Boston, 1896); Sally Gregory Kohlstedt, "Maria Mitchell: The Advancement of Women in Science," *The New England Quarterly,* 1978, *51:*39–64.

4. Mitchell's short paper, describing her discovery, is one of the "ghost" publications of the Smithsonian. It was received by the Smith-

sonian prior to September 9, 1848, supposedly sent off to referees in late September, and accepted for publication in SI Contributions, volume 2. The executive committee of the Board of Regents even voted Mitchell a premium of $50 in recognition of her discovery. The paper, however, was never published. As late as 1857, Henry was considering publishing it as an appendix to the 1858 annual report. Charles P. Russell to Henry, September 9, 1848, Henry Papers, Smithsonian Archives; Henry to William Mitchell, September 19, 1848, and February 13, 1857, Maria Mitchell Papers, Maria Mitchell Science Library, Nantucket, Massachusetts; *Smithsonian Report for 1849,* p. 10; Rhees, *Journals,* pp. 469, 474.

5. Edward Bromfield Phillips (1822 or 1823–1848), a Harvard classmate of George P. Bond's (assistant to his father at Harvard College Observatory), had committed suicide and left a legacy of $100,000 to the observatory. The income was used to pay salaries, purchase books and instruments, and repair instruments. Bessie Z. Jones and Lyle G. Boyd, *The Harvard College Observatory: The First Four Directorships, 1839–1919* (Cambridge, Massachusetts, 1971), pp. 96–97; *Annals of the Astronomical Observatory of Harvard College,* 1852–1853, *1,* part 2:lx.

6. A false rumor.

7. Perhaps a reference to the project Bache mentioned in Doc. 213.

188. TO JAMES CARNAHAN

Princeton June 27th 1848

To the Rev. James Carnahan D.D.
Dear Sir

I beg leave through you to tender, in full, my resignation of the chair of Natural Philosophy in the college of New Jersey;[1] and again to express my grateful sense of the continued kindness and confidence with which I have been for so many years favoured by the Trustees.ᴬ Though nominally seperated from the college I shall always be connected with it by feelings of the warmest attachment and ever consider myself identified in interest with its prosperity and reputation.

> I remain very respectfully
> and truly your obt servt.
> Joseph Henry

Letters, Maclean Papers, Princeton University Archives, Seeley G. Mudd Manuscript Library, Princeton University.
Draft: Henry Papers, Smithsonian Archives.

1. Henry had initially submitted his resignation in December 1846. At that time he offered to complete his senior course, an offer the Princeton trustees accepted. He continued to shuttle between Princeton and Washington during the academic year 1847–1848, again teaching natural philosophy to the seniors. He turned his salary over to the Smithsonian. This second letter of resignation signaled Henry's commitment to the Smithsonian, his recognition that he could no longer spare the time to teach, and perhaps the mutual recognition that Princeton needed a full-time professor. *Henry Papers*, 6:597–598; Rhees, *Journals*, p. 488.

189. TO EPHRAIM GEORGE SQUIER

Princeton June 28ᵗʰ 48

Dear Sir

I have the pleasure to inform you that the Trustees of the College of New Jersey have this day confered upon you the honorary degree of A.M. These letters you will please to insert after your name on the title of the memoir as well as M.D. after that of Dr Davis. These titles will have a good effect on the reception of the work abroad and will detract nothing from its respectability at home.[1]

The effect of every additional honor confered on a man of properly balanced mind is that of a stimulent to new exertions in the way of intellectual and moral attainment and I presume this result will be produced in the present case.

With reference to the words delineated &c on the title of the map I think their insertion too small a matter to form a subject of discussion between Dr D. and yourself and since they are at present on the bottom it is scarcly necessary to put them in the title.[2]

I shall be in Washington on Friday[3] and after that time no detention will be experienced in the return of the proofs. I found it impossible to send a message to Mr Marsh by means of the telegraph while I was in

New York. I wrote to Washington on the subject of the proofs and also telegraphed Mr Marsh after my arrival in Princeton.

I remain truly yours &c
Joseph Henry

E. George Squier

Squier Papers, Library of Congress.

1. In a letter to his father, Squier commented upon the honorary degree: "I value it chiefly from the fact that it was entirely spontaneous, and came without suggestion or application on my part." E. G. Squier to J. Squier, July 5, 1848, E. G. Squier Papers, New-York Historical Society.

2. Typically, a map title in Squier and Davis's

Ancient Monuments consisted of the name of the archaeological subject, its location, and the names of the surveyors. The name of the delineator (who was frequently Squier), if given, was placed at the bottom of the map. For example, see Plate X.

3. June 30.

190. FROM LEWIS C. BECK

New Brunswick June 29th '48

My dear friend

In accordance with the promise which I made yesterday, I now sit down to give more full & definite details on the matters which we talked over ~~yesterday~~. And first in regard to the "Report on Agricultural Chemistry." I have not worked at it ~~much~~ lately, as I have been much engaged in the Researches on Breadstuffs, & as[A] you had not come to a definite conclusion in regard to it. The following is the general plan which I have laid out.

1. General Remarks on the relations of the Natural Sciences to Agriculture.
2. Importance of Agricultural Chemistry
3. Sketch of the progress of Agricultural Chemistry.
4. What has been accomplished by the researches ~~upon~~ ↑in↓ this department of Knowledge.
5. Prospects for the future.
6. Points for observation— Directions (plain & simple) for the analysis of soils, grains &c— With figures of apparatus—

Now if you like this programme, let me know to how many pages the Report should extend.— Also the time when you wish it completed & what expense you can incur for the cuts. I like precise[B] & definite information on all these points, & then I can work up to the prescribed plan. I can carry this along with my Breadstuffs Researches & can have it ready during the next winter, if you wish—that is if I keep my health— Perhaps you will have some modifications to propose in regard to the above programme.— Please let me know definitely about the whole thing as soon as convenient.

About the other matter, viz the "Adulterations of Medicines."— The bill recently passed authorizes the appointment at New York, Philadelphia, &c of an Examiner, whose business it shall be to determine the purity or impurity of certain articles imported under the general terms, "drugs & medicines."[1] This plan, although it ↑will↓ not prevent adulterations in this country, will do ~~some~~ ↑much↓ good, if properly managed. The Examiner should, of course, be a good practical chemist, acquainted with drugs & medicines—& should, moreover, be an honest man. If, in digesting the plan, Mr. Walker should find it necessary or useful to have some chemist in chief, to see that the examiners work in a uniform manner & adopt unexceptionable processes & who could be referred to ↑in↓ the disputed cases, (which I think will occur,) I should have no objections to taking such a commission & executing[C] the trust as faithfully as I can. I know not that the Secretary will view the subject in this ↑way,↓ nor do[D] I know that the bill contemplates such an appointment;[2] but from the nature of the case, I think some such person will be required. I do not wish to apply for any office, nor do I wish to thrust myself forward—but this is a subject upon which I have talked to my Medical Classes for the last ten years—& it ↑is↓ perhaps not too much to say that my book on the subject has helped[E] greatly to wake up the profession to its importance[3]— All I now desire is, that the plan proposed as a remedy should be faithfully & efficiently carried out.

But I have already said more on this point than I had intended. I give you the above views, so that if the matter should be presented to you, you[F] may be able to give answers to queries & perhaps prevent the appointment of incompetent persons.

> With my best regards to Mrs Henry
> & your children I remain
> Yours sincerely
> Lewis C. Beck

Prof. Henry.

Henry Papers, Smithsonian Archives.

1. On June 26, 1848, President Polk signed into law an "Act to Prevent the Importation of Adulterated and Spurious Drugs and Medicines," which ordered that

all drugs, medicines, medicinal preparations, ... and chemical preparations used wholly or in part as medicine, imported into the United States from abroad, shall, before passing the custom-house, be examined and appraised, ... in reference to their quality, purity, and fitness for medical purposes. [*U.S. Statutes at Large, 9:*237–238.]

For background, an account of the debates in Congress, and the history of enforcement, see James Harvey Young, *Pure Food: Securing the Federal Food and Drugs Act of 1906* (Princeton, 1989), pp. 6–17.

2. The legislation did not provide for any "chemist in chief." Instead, it ordered the appointment of six "special examiners," one for each of the major ports, to be selected, if pos-

sible, from current customs employees at the respective ports. *U.S. Statutes at Large, 9:*238–239.

3. Historians agree with Beck's assessment. Beck's *Adulteration of Various Substances Used in Medicine and the Arts, with the Means of Detecting Them* ... (New York, 1846) has been called "the first *comprehensive* work in English devoted to the subject of drug adulteration and its detection" (Stieb, p. 249; italics in original) and "a major landmark" (Young, p. 8). Stieb has claimed that "there is good reason to believe this work provided the necessary documentation leading to the American Drug Import Law of 1848" (p. 249). Ernst W. Stieb, *Drug Adulteration: Detection and Control in Nineteenth-Century Britain* (Madison, 1966).

191. FROM ASA GRAY

[Late June 1848][A]

[...] As soon as I get my cue from you, I will secure some drawings[B] of those subjects I want in part 1.—and put things in train about it this season.

2. Now for the Genera Illustrated.[1] I send you by mail a copy of vol. 1.—in paper cover only—as most convenient for transmission thus— (postage should be only 31 cents.) I presume the Smithsonian Library will subscribe for one copy at least.—

Now, I am proud of the production, and think it does more credit to my ↑scientific↓ reputation than any thing I have done. The plates for the 2ᵈ vol. are preparing[C] and engraving,—the drawing &c. of higher order than in this first vol. I am very anxious to carry it on: but feel discouraged. The State of Europe cuts off entirely all hope of foreign (at least Continental) sale, on which I had a good deal relied, to help pay the bills. And some of our rich men, who entered into the scheme as subscribers with spirit, have behaved very shabbily, (the poorer ones, however, all fulfil their engagements with alacrity).— I must not continue to sink money, & time, and Sprague's invaluable talents in it, unless it will remunirate him, & free me from actual loss,— —which I fear it will not do.— I know no more national work; my friends assure me it does great credit to our country abroad. I will soon give you their statements on that point from abroad.

The plan I venture to suggest is, to let the Smithsonian take a part of the edition—with a new title page, or prefix, identifying the work with your operations,—which you may distribute to the principal societies abroad,—whose transactions and other publications you want to obtain, complete from the begining for your library. It will be some time before you will have enough published of your own to command all you want by mere exchange. Would not a few—(2 or 3) hundred dollars invested in this turn to most useful account in the building up of your library— far beyond what the sum would do applied directly to the purchase of memoirs—while at the same time it would stimulate and keep alive a work of pure original investigation (which this strictly is), but which otherwise must I fear be given up.

Let me know early how this strikes you, for I must soon decide upon thes the size of the ed. for the 2^d volume, and also whether the stones for the 1st vol. shall be obliterated without taking any more impressions. I am so far advanced that I must in any case bring out a 2^d volume.

The price is $6.00 pr. volume of 100 plates, & letter press as you will see,— —which is thought very cheap.— You can have them very much cheaper.—

Mrs. G. is now with her father,[2] who is laid up with a bad sprain. Were she here, she would most cordially join in the expression of sincere thanks to Mrs. Henry & yourself for your kind attention to us at Washington, and in best regards to you both. We hope yet to see you here before winter.—

Yours faithfully
A. Gray

Prof. Henry

Henry Papers, Smithsonian Archives.
The number "2" appears in parentheses in the top center of the first sheet, suggesting that this is the second set of four pages as a continuation of a first set, which is missing. Reply: Doc. 197.

1. Asa Gray, *Genera Florae Americae Boreali-Orientalis Illustrata. The Genera of the Plants of the United States Illustrated by Figures and Analyses from Nature, by Isaac Sprague,* 2 vols. (Boston, 1848–1849). His goal was a ten-volume publication in which each genus would be represented by a definitive description and illustration of a representative species. Henry and Gray were unable to agree on a strategy to save the publication, and Gray terminated it after two volumes. Dupree, *Gray,* p. 168.

2. Charles G. Loring (1794–1868), a Boston lawyer and member of the Harvard Corporation. Dupree, *Gray,* pp. 178–180; Thomas W. Herringshaw, *Encyclopedia of American Biography of the Nineteenth Century* (Chicago, 1905).

192. FROM AMOS DEAN[1]

[June 1848][A]

Joseph Henry LLD
My Dear Sir—

Some time since a company of us here consisting of J<u>no</u> Keyes Paige,[2] Samuel Stoens, Theodore Olcott,[3] Benjamin Nott,[4] John P. Pepper,[5] George H. Cook,[6] a young man formerly at the head of the Rensselaer Institute in Troy and myself organised for the purpose of manufacturing an article termed Argillo,[7] our expectations of success being based upon the results of a long course of experiments made by M<u>r</u> Pepper. My friend M<u>r</u> Brownell[8] from Hartford who has also become interested so far as the manufacture of it for flooring and table tops is concerned, has recently been in Washington to exhibit specimens[B] to Congress with the view of securing the Government patronage in the use of it for flooring &c for publick buildings. He has I am told received many assurances, and much encouragement, and a resolution has passed the Senate appointing a committee to frame and present a Bill providing for the use of it for that purpose.[9] As, however, it was a matter of great importance it was thought proper to refer to some publick scientific man or men, to get ~~th~~ his or their opinion as to its merits and utility for the purposes contemplated in its use. I was extremely happy to hear that you were referred to for this purpose,[10] because I knew that if you would give it your attention the conclusions you would arrive at would be satisfactory to all parties; but the difficulty I apprehended was that in your multitudinous engagements you would be unable to find any time to devote to such a subject. Besides I have little doubt but that situated as you are you have applications of a nature kindred to this sufficient to use up much of your time, and not unlikely some of your patience. Now my principal purpose in writing you this line is to ask of you as a personal favour that you will take sufficient time and opportunity to examine this article, to test it by all the tests that occur to you as necessary, and then state the conclusions you arrive at in relation to it. There is not here that I know of any doubt existing in regard to its being a genuine article, and one well fitted to answer all the purposes proposed— Still we may not have used all the tests necessary for ~~th~~ determining its utility, and if there is any one that will prove its insufficiency, we—of course, would wish to know it. I am deeply interested in its success, and although I am as reluctant, I believe as any one can well be in troubling my friends in matters that do not directly concern them, yet I cannot well avoid asking this favour at your hands. I do not, however, neither does the Company, wish you to render a gratuitous service. We are asking for the results which your scientific attainments can afford in this matter, and we shall be happy to pay you a liberal compensation, such as shall amply make you good for any time, attention—or scientific research you may devote to the subject. Not only that, but the responsibility you may assume in your conclusions is as legitimate an item as any other in the way of compensation. Now I shall venture to hope that you will do me the f great favour of giving to this subject your attention, and any balance that the Company may fail of ~~satis~~ abundantly satisfying you therefor, you may consider as a fund laid up by me for your benefit, and subject to your draft at sight, either for yourself or for any friend you may desire to accommodate, that I can be of service to.

Please present my respects to Mrs Henry and Believe me

as I ever have been
Truly Your Friend
Amos Dean—

I suppose the question will be between the Argillo and Marble so far as relates to flooring & table tops— I think Mr Pepper will be at Washington this week with specimens in form. If you find it convenient to comply with this request be good enough to send your conclusion in the form of a certificate directed either to myself or to John Keyes Paige who is the President of the Company. We may probably wish to make use of it in Europe, as it is intended to get out the article there during the present season.

Henry Papers, Smithsonian Archives.

1. An old acquaintance of Henry's from Albany, Dean was a lawyer and professor of medical jurisprudence at the Albany Medical College. *Henry Papers*, 2:26n–27n.

2. Former president of the Canal Bank of Albany (which collapsed in July 1848) and former mayor of Albany (1845–1846), John Keyes Paige (1788–1857) was also a regent of the University of the State of New York from 1826 until his death. George Rogers Howell and Jonathan Tenney, eds., *History of the County of Albany, N.Y., from 1609 to 1886* (New York, 1886), pp. 531, 664–665; Cuyler Reynolds, comp., *Albany Chronicles: A History of the City Arranged Chronologically* (Albany, 1906), no. 44.

3. The cashier of the Canal Bank. Howell and Tenney, p. 531.

4. He had an office at the Albany glass works. Albany City Directory, 1847–1848.

5. A marble worker who formerly lived in Washington, D.C. Washington City Directory, 1846.

6. George Hammell Cook (1818–1889) had graduated from and later taught geology at Rensselaer Polytechnic Institute. From 1846 through 1848 he was engaged in glassmaking in Albany. In the latter year he was named to Henry's old chair at the Albany Academy. He subsequently became professor of chemistry and natural science at Rutgers and the state geologist of New Jersey. *DAB.*

7. Derived from the Latin word meaning "clay."

8. H. Tudor Brownell. U.S. Senate, 30th Congress, 1st Session, Senate Reports, No. 224 (1848), p. 1.

9. Dean was referring to the select committee appointed to consider Brownell's memorial

on behalf of the Hartford Argillo Manufacturing Company. The Senate committee examined specimens of the Argillo and read a report prepared by Walter R. Johnson and Zenas C. Robbins. However, the committee concluded only "to recommend its use as a substitute for mar-

ble in the public buildings." No specific legislation was suggested. Senate Reports, No. 224 (quotation on p. 1).

10. There is no evidence that Henry was ever involved in evaluating Argillo.

193. TO ALEXANDER DALLAS BACHE

Private
Bulletin no 2

Washington July 4th/48

My Dear B

I have just returned from the north after an absence of about two weeks and find all things pertaining to the smithsonian in about the same state as when I left. I regretted to learn on my return that the magnetic commission of Dr Locke had not yet been sent to him but I am now assured that it will be forwarded immediately. I find that all matters pertaining to the operations of the Government require constant pushing.

I am sorry to inform you that our friend Peale has lost the appointment of principal examiner and has refused the offer of that of assistant with a salary of 1500 dollars and the prospect of speedy promotion. His friends in Phil[d] cannot blame us for the failure in securing him a position in Washington. You suggested the idea of the application and did all you properly could to advance his interest. I also made all the exertions necessary to influence the commissioner[1] and others in his favour. Mr Burke had concluded to give him the appointment and would have done so had not the removal from the departement at the last hour of Mr Clinton the older assistant examiner[2] given him an opportunity of promoting Dr Gale[3] a course which he had determined on from the first[A] and which he was prevented from carrying into execution on account of Clinton who stood in the way. Dr Gale is a good man and was the best entitled to the office he had been induced to apply for the office of assistant with the prospect of promotion. Immediately after the above mentioned change had taken place Mr Burke sent for Mr Peale and offered him the office of assistant with the assurance of a good prospect of a speedy promotion this was promptly declined. Had I been in the city I would have urged Mr Peale to accept the appointment and would have told him that if he did not accept he could expect no other assistance.[4] I have not yet seen him the foregoing account I had from Mr Burk. Lane has been appointed as the assistant to Dr Page and Cooper[5] has been nomenated as that of Dr Gale.

You have probably seen by the papers that Loomis has been appointed to my chair in Princeton.[6] Rogers[7] at the last moment withdrew his resignation of the chair in the University with the hope that his Lady love would consent to reside at charlottsville. This threw our friend Dicky into a quandary—the trustees of Princeton would not wait and McCullough could not give up the prospect of virginia.[8] In this state of things I was called upon by the Trustees informally to nominate a candidate and I accordingly gave as ↑that of↓ the best available man the name of Loomis. He had not been consulted on the subject but I presume he will accept. I would on one accounts[B] had I consulted my own feelings prefered McCullough but I think Loomis is the proper man. In severing my connection with Princeton I was actuated by a desire not only to do right but also to avoid the imputation of doing otherwise and though I felt unpleasantly in resigning in full my connection with an institution with which I had been so long and pleasantly connected yet the kind feeling exhibited toward me by the act of the trustees was exceedingly gratifying. They resolved to continue the payment of the yearly due on the insurance they effected upon my life some years ago and elected me Professor Emeritus.

The memoir of Squier & Davis is now passing so rapidly through the press that I think the whole volume will be out before the adjournment of congress. The number of pages will not be as great as was at first calculated but with the plates it[C] will still make a good sized quarto. Dr Davis is an MD and to adjust the titles of the two gentlemen [?consistently] I procured for squier the degree of A.M.

The Smithsonian Reports are still in the hands of the printer. Just before I started a proof was given me of my report with the information that it must be returned as soon as possible for the paper I had furnished for the extra copies had been "wetted down" several days and in the warm weather would spoil.[9] I had not therefore an opportunity of sending a proof to you or of submitting it to Mr Johnson as I intended he being at the time in Phil[d] attending the political Convention.[10] I submitted a copy to Mr Marsh who made no alterations except in the way of pointing. I regret this occurrence for it would have given me more confidence to have had your revision.

Dr Gray of Cambridge has been appointed to the charge of the botany of the exploring expedition. Wilkes went on to Boston to engage him without consulting Dr[D] Torrey with whom he had made a previous

353

though not a definite engagement.[11] The appointement of Dr Gray to this duty will not interfere with his going on with the Report on the Forest Trees of the united states. He cannot however finish the work in one year and thinks it ought[E] to be given in parts and spread over two or three years. The subject he considers of great interest and importance on which he wishes to put forth his whole strength.

I have been applied to for assistance to enable Professor Baird of Pennsylvania to give to the public his researches on Embriology in the way of procuring a draftsman[F] for his illustrations and I have refered the subject to Dr Morton and Professor Haldeman who report very favourably on the labours of Prof Baird and recommend a small appropriation. I think this a proper case for the application of the Smithsonian funds and with the approbation of the executive I will make a small advance.[12] The paper of the Professor of course will appear in the Smithsonian contributions.

One object of my going to the north was that of conveying[G] Mrs H and the little girls to Princeton. I left them there where they will remain until the warm weather is over. William was left with Mr Nourse his teacher.[13] Mrs Henry received in Princeton the kind letter of Mrs Bache and has I presume answered it before this. Your good Lady has been of as much comfort to Mrs H as you have been to me. I have hired two rooms in the house on the N.W. corner of C & 4½ Streets[H] and take my meals in a Hotel near by.[14]

Mrs H. sent one vol. of "mental relaxation" in the form of a new novel for Mrs B. and directed me to procure another. This I have sent to the coast survey office.

Young smith[15] whom you appointed to the coast survey on my recomendation has retured to Princeton. His eyes gave out. I am not well please with the occcurrance and always feel some responsibility when I recommend a person. I should as soon have though of recommending a spavin horse for a race as a man with bead eyes for a draughts man.[I] The case however is not quit so bad is if I had imposed upon you an unworthy[J] fellow of whom you found it difficult to get rid.

I have little to communicate relative to the operations of the national Institute— The sub-committee have had one meeting during my absence but I know not what has been done.[16] Vattemares bill has passed and he now proposes to ask that a commission or set of trustees be appointed to take charge of the articles he may send to the Government of the united states in the way of exchange and that these consit of the superintendent of the coast survey the sec of the Smith. Institution the superintendent of the observatory the heads of the Topographial and the Engineer department.[17]

Draft, Bache Papers, Smithsonian Archives.

1. At Peale's request, Henry met with Burke on June 9 regarding his suitability for the post of patent examiner. Titian R. Peale to John F. Frazer, June 10, 1848, Frazer Papers, Library, American Philosophical Society.

2. Thomas G. Clinton, a native of Ireland, became an assistant patent examiner about 1845. In March 1848, after his application to become a principal examiner was rejected, Clinton accused Burke of malfeasance and dereliction of duty. He made these charges first to the secretary of state, then to the president, and finally to a grand jury; all found them groundless. In the meantime, Burke barred Clinton's access to the Patent Office. In July, Clinton petitioned the House of Representatives about his complaints. On August 10, 1848, the House Committee on Patents reported that Clinton's allegations were unsubstantiated. U.S. House, 30th Congress, 1st Session, *Edmund Burke, on the Complaint of Thomas G. Clinton,* House Reports, No. 839 (1848), especially pp. 29, 181, 238–240, 265.

3. Leonard D. Gale became a principal examiner on July 1, 1848. House Report No. 839, p. 53.

4. In a letter to Burke of July 10, 1848 (Henry Papers, Smithsonian Archives), Henry stated that Peale, urged on by his supporters, would likely accept if offered the post again.

5. Samuel Cooper, a former military engineer, was an assistant and later a principal examiner in the Patent Office until 1852, when he resigned and became a patent agent in Boston. Robert C. Post, *Physics, Patents, and Politics: A Biography of Charles Grafton Page* (New York, 1976), pp. 46, 118.

6. On June 28, the Princeton trustees appointed Elias Loomis as Henry's successor in the chair of natural philosophy, with a salary of $1,300 per year plus free housing. Loomis hesitated about accepting the offer. As of late August he still had not made up his mind, and, as Henry observed, "[t]he good people of Princeton are beginning to be·very uneasy about" his acceptance. Henry agreed to deliver a few lectures, albeit reluctantly, until Loomis made his intentions clear.

Trustees' Minutes, vol. 3, p. 499, Princeton University Archives, Seeley G. Mudd Manuscript Library, Princeton University; Henry to Anonymous, August 26, 1848, Mary Henry Copy, Henry Papers, Smithsonian Archives.

7. William B. Rogers.

8. Rogers resigned his chair at the University of Virginia after the family of his fiancée, Emma Savage of Boston (whom he married in 1849), urged "that in my new domestic arrangements my home should be less remote from them, & in a free state." Yet the prospects of "giv[ing] up an employment in which I have for so long a time found almost daily pleasure," and leading "an unprofessional life in Boston" made Rogers have second thoughts. Knowing that Richard Sears McCulloh was interested in his chair, Rogers considered applying for Henry's vacant chair at Princeton. Ultimately, however, he withdrew his resignation. Elliott, *Dictionary,* s.v. "Rogers, William Barton"; Rogers to Henry, June 9, 1848, Henry Papers, Smithsonian Archives (quotations).

9. Prior to printing, paper was wetted down so that it would "receive the impression of the ink in a far more perfect manner." In humid weather, mildew formed if the dampened paper was not used quickly. W. T. Brande, ed., *A Dictionary of Science, Literature, and Art* (New York, 1843), p. 985 (quotation); Thomas MacKellar, *The American Printer: A Manual of Typography* (Philadelphia, 1885), pp. 255–257.

10. The Whigs held their national convention in Philadelphia early in June. Richard B. Morris, ed., *Encyclopedia of American History* (New York, 1953), p. 209.

11. Gray had traveled to Washington in June, at Wilkes's request, to discuss his appointment to oversee the tropical botany of the United States Exploring Expedition. Far from being ignorant that Wilkes wanted to appoint Gray, Torrey wrote Gray in May 1848 that he was "not surprised at Wilkes' late movement, & hope you will make a good bargain with him." Gray to Henry, June 2, 1848, Archives of the Hunt Institute for Botanical Documentation, Carnegie Mellon University; Torrey to Gray, May 30, 1848, quoted in Andrew D. Rodgers, III, *John Torrey: A Story of North American Botany* (1942; New York, 1965), p. 183; Dupree, *Gray,* pp. 184–186.

12. At the executive committee meeting of

July 6, 1848, Henry stated his plan to advance Baird occasional sums of $50 for his embryological research. Rhees, *Journals*, p. 463.

13. Joseph Everett Nourse (1819–1889), an 1837 graduate of Jefferson College, taught at the Rittenhouse Academy in Washington until 1840, when he became its principal. During his tenure, the school became "one of the most flourishing academies" in the city. *The Twentieth Century Biographical Dictionary of Notable Americans* (Boston, 1904); Henry to Ormsby M. Mitchel, May 23, 1849, Henry Papers, Smithsonian Archives (quotation).

14. Henry and William Henry occupied a second-story flat in a house owned by C. H. Van Patten, a dentist who knew Jane Ryley, the Henrys' old family friend. Henry to Harriet Henry, July 1, 1848, Family Correspondence, Henry Papers, Smithsonian Archives; Washington City Directory, 1846.

15. Louis Henri Smith was the son of Louis P. Smith, cashier of the Princeton Bank. *Henry Papers*, 3:90n; *Catalogue of the Officers and Students of the College of New Jersey, for 1844–1845* (Princeton, 1845), p. 13; Louis P. Smith to Henry, April 20, May 11, May 13, 1848, Henry Papers, Smithsonian Archives.

16. At a meeting on June 10, members of a committee on the future of the National Institute appointed a sub-committee—composed of Henry, Charles Wilkes, Matthew F. Maury, John J. Abert, and Peter Force—to consider "the wants of the Institute & the best mode of restoring it to activity & usefulness." The sub-committee met first in June (the meeting Henry missed), and again on July 13 (see Doc. 195). Minutes of National Institute committee meeting, June 10, 1848, Box 13, RU 7058, Records of the National Institute, Smithsonian Archives (quotation); Charles F. Stansbury to Henry, July 11, 1848, Henry Papers, Smithsonian Archives.

17. On June 26, 1848, Congress passed an act directing its Joint Committee on the Library to nominate an agent to manage a program of international exchanges of documents and publications; the act appropriated $2,000 to implement the program. Congress subsequently followed the committee's unanimous recommendation and named Vattemare as its agent for international exchanges. Vattemare was no stranger to such a program. In 1840, backed by several state legislatures, he had successfully memorialized Congress for a bill authorizing an international exchange of duplicate public documents; since then, he had overseen the exchanges of several thousand volumes between France and the United States. Congress never established the exchange commission that Vattemare sought.

Rhees, *Documents* (1901), 1:466–467; George H. Boehmer, "History of the Smithsonian Exchanges," in *Smithsonian Report for 1881*, pp. 703–810, especially pp. 705–708.

194. TO HARRIET HENRY

Washington, July 13th, 1848.

Dearest: I suppose you will think yourself badly treated if you do not have a letter every day,[1] and therefore I seize a leisure moment after breakfast, while I am waiting the arrival of several persons who are to pay court to me this morning in my basilica. Indeed, seated as I am in a gothic chair, with a large gothic table[2] before me and my morning gown on, I need but a wig, of the reign of Charles the Second, to convert me in appearance into a respectable looking judge of the court of Kings Bench. Yesterday was a busy time for me, I had several engagements on hand, when Dr. Hare was announced and of course I wished to pay him all due attention. We first went to the building, then to the monument,[3] then to the President's, took tea with Mrs. Bell[4] and passed the remainder of the evening at Mr. Walker's.[5] The Dr. appeared much pleased with his reception and has concluded to give all his apparatus to the Smithsonian; he is well pleased with the arrangements I have proposed for the exhibition of the articles. We are to visit the building again this morning to settle upon a place for his large electrical machine.[6] I have now to call a meeting of the establishment—which consists of the President, the Vice-President, the Secretaries of State, of War, of the Navy, and of the Treasury—to elect Dr. Hare the first honorary member of the Institution.[7]

This gift of Dr. Hare will I think be a matter of great importance to the Institution, not only on account of its intrinsic value, but also as forming a precedent for other gifts; as well as serving to increase the confidence of the public, in the stability and usefulness of the Institution. . . .

Mary Henry Copy, Family Correspondence, Henry Papers, Smithsonian Archives.
Mary Henry used three of Henry's 1848 letters to Harriet to compile her copy—July 11–12 (Family Correspondence, Henry Papers, Smithsonian Archives), July 14 (Doc. 195), and a third, dated by her as July 13, which we have not found. We have deleted the materials clearly taken from the letters of July 11–12 and 14, and are printing only the first two paragraphs of her copy.

1. In addition to the letter of July 11–12 cited above, Henry's letters to Harriet of June 30 and July 1, 6, 7, and 8–9, 1848, are in the Family Correspondence, Henry Papers, Smithsonian Archives.

2. The table and chairs were part of a set designed by James Renwick for the Smithsonian Building; although some of the chairs were apparently destroyed in the 1865 fire, others survive as part of the Office of Architectural History and Historic Preservation's "Castle" Collection. Cynthia Field, OAHP, Smithsonian Institution, private communication; Henry to Harriet Henry, July 6, 1848, Family Correspondence, Henry Papers, Smithsonian Archives.

3. That is, the site of the Washington Monument, the cornerstone of which was laid—in a ceremony marked by considerable fanfare—on July 4, 1848. Constance McLaughlin Green, *Washington: A History of the Capital, 1800–1950*, 2 vols. in 1 (1962; Princeton, 1976), *1:*170–172.

4. Jane Erwin Bell, the wife of Senator John Bell of Tennessee. *DAB*, s.v. "Bell, John."

5. Robert J. Walker.

6. Mounted on an elevated platform, Hare's electrical machine became "the most prominent object" in the Smithsonian Building's apparatus room. William J. Rhees, *An Account of the Smithsonian Institution, Its Founder, Building, Operations, Etc.* (Washington, 1857), pp. 25–26 (quotation on p. 25). Rhees illustrated the machine on page 26 of his book.

7. The first section of the act creating the Smithsonian provided for an "Establishment," whose members included, in addition to those given by Henry, the attorney general, the postmaster general, the chief justice, the commissioner of patents, and the mayor of Washington. This body could elect other individuals as "honorary members." At its first meeting, on August 1, 1849, the Establishment so elected Hare, Albert Gallatin, Benjamin Silliman, and Washington Irving (1783–1859, *DAB*), the celebrated novelist and man of letters. Rhees, *Journals*, p. 771.

195. TO HARRIET HENRY

Washington
July 14th 1848

My dearest

What an admirable invention is that which enables us to converse with those we love though they may be hundreds of miles distance. I have been out all ↑the↓ day & have just returned to my room after a pretty severe attack on the organized remains of a dinner table. This is a very warm day but I have been careful not to expose myself but little. I was however in rather an exposed position for a few minutes on the roof of the capitol. I went up to see the gilt ball which formed the top of the lantern which was lying at the foot of the dome. When it was taken down it was found to be preforated in four holes by lightning. I heard of this but could scarcely credit it—but there is no mistake.[1] The commissioner of Bubli Buildings has given the article[A] to be placed in the museum of the smithsonian. I must send Mc Peak with a mechanic to cut it off from the stem. This will give rise to sage remarks on the part of Mc Peak. Dr Hare is still in the city though I have been so much engaged as not to be able to see him. I called for that purpose—yesterday was also a very busy day with me. I had engagements from 8 o'clock in the morning until 12 at night. I attended in the evening a meeting for the amelioration of the condition of the National Institute at Col. Aberts.[2] We remained in session until I found it about 12 o'clock before I got home. Will. was fast asleep and the candle which he had placed in the entry for me almost[B] burned down. There is an occupant of the room above ours who is company for Will. when I am out otherwise I would not leave him alone. He is however sufficiently able to take care of himself and would be offended were I to hint that he was unwilling to be left alone. Mr Mc Peak has just come in with a calico bed cover which I directed him to procure to hide the cotton sheets which bespred our couch. He has procured of the same material a curtain for hanging over our clothes. We keep on thus[C] making improvements our apartments will soon be not only well but elegant furnished our gothic chairs table pictures of the Institute &c &c. I have been engaged the principal part of the day in seeing persons relative to the affairs of the coast survey. The appropriation bill has been up several day in sucession[D] and that part of it relative to the coast survey was to come up to day. A discussion hower occurred on some other subject and the matter has rested. Among the applications which I have had for advise there is one which I received to day³ of rather a singular kind. A gentleman is engaged to write the will of an old man possesed of a property worth 80 thousand dollars wishes to found ↑at his death↓ with it an institution for the diffusion of knowledge in a given district and the question is what kind of an institution will best s[p]end so small a sum and be most effectual in producing good results.⁴ Will has just come home complains some what of the heat appears however very well—has improved in flesh since I returned—has a good apetite, and is in good health.— He bids me say that if you make any more collars let them be like the one you sent though he is not sure that he shall want any more. I should delight to be with you to night—I hope you and ours are well—do not take the world to hard we are very comfortably situated and were it not that I am seperated from you I would think my self well off. This situation is quit cool while the other parts of the city are warm. A bill has passed one part of ~~the~~ congress to fence in all the public grounds including the whole mall and plant them with trees.⁵ This will obviate the necessity of puting a fence around the Smithsonian or of planting it with trees at the expense of the Institution.⁶ I have now written you a long letter and I am too lazy to read it over. You will I hope not consider it merely twaddle though it may contain not a silable of any interest. The fact of its having been written by me will be sufficient to make it of some value to you. Perhaps however you will not think it of much interest when I inform you that it has been written as much for my own gratification as for yours. It has given me much pleasure to scribble thus to you for several days past and is an agreable relief to the labor of business. I have been honored by no less than four calls since I commenced this epistle. The last was from Professor Hubbard and his wife.⁷ The Lady did not however come up stairs but remained in the carriage. An other person has just come in to keep an engagement with me to call upon col. Totten. We shall take an omnibus and return as soon as possible. I may not however have an opportunity of closeing this letter again before this evening and there I will end by assuring you that you are the dearest object of my existance that I shall love you while^E life lasts and hope to enjoy a spiritual existence with you beyond the grave.

Adieu Dearest

Family Correspondence, Henry Papers, Smithsonian Archives.

1. Henry's on-site inspection apparently resulted from a report to Congress in April 1848 by Charles Douglas, commissioner of public buildings, on damages caused to the Capitol by James Crutchett's gaslighting system. Douglas cited the strains imposed on the dome, and especially on its skylight, by the sway of the lantern mast in the wind. Of more concern, however, he wrote, was the continuing threat posed by lightning. Douglas observed that while "ju-

dicious plans" had been devised to conduct electricity away from the dome, these were not foolproof, and the chance remained "that the electric fluid may pass down the iron braces that sustain the pole, between the two wooden [outer and inner] domes." He warned of "a direful catastrophe" should this happen: the domes would likely be "set on fire and consumed, to the great injury of the capitol, and possibly to the destruction of many valuable lives."

In May, after Congress received Douglas's report, Representative John W. Houston of the House Committee on Public Buildings asked Henry's opinion as to whether the mast was "so connected with [the Capitol dome], as to endanger the edifice from charges of electricity during the summer season." We have not found Henry's reply. After the on-site inspection showed that the mast had been struck by lightning several times, however, in August Congress appropriated $323 to remove it from the dome.

U.S. House, 30th Congress, 1st Session, *Injury to the Capitol from the Introduction of Gas,* House Executive Documents, No. 61 (1848), pp. 2–3 (quotations on p. 3); Houston to Henry, May 8, 1848, Henry Papers, Smithsonian Archives; *U.S. Statutes at Large,* 9:293.

2. The meeting was held to consider a report prepared by Abert's subcommittee on the future of the institute. The report rejected as too extreme all but one of the suggestions for reorganizing the institute, the sole exception being the plan advanced by George P. Marsh. Under it, Congress would grant land to the institute and place it under the immediate control of "certain government functionaries [who were not specified] as trustees for the U.S." After stipulating that the institute's charter should also be extended, the subcommittee recommended that the institute seek relief from Congress along the lines suggested by Marsh. "Report of the Subcommittee upon the Different Plans for Amending the Nat. Institute," July 13, 1848, Box 13, RU 7058, Records of the National Institute, Smithsonian Archives.

3. Not found.

4. In another letter, Henry identified the testator as a "Gentleman in the South." The individual engaged to write his will may have

been Virginia representative James McDowell, to whom Henry sent documents relating to the New York State Normal School; Henry had solicited the information from George Roberts Perkins (*Henry Papers,* 6:167), the school's professor of mathematics and an old acquaintance. (Henry also requested information from Eben Horsford; see Doc. 208.) We have not found any information on the subsequent disposition of the will. Henry to Perkins, July 26, 1848 (quotation); Perkins to Henry, August 1, 1848; Henry to McDowell, retained copy, August 3, 1848, all in Henry Papers, Smithsonian Archives.

5. Congress appropriated $2,300 for erecting wooden fences around the public grounds to the north, south, and west of the Capitol, and also to the south of the White House; $1,000 for grading these grounds to alleviate flooding from Tiber Creek; and $500 for "suitable trees, for planting [a] Nursery" on the grounds west of the Capitol. The work progressed more slowly than anticipated, however, and while some trees were planted during the summer and fall of 1848, further planting was postponed until the following spring. "Estimates for the Public Buildings and Grounds, for the Fiscal Year, Commencing July 1st, 1848," p. 2 (quotation), HR 30A-D25.8 (Estimates from Commissioner of Public Buildings and Grounds, House Ways and Means Committee, Committee Reports and Papers, Legislative Proceedings, 30th Congress), Folder 2, Records of the House of Representatives, RG 233, National Archives; U.S. House, 30th Congress, 2d Session, *Annual Report of the Commissioner of Public Buildings and Grounds,* House Executive Documents, No. 34 (1849), pp. 6, 7, 9–12.

6. On January 28, 1847, the regents had authorized expenditures of up to $10,000 for permanently enclosing, and up to $4,000 for landscaping, the Smithsonian grounds. In 1847, the building committee spent $520 to erect a temporary fence around the grounds. Rhees, *Journals,* pp. 29, 593.

7. Joseph Stillman Hubbard, professor of mathematics at the United States Naval Observatory, and the former Sarah E. L. Handy, whom he married in 1848. *Henry Papers,* 6:76n; Elliott, *Dictionary.*

196. TO JARED SPARKS[1]

Washington July 14th 1848

My dear Sir

Mr Henry Stevens has submitted to me as Secretary of the Smithsonian Institution his proposition to prepare a bibiographical account of books relating to or printed in America prior to the Year 1700,[2] the details of which he informes me have been submitted to you. I beg leave to request an expression of your opinon as to the importance of such a work,[3,A] and whether it would be of sufficient interest to the Student of American History to warrant its publication in the series of volumes forming the Smithsonian Contributions to Knowledge.

My object in making this request is to satisfy the Regents as to the propriety of giving Mr Stevens the necessary encouragement[B] on the part of the Institution relative to the preparation of the work. In conformity to the rule adopted in the Smithsonian publications, it will not be accepted by the Institution until it has been approved of as to character and execution by a Commission of competent Judges.[4]

I remain very respectfully and
truly yours
Joseph Henry

Jared Sparks LLD

Sparks Mss 153, Sparks Papers, Houghton Library, Harvard University.
In Charles P. Russell's hand, with Henry's signature. Reply: July 24, 1848, retained copy in same location; reprinted in *Smithsonian Report for 1848,* pp. 59–60.

1. A pioneering documentary editor, Sparks (1789–1866) since 1839 had been McLean Professor of History at Harvard. *DAB.*

2. To compile his bibliography, which he estimated would list some five thousand titles, Stevens proposed to survey the holdings of public and private European and American libraries which agreed to subscribe to the project. The subscriptions were intended to defray the expenses (which he figured at $5,000) of compiling the work and preparing it for publication. Touring the United States in 1848 to enlist support, he visited Henry at Princeton in June. According to Stevens, Henry said that the plan "met fully his views," promising that the Smithsonian would contribute as much as $1,000 toward the work, and publish it "in the best style." On July 7, 1848, Stevens sent Henry (and Jewett, whom he named as co-recipient) a formal prospectus for "Bibliographia Americana: A Bibliographical Account of the Sources of Early American History." His letter and prospectus were printed in *Smithsonian Report for 1848,* p. 57 and pp. 55–56, respectively; we have not found the originals.

Stevens to "Pink" [William Page], June 25, 1848, microfilm, reel 20, frame 78, William Page and Page Family Papers, Archives of American Art, Smithsonian Institution.

3. On the same date, Henry sent a similar letter to John Gorham Palfrey (not found) and Peter Force (Force Papers, Library of Congress). Henry's letter was reprinted in *Smithsonian Report for 1848,* p. 58.

4. In his reply, Sparks strongly endorsed Stevens's project, writing that the bibliography, if "completely and faithfully executed," would form "a most important acquisition to our historical literature," and would prove invaluable to scholars and librarians alike. Given the project's cost and prospect of low sales, Sparks concluded "that few works in the literary class are more worthy of the patronage of the Smithsonian Institution, or more in accordance with its

original design." Palfrey and Force sent similar endorsements, both dated July 15, 1848, the latter pledging $250 toward the project. (Palfrey's letter has not been found; Force's retained copy is in his papers at the Library of Congress. Both letters were reprinted in *Smithsonian Report for 1848*, pp. 58–59.)

Henry and Jewett gave Stevens a certificate, dated July 17, stating their own support for his plan and affirming the institution's desire to publish the bibliography in SI Contributions, "provided the execution is found satisfactory to a commission of competent judges" (*Smithsonian Report for 1848*, p. 58). The certificate enabled Stevens to procure subscriptions from the congressional Joint Committee on the Library, from libraries and societies, and from private individuals, before he returned to England to begin work on the bibliography (see *Smithsonian Report for 1848*, pp. 17, 60).

Notwithstanding this promising start, Stevens's efforts soon proved desultory; despite prodding from Henry and promises from Stevens, the project dragged on with no apparent end in sight. Ultimately, Stevens never completed his bibliography. Henry to Stevens, November 14, 1850, and January 9, 1854, Henry Stevens Papers, Department of Special Collections, University Library, University of California at Los Angeles.

197. TO ASA GRAY

Washington
July 17th 1848

My dear Sir

On my return from the North I found your letter[1] on my table and I have waited from day to day that I might be enabled to acknowledge the receipt of the book you mention; but owing to some unexplained delay, it has but just come to hand. I shall not fail to show it to Mr Pearce and to the other members of the Board of Regents now in Washington. I agree to your several propositions as to the Report.[2] Funds can be advanced from time to time to defray the necessary expense during the progress of the work. I should like to have a programme of the plan to present in my next Report, and then the first number may ↑appear↓ in the Autumn of next year. I am pleased with the idea of illustrations from original sketches, and in all cases of illustrations it will be well for us to procure original drawings and not to follow the ordinary custom of copying from Stereotyped[A] figurs. With regard to compensation the method you propose will be adopted provided Congress should not see fit to print the work as a Public Document.[B] In that case an equivalent remuneration to the one proposed will be made you. Even should the work be adopted by Congress, we can strike off another edition on better paper for sale.

As to The Genera of the Plants of the United States I cannot speak at this moment so definately, tho I have little doubt that the assistance in amount you mention may readily be procured. The only question in my mind is the proper method of effecting it without interfering with our general plan and establishing an inconvenint precedent. Were the work in the form of a quarto. volume such as we could adopt as a part of our Contributions to Knowledge there would be no difficulty in the case. Perhaps the simpler plan will be for us to subscribe for a certain number of volumes. Send me as early as convenint the testimonials you mention and I will confer with the Regents in Washington.

I have just received a letter[3] from M E. Desor the friend of Agassie, asking to be employed in the preparation of a Report on Natural History.[4] Inform me confidentially as soon as possible, if you consider him a proper person for this work.

I remain Very
truly yours &
Joseph Henry

Dr A. Gray

Historic Letters, Archives, Gray Herbarium Library, Harvard University.
In Charles C. Jewett's hand, with Henry's signature. Drafts (dated July 8 and 11), in Jewett's hand, missing final paragraph: Henry Papers, Smithsonian Archives. Reply: Doc. 201.

1. Doc. 191.
2. That is, Gray's contemplated report on forest trees.
3. Not found.
4. Pierre Jean Édouard Desor (1811–1882), a German-born law student, in 1837 was hired by Agassiz to oversee the employees of his Neuchâtel publishing house and laboratory. Agassiz tutored Desor in natural history and glaciology, and he soon became a valued associate. Early in 1847, Desor followed Agassiz to the United States, planning "to strike out on his own and win equal recognition as a great European naturalist come to explore America." At the same time, however, he began publicly savaging Agassiz's character. By the spring of 1848, they had severed their relationship. Their ensuing bitter and highly visible feud threatened to divide the Boston scientific community. *DSB;* Edward Lurie, *Louis Agassiz: A Life in Science* (1960; Chicago, 1966), pp. 108, 112–113, 141, 153–162 (quotation on p. 153).

198. TO ALEXANDER DALLAS BACHE

Washington July 29th, 48

My dear B.

I started last week on Wednesday[1] at the request of Dr Hare for Phil[d] to make arrangements about his apparatus— Met him in the city next day inspected the articles found an immense number sufficient with the chemical materials to fill a sloop or at least a canal boat— Does not give his tools also keeps his balances[2]—has promised one of the blow pipe apparatus[3] to the Franklin Institute. Engaged a man the Drs assistant[4] to clean and pack the articles attempted to strike for higher wages but I think will take what Dr gave him 10 dollars per week.

I telegraphed to Princeton informing Mrs H that I was on my way to Phil<u>d</u> and requesting her to meet me there—found the Lady waiting for me at Dr Ludlow's when I arrived—stoped a day in phil<u>d</u> saw Dr James and the younger Dr Rogers[5] was informed that William has hopes of retaining his Virginia Professorship without loosing his Boston bride— I fear our friend Richard[6] will be the ass betwen the bundles of hay— Arrived in Princeton in time to attend a grand wedding that of the nece of Capt Stockton Miss Potter to a young gentleman from the South a former Student in Princeton College[7]—met Capt S and next day was presented through the Captain by the railway company with a free ticket through N.J.[8] was pleased with the compliment the ticket came rather late but must not look a gift horse in the mouth. Same compliment paid General Scott[9] at the same meeting— How we apples swim![10]— Started next morning for New York found all things going on as well as could be expected book nearly all printed[A] little man Squier in good spirits & Dr Daves likewise. The weather was excessively warm in New York was much oppressed with the heat same in Phil<u>d</u> have been this summer more comfortable in Washington than elsewhere present location cool and pleasant— Got back to Princeton[B] on saturday night spent the evening with Dr Hodge[11]—left for Washington on Monday morning came down in the boat with Col. Fremont[12] who will do all he can to forward the meteorological campeighn by establishing observers in California[13] for which place he starts in about 10 days. Expects to get across the mountain before the heavy snow falls—takes a more southern pass—will have three sections across the country.[14] His wife goes in a steamer from New York through the Streights of Magellan meets him in California.[15] I stoped in Baltimore arrived in Washington next morning—found Will whom I had left to take care of the house in good condition had been rather lonely—found a pile of letters on my table among which were several highly approving the scheme of Mr Stevens. Also a very friendly communcation from Prof Jewett[16] also approving the plan of the Stevens publication. Since my return weather has been too warm for me to go out except in the evening—have been engaged several days with Mr Espy on subject of meteorology—he has agreed to cooperate with the Smithsonian and I think will work very will—I have advised him to present the matter which he has now in ha[n]d and which he has been endeavouring to get printed as his report for next winter[17] and in the mean time join me in the examination of barometers the digesting of a plan of observations &c. I think he will be willing to be directed ~~in this matter~~ ↑by you and myself↓ and to act as an assistant in carrying out the plans we may ~~settle~~ ↑agree↓ on. When he first called he was fierce for issuing his circular and for calling in observations on the old plan[18] ~~but he appears now to be perfectly willing to be directed in this matter by you and myself~~. I dined last evening at Col. Benton's[19] met a gentleman from the far west ↑one of↓ the proprietors of Bents fort who agreed to take charge of a set of meteorological observations and to have them transmitted to us every six months. I shall provid him with instruments to take with him.[20] I have had ~~a short~~ ↑an↓ interview with Mr Gregory[21] but but had not an opportunity of introducing the subject of the C.S. I am to call upon him this evening and will get him to introduce me to Mr Talmage.[22] Another guest[C] of Col B was the Democratic nominne for Vice President with whom I was pleased to make an acquaintance.[23]

Draft, Bache Papers, Smithsonian Archives.
A Mary Henry Copy of the same date, with some textual variations and with materials taken from Doc. 199, is in the Henry Papers, Smithsonian Archives.

1. July 19.

2. In addition to the items mentioned, Hare, "contemplating the pursuit of Agricultural Chemistry" (p. [4]), planned to keep his own laboratory retorts, reagents, and "sundry portable articles which might serve to amuse, or instruct my family and friends" (p. [5]). However, due to a miscommunication with Henry, nearly all of his equipment was shipped to the Smithsonian. The result was a long dispute between Hare and the Smithsonian over which items were rightfully his and which now belonged to the institution. Hare to Henry, retained copy beginning "It may be expedient," n.d. but circa 1852, Robert Hare Papers, American Philosophical Society.

3. Invented in 1801, Hare's oxyhydrogen blowpipe produced temperatures higher than had been attained previously. For this device, "the earliest and perhaps most remarkable of his original contributions to science," Hare received the Rumford Medal of the American Academy of Arts and Sciences. "The Late Dr. Robert Hare," *Silliman's Journal*, 1858, 2d. ser. 26:100–105 (quotation on p. 101); see also *Henry Papers*, 2:202n.

4. William R. De Beust, a Philadelphia blacksmith and machinist, until recently had been Hare's laboratory assistant. He was later employed by the Smithsonian, where Henry termed him "a very ingenious and skilful workman acquainted with special branches of practical chemistry and the general application of electricity to the useful arts." Philadelphia City Directory, 1848; Henry's letter of recommendation for De Beust, May 18, 1865, Outgoing Correspondence, Office of the Secretary, RU 33, Smithsonian Archives; testimony of De Beust, in U.S. Senate, 38th Congress, 2d Session, *Report of the Special Committee of the Board of Regents of the Smithsonian Institution Relative to the Fire*, Senate Reports, No. 129 (1865), pp. 27–28.

5. James Blythe Rogers and his brother, Robert Empie Rogers (*Henry Papers*, 5:268n), professor of general and applied chemistry at the University of Virginia.

6. Richard Sears McCulloh.

7. One of the six daughters of James Potter (1793–1862), a South Carolinian who summered in Princeton, married Philip Poullain (d. 1880), of Greensborough, Georgia, an 1846 graduate of the college. James Potter's sister, Maria, was the wife of Robert Field Stockton. Hageman, *Princeton*, 1:313–315, 336; *Catalogue of the Officers and Students of the College of New Jersey, 1845–1846* (Princeton, 1846), p. 9; *Princeton Catalogue*, p. 170.

8. Commander of the ill-fated *Princeton* and a controversial hero of the Mexican War, Stockton (*Henry Papers*, 2:82n) was associated with several New Jersey canal and railroad companies. Hageman, *Princeton*, 1:253; [S. J. Bayard], *A Sketch of the Life of Com. Robert F. Stockton* (New York, 1856), pp. 65–67.

9. Winfield Scott (1786–1866), general-in-chief of the army and conqueror of Mexico. *DAB*.

10. An earthy (for Henry) allusion to one of Aesop's fables, "Apples and Horse Turds," in which a pile of horse dung and a heap of apples were swept away together by a flood. Seeing the

fruit bobbing alongside them, the droppings cried out "Alack-a-day! *How wee apples swim!*" Roger L'Estrange, trans. and ed., *Fables of Aesop and Other Eminent Mythologists: With Morals and Reflections* (London, 1692), p. 124.

11. Charles Hodge.

12. John C. Frémont (1813–1890), "the Pathfinder," as a member of the Corps of Topographical Engineers led three quasi-governmental scientific expeditions to explore the Far West between 1842 and 1847. The last coincided with Stockton's capture of California; declaring California a territory, Stockton named Frémont military commandant, and later civil governor. However, Stockton's assistant, Stephen W. Kearny, refused to recognize Frémont's authority and had him court-martialed. Frémont was convicted of insubordination and mutiny, but President Polk granted him clemency; he then resigned from the army. *DAB;* Ferol Egan, *Frémont: Explorer for a Restless Nation* (Garden City, New York, 1977); Andrew Rolle, *John Charles Frémont: Character as Destiny* (Norman, Oklahoma, 1991).

13. This would have achieved a major goal of the Smithsonian's meteorological project, namely, to create a system of observers that extended "as far as possible over the North American continent." Few meteorological data existed from the Far West, other than readings taken by surgeons at military outposts in Oregon and the Indian Territory. As Elias Loomis noted in his "Report on the Meteorology of the United States," such data were important for understanding how storms were modified as they passed over the Rocky Mountains. On August 10, 1848, Henry informed the executive committee of his intention to send sets of meteorological instruments to California. In November, the steamer *Panama* left New York, carrying six sets of instruments for California (and also for Oregon). It is not known whether these instruments reached their destination. However, it was not until 1854 that the Smithsonian began regularly receiving meteorological observations from California and Oregon. *Smithsonian Report for 1847*, pp. 190, 195, 204–207 (quotation on p. 190); *Smithsonian Report for 1848*, p. 15; Rhees, *Journals*, pp. 465, 466; Charles J. McIlvaine to Henry, November 20, 1848, Henry Papers, Smithsonian Archives; *National Intelligencer*, November 30, 1848; *Smithsonian Report for 1853*, p. 63.

14. Eager to redeem his name, Frémont was planning another trip west, to survey a route for a transcontinental railroad. Various proposals existed for a northern or southern route to the Pacific, but Frémont and his father-in-law, Missouri senator Thomas Hart Benton (1782–

1858, *DAB*), promoted a third, central route. It would run west from St. Louis along the thirty-eighth parallel to Colorado's San Luis Valley, where Frémont expected to find a pass over the Continental Divide. Privately funded by Benton and several St. Louis merchants, Frémont's party left Westport, Missouri, late in October, and soon met with disaster when it was stranded in the mountains during a blizzard. Many died, and it was later alleged that some of the survivors had engaged in cannibalism. Frémont himself survived and eventually reached California. Egan, pp. 464–477; Rolle, pp. 111–123; William Brandon, *The Men and the Mountain: Frémont's Fourth Expedition* (New York, 1955).

15. Jessie Benton Frémont (1824–1902) married John Frémont in 1841. She helped her husband write his reports, and became a noted author in her own right.

Her travel differed from what Henry stated. With her young daughter, Elizabeth, Benton left New York in March 1849, sailed to the east coast of Panama, crossed the isthmus, and then took a second steamer from Panama City to San Francisco. *DAB;* Pamela Herr, *Jessie Benton Frémont: A Biography* (1987; Norman, Oklahoma, 1988), especially pp. 179–197.

16. Not found.

17. Espy submitted his *Second Report on Meteorology to the Secretary of the Navy* on November 12, 1849; it was printed, with his *Third Report on Meteorology*, as U.S. Senate, 31st Congress, 1st Session, Senate Executive Documents, No. 39 (1851).

18. By "the old plan," Espy meant the procedure he adopted in the 1830s as chairman of the joint committee on meteorology of the American Philosophical Society and the Franklin Institute. The committee sent circulars to select individuals, asking them to keep journals of meteorological observations according to a format set forth in the circular; observers then furnished monthly reports to Philadelphia. James P. Espy, *The Philosophy of Storms* (Boston, 1841), pp. 77–81; *Smithsonian Report for 1848*, pp. 207–208; Fleming, *Meteorology*, pp. 56–58.

19. In a Mary Henry Copy dated July 29, 1848, Henry told Harriet about his dinner at Benton's, noting that the senator "was quite facetious and related several amusing anecdotes relative to the history of our country." Henry Papers, Smithsonian Archives.

20. The proprietor in question was Ceran de Hault de Lassus de St. Vrain (1802–1870, *DAB*), a Missouri fur trader who, in the mid–1820s, formed a partnership with two St. Louis trappers, Charles Bent (1799–1847, *DAB*) and his brother, William (1809–1869, *DAB*). In

1832, they opened "Bent's Fort," on the Arkansas River near present-day La Junta, Colorado; it became a prosperous trading post. After Charles Bent's death, his younger brother and St. Vrain ran the business.

On August 10, 1848, when Henry told the executive committee of his plans to send meteorological instruments to California, he also stated that he would provide sets for Bent's Fort and Santa Fe. The latter set was intended for one Hough N. Smith of Santa Fe, who met Henry in Washington during the summer of 1848 and "accepted [the] proposal for taking charge of some philosophical apparatus & making certain observations therewith." However, it was not ready when St. Vrain, who was to carry both sets with him, left for St. Louis; it is not known if the other set reached Bent's Fort. Lists of Smithsonian meteorological observers through 1872 show no observations from either location. Rhees, *Journals*, pp. 465, 466;

Smithsonian Report for 1848, p. 15; Lewis A. Edwards to Henry, March 29, 1849, Letters Received, Records of the Smithsonian Meteorological Project, Records of the Weather Bureau, RG 27, National Archives (quotation).

21. Dudley Sanford Gregory (1800–1874) served one term as a Whig representative from New Jersey. *BDAC*.

22. Frederick Augustus Tallmadge (1792–1869), a Whig representative from New York, also served a single term. *BDAC*.

23. William Orlando Butler (1791–1880), a hero of the War of 1812 and the Mexican War, and a former representative from Kentucky, ran with Lewis Cass on the Democratic ticket. *DAB*.

In his letter to Harriet of July 29, Henry described his meeting with Butler, terming him "a very unassuming man, with little of the appearance of the warrior about him."

199. TO ALEXANDER DALLAS BACHE

[July 31–August 1, 1848][A]

[...] thought of turning him over to the observatory—had not himself recommended the appropriation but merely transmitted to the committee some papers on the subject given him by Mr Brown of Penn[a] I was somewhat surprised at these remarks and set myself at work to disabuse the secretary as to the character of Mr Espy and the merits of his theory.[1] I had however but a short time with him but before I left he assured me that he would be happy to turn Mr Espy over to me and to render me any assistance in his power in carrying into operation the meteorological scheme. The appropriation ↑bill↓ has passed both Houses of congress and I have advised Mr. E. to see Mr Brown and get him to secure the meteorological appropriatio to the salary for which it was intended.[2]

Aug 1st 9 o'clock in the Evening

Your letter of the 30th was received[3] this Evening. Mc.Fuss did not go to the office[B] this morning, for which I gave him a repremand. I have visited the building this evening—find the roof of the 2nd connecting range[4] on and the foundation of the main building commenced. The architect[5] informes me that he wishes to push the work during the present good weather and that he certainly shall not spend more than 41 thousand dollars within the year— Should not I insist on an inspection of the accounts?— Does Col Totten know any thing about these finantial matters? These are points which give me uneasiness every time I think of them. The second wing I think will be very hadsome I do^C not like the first[6] neither interiorally or exteriorally. I think it would be an improvement when the large lecture room is finished and when the smaller one will be of little use to remove the present seats chemical rooms &– and throw the whole wing into one room with a Galery^D around it and a large table in the midle for the use of the savants which may be annually assembled for the discussion of scientific subjects. The wall to be occupied with cases for apparatus. The chemical rooms may be put below stairs where there is good room in abundance. This however is a scheme for the future. The alteration according to Renwick could be made for 600 dollars.[7]

I shall not fail to see Breese on the subject you mention and could I do it safely I would broach the subject to Fremont. I am to have several interviews with him relative to meteorology before he starts and he has expressed a desire to see your Physical atlas translated from the german & published in Edinburge.[8] I allude to the large one which was on your table on the Evening of your scientific gathering last winter. Can I get it from the coast survey? write to me relative to my course with Fremont. I will be more cautious with your affairs than with my own.

I did not attend the meeting of the Institute in full[9] but I did those of the committee. Our first meeting[10] or rather that of the subcommittee was held at the house of Col Abert besids myself Lieut Maurry was presant. Col. Abert presented the Report he had made recommending that Congress be petitioned to make a grant of land for the support of the Institution on the old plan.[11]

Draft, Henry Papers, Smithsonian Archives.
Missing first page and possibly others. This may be a continuation of the draft printed as Doc. 198, although the two are written on different paper. Together, the drafts would form a six-page letter, with one or more internal pages missing. In a letter to Harriet of August 3, 1848 (Family Correspondence, Henry Papers, Smithsonian Archives), Henry stated that he sent Bache a sixteen-page "bulletin" (including a note from Harriet to Bache's wife) on August 2. A Mary Henry Copy, dated July 29, 1848, which paraphrases or incorporates materials from both the present document and Doc. 198, or from another draft or Henry's outgoing letter, is in the Henry Papers, Smithsonian Archives.

1. Henry was referring to the involvement of Navy Secretary John Y. Mason and Representative Charles Brown in the effort to renew federal funding of James P. Espy's meteorological research.

2. Enacted on August 3, 1848, the 1849 appropriations bill provided $2,000 for "meteorological observations to be conducted under the Secretary of the Navy." Espy's appointment became effective on August 10. His salary was set at $125 per month. *U.S. Statutes at Large,* 9:266; Mason to Espy, October 25, 1848, General Letter Books, Volume 40, Miscellaneous Letters Sent, Office of the Secretary of the Navy, Naval Records Collection of the Office of Naval Records and Library, RG 45, National Archives (quotation).

3. Letter not found.

4. That is, the connecting range adjacent to the west wing of the building. Rhees, *Journals,* p. 695.

5. James Renwick, Jr.

6. The east wing of the building.

7. Many of these ideas were implemented in 1849.

8. Alexander Keith Johnston, *The Physical Atlas; A Series of Maps & Notes Illustrating the Geographical Distribution of Natural Phenomena* (Edinburgh, 1848). It was based on Heinrich Karl Wilhelm Berghaus's *Physikalischer Atlas* (Gotha, 1838–1848).

9. The National Institute held a special meeting on July 29, 1848, to consider the report of Abert's committee. After his report was read and discussed, members authorized the committee to petition Congress regarding modifications to Marsh's bill for rechartering the institute. They also directed the committee

to express the institute's support for Alexandre Vattemare's international exchange system.

Henry did attend the next meeting of the committee, on August 3.

Journal of Meetings, No. 2 (1842–1849), Box 11, Records of the National Institute, RU 7058, Smithsonian Archives; Henry to Harriet Henry, August 3, 1848, Family Correspondence, Henry Papers, Smithsonian Archives.

10. That is, the meeting on July 13, 1848.

11. The Mary Henry Copy has two final paragraphs. In the first, Henry said he was "overwhelmed" by the press of visitors who called on him. He also termed Washington "certainly a place of unrest," but added that he had not found it unpleasant. In the second, Henry closed with a poignant note: "Without wife and children, Mrs. Bache and yourself, I am in a lonely condition."

200. THOUGHTS REGARDING THE MALL

July, 1848

The idea has occurred to me that the Mall might be made one of the most deleghtful places in the United States by filling up the canal[1] planting the ground with clumps of native ornamental trees & making a broad gravel road entirily around the whole extending from the foot of Capitol Hill to the monument. This would be one of the finest "drives" in the World.[2]

Henry Pocket Notebook [13279], p. 57, Henry Papers, Smithsonian Archives.

1. Opened in 1815, the Washington Canal extended along the northern side of the Mall from the Potomac River on the city's western edge to the "Eastern Branch" (now known as the Anacostia River) near the Washington Navy Yard. By the 1840s, heavy silting had rendered it all but unusable. Constance McLaughlin Green, *Washington: A History of the Capital, 1800–1950,* 2 vols. in 1 (1962; Princeton, 1976), 1:3, 28–29, 193; Rhees, *Journals,* pp. 321, 343–344.

2. In the half-century since Pierre Charles L'Enfant prepared an urban design for Washington which would make the Mall into "the aesthetic focus of the city" (Schuyler, p. 68), many proposals had been offered for utilizing this space. They ranged from public prome-

nades, sculpture gardens, and conservatories, to a model farm, a church, an observatory, and the campus of a national university. Congress failed to appropriate money to implement any of these ideas, however, and by the 1840s, the Mall was little more than a barren, rubbish-littered common occupied by a few squatters. The decision to locate the Smithsonian Building in a nineteen-acre tract on the south half of the Mall gave fresh impetus to thinking about how this public space might be improved and beautified, as did the laying of the Washington Monument cornerstone in July 1848.

Inchoate here, Henry's ideas would be expanded upon by the noted landscape designer, Andrew Jackson Downing, in the comprehensive plan for the Mall which he developed in 1850–1852, as will be seen in the next volume of the *Henry Papers*.

David Schuyler, *The New Urban Landscape: The Redefinition of City Form in Nineteenth-Century America* (Baltimore and London, 1986), pp. 67–69; Pamela Scott, "'This Vast Empire': The Iconography of the Mall, 1791–1848," and Therese O'Malley, "'A Public Museum of Trees': Mid-Nineteenth Century Plans for the Mall," in *The Mall in Washington, 1791–1991*, ed. Richard Longstreth (Washington, 1991), pp. 37–58 and 61–76.

201. FROM ASA GRAY

Cambridge Aug 3[d] 1848.

My Dear Friend,

I was away for a fortnight when your letter of the 17[h] ult[1] arrived,— and must now reply briefly.

In a day or two Sprague & myself will sit down to shape the Tree Report. Remind me, before you need it for your Report and I will send you a sort of programme.— I have not time to bend my mind to it now, any farther than to secure drawings of fruits, flowers &c— ~~as they~~ of trees that fall within the limits ~~of the~~ which I have assigned for the first part.

I want to see you before autumn.— I will now merely say that Common Congressional printing will not do for wood cuts, if the illustrations are done on wood, which is most desirable.

In Respect to testimonials, I have at present only statements in private letters, mixed up with other things. I will send some if you wish. But I have yet to answer some of the letters. There is a notice in Hooker's London Journal of Botany for July.[2] If the Smithsonian were to subscribe for 100 copies, it would make the continuation of the work sure. In my opinion, it is deserving of that encouragement.

I think it would be well to employ Desor for a Nat. History Report. He is extremely Capable, and somewhat in want.

It happens that I do not know him at all intimately myself; But Agassiz has the highest opinion of his talent,[3] and I know would like he should have such an engagement with you. A. is now at Lake Superior.[4]

In haste
Yours faithfully
Asa Gray

Prof. Henry.

Archives of the Hunt Institute for Botanical Documentation, Carnegie Mellon University. Reply: October 5, 1848, Historic Letters, Archives, Gray Herbarium Library, Harvard University.

1. Doc. 197.

2. Favorably noticing the first volume, William J. Hooker's journal asserted that "if carried to completion," Gray's *Genera Illustrata* would "rank among the most valuable and useful works that have appeared in any country." "Notices of Books," *The London Journal of Botany*, 1848, 8:389–390 (quotation on p. 389).

3. As his remark suggested, Gray was unaware of the bitter dispute between Desor and Agassiz, which had led to a break in their relationship in the spring of 1848.

4. Agassiz spent the summer of 1848 exploring and collecting along Lake Superior's north shore. He published the results of the expedition in his *Lake Superior: Its Physical Character, Vegetation, and Animals, Compared with Those of Other and Similar Regions . . .* (Boston and London, 1850). Edward Lurie, *Louis Agassiz: A Life in Science* (1960; Chicago, 1966), pp. 148–150.

202. TO HARRIET HENRY

Washington Aug 5th 1848

Dearest

My last letter[1] I fear did not reach you quit as soon as I intended it should do. It was put into the Box at the Post office instead of the bag at one of the public Hotels— I was all day yesterday out of my office— In the morning at the capitol making an examination of the system of ventillation adopted by congress[2] and in the afternoon at the building directing the alteration of some cases or at least I went for that purpose. On my return I felt quite tired and though of sending a short note to you and immediately afterwards going to bed but just as I commenced the epistle F. Stansbury[3] came in who had been appointed with me to draw up some resolutions relative to the Washington Institute. We commenced operations and, at a little after eleven finished the business to our mutual satisfaction— I then went to bed slept soundly until near six o'clock when I was awakened by Mr Skerving the ventillator of the capitol[4] who in accordance with previous agreement came at that hour[A] to give me some farther information as to his plans— You see that I am kept pretty busy and indeed it is as well that I am so otherwise I should begin to immagine my self sick and to find the separation from you and my children insupportable. I feel to day unusually well— The day is quite warm I came from the capitol before 10 o'clock and therefore did not feel the heat much. I am to attend a meeting this evening at Mr Markoe's—to meet Mr Ingersoll[5] Mr Marsh[B] and others on business of science. I met Mrs Nesbit[6] this morning with Miss. Sarah Howard going (they were) to the capitol.[C] I promised Mrs N. to take tea with her some evening soon and I am to see her at church tomorrow. She thinks[D] herself delightfully situated. The present occupant of her house will not give her possession until the first of Sept.— Dr Page informed me last

371

night that the house next to the one he occupies will be for rent after
the adjournment of congress and that the price to one of the senators
was 600 a year or 50 a month with all the furnature. I think that this
can scarcsly be true though the Dr affirmed that he was not mistaken.
Also it is probable that the house occcuped by Senator Dix will be for
rent next winter though I do not know this certainly—

You do not know how[E] much I want to see you—it appears months
since I parted with you at Princeton. The time appears longer to me in
the retrospect than it does to you on account of the variety of objects
which now engage my mind.— I received a letter from Mr Hope evinc-
ing great anxiety and flusteration as to a draft on his Fatherinlaw.[7] My
answer I enclose to you[8] which after reading you will please to seal and
send him as soon as it arrives.

Lat night we had quit a large procission with a display of rockets[F]
from near the the Union office at the corner of $\overline{\text{E}}$ street and the avanew.
General Butler addressd the Democrats[G] of the city—I did not howeve
put out my head to see the display though the procession passed hard
by I was too tired after my day's labour—

I have just received a letter from Dr Gray[9]—who is about to undertake one of the reports. Love to the children & Grandmother and the
assurance to yourself that I remain as ever your own H.—

Write again to Mrs B. The book you sent her had been forwarded
before he came in I mean to say that she had a copy of it. I therefore
presented it to Mrs Page who was so kind as to invite me to dinner &
tea on Thursday last[10] but I regret to say that I neglected the engagemt
and was obliged to make an apology.

I saw Mr Burk yesterday who has got through with his trial and tri-
umphantly refuted the charges made against him.[11] He promised to
appoint Mr Peale to the vacant office— Poor man he has been to see
me every day for a week past. He called this morning when I was out
which I regret on account of wishing to give him the information of Mr
Burk's promise.

H–

Family Correspondence, Henry Papers, Smithsonian Archives.

1. August 3, 1848, in same location as this document.

2. Between 1842 and 1847, Congress appropriated $23,292 to improve the heating and
ventilation of the Capitol, as part of the construction of a new hall for the House of Representatives. Congress considered various
proposals before it adopted, subject to trial, the
plan of John Skirving (see note 4) to use furnaces, flues running from the basement to the
House and Senate chambers, and grates
around these rooms which would "draw off the
vitiated air from the ceiling and gallery, by
combustion and rarefaction" (Skirving, p. 8).
According to the New York *Saturday Evening
News* of December 4, 1847, Skirving's "arrange-

ment has worked well, and it is thought preferable to the plan which has been adopted for similar purposes in the new House of Parliament in London." (On the latter plan, see *Henry Papers,* 3:210.) After 1847, however, Congress made no further appropriations for Skirving's system.

Henry's interest in Skirving's system presumably arose because James Renwick had offered a similar plan for heating and ventilating the Smithsonian Institution Building. Installed in 1849, this plan proved unsatisfactory, due "to the difficulty in conveying the heated air horizontally" (Rhees, *Journals,* p. 701).

U.S. House, 28th Congress, 1st Session, *Hall of Representatives,* House Reports, No. 516 (1844), pp. 1–24, especially pp. 10–18; John Skirving, "Ventilation: A Great Preventive of Consumption and Cholera" (Washington, n.d. but ca. late 1848), pp. 1–15; Glenn Brown, *History of the United States Capitol,* 2 vols. in 1 (1900–1903; New York, 1970), 1:107, 108, 109, 339–340; Rhees, *Journals,* pp. 700–701.

3. Charles Frederick Stansbury (1821–1881), the son of Arthur J. and Susanna B. Stansbury, in 1840 graduated from Princeton, where he had served as Henry's student assistant. During the mid-1840s he taught natural philosophy and chemistry at a classical school in Burlington, New Jersey. After the deaths of his wife and infant child, he moved to Washington, where he became the National Institute's recording secretary. *Princeton Catalogue,* p. 159; E. C. Wines to Henry, September 9, 1847; C. F. Stansbury to Henry, May 30, 1848, both in Henry Papers, Smithsonian Archives; Frederick Howard Wines, comp., *The Descendants of John Stansbury of Leominster* (Springfield, Illinois, 1895), p. 21.

4. Skirving was identified as a bricklayer in Philadelphia city directories for 1840 and 1842, and in a Washington city directory for 1843; Washington directories for 1846 and 1850 listed him as an "architect." In a letter to the House Committee on Public Buildings of February 3, 1845, Bache described Skirving as "a most ingenious and trustworthy mechanic" who was "well acquainted with methods of ventilation in use both at home and abroad, in large buildings." He worked on numerous public and private building projects in England, France, and the United States. Skirving, pp. 12, 14–15 (quotation on p. 12).

5. Joseph R. Ingersoll.

6. Harriet Nesbit, the widow of John Nesbit of Athens, Georgia, lived in Georgetown. She had met the Henrys in Princeton in 1846. *Henry Papers,* 6:486, 530.

7. Matthew B. Hope had written Henry on August 2 about a balance of some £15 on a manikin which his father-in-law, Matthew L. Bevan, a Philadelphia merchant, had imported from Europe. It, and other apparatus made by the Paris instrument firm of Louis F. C. Breguet, were intended for use at Princeton. Hope to Henry, December 27, 1847; January 4, August 2, 1848, all in Henry Papers, Smithsonian Archives; Philadelphia City Directory, 1846.

8. Not found, but dated August 5, according to Hope's reply of August 8, 1848, Henry Papers, Smithsonian Archives.

9. Doc. 201.

10. Either July 27 or August 3.

11. Henry alluded to the allegations made by Thomas Clinton against Edmund Burke, for which see Doc. 193.

203. TO HARRIET HENRY

Sunday night 9 o'clock
Aug 6th[–7] 1848

Dearest

I have just come in and feel inclined to go to bed but before I retire I must devote a few minutes to my own dear little wife. When I returned from church this morning I found your very acceptable letter[1] on my table and though I was weary with the long hot walk through the sun it aroused my feelings of love and tenderness to such a degree that had it not been sunday I would have been tempted to leave Washington for a few days and have started with the next train for Princeton. I read it several times and found my heart going out to ↑meet↓ you and our dear children—you and they are by far the most precious objects to me in life and were I to loose you though I might live on and endeavour to discharge the duties relative to my fellow men which Providence has devolved on me yet on my own account life would be valueless. Ours are indeed precious children and they owe their moral developement to your affectionate and untiring attention to them. I know that I have frequently given you cause to think that I do not properly appreciate your labours in this respect but my Dearest I beg to assure you that I am fully sensible, when I reflect at all on the subject, of your merits as a mother as well as your estimable qualities as^A a wife. No other woman could have been the wife of my bosom nor ~~such a~~ ↑the↓ mother of^B my children. It is true you are not perfet and that your peculiarities are such as may be disearned^C and magnified by the eyes of a Mrs C. but bad as you are I would not give you for a wife compounded of the virtues of a thousand shuch as she. You have done well in your family and instilled into your children the precepts and practice of religion and virture which will I trust enable them to pass through this world without being tainted by its vices. You have taught them the way they should go and when they are old they will not depart from it but will bless your memory for having directed them in it. I have been so much immersed in other matters that I have left too much to you but I think all things are as well as if I had attempted to meddle more in matters which you^D have conducted as well as I could have hoped they might be.

Monday Evening^E— I have been as usual quite busily engaged all day—have been well though I did not sleep very soundly— I got your letter of Saturday[2] to day; am glad that Jane Riley is with you. She^F will serve to cheer you in my absence. She was once almost every thing to you but now She^F has very powerful rivals for your love in the persons of your Husband and children.*

On saturday night I went up to Markoe's spent the evening there until half past 11 o'clock^G found Mrs M.[3] very agreeable and on the whole was well pleased with my visit though I went on business.

I called yesterday at the door of Mr Schoolcraft as I was going to church saw the lady[4] and gentleman. She looked very poorly—quite

Give her my kind regards.

pale dressed in black lips almost blue complained of pain in her side. He appea[re]d better than when I last saw him. Old Mrs Howard[5] and the general[6] arrived on saturday night. Jhon[7] is in new york but is comming on to Washington. General Howard is going to some watering place to spend the summer. I found the walks to the church[8] from this place almost too much for me—the sun was very hot and the reflection from the pavement almost intollerable were it not that I do not like to be out of my pew I would have gone to the church hardby[9]—We had two rather eloquent sermons the one in the morning from Mr Elliot the former chaplan of the exploring expedition[10] under Capt Wilkes he was tried by the presbyterian church for slander—the other was from the Mr Wilson[11] who was repremanded before the last general assembly for habitual railing.

I shall attend to your remark about the account of clow[12]—I feel sorry for this man I think him a well meaning man but when we are embarrassed and oppressed with poverty we are sorely tried and without intending to do wrong[H] it is difficult to know precisely what is right.

Give Helen my love and thanks for nice little letter[13] I found no difficulty in reading it and received much pleasure in the act. This fact I am sure will induce her to favour me with another epistle at her earliest convenience. Tell Carry I am very glad she is so attentive to her book. She must persever and it is very difficult yet when she once gets agoing she will I am sure learn quite fast. She will I am sure take much pleasure in reading and we have as she knows a great many very fine[I] books. Mary and Will.[J] are above prase they are almost grown up to man and woman's estate. I hope they comport themselves in accordance with their stature.

I received to day an other present for the Smithson a bronze bust of Therwalsden the great Danish sculptor[14]—two volumes of illustrations of his work[15]—a copy of the Holy Bible printed upwards of two hundred years ago and some other books from Mr Irwin late minister to Denmark.[16]

I hope the letter I sent you on saturday[17] enclosing one to Mr Hope was received. I shall probably here from him tomorrow.

> I am now rather fatigued and
> shall retire to bed with the
> assurance to you that I
> remain as I ever shall
> in this world only your
> H

Family Correspondence, Henry Papers, Smithsonian Archives.

1. Not found.

2. Not found.

3. Mary Galloway Maxcy Markoe was the daughter of Virgil Maxcy (1785–1844, *DAB*), a diplomat and solicitor of the treasury. Information files, Catalog of American Portraits, National Portrait Gallery, Smithsonian Institution.

4. Mary E. Howard Schoolcraft.

5. Elizabeth Bowles Hogg-Howard, the wife of James Hogg, Jr. (who changed his surname to "Howard" about 1815), was the mother of Mary E. Howard Schoolcraft. Chase S. Osborn and Stellanova Osborn, *Schoolcraft-Longfellow-Hiawatha* (Lancaster, Pennsylvania, 1942), p. 623.

6. John H. Howard (born John H. Hogg), Mary E. Howard Schoolcraft's brother. Osborn and Osborn, pp. 542, 623.

7. John Johnston Schoolcraft (1829–1865), the second son of Henry Schoolcraft and his first wife, Jane Johnston. He attended a private school in Princeton during the late 1830s. Osborn and Osborn, pp. 524, 548, 568.

8. The Fourth Presbyterian Church, located on Ninth Street, NW, between G and H streets.

9. That is, the First Presbyterian Church, which was located on Four-and-a-half Street, NW, near C Street.

10. Jared Leigh Elliott (1807–1881), a graduate of Princeton (1831) and Princeton Theological Seminary (1834), was ordained in 1835. Three years later he became a navy chaplain, and, in that capacity, sailed with the United States Exploring Expedition. He was currently an army chaplain. Alfred Nevin, ed., *Encyclopaedia of the Presbyterian Church in the United States of America* (Philadelphia, 1884).

11. Perhaps David M. Wilson, who, in 1828, helped found, and was appointed ruling elder of, the Fourth Presbyterian Church. *Centennial and Dedication of New Edifice, the Fourth Presbyterian Church, Washington, D.C.* (Washington, 1928), pp. 1, 2.

12. Either Henry Clow, the steward of Nassau Hall from 1816 to 1845, or his son, William, steward of Nassau Hall from 1846 to 1848 and also steward of Princeton's new refectory until 1846. *Henry Papers*, 2:371n; 6:442n; *Princeton Catalogue*, p. 81.

13. Not found.

14. Bertel (or Albert) Thorvaldsen (or Thorwaldsen) (1768 or 1770–1844), a native of Copenhagen, was a sculptor who became "the most celebrated artist of his time." His works included numerous classical relief sculptures, monuments, and equestrian statues. *Encyclopedia of World Art* (1958; New York, 1967).

15. Just Mathias Thiele, *Thorvaldsen og hans vaerker. Texten forkortet efter Thiele, ved F. C. Hillerup,* 2 vols. (Copenhagen, 1842–1843).

16. William Wallace Irwin, a brother-in-law of Alexander Dallas Bache, was chargé d'affaires to Denmark from 1843 to 1847. *Henry Papers*, 5:450n–451n; *BDAC*.

17. Doc. 202.

204. ALBERT GALLATIN TO GEORGE PERKINS MARSH

New York August 7ᵗʰ 1848

My Dear Sir

Professor Henry is a first rate man in his line, but he has a defect, he is not at all a man of business. I had advanced 150 dollars for the engravings which were to accompany Mʳ Squier's work on the Western Tumuli."[1] Mʳ Henry undertook, on the part of the Smithsonian institute, to publish the whole work of Mʳ Squier's[A] at large, instead of the abridgement which he was preparing for the Ethnological Society,[2] which we agreed too, on condition that he would repay us the money advanced for the engravings, of which he had the benefit; and he was also to repay to 20 dollars advanced by Mr Barttlet for the same purpose. More than twelve months have elapsed since that time; and not withstanding our repeated applications, some of which passed through your hands,[3] we have not yet been paid. To these 170 dollars must be added 24 for maps of the same character[B] the account for which had not been presented till lately. The second volume of the transactions of our Society which is all printed, the publication of which is retarded only by the want of Fremont's Map,[4] and which will cost us at least 1000 dollars, is published at our sole risk and expense; and you will at once perceive that the immediate repayment of these 194 dollars is really important to us. I pray you to use your endeavours to obtain it.[5]

> I have the honour to be respectfully
> Dear Sir Your most obedt Servant
> Albert Gallatin

The hon^ble Mr Marsh
of Vermont
in Congress

Marsh Papers, Bailey/Howe Library, University of Vermont.
Draft: Gallatin Papers, New-York Historical Society. Reply: August 10, 1848, also in Gallatin Papers.

1. This was but one instance in which Gallatin (either himself or through the American Ethnological Society) acted as Squier's patron. Early in 1848, he loaned Squier $350 to help defray the cost of printing a private edition of *Ancient Monuments of the Mississippi Valley.* Thomas G. Tax, "E. George Squier and the Mounds, 1845–1850," in *Toward a Science of Man: Essays in the History of Anthropology,* ed. Timothy H. H. Thoresen (The Hague and Paris, 1975), pp. 104–105, 112, 116.

2. E. G. Squier, "Aboriginal Monuments of the Mississippi Valley," *Transactions of the American Ethnological Society,* 1848, 2:131–207.

3. None of these requests have been found.

4. This map presumably was intended to accompany John R. Bartlett's essay, "The Progress of Ethnology," which appeared as an appendix to the second volume of the American Ethnological Society's *Transactions.* On pages 20–21, Bartlett discussed Frémont's expedition of 1843–1844 to explore "the vast region lying between the Rocky Mountains and Upper California and Oregon" (p. 20). The essay contained no maps.

5. In his reply, Marsh promised to see Henry about the repayments, and stated that he had sent him a note (not found) about them. He later recalled that "immediately after [Gallatin] called my attention to it during the last session," he had discussed the matter with Henry, "who promised that he would immediately look into it & do what should seem to be right." But the repayments were not made, apparently due to some confusion over the amount owed. Later in 1848, after again urging Henry to reimburse the money, Marsh assumed he had done so. However, Marsh learned, on receiving a note from Bartlett on January 6, 1849, that neither he nor Gallatin had yet been repaid; the same day, he saw Henry "and begged him to delay it no longer." Once again, Henry assured Marsh he would see to the repayments.

Marsh to Gallatin, January 6, 1849, Gallatin Papers, New-York Historical Society (quotations); Desk Diary, January 6, 1849.

205. TO HARRIET HENRY

Washington Aug 8th[–9th] 1848
½ past 9 o'clock

Dearest

I have just returned from a vesit to Miss Dix.[1] She left a package or sent it to my office this morning requesting me to call upon he[r] relative to a message she had for me from Dr Hare.[2] I spent more than an hour with her and as usual found her very agreeable— She has lately returned from a visit to Dr Hare's farm where she went with Mrs Bell[3] who has taken her little girld to the country the child is[A] still feeble. Miss Dix sent her love to you and said she hoped to see you in the winter if not before since she will be obliged to return to Washington next session as her bill cannot be reached this term.[4] Mr Bell just came in as I was about to leave he had been in the senate chamber from 8 oclock AM until 9. P.M.

I received your kind letter of yesterday[5] this morning I am sorry to learn that Will. is so afflicted and hope he will not have a teadious time of it. He cannot afford to loose much of his vacation, but I trust the illness will be but temporary.— You are very good to write to me so often though the receipt of your letters gives me much pleasure yet I know that you have much to do and that it is not convenient in all cases to break off from an engagement and write even to an absent husband. I shall be content to receive a letter every other day though I shall not complain if I get one every day.

I spent this morning in my room[B] in the patent office arranging books and apparatus—the little den is well filled with[C] articles not quite in as good order as they might be. I received a letter from the printer[6] informing me that the last form of the memoir of Squire and Davies would be passed through the press this week and asking me to prepar the preface. I shall therefore be busily engaged on this work for several days to come—perhaps not so long. I have also to prepare an account of the Smithsonian for a review[D] but this will not occupy much time since it will be merely a notice.[7] I am living almost enterely on peaches we have abundan at the table and with milk they go very finely they are selling in market a shilling a peck or 50 cts the bushel. I hope you are feasting on the rich production of New Jersey of the same kind.— I feel now rather inclined to close my eyes in slumber and with the expression of the prayer that you and our dear children may be preserved from all harm and that we may be speedly restored to each other I bid you an affectionate

good night
Dearest—

Aug 9th

The servant came so late this morning that I could not[E] send this letter by the morning train. This is a very pleasant day as to termperature apparently inclined to rain. I slept well and feel quite bright. By the by[F] the cotton mattrass does very well and is much more plesant than the bed we use at Uncle's which sinks so much in the middle as to be uncomfortabl. Mrs Nesbit has manufactured a number of cotton mattresses[G] which cost her about 3½ dollars including making and all. She understands the process—the article requires a peculiar kind of cotton. It it will be well for you to take some lessons from her on this point.

The carriage has called to take me to the treasury department and therefore I must be off. I am now about organizing the Smithsonian establishment[H] Consisting of the Heads of the departments and the President and vice President of the United States. I am however obliged to act with much caution in this matter and to see well my ground.

Adieu dearest

Family Correspondence, Henry Papers, Smithsonian Archives.

1. Dorothea Lynde Dix (1802–1887), the noted educator, humanitarian, and social reformer, who worked tirelessly to alleviate the condition of the mentally ill. Although this is our first record of Henry's contact with Dix, his letter indicates that he likely had known her for some time, perhaps due to her interest in natural science and science education. The Henrys and Dix also had several mutual friends, including Senator John A. Dix of New York (no relation), and Robert and Harriet Clark Hare, with whom Dix frequently stayed when in Philadelphia.

Dix and Henry formed an intimate and lasting friendship. She fondly referred to him as one of only a few people (including Robert Hare) "whose virtues, truth, and abilities secure a respectful attachment which it is grateful to cherish."

DAB; Helen E. Marshall, *Dorothea Dix: Forgotten Samaritan* (New York, 1937), pp. 130, 131, 134–135, 261; Dix to Henry, April 10, 1849, Henry Papers, Smithsonian Archives (quotation).

2. Dix's note of August 8, accompanying the parcel from Hare, asked Henry to call on her that or the following evening to discuss the disposition of Hare's apparatus. Henry Papers, Smithsonian Archives.

3. Jane Erwin Bell. Dix came to know the Bells in 1847, when she resided in Nashville while successfully lobbying the Tennessee legislature for a bill to replace the existing state insane asylum with a new hospital and farm. John Bell, then a member of the legislature, became "one of her most loyal supporters." Their friendship continued after the Bells moved to Washington. Dorothy Clarke Wilson, *Stranger and Traveler: The Story of Dorothea Dix, American Reformer* (Boston, 1975), pp. 167–169 (quotation on p. 169).

4. On June 23, 1848, Dix memorialized Congress, asking for legislation to set aside five million acres of public land "for the relief and support of the indigent curable and incurable insane in the United States." Her proposal marked the first such appeal for federal aid for the insane. John A. Dix introduced her memorial on June 27 and sponsored a bill on her behalf; it was referred to a select committee,

which favorably reported on it on July 21. Dorothea Dix personally lobbied for the bill's passage, but Congress adjourned on August 14 without voting on it. She returned to Washington during the next session to renew her efforts. This time, however, the bill's sponsors, faced with growing sentiment against land bills, declined to bring it up for a vote. Dorothea L. Dix, *Memorial . . . , Praying a Grant of Land for the Relief and Support of the Indigent Curable and Incurable Insane in the United States,* U.S. Senate, 30th Congress, 1st Session, Senate Miscellaneous Documents, No. 150 (1848), pp. 1–32 (quotation on p. 1); Marshall, *Dorothea Dix,* pp. 129–139.

5. Not found.

6. Edward O. Jenkins, whose letter has not been found.

7. We have not identified any such notice.

206. FROM FREDERICK SIDNEY GIGER

Baltimore August 9ᵗʰ 48

My dear Sir.

The bearer of this Mr Montgilion of Elkridge Landing,[1] has contrived a Cow Catcher, which he concieves to be an invention. I happened to stop at the artist's who was drawing a sketch of it and promised to give Mʳ M a letter to you. He, with the exception of a few moments conversation is a stranger to me, but as the machine exhibited some considerable degree of ingenuity, and especially as I found that although a shoemaker, he had devoted his time and ingenuity, ~~upon~~ ↑to↓ a machine whose professed object is to save life I thought that you wld excuse me ~~from~~ for thus troubling you. Recollecting the remark which you made in yr lectures years ago upon the useless expense which these aspirants went to, as well as the pecuniary ruin they entailed upon themselves in imaginary discoveries, I felt a desire that, this man should clearly know wether his was an invention, wether it was adapted to the purpose proposed, & wethe[r] it was likely to be a profit or loss to him— I think such men ought to be in some way or other secured from unnecessary loss by the information of those who have mastered the laws, of physics—for I hold that as soon as a man leaves the dull routine of his mechanic employment & tries his own powers in an unbeaten track for the purpose of discovery he is entering the province of true Philosophy whose practical object & fruit is, to increase the well being and elevation of the human race[2]— I would be glad therefore if you wld examine Mr M's machine and give him all necessary advice & information about it—

My health since my return has been quite good the trip to Princeton did me a great deal of good although my professional labours have been quite severe and unremitting, yet the work has not made much impression upon me. The Smithsonian institute is becoming more and more the theme of conversation among all classes—there is such an increased interest felt on the subject of education throughout the country that an institution such as that excites ten times more extensive interest than it would have done even 5 years ago much is expected from it, and I feel proud that you are to direct and shape its destinies. I will endeavour to pay you a visit during the winter if my health should continue as good as it is now. My uncle and mother[3] desires to be remembered to you,—

Yrs truly
F. S. Giger.

Henry Papers, Smithsonian Archives.

1. Lewis Montgilion (b. 1820 or 1821) lived in a manufacturing village south of Baltimore. Seventh Census of the United States, 1850, Maryland (NARA microfilm M432, reel 278, frame [319]); J. Thomas and T. Baldwin, eds., *A Complete Pronouncing Gazetteer, or Geographical Dictionary, of the World*, 2 vols. (Philadelphia, 1858), s.v. "Elk Ridge Landing."

2. Not surprisingly, Giger's views paralleled those of his former instructor. For Henry's thinking on the role of the scientist in enlightening practical mechanics, see Arthur P. Molella and Nathan Reingold, "Theorists and Ingenious Mechanics: Joseph Henry Defines Science," *Science Studies*, 1973, *3*:323–351, and Molella, "At the Edge of Science: Joseph Henry, 'Visionary Theorizers,' and the Smithsonian Institution," *Annals of Science*, 1984, *41*:445–461.

3. George Washington Musgrave, pastor of the Third Presbyterian Church in Baltimore and a director of Princeton Theological Seminary, and his sister, Eliza Musgrave Giger. *Henry Papers*, *6*:441n; Donald Drew Egbert, *Princeton Portraits* (Princeton, 1947), p. 105.

207. TO CHARLES ELLET, JR.[1]

Washington
August 12th, 1848

My dear Sir

Accompanying this letter I send you a programme of organization of the Smithsonian Institution which I hope will meet your approbation. In accordance with it, the first Volume of a series of original memoirs under the name of Smithsonian Contributions to Knowledge, is just through the press. The second will be commenced in the course of the coming Autumn, and it has occurred to me that a descriptions with plans, elevations ↑&↓ perspective drawings of your Sublime work at Niagara would form an interesting Contribution to general Knowledge; and I would therefore suggest the preparation by[A] yourself of a paper on this subject.[2] The Article will be published in the best style of American typography and no cost will be spared in the preparation of the plates; As many copies as may be necessary for distribution among your freinds will be presented you and the free use of the plates for striking[B] off additional copies will also be granted you. The size of the plate adopted for our publications is given by the black line on the opposite page. A long folded perspective drawing of the bridge might be admitted. In that case it should be of the same width as the length of the usual plate.

I remain with much
respect your friend
and Servant
Joseph Henry

Charles Ellet Jr

Ellet Papers, Department of Rare Books and Special Collections, University Library, University of Michigan.
In Charles P. Russell's hand, with Henry's signature. Third page blank except for an ink rectangle approximately 18 centimeters by 24.5 centimeters.

1. One of the leading civil engineers of the United States. *Henry Papers, 6:*272n.

2. In November 1847, Ellet was awarded the prestigious contract to erect a railroad suspension bridge across the Niagara River below the falls. Throughout 1848, his reputation grew with the project, yet at the same time his relations with the Canadian and New York companies that were financing the bridge deteriorated. Ellet was dismissed as engineer in mid-August 1848; his rival, John Roebling, completed the work in 1855.

Henry reiterated his request on October 21; sometime between then and the following March, Ellet agreed to write the memoir. But it is not surprising that, given his disagreeable departure from the Niagara project, the proposed article never appeared.

Gene D. Lewis, *Charles Ellet, Jr.: The Engineer as Individualist, 1810–1862* (Urbana, 1968), pp. 107–117; *Spanning Niagara: The International Bridge, 1848–1962* (Seattle, 1984); Henry to Ellet, October 21, 1848, and March 9, 1849, in same location as this letter.

208. FROM EBEN N. HORSFORD

Cambridge, Aug. 15, 1848.

Dear Sir,

Your letter of the 26th ult. in relation to the appropriation of $80.000 to found an Institution for popular instruction has occupied much of my thought since its receipt.[1]

The Lowell Institute has a foundation of about half a million. Among its distinguishing features the following may be mentioned.

It can never own, but must always rent apartments, as well for its collections as for its lecture hall.

The money—the income—must be expended in supporting lecturers by furnishing them with needed apparatus, hall and direct salary.

Its sole Trustee is Mr. John A. Lowell,[2] a^A relative of the founder, responsible to himself alone.

It occurs to me after reviewing the various plans that have presented themselves, that if the right man could be found an Institution like that of Fellenberg in Switzerland,[3] with this foundation would be more useful than any other that could be selected.

Next to that I am disposed to think that something like our scientific school[4] would be best.

I trust it will be in my power to submit to your consideration a memoir for the Smithsonian Contributions to Knowledge.

It will gratify you, I know, to learn that my new laboratory is nearly ready for receiving students. It will be opened on the 1st of September and already there are sixteen applicants for places.

A recent letter from Prof Liebig,[5] speaks of you in reply to an account of the S. Institute I had furnished him. He (Prof L.) will be among us in the course of two or three years at the farthest.[6]

Please remember me kindly to Mrs. Henry, and believe

> me respectfully
> and truly yours,
> Eben N. Horsford

Prof Henry.

Henry Papers, Smithsonian Archives.

1. Henry's letter (Horsford Papers, Rensselaer Polytechnic Institute Archives) adds to this only that the institution would be founded through the proposed bequest of a "Gentleman in the South," and that Henry had been asked to inquire specifically about the Lowell Institute. On the same date, Henry sent a similar letter to George Roberts Perkins of the New York State Normal School in Albany, for which see Doc. 195, note 4.

Henry enclosed a copy of his "Programme of Organization" and solicited Horsford, in a general way, for a paper for the SI Contributions.

2. John Amory Lowell (1798–1881), a wealthy Boston merchant and philanthropist, and a member of the Linnaean Society of London and the American Academy of Arts and Sciences. Harriette Knight Smith, *The History of the Lowell Institute* (Boston, New York, and London, 1898), pp. 14–17; Delmar R. Lowell, comp. and ed., *The Historic Genealogy of the Lowells of America from 1639 to 1899* (Rutland, Vermont, 1899), pp. 116–117.

3. The innovative school system founded by Philippe-Emanuel von Fellenberg (1771–1844) at Hofwyl, outside Bern, in 1799. Influenced by the educational doctrines of Rousseau and Pestalozzi, Fellenberg structured his educational system around practical knowledge and moral development, and included some manual labor. His work was strongly democratic, in that he believed in the education of both rich and poor, who followed similar courses, though not in the same school. Fellenberg founded schools for female education, for young children, and for teacher training. By the 1830s he had strongly influenced Swiss education, both in and around Bern and nationally. His schools attracted great attention in Britain.

In the fall of 1845, Horsford visited Fellenberg's complex, including the separate agricultural school at Kutti, near Hofwyl. He described the school and its course of instruction in great detail in his letter printed in the *Cultivator*, 1846, n.s. 3:73–78. At this time, the school was being run by Fellenberg's son, Wilhelm.

Dictionnaire historique & biographique de la Suisse, s.v. "Fellenberg"; Richard William Leopold, *Robert Dale Owen: A Biography* (1940; New

York, 1969), pp. 10–13; Samuel Rezneck, "The
European Education of an American Chemist
and Its Influence in 19th-Century America:
Eben Norton Horsford," *Technology and Culture,*
1970, *11*:373.
4. That is, the Lawrence Scientific School at
Harvard.

5. The eminent German chemist Justus von
Liebig, whom Henry had met in Europe in
1837, and under whom Horsford had studied.
Henry Papers, 3:507n.
6. Liebig never visited America.

209. TO FRANCIS MARKOE, JR.

Washington
August, 16th 1848

Dear Sir

I am informed by Mr Stansbury[1] that it is proposed to publish in detail the proceedings of the meetings for ↑"↓ameliorating the condition of the National Institute↑"↓, and with these the report of the subcommittee of which Colo. Abert Lieut Maury myself and others were members.[2] I hope this proposition will not be carried into effect. There is, at present, a diversity of opinion as to the best plan of reviving the operations of the Institute and I should think the publication of the report at this time rather premature. I cannot myself subscribe to all parts of it. The present organization is calculated to answer a good purpose in the way of making extensive collections, but I do not consider it so well adapted to promote original research. In order to do this effectually it will be necessary to call into our aid all the working men of the country in the way of science, not as mere honorary members,[A] but as co-operators in conducting the business of the Classes. If the Institute is designed to stand before the world as the exponent of American Science, the active contributors on whom the reputation of the reputation[B] of the country really depends should be consulted and their names appended to the memorial presented to Congress.[3] If, hower, the Institute, in accordance with the views of Colo Abert, is to be considered merely a local Association for the promotion of Knowledge in the District, the report may be sufficient. I think however that a majority of the members of the Institute consider it as intended for something more.[4]

I remain very respectfully
and sincerely yours &—
Joseph Henry

Francis Markoe Esq

Retained Copy, Henry Papers, Smithsonian Archives.
In Charles P. Russell's hand, with Henry's signature. Draft (in Russell's hand, with Henry's correc-

tions, closing sentiments, and signature) in same location. Copy, with copies of Markoe's reply of September 5 and of John J. Abert to Markoe, September 2, 1848 (all three in Caspar W. Hodge's hand), in same location. Replies: Markoe to Henry, August 19 and September 5, 1848, in same location.

1. Charles Frederick Stansbury.

2. At the July 29 general meeting of the National Institute, Markoe had proposed that Stansbury draw up a report of the committee's proceedings for publication, "that the friends of the Institute may be made aware of the present proceedings in its favor." This proposal was adopted. Journal of Meetings, No. 2 (1842–1849), Box 11, Records of the National Institute, RU 7058, Smithsonian Archives.

3. At an August 3 meeting of the committee, Henry was appointed a member of a new subcommittee to draw up this memorial to Congress, based on the report. Other members included J. M. Gilliss, Charles Wilkes, and Stansbury. Henry and Stansbury had already drafted a memorial when the subcommittee decided to delay matters until the new session of Congress. "Committee Appointed at the Meeting of May 27, 1848 . . . ," Box 13, Records of the National Institute, RU 7058, Smithsonian Archives.

4. Markoe's reply of August 19 stated that only a précis of the report would appear in the proceedings, and that, as Henry wished, the memorial, rather than the report, would carry the brunt of the argument for revitalizing the institute. On September 2, however, he showed Henry's letter to Abert, a strong force behind the revitalization of the National Institute.

Abert reacted angrily, especially to Henry's proposal to include names of eminent scientists on the memorial. His letter to Markoe of September 2 said:

This application does not want the names of other persons—they would be out of place. It is an application to Congress by the Institute, & in the name of the Institute, & by direction of the Institute, & need only have signed to it the name of the presiding officer at the meeting.

The sole duty of the committee is to draw up a petition, or application, to Congress, in accordance with the directions of the Institute, & then, at a meeting of the Institute, to submit the petition for its final adoption. On this occasion Mr. Henry can, in form of motions to amend, bring forward any of his peculiar notions. . . .

What is the use of having meetings of the Institute, & of invoking its formal action, if the opinion of any member is afterwards allowed to have a control over such action?

Abert insisted that his reply be shown to Henry. In the event, the report was not placed in the minutes, no proceedings were published from 1846 to 1855, and the memorial only bore the names of local—though prominent—scientists.

210. TO EPHRAIM GEORGE SQUIER

Princeton Aug 18th, 48

My dear Sir

I arrived here last night and intend to be in New York on Monday[1]— Owing to a new arrangement of the mails I have been prevented from sending on your proof until this evening—it goes with this letter. I am on the whole well pleased with your preface though I think it requires some alterations— The parts relating to the press should be given in the Smithsonian advertisement which precedes your preface. You have forgotten that the preface is that of a memoir presented to the Smithsonian Institution for publication and not that[A] of a work published by its author and that therefore every thing relative to the press must come from the Institution.[2] I also think it would be well for you to allude, at the close of the article to the fact of the memoir being presented to the Institution for publication and it might be well to give the reasons for the presentation namely the cost of the illustrations would be too great for your means and could not be paid from the sale of the work and that the memoir might be examined by a commission of competent judges— It might perhaps be well for you to express the hope should the memoir be accepted[B] and the subject found interesting that an appropriation would be made from the income of the Smithsonian bequest to carry on farther researches— Such an appropriation being in strict accordance with the intention of the donor of increasing knowledge among men.[3]

I would also suggest the propriety of dating your preface to correspond with the date of your letter to me.[4] I have said that I am on the whole well pleased with the preface though I think it would be improved by a littl less (excuse the expression) of what appears like pretension. Your work is one of great merit and the world will find this out—do not however proclaim it even by implication yourself— For this reason I would soften the expressions relative to Dr Davis and yourself[5]— I may be too sensitive on such points but you will find it best to err on the safe side.

Mr^C Marsh has gone on to New York.[6] I left him in Phil^d he probably went on to day— I received your communication relative to the western exploration and read it with much interest. I will confer with you relative to the subject when we meet.[7]

I fear you will find some difficuty in[D] deciphering[E] this scrall—pen ink & paper are execrable as well as my chirography[F] at the best.

I remain truly yours &c
Joseph Henry

E G Squier

Squier Papers, Library of Congress.

1. August 21.

2. The front matter of Squier and Davis's publication consisted of a Smithsonian "Advertisement," giving a brief description of the history and organization of the Smithsonian and detailing the procedure that led to the memoir's acceptance for publication; lists of officers, regents, and members of the institution; title page; table of contents, lists of engravings and woodcuts; and the authors' "Preface." We have not found Squier's original manuscript, but the published version placed information about printing, press supervision, proofing, and preparation of illustrations within the "Advertisement." *Squier and Davis*, p. x.

3. No such language appeared in the "Preface."

4. The "Preface" appeared over the dateline of "Chillicothe, Ohio, June 1847." However, the constructed letter of submission of the manuscript bore a date of May 15, 1847, as it appeared in the "Advertisement." *Squier and Davis*, pp. viii, xxxix; Doc. 67, note 3.

5. Not having access to Squier's original

draft makes it difficult to determine Henry's reference. Even the published version, however, was not shy in pointing out the superiority of the work over previous efforts:

> [Earlier] compilations, however, have proved eminently unsatisfactory .... It was under an impression of existing deficiencies in these respects,—the paucity of facts and the loose manner in which most of them had been presented,—that the investigations recorded in this memoir were commenced and prosecuted. At the outset, as indispensable to independent judgment, all preconceived notions were abandoned, and the work of research commenced *de novo*, as if nothing had been known or said concerning the remains to which attention was directed. [*Squier and Davis*, p. xxxiii.]

Thus while the preface was generous in naming those who had labored before and those who had assisted, their contributions were decidedly subsidiary to this great work of erudition.

6. That is, upon the adjournment of the first session of the Thirtieth Congress on August 14.

7. The communication has not been found, but it clearly related to Squier's proposal to survey the mounds of western New York State. As early as late 1847, Squier had become concerned with getting his next project underway. He had initially considered the Smithsonian as a possible source of funding, but was advised by George Perkins Marsh that "this will depend in some measure on the manner in which the first memoir shall be received by the public." Squier declined to approach the institution, and thought of going to Congress for funding. Instead, around the end of June 1848 he directed his efforts to the American Antiquarian Society. In a letter from Samuel F. Haven, July 18, 1848, he learned that that society would not sponsor his work, and he likely contacted the Smithsonian shortly afterwards. Henry's response to Squier's proposal is Doc. 223.

Marsh to Squier, January 7, 1848; Haven to Squier, July 18, 1848, both in Squier Papers, Library of Congress; Thomas G. Tax, "E. George Squier and the Mounds, 1845–1850," in *Toward a Science of Man: Essays in the History of Anthropology*, ed. Timothy H. H. Thoresen (The Hague, 1975), pp. 116–117.

211. FROM WILLIAM BARTON ROGERS

Boston August 24.. 1848.

My Dear friend.

At Prof^r Peirces request I forward to you a bundle of circulars[1] asking that you would aid the Committee by distributing them to the Scientific gentlemen in Ohio, & the other North-western states, as well as to those in the District of Columbia. We have thought that from your central position you might more readily learn the names of the cultivators of science in that region, than it would be in our power to do, & that Prof^r Johnson[2] would be able to afford you assistance in the matter.[3]

I hope you will not fail to aid the new organisation by your presence & counsels, & I will strive although at much sacrifice to meet you there.

With kindest wishes—I remain very truly—

Your friend
W^m B
Rogers.

The bundle is sent by
Harnden's Express—

Henry Papers, Smithsonian Archives.

1. The undated, printed four-page "Circular" contained two pages of "Objects and Rules of the Association," followed by an explanatory essay. At the last meeting of the Association of American Geologists and Naturalists in September 1847, Henry D. Rogers, Louis Agassiz, and Benjamin Peirce were appointed a committee for revising the constitution as the organization converted itself into the American Association for the Advancement of Science. For a discussion of this new constitution, the authorship of which she refers predominantly to Rogers, see Kohlstedt, *AAAS,* pp. 80–87.

2. Walter Rogers Johnson was formerly professor of mechanics and natural philosophy at the Franklin Institute and professor of chemistry and natural philosophy at the Pennsylvania Medical College. At this time, he was based in Washington, working as a technical consultant on coal and soil analysis and editing technical publications. He was the secretary of the American Association for the Advancement of Science. *Henry Papers,* 2:188n–189n; George E. Pettengill, "Walter Rogers Johnson," *Journal of the Franklin Institute,* 1950, 250:93–113, especially pp. 101, 111–113.

3. Henry passed on the task of assembling names to Charles G. Page, and promised him the assistance of Charles Russell of his own staff. But the mass distribution that Rogers wanted was stymied by Johnson's insistence that only those with an expressed interest in science could be members of the new association. Henry to Page, September 11, 1848, and Page to Henry, September 14, 1848, both in the Henry Papers, Smithsonian Archives; Kohlstedt, *AAAS,* p. 87.

212. TO MARGARET POLLARD ESPY

Princeton Aug 24th 48

Mrs Prof. Espy
My dear Madam

On my return from New York I find your letter of the 21st on my table[1] and I hasten to assure you that I think the Professor's Commission will be received by him in due time. Congress remained in session so long that all the Officers of government were weried out and all who could get away from the city left immedeatily after the adjournment & I presume the commission has been delayed on this account. I saw the Secretary of the Navy[2] the evening before the adjournment of congress and he informed me that Mr Espy would be directed to connect his Meteorological investigations with those of the Smithsonian Institution on the same subject.

My advise to the Professor was that he should go to Harrisburgh and recruit himself until about the beginning of Nov. then return to Washington and commense operations with renewed vigour.

He has at present sufficient matter to make a very important report and before the next meeting of[A] Congress in 1849 he will be ready for another Communication.

I have left Washington for a few weeks with the hope of enjoying a little rest from the perplexities and labours of the Smithsonian Secretaryship but I am obliged to bring my work with me at least in part.

I regret to learn that you are so unwell as to despair of recovery. Recollect that while there is life there should be hope—that the mind and body ~~have a~~ reciprocally[B] action on each other to such an extent that ~~an unhealthy~~ state of the one frequently produces a corresponding condition of the other and that therefore we should cherish a lively hope of recovery in all cases in which hope is possible.

We shall hope to see you in better health and sperets next winter in Washington. I say we for Mrs H. who is on the opposite side of the table while I am writing this joins me in kind regards to Professor E. and yourself.

> I remain as ever
> with much respect
> truly yours &—
> Joseph Henry

General Manuscripts Collection, Department of Special Collections, University of Pennsylvania Libraries.
Retained copy: Henry Papers, Smithsonian Archives.

1. The letter (Henry Papers, Smithsonian Archives), written without the knowledge of her husband, James, asked about his commission as meteorologist working in the Department of the Navy. Because of Margaret Espy's condition—she suffered from uterine cancer, with frequent and severe hemorrhages—he had to remain with her in Harrisburg, Pennsylvania, and could not travel to Washington to inquire for himself. See also Doc. 300.

2. John Y. Mason.

213. FROM ALEXANDER DALLAS BACHE

> near Manchester N.H.
> Sept 1, 1848.

My dear friend.

The Smithsonian Contrib[s] has just reached me[1] & I give you my ideas as they come, premising that you could not have a much worse authority in matters of etiquette than your friend on Unkonoonuc.[2] I should submit the case to Hon J. R. Ingersoll.

1. Is it James K. Polk who is ex-officio President? Or is it The President of the United States.[3]
2. Ditto for the Vice President.

3. George M. Dallas, ex nomine was elected Chancellor by the Board of Regents. I incline to the following.
    1. The President of the United States
    Ex officio Presiding Officer of the Institution, if that is the title in the Act of Congress.
    2. The Vice President of the United States
    Ex officio, Second Presiding &ᶜ. if that is the title &c.
    3. ~~Hon~~. George M. Dallas
    Chancellor of the Institution
    4. Joseph Henry
    Secretary of the Institution.
    5. Charles C. Jewett.
As to prefixes of titles or suffixes of ditto I doubt, inclining to the literary titles as Joseph Henry LLD & Charles C. Jewett A.M. if he is so, and yet considering that if these are used the political titles must also be used Hon George M. Dallas.[4]
    6. Is the executive Com. of the Regents also Exec. Com. of the Institution.
    Hon. W. W. Seaton
    Alex. D. Bache LL.D.   } Executive Com. would look better
    Hon. James A. Pearce } to my eye than the plain names.

Page 2.

    7. No titles on page 1 & all titles on page 2 I suppose to be experimental.
    8. Once an Hon. always an Hon. So Rufus Choate is still an Hon. & so is Wᵐ C. Preston & if not so then is Richard Rush not an Hon.
    Alex. D. Bache is an LL.D. if the other gents. are Honˢ & J G Totten a Col.
    The names of A.D.B & J G T come in last, & they are not citizens of the U.S. but (!!) Members of the National Institution or National Institute (which?)[5] of Washington. So says the law unless I mistake. Pity 'tis 'tis true!

page 3.

    The attorney gen. is no longer Nathan Clifford.[6]
    "An election" for "the election"
    of the Institution for "of the Officers of the Institution." or of the members of the Institution.[7]

Advertisement. I suggest a few changes on the proof.
    Six citizens are not appointed at large if I remember aright, since two must be members of the Nat. Inst.

The directions of Smithson embraced two objects,—one, the increase of knowledge &ᶜ. or The plan of organization ↑(of the institution)↓ embraces two objects.

I do not understand "leaving to the Regents &ᶜ." & suppose the printer has made some mistake.

page IX.   collection & publication of articles of science, &ᶜ.
There is some looseness in the phrase.

page X   "The treatises should, in all cases",
The treatises to be submitted &ᶜ.

page XI.   ↑"besides the Secretary,↓ "no permanent assistant will be required &ᶜ"
only one permanent to the Secretary will be required, who will act as librarian.

page XII.   Has Mʳ Gallatin two lls in his name? I think so on
& XIII   writing it but it is best to be sure.

Contents.
I do not see what origination of Smithsonian Institute has to do with this memoir of which the Contents and not those of the Vol. are enumerated.[8]

List of Plates   Is it Cuyohoga County.
" Lorain   "
" Pickaway   "

List of Wood Engravings
Is not Plain put for Plan.
18. Is it Parkerburgh or Parkers
58. Is this Oergon?
195. Brown of same. What is this?

page XXXIII   It seemed line 17
seemed   " 19
XXXV   9 lines from bottom Topographical
XXXVII.   Charles Sulivan?
line 17 from bottom uninterested? is that the same as disinterested. I have always supposed one to mean notᴬ caring, and the other expecting no reward.

Finis

When in Cambridge Prof. Peirce showed me the memoranda for a catalogue raisonnée of all memoirs on analytical mechanics the beginning of such a catalogue I mean. He intends to take up theᴮ subject in parts & to present successive memoirs to the Amer. Acad. He would like the Smithsonian to print them in volumes, he to receive from them 150 copies for his labour & to waive the Acad. copies so that the Smithsonian might arrange for the printing with the Academy. I told him that I would communicate with you.[9]

I rather urged him to the application of his recently developed formulae of Uranus & told him that you had funds to provide mechanical computers[10] if he would superintend the work. He spoke of seeing you soon in Cambridge. Is this likely?

I had a conversation with him about Davis. He says that it must be Davis' Navy friends who present such views, for his Cam. friends entertain the opposite.[11] More of this anon, for I had a full talk on the modus operandi &c.

Mrs. B. unites with me in regards to you & yours.

A.D.B.

Henry Papers, Smithsonian Archives.
Reply: Doc. 214.

1. Proof sheets of the front matter to Squier and Davis's *Ancient Monuments*.

2. From August 28 to October 7, Bache worked at the Coast Survey station on this mountain in southern New Hampshire. *Coast Survey Report for 1848,* p. 17.

3. Henry had composed a list of "officers" of the institution, comprising the president and vice-president of the United States, who according to section 8 of the Smithsonian act served as the presiding officers of the Establishment; the chancellor of the institution; the secretary and the assistant secretary, the working officers; and the three-man executive committee of the regents. He had apparently identified all these positions by their current incumbents. But as the presiding officers held their positions by statute, while all others were elected or appointed to their posts by the regents, Bache proposed that titles be used for the former, and proper names for the rest. One result of this suggestion was that George M. Dallas's name would appear once, not twice, for he was vice-president of the United States as well as chancellor of the Board of Regents. *Squier and Davis,* p. xi.

4. No prefixes or suffixes appeared on any of the lists of officers, regents, or members. *Squier and Davis,* pp. xi–xiii.

5. When it was founded in May 1840, the organization bore the name "The National Institution for the Promotion of Science," but when it received its congressional charter in 1842, "Institution" had become "Institute." Sally Kohlstedt, "A Step toward Scientific Self-Identity in the United States: The Failure of the National Institute, 1844," *Isis,* 1971, 62:341, 345.

6. Clifford resigned March 18; his successor, Isaac Toucey, took office June 29. *BDAC.* Bache was reviewing information relating to the members of the Establishment.

7. These lines most probably refer to the election of honorary members of the institution.

8. The table of contents was part of Squier and Davis's memoir, hence it would not include Henry's "Advertisement," which preceded the SI Contributions volume as a whole. It was only happenstance that this volume contained only one memoir.

9. Nothing came of this project.

10. That is, to aid in the calculations for Peirce's paper on the mutual effects of Neptune and Uranus, proposed for the SI Contributions. *Smithsonian Report for 1849,* pp. 9–10.

11. Charles Henry Davis, Peirce's brother-in-law. Perhaps Bache's reference is to preliminary plans for the *American Ephemeris and Nautical Almanac,* begun in 1849 and edited by naval officer Davis from Cambridge, Massachusetts. *Henry Papers,* 6:263n.

214. TO ALEXANDER DALLAS BACHE

Princeton Sept 9th 1848

My dear Bache

I send you with this a communication from Professor Jewett[1] which he requests me in an accompanying note[2] to forward to you after I have read it. Iinformed him in answer[3] that I concurred in the opinion of the importance of taking advantage of the present condition of things in Europe in the way of purchasing books and that had we the funds I would be in favour of immediate action but that I did not see how any thing[A] could be done before the meeting of the Board.

I also wrote to him about 10 days ago,[4] asking him to meet me in new york that we might confer about future operations and that I might have his advice and assistance in bringing out and distributing the first vol. of the contributions my letter however could not have reached him since he makes no mention of it in his last communication to me.

I have been constantly oscillating between New York and Phil[d] since I came north and as yet have found no rest for the sole of my foot or that of my body. Your critical letter[5] was forwarded to me in New York and arrived just in time. The alterations in the advertisement you suggested I had made— The proposition of substituting the President of the U.S. for J K Poke &c was immediately adopted— The word, "at large" was stricken out of the text in the expression "citizens at large" and Mem. Nat. Washington put after your name & Gen. Totten's—an exertion of will was ↑however↓ required to over come the disinclination. _____ As to retaining the titles I am still at a loss. Had I not presented the case to the chancellor[6] and had he not decided[B] against all titles even that of esq to the name of Smithson I would immediately have adopted the side to which you incline. The esthetical effect is better with the addition of LL.D &c. Some gentlemen in N.Y. to whom I spoke on the subject advise the omission of titles and refered to the course of Silliman on the title page of his journal. Dr Torrey is in favour of the titles. The book is for the world and we have no right to change the usages which pertain[C] in other countries. Ther is this consideration which impresses me; have we a right to take the liberty of striking off a suffix to which the individual to whom it may belong attaches great value? I shall write to Mr Ingersoll on the subject. Marsh is opposed to titlees and as the question now stands sienc is rather in favour Politics against—perhaps the[D] ↑latter↓ fear the suffixes will be considered of more value[E] than the prefixes.

I found the chancellor in a very pleasant state of mind— As usual he received me very kindly—fully approved of the exposition I had given in the advertisement and of the plan of calling a meeting of the Establishment. He suggested that besides the names I mentioned those of Faraday & Arago should be added.

He will I think consent to give the first lecture at the opening of the new House. I proposed this to him and he did not decline.[7]

I have received a letter from Downs[8] ↑stating↓ that the computations for the occultations of next year ↑are↓ completed they embrace all the stars which will be used in our Mexican boundary surveys[9] and should on this account be paid for in part out of the appropriation of the government for this purpose.[10]

Dr Hare's apparatus is all packed and ready to be shipped as soon as I can hear that the rooms are ready in Washington to receive them.

I received to day a memoir from Miss Mitchell relative to the discovery of her comet also the transfer of a paper from the Amer Acad$^{\underline{my}}$ by Dr Torrey to the Smithsonian. The transfer is by the consent of the Ac$^{\underline{d}}$. Dr T. did not find himself able to pay the expense of the engravings— When the paper was presented to the acad$^{\underline{my}}$ it was supposed that the plates would be paid for by Fremont but the failure of his bill has prevented this.[11]

I do not fully understand your account of the proposition of Prof Pierce. Does he intend to prepare a catalogue like that in the 2nd vol of Dr Young's book[12] or an abstract of all important papers on analytic mechanics?

Travelling in the hot weather has not agreed with me. I spent four days ↑of↓ this week in New York and was too unwell to go out. I transacted my business principally in my room. I am now hower thanks to the recuperative influence of Mrs H in a state of convalesence— She has a life interest in me and will do all she can to keep me a live. I hope Mrs B and yourself are taking good care of each-other. We^F have an interest in you and could better offord to loose many who esteem themselves better than they esteem you.

I remain as ever truly
Yours
H.^{G}

P.S. I have added to my letter to Prof Jewett that the extra meeting of the board would^H cost nearly a 1000 dollars and that it could not be effected in less than six weeks from this time. The regular meeting takes place in less than double that time.[13]

Bache Papers, Smithsonian Archives.
Draft in same location.

1. Jewett to Henry and the Library Committee (Bache, Choate, and Marsh), August 12, 1848, Henry Papers, Smithsonian Archives.

Jewett called attention to the distressed conditions in Europe on account of the revolutions. He thought that this provided an excellent opportunity for book-buying, and he reminded Henry that the board had authorized $20,000 for the library at one of its earliest meetings and had still not spent this money. He pointed out that the current budget (which only allowed $1,000 for book purchases) had been set without knowing that this opportunity—"the very moment of centuries"—would arise and called for a special meeting of the board, if necessary, to make that $20,000 appropriation.

2. Not found.

3. Not found.

4. Not found.

5. Doc. 213.

6. George M. Dallas.

7. Dallas did not inaugurate the Smithsonian lecture series.

8. The letter from John Downes is not found.

9. Article 5 of the Treaty of Guadalupe Hidalgo, ratified in May 1848, provided for a joint commission to survey and mark the boundary between the United States and Mexico, with a commissioner and surveyor from each country. Work was to begin no later than May 30, 1849. William H. Goetzmann, *Army Exploration in the American West, 1803–1863* (1959; Austin, Texas, 1991), pp. 154–159.

10. With Bache's consent, later ratified by the executive committee, Henry had Downes continue his 1848 occultations with *Occultations Visible in the United States during the Year 1849* (Washington, 1848). We have no evidence that

the government provided a subvention toward this work, for which Henry proposed Downes be paid $300. Rhees, *Journals,* pp. 466, 468.

11. Torrey published this material—eventually including descriptions of specimens from all four of Frémont's expeditions—in *Plantae Frémontianae; or, Descriptions of Plants Collected by Col. J. C. Frémont in California,* 1853, Smithsonian Contributions, vol. 6 (Washington, 1854). (An abstract of the material was presented as "On Some New Plants Discovered by Col. Fremont, in California," AAAS *Proceedings,* 1850, *4:*190–193.) The publication was accompanied by ten quarto plates.

Frémont had apparently expected to underwrite the cost of the plates from a congressional grant, ostensibly in support of his fourth expedition of 1848–1849. He had petitioned Congress for $30,000, and, though the Senate agreed, the House of Representatives strongly rejected the proposal on July 24. Andrew Rolle, *John Charles Frémont: Character as Destiny* (Norman, Oklahoma, 1991), p. 111.

12. Thomas Young, *A Course of Lectures on Natural Philosophy and the Mechanical Arts,* 2 vols. (London, 1807), whose second volume contained a detailed catalog of works of mathematics, mechanics, natural philosophy, and the practical arts, from antiquity up to the early nineteenth century.

13. Section 3 of the Smithsonian act specified that three regents could request a special meeting by contacting the secretary, who then had the responsibility to inform all regents of the meeting; five would constitute a quorum. After the adjournment of Congress, though, few regents remained in Washington. The next regular meeting was scheduled for December 13, 1848. Rhees, *Journals,* p. 49.

215. FROM WILLIAM C. REDFIELD

New York 15ᵗʰ Sept 1848

Prof Joseph Henry, Secretry
of Smithsonian Institute.
My dear Sir,

I hope it is not too late to express my sincere regret that I was not at home when you called at my house last winter and to acknowledge, also, the receipt of your circular from the Smithsonian Institute relating to storms and meteorology.[1] Although my labors in meteorology, as regards writing, have been wholly interrupted for nearly two years, it has been my constant purpose to write to you on the subject of the circular at the first leisure[A] I could command, and thus time has stolen on, regardless of my wishes as well as of other and urgent claims on my attention.

I must not however conceal from you that some embarrassment has arisen from the terms of your circular (not now before me) so far as the same relates to solving the problem of storms: as involving an ambiguity or conclusion which to me is necessarily embarrassing, even if I could find time to make suggestions or take any other part in in the objects of the circular. But it seems now too late for any effort on my part, and I can only claim your indulgence for the delay in acknowledging your circular. I may state also that a work on storms has lately been published by Mr Piddington of Calcutta entitled "the sailors Hornbook for the Law of Storms",[2] which seems well entitled to the notice of inquirers. It is sold by ↑John↓ Wiley, & Putnam.

There is another subject which I have long wished to bring to your notice as connected with the utility of the Smithsonian Institution, viz., the investigation of the fossil fishes of the United States. Prof. Agassiz has already engaged in this important service with only such aid as myself & Mr John H. Redfield[3] may be able to afford him. But nothing satisfactory can be accomplished without considerable outlay for good drawings & figures of the several species and for publishing the same in a proper form. This expenditure appears to be beyond the limit of our present resources. I beg leave to refer you to Profr. Agassiz and to our geologists for further information in regard to the difficulties of this enterprise and its importance to American science.[4]

Respectfully & truly yours
Wm C. Redfield

Retained Copy, Redfield Letterbook, Redfield Papers, Beinecke Rare Book and Manuscript Library, Yale University.
Reply: Doc. 224.

1. Doc. 135.

2. Henry Piddington, *The Sailor's Horn-Book for the Law of Storms* (New York and London, 1848). Piddington (1797–1858), a former merchant and shipper in the East Indian and China trade, retired and became involved in the local scientific society in Calcutta. He began systematically investigating the weather, collected logs and information from different ships, and, from 1839, had the backing of the Indian government, which announced his activities and provided free postage for observations sent to him. The *Sailor's Horn-Book* became a standard reference work. Redfield championed Piddington's book, which he saw as supporting his own theories, at the meeting of the American Association for the Advancement of Science in Philadelphia later in the month. He later proposed the work to the United States Navy as a standard for both navigation and teaching. *DNB;* Fleming, *Meteorology,* pp. 96–97.

3. John Howard Redfield (1815–1895), Wil-

liam's son, was a botanist in New York City. His livelihood came from his participation in the New York City steamship line, the Steam Navigation Company, cofounded by his father. He was a member of the New York Lyceum of Natural History, and, from the age of twenty-one, its corresponding secretary. Redfield also had studied the fossil fishes of Connecticut and Massachusetts. Priscilla Redfield Roe, "Epi-

logue," in *Life in the Connecticut River Valley, 1800–1840, from the Recollections of John Howard Redfield*, ed. Edmund Delaney (Essex, Connecticut, 1988), pp. 87–95.

4. In 1848, Agassiz had planned a collaborative monograph on the fossil fishes of the United States, but the project never materialized. Edward Lurie, *Louis Agassiz: A Life in Science* (Chicago, 1960), p. 145.

216. FROM JAMES P. ESPY

[Mid-September 1848][A]

My Dear Sir,

I suppose you will be at the Meeting of the American <u>Savans</u> on the 20th of this month at Phil[a].

I hope I shall be able to bring Mrs. Espy down to Phil[a] next week, and if so we shall remain there till after the Meeting. Mr Wm. M[c]Ilhenney of the Athenaeum[1] will be able to tell you where we put up. I want to see you as soon as you come to town.

I wish you would order the "double nephelescope""[2] to be sent from Boston to Philadelphia that it may be there at the time of the Meeting. Whether we may choose to exhibit it or not—it will probably need some alterations which can be made in Phil[a], better than in Washington—

It is highly important that[B] we get out our "Circulars to the friends of Meteorology"[3] immediately, as it will be a long time at all events before[C] we shall be able to begin to collate journals of the weather, to be received from so wide a territory.

Would it not be well to send out our circulars together, each of us referring to the other?

For example, I might say at the conclusion of mine—
"you will see by the "Circular" of Prof[r] Henry herewith communicated what the Smithsonian Institution is about to do on this subject, and as all the correspondence which each of us[D] may obtain will ↑be↓ accessible to both, it is manifest that a much more efficient Meteorological campaign than has ever yet been made, may be expected to result from the ~~united~~ forces of the General[E] Government and the Smithsonian Institution ↑thus↓ united."

As one means of stimulating amateurs to become our correspondents during the meditated campaign, I intend to embody in my circular the generalizations which I have formed from preceeding investigations, stating the importance of having these generalizations confirmed, modified, or refuted.

I wish you would be in Phil^a by the 18th Inst. that we may compare our views on various points connected with our plans: perhaps we will then be able to issue our circulars together soon afterwards.

We acknowledge the receipt of your letter to Mrs. Espy[4] which was very satisfactory.

Mrs Espy is still very unwell—she joins me in love to Mrs. Henry and yourself.

Yours truly
James P. Espy

Prof^r Joseph Henry
Sec. Smith. Iins^t

Henry Papers, Smithsonian Archives.

1. Secretary of the Philadelphia Athenaeum and consul for Venezuela. Philadelphia City Directory, 1848.
2. This device was an improvement over the "nepheloscope" that Espy had used for his meteorological researches in the 1830s. Espy thought that the cooling of air by expansion was a major factor in the production of weather. The nepheloscope was a closed vessel, connected to a manometer, which opened to the outside air by means of a stopcock. The double nepheloscope consisted of two such devices, with vessels of different sizes, joined through a valve. By compressing or evacuating the air in each vessel, Espy could create a range of experimental conditions. Starting in 1849,

Espy used the instrument to experiment on atmospheric air, various gases, and water vapor. The device was constructed by the Boston firm of N. B. & D. Chamberlain, makers of pneumatic instruments. It was apparently completed in Boston and shipped in mid–1849.

Fleming, *Meteorology*, pp. 25–26, 98–99, with an illustration of single and double nepheloscopes on p. 99; *A Catalogue of Pneumatic Instruments Manufactured and Sold by N. B. & D. Chamberlain* . . . (Boston, 1844); Doc. 286.
3. Espy's plan was to issue two circulars. Instead, one circular signed jointly by Espy and Henry (Doc. 229) was issued by the Smithsonian. Fleming, *Meteorology*, p. 79.
4. Doc. 212.

217. [CHARLES COFFIN JEWETT]
TO [GEORGE PERKINS MARSH]^A

Boston, Sept 19. 1848

My dear Sir,

I did not receive till yesterday, your note dated the 8th inst. I have been for several days past in New York & Princeton. I had sent the letter concerning the purchase of books ↑to Prof. Henry↓[1] & he had replied to it immediately[2] requesting me to go to New York for the purpose of conferring with him on that & other subjects. I found him disposed to make our appropriation as soon as possible. His ideas were limited however to about five thousand dollars. He said it[B] would not be possible to make an appropriation or to use that of $20000 without the further action of the Regents. It would be impossible to call a special meeting in less than six weeks, whilst the regular meeting would take place in 2½ months. I saw it was of no use to urge the matter further. Mr Bache had not been heard from. I have no expectation however that he will be more favorable to our views than Prof. Henry. Our demonstration now will I think without doubt secure an appropriation for the Library at the next meeting of the Board. Much will therefore be gained. The Library will be safe—if not flourishing.[3] A very great change has taken place in Prof. Henry's feelings, as I think. He seemed very cordial to me, spoke of you as of one of his most trustworthy & judicious advisers, was willing to do all that I suggested for the benefit of my department. He said that he had been worked & harassed almost beyond endurance, that he wanted me with him all the time, to consult with him & assist him. He is beginning to see the impracticability or rather the difficulty (for I suppose he does not yet regard it as impracticable) of carrying out a scheme like his with an organization like ours. I am more & more satisfied that this plan of publishing cannot long succeed. We shall be continually troubled by the authors of memoirs accepted & memoirs rejected, by disappointed booksellers[C] printers & binders, by quarrels about copyright, by complaints of partiality in distribution &c &c &c— & Ten to one, we publish within three years some articles which will bring down upon us the ridicule of the learned world.[D]

Marsh Papers, Bailey/Howe Library, University of Vermont.

1. August 12, 1848; see Doc. 214, note 1.
2. Not found.
3. At the next meeting of the board, authorization for the library reached $3,000 (not counting Jewett's salary and incidental expenses), with $2,000 of that for book purchases.

This substantially increased the $1,000 for book purchases approved at the previous meeting, though it was still less than half of the non-building expenditures. Rhees, *Journals*, pp. 43, 53.

218. TO ALEXANDER DALLAS BACHE

Princeton Sept 20th 1848

My dear B.

I have been unable to obtain access to any account of the electrical clock since I last wrote. My books are all packed and my last stay in NY was so short that I could make no researches of the kind there.[1] I am however well pleased with the plan proposed[A] by Mr Bond[2] and see no reason why it should not succeed in practice.[3] There is perhaps one point which may require attention in regulating the instrument. I allude to the probable difference in the rate of the clock while in and out of the circuit. You probably recollect that there is a repulsive action between the several consecutive parts of an electrical current which tends to break a conductor into parts at right angles to the axis ~~of the conductor~~ and that I once made a machine of wire which oscillated under the action of this force.[4] It appears to me that the operation of this force may be sufficient to accelerate the beats of the clock while the instrument is in the circuit. It may not however be sufficiently intense to produce any practical effect.

Enclosed I send you a copy of my correspondence with Markoe & Col. Abert.[5] I received a previous letter from Markoe[6] in which he fully agreed with me ↑in opinion↓ that the publication of the report would be premature. I have thought of respectfully declining any farthe cooperation with these gentlemen. I was solicited to attend their meetings and gave my views candidly and kindly. I have no objections[B] to the resucitation of the Institute for the purpose of establishing a museum in Washington and would make no objections to transferring to the society the great museum of the patent office. But I think for the honor of the country that the organization of the institution should not be such as to present it to the world as the exponent of american science when it has no claim to such a character. These are the views I presented in my conversation with Col. Abert. I was not at the large meeting.[7]

I am off this morning to Phil[d] to attend the association. I will give you an account of the proceedings.

Prof. Jewett gave me a visit on Friday last.[8] He accompanied[C] me to NY and entered with zeal into the business of distributing the first vol. of the Contributions. He said very little about the purchase of European books and appeared to have satisfied himself by shifting the responsibility of not taking advantage of the times from himself to the committee &c.

He appears well disposed to take hold and and work in harmony.

I see by the papers that the "builders" of the Smithsonian have stolen a little of our thunder in announcing the donation of Dr Hare in connection with the edifice.

Mrs Henry under ↑went↓ the operation of tooth pulling on tuesday last while under the influence of chloriform. The operation was very successful though she was not entirely insensible. She joins me in kind regards to Mrs B.

Loomis enters upon his duties at this place almost immediately. Daves steps into his shoes in New York.[9]

> I remain as ever
> Yours &c
> J.H

Bache Papers, Smithsonian Archives.

1. In a letter of August 28, 1848, from New Hampshire (Henry Papers, Smithsonian Archives), Bache had requested Henry to look up an account of Wheatstone's electromagnetic clock, a device Wheatstone invented in 1840 for ballistics experiments. Though first described in French in the *Comptes rendus*, an English translation appeared as "Note on the Electro-Magnetic Chronoscope," Walker's *Electrical Magazine*, 1845–1846, 2:86–93; this journal is in the Henry Library. *Henry Papers*, 5:295n.

2. William Cranch Bond (1789–1859), an astronomer and precision instrument maker, Phillips Professor of Astronomy at Harvard College, and director of its observatory. *DAB*.

3. Bond had proposed a device whereby the escapement mechanism of a clock would send a telegraphic signal. This would allow widely separated observers to agree on one standard time, which, when compared with local solar time, would establish the difference in longitude between the stations. Trials between Elias Loomis in New York and Bond in Cambridge had taken place in July and August 1848, followed by Bond's proposing his device to Bache. In his letter of August 28, Bache asked Henry for his evaluation before commissioning the device for the Coast Survey.

Sears Cook Walker and John Locke proposed similar devices. The question of priority and especially of which device the Coast Survey would use became a contentious issue among American scientists over the next years. Elias Loomis, *The Recent Progress of Astronomy; Especially in the United States* (New York, 1850), pp. 212–236, especially pp. 217–221, 223.

4. For Henry's thoughts on consecutive repulsion, see "Contributions to Electricity and Magnetism. No. III:—On Electro-Dynamic Induction," *Transactions of the American Philosophical Society*, 1839, 2d ser. 6:303–337, paragraphs 126–127; for his electric motor, see his "On a Reciprocating Motion Produced by Magnetic Attraction and Repulsion," *Silliman's Journal*, 1831, 20:340–343.

5. Probably the combined document, in Caspar W. Hodge's hand, comprising Henry to Francis Markoe, Jr., August 16, 1848; John J. Abert to Markoe, September 2, 1848; and Markoe to Henry, September 5, 1848. Henry Papers, Smithsonian Archives.

6. August 19, 1848, Henry Papers, Smithsonian Archives. For its contents see Doc. 209, note 4.

7. That is, the full meeting of the National Institute on July 29, 1848.

Henry did keep up his participation in the movement to revive the National Institute. He apparently continued his work on the committee to petition Congress, and, as vice-president of the organization, on November 14, 1848, he joined his name with five other officers on the resulting memorial. That memorial was presented at a general meeting of the institute and adopted on December 9, 1848, with George Perkins Marsh to introduce it in the House and Democrat Edward Allen Hannegan of Indiana to present it to the Senate.

The National Institute asked three things of Congress in its memorial. Giving as a reason that the government was the "residuary legatee" of the institute, it asked "a proper extension of the Patent Office" in which to exhibit its collections. Second, it asked for an appropriation—of an unspecified amount—in order to increase by exchange the government collections of which it had the charge (not those of the Wilkes Expedition) and to provide for the safekeeping and proper exhibition of both the government's collections and its own. Finally, the National Institute asked that collections from the Wilkes Expedition be given it and not deposited with the Smithsonian Institution. This the institute characterized as "a private establishment . . . intended to increase the fame and perpetuate the name of a private individual," while "the first and greatest Expedition of purely a scientific character, which this Country has ever undertaken upon the high seas" had produced a "truly National Collection, the fruit of so much American labor and American toil." Placing this collection in an institution founded by a foreigner, the institute argued, would be inappropriate, as well as an undue burden on the Smithson bequest.

For inexplicable reasons, presentation of the memorial to Congress was greatly delayed. The memorial was explicitly referred to the institute's board of directors in April 1849, but only in the spring of 1850 did it make its way to Congress. Joseph R. Chandler, Democrat of Pennsylvania, presented the memorial to the House and Whig Solon Borland of Arkansas to the Senate. The memorial was referred to the Joint Committee on the Library on April 30, 1850, but no further action was taken. By the end of that year, Charles Stansbury, the recording secretary of the institute, lamented "the refusal of aid by Congress."

Memorial of the National Institute, November 14, 1848, signed by Peter Force et al., Petitions and Memorials Referred to the Committee on the Library, 31st Congress, Records of the United States Senate, RG 46, National Archives; Journal of Meetings, No. 2 (1842–1849), meetings of October 9; December 4 and 9, 1848; and April 2, 1849; and No. 3 (1849–1856), meeting of May 6, 1850, Box 11, Records of the National Institute, RU 7058, Smithsonian Archives; *Report of the Recording Secretary of the National Institute for the Year 1850* (Washington, 1850), p. 9 (quotation).

8. September 15.

9. Mathematician Charles Davies took the position of professor of mathematics and natural philosophy at the University of the City of New York (now New York University) for the academic year 1848–1849. *Henry Papers, 1:*280n; Joshua L. Chamberlain et al., eds., *Universities and Their Sons: New York University* (Boston, 1901), pp. 50–51.

219. FROM JOHN HENRY ALEXANDER[1]

Prof. Joseph Henry

Baltimore 26 September 1848.

Dear Sir

I take the liberty with this of introducing to your acquaintance my friend Mr. Philip T. Tyson[2] of this place; a gentleman universally esteemed here for the many excellent traits of his character and, in what farther concerns the present writing, remarkable in our little scientific circle for the accuracy and fidelity of his acquirements in mineralogy and geology and his skill in chemical manipulations. I have no doubt, therefore, of your finding ample interest in his society.

Another motive which I have for presenting him to you is that he visits Washington at the moment in connection with a design that, in view of the position which you so worthily hold, ought I think to be early communicated to you; and that I am sure you will not fail to appreciate and, as much as circumstances may allow, farther. The design was this.[A] Mr. Tyson intended to visit California upon a scientific exploration of the Country, for his own gratification and the prosecution of possible ulterior views. It was suggested upon that determination that the Government would do well to avail of the opportunity for acquiring information not only of scientific interest but of commercial importance; and such a suggestion made to the Secretary of the Navy[3]—Gov. Marcy's[4] absence prevented its being made to him also—is held, I believe, under advisement. The system of our Government justly prescribes caution in the exercise of Departmental powers; and the limitation to the expenditure of public monies upon any object not specially authorised by law, very wisely intended, is always found to act very emphatically upon cases of this kind where the practical utility (i.e. the money-value) of the knowledge to be acquired is not so immediate and apparent. In the present instance, however, irrespective of any interest I might feel in the party making the suggestion, I think it a very fair and proper case for the interference and action of the Government. We have acquired extensive territories on the Pacific at great cost; and it is both our interest and duty to provide as soon as may be for their developement and peopling. Such provision can only be made by furnishing authentic and reliable information upon their resources. For instance, even the very means of conveyance there, if it be steam-vessels which are undoubtedly the speediest and most suitable, is crippled by the absence of any known deposites of fuel; while the cost of artificial depôts is enormous. Coal imported there costs the Government at least $16.— per ton.[5] Now on the other hand, there is every reason in the little that we know of the geology of the region, to expect the occurrence of coal; the rocks there are at least suitable to such occurrence; and the recent discovery of mines of that article on Vancouver's Island[6] renders it highly probable that a brief research w^d be rewarded in finding similar beds in our own territory. I have no doubt that if such discovery could be guaranteed, the Government w^d find no difficulty in making the necessary expenditure, though a very large one, for its avail; it seems to me, therefore, that there would be equal justification in an expenditure towards such discovery, which should bear a similar proportion to the existing probability: that is to say, (the question being not the procurement of the money but the relative merit of its application) if the probability of coal being found at all be only 1/10, it would be allowable to expend in the search for it one tenth of what would be expended to[B] realize the certainty.

This view implies arrangements for a special research which however is neither called for nor proposed at present. Recognizing the propriety and duty of protecting at whatever expense the territory we have acquired, the Gov^t is in fact about sending out a Commission of Officers of the Navy and Engineers to investigate the appliances to be made for Sea-ward defence.[7] The cost of annexing a Geologist to that Expedition would be very small in comparison with the aggregate either with or without the addition; while the advantages would be incomparably en-hanced.[A] I have made so long a story quite unintentionally; and permit it to stand only that you may see the foundation of the whole subject. Otherwise for you and myself, whose business is not with Government policy or National expend[itur]es,[C] the contributions that might be looked for from the measure to Physical Geography form an ample in-ducement to encourage it.[A] In view of this and of the National promi-nence and weight that the Institution over which you preside justly has, I thought that you might find occasion in some way best judged by yourself to contribute to such[D] encouragement;—your known devotion to the cause of science and advancement of knowledge guarantees your good will—your position might enable that will to be felt efficiently.

If my friend Bache were in Washington, I should have no doubt of interesting his co-operation; but a recent letter informs me of his busy occupation at a distant station and besides that I w[d] not like to impose upon him the task of correspondence, the delay in its transmission would probably over run the period of Mr. Tyson's arrangements for his departure. So the scientific urgency has ~~bee~~ to be left with you.

I have throughout looked only to your own individual advice and countenance. You will excuse me, I know, for suggesting in conclusion that it might not be amiss for the Smithsonian to signalize at the outset its means to give impulse to such praiseworthy undertakings; and that any communication you might see fit to hold with the Departments might be not individual only but official.[8]

I remain, my dear Sir,
Very respectfully and faithfully
Y[ours] J[n] H[y] Alexander

Henry Papers, Smithsonian Archives.

1. Chiefly interested in applied science, and especially the rational development of mineral resources, Alexander had conducted a topo-graphical and geological survey of Maryland between 1834 and 1841. *Henry Papers, 6:*565n.

2. Philip Thomas Tyson (1799–1877), a ge-ologist and chemist from a Baltimore family that engaged in industrial chemistry and min-ing. *National Cyclopaedia of American Biography, 13:*543.

3. John Y. Mason.

4. Secretary of War William L. Marcy.

5. Thomas Butler King found coal selling for "$60 to $100 per ton" in San Francisco in 1849. T. Butler King, *Report . . . on California* (Washington, 1850), p. 50.

6. In 1835, Hudson's Bay Company traders found coal on Vancouver Island, lying in seams close to the surface. After a mail contract was let for the Panama-Oregon route in 1848, the Hudson's Bay Company began to mine the coal in 1849, to supply the mail-carriers. At that time the beds were found to be worthless, but successful mining of inland coal on the island began in 1853, to last until 1950. Charles Lil-lard, *Seven Shillings a Year: The History of Vancou-ver Island* (Ganges, British Columbia, 1986), pp. 97–104.

7. Despite noting numerous, though scat-tered, references to this commission through-out 1848–1850, we have found no other infor-mation on its commissioning or activities.

8. The State Department appointed Thomas Butler King (1800–1864), congressman from Georgia, as an agent to report on California, but Marcy provided Tyson with a letter that allowed him the aid of the army while in California. He undertook a private tour, arriving in San Francisco in June 1849, and accompanied King on his survey, under the direction of General Persifer Smith. The tour took them over the coastal ranges into the Sacramento Valley and up into the Sierra Nevada mountains. Tyson toured the gold fields, came back down to the south, went briefly into Sacramento, and then returned to San Francisco. He visited San Diego and departed California in October 1849. Contrary to Alexander's hopes, Tyson saw no indications of coal in California. He did, however, make a small collection of minerals and fossils, some of which he promised to the Smithsonian.

Mary C. Rabbitt, *Minerals, Lands, and Geology for the Common Defence and General Welfare*, 3 vols. (Washington, 1979–), *1*:92; Philip T. Tyson, *Geology and Industrial Resources of California* (Baltimore, 1851), especially pp. xiii–xiv, 3–5, 38, 72; *BDAC*.

220. FROM JAMES MELVILLE GILLISS[1]

Washington 26th Sept[r] [1848][A]

Dear Sir,

I had an interview with Judge Mason[2] this morning, in which the meteorological instruments for the southern expedition[3] formed one of the subjects of conversation.

As he considers every expense incurred for instruments must be paid from the small appropriation granted by Congress, and makes no objection to my obtaining instruments from the Smithsonian Institution, rendering to it due credit therefor, I should be glad to know whether you can give me a complete fit out, and what further steps are necessary for me to take in the premises.

In looking over your "programme of organization" it has occurred to me, that you might also furnish me with a larger telescope than the 5 feet instrument belonging to the Navy which is now at my control. A parallactically mounted telescope of 6 (French) inches aperture and 8 feet focal length with clock motion &c can be obtained from Frauenhofer's[4] establishment for somewhat less than $1800 and it would double the value of results attainable in extra-meridian observations with the instrument at my control.

It is of much consequence that I should have a telescope with which good work may be done; for Prof: Peirce agrees with me in belief that a parallax of Mars is obtainable in the manner I propose, from which that of the Sun may be derived with a probable error of only 0"02. Encke's[5] you remember, resulting from the transit of Venus, he states cannot exceed 0"05.

If the Smithsonian Institution can supply such an instrument I shall be greatly rejoiced, for the larger half of my whole appropriation will be swallowed in the Meridian Circle, and the purchase from it is absolutely impossible.

May I beg a reply at your earliest convenience, and believe me

Very truly & Respectfully yours
J.M.G.

Prof: Joseph Henry
Sect^y Smithson^n Instit^n
Princeton N.J.

Retained Copy, Letters Sent, Records of the United States Naval Astronomical Expedition to the Southern Hemisphere, Records of the Naval Observatory, RG 78, National Archives. In an unknown hand. Reply: Doc. 221.

1. The effective creator of the Naval Observatory, though denied its first directorship, Gilliss (1811–1865) was currently employed on the Coast Survey. *DAB;* Elliott, *Dictionary.*

2. John Y. Mason, secretary of the navy.

3. The navy's astronomical expedition to South America. This project had begun in 1847, when a German scientific correspondent of Gilliss's, Christian Ludwig Gerling of the University of Marburg, suggested that observations of Venus at its point of maximum elongation, undertaken by observatories of the same longitude but of greatly different latitude, would enable a more precise calculation of the solar parallax, a measurement that would yield the absolute dimensions of the solar system. Gilliss launched a campaign in late 1847 to have the government undertake an expedition to the southern hemisphere to make observations, to be matched with similar ones in Washington. Gilliss proposed to add observations of Mars, a catalog of southern stars, and, at Bache's suggestion, magnetical and meteorological observations. On February 10, 1848, Gilliss applied to Mason, who refused approval, but passed the proposal to the Naval Affairs Committee of the House of Representatives. In spite of M. F. Maury's opposition, a bill authorizing the expedition and appropriating $5,000 became law on August 3.

Wendell W. Huffman, "The United States Naval Astronomical Expedition (1849–52) for the Solar Parallax," *Journal for the History of Astronomy,* 1991, 22:208–220; J. M. Gilliss, "Origin and Operations of the U.S. Naval Astronomical Expedition," in Gilliss, *The U.S. Naval Astronomical Expedition to the Southern Hemisphere, during the Years 1849–'50–'51–'52,* U.S. House, 33d Congress, 1st Session, House Executive Documents, No. 121, 4 vols. (1855–1856), 3:i–xxx; Rhees, *Journals,* p. 44; Gilliss to Henry, January 27, 1848, Henry Papers, Smithsonian Archives. The favorable report of the Naval Affairs Committee, including Gilliss's extensive correspondence on this project with Gerling and other European and American scientists, is U.S. House, 30th Congress, 1st Session, *Astronomical Observations,* House Reports, No. 470 (1848).

4. Joseph Fraunhofer, an optical instrument maker and researcher in Munich. *Henry Papers,* 2:273n.

5. Johann Franz Encke, a German astronomer and director of the Berlin observatory. *Henry Papers,* 6:380n.

221. TO JAMES MELVILLE GILLISS

Princeton Sept 27th 1848

My dear Sir

Your letter[1] dated this moring has just been received and I hasten to answer it in time for the return mail.

It is true there is nothing in the programme of the S.I. to prevent our furnishing you with the telescope you mention; but the state at present of our funds will prevent us from making any appropriation which approximates in magnitude to the amount required for the purchase of the instrument[2]—.

According to the plan adopted for permanent operation one half of the annual income is to be given to the library & the museum the other half to carry on the active business of the institution in the way of publications lectures scientific & other investigations &c &c. This plan however does not go into full operation until the end of three years from next march, in the mean time one half of the whole income is to be devoted to the building; and the other half alone is appropriated to carry on all the operations.

I think we may venture to appropriate 150 dollars for the purchase of Meteorological instruments. If you do not start until after the meeting of the Regents which takes place in the beginning of Dec. we may perhaps increase this sum.

Please inform ↑me↓ as to the cost of a complete set of instruments of meteorology. I shall be in Washington in the course of a week or two but it will be best to drop me a lin[e.][3,A]

The scientific meeting was very successful.[4] No meeting has ever taken place in this country at which there were so many papers presented of a strictly scientific character and consisting of original materials. At first the Savans[B] of Philadelphia did not join in very cordially but towards the end they united very heartily in the discussions. I regret that you did not remain longer and give the association an account of your intended expedition.

> I remain very truly & resp
> Yours &c
> Joseph Henry

Lieut Gilliss
Washington

Letters Received, Records of the United States Naval Astronomical Expedition to the Southern Hemisphere, Records of the Naval Observatory, RG 78, National Archives.
Reply: September 30, 1848, Letters Sent, Records of the United States Naval Astronomical Expedition to the Southern Hemisphere, Records of the Naval Observatory, RG 78, National Archives.

1. Doc. 220.
2. Gilliss did not take this as an outright refusal. In his reply, he pointed out the advantage of an achromatic equatorial telescope to the Smithsonian permanent collections, and referred Henry to their mutual "Astronomical friends," as to whether the investigations of the expedition did not constitute "a special cause for anticipating the purchase somewhat." He thought that returning to Congress for additional funding might jeopardize the whole project.

His letter was persuasive. On October 2 Henry responded, saying, "I think it not improbable that some means may be devised, by which, with a union of our forces, the object may be attained." On October 26, he again wrote, saying that those members of the executive committee who were in Washington had met and proposed to offer Gilliss the assistance he required. However, the Smithsonian did not ultimately bear the cost of this telescope. Another congressional appropriation, passed January 26, 1849, provided $6,400, which paid for all the instrumentation—astronomical and geophysical—which the Smithsonian had bought for the expedition to use.

Gilliss to Henry, November 25, 1848, and March 7, 1849, in same location as reply; Henry to Gilliss, October 2 and 26, 1848, and March 20, 1849, in same location as this document; *Smithsonian Report for 1848,* pp. 17–18; *Smithsonian Report for 1849,* p. 11; Rhees, *Journals,* pp. 467–468.

3. Gilliss's response stated that, in 1843, he paid just over £30 for a complete set of meteorological apparatus, which he specified as a standard barometer, standard thermometer, self-registering versions of each, wet-bulb thermometer, solar radiation thermometer, a "radiation to sky" thermometer (with parabolic reflector), rain gauges, and wind vane. Henry authorized the money with his letter of October 2, and, in his letter of October 26, added to Gilliss's scientific mission, asking for observations in seismometry and offering to supply an instrument. By December 9, Henry had authorized Gilliss to purchase magnetic instruments in the name of the Smithsonian as well. Gilliss ordered the same instruments from the same manufacturers as Henry's previous order: a declinometer and unifilar magnetometer from Thomas Jones, and a dip circle from Henry Barrow.

Gilliss to Edward Sabine, October 25 and December 9, 1848, February 19 and June 29, 1849, BJ3/25, Letters from Americans re Magnetic Observatory in US, 1839–1854, Sabine Papers, Records of Kew Observatory, Public Record Office, London.

4. Henry was an active participant in the first meeting of the American Association for the Advancement of Science, held in Philadelphia from September 20 through 25. He was elected a member-at-large of the Standing Committee, an executive committee to ensure the continuity of business during and between meetings; chair of the Section of General Physics; member of a committee in aid of M. F. Maury's work on ocean winds and currents; and president of the association for the succeeding year. He took part in the discussions, notably on one paper on the telegraph, and made a presentation on the organization of the Smithsonian. In Bache's absence, he was one of the chief Washington scientists at the meeting. AAAS *Proceedings,* 1848, *1:*25, 62, 67, 82–90, 92–94; *Silliman's Journal,* 1848, 2d ser. *6:*393–401.

222. TO JAMES HENRY COFFIN[1]

Princeton Sept 30th 1848

My dear Sir

In looking over my book of memoranda this morning I found a note which states on the authority of Professor Nichol of Glasgow that the manuscripts of the long seriees of meteorological observations by Dr. Holyoke[2] are deposited in the library of the American Academy in Boston and that the part of the series relating to the wind has never been published.[3] Professor Nichol mentioned this fact for the purpose of inducing the publication of the whole series in the Smithsonian Contributions. Is it true that the part of the series of Dr H's observations which relates to the wind has never been published? Have you examined the manuscripts and ↑have↓ the records of the winds in these observations been incorporated in your extended series? I forgot to question you on this subject when I saw you in Phil^d and lest I should forget it again I have concluded to put my enquiry thus on paper.[4]

There is also another subject on which I wish to address you namely that of ↑the↓ vacancy in the office of President of your College.[5] I mentioned to you in connection with this office the name of my freind Dr Bullions of albany. You informed me that the office would probably be filled by the election of the present Professor of Languages.[6] It has since occurred to me that if this should happen the chair of languages would become vacant[7] and in that case I would nomenate Dr Bullions for the position. He is a gentleman of very extensive acquirements and through his publications is widely known^A to the community. Such an election would I think do much towards sustaining and advancing the character of the Institution. I have not had any communication with Dr. B. on this subject and do not know that he would accept the appointment. I do know however that he is now out of employment[8] and that he is too good a man to be thus situated for any length of time. Please drop me a line on these points at your convenience and be assured that

I remain truly yours &—
Joseph Henry

Professor James H. Coffin
Lafayette College
PS Should^B there be a probability of a vacancy in the chair of Languages please inform me as to the salary whether there is a dwelling house or other perquisits attached to the office.

J.H.

PPS Since the foregoing was written your letter asking for information as to the Smithsonian Institution has been received.[9] I will send you a copy of my exposition of the organization and progress of developement of the institution as presented to the New Jersey Historical society a few days ago as soon as I can procure ~~a copy of the same~~ one.[10]

I think it was understood when we parted that you were to put your paper in order for publication in the Smithsonian Contributions.[11]

J.H.

Box 5, Coffin Correspondence, Henry Papers, Smithsonian Archives.

1. Meteorologist and professor of mathematics and natural philosophy at Lafayette College, Easton, Pennsylvania. *Henry Papers,* 5:266n.

2. Edward Augustus Holyoke (1728–1829),

a prominent physician of Salem, Massachusetts, a founder and president both of the Massachusetts Medical Society and of the American Academy of Arts and Sciences. *DAB.*

3. Henry's "book of memoranda" was Henry

Pocket Notebook [13279]; the note on this material is on page [90].

Holyoke kept meteorological and astronomical, as well as personal, diaries, but the manuscript meteorological observations apparently no longer survive at the American Academy of Arts and Sciences. They probably covered the years 1786 through 1829, as Holyoke's journal for that time was published: Edward A. Holyoke, "A Meteorological Journal from the Year 1786 to the Year 1829, Inclusive," *Memoirs of the American Academy of Arts and Sciences,* 1833, new ser. *1:*107–216; Peggy Murphy, American Academy of Arts and Sciences, private communication; *National Union Catalog,* s.v. "Holyoke, Edward Augustus."

4. Henry was responding to Coffin's "Report on the Winds of the Northern Hemisphere," presented at the meeting of the American Association for the Advancement of Science (AAAS *Proceedings,* 1848, *1:*34–35; *Henry Papers, 6:*310n). His later work (see note 11, below) did note Holyoke as an observer of the winds, but it is impossible to determine to what extent Coffin used Holyoke's observations.

5. George Junkin (1790–1868) had resigned as president effective September 19, to take up a similar position at Washington College, Lexington, Virginia. *DAB;* William T. Kosanovich, Jr., *Lafayette College: 1826–1976* ([Easton, Pennsylvania], 1976), pp. 11–12.

6. Charles William Nassau (1804–1878), the professor of languages since 1841, was elected president in the spring of 1849. Kosanovich, p. 12; David Bishop Skillman, *The Biography of a College: Being the History of the First Century of the Life of Lafayette College,* 2 vols. (Easton, Pennsylvania, 1932), *1:*190; Edward Howell Roberts, *Biographical Catalogue of the Princeton Theological Seminary, 1815–1932* (Princeton, 1933), p. 27.

7. Instead of hiring a new professor of languages, in 1849 the college called back lawyer Washington McCartney (1812–1856), who had been intermittently on the faculty since 1835, as the part-time professor of mental and moral philosophy. Skillman, p. 190; *DAB.*

8. In a crisis in the fortunes of Albany Academy, the trustees dismissed the principal and entire faculty, including Bullions, in the winter of 1848. *Henry Papers, 6:*457n–458n; Cuyler Reynolds, *Albany Chronicles: A History of the City Arranged Chronologically* (Albany, 1906), p. 578.

9. Not found.

10. Henry addressed the New Jersey Historical Society on September 27, at Princeton, presenting essentially the same talk that he had given to the American Association for the Advancement of Science four days previously in Philadelphia. The speech was quite similar to Henry's "Advertisement" prefacing Squier and Davis's *Ancient Monuments* (pp. iii–vii). It consisted of a brief account of the history, organization, and current projects of the Smithsonian, and included the edited version of his "Programme of Organization" that appeared in Squier and Davis. The address was later published as *Smithson's Bequest . . .* ([Washington, 1848]). (In various compilations of Smithsonian publications, this is incorrectly given the date of 1847.) See also AAAS *Proceedings,* 1848, *1:*82–90, which differs from the separate pamphlet only by the addition of a paragraph announcing Robert Hare's donation of his apparatus.

11. Coffin's AAAS presentation was greatly revised and expanded, and eventually published as *Winds of the Northern Hemisphere,* 1853, SI Contributions, vol. 6 (Washington, 1854).

223. TO EPHRAIM GEORGE SQUIER

Princeton Sept. 30ᵗʰ 1848.

My Dear Sir,

I have been absent from Princeton for about a week, & have found so much to occupy me on my return, that I have been unable to give attention to your letter[1] until this morning. I think I may venture to promise you an appropriation of $100, to assist in defraying the expenses of the exploration of the ancient monuments in the northern part of the State of New York, provided that a full account of the results of the exploration be presented to the Smithsonian Institution for publication in its Contributions[A] to Knowledge— The plates & woodcuts which may be prepared for the illustration of your communication will be loaned to the Historical Society, on condition that due credit be given to the Smithsonian Institution for the same[2]—

I act in this matter entirely on my own responsibility, and should the regents refuse to grant the appropriation I shall be obliged to pay the money myself. I cannot however advance to you immediately— Such large drafts have been made by the building committee during the last few months, that I have found difficulty in procuring money to discharge bills which are now pressing for payment. I shall probably be in N.Y. at the beginning of the week, & will then have farther communication with you on this subject. In the meantime,

I remain very respectfully & truly yours
Joseph Henry

E. G. Squier

Squier Papers, Library of Congress.
In Caspar W. Hodge's hand, with Henry providing the correction, signature, and internal address.

1. Not found.
2. Henry's pledge was matched by members of the New-York Historical Society, providing enough to sponsor Squier's quick tour of New York State in the fall of 1848. He published his memoir on the mounds that he surveyed and excavated as *Aboriginal Monuments of the State of New-York*, 1850, SI Contributions, vol. 2 (Washington, 1851), while his talk to the New-York Historical Society appeared in its 1849 *Proceedings* (pp. 41–61) as "Report upon the Aboriginal Monuments of Western New York." Thomas G. Tax, "E. George Squier and the Mounds, 1845–1850," in *Toward a Science of Man: Essays in the History of Anthropology*, ed. Timothy H. H. Thoresen (The Hague, 1975), pp. 116–117; *Smithsonian Report for 1849*, p. 11.

224. TO WILLIAM C. REDFIELD

Princeton Oct. 2nd. 1848.

My Dear Sir,

Your letter of the 15th ult.[1] has just reached me this morning from Washington. I regret that we did not meet last winter, since had we done so, the offensive expression in the Programme, which you notice, would have been either omitted, or so modified as to render it unobjectionable.[A] I can only assure you that there was no intention to throw discredit upon your mechanical theory of the motion of storms, & that in the course of the investigations which may be established by means of the Smithsonian Institution, a due regard, so far as I have any influence, shall be paid to your previous investigations. Whatever may be the true nature of storms, the public mind is not yet set at rest on this point, & the object of the S.I. in setting on foot these investigations, is to collect data which may serve to establish the truth in the mind of the public generally. The subject is certainly not exhausted, & farther research is needed to determine, as far as may be, the numerical relation of the several phenomena. I think it highly important that you should direct us to points of observation which may have a bearing upon your theory.

I hope Prof. Agassiz & yourself will proceed as rapidly as possible with your memoir on the fossil fish of the country, & I beg to assure you that every facility compatible with the means & organization of the Smithsonian Institution, will be afforded you in its publication—

I remain truly your friend
& obdt. serv[t]
Joseph Henry

W C Redfield Esq

P.S. Please excuse me for not addressing you in my own hand. I am so much oppressed with correspondence that I am obliged to dictate many of my letters to an amanuensis.

J.H.

Redfield Papers, Beinecke Rare Book and Manuscript Library, Yale University.
In Caspar W. Hodge's hand up to the signature, with the remainder by Henry.

1. Doc. 215.

225. TO SPENCER FULLERTON BAIRD

Princeton Oct. 2nd. 1848.

My Dear Sir,

Your communication of Sept. 28th[1] has just reached me at Princeton— Prof. Agassiz & Mr. Redfield have in preparation a memoir on the fossil fish of North America, which they intend to present to the Smithsonian Institution for publication in the volumes of the Contributions[A]— In connection with this, Prof. Agassiz spoke to me of the preparation of a monograph of the fish of this country, also to be presented to the Smithsonian Institution[2]— I agree to the proposition that the engravings on stone for both these memoirs should be prepared by the artists now in the employment of Prof. Agassiz,[3] provided that the work can be done as cheaply as by other artists who might be employed. The

Professor also mentioned to me your desire of having your illustrations[4] prepared by the same artists— To this I have no objection; & I shall be pleased to learn that he & you have made an arrangement by which the Ichthyology of our Country will be more fully developed. You may be assured that the Smithsonian Institution will afford you every facility in the way of publication compatible with its limited means & with the plan of organization which has been adopted.

With my best wishes for your continued success in the prosecution of your interesting researches,

I remain very truly your obt serv
Joseph Henry

Professor S F Baird.

Baird Papers, Smithsonian Archives.
In Caspar W. Hodge's hand through "remain" in the closing, with the remainder by Henry. Previously printed in William Healey Dall, *Spencer Fullerton Baird: A Biography* (Philadelphia, 1915), pp. 185–186.

1. Not found.

2. In collaboration with Baird, Agassiz planned a work on the freshwater fishes of North America similar to the study he had done of European freshwater fishes. This became one of many projects that Agassiz started but never finished. Lithographs of six species were completed in 1849, however; these were published by the Smithsonian forty years later as *Six Species of North American Fresh-Water Fishes. Six Lithographs from Drawings by A. Sonrel. Explanation of Plates by David Starr Jordan* (Washington, 1889). Edward Lurie, *Louis Agassiz: A Life in Science* (Chicago, 1960), pp. 145, 186–189; Jules Marcou, *Life, Letters, and Works of Louis Agassiz*, 2 vols. (New York, 1896), 2:74–75.

3. Probably Antoine Sonrel, "one of the out-

standing lithographic artists of that era," and the artist Jacques (or Jaques) Burkhardt, both of whom had worked with Agassiz in Neuchâtel and followed him to Boston. Lurie, pp. 109, 130, 146, 176, 204–205; Elizabeth C. Agassiz, *Louis Agassiz: His Life and Correspondence*, 2 vols. (Boston, 1885), 1:320–321, 2:442–443; George C. Groce and David H. Wallace, *The New-York Historical Society's Dictionary of Artists in America, 1564–1860* (New Haven, 1957), p. 593; Elmer Charles Herber, ed., *Correspondence Between Spencer Fullerton Baird and Louis Agassiz—Two Pioneer American Naturalists* (Washington, 1963) (quotation on p. 27).

4. Probably those for his own work on amphibia, which Henry had agreed to partially support.

226. FROM JARED SPARKS

To Joseph Henry, Esq.
Sec[y] of the Smithsonian Institution.

Cambridge, Mass. Oct. 7. 1848.

Dear Sir,

I observe in the Plan of Organization of the Smithsonian Institution, adopted by the Regents, that one of the topics under the head of ↑the↓ Increase of Knowledge is,

"Historical Researches, and accurate surveys of places celebrated in American History."

It has occurred to me that this topic would properly embrace the topography of the military operations of the Revolution. Whoever has given attention to this subject has observed the extreme deficiency of nearly all the maps and drawings illustrative of these operations. There were few skilful engineers in the American army, and whatever reasons we may assign for the cause, the fact is nevertheless certain, that the topographical sketches of battles and marches now left to us exhibit marks of having been executed in haste, and are very imperfect.[1] The atlas accompanying Marshall's Life of Washington[2] is a convincing proof of this fact. This atlas was compiled in part from General Washington's papers, but the originals were never returned to the family, and they are supposed to have been lost in Philadelphia, or destroyed in the process of copying them for the use of the engraver.

The British engineers drew the plans of several battles. Some of these are good, such as those of Burgoyne at Saratoga,[3] but the larger part of them are defective and erroneous, because the engineers knew little of the movements of the American army, or of the ground they occupied, and seldom made surveys with any degree of accuracy.[4]

Would not a volume of maps and plans of battles, embracing all the prominent military operations of the revolution, founded in some instances on new surveys of localities, with an accurate description accompanying each map and plan; would not such a volume be a valuable contribution to the knowledge of American history, and worthy of the patronage of the Smithsonian Institution? From my own experience in researches of this kind, I am strongly impressed with the belief that it would, and it seems to come within the topic extracted above from the Plan of Organization. It is moreover an enterprise which no individual can undertake.[5]

I throw out this hint for your consideration; and am

Very respectfully yours,
Jared Sparks.

Retained Copy, Sparks Letterbook 147 h, Sparks Papers, Houghton Library, Harvard University. In an unknown hand.

1. Sparks had worked extensively with documentary materials from the revolutionary period, for example in his edition of *The Diplomatic Correspondence of the American Revolution* (Boston, 1829–1830). Although later historians have echoed his assertion that the mapmaking skills of the American army during the Revolution were inferior, several experts have suggested a need to reevaluate the American effort.

The American army's mapmaking unit, approved by Congress in 1777 at Washington's urging, never exceeded twenty men and was not large enough to satisfy the demand. Its work was supplemented by that of engineers trained in mapping fortifications, line officers with mapmaking skills, and correspondents. A study of surviving maps showed that the training of the mappers "ranged from nil to extensive formal education as surveyor, draftsman or trained mathematical cartographer." Despite the traditional view of the American effort as inferior, J. B. Harley has pointed out significant similarities between the mapmakers in the American and British armies, including a common continental source of professional knowledge and analogous roles within their armies.

The nature of the conflict, a mobile war fought over an immense area, accounted for some of the deficiencies in mapping. It was more likely that a battle map, which showed basic terrain and was usually drawn shortly after a battle, would be made to record an important battle, particularly a victory, or a battle in an accessible coastal area.

Sparks may not have been aware of the great number of battle maps that had been made. One source estimates as many as twenty thousand British maps once existed. Although some of these were forwarded to London and rapidly printed, others were sent to the War Office and King George III. Still others were retained by participants. By mid-century, the surviving battle maps had been widely scattered.

J. B. Harley, "The Contemporary Mapping of the American Revolutionary War," and "The Spread of Cartographical Ideas between the Revolutionary Armies," in *Mapping the American Revolutionary War,* ed. J. B. Harley, Barbara Bartz Petchenik, and Lawrence W. Towner (Chicago, 1978), pp. 1–78; Douglas W. Marshall and Howard H. Peckham, *Campaigns of the American Revolution: An Atlas of Manuscript Maps* (Ann Arbor, 1976), pp. iv–v; Peter J. Guthorn, *American Maps and Map Makers of the Revolution* (Monmouth Beach, New Jersey, 1966), pp. 4–5 (quotation on p. 4); Kenneth Nebenzahl and Don Higginbotham, *Atlas of the American Revolution* (Chicago, 1974), pp. 9–10; Walter W. Ristow, *American Maps and Mapmakers: Commercial Cartography in the Nineteenth Century* (Detroit, 1985), pp. 35–47.

2. John Marshall, *The Life of George Washington,* 5 vols. (Philadelphia, 1804–1807). An accompanying atlas consisted of subscribers' names and ten plates of maps.

3. John Burgoyne (1722–1792, *DNB*) published maps of the battle in 1780 as part of his defense of his actions. Nebenzahl and Higginbotham, pp. 108–111.

4. The British were relatively confined for much of the war, with little opportunity to make topographical surveys. Harley, pp. 32–33, 83–84.

5. Over two hundred battle maps were published between 1775 and 1795. Shortly after the war, William Faden, the king's geographer, published a selection of maps in his *Atlas of the Battles of the American Revolution . . .* (London, 1793), which was republished in 1845 by the American firm of Bartlett and Welford. Lawrence W. Towner has found it surprising that nineteenth-century American histories made so little use of Revolutionary maps, "given the nationalistic need for a historic myth, [an] intense interest in the battlefield, and the remarkable series of nobly conceived and executed contemporary maps already available" (p. 113). Those that were used were based on old maps with no attempts to survey terrain or consult accounts of battles. He concludes that during this period of rapid national expansion, more effort was necessarily devoted to contemporary maps than to historical maps, and that there was a strong tendency to celebrate the Revolution rather than to analyze it.

Despite Sparks's pessimism about the scope of the project, he supported an individual who took up the challenge. Benson J. Lossing (1813–1891, *DAB*) traveled over twelve thousand kilometers in five months to visit the sites of Revolutionary War battles. His *Pictorial Field Book of the Revolution* (New York, 1851–1852) included only seventy-six maps. He did, however, attempt to compare existing maps with terrain, interviewed survivors, and consulted privately-held manuscripts.

Lawrence W. Towner, "The Mapping of the American Revolutionary War in the Nineteenth Century," in Harley, Petchenik, and Towner, pp. 111–124; Harley, pp. 41–42; Ristow, p. 35.

227. TO EDWARD SABINE

Smithsonian Institution
Washington—Oct. 13th 1848

My Dear Sir,

Your favor of May 12th '48[1] was duly received, and should have been answered before this, but I have waited with the hope of being able to announce to you the safe arrival of the instruments the construction of which you were so kind as to take charge of. They have not as yet however come to hand; neither have I heard anything from the workmen concerning them. We shall endeavour to put them to use as soon as possible after they are received.

The project relative to a system of meteorological observations, embracing the U.S. and Canada, has not been abandoned. The board of Regents of the S.I. made a grant for the purpose of $1000, and will probably appropriate an equal sum at their next meeting. The whole cost of instruments necessary to begin operations will be at least $3000. We hope to engage the cooperation of a number of the states of our Union, and perhaps may induce Congress to render us some assistance. I have now in process of construction, ten sets of instruments, including barometer, thermometer, and rain-gage, to send to the coast of Oregon & California—and also two sets for use on the eastern side of the base of the Rocky Mts.[2] The plan cannot be matured & carried into operation immediately, but I have no doubt of its ultimately successful operation.

My mind has been occupied, during the last 18 months, almost entirely with organizing & commencing ↑the↓ operations ~~with~~ ↑of↓ the S.I. I beleive I sent you a programme of the proposed plan of organization;[3] though as you do not mention it in your letter it was probably not received. The first volume of the Smithsonian Contributions to Knowledge is now in the hands of the binder, and will be ready for distribution to literary and scientific societies in the course of a few weeks. I will send you a copy; and must ask in return that you will give me an expression of your opinion, (a favorable one, of course) of the plan which was advocated by Dr. Bache & myself, and which has been provisionally adopted. You will find this plan set forth in the advertisement to the volume—it is the same as that of the programme I sent you. I shall also send a copy to the Royal Society, with the hope that the philosophical Transactions will be sent in exchange for our series of volumes, and to bring about so desirable an object, I must bespeak for the Institution your kind offices. It must be recollected that Smithson, under the name of M Macie[4] was long a member of the Royal Society, & a contributor to its volumes; and therefore the Institution, founded by his munificence for the increase & diffusion of knowledge among men, should have perhaps some preference in the exchanges of your Society.

We are not entirely at a stand, with reference to magnetism. Dr. Locke was engaged under the direction of the U.S. geologists, in making a series of magnetic observations in the region round Lakes Michigan & Superior; and at my earnest solicitation, he has been employed this season by the Sec. of the Treasury to continue these observations, independently of any supervision, the results to be presented to me for publication in the Smithsonian Transactions.

I shall be pleased to receive from you any suggestions as to the plan of organization of the meteorological observations.

I beg leave to state that I shall be happy to pay all the expenses you may incur in the way of postage, carriage hire, &c &c, while attending to the business you have so kindly undertaken to transact for the S.I.

Prof. Bache is now in the field at one of the stations of his primary triangulation in New Hampshire. The work under his care is making admirable progress.

> I remain very respectfully &
> truly yours &c &—
> Joseph Henry

Lieut Col Sabine

BJ3/49, Letters to Sabine from Renwick and Henry, 1845–1853, Sabine Papers, Records of Kew Observatory, Public Record Office, London.
In Caspar W. Hodge's hand up to the closing, with the remainder by Henry.

1. Not found.
2. See Doc. 198.
3. See Doc. 91.

4. James Smithson was known as James Louis (or Louis) Macie until 1801. *DSB.*

228. TO LEWIS C. BECK

Washington Oct. 28th, 48

My dear Sir

I beg that you will not write to Mr Burke until you have heard again. I will see him on monday[1] and will endeavour to ascertain his views relative to the appropriation.[2] I fear from Mr Burke's previous silence and the attacks you have seen on him[3] in the newspapers that you are a little inclined to be distrustful of him and to interpret his remarks unfavourably. I have always found him a man of his word and beleive that he intends to act justly and liberally with you and in truth I cannot at present see any thing contrary to this in his letter to you.

The appropriation by Congress was for a specific object and the amount was intended to cover all the expense and I presume Mr Burke does not consider himself at liberty to apply any other funds to this purpose. It is probable that the expenses he mentions will amount ↑to↓ but little and that nearly the whole sum voted by congress will be paid to you. I shall speak to him on this point and let you know his views. You must recollect that government is no respecter of persons and that no money can be paid without vouchers of a prescribed form. I have no doubt that Mr Burke will pass your account in a form as agreeable to yourself as the established practice of his office will permit. I have no fear in this case of an exposure a posteriori. I feel myself implicated in this offair and trust you will not give up the investigation without the most positive assurance of intentional wrong on the part of the commissioner.

I remain truly your friend
and obt. servt.
Joseph Henry

Dr L C. Beck

Retained Copy, Henry Papers, Smithsonian Archives.

1. October 30.
2. Beck wrote Henry on October 24 (Henry Papers, Smithsonian Archives) to complain of his latest correspondence with Burke. On October 9, Beck had written to the commissioner of patents to apprise him of the progress of the breadstuffs investigation and to find out how Burke intended to compensate him. In response, he received "a singular letter" from Burke, dated October 20, in which Burke said the appropriation had to cover all related expenses, including payment to those who collected and shipped specimens to Beck. He asked Beck to "distinquish between actual expenses for materials for conducting the analysis & for your own time & labor &c." Beck refused to "furnish this 'bill of particulars,' to be paraded, perhaps, in some Congressional document" and complained that Burke intended to pay him "like a laborer." Irritated also that Burke had only just informed him of the passage of the appropriation, which took place in August, Beck vowed to "close up the business as soon as possible, or carry it on in a way more agreeable to my feelings."

3. Probably those launched by Thomas G. Clinton, who was passed over for promotion to principal examiner. Clinton's twenty-one charges against Burke included one for improper authorization of payment for services rendered.

229. CIRCULAR ON METEOROLOGY[1]

COPY TO [JAMES HENRY COFFIN][A]

Washington Nov[r] 1st 1848.

Sir

The Regents of the Smithsonian Institution at their last meeting[2] resolved to establish an extended system of Meteorological observations, particularly with reference to American Storms, embracing as far as possible the surface of this Continent.— In order that the Meteorological observations ordered by Congress at their last Session may not interfere with this enterprise, but cooperate with it, the Secretary of the Navy has directed Prof Espy to join his labours to those of the Secretary of the Institution.—

As a preliminary step, it is important to ascertain the number and locality of the persons who will assist in this enterprise, & what available instruments are now in the Country. For this purpose those who are disposed to join in these observations are respectfully requested to signify their willingness to do so by a line addressed to the Navy Department, with the word "Meteorology" written on the envelope.[3]

Though it would be of great importance that each observer should be provided with a perfect set of compared instruments yet it is believed that much valuable information, relative to the velocity, the duration, and extent of Storms, may be obtained even without instruments from a mere record of the face of the sky, the direction & force of the wind, & the beginning & ending of rain and snow provided the observations are of sufficient extent & duration. Blank forms free of expense will be sent to those who are disposed to join in the observations,[B] & as soon as the amount of funds for this purpose is sufficient, full sets of instruments will be furnished to careful observers in important localities.

> Very respectfully,
> Your obedient Servants.
> Joseph Henry Sec: Smith: Inst:
> James P. Espy Meteorologist
> Under the direction of the Sec: of Navy

Box 5, Coffin Correspondence, Henry Papers, Smithsonian Archives.
Lithographed circular, including Henry's and Espy's signatures. Reply: Possibly Coffin to Espy, January 20, 1849, Letters Received, Records of the Smithsonian Meteorological Project, Records of the Weather Bureau, RG 27, National Archives.

1. This circular was distributed through members of congress to over four hundred people and was also published in newspapers. In March 1849, Henry reported that he had received about two hundred responses. In his annual report for 1849, Henry wrote that about one hundred and fifty observers were making daily observations of the weather and reporting regularly each month. Fleming, *Me-* *teorology,* p. 79; Rhees, *Journals,* pp. 469–470; *Smithsonian Report for 1849,* pp. 12–15; *Smithsonian Report for 1851,* pp. 68–69.

2. On December 15, 1847. Rhees, *Journals,* pp. 41, 42–43.

3. The responses are in Letters Received, Records of the Smithsonian Meteorological Project, Records of the Weather Bureau, RG 27, National Archives.

230. TO ALEXANDER DALLAS BACHE

Washington Nov [13][A] 48

My dear B.

Though I have nothing of importance to communicate I must write to you if for nothin else but to keep up my character of a good correspondent. Capt William's[1] called before he left for your camp and though I prepared a note to send by him he was permitted to start without it thanks to the prompness of Mc Fus— What an overturn in politics![2] Many changes will be made among the office holders. Speculation is quite busy here in forming the new cabinet. Truman Smith[3] Mr Choat[4] & Mr Evans[5] are spoken of for the Treasury[6] also Abot Lawren for the same office.[7] Some say Smith is to go into the Post Office[8] that Crittenden[9] is to be appointed Secretary of State[10] others that Mr Reeves of Virginia is to be elected to this position.[11] My friend Mr Burke will I presume be obliged to vacate the Patent Office. What whould you say to George P Marsh as his sucessor? You would I presume prefer him to W. R. Johnson. Dr Page informes me that Marsh's name has been mentioned and that he would be will received in the Office. A worse man might I think be found to take the place.[12]

I have boarded with Mrs Whitwell[13] since my return and have at her table come in communication with Truman Smith and Mr Holmes[B] of S.C.[14] The former became quite sociable and promised of his own accord to procure the franking privilege for the Smithsonian Inst.[15] We had long taks on subjects of sc[i]ence[C] and should he get into power my accidental acquaintan may ↑perhaps↓ be turned to some account in the way of doing good. Holmes is a very strange man. I have been amused and instructed by him the latter not in the line of profound philosophy but in that of Political History.

Mr Jewett left here this morning. He came on to get instructions relative to the distribution of the books and to look out I presume for a house. I was very glad to see him for I began to fear that he had taken a *Stunner* at the alterations in the circulars and intended to give up the work of destributing the books.[16] He is very anxious to commence his engagement in full with the Inst at the beginning of the year. We shall have enough to do and if he continues to exhibit the same willingness to fall into the harness and draw kindly I shall not object. I am now very busily engaged with my Report with the examination of the accounts and other matters relative to the Smithsonian. I have borrowed from Dr Hodge his son Wistar[17] for a few weeks and with him I am or consider myself some thing of a man.

Mr Seaton has turned over the accounts to Mr Bradley[18] of the Bank not[D]

Bache Papers, Smithsonian Archives.

1. James S. Williams, an assistant on the Coast Survey. G. W. Cullum, *Biographical Register of the Officers and Graduates of the United States Military Academy at West Point, New York*, rev. ed., 2 vols. (New York, 1929), *1*:396.

2. General Zachary Taylor, with Millard Fillmore as his running mate, had just won the presidency over the Democratic ticket of Lewis Cass and William O. Butler. Although Taylor had no experience whatsoever in government, had not belonged to either party, and had never even voted, his Mexican War popularity gave the Whig party the victory. Succeeding Democrat James K. Polk, who had declined to run for a second term, Taylor was an unknown quantity politically and there was a great deal of speculation about his intentions. Holman Hamilton, "Election of 1848," *History of American Presidential Elections, 1789–1968*, ed. Arthur M. Schlesinger, Jr., and Fred L. Israel, 4 vols. (New York, 1971), *2*:865–918.

3. Truman Smith (1791–1884, *DAB*) was a Whig congressman from Connecticut who had run Taylor's campaign. Elected to the Senate, he assumed a seat there rather than take a position in Taylor's cabinet.

4. Following the expiration of his term as senator in 1845, Rufus Choate had resumed the practice of law in Massachusetts. Although a loyal Whig who was sought after by party leaders, he repeatedly declined higher offices, preferring private study and the law. *DAB*.

5. George Evans, a former Whig senator from Maine and a former Smithsonian regent, was an acknowledged expert on public finance. His support of the Webster-Ashburton Treaty, unpopular in Maine, may have cost him a cabinet appointment. *DAB*.

6. William M. Meredith of Pennsylvania became secretary of the treasury, succeeding Bache's brother-in-law, Robert J. Walker.

7. Abbott Lawrence had been considered for Taylor's running mate and had campaigned actively for the ticket. An industrialist and former representative from Massachusetts, Lawrence turned down Taylor's offers of the navy and the new Interior Department and eventually agreed to serve as minister to Great Britain. *DAB*.

8. The position went to Jacob Collamer of Vermont.

9. John Jordan Crittenden, a former senator from Kentucky, was an early supporter of Taylor's candidacy. After Taylor's election, Crittenden turned down offers of a cabinet position and became governor of Kentucky. *DAB*.

10. John M. Clayton of Delaware became secretary of state.

11. William Cabell Rives was a former congressman, senator, and minister to France under Andrew Jackson. He became minister to France again in Taylor's administration. *DAB; Henry Papers*, *2*:413n–414n.

12. Taylor appointed Thomas Ewbank commissioner of patents. George P. Marsh became minister to Turkey. Walter Rogers Johnson had no formal position during these years (Elliott, *Dictionary*).

Several days after this letter, Caspar Wistar Hodge described Henry's political stance as follows:

By the way, the Prof. is very quiet about politics— He belongs to the party that is in power, & can do most for the Institution— But it is amusing to hear the way that he &

his scientific visitors talk about the Whigs & Locos. I have heard them say several times in relation to men from whom they wished to get aid for any scientific project in the way of appropriations from Congress &c, "Oh he is a Whig—you know they are very liberal—we can get anything out of him." They all say, Whigs & locos themselves that they can get this or that bill through Congress, for all the Whigs will vote for it & quarter of the locos. I guess the Prof. will be converted before he is here long. [C. W. Hodge to Sarah Hodge, November 17, 1848, Charles Hodge Papers, Manuscripts Division, Department of Rare Books and Special Collections, Princeton University Libraries.]

The Locos, or Loco-Focos, were a radical reform wing of the Democratic party. Richard B. Morris, ed., *Encyclopedia of American History* (New York, 1953), p. 176.

13. Proprietor of "one of the most recherché boarding houses in the city," according to Henry. In 1848, Mrs. Whitwell's was on the west side of Four-and-a-half Street between C Street and Louisiana Avenue. According to Hodge, Henry rented four rooms in a nearby house, presumably the same one in which he began renting two rooms on July 1 (Doc. 193). C. W. Hodge to Charles Hodge, November 11, 1848, Charles Hodge Papers, Manuscripts Division, Department of Rare Books and Special Collections, Princeton University Libraries (quotation); *Congressional Directory for the First Session of the Thirtieth Congress* (Washington, 1848), p. 32.

14. Isaac Edward Holmes (1796–1867) of Charleston served twelve years in Congress. A lawyer and proslavery advocate whose speeches one judge called "inflammatory," Holmes was considered socially congenial. *DAB.*

15. The franking privilege would enable the Smithsonian to send mail free of charge. It was limited to specified government officials and members of Congress and covered the mailing of official correspondence and publications. The Smithsonian did not receive the full privilege until 1879. United States Post Office Department, *Postage Rates, 1789–1930* (Washington, 1930), p. 45.

16. We have found no evidence relating to changes in the November 17 circular (Doc. 231). Jewett did distribute the volumes, as he recounted in his letter to Henry of November 17, in the Archives Collection, Brown University Library.

17. Caspar Wistar Hodge (1830–1891), a son of Henry's close friend Charles Hodge, had just graduated from Princeton and was serving as Henry's secretary. He later attended the Princeton Theological Seminary and became a professor there. Francis Bazley Lee, ed., *Genealogical and Personal Memorial of Mercer County, New Jersey*, 2 vols. (New York, 1907), 2:463.

18. Probably William A. Bradley (1794–1867), a former mayor of Washington who was affiliated at various times with the Bank of Washington and with the Patriotic Bank. Following Taylor's election he became postmaster of Washington City. This is probably the same Mr. Bradley who was later clerk of the executive committee of the Smithsonian Board of Regents, a position whose duties were defined in the executive committee report of January 1, 1849, as those of an accountant and bookkeeper for that committee as well as for the secretary, the building committee, and the Board of Regents as a whole. Madison Davis, "A History of the City Post-Office," *Records of the Columbia Historical Society*, 1903, 6:187–189; Rhees, *Journals*, pp. 475, 484.

231. CIRCULAR ON PROGRAMME AND LIBRARIES[1]

COPY TO SAMUEL FOSTER HAVEN

Smithsonian Institution,
Washington, 17 November, 1848.

To the Secretary of the American Antiquarian Society,
Sir,

On the part of the Smithsonian Institution we have this day addressed to your care, and deposited with J. P. Jewett & C⁰ 23 Cornhill,

Boston,[2] subject to your order, the first volume of the "Smithsonian Contributions to Knowledge," published in accordance with the Programme of the Institution, a copy of which is herewith transmitted to you.[3]

Should the Programme meet your approbation, we beg leave to request, that you will favor us with a written expression of your approval, that you will furnish us with any suggestions relative to the subject which may be deemed of importance, and give us your co-operation in cases where it may be required.[4]

In pursuance of the plan given in the second part of the Programme, of making the Institution a centre of bibliographical knowledge, it will be necessary to procure the catalogues and statistics of all the public Libraries in the United States; and in furtherance of this object, we trust that you will furnish us with the materials needed relative to your institution. We beg leave, therefore, to call your attention to the accompanying sheet,[5] and also to request three copies of the last printed Catalogue of your Library.

Please to inform us in what way we can most conveniently send to you the future publications of the Smithsonian Institution.

> Respectfully,
> Your obedient servants,
> Joseph Henry, Secretary,
> Charles C. Jewett, Assist. Sec'y,
> Acting as Librarian.

American Antiquarian Society Correspondence, American Antiquarian Society.
Printed circular with addressee and "J. P. Jewett . . . order," added in C. C. Jewett's hand. Reply: February 6, 1849 (RH 3250), enclosing committee report of January 31, 1849 (RH 2640), Rhees Collection, Huntington Library (printed in Rhees, *Documents* [1879], pp. 985–989).

1. Over nine hundred copies of this circular were sent out to institutions in the United States. Jewett collected the responses relative to libraries and presented the information, organized geographically, in his *Notices of Public Libraries in the United States of America* (Washington, 1851). He included the libraries of states and colleges (both institutional and those of student societies), learned, religious and social societies, and public schools. Although he initially intended to rely solely on the responses to this circular for his data, he found the results inadequate. Many were not answered, "others were filled up hastily, and gave but a meagre account of the collections; others, again, simply referred to some sources from which authentic details might be gathered" (Jewett, p. 5). De-

spite the difficulties, Jewett was able to collect statistics on 644 libraries (excluding district school libraries), which reported an aggregate of over two million volumes. *Smithsonian Report for 1849*, p. 38.

2. John Punchard Jewett (1814–1884), Charles Coffin Jewett's older brother, was a bookstore owner and publisher in Boston. *Who Was Who in America: Historical Volume, 1607–1896*, rev. ed. (Chicago, 1967).

3. SI 1.1, Federal Government Documents Collection, American Antiquarian Society.

4. The society's publishing committee, chaired by Haven, prepared a ten-page report which was approved by the council on January 31, 1849. The committee congratulated the Smithsonian for not spending all of its funds on

costly buildings and for not restricting its mission to the establishment of a national library. It applauded

the plan of rendering it the seat and centre of vital energy and activity to the science and literature of a youthful republic,—an ever pulsating heart, distributing life and strength throughout the body politic of letters, prompting, sustaining, and guiding, every department of intellectual exertion here, and thus effecting an influence upon mankind at large.

The institution could fulfil Smithson's intent by acting

as an exponent of universal science for our whole country; as the head quarters of bibliographical information; and as a register of the progress of knowledge, where the latest achievements of the human mind may be found—in mercantile phrase—"posted up" for convenient reference, and the farthest footsteps of the last traveller in the paths of learning duly noted for the benefit of subsequent adventurers.

Forty-six other responses, most quite brief, are printed in Rhees, *Documents* (1879), pp. 970–994; the originals of most of them, as well as some responses which do not mention the "Programme of Organization" and are not printed in Rhees, are in the Rhees Collection, Huntington Library.

5. The list of nineteen questions Jewett enclosed was reprinted in Jewett, pp. 4n–5n. In addition to asking for the name, date of founding, and number of volumes of each library, he requested information on acquisitions budgets, staff and buildings, shelving systems, catalogs, hours, admission policies, and lending procedures.

232. FROM JOHN LOCKE

Cincinnati Nov. 23[d] 1848[A]

Prof. Henry
Dear Sir,

Your late favour[1] was duly received. I had been ambitious to return to Lake Superiour early enough to do a good seasons work. I at last despaired of receiving the appointment and engaged in such ~~duties~~ ↑pursuits↓ as did not permit me to assume the duties it imposed. Still however I struggled so to arrange my affairs that I might leave them but it was impossible without sacrifices which I was not justified in making. The disappointment in itself was painful and it was rendered more than doubly so by the ~~refle~~ very reflection ↑to↓ which your note alludes, namely, that my friends at Washington had made no small exertions to procure the appointment, and on the whole I have suffered severely both from our climate and from ~~an~~ excessive anxiety during the past summer. I have for years rather neglected my private interests for my favourite pursuits and now with a large and perfectly helpless family, dependent so far solely on the continuance of my own health and activity for their support I have been admonished by an occasional attack of illness to provide if possible for their future interests. This I have been endeavouring to do. When the task which I have on hand shall have been performed I shall I hope resume my former pursuits. I shall probably revisit the Atlantic in the spring and unless you ~~th~~ have altered your views I may be able in March next to ↑make↓ the tour of Magneticals by way of New Orleans.

I did not recieve my appointment until July 11th when Owen and Jackson were already in the woods and on them I was dependent for outfit and supplies. In August, open boat movements begin to be seriously impeded by blustering and boisterous weather on the Lakes while the horrible wilds of that region require time to seek information from Indians and to seek out Indian trails, used mostly by them in Winter and in their hunting seasons, being scarcely traceable in the full foliage of summer. All difficulties I would have encountered but for the reasons I have assigned to you. I have since learned that the delay of my Appointment was caused by a want of seasonable Appropriations by Congress a circumstance unknown to me at the time.

I have no doubt you have done every thing to make the work of Messrs Squiers & Davis such as it should be in regard to giving proper credit; and I find it vastly better than I had supposed it would be from the manner of talking ~~of~~ peculiar to one of the parties, Still I see several special items of my own labours which as the text reads do not appear as mine, as for example: The ascertaining of the age of the two large trees on the Fort hill embankment,[2] and the section of the Colerain embankment showing its artificial origin from the fact that the loam was excavated first and thrown over to the <u>far</u> side, while the subjacent gravel was thrown upon the <u>contiguous</u> side.[3]

I have lost something of my parental doting upon my Magnetical children, but still if it be thought best to publish we can talk of that matter when I shall see you.

Your much obliged friend
John Locke

Henry Papers, Smithsonian Archives.

1. Not found.
2. Although Locke was not specifically credited for the estimate that a large chestnut tree at Fort Hill, near Chillicothe, Ohio, was at least one thousand years old, the entire section was prefaced by the following statement:

This work was first described, though not first surveyed, by Professor LOCKE, of Cincinnati, in 1838. His description and plan—to the accuracy and fidelity of which every visitor can bear witness—were published in the

"Second Annual Report of the Geological Survey of Ohio." [*Squier and Davis,* pp. 14–16, quotation on p. 14n.]

Locke was generally credited in the preface as one of the authorities used (p. xxxiii) and was credited specifically elsewhere in the work (for example, pp. 19–20).

3. There is no mention of Locke in connection with the Colerain embankment, an earthworks near Cincinnati, the source being given instead as James McBride. The passage in question is on pages 35–36.

233. CASPAR WISTAR HODGE TO CHARLES HODGE

Washington Nov. 27th [1848][A]

My Dear Father,

You expect me to write often because Washington is such a teeming place, while the truth is, that I get all my knowledge of what is going on in it from the New York papers. I beleive that I have seen most of the scientific men in the place— At any rate no more come to Prof. H.'s office. I am just as quiet as if I were at home— I suppose it will be somewhat different next week, when Congress reassembles— I called at Mrs. Eckhard's the other day, & found that all her children were just recovered from the measles. They were going out for the first time that day, which was the day before thanksgiving.[1] Mr. Eckhard[2] called ↑to day↓ to invite me to dine with them to morrow, to which I acceded. The Prof. & I rode out to the National Observatory[3] on Saturday[4] to test some barometers by a standard, & to try a piece off apparatus for determining elevations by means of the boiling point of water;[5] destined for Col. Fremont— I saw there Lieut. Maury, the Superintendent— He talked with the Prof. about the exploring expedition's museum, & said that there was a good deal of feeling in the navy against making it over to the Smithsonian, & merging it with their subsequent collections. It is considered as a navy monument, & ought to be made the foundation for a National, & not a Smithsonian Museum.[6] All that I have heard speak of it, feel the injustice of it being imposed on the Inst[n], so that the Prof. is considerably encouraged as to the prospects of getting rid of it— And what makes it better for him is that the government has no place to put it in. The Patent office is so crowded that it is absolutely necessary to turn it out of its room there; so that uncle Sam will have to buy a part of the Smithsonian building, for which he will be charged $200.000, leaving for the Inst[n] only the two wings— This will be but fair, for the building was resolved upon by the Regents only on the plea of accomodating the museum. There is also considerable effort making to revive the defunct National Institute, with the hope of getting the museum under its direction. Now that the Whigs are in power, the prospects are brighter. The museum is a very valuable one in itself—Agassiz says that it is one of the most complete collections ever made—though of course not a very large one yet— We were so busy boiling thermometers &c at the Observatory that I did not see much of it. I was in the observing room, & saw the telescope, chair &c., but did not go up stairs. I met young Mc Culloh[7] there, who said[B] that he was going on to Princeton— I was carried out to tea the other night by Prof & Mrs. H., to Mrs. Nesbit's, a Georgian lady, with whom they are intimate, & who staid at Mrs. Skelly's in Princeton a year or two ago—had Charley King[8] under her protection— Last Saturday evening we moved off in procession, preceded by a furniture wagon & Major McPeak, & took possession of the new house in the rear of the Patent Office.[9] It is a very snug, well lighted little house, not so very little either. Will & I are to have two of the upstairs rooms between us, to arrange as we please. The probability is that there will be a stove in one, in which we will study, & the other will be used for sleeping— There is a stable, which Push inhabits, & a bath house, not yet in operation— You caution me against the deceitful allurements of the Episcopal Church. What will you say when I tell you that yesterday week I went to the largest Catholic Church in the city?[10] The ceremony in itself did not meet my expectations—in its effects on myself, it surpassed them. The music was most melting—I recognized, Lord Remember David.[11] The sermon was entirely exhortatory— It reminded me of one of Dr. Rice's[12]—not in manner however. I have heard Mr. Bannatyne,[13] Mr. Ballentine,[14] & the Catholic priest[15] all preach, & they all together could not preach as good a sermon as the Episcopal Mr. Butler.[16] I like Mr. Bannatyne very well, but Mr. Butler is decidedly above par. His manner is negative—his voice deep & monotonous, but his sermons are fine. You need not fear for me, for I go to the conventicle twice a day, & to Mr. Butler's only in the evening, when, as far as I know, his is the only church open. That is a rather hypocritical excuse, I confess, for I should go there if they were all open— The Congressional library is open now three days in the week—I begin my visitations to morrow. Walking with the Prof. the other evening I met a Mr. Dalton,[17] an auditor of the Treasury Department, who told me that he was in College with you— He invited me to his house— The Prof. seems to like him very much— I wrote to Mary[18] the other day— If you write to Arch[19] before I do, tell him that the Prof. has got him a very nice working model engine—not first rate, for such a one would cost $400 or 500, but a very good one[20]— There is a strong compound horse shoe magnet here, which I am going to bring on for him. If he does not remember himself, I must tell him how to retouch it. It can be kept saturated, with ease.

Your affectionate son
C. W. Hodge—

Charles Hodge Papers, Manuscript Division, Department of Rare Books and Special Collections, Princeton University Libraries.

1. In the District of Columbia, Thanksgiving was on Thursday, November 23, in 1848. *Laws* *of the Corporation of the City of Washington . . .* *(1848–49)* (Washington, 1849), p. 43.

2. Probably James Read Eckard (1805–1887), a graduate of the University of Pennsylvania (1823) and the Princeton Theological Seminary (1833) and pastor of the New York Avenue Presbyterian Church in Washington from 1848 to 1858. Edward Howell Roberts, comp., *Biographical Catalogue of the Princeton Theological Seminary, 1815–1932* (Princeton, 1933), pp. 78–79.

3. An alternate name used in the early years of the Naval Observatory.

4. November 25.

5. A reference to a hypsometer, an instrument based on the principle that the boiling point of water varies with barometric pressure, which in turn varies with elevation. It was an alternative to the more delicate mercurial mountain barometer, particularly for surveyors working in rough areas. A description of a portable hypsometer is given in Louis P. Casella, *L. Casella's Catalogue of Meteorological Instruments* (London, 1860), p. 7. W. E. Knowles Middleton, *Meteorological Instruments* (Toronto, 1941), pp. 12, 47.

6. Eager to have the Smithsonian avoid responsibility for collections belonging to the government, Henry gladly adopted this argument, using it in his annual report a year later:

> This museum was collected at the expense of the government, and should be preserved as a memento of the science and energy of our navy, and as a means of illustrating and verifying the magnificent volumes which comprise the history of that expedition. If the Regents accept this museum, it must be merged in the Smithsonian collections. [*Smithsonian Report for 1849*, p. 20.]

7. Probably Richard Sears McCulloh.

8. Probably Charles Barrington King, who graduated from the Princeton Theological Seminary in 1848. Roberts, p. 143.

9. The house was at Eighth and G Streets, NW. Washington City Directory, 1850.

10. Probably St. Patrick's on F Street near Tenth Street, NW. James Goode, *Capital Losses: A Cultural History of Washington's Destroyed Buildings* (Washington, 1979), pp. 194–195; Wilhemus Bogart Bryan, *A History of the National Capital*, 2 vols. (New York, 1914–1916), 2:189–190.

11. From the oratorio *Redemption* by Samuel Arnold (1740–1802, *DNB*). It was based on an aria from Handel's opera *Sosarme* (1732).

12. Benjamin Holt Rice, pastor of the First Presbyterian Church of Princeton. *Henry Papers*, 4:329n.

13. Ninian Bannatyne (1814–1849), an 1845 graduate of the Princeton Theological Seminary and pastor elect of the F Street Presbyterian Church in Washington from 1845 to 1849. Roberts, p. 125.

14. E. Ballentine, pastor of the First Presbyterian Church in Washington. Washington City Directory, 1850.

15. Probably William Matthews of St. Patrick's. Goode, pp. 194–195.

16. Clement Moore Butler (1810–1890), rector of Trinity Episcopal Church in Washington from 1848 or 1849 to 1854, and 1859 to 1861. *National Cyclopaedia of American Biography*, 10:34; *Historical Sketches of the Parishes and Missions in the Diocese of Washington* (Washington, 1928), pp. 22–23.

17. Aaron Ogden Dayton (d. 1858), a graduate of Princeton (1813) and fourth auditor of the Treasury Department from 1838 to 1858. *Princeton Catalogue*, p. 125.

18. The writer's older sister, Mary (1825–post 1903), who married William M. Scott (1817–1856) in 1848 and joined him in Danville, Kentucky, where he taught at Centre College. Hugh L. Hodge, *Memoranda of Family History* ([Philadelphia, 1903]), pp. 113–114; Roberts, p. 133.

19. Charles Hodge's oldest son, Archibald Alexander Hodge (1823–1886), a former student of Henry's at Princeton (B.A., 1841) and a graduate of the Princeton Theological Seminary (1845). Hodge had gone the year before to Allahabad, India, to serve as a missionary. Advised to leave because of his wife's poor health, he returned to the United States in 1850. *DAB*; Hodge, p. 112.

20. Charles Hodge wrote on July 6, 1849 (Henry Papers, Smithsonian Archives), to let Henry know of an opportunity for sending the apparatus to his son. For an earlier instance of Henry's sending philosophical apparatus to Allahabad for one of his former students to use in his missionary work, see *Henry Papers*, 5:375–376.

December 1, 1848

234. TO CHARLES COFFIN JEWETT

Washington Dec. 1ˢᵗ 1848.

My Dear Sir,

I have received a number of answers to the circulars[1]— I fear however that, owing to our separation, a mistake has been made in the direction— I intended that the[A] ↑letters↓ should be sent to the Presidents of Colleges, the Secretaries[B] of learned Societies, & the Librarians of public libraries— The college librarian is in many cases a young man— perhaps an under graduate,[2]—unqualified to give an opinion as to a general plan, particularly with regard to the Scientific part, & uninfluential with reference to a recommendation. The remarks thus far have all been favorable; but ↑they are from persons unknown↓ the value of opinions should be ~~obtained~~ ↑estimated↓ by weight as well as by number.

Prof. C. C. Jewett.

Draft, Henry Papers, Smithsonian Archives.
In Caspar W. Hodge's hand, with corrections by Henry.

1. Doc. 231.
2. The evidence does not entirely support Henry. Most college librarians were members of the faculty, who oversaw the library as a part-time responsibility. For example, the librarian at Princeton during Henry's tenure there was John Maclean, Jr. However, at least one observer believed that the position of college librarian in the mid-nineteenth century "was a haven for the incompetent or the decrepit." W. N. Chattin Carlton, "College Libraries in the Mid-Nineteenth Century," *The Library Journal*, 1907, 32:479–486; Arthur T. Hamlin, *The University Library in the United States: Its Origins and Development* (Philadelphia, 1981), pp. 22–44 (quotation on p. 44); *Princeton Catalogue*, p. 76.

235. FROM AUGUSTUS WILLIAM SMITH[1]

Wes. University Dec 2ⁿᵈ 1848

Dear Sir

Your favour[2] with accompanying blank forms for reduction of observations of occultations &c, and copy of your first report, were duly recᵈ and I beg you will accept my thanks for your kindness in the matter, and should a convenient opportunity present, that you would tender the assurance of my very great obligations to Dr Bache.

I had previously recᵈ a copy of the "Programme of organization of the Smithsonian Institution" and examined it with some care. I have again carefully reperused and considered ↑the details↓ as therein presented with your "explanations and illustrations."

In common with many others I presume, I had indulged some apprehensions on the subject of the mode in which the intentions and

429

purposes of the Testator <u>could</u> and <u>would</u> be carried out by the Trustee. These apprehensions were not diminished, on reading the reports of the widely different views and plans which seemed not merely to divide but to distract congress while the subject was under discussion. They were however greatly removed by a sight of the programme.

Those portions of the plan which seem to result directly from the will of the Testator, by the action of yourself and Board of Regents, have a character conformable to the designs of the Testator, and much more of symmetry, than the novel character which the Institution was to bear, warrented the hope of realizing so early in its history. I reread the whole with the special purpose of raising objections and finding occasion to make suggestions, but I freely[A] confess I do not see wherein the portion referred to, could be improved, especially as the details are conditioned on their practical and successful[B] character when tested by experience. Neither[C] am I prepared to condemn the appropriation of the means of the institution by the positive enactments of congress to the formation of a library—especially the kind of library contemplated. But with regard to Cabinets &c I do not clearly see in what it will ultimate. More is however to be feared from ~~th~~ a disposition to modify and change, under the pretence of improving the plan, by the numerous Sages who, as members of Congress will become its Guardians-in-Law.

My hopes of its success and utility are strong ↑while↓ under its present direction, if untramelled by new restrictions and left free to act.[D] On the whole, the country and the friends of Science may well congratulate themselves upon the prospects of the Institution, and especially (allow me to say it in all sincerity) upon the choice of the individual selected to direct and superintend its interests, with regard to whom public sentiment is unanimous so far as I have heard an expression of opinion.

I am Dr Sir very Respectfully Yours
Aug. W. Smith

Joseph Henry LL.D.

P.S. After writing the above I understood that our President[3] had rec^d a programme and that probably a consultation on the matter might be called for and a united expression of opinion prepared and forwarded to you. Our term has closed and nearly all my collegues have left town. I therefore delay no longer.

A.W.S

Dec 25th 48

RH 3853, Rhees Collection, Huntington Library.
Previously published with deletions in Rhees, *Documents* (1879), pp. 974–975.

1. Smith (1802–1866) was professor of astronomy and mathematics at Wesleyan University from 1831 to 1857. *National Cyclopaedia of American Biography,* 9:430.

2. Henry to Smith, October 26, 1848, Smith Papers, John Hay Library, Brown University. In that letter, Henry asked Smith for "a written statement of your approval provided it [the "Programme of Organization"] meets with your approbation." Henry also enclosed a copy of the forms used by the Coast Survey for computing occultations and moon culminations.

3. Stephen Olin (1797–1851), a Methodist clergyman, served as president of Wesleyan from 1842 until his death. *DAB.*

236. FROM BENJAMIN SILLIMAN, JR.

Confidential

Yale College December 4 1848.

Prof Joseph Henry
Smithsonian Institution
Washington D.C.

My Dear Sir I have your favor of Nov 30th and note its contents.[1] In regard to the gentleman in question it is true he was here 9 months and during that time from almost total ignorance of scientific Chemistry he came to have a very competent knowledge of its <u>general principles</u> and commenced some investigations on points in agricultural Chemistry— but I cannot say that I consider him fitted to untertake the subject proposed one of the most delicate and unsettled in Chemical physiology of plants. He has a decided tact at investigation & ought to be encouraged to go forward & <u>fit himself</u> for it. His habits are not suffiently careful or acute to make his results trustworthy although they may become so. I do not wish to say that he may not arrive at interesting results in a course of investigation like that proposed on excretion. But I certainly should be unwilling to publish his results unless the research had been reviewed & verified by abler hands.

You of course do not need my advice—but I will venture to say that the most it would be prudent to say to him would be that if on the completion of his researches the results should be by a competent academic body, judged of sufficient interest that the S. Institute would pay the cost of the researches.

I remain Dear Sir

Yours very Respectfully
& truly
B Silliman, Jr.

Henry Papers, Smithsonian Archives.

1. Letter not found.

December 15, 1848

237. FROM JOHN WISE[1] TO JOSEPH HENRY AND JAMES P. ESPY

Lancaster Decr 15th 1848

M^ssr Espy & Henry.—

Agreeable to your notice on the subject of Meteorology[2] I will most cheerfully make such observations in the meredian and latitude of Lancaster City Pa. as you may direct. A Hygrometer and Thermometer are the only instruments I have in use, which, if of any service in the cause, I will keep a record of. I find the Hygrometer a very useful indicator of Rain since I have got well acquainted with it and keep ↑it↓ at a particular place. I have in my numerous Ascensions noticed Phenomena in air currents that cannot be ascertained on the earth—their electrical conditions—sometimes shallow Strata, with three currents playing at the same time. Tornadoes, or hail-storms, do not move strait forward as fast, as the high current does from west to east—this always blows in high regions. Sometimes there are two distinct cloud strata—the lower giving out rain, the upper not—the upper at the time being a "mackerel sky" and being from 5 to 800 feet apart. Clouds, or cloud stratum partakes of the same form with the earth over which it lies in time of rain—the shape of the cloud surface being ~~nearly~~ nearer a level—I refer here to mountain ridges and valleys. There are currents in the atmosphere analogous to the currents of the ocean.[3] Clouds giving out rain are accompanied with a warmth over their top surface—they look more milky in time of rain than otherwise, when seen in their midst. Clouds do not mingle into a common mass by contiguity. I have noticed more than I can at this moment relate.

Address Lancaster City Pa.

Yours respectfully. John Wise

Letters Received, Records of the Smithsonian Meteorological Project, Records of the Weather Bureau, RG 27, National Archives.
Address: "Meteorology, Navy Department."

1. A pioneer American balloonist. Henry had witnessed his first ascent. *Henry Papers*, 2:387–388.

2. Doc. 229.

3. Wise's observations were not new, nor was his analogy. For example, after describing the atmosphere as being divided into different strata with different wind conditions, John Frederic Daniell wrote:

This state of the upper and under surface of the atmosphere is not unaptly represented to us by the state of the fathomless ocean. . . The currents of the great deep flow in opposite compensating streams, like those of the atmosphere.

Elements of Meteorology, 3d ed., 2 vols. (London, 1845), *1:*158.

238. FROM AARON PITNEY DALRYMPLE[1]

Nottingham Dec. 16. 1848.

Honorable Sir:

In looking over the columns of a newspaper a short time previous I accentally fell upon an article from Prof. Henry; requesting all persons w[ho]^A are willing to enter upon^B a series of 'Meteorological Observations, to signify it by a note addressed to the Navy Department".[2]

It is with pleasure that I would offer my services in that branch of the Sciences, not only from the interest I feel ~~of its~~ in such a National Undertaking; but from the source which the request came from:—Prof Henry with ↑whom↓ I have the honor of acquaintance^C; being a member of the Senior Class at Princeton, which [receiv]ed^A his valuable lectures on Nat. Phil. during the years of '46 and '47.

I reside now on the Patuxent River in Prince George's, Md., about five miles from the Chesapeake; a position in this part of the country very advantageous, having the benefit, both of inland storms and those along or near the Ocean. No high mountain ridges break off or shield this part of the country from the storm that may rage upon the land; and ↑the↓ storms^D that spwees over^E the broad surface of the Chesapeake^F affords a good i[?mage]^A to that which is raging upon the Atlantic.

I have been making some observations of late; but having no instruments ↑except the ~~the~~ thermometer↓, they must be of course somewhat limited. I think a barometer and hygrometer would be of much service at present; which I intend^G to get soon.

Any late treatise on storms; books for registering, or any communication whatever would be kindly received by addressing A. P. Dalrymple. Nottingham. Prince George's Co. Md.[3]

With much respect
I remain your most Obt.
A. P. Dalrymple

Prof. Joseph Henry.
Secretary of Smithsonian Institute.

Letters Received, Records of the Smithsonian Meteorological Project, Records of the Weather Bureau, RG 27, National Archives.

1. Dalrymple (d. 1894) graduated from Princeton in 1847 and the College of Physicians and Surgeons in 1851. During the Civil War he served as a surgeon with the Union Army. *Princeton Catalogue*, p. 171.

2. A reference to the reprinting of the circular on meteorology (Doc. 229) in various newspapers. One example was the *National Intelligencer* for November 30, 1848.

3. Although no reply has been found, Henry did send Dalrymple blank meteorological journals, which he received on February 14, 1849.

Dalrymple served as a meteorological observer for less than a year. Dalrymple to Henry, March 1, 1849, in same location as this letter; *Smithsonian Report for 1868*, p. 74.

239. TO EPHRAIM GEORGE SQUIER

Washington Dec. 16ᵗʰ 1848—

My Dear Sir,

Your letter of the 14th[1] did not reach me until last evening, & I now hasten to answer it at my first moment of leisure. Mr. Bartlett wrote to me[2] some time ago to send him the money promised for the explorations of antiquities— I could not however send him the amount[A] until after a new appropriation for objects of this kind should be granted. The one made at the last meeting of the Board has been exhausted, & I have had so many calls of late upon my own funds that I could not make the advance myself. The Board is now in session, & I presume the appropriations will be made in the course of next week.[3] The fund which can be devoted to research, publications &c will be small, as half the income on the original bequest is devoted for the next three years to the building; & the remainder, after deducting salaries, incidental expenses &c, will be divided between publications on the one hand, & collections on the other. This division is necessary for the next year on account of the entrance of Mr. Jewett on his duties as librarian.

I have made no arrangement for transmitting copies of the Antiquities to the gentlemen you mention. I do not intend to take upon myself the responsibility of presenting a single copy to any individual. I am authorized to distribute the work to Colleges & other public institutions,[4] but no resolution has been adopted by the Board relative to presentation to individuals. The copies presented to the gentlemen you mention, if they are considered as contributors to the work, will be included among those appropriated to the authors.

I remain very truly
Yours &c
Joseph Henry

E. G. Squier Esq.

Squier Papers, Library of Congress.
In Caspar W. Hodge's hand.

1. Not found.
2. Not found.

3. The appropriation was not passed until January 3, 1849. Rhees, *Journals*, p. 53.

4. Henry is probably referring to the "Programme of Organization" provision that the Smithsonian Contributions to Knowledge were to be "exchanged for the Transactions of literary and scientific societies, and copies to be given to all the colleges and principal libraries in this country." Not coincidentally, when Henry reported to the Board of Regents on the distribution of the Contributions, at the meeting of December 20, 1848, he specifically mentioned that no copies had been given to individuals. Rhees, *Journals*, p. 51.

240. FROM JAMES HALL[1]

Albany Dec. 18th 1848[A]

Prof Henry.

Dear Sir,

The state of my health, of which I spoke to you in Philadelphia, makes me very anxious to leave, for a time, the work in which I am engaged and take some more active and out-of door employment— I intend to remain here to get out my second volume of the Palaeontology however, before leaving.[2]

I have written to Washington, through Mr. Thomas W. Olcott[3] and also by myself to make some interest to be sent out to California as Geologist to explore the Gold Region— I could give a year to that duty and then return here, reinstated in my health, which is now debilitated[B] from over work and confinement. I write you to ask your influence to secure me this appointment should such a law pass Congress. I know that Your influence will have great weight, and I hope you may feel willing to exert it for me. If you wish any testimonials beyond my published works I can refer you to persons both in this country and abroad who have on several occasions expressed a favorable opinion of my labors—

I think such a survey would be of great benefit to the country as showing not only the extent and limits of the metaliferous portions of the Country but also the nature of the rocks and soils of the other portions. I think moreover that other departments of Nat. Hist. and the Physical Sciences should not be neglected if an investigation is undertaken— I hope you may think favorably of the subject, and that it may furnish, at the same time, the means of extending observations in which you are more particularly interested.

I shall feel greatly obliged if you can suggest any steps that may be taken to facilitate my object— Should any person have previously applied to you and to whom you are pledged I shall feel very grateful if you will inform me— I shall not enter into a competition for any place

435

of the kind, and I do not wish to ask my friends to pledge themselves for me unless there is a fair prospect of success.

I am told that the Hon. Mr Walker Secretary of the Treasury has much influence with the President but I do not know how to secure his favorable consideration except through your kindness. I shall write to prof. Agassiz this evening, both to ask his recommendation and advice—

> I am very[c] sincerely
> Your obedient Servant
> James Hall

Henry Papers, Smithsonian Archives.
Reply: Doc. 242. Gloss of reply on third sheet.

1. State paleontologist of New York. *Henry Papers*, 6:136n.
2. Hall did not finish the second volume of the *Paleontology of New-York* until 1852. While he was working on it, he took on a number of other projects. Michele L. Aldrich and Alan E. Leviton, "James Hall and the New York Survey," *Earth Sciences History*, 1987, 6:29.
3. President of the Mechanics and Farmers Bank of Albany. *Henry Papers*, 5:386.

241. TO ASA GRAY

Washington Dec. 22nd 1848.

My Dear Doctor,

The Board of Regents is now in session, & all things relative to the Smithsonian are apparently in a harmonious & prosperous condition. The east wing of the building is finished, and will be ready for use as soon as the heating apparatus is arranged. Prof. Jewett will enter on his duties immediately, & will relieve me from much that is irksome & unprofitable to me. Mr. O. is no longer a regent, & by the loss of his election to the senate, will probably not be able again to secure a place in the Board.[1]

My Report will be given in to Congress about New Year, & if in the course of a few weeks you can furnish me with the promised programme of your Report on forest trees, I shall be much pleased. It may be printed as an appendix at any time during the session of Congress, though it would be best to have it prepared as soon as possible[2]—

I am not yet quite clear as to the manner in which we can assist you in the continuation of the publication of your work on Botany.[3] Agreeably to the financial arrangements adopted at the last meeting, one half of the income of the original bequest is to be devoted for the next three years, or until the building is completed to the building fund. This arrangement was at first proposed with the idea that all operations relative to the collection of a library would be postponed until the building should be completed. The friends of the library however would not consent to this, & they insisted upon calling in the services of Mr. Jewett at the beginning of the present year. This was agreed to, & both parts of the general plan will hereafter be carried on jointly, the portion of the income remaining from the building being divided between them. Though I do not think that we shall adhere rigidly to this arrangement, since we shall require more money to develope the plans of the Institution,—yet much economy will be required in conducting our operations, & but little expenditure will be allowed for objects not immediately embraced in the programme. I think it however highly important that your work should be continued, & I regret that it was not at first presented as a Contribution to the Institution— Cannot parts of it still be presented in this form, so far as they are original, & afterwards be republished in your volumes? You might in this way save the expense of the plates. If you still think we could most effectually aid you by the purchase of—say a hundred copies, I will place the proposition before Mr. Marsh & those most interested in the library, in order that part of the purchase money, if not the whole, might come from the library appropriation. If our funds were entirely free at this time, I think there would be no difficulty in adopting the plan proposed, & if you can wait until three years from next March I doubt not that the required assistance can be rendered. I hope however that you intend to visit Washington during the present session of Congress, & that we may have an oppertunity of ascertaining definitely what can be done.

What is the state of the paper in preparation for the second volume of the Smithsonian Contributions, on which I have advanced $100 to Dr. Torrey?

We have just got into a new house, & shall be happy to furnish Mrs. Gray & yourself with accomodation, when you next come to Washington, under our own roof.

If the east wing of the Smithsonian building is ready to be occupied before the close of the present session of Congress, lectures will be commenced in it; & if so, cannot you oblige us by giving a short course? Our funds will not allow us to pay much at present; we might however give you enough to defray your expenses here & back, which might be an object if you are obliged to visit the city.[4]

There is an attempt making here to revive the National[A] Institute, & Bache & myself have been solicited to allow our names to be included in the list of officers. We have however declined; though it is a difficult

437

matter to know what is the proper course. The expense of keeping the Museum of the Exploring Expedition ought not be put upon the Smithsonian fund, while on the other hand the collection should be under the care of some institution properly organized. If the National Institute would confine its operations for the present merely to the care & increase of the collections now in Washington, it might render good service to the Country, & in time, under other directors retrieve its character. It cannot however ever become a National Institution in the proper sense of the term without[B] securing the coöperation of all the real men of science in the country. But this can scarcely be accomplished because thay are so widely separated. Washington is not, like Paris, a nation in itself.

Mrs. Henry joins me in kind regards to you & yours—

> I remain, as ever
> truly yours
> Joseph Henry

Dr. Gray.

P.S. I have now a confidential assistant who relieves me very much by writing to my dictation. J.H.

Historic Letters, Archives, Gray Herbarium Library, Harvard University.
In Caspar W. Hodge's hand, except for the signature and postscript. Reply: Doc. 258.

1. Robert Dale Owen had lost his election to the House of Representatives, not the Senate.
2. The congressional session ended March 3. The *Smithsonian Report for 1848* was presented to the House of Representatives on February 19 and to the Senate on February 22. It did not contain a report by Gray. Rhees, *Documents* (1901), *1:*465.
3. *Genera of the Plants of the United States.*
4. Gray did not lecture at the Smithsonian until the winter of 1854–1855.

242. TO JAMES HALL

Washington Dec. 23[d] 1848.

My Dear Sir,

Your letter of the 18th inst.[1] was duly received. I have, I think, received four letters applying to me for interference with regard to securing appointments for explorations in California.[2] I have promised to speak favorably of one of the gentlemen should an exploration be ordered.[3] I should think that recommendations from individuals well known in the line of sciene would have great weight in a matter of this kind. The names of Dr. Silliman,[4] Agassiz &, Dr. Hitchcock, would be important. I will myself speak to Mr. Walker on the subject, though I cannot with propriety give you a recommendation, unless the other person should withdraw,[A] or be considered ineligible.

Lieut. Gilliss will start next summer on an astronomical expidition[B] to Chili, & may possibly take a naturalist with him.[5] Should he do so, & should you like the situation, I think it not improbable that you might obtain it.

> With much respect
> I remain your friend &serv[t]
> Joseph Henry

James Hall Esq.

PS Since inditing the foregoing I have seen the secretary[C] of the Treasury Mr Walker who informes me that he does not think any explorers will be sent to the new Teretories by this administration.

> JH

Monday Dec 25th 1848

I have this morning had an interview with the Hon Butler King[6]—he thinks an expedition will be sent out or rather a geologist with the Surveying parties which are to formed. He is anxious to have an exploration made of the Alutian Island's for the descovery if possible of any coal[D] fields which may exist along the route to Japan.

> J–H

State Geologists' and Paleontologists' Correspondence File, Series B0561, New York State Archives.

In the hand of Caspar W. Hodge, except for the signature and postscripts. Copy: Partial Mary Henry Copy, Henry Papers, Smithsonian Archives.

1. Doc. 240.

2. We have identified three: Doc. 219; Samuel G. Morton to Henry, October 27, 1848, Box 784, Consolidated Correspondence File, Records of the Office of the Quartermaster General, RG 92, National Archives, recommending William H. Pease, a naturalist; and T. Abbott to Henry, December 13, 1848, Henry Papers, Smithsonian Archives, recommending Timothy A. Conrad, a geologist.

3. We do not know who Henry supported. No responses have been found to any of the above letters, nor have we found letters supporting a particular candidate. Henry did write Secretary of War William Marcy on November 3, 1848 (Box 784, Consolidated Correspondence File, Records of the Office of the Quartermaster General, RG 92, National Archives), asking that Pease be given "a free passage in one of the public ships about to sail for Oregon," but this was to facilitate Pease's personal collecting. There is no mention in the letter of a government position for Pease.

Hall served as a consultant to the Mexican Boundary Survey, but he never did field work in the West. William H. Goetzmann, *Exploration and Empire: The Explorer and the Scientist in the Winning of the American West* (New York, 1966), p. 317.

4. Benjamin Silliman, Sr.

5. Instead, Gilliss asked Edmond Reuel Smith, the clerk of the expedition, to take responsibility for natural history. However, no systematic collecting was done. Whatever collections Gilliss did acquire at his own expense were given to the Smithsonian in 1853. Wayne D. Rasmussen, "The United States Astronomical Expedition to Chile, 1849–1852," *Hispanic American Historical Review*, 1954, *34:*104, 106, 110.

6. King was a strong advocate of internal improvements and Asian trade. Edward M. Steel, Jr., *T. Butler King of Georgia* (Athens, 1964).

243. TO FRANCIS LIEBER

Washington Dec. 23ᵈ 1848.

My Dear Sir,

The gentleman in the state of New York to whom I sent your circular was the Hon William J. Hough, formerly one of the Regents of the Smithsonian Institution. He resides at a place called Cazenovia—

I regret that I did not have an oppertunity of seeing you on your return from Europe. You have doubtless much to tell which I should be delighted to hear. I hope you intend to visit Washington, & that I shall soon see you at my house—

I have written to Dr. Howe on the subject of a memoir relative to Laura Bridgeman,[1] & have requested him to give a simple account of all the circumstances of her case. He appears I think from his letter,[2] inclined to undertake the task, & if he should conclude to do so, I should be pleased to have his memoir accompanied by one from you giving such theoretical inferences as you may have arrived at by an induction from the facts. In order however not to violate our rules as regard hypotheses, the two memoirs should be connected; & it would be well if your inferences could lead you to results which might be tested by actual observation of the girl in her present state of mental developement, or by inquiries which might be put to her. I have stated to Dr. Howe that it would be well to illustrate the memoir with a portrait of Laura, & with drawings of all the implements used peculiarly in the course of her instruction.[3]

The Smithsonian Institution I think is gradually developing itself in the way of doing much good. The plans are beginning to be generally understood, & scarcely a day passes without offering some occasion for a proper application of our aid. I will send you a copy of my Report for this year as soon as it is printed, & it would give me much pleasure if I could present you with a copy of the first Volume of the Contributions to Knowledge. But this I am at present unable to do. No copies as yet have been given to individuals—

I remain very truly
Your friend & servᵗ
Joseph Henry

Professer Lieber—
P.S.

Please excuse me for having employedᴬ an amanuensis in writing this letter. I am now so much oppressed with correspondence that I cannot otherwise get along.

In examing the date of your letter I am surprised to find it the 9th of Nov.[4] It has just been received by me through Mr J. R. Ingersoll. Can I be of any service to you in the distribution of your circular? Professor Jewett enters[B] upon his duties as Assistant Secretary and will I trust relieve me of some of the details of the business of the Institution.

Yours

JH

LI 1626, Lieber Papers, Huntington Library.
In Caspar W. Hodge's hand, except for signature and postscript in Henry's hand. Reply: December 30, 1848, Henry Papers, Smithsonian Archives.

1. Letter not found.
2. Not found.
3. The Smithsonian never published a memoir by Howe.
4. Not found, although possibly the Lieber letter with Henry's file date of November 10, 1847, located in the Henry Papers, Smithsonian Archives. It consists of only the last two pages.

244. TO EPHRAIM GEORGE SQUIER

Washington

Dec 25th 1848

My Dear Sir

I received your letter of the 22nd yesterday[1] and I am sorry to inform you that I cannot without much inconvenience meet the draft you mention— You must apply the funds I sent to you to the payment of your note in New York and I will pay the expense of the protest. I will also explain to the cashier in this place to whom the draft may be sent the reason why it is not accepted. This is all I can do for you.

The remonstrance you speak of to the Board of Regents can produce no effect except evil.[2] The Board will not acknowledge the obligation to give you more than comparatively a few copies for distribution; this was all I promised you with their authority and to attempt to[A] establish the position you state in your letter would bring on a discussion which might be attended with unplesant consequences. Nothing as yet has been done in the Board which in the least degree reflects improperly upon Dr Davis or yourself. All[B] that will appear on the minutes is the simple fact of the grant of the 200 copies. The delivery of the copies will be intrusted to myself and the executive committee and we shall endeavour to ascertain previous to the act whether the Institution is likely to suffer in reputation or otherwise by the litegations which may

441

grow out of the difficulties between Dr Davis and yourself. I trust however that we shall have no cause to with hold the copies and that Dr Davis and yourself will be able to effect a conventional adjustment if not an amicable settlement of your difficulties.[3]

> I remain very truly
> Yours &c
> Joseph Henry

E G Squier Esq

Squier Papers, Library of Congress.

1. Letter not found.

2. We suspect that the tone of Squier's letter to Henry matched that of his of the same date to G. P. Marsh (Marsh Papers, Bailey/Howe Library, University of Vermont). The Board of Regents was threatening to hold up the distribution of the authors' copies of the Squier and Davis publication, pending the settlement of a financial dispute between the authors. In his letter to Marsh, Squier claimed that his contract with Davis provided for unconditional equal distribution between the authors. He also stated that he planned to write the "President of the Board of Regents, enclosing a copy of my contract with Davis." Squier's letter to the board, not found, was read and referred to Henry and the executive committee on January 6, 1849 (Rhees, *Journals,* p. 54). If it was similar to the draft dated December 27, 1848 (Squier Papers, Library of Congress), then Squier ignored Henry's advice. Squier quoted his contract with Davis and claimed that the dispute between the two men was irrelevant as far as the Smithsonian was concerned. He asked for his one hundred copies.

3. It was not until February 6, 1849, that Henry was ordered by the executive committee to distribute the authors' copies of Squier and Davis's publication. The order was issued only after a joint letter, not found, was sent to the Smithsonian by the two men. Rhees, *Journals,* p. 468.

245. TO ELIAS LOOMIS

Washington, Dec[r] 28th 1848

My dear Sir:

Your letters[1] were duly received, but I have been so much pressed with business relative to the meeting of the Board of Regents, that I have not been able to keep up with my correspondence. The edition of the report in which your meteorological essay was published[2] is, with the exception of a few copies, exhausted. Arrangements, I think, however, will be made for its republication, which will enable you to make any corrections which you may deen necessary. I am glad to learn that the report on astronomy is so nearly completed. I cannot tell, just at this time, when I shall want it, probably, however, before the adjournment of the present session of Congress. I will give you notice a few days before it will be required.

I hope you have done especial justice to the labors of American Astronomers. It is time that we should have among us a scientific <u>esprit du corps</u>. I presume you have mentioned the intended expedition, ↑of Leut.↓ Gilliss', to the coast of Chilli—tho this is among the things that are to be. I have a long communication from him[3] on the subject which if you would like to see, with his permission, I will send to you.

M[r] S. C. Walker has lately presented to Prof. Bache a plan of application of the electrical telegraph to the registry of the time of occurrence of astronomical phenomena.[4,A] The electrical circuit is connected with the escapement of a clock, and, at each second, a mark is made on a slip of paper passing with uniform velocity under the magnetic pen. At the moment of the appearance of a phenomenon,[B] the observer touches a key which imprints an intermediate mark, the position of which on the paper gives the time in small fractional parts of a second. Thus,

if the marks, 1., 2., 3., &[c], represent the seconds, and <u>a</u> the time of a phenomenon[B] the proportional part of a second may be estimated by the[C] distance ↑of a↓ from the nearest second by the application of a proportional compass or of a graduated scale.

M[r] Walker proposes to introduce a large number of spider webs into the transit and other instruments and by means of the above apparatus[D] to multiply[E] the number of observations many times. I remain

Very truly yours, &c
Joseph Henry

Professor Loomis

Loomis Papers, Beinecke Rare Book and Manuscript Library, Yale University.
In Charles C. Jewett's hand, except for signature and inside address. Undated draft in Henry Papers, Smithsonian Archives.

1. Not found.
2. *Smithsonian Report for 1847*, pp. 193–207.
3. Not found.
4. As early as 1844, astronomers began utilizing Morse's telegraph to determine longitude by comparing chronometers or observations. The Coast Survey became the primary patron of such activities. Initially, the signals were transmitted by a human operator. Astronomers soon realized, however, that a system in which the beats of the clock were transmitted directly to the telegraph line was more accurate. In August 1848, William Bond, director of the Harvard College Observatory, developed a method of automatically breaking the circuit every time the clock beat. His device was not completed until 1850. Meanwhile, in the fall of 1848, John Locke invented his electro-chronograph. It consisted of a toothed wheel which attached to the axis of a clock's escapement wheel. As a result of the wheel's motion, a hammer was alternately lifted and dropped, which in turn broke and completed the electric circuit.

Sears Cook Walker's report credited Charles Wheatstone with the invention of the "automatic clock register." He also mentioned Bond's efforts, experiments that he and O. M. Mitchel performed in October 1848 in the Cincinnati Observatory, and Locke's instrument. Walker also included a number of suggestions for improving the apparatus. U.S. House, 30th Congress, 2d Session, *A Report by the Superintendent of the Coast Survey, on an Application of the Gal-*

vanic Circuit to an Astronomical Clock and Telegraph Register in Determining Local Differences of Longitude, and in Astronomical Observations Generally, House Executive Documents, No. 21 (1849) (quotation on p. 3).

As subsequent letters in this volume will show, Walker's report triggered a controversy with John Locke over priority. Fueling the acrimonious interchange was a $10,000 congressional appropriation for Locke, in exchange for the free use of his invention by the United States and the construction of a clock at the Naval Observatory. The appropriation passed on March 3, 1849. Subsequently, Locke accused Mitchel, Walker, and Bache of having engaged in a "conspiracy" against him (Locke, *Invention of the Electro-Chronograph*, p. 73).

The most balanced contemporary account of the dispute is Elias Loomis, *The Recent Progress of Astronomy; Especially in the United States* (New York, 1850), pp. 212–236. Locke presented his attacks and defense in three pamphlets: *Documents Relative to the Electro-Chronograph, Invented by John Locke, . . .* (Newark, 1849) (Locke's annotated version of Walker's report appears on pp. 9–22); *On the Invention of the Electro-Chronograph. A Letter to Nicholas Longsworth, Esq.* (Cincinnati, 1850); and *Report of Professor John Locke, . . . on the Invention and Construction of His Electro-Chronograph . . .* (Cincinnati, 1850). At the 1849 meeting of the American Association for the Advancement of Science, Walker credited the Coast Survey with almost every advancement in longitude determination by telegraph, and almost entirely ignored Locke's contributions; AAAS *Proceedings*, 1849, 2:182–192. At the same meeting, Mitchel presented a paper on his "Improvements in the Application of the Magnetic Telegraph to Astronomical Observations," which gave rise to "an animated discussion" between Mitchel, Henry, Benjamin Peirce, Bache, and M. F. Maury; AAAS *Proceedings*, 1849, 2:274. William Bond publicized his contributions in *Annals of the Astronomical Observatory of Harvard College*, 1852–1853, *1*, part 2:xxi–xxx.

246. FROM JOHN LOCKE

Cincinnati Dec. 31 1848

Prof Henry
Dear Sir.

Enclosed is a specimen of the work performed by my Telegraphic clock for determining Longitude.[1] The seconds you see are marked by dashes about half an inch long. The commencement of every minute is marked by the <u>omission</u> of a break between two seconds when there occurs a dash say 1 inch long. Every 5 minutes the minute zero is <u>followed</u> in two or 3 seconds by a second dash say 3 seconds long. The commencement of an hour is indicated by a long dash <u>preceding</u> the minute zero a few seconds. The specimen encl[os]ed[A] does not include the hour signal. Observat[ion]s[A] are entered by breaks or blanks the co[mm]encement[A] of which is the punctum of time. I have just invented a key which shall measure the break or blank in such a manner that each end of it shall be a known punctum of time. I have communicated in detail the steps of my invention to Prof Bache[2] who may have mentioned it to you. To you the advantages of such a machine will be very apparent. But the one clock is needed in determining longitude. Say that clock is going at Washington and is registering its time both there and at Cincinnati. Observations both there and here are entered by simply breaking the circuit, and a duplicate register, made by the clock. The rate of the clock is determined by its own registration of star transits of known difference of right ascension. Nor will its use be scarcely less in the local Observatory, when the observer will be relieved of all anxiety of looking at, and listening to, the clock beats and of estimating the fraction of a second. The ↑electrical↓ machinery of my clock does not interfere in the least with the pendulum and seems not sensibly to affect the rate.

yours
John Locke

Henry Papers, Smithsonian Archives.

1. The enclosure has not been found, but from the description it resembled the specimens in *Report of Professor John Locke, . . . on the Invention and Construction of His Electro-Chronograph . . .* (Cincinnati, 1850), p. 47.

2. Locke printed his five letters to Bache, of November 17, 18, 19, 20, and 23, 1848, which laid out the development of his invention, in *Report of Professor John Locke,* pp. 42–48.

◈ 1849 ◈

247. FROM ASA GRAY

Cambridge. Jany 1, 1849.

My Dear Friend

Lieut. Davis[1] going on to Washington, gives me the opportunity to send a hasty line—to ask you to answer—by however brief a line—a late letter of mine,[2] about having a botanical explorer attached to the Mexican Boundary survey.[3] If you can not say whether Mr. Marcy will entertain my proposition, please say whether I should make a direct application to him, or to some other functionary.

I have labored hard since I saw you, but under many discouragements, my wife having been sick all the autumn, and ↑still↓ quite feeble—though convalescent,—so that I have not had the help I anticipated and needed.— You must lay it therefore to real necessity of the case—that I have not felt like placing[A] myself under direct engagements to get out a part of Report on Trees the coming summer—as much depends on the future state of her health. I see no reason why it should not be good, but thus far it has not been so.

I should like to hear from you about the <u>Genera Illustrated</u>— I soon begin to print the 2nd vol.—

My wife joins in best wishes and regards to Mrs Henry—

Yours cordially
Asa Gray

P.S.

I am mortified at our good friend Torrey's defeat at New York.[4] I fear he will feel it sensibly—

A.G.

Henry Papers, Smithsonian Archives.
Reply: Doc. 253.

1. Charles Henry Davis.
2. Not found.
3. The Mexican Boundary Survey served as "a kind of graduate school for collectors." Before it was completed in 1857, the survey employed five field collectors at one time or another, all under the general supervision of John Torrey. Dupree, *Gray,* pp. 205–206 (quotation on p. 205); William H. Goetzmann, *Exploration and Empire: The Explorer and the Scientist in the Winning of the American West* (New York, 1966), pp. 314, 321–322; Andrew Denny Rodgers III, *John Torrey: A Story of North American Botany* (1942; New York, 1965), pp. 219–230.
4. Torrey had applied for the chair of chemistry at the New York Free Academy (now College of the City of New York). Although he had been favored by the nominating committee, the election was won by Oliver Wolcott Gibbs. Rodgers, *Torrey,* pp. 211–213.

248. FROM LEWIS C. BECK

New Brunswick Jany 6th
1849

My dear Sir

Your letters of Oct 28th,[1] Novr 2^d & Decr 29th,[2] were duly rec^d; the last, via Albany, which place I left for home on the 23^d ult. where I hope I shall now remain for the next 9 months— The two first of your letters seemed to require no immediate answer, as I determined to leave the whole arrangement of the amount of my compensation to Mr Burke himself.— I thought it somewhat singular that he should not have apprized me of the Congressional appropriation, when even the continuance of the work seemed to depend upon it. I regret that any thing of an unpleasant nature should have passed between us. In every thing else I have found Mr B. polite & corteous. But the longer I live the more I am satisfied that a good deal of the trouble which occurs in these matters, arises from the want of <u>definite</u> arrangements in regard to compensation for services of this kind. I cannot accuse myself of any great fondness for money, but when one engages in a work of this sort, it is, I think, not unreasonable that the quid pro quo should be understood on both sides. I know not that the Investigation will be continued—this I suppose will depend upon the action of Congress. If it is, I hope all unpleasant correspondence[A] will be avoided by a plain understanding of this matter in the outset—

I have at length completed my Report & hope it is now in Mr Burke's hands. I may say to you as I have said to him, that I have worked at the Investigation almost daily & nightly, for 10[B] months. Whatever difference of opinion there may be in regard to the merits of the Report, I am aware of no want of Industry to render it what it should be. But it is after all only a beginning. The samples came in at too late a date & were not all of the kind that I wished to have. Many points are therefore left for the future— But whether I shall follow them out, depends in a measure upon the contingency to which I have before referred— I regret at times that the Researches on the 'Breadstuffs' could not have been carried on under the auspices of the S.I. or independently. My principal reason for this wish is, that the Reports would then have been published separately & if they had any merit would have been more apt to attract attention. I fear that being published with a mass of other documents, it will form so small a part of a large whole, as to be overlooked. But I propose if the work goes on, to embody all the important facts in the shape of a Final Report & this may perhaps be voluminous enough to stand alone somewhere.

This ~~perhaps~~ rather tedious account of my operations, in regard to the 'Breadstuffs', will perhaps prepare you for what I have to say concerning the Agricultural Report. The truth is my mind & my hands too were so wholly occupied with ↑that↓ work, that I could not attend to any thing else. I lost 3 or 4 months ↑on your Rep.↓ during the summer for reasons heretofore explained. Nevertheless, I have done something—& ~~which~~ if I keep my health, I hope to be ready by the time you will want to print. I have a number of drawings for wood cuts, but I must advance further in the Text before I decide definitely in regard to them. The Report should be carefully prepared & I often have misgivings— You will be able to learn something of my mode of treating of kindred subjects from my Breadstuff Report. My wish is to Make the Rep. on[C] A. Chemistry—a hand book in this branch, as well as to include in it a sketch of the history & illustrations of the importance of the science.

I thank you much for your kind invitation to visit you in Washington. At some future time time I may accept it, but just now it is out of the question, as in addition to other work, I have to attend to my duties in the College.

In haste.

> With my regards to Mrs H. in which
> Mrs B.[3] begs to unite with me
> I remain yours truly L.C.B.

Prof. Henry—

Henry Papers, Smithsonian Archives.

1. Doc. 228.

2. Neither letter has been found.

3. Hannah Maria Smith Beck (b. 1806) married Beck in 1825. Lewis B. Sebring and Lewis B. Sebring, Jr., *Life of Lewis C. Beck, M.D.: Physician, Traveler, Geologist, Author, Educator* (typescript, 1934), pp. 7, 8.

249. FROM ROBERT DALE OWEN

Washington, Jany 10. 1849.

My dear Sir:

I received, last evening by Mr Bache the advertisement & preface.[1] I had previously seen Genl Totten & Mr Seaton, & mentioned to them y^r wishes as to the omission of the resolution. To this they consent. If, therefore, I don't hear further from you, I shall print the advertisement as it is, omitting the resolution. I shall also submit ↑it,↓ as you suggested, along with the two concluding chapters to Messrs Everett,[2] Kemble[3] & Kane.[4]

The enclosed letter[5] I^A received ~~a cop~~ a day or two since. Dr Buchanan[6] is Professor in a Medical College in Cincinnati, a man of decided talent; whether a practical man & accurate observer I know not. In former years when I knew him, he seemed to me misled by imaginative theories, beyond the strict results of dispassionate experiment.

I am desirous to obtain a copy of the last report of the Building Committee recently prepared by Genl Totten, to get from it accurate data as to the cost of the Institution Building, &c. ~~If you~~ I asked Genl Totten for it yesterday but he told me it was in your hands. If you can spare it for a couple of days, I will get Miss Mills[7] to copy it & return it to you, & to send me the copy to New York; for which place I start this afternoon.

Also you will oblige me by lending me per bearer the Journal of the

Executive Committee, as Miss Mills wishes me to aid her in making up her account for engrossing.

I am, my d Sir
Truly y^{rs}
Robert Dale Owen

Joseph Henry, L.L.D.

Henry Papers, Smithsonian Archives.

1. To Owen's *Hints on Public Architecture* (New York, 1849).
2. Edward Everett.
3. Gouverneur Kemble (1786–1875) was a cannon founder, railroad entrepreneur, and former congressman. *DAB*.
4. John K. Kane. Everett, Kemble, and Kane were selected by the building committee of the Smithsonian Regents to referee Owen's publication. *Hints on Public Architecture*, pp. iii–iv.
5. Not found.

6. Joseph Rodes Buchanan (1814–1899) was on the faculty of the Eclectic Medical Institute of Cincinnati. He had developed theories of illness, diagnosis, and treatment which were eccentric and were rejected by the established medical profession. *DAB*.
7. Ann Mills had been employed by the Smithsonian periodically since April 1847 for copying and engrossing. Smithsonian Daybooks, vol. 1, pp. 17, 21, 27, 32, 35, 44, 68.

250. EXCERPT, MINUTES, NATIONAL INSTITUTE

Ordinary Meeting, Jan 15. 1849

Institute met at 7 oclock P.M.

Prof Henry, Vice President, in the chair.

Present,	Capt. Wilkes
Prof. Johnson	Mr Schoolcraft
Lt. Gillis	" Cutts[3]
Mr Easby[1]	" Stansbury
" Elliot[2]...	

Donation to the Library

Prof Henry presented to the Library a Copy of the "Smithsonian Contributions" on Occultations, & also several copies of his report on the Organization of the Smithsonian Institution.

Verbal Communications . . .

Prof Henry said that, in connection with the subject of California, he would mention certain facts stated by Col Frémont with regard to the country between the Sierra Nevada & the Rocky Mountains, which he regarded as of interest in a meteorological[A] point of view. Col Fremont stated that the country on the West slope of the Sierra Nevada was well watered, whereas that to the East of the same range was a dry and arid desert;[4] and, moreover, that the plain or table land between the Sierra Nevada & the Rocky Mountains, was warmer than the country of the same elevation on the West of the Sierra Nevada.[5]

The explanation given by Prof Henry of these two phenomena was as follows.

1st The prevailing wind of that region is from the West. The air in its ascent along the side of the mountain ridge is brought constantly into a colder region, & must therefore precipitate its moisture, & if the ridge be sufficiently high the air which passes over it must be nearly dry.

2[d] A current of perfectly dry air in passing over a high mountain ridge will have the same temperature when it descends to the same level on the other side; for the sensible heat which becomes latent in the ascent & consequent expansion, will again become sensible in the descent. But if the current of air be surcharged with moisture the effect will be different: the moisture will be condensed in its passage over the ridge, & its latent heat will be added to that of the air, which will, consequently, when it arrives at the same level on the opposite side, be of a higher temperature than that of its normal condition.

These facts are in striking accordance with Espy's theory[6]. . . .

Journal of Minutes, No. 2 (1842–1849), Records of the National Institute, RU 7058, Smithsonian Archives.

1. William Easby, who was appointed commissioner of public buildings for the District of Columbia in 1851. *Third Bulletin of the Proceedings of the National Institute for the Promotion of Science* (Washington, 1845), p. 392; Charles Lanman, *Biographical Annals of the Civil Government of the United States,* 2d ed. (New York, 1887).

2. William Parker Eliot (1807–1854), a patent agent in Washington. Douglas E. Evelyn, "The Washington Years: The U.S. Patent Office," in John M. Bryan, ed., *Robert Mills, Architect* (Washington, 1989), pp. 112, 138–140; *Third Bulletin,* p. 392.

3. James Madison Cutts (1805–1863), author of *The Conquest of California and New Mexico, by the Forces of the United States, in the Years 1846 and 1847* (Philadelphia, 1847), became second comptroller of the treasury in 1857. *Third Bulletin,* p. 392; Lanman; Oscar Fay Adams, *A Dictionary of American Authors,* 5th ed. (Boston, 1904).

4. Drawing upon the observations made during his 1843–1844 expedition, Frémont made the comparison between the moist western side and the arid eastern side of the Sierra Nevada Mountains in U.S. Senate, 30th Congress, 1st Session, *Geographical Memoir upon Upper California, in Illustration of His [Frémont's] Map of Oregon and California,* Senate Miscellaneous Documents, No. 148 (1848), pp. 6–7.

5. In his description of the Great Basin, Frémont noted that its climate "does not present the rigorous winter due to its elevation and mountainous structure." Frémont, p. 12.

6. According to Espy, moist air rises and expands. As the expanding air cools, the water vapor will condense out. "On the leeward side of very lofty mountains, there cannot be rain," for the very reasons stated by Henry. James P. Espy, *The Philosophy of Storms* (Boston, 1841), pp. viii–xvii (quotation on p. xvii).

251. FROM FRANCIS LIEBER

Columbia S.C.
16 January [1849][A]

My dear Sir,

I suppose it will be easy for You to have a copy of the S.I. Transactions delivered for S.C. College[1] at John Wiley's, Publisher at N.Y. If it be directed to us, he will send it, as we are in the habit of receiving books from him.

I have not yet received the Congressional Directory,[2] but beg You to accept my thanks.

Dr Howe has not yet answered. I cannot agree with Mr Owen's enthusiasm for the Norman architecture. It is proper in its place, like all other sublunary things; but battlements and turrets of the middle ages do not agree with scientific purposes of the 19[h] century, it would appear; still less does the Smithsonian seem to be the proper organ to diffuse such Knowledge, if Knowledge it be. I am sorry, for it will serve as a handle against the institution.

I trust that You will soon find time again to pursue Your scientific objects. To gain You at that cost would lead one to "calculate the value" of the bargin.

Most truly Yours
F. Lieber

Henry Papers, Smithsonian Archives.

1. In his letter to Henry of December 30, 1848 (Henry Papers, Smithsonian Archives), Lieber informed Henry that the South Carolina College library had not yet received a copy of the SI Contributions, and inquired whether it should have.

2. In the same letter, Lieber asked for a list of members of the House of Representatives. He was trying to identify a New York congressman to whom he wanted to send a pamphlet.

252. FROM EDWARD FOREMAN[1]

Baltimore Jany. 17 1849

Profr Henry

Dear Sir   I sent down yesterday to your address a packet containing 12 copies of the circular[2] to be issued to those who may be induced to collect specimens of building stone for our Experiments.[3] As the printed queries are by this time ready I deemed it better, not to cause any delay & transmit them at once. I would suggest that a copy be sent to the following persons—Dr Charles. T. Jackson Boston, Ms. or to Mr F. Alger[4] of the same place.— Profr Edwd Hitchcock, Amherst D̶r̶ Profr H. D. Rogers[5] Phila^a— Profr James Hall, Albany, or to Profr Beck Mineralogist of the N.Yk. Geolog^c Survey,—or to Robt. Carey Long[6] Esqr Architect o̶f̶ N. York.— Profr J. C. Booth Geologist of Delaware (if he be in Philadelphia which is his residence—a̶n̶d̶ Mr J. G. Percival[7] who surveyed the State of Connecticut—& Profr. B. Silliman Jun New Haven.

I will procure specimens of the building stone from this vicinity. We will probably be in possession of sufficient materials to commence Experiments by the time we have prepared suitable fixtures. ↑We may want↓ For this purpose apparatus for taking the Specific Gravity— An arrangement to shew the effect of a crushing weight, as figured in the 7th Meeting Rep^t of the Br. Assoc.[8] & means for making Chemical Analyses— An air pump, Freezing Apparatus and a boiler for generating Steam under high pressure. I have access here to the Annales Des Mines, Annales De Chimie, ↑&↓ various other recent French works on Chemistry & Mining, in private hands, and to Silliman J^l, Journal of Franklin Inst^e Reports of Institution of Civil Engineers in London Atheneum in Balto Library—and works in my own Library. I shall therefore occupy myself a few days in preparing a digest of what has been done & what is known upon the subject.

Some items of information upon the subject of Meteorology have come under my notice—I deem it my duty to lay them before you. There is extant here & for the most part in printed form a meteorological journal for some ten years carefully kept by Capt. Brantz[9]— The Thermom^r Barometer Rainguage direction of Wind—were observed. Another series more recent & now accumulating, of 10–12 years duration, is in possession of Dr Thos Edmondson[10] of this city. He has very fine instruments and is very punctual. He adds observations on the Hygrometer—using Mason's.[11] He would allow a copy to be taken & a copy of Brantzs can be had from Mr J. Green[12] the Instrument maker. My series extends from 1838 to 1848. Mr Green has shown me the "Aneroid Barometer"[13] a French instrument which probably you have become acquainted with. It consists of a box made of plates compensated for t̶e̶m̶ Expansion—partially exhausted, to exaggerate the effect produced by the ever varying density of the Atmosphere—rendered sensible by a system of levers connected with a multiplying arrangement— Indexes on the face point to the inches tenths & hundredths— It is of the diameter of an ordinary Chronometer & coincides very closely with the common barometer as I made the comparison yesterday. Price $20. An intelligent Sea captain has told me that being less liable to damage or derangement they are rapidly getting into use & displacing the mercurial Instrumnt in all ships sailing out of Liverpool &c.

Profr N. R. Wright[14] (my successor here) has fair instruments for meteorology and if blanks are sent to him would furnish regular reports.

Profr Frs. P. Mettauer[15] Prince Edward Court House Virginia wishes to be an applicant for a set of Instruments when they are ready for distribution. He is a man of Science, perfectly trustworthy, very assiduous in this business and occupies a station which Espy strongly recommends to notice as a very important focus of atmospheric vicissitudes. If blanks were sent to him, as preliminary to further correspondence & acquaintance some estimate might be formed of his probable usefulness.

I have had complaints made to me that intelligent ship owners & captains have sent propositions to Mr Espy to record observations made during their voyages, if he would issue ~~any~~ blanks for the purpose— and that they have received no reply.

If the rules of the Smith". Instit^n permit it I would recommend that any publications of an Astronomical character now on hand may be sent to Profr. Verot St Marys College[16] Baltimore— It would confer a favor on that gentleman, & he has been of service to us, lately.

I would be very much obliged if you will send a messenger to the P. Office in Your city, take out one or more letters now lying there addressed to me & envelope them to my address here— They must be prepaid— I will refund.

I perceive that Mr Putnams list of books to be published contains the following "Researches on Building Materials, and hints on Public Architecture, issued under the direction of the Smithsonian Institution by R. D. Owen M.C. numerous illustrations in the finest style of Art."

To a previous list add Profr Wm B. Rogers, Charlottesville Va.

I remain very respectfully, Your Ob^t Servt
E Foreman

Henry Papers, Smithsonian Archives.

1. Originally offered $2 a day "to assist Prof. Henry in collecting building materials for experiment and probably in the experiments themselves," Edward Foreman (1808–1885), a former professor in the Medical Department of Washington University in Baltimore, was hired as Henry's general assistant in early January 1849. Among Foreman's responsibilities was the meteorological correspondence. Half of his salary was paid by the Smithsonian, half by the

Department of the Navy through the appropriation in support of Espy's work. At its July 1850 meeting, the Board of Regents authorized Henry to hire a general assistant for the Smithsonian at the salary of $1,200 per annum. Foreman was immediately appointed to that permanent position. Foreman remained with the Smithsonian until 1853, when he took a position as a patent examiner. He returned to the Smithsonian in 1867 to assist in the accessioning of ethnological specimens, remaining until 1884. Curtis M. Hinsley, Jr., *Savages and Scientists: The Smithsonian Institution and the Development of American Anthropology, 1846–1910* (Washington, 1981), pp. 71–72; Robert C. Post, *Physics, Patents and Politics: A Biography of Charles Grafton Page* (New York, 1976), pp. 73–74; Rhees, *Journals,* pp. 67–68, 474; Alexander Dallas Bache to Foreman, January 5, 1849, Box 1, Bache Papers, Smithsonian Archives (quotation).

2. Not found.

3. Perhaps Henry was finally following up on the Board of Regents' resolution of March 1, 1847, appropriating $500 for experiments "to determine the economical value of the different building materials used in the United States" (Rhees, *Journals,* p. 39). Whatever the ultimate purpose of the intended experiments, they were never conducted. In 1853, Henry reported that "other duties and a want of funds prevented the intention being carried into execution" (Henry to M. C. Meigs, May 6, 1853, Testing Materials (Strength of Materials), Capitol Extension, House and Senate Wings, 1851–1856, Office of the Curator, Office of the Architect of the Capitol).

4. Francis Alger (1807–1863) was a businessman and mineralogist with numerous publications. Elliott, *Dictionary.*

5. Henry Darwin Rogers was former state geologist of Pennsylvania and former professor of geology and mineralogy at the University of Pennsylvania. At this time he was living in Boston, not Philadelphia. *Henry Papers,* 2:290n; *DSB.*

6. Born in Baltimore and trained in New York, Robert Cary Long (1810–1849) practiced architecture in both cities. Best known for his churches, he was working on the plans for the Astor Library when he died in June. *Macmillan Encyclopedia of Architects.*

7. James Gates Percival (1795–1856) was renowned both as a poet and a geologist. The state geologist of Connecticut from 1835 to 1838, he would hold a similar position in Wisconsin from 1854 through 1856. *DAB.*

8. A reference to the apparatus illustrated in Eaton Hodgkinson, "On the Relative Strength and Other Mechanical Properties of Cast Iron Obtained by Hot and Cold Blast," *British Association Report for 1837,* p. 341.

9. Lewis Brantz had been a member of the Meteorological Committee of the Maryland Academy of Science and Literature. *Transactions of the Maryland Academy of Science and Literature,* 1837, *1:*142. His tables of meteorological observations appeared annually, under varying titles, beginning with his observations for 1817.

This is an example of the historical meteorological data that the Smithsonian gathered. Such data was useful in investigating climatological questions, such as the relationship between climate and health. For background, see Fleming, *Meteorology,* pp. 2–7.

10. Trained as a physician, Thomas Edmondson (1808–1856) was a horticulturalist, book collector, and one of Baltimore's major patrons of the fine arts. The Walters Art Gallery, *The Taste of Maryland: Art Collecting in Maryland, 1800–1934* (Baltimore, 1984), pp. 13–14.

11. Alva Mason, a Philadelphia instrument maker. *Henry Papers,* 2:269n.

12. Born in England, James Green (b. 1808) established himself as an instrument maker in Baltimore in 1832. By 1844, he had moved to New York City. Guyot selected Green to produce the standard barometers and thermometers for Smithsonian meteorological observers and for the New York State system. W. E. Knowles Middleton, *The History of the Barometer* (Baltimore, 1964), p. 343; Deborah Jean Warner, National Museum of American History, private communication; Fleming, *Meteorology,* pp. 119–120.

13. The name and modern form of the "aneroid barometer" (without liquid) is credited to Lucien Vidi or Vidie (1805–1866), a French steam engineer, who patented a barometer in 1844 that was based on a thin diaphragm of metal which reacted to changes in pressure. His invention was ridiculed by François Arago, director of the Paris Observatory, and therefore not readily accepted in France. Vidi found a warmer welcome in England, where the respected chronometer-maker Edward J. Dent acted as his agent. Middleton, *History of the Barometer,* pp. 398–409.

14. Reginald Norwood Wright (1819 or 1820–1865) graduated from Jefferson Medical College in 1844. He served as professor of chemistry at Newton University in Baltimore, and, following Foreman's resignation, simultaneously as professor of chemistry at Washington University. Baltimore City Directories, 1847–1854; *Catalog of Graduates of the Jefferson Medical College from Its Organization* (Philadelphia, 1879); *Baltimore Sun,* June 16, 1865.

phia, 1879); *Baltimore Sun,* June 16, 1865.

15. There were two members of the faculty of the Medical Department of Randolph-Macon College, nephew and uncle, named Francis Joseph Mettauer. One of them was a Smithsonian meteorological observer from 1849 until 1852. Howard A. Kelly and Walter

L. Burrage, *American Medical Biographies* (Baltimore, 1920), p. 786; *Smithsonian Report for 1868,* p. 84 (where the name is rendered "Frs. J. Nuttaner").

16. Jean Marcel Pierre Auguste Verot, professor of mathematics and science. *Henry Pa-*

253. TO ASA GRAY

Washington Jany 18th 49

My Dear friend

Your favour of the 1st of Jany[1] was received last week by the hands of Capt Davis and I have delayed answering it until I could get some definite information as to the appointment of a botanist to the boundary survey.

I wrote immediately to Col. Emory who has been appointed to command the expedition but did not get a reply until yesterday. I enclose his letter.[2]

You have no idea of the difficulty of transacting business in this place and how much my time is cut up and dissipated by visitors and correspondence of an unimportant kind. To obtain a single interview with one of the heads of Departments during the session of Congress members having precedence of all others sometimes costs me several calls. Most of the business has to be transacted at this season of the year by letter and these answered by clerks. I make these remarks to excuse my self in part for the seeming neglect of your commission.

Naturalists of late have become quite plenty. I have now on my table six applications for assistance in obtaining situations as explores of California.

I doubt whether any appointment of the kind will be made this session. Benton[3] thinks all operations of this nature should be performed by the officers of the Army or Navy. He has introduced or asked leave to introduce a bill for the discharge of all civilians from the Coast surey[4] has attacked the geological surveys & the exploring expedition.[5] Though he has but little influence at present yet he is feared.

I will see the secretary of state[6] on the subject of your letter and endeavour to learn diffenty whether an appointment of the kind can be hoped for from the present administration.

I am sorry to learn that Mrs Gray has been unwell but hope she will soon be restored to health. When you come again to Washington we shall be able to offer you and yours a room. We have taken a very pleasant house directly in the rear of the Patent Office and are now comfortably situated. The affairs of the Smithsonian are now getting into order. Prof. Jewett has entered on his duties and will relieve me of some of the drudgery to which I have been subjected as man of all work for the last two years.

The Board of Regents have adjourned after a very harmonious session. All the arrangements I was anxious to have made have been settled to my satisfaction. Your report will be printed as soon as it can be prepared— I think we shall be able to purchase 100 copies of your book provided you can wait until the end of three years. I received ↑a copy of a↓ a plate from Agassiz which I presume he intends for one of his papers in the Smithsonian Contributions.[7] It is very beautiful.

> I remain as ever
> truly yours &c
> Joseph Henry

Dr Gray

Historic Letters, Archives, Gray Herbarium Library, Harvard University. Reply: Doc. 258.

1. Doc. 247.

2. Not found, but in Henry's Desk Diary entry of January 17, 1849, he summarized Emory's letter: "Law does not provide for botanist—apply to secretary of state organization not yet made—have promised influence to Mr Halstead." For Mina Halsted, see Gray's reply.

3. Senator Thomas Hart Benton of Missouri. *Henry Papers,* 6:593n.

4. On February 17 Benton proposed deleting all funds for civilian employees of the Coast Survey from the 1849–1850 appropriations bill, and turning all the work over to the navy. Benton attacked the Coast Survey on two grounds: first, that it was engaged in activities far beyond its mission, including abstract science; second, that it was too expensive. Alert to the danger, Bache and his supporters orchestrated support from the mercantile, commercial, and scientific communities. Both James A. Pearce and Jefferson Davis rose in defense of the Coast Survey and Bache. In the end, Benton withdrew his amendment. *Congressional Globe,* 30th Congress, 2d Session, 1849, *18,* appendix, pp. 196–212; U.S. Senate, 35th Congress, 2d Session, *Report of the Secretary of the Treasury, Communicating, in Answer to a Resolution of the Senate, a Report Showing the Amount Expended and the Progress Made in the Coast Survey, and also the Weights and Measures Furnished the Several States and Custom-houses and Their Cost,* Senate Executive Documents, No. 6 (1858), pp. 148–177; Hugh Richard Slotten, "Patronage, Politics, and Practice in Nineteenth-Century American Science: Alexander Dallas Bache and the United States Coast Survey" (Ph.D. diss., University of Wisconsin-Madison, 1992), pp. 171–174.

5. The attack was not made by Benton, but by Representative William Sawyer, Democrat from Ohio. On January 16, Sawyer criticized many aspects of the appropriations bill for 1849–1850. Among his targets were the Wilkes Expedition, the Coast Survey, the Naval Observatory, and, in general, "national observatories, and exploring and scientific expeditions at the public expense." *Congressional Globe,* 30th Congress, 2d Session, 1849, *18:*271–272 (quotation on p. 272).

6. James Buchanan.

7. For a proposed memoir on fossil whales. See Doc. 263.

254. TO ROBERT HARE

Washington
Jany 19th 1849

My Dear Sir

I called at Gadsby's the day you left and was much disappointed to learn that you had started with the early line. I had gi[v]en[A] orders to Mr Gadsby not to present his bill to you but to charge it to the Institution. He happened however to be out at the time the bill was called for and the Barkeeper presented it to you not knowing the order I had given. The executive Committee of the Institution authorized me to pay your expenses in this city when you came on business relative to the apparatus which you have presented and as your late visit was at least in part of this kind I think your bill at the Hotel should be paid.[B] As[C] to the employment of De Beust with a salary of 700 Dollars a year, I do not think we can accomplish it at present. Our in[c]ome[A] which can be devoted to science is too small. One half of all the interest of the original fund is devoted to the building and until this is completed we shall be very much straitened for funds to carry on the active operations of the Institution. I hope however to be able in another year to make a diferent[D] arrangement and draw a larger amount for the Scientific operations.

Your essay on credit has been received[1] and at my first leisure I shall endeavour to study it. A mere reading will not answer. I have however derived my ideas of [c]urrency[A] from Adam Smith[2] and to use an expressive saying of your own, it is hard to teach old dogs new tricks, or old men new theories.

At the age of 45[E] a man is pretty well made up on the ordinary subjects of life and though he may constantly grow in Knowledge yet at this age his den, in the language of Bacon, has been excavated and all subjects are viewed by its light.[3]

Recollect when you come again to Washington you are to be my guest.

Miss Dix is now in the city at her friend's Mrs Bell's.

I remain as ever truly
your[s][A] &[...][A]
Joseph Henry

Dr Robert Hare
Phil^d

Hare Papers, Library, American Philosophical Society.
Draft: January 12, 1849, Henry Papers, Smithsonian Archives.

1. *Proofs That Credit as Money, in a Truly Free Country, Is to a Great Extent Preferable to Coin* (Philadelphia, 1834). A revision of a pamphlet published in 1810, *Proofs* argued the superiority of credit, including paper currency, over specie, in commercial dealings. It also argued that banks, including a national bank, were very important. Although Hare's publication appeared during the political and economic conflict between Andrew Jackson and supporters of the Second Bank of the United States, Hare denied he had any political objectives in mind.

2. A copy of Smith's *An Inquiry into the Nature and Causes of the Wealth of Nations*, 11th ed., 2 vols. (Hartford, 1811), survives in the Henry Library.

Whereas Hare (*Proofs*, p. 4) termed credit "an original medium of commercial interchange, constituting in fact a species of money," Smith contended (*1:*210) that "the whole paper money of every kind which can easily circulate in any country never can exceed the value of the gold and silver, of which it supplies the place."

3. A reference to Bacon's idols of the den or cave, the individual idiosyncrasies which result in attaching excessive importance to personal perspective or experience. Francis Bacon, *Novum Organum*, Aphorisms 53–59.

255. TO JOHN TORREY

Washington
Jany 19ᵗʰ, 49

My Dear Dr

I hope you will pardon me for suffering your letter[1] received last week to remain several days unanswered. My excuse is the constant press of engagements which during the session of congress absorbs[A] all my time.

I deeply sympathise with you in the result of the election in the free Academy. You and your friends have however the[B] consolation of knowing that in this case as in every act of your life you have ↑been↓ governed by higher principles than those by which the majority of men are actuated and that if you have failed in any instance to secure an appointment to which your standing and reputation justly entitled you it has been because you could not so far compromise your self respect as to allow of recourse to the low arts of the politician.[2]

I know not what is the state of the proposition relative to the establishment of a mint in New York. If the law[C] should pass[3] and I think it will sooner or later several desirable situations would be created which would not interfere with your professorship. If you start as a candidate for any situation it must be with a more thorough understanding among your friends with reference to an organization of effort. Though you cannot stoop to the ordinary artifices of the general office seeker yet your friends should be allowed to take such measures as would neu-teralize unfair opposition.

All things relative to the Smithsonian are now apparently in a pros-perous condition with the exception of the publication of a book by owen on architecture under the direction not of the Institution but of the building committee. This you may recollect was ordered while he was a Regent and before the plans had been fully matured. The Board are now fully aware of the impolicy of the publication but no one wishes to meddle with it.

What would you say to the proposition of your preparing a report on botanical physiology? giving the pith of your lectures on this subject particularly a developement of the theory of morphology illustrated with wood cuts. I think a report on the present state of this subject would be highly interesting to the general reader and important to you. It is one of the objects of the S.I. to do justice in the way of presenting to the public those who are really men of science a species of popular knowledge much required among us. The pay cannot be much. I will give you say 200 Dollars at first and something on the sale.[4]

We shall always give a warm welcome to any of your family and think it will ↑be↓ most interesting to Margaret to be with us at the time of the Inauguration.

I remain as ever,
truly your's &—
Joseph Henry

Dr. John Torrey—
New-York.

Torrey Papers, Library, New York Botanical Garden.
Replies: Doc. 259 and February 5, 1849, Henry Papers, Smithsonian Archives.

1. In his letter of January 8, 1849 (Henry Papers, Smithsonian Archives), Torrey un-leashed a litany of complaints: the manner of the election of the professor of chemistry at the New York Free Academy and the "tactics em-ployed by the friends of Gibbs that I would not condescend to use," the deficiencies in Prince-ton's social life, and the lack of remuneration from lecturing at the College of Physicians and Surgeons.

2. According to Torrey, the appointment power at the Free Academy was in the hands of "ordinary ward politicians, who were besieged day & night by those who wished Gibbs elected."

3. Serious discussion of a branch mint in New York City had begun in late 1845. How-ever, the bill did not pass. After considerable debate, Congress finally voted in 1850 to open a branch mint in San Francisco instead. In 1853, Congress authorized only an assay office in New York. Bauman L. Belden, *A Mint in New York* (New York, 1930).

4. This proposed report was never pre-pared.

256. FROM JOHN LOCKE

Cincinnati Jany 23, 1849

Dear Sir,

It has transpired here that Sears C Walker, after witnessing certain experiments made here by Prof Mitchill[1] ~~and others made by me~~ in which he attached a wire to the lower end of a pendulum allowing it to pass through a mercury cup in its excursion and thus form and break circuit, while connected with a receiving magnet, causing it to reciprocate and perhaps causing the fillet of the Register to be impressed by dots; and doing nothing more—after witnessing again my experiments and being satisfied by them and by my subsequent publications and letters to him and to Prof Bach that I had invented the Automatic ↑clock↓ with all of the properties which I have claimed for it especially that of being enabled to register in very exact time the observations of the astronomer, after reporting to Mr Bache and to others and writing to ↑me↓[2] &c. &c, ↑that I was the inventor↓ has written a letter to Prof Mitchill, which I have seen, in which he says in effect as follows: I have reported to Mr Bache that you ~~are~~ have priority in the invention of the "Automatic clock".!!

Our community and myself stand astonished at this and other transactions which have lately appeared here. And Mr Mitchill himself is surprised and says to me today that he claims no such invention.[3] Why is it that the Coast^A Survey has set up several ~~plea~~ special pleas against my receiving any benefit from my invention and has now in its archives such a document as that, which all of our community know is not true, even Prof Mitchill admitting the same!!!

Judge Walker, the active friend of myself and of the Survey has written with the most anxious solicitude to both of his brothers[4] for some explanation of still other extraordinary moves of the Coast Survey.

As you and I and all of us are interested in these transactions, I have laid them thus before you ↑that you↓ may have them under your consideration.

> I have the honour to be
> Your sincere friend &
> Humble servant
> John Locke

P.S. After Mr Walker applied to me to make some clock experiments Prof M, on the same evening being some what emulous made the above experiments, which were never communicated to me until lately. Mr. Walker mentioned that some one had <u>proposed</u> the Mercury cup which neither of us supposed would be available in practice; for I had made it a condition of my invention that no machinery should interfere with the pendulum. I still deem this essential.

Henry Papers, Smithsonian Archives.

1. O. M. Mitchel.

2. Timothy Walker (1802–1856) of Cincinnati was a member of the Ohio judiciary. *DAB*.

3. According to Locke's published account, Walker had written Mrs. Mitchel, telling her that he had given Mitchel priority. When Mitchel, who had been out of town, returned to Cincinnati and discovered Walker's letter, he met with Locke and rejected Walker's claim. John Locke, *On the Invention of the Electro-Chronograph. A Letter to Nicholas Longsworth, Esq.* (Cincinnati, 1850), p. 23.

Locke was responding to a sentence in Walker's report to Bache in which Walker referred to "an experiment of the combination of an electro-magnetic clock and Morse's telegraph register . . . made by Professor Mitchell and

myself at the Cincinnati observatory, on the 26th of October last." According to the same report, Locke did not invent his clock until November 6. U.S. House, 30th Congress, 2d Session, *A Report by the Superintendent of the Coast Survey, on an Application of the Galvanic Circuit to an Astronomical Clock and Telegraph Register in Determining Local Differences of Longitude, and in Astronomical Observations Generally*, House Executive Documents, No. 21 (1849), p. 4.

4. The third brother was Ezra Otis Kendall (1818–1899), a half-brother. Kendall was professor of mathematics and astronomy at Philadelphia's Central High School, as well as S. C. Walker's collaborator in astronomical research during the years both men lived in Philadelphia. Elliott, *Dictionary*.

257. FROM SAMUEL TYLER

Frederick Maryland
23rd Jan'y 1849

My dear Sir.

Since I received your favor of the 29th ult.[1] I have determined to prepare for the Smithsonian Institution, a work, the nature of which, as the subject now presents itself to my mind, may be indicated by the title, "The Logic of Philosophy."[2] I propose to take a wide range through the labyrinths of human thought; and I hope to be able to expose error, and to expound truth in important matters more fully than has been done. I will be as brief as satisfactory analysis will permit; for the great thing to be attained in this age of books, is brevity. But to what size my thoughts may grow, I can form no very definite estimate, as the subject to be considered is so boundless.

Like yourself, I have no very profound regard for Prof: Whewell[3] or M[r] Morell[4] as philosophers. I think I shall be able to show both of them to be rather superficial thinkers; and that both are caught by the same false shows of the a priori philosophy. Indeed, so far as logic in its most comprehensive sense is concerned, M[r] Morell is evidently a mere tyro.

His history of Philosophy[5] shows this in all its parts. And as to the psychological basis of Induction, which is the great problem which lies at the foundation of all Prof: Whewell's speculations, and is the fundamental problem of the inductive philosophy, I consider Prof: Whewell entirely ignorant of it. He is learned, abounding in the most ample resources of knowledge, with an extraordinary command over brilliant illustrations, comprehensive and at the same time minute in his mental apprehension, and endowed with a perseverance in investigation, but still there is a want of a certain[A] clear vision that is necessary to make up the mind of a philosopher. Both he and Mr Morell are lacking in this faculty.

I should like to talk with you for the sake of information and instruction, on the correlation of the physical forces or the connection of polarities. This subject has at times greatly interested me: but as physical researches require experiment in open trials with external phenomena, I can never have opportunity to do any thing in that way of thought. Hence I am constrained to confine my reflections, in a great measure, to philosophy where all the data is easily obtained. Magnetic, electrical, chemical, crystellographical, optical and dynamical polarities have all been brought into such connection[6] by the discoveries of Oersted[7] and Ampere,[8] Davy,[9] Farady and yourself, Haüy[10] and Mitscherlich,[11] and Brewster[12] and Fresnell;[13] and all these again have been so marvellously supported by the experiments in physiology with some of these forces, by Prof: Matteucci[14] of Pisa, as to seem to prove that they all are but modifications of the same thing. This is an important truth if it be one, in developing the logic of natural theology.

You overestimate me, my dear Sir, when you say it is my mission to expose and dissipate the philosophical errors of the times. That I have some capacity for philosophical research, I must believe, when under every disadvantage of education, of opportunity, of social intercourse, and of occupation, I have been able to produce a work which many of the first minds in the country think superior to any other on the same subject.[15] Whatever I have done, has been without even a conversation with a single person who could appreciate the high argument. I was never for a moment out of this place while I was writing the book, and was most of the time little else than a nurse of sick members of my family wasting under protracted disease. I was literally chained to a stake. These considerations induce me to think that with proper opportunities in the future, I might do something towards rearing up in our country a system of true philosophy. But the calls of my profession, which necessity renders imperative, must ↑be↓ answered before all things. I have been engaged for some time, in a law suit, which has lead and is still leading, to the discussion of a branch of the law that is important, extremely complex, subtle, and but little developed; and I feel it due to my profession to contribute a treatise on this[B] subject, after the case is disposed of. Such are necessities which my place in life impose on me. If the fields of philosophy and science could be exchanged for the arena of practical life, how gladly would I leave it, where I must fall like a dying gladiator with hardly more sympathy for my vocation. But we are all marshalled[C] according to a divine tactic and every man must perform the duties of his post.

> With assurances of my profoundest respect I am your friend and servant
> Sam.[l] Tyler

Joseph Henry L.L.D.

Henry Papers, Smithsonian Archives.

1. Not found.

2. No Tyler publication appeared under this title, but Tyler examined some of the themes he mentions below in *The Progress of Philosophy in the Past and in the Future* (Philadelphia, 1858).

3. William Whewell was master of Trinity College, Cambridge. Henry was unimpressed by Whewell's philosophy, but Tyler was vicious in his analysis: "In truth, Dr. Whewell is as crude and confused a thinker as ever aspired with such laborious ambition to be a philosopher." *DSB; Henry Papers*, 2:135n; 6:55n, 381; Tyler, p. 122.

4. John Daniel Morell (1816–1891), who had studied philosophy with Johann G. Fichte, a German idealist, was the inspector of schools in England. According to the *DNB*, philosophically he was "an eclectic, with a decided leaning to idealism." He greatly impressed his English contemporaries. In contrast, Tyler thought Morell's work derivative, especially of the French philosopher Victor Cousin. Tyler dismissed Morell's comments on John Locke, the English philosopher, as "stale criticisms." *DNB;* Tyler, pp. 103–104 (quotation on p. 103).

5. *Historical and Critical View of the Speculative Philosophy of Europe in the Nineteenth Century*, 2 vols. (London, 1846). The book was sufficiently popular to require a second edition in 1847, demonstrating that Tyler held a minority view.

6. A review of the efforts of the international physics community to discover the relations between electricity, magnetism, light, and heat, one of the major themes of physics research during the first half of the nineteenth century, is given in Charles I. Weiner, "Joseph Henry's Lectures on Natural Philosophy: Teaching and Research in Physics, 1832–1847" (Ph.D. diss., Case Institute of Technology, 1965), pp. 81–103. Tyler may have been familiar with W. R. Grove's *On the Correlation of Physical Forces . . .* (London, 1846), which argued that "Heat, Light, Electricity, Magnetism, Chemical Affinity, and Motion are all Correlative, or have a reciprocal dependence" (p. 8).

7. Hans Christian Oersted, the Danish physicist who discovered that a galvanic current produced magnetic effects. *Henry Papers*, 1:158n.

8. The great French theoretician in electricity and magnetism. *Henry Papers*, 2:65n.

9. Davy was renowned for his work on the relationship between chemical affinity and electricity. Grove, pp. 27, 38.

10. A French mineralogist and member of the Academy, René-Just Haüy (1743–1822) was concerned with the relationship between crystallographic and chemical determinations of mineral species. He argued that crystal angles were characteristic of a given substance. *DSB*.

11. Eilhard Mitscherlich (1794–1863) was professor of chemistry at the University of Berlin. In 1822 he had announced the discovery that different chemical compounds have similar crystalline forms, or isomorphism, refuting the theory of Haüy. *DSB*.

12. Tyler was probably referring to Brewster's experiments on polarization and depolarization, and his contributions on behalf of the corpuscular theory of light. *Henry Papers*, 3:477n–479n.

13. Augustin Jean Fresnel, an advocate of

the wave theory of light, and famous for his work on optical interference. *Henry Papers,* 3:383n, 470.

14. Professor of physics at the University of Pisa, Carlo Matteucci was known for his work in electrophysiology. *Henry Papers,* 5:14n.

15. Contemporaries praised Tyler as Ameri-

ca's greatest living philosopher. See George H. Daniels, *American Science in the Age of Jackson* (New York, 1968), pp. 69–70. Henry thought Tyler's *Discourse on the Baconian Philosophy* (Baltimore, 1844) "a very valuable production" and recommended it to his students at Princeton. *Henry Papers,* 6:563.

258. FROM ASA GRAY

Cambridge, Jany. 23^d 1849—

My Dear Friend,

Many thanks for your favor of the 18^h. inst,[1] and for the trouble you have taken.

D^r. Halstead[2] being, I believe, otherwise provided for, I trust Mr. Wright[3] may have a chance to go on the boundary survey.

Since your last was received—only yesterday indeed, I found in the Boston P. Office (your clerk having addressed it to Boston, instead of Cambridge) your favor of the 22nd December.[4] Perhaps you noticed that my letter[5] of Jany 1st—made no mention of having received ~~yous~~ yours.— Had it reached me I should have replied at once.

I do not contemplate being at Washington this winter. Perhaps, I may come on in the spring, and if I do I shall avail myself of your hospitable offer; for which Mrs. Gray joins me in many thanks, and in kind remembrances to Mrs Henry. Perhaps I shall not see you till the meeting here next August, when as my guest we can talk over many things at leisure.—

Mrs. Gray is getting on well now,—tho. yet by no means strong. I think we may expect her restoration to robust health soon. Her illness and other mischances have been a great drawback to me, preventing me from accomplishing half as much as I expected,—tho. I have done the best that could be done under the circumstances.—

Mr. Sprague, my artist, too, have been detained at the sick- bed of his wife much of the time for the last 3 months. She died a fortnight ago. Mr S. has ~~been~~ since changed his residence, and now getting settled in a new house, is preparing to go on with his work again.— This explains why we have had no progress to report as to the drawings & plates (beyond the first) for D^r. Torrey's paper for you. It has also kept back the 2^d vol. of Genera— But now, after finishing one or two more plates for that, he goes directly at those for D^r. Torrey & will finish them up. You must have patience for ~~he~~ Sprague has been severely tried and under great discouragements. But a few months now will set him up again.

In a few days I will see what the financial state of the Genera Illustrated is, and whether I can keep it alive for three years without the aid of a subscription of 100 copies from you. I can bring out the 2^d Vol.— for which I have already paid much—but that I fear will exhaust me quite.

Of the 1st vol. I had 750 copies of the text printed, but only 400 copies of the plates struck off, but have saved up the stones thus far.— If I strike off more, I shall make several alterations & corrections in some of the plates. To reprint the text (If you want would cost little. The question should be considered now, (rather than after another volume is issued) whether we^A cannot retrieve our steps, and by thus issuing a 2^d edition of the 1st vol, at the same time with the second vol, as a Smithsonian Contribution. I do not think you could have any thing more truly original, of higher standard so far as botanical science goes—(& the illustrations for the 2^d vol. are of still higher character & beauty). That would secure the progress and completion of the work, if Sprague & I live.

But if the Contributions must needs all be of the 4to form—then could it not come into your 8vo series, which tho. called Reports—is^B likely to embrace systematic treatises. The only objection is that this work is addressed to men of Science & real botanical students—rather th and not ad populum, but that will be the case with many contributions you will have for that series.

If you will adopt^C the work, & pay for the drawings, as I pay for them—& to execute the engraving & print them does not cost much— I will ask nothing on my own part but the right^D of having a small private edition struck off at my own charges.

I have spoken of this, because, in reflection, I cannot but think that the simplest & best arrangement for the Institution and for Sprague & I would be for you now to adopt the work as your own.

If carried out, it will ↑we shall↓ certainly accomplish—as Hooker says, what no country yet has done for its Flora.

Let me hear your views, before it is necessary for me to bring out the 2^d Vol.— To meet the expenses I have for To replace the funds I have advanced Sprague—on it—to relieve him from difficulty—the 2^d vol. should be out in two months from this. But—though I go now directly at work on the text, it cannot be out for nearly three months.

I hope soon that Sprague will show you evidences of progress in the plates for Torrey's paper. He will do extremely well all he undertakes.—

I feel much interest in the Report on Trees, and am making arrangements & gradually shaping things about it. But I am so sadly pressed & so far behind where I expected to be at the beginning of the new year, that I do not want to promise anything as to time now.

I shall soon send you a copy of a Memoir which represents 6 months labor at least.

> I remain Very sincerely & cordially Yours,
> Asa Gray

Prof. Henry.

Henry Papers, Smithsonian Archives.
Reply: Doc. 263.

1. Doc 253.
2. Mina B. Halsted (d. 1860) graduated from Princeton in 1843 and from the College of Physicians and Surgeons in 1846. He developed an interest in botany. After service in the United States Army as a surgeon, in January 1849 he joined the survey of Panama which was to identify a route for what became the Panama Railroad Company. *Princeton Catalogue*, p. 164; Jane Loring Gray, ed., *Letters of Asa Gray*, 2 vols. (Boston, 1893), *1*:360; John H. Barnhart, *Biographical Notes upon Botanists*, 3 vols. (Boston, 1965), *2*:116; Joseph L. Schott, *Rails Across Panama: The Story of the Building of the Panama*

Railroad, 1849–1855 (Indianapolis, 1967), pp. 19–20; *New York Tribune*, January 25, 1849.
3. Charles Wright (1811–1885) had spent the winter of 1848–1849 working with Gray at Harvard. He was not appointed botanist to the Mexican Boundary Survey until 1851. In the interim, he collected plants in New Mexico and Texas, with financial support from a number of individuals and institutions, including the Smithsonian. Elliott, *Dictionary; Smithsonian Report for 1849*, p. 16.
4. Doc. 241.
5. Doc. 247.

259. FROM JOHN TORREY

New York. Jan[y]. 25, 1849.

My dear friend—

Yesterday I received your letter,[1] & I thank you for the interest you take in my welfare. As to the Free Academy, I don't care much about that now—except the mortification of having been defeated by a mere boy. The pay is only $800 a year—& they have assigned to the Professor the whole of heat, Light, Electricity & Magnetism.— Then, too, as Ross[2] & Webster[3] are not familiar with the use of apparatus,[4] the experiments in several departments of Physics will be performed by the Prof. of Chemistry. So the office will be no sinecure.

Ellet[5] is another disappointed Candidate. He is in the city, & calls on me several times a week. He can live plainly without business, but, nevertheless would be glad of some employment in his line.

As to the Report on Botany to which you allude, I could not undertake it till I finish the Oregon & Californian plants of the U.S. Exploring Exped[n]—& even then I fear my ability to do the subject justice. There are so many valuable works in German—not yet translated—& almost unintelligible to me, that, unless I had a scientific High[A] Dutch friend to assist me, I should be apt to miss some important facts.

From some indications in Congress, I think there will be an attempt made to defeat or greatly diminish the appropriations for the Coast Survey & the publications of the Exploring Expedition. That Ishmaelite Greely[6] will head the noisy pack—& I have fears that Benton will join in the cry. Should the appropriation[B] for the Expl. Exp[n] be withheld my services would be dispensed with. Are you intimate enough with Benton to speak to him on the subject? He has great respect for you, & would be much influenced by your opinion.[C]

Hastings Grant[7] is a candidate for the office of Librarian, in the Mercantile Lib[y]. The late Libr[n] resigned two days ago. The Pres[t] of the Assoc[n] & several[D] of the directors are desirous of appointing Hastings. The situation is vastly easier than his present one, & will interfere less with his health, as two assistants do all the writing. There will be little[E] fear of failure on the part of H. if he has two or three letters from responsible persons. You know him to be a well informed, gentlemanlike, steady & amiable person— He is exceedingly well[F] acquainted with the character, prices &c. of books—& his business habits are of the first order. Of his integrity there can be no doubt. Now a line to this effect, addressed to the President & Directors of the Mercantile Library Association, N.Y. & enclosed to me—at your earliest convenience, will probably do much in securing several votes.[8] There are twelve directors, who fill the offices. The Lib[n] receives $800 a year. Give my kind regards to Mrs. Henry—& to Prof[t] Alexander if he is still with you—

Very cordially yours
John Torrey.

Henry Papers, Smithsonian Archives.

1. Doc. 255.
2. Edward C. Ross (1801–1851) was professor of mathematics and natural philosophy at the Free Academy of New York. *National Cyclopaedia of American Biography, Supplement:*782.
3. Horace Webster (1794–1871) was principal of the Free Academy. *National Cyclopaedia of American Biography, 19:*320–321.
4. Both Ross and Webster had been professors of mathematics before coming to the Free

Academy, Ross at Kenyon College and Webster at Geneva College.
5. W. H. Ellet.
6. Editor of the *New York Tribune*, Horace Greeley (1811–1872) served in the House of Representatives from December 4, 1848, to March 3, 1849. He was an opponent of Henry's vision for the Smithsonian. *BDAC;* Robert Post, "Science, Public Policy, and Popular Precepts: Alexander Dallas Bache and Alfred Beach as

Symbolic Adversaries," in *The Sciences in the American Context: New Perspectives*, ed. Nathan Reingold (Washington, 1979), p. 84.

7. Seth Hastings Grant had lived with the Torreys. *Henry Papers*, 5:384n–385n.

8. Although Henry never sent the requested letter, Grant did get the job. Torrey to Henry, February 5, 1849, Henry Papers, Smithsonian Archives; Henry to Torrey, February 7, 1849, Torrey Papers, Library, New York Botanical Garden.

260. FROM LEWIS C. BECK

[New B]runswick[A] Jany 29 '49.

My dear Sir,

I received your letter of the 12th inst.,[1] but the preparation of a couple of lectures on "Mines & Metals" which I was requested to give, in addition to other duties, have kept me more closely occupied than usual; & I have therefore delayed answering it.

Your suggestion in regard to an Index of Scientific Subjects[2] is one that strikes me very favourably, of course. I have ↑often↓ thought of something of the kind, & in the first edition of my Manual of Chemistry I introduced, I believe for the first time, at least in American publications, the plan of references under each article.[3] I always fancied that if the book possessed any merit it was due to this feature, for in other respects, it was of course, as most text books are, a compilation. In the selection of the references, I consulted my brother's M.S.[4] but added many others. T[he wor]k[A] is very valuable, but it has not been posted up for several years & I do not think my brother could now command the time to do it. It would however be useful in the prosecution of a work such as you propose—

Agasiz has made an attempt of this kind in regard to Natural History,[5] but I think it is wanting in American References— The[B] work has been published by the Ray Society.[6] In getting up such an Index as would be really useful, the services of some person would be required who could digest & direct the plan—to be assisted by one or two others whose business it should be to arrange the titles of papers &c. No one who is fit to direct such a business would be willing to submit to the drudgery of making a list of papers from the various periodicals. But this would involve a considerable expenditure, perhaps more than either the Commissioner of Patents or the Regents of the Smithsonian, would think it worth while to incur. My views in regard to the details of the work I could give you in a half hours talk, but writing on these matters is very unsatisfactory—

It has occurred to me that a very useful work might be got up [---] containing tables of weights & measures, values of coin, degrees of heat on different thermometric scales, &c. I presume my experience is that of most persons engaged in scientific researches, & I have found this to be one of the most puzzling matters connected with the examination of a subject through different Authors. For example, I was puzzled ↑very much↓ the other day to find out the exact value of the Marc, & only accidentally ascertained it in a note to an article in Ure.[7] Now a small manual in which all foreign weights, measures, coins, &c. should be reduced the U.S. standards, would save a great deal of time; & would, I think, be the most acceptable[C] present that could be made to a scientific or an unscientific man. I should think this might be got up without much difficulty. The work should include the Jewish, Roman & Greek ancient standards as well as those of Modern times—

My Report is going on slowly. I have ~~had~~ in some measure changed the plan, I think for the better; but I will soon write more in detail on this point.

In regard to 'Breadstuffs' I am now waiting to learn what will be the action of Congress. I should like to know as soon as may be whether I am to go on or not— Should the Appropriation be discontinued, I have some other plans in regard to the work which I should like to urge forward—

yours truly
L C Beck

Prof Henry—

Henry Papers, Smithsonian Archives.

1. Not found.

2. This is the first mention of Henry's proposal for an international index of scientific articles. Officially, the Royal Society *Catalogue of Scientific Papers* "originated from a communication from Dr. Joseph Henry, Secretary of the Smithsonian Institution, to the Meeting of the British Association in Glasgow in 1855." However, one historian has argued that Henry derived the idea of this catalogue from the bibliographic activities of Edward Bissell Hunt, an army officer attached to the Coast Survey. This letter demonstrates that Henry was thinking of a bibliography of scientific publications long before his meeting with Hunt in 1855. Royal Society of London, *Catalogue of Scientific Papers. (1800–1863)*, 6 vols. (London, 1867–1872), *1*:iii (quotation); Donald deB. Beaver, "The

Smithsonian Origin of the Royal Society Catalogue of Scientific Papers," *Science Studies*, 1972, 2:385–393.

3. Each section of Beck's *A Manual of Chemistry . . .* (Albany, 1831) concluded with a list of references, ranging from entire books to specific pages in books, articles, and encyclopedia entries.

4. An allusion to T. R. Beck's "manuscript book of chemical references." Beck, *Manual of Chemistry*, p. iv.

5. Louis Agassiz, *Bibliographia zoologiae et geologiae. A General Catalogue of All Books, Tracts, and Memoirs on Zoology and Geology*, 4 vols. (London, 1848–1854).

6. Founded in 1844, the Ray Society was dedicated to publishing volumes in natural history. John L. Thornton and R. I. J. Tully, *Sci-*

entific Books, Libraries & Collectors: A Study of Bibliography and the Book Trade in Relation to Science, 3d ed. (London, 1971), p. 274.

7. Andrew Ure, *The Philosophy of Manufactures: or, An Exposition of the Scientific, Moral, and*

Commercial Economy of the Factory System of Great Britain, 2d ed. (London, 1836). In a note on p. 472, on the silk trade in France, Ure defined the ounce poids de marc of Lyon in terms of the ounce troy.

261. FROM WILLIAM WILLIAMS MATHER[1]

Ohio University Athens Ohio
Jan 31st 1849.

Prof Henry
My Dear Sir.

I have the honor to acknowledge the receipt of your circular on meteorological observations, & Downe's Occultations for 1849, through the kindness of Mr Vinton (MC).[2]

I will willingly cooperate in making meteorological observations, and have them made both here and at my family residence 40 miles SW of this place (Jackson C.H.), if two stations so near each other should be deemed desirable; but must request that the Smithsonian Institution or the Navy Dep't, furnish the necessary instruments that shall have been compared with standard instruments. I have also written Mr Espy[3] upon this subject and to the same effect.

Should Congress authorize a geological examination of Oregon, California, & New Mexico, I should like the opportunity of making the explorations under an appointment from the Government; and if you deem it proper; and you think I would be useful to the cause of science in that capacity, you will much oblige me by recommending me for that purpose.[4] You know something of my labors in the geological explorations in New York Ohio & elsewhere, & probably you may have my report to NYork in the Natural History of New York (quarto) either in your private library[5] or in that of the Smithsonian Institution. The sedentary occupations of a professorship do not suit me as well as more active employments; & I believe I could be more usefully engaged in geological explorations than in my present situation.

Have Messrs Davis & Squier noticed any connection between the position of mounds and the topography of the adjacent country. I have not seen their work. While making some very minute topographical surveys and maps of some large tracts of land in this State last summer, I noticed that where there were groups of mounds, the lines joining them indicated the direction[A] of the dividing ridges between streams, the largest mound being toward the main divide. On the hills where the ridges branch, and the eye in the forest cannot distinguish the main ridge, the position[B] of the mound indicates it. Those on the hills or on the low divides between the heads of streams indicate the direction of the dividing ridge, & but for these, a traveller might leave the main ridge & follow a spur between the little branches. Since the first observations were made on this subject last summer, I have observed when I have had opportunities, and have as yet found no exception to the situation as mentioned above. The mounds may have been way marks to guide the former inhabitants in journeying from one centre of population to another along the dry ridges, or ↑points of↓ boundaries along the divides of the waters between tribes or families, as well as places for the dead or for religious rites. It would be interesting to ascertain if the[C] distribution of mounds generally follows the same rule.[6]

> I have the honor to be
> Your Ob'dt Serv't
> W W Mather

Letters Received, Records of the Smithsonian Meteorological Project, Records of the Weather Bureau, RG 27, National Archives.
Reply: Draft in Charles Coffin Jewett's hand, February 22, 1849, on separate sheet immediately following this letter.

1. A former army officer, geologist on the New York Natural History Survey, and organizer of the Ohio Geological Survey, Mather (1804–1859) was serving as vice-president of Ohio University and its professor of natural science. He was an expert on coal geology. *DSB*.

2. Samuel Finley Vinton (1792–1862), a Whig from Ohio. *BDAC*.

3. Mather's letter to Espy of January 30, 1849, is in the same location as this letter.

4. Mather did not participate in geological exploration of the West.

5. No copy of *Geology of New York, Part I, Comprising the Geology of the First Geological District* (Albany, 1843) survives in the Henry Library.

6. In his reply, Henry invited Mather to submit an article on his observations of the mounds for SI Contributions.

262. FROM ZADOCK THOMPSON[1]

> Burlington, Vt. Feb. 3. 1849.

Sir,

Through our Rep. in Cong. the Hon^le G. P. Marsh I have recently received the joint circular of the Smithsonian Institution and of the Navy Department, on the subject of meteorological observations,[2] and have returned an answer to the Navy Department.[3]

I have ever felt[A] a deep interest in the progress and success of the

Smith. Inst. especially since I listened to your exposition of the plan of it, before the Asso. of Geol. & Nat. at Boston in 1847. That part of the plan which related to the publication of occasional Reports of the progress of science in its several departments, struck me as calculated to remedy, in a great measure at least, the inconvenience, which those, in the country, who are at a distance from public libraries and who have not the means to purchase books for themselves, experience, whenever they attempt to become acquainted with any particular branch of Nat. Hist.

Of the difficulties in the way of studying Nat. Hist. without access to cabinets and suitable books, and without means to purchase them, I can speak from experience,[4] and on that account I venture these remarks. I at first gave my attention to Ichthyology, and the only book I had on that subject for some time was Dr Mitchel's paper on "The Fishes of New York."[5] I afterwards received as a present from my esteemed Friend, the Hon. G. P. Marsh our distinguished Rep. in Cong. the vol. of Dr Richardson's Fauna Boreali Americana, which relates to Fishes[6] and found it of very great service. Since then I have obtained Dr Storer's and DeKay's reports[7] and had access to various other works in this department. My experience has been very nearly the same, in relation to the other branches of natural science; and I mention the subject because I know that many others are laboring under the same difficulties, which I have experienced; and who might, if they had the means within their reach, afford much assistance in developing the Nat. Hist. of the country. Since my History of Vermont (a copy of which I beg you to accept, either for yourself or the Smith. Library) was published and circulated in our state, I have frequently received letters, making inquiries respecting books in the different departments of Nat. Hist.— pricees, &c—

Judging from my own experience and limited observation I have thought that the Smith. Inst. could do nothing, which would so much increase and diffuse a knowledge of Nat. Hist. among men, as the publication of Manuals for the principal departments, containing clear descriptions of all the species known at the time of publication;—and after that, issue, occasionally, reports, exhibiting the progress made in each department; and, then, having these furnished at so cheap a rate as to bring them within the reach of the poorest country lad, whose taste should lead him to the cultivation of any particular branch of Nat. Hist. These reports, being culled from all the scientific journals in the world, would be, in a great measure, a substitute for them all, without their expense, and would be even better than all, to most persons, on account of the arrangement of the materials under distinct and appropriate heads.

A good manual of Entomology appears to me to be a desideratum, which is not likely to be soon supplied, unless by the aid of the Smith. Inst. or some other, and without such a work the progress of Am. Ent. must be slow.

Manuals of Herpetology and Ichthyology seem also to be much needed. The general works on these subjects are too expensive to be within the reach of a great part of our young men, whose tastes would lead them to cultivate these sciences. Other departments seem to be somewhat beter supplied.

I hope you will pardon my presumption in offering these suggestions. I should not have done it, had I not felt great anxiety to see the plan, with regard to the publication of reports, (as I understood it from you at Boston,) carried into effect.

Very respectfully, Sir,
Your Obed.ᵗ Servant
Zadock Thompson

Prof Joseph Henry
Sec. Smith. Inst.

Letters Received, Records of the Smithsonian Meteorological Project, Records of the Weather Bureau, RG 27, National Archives.

1. A graduate of the University of Vermont (1823) and the author of several publications on the state of Vermont, Thompson (1796–1856) in 1845 was appointed an assistant on that state's geological survey. In 1847, after the legislature refused to fund the completion of the survey, he was placed in charge of the state's international exchange efforts. Elliott, *Dictionary;* George F. Houghton, "Obituary of Professor Zadoc Thompson," *Silliman's Journal,* 1856, 2d ser. 22:44–49.

2. Doc. 229.

3. January 24, 1849, in same location as this document.

4. Thompson's *History of Vermont, Natural, Civil, and Statistical* (Burlington, 1842), for example, "cost him ... much travel, research, time and expense in its preparation." Lacking access to specimens and books, he re-

lied upon correspondents for assistance. Houghton, pp. 45, 46 (quotation on p. 45).

5. Samuel Latham Mitchill, "The Fishes of New York Arranged and Described," *Transactions of the Literary and Philosophical Society of New York,* 1815, *1:*355–392.

6. That is, Sir John Richardson's *The Fishes,* part 3 of his *Fauna Boreali-Americana, or, The Zoology of the Northern Parts of British America ...,* 4 vols. (London, 1829–1837).

7. David H. Storer, "Reports on the Ichthyology and Herpetology of Massachusetts," in Massachusetts Zoological and Botanical Survey, *Report on the Fishes, Reptiles and Birds of Massachusetts* (Boston, 1839), pp. 1–253; James Ellsworth De Kay, *Fishes,* part 4 of his *Zoology of New York, or, The New York Fauna ...,* 5 vols. (Albany, 1842–1844).

263. TO ASA GRAY

Smithsonian Institution
Feby 7ᵗʰ 1849

My Dear Dr

I have called upon the Secretary of State[1] and though he professes himself very favourably disposed to advance the cause of science he does not give me the slightest encouragement[A] relative to the appointment of a botanist on the boundary survey. He informs me that there is nothing in the Act directing the survey which will authorize such an appointment.

I am sorry to say that I do not see our way very clearly as to the adoption of your botanical book. Were the matter to do again we could manage it without difficulty by adopting the whole as a part of the contributions. Now it must either be adopted as one of the Reports or we must purchase a sufficient number of copies to enable you to go on with the publishing. There ↑are↓ difficulties in each course but the latter appears the most feasible though we cannot adopt it until the building is finished. I hope however to have a long confabulation on this and other matters when we meet. In the mean time I hope you will not forget the Report on forest trees. Could not a considerable part of your other work be introduced into this?

I wrote to Agassiz[2] a few days ago authorizing him to go on with the preparation of his plates for the illustration of the paper on the cetacean remains.[3] He sent me one of the copies as a sample which I think very beautiful.

We hope to get out a volume of our Reports in the course of the next summer. Among the number will be one on the application of science to arts, giving the more recent improvements.

Remember me to Prof. Peirce and your good Lady and receive for yourself the assurance

That I remain as
Ever Yours &—
Joseph Henry

Dr. A. Gray
Cambridge

P.S. I have written to Dr Torrey[4] to prepare a Report on the present state of our knowledge of the Physiology of[B] Botany.[C] He does not hower seem willing to engage in it for the present at least.

Historic Letters, Archives, Gray Herbarium Library, Harvard University.

1. Henry may have meant the meeting noted in his Desk Diary entry of February 1, 1849.

2. Letter not found.

3. Agassiz planned to prepare an extensively illustrated memoir "on the gigantic fossil cetacean remains which are found in the southern and western States of the Union." He apparently intended this as a fuller version of the brief account which he gave to the American Academy of Arts and Sciences in October 1848 of seven species of fossil whales. This memoir never appeared, however. *Smithsonian Report for 1848*, p. 12 (quotation); *Proceedings of the American Academy of Arts and Sciences*, 1848–1852, 2:4–5.

4. Doc. 255.

264. FROM ASA GRAY

Cambridge Feb[y] 8[h] 1849.

My Dear Friend

This will be handed to you by my brother Chas. G. Loring Jr.[1]—a student of our Scientific School here,—who makes a flying visit to Baltimore and Washington to recruit his health a little. He will look, with pleasure & profit, at matters of scientific interest, having some inclination to engineering as a profession—but not yet decided. He accompanied Agassiz to Lake Superior last summer.

I have asked him to seek an opportunity of delivering a copy of the sheets of my Memoir on Fendler's Santa Fe collection, as far as yet printed,[2] and a letter[A] to Gov. Marcy, (who granted to Fendler free transportation to Santa Fe—with the troops)—asking the same favor anew[3]—and also rations—with the Regiment of Mounted Rifles,[4] in his way to the region we have now decided on his attempting to explore, viz. the country around & south of the Great Salt Lake and Mormon City, a very novel region. The reason I send by my brother is, that, if possible I may get an answer by him, or an intimation at least, whether the application will be favorably noticed. For Fendler (now at St. Louis) must soon be ready, if he goes.[5] He will undertake any simple physical, meteorological[B] & magnetical observations you may choose to intrust him with.

Greatly as your time must be occupied, perhaps, if you think it will be useful, you may take Loring to the Secretary's house or office that he may deliver his letter & package.

As to Society he has letters to his father's friends, Winthrop,[6] Webster,[7] Palfrey, &c—and I have given one to Lieut. Davis,[8]—so he will be well enough cared for.—

475

I am getting more and more anxious that you should adopt my Gen-era, U.S. Illustrated as a Smithsonian Contribution of the Report Se-ries—of a more strictly scientific character (while the work on trees will be more directly popular in its form.) We could then reduce the price still lower of the copies sold and insure it a wide circulation. I have 400 copies in sheets of the text (or it could be reprinted for 180^C dollars—not counting the paper—): a new ed. of the plates could be struck from the stones, and we could make such arrangements as that the cost to you would not be great.

All my savings are invested in it, and I begin to feel the burden pretty heavy. The 2^d vol. is almost ready. Let me hear from you on it. I send a letter^D from Prof. Fischer, Director of the Imp. ~~Garde~~ Botanic Garden of St. Petersburgh.[9]— Please send back by Mr. Loring.

My messenger waits.

Kind^E regards to Mrs. Henry.

Yours ever
A. Gray

Henry Papers, Smithsonian Archives.
Reply: Doc. 267.

1. An 1848 Harvard graduate, Loring (1828–1902) became a Civil War hero and a leading American Egyptologist. He was Gray's brother-in-law. *National Cyclopaedia of American Biography,* 25:301–302.

2. Gray referred to his "Plantae Fendleria-nae Novi-Mexicanae: An Account of a Collec-tion of Plants Made Chiefly in the Vicinity of Santa Fé, New Mexico, by Augustus Fendler; with Descriptions of the New Species, Critical Remarks, and Characters of Other Unde-scribed or Little Known Plants from Sur-rounding Regions," *Memoirs of the American Academy of Arts and Sciences,* 1849, 2d ser. *4*:1–116. Although a "to be continued" note ap-peared at the end of the memoir, Gray never published a sequel.

Fendler (1813–1883), a Prussian-born lamp manufacturer, emigrated to the United States and settled in St. Louis, where he began collect-ing Midwestern plants for European herbaria. This activity brought him to the attention of Gray, who recruited him to collect plants in New Mexico. Fendler traveled there in the fall of 1846 and stayed until the following spring, gathering many new specimens. In 1849, the Smithsonian paid $20.50 for a large set of his plants. Gray, "Plantae Fendlerianae," pp. 1–3; Dupree, *Gray,* pp. 162–164; Elliott, *Index;*

William M. Canby, ed., "An Autobiography and Some Reminiscences of the Late August Fendler," *Botanical Gazette,* 1885, *10*:285–290; *Smithsonian Report for 1849,* pp. 16, 23.

3. Gray's letter to Marcy has not been found, but see Gray to George Engelmann, February 25, 1849, in Jane Loring Gray, ed., *Letters of Asa Gray,* 2 vols. (Boston and New York, 1893), *1*:361–362. On his prior efforts to secure free transportation for Fendler, see Dupree, *Gray,* p. 163, and Canby, p. 288.

4. In 1849, under the command of William Wing Loring (1818–1886), a cousin of Charles G. Loring, Jr., the Regiment of Mounted Rifles went on a march to Oregon via the Oregon Trail. *DAB.*

5. Fendler hoped Gray would let him collect in California; Gray prevailed, however, and Fendler left St. Louis for the Great Salt Lake in the spring of 1849. He had not traveled far be-fore he lost his gear in a flood and returned home, only to find that all his possessions had been destroyed in a fire. Hearing of Fendler's plight, Henry offered to subscribe up to $150 toward a new expedition to Salt Lake, but Fen-dler never collected in the West again. Gray to George Engelmann, August 28, 1849, Engel-mann Papers, Missouri Botanical Garden Li-brary; Dupree, *Gray,* p. 164; Canby, p. 289.

6. Robert Charles Winthrop (1809–1894), Whig representative from Massachusetts and, since 1847, speaker of the House. *DAB*.

7. Daniel Webster.

8. Charles Henry Davis.

9. Frank Ernest Louis Fischer (1782–1854), who in 1823 became the first director of the Imperial Botanic Garden of St. Petersburg, shaped it into "the major botanical institution of Russia." *World Who's Who of Science;* Stanwyn

G. Shetler, *The Komarov Botanical Institute: 250 Years of Russian Research* (Washington, 1967), pp. 28–30 (quotation on pp. 29–30).

In his letter, Fischer praised Gray's *Genera* as "an immense undertaking and a most meritorious one," adding that "there is no country which can boast of an analogous work." Fischer to Gray, August 23/September 4, 1848, Historic Letters, Archives, Gray Herbarium Library, Harvard University.

265. FROM BENJAMIN PEIRCE

Harvard University
Febr 13— 1849

My Dear Sir,

I enclose you a copy of an award which has just been made, and which will sufficiently explain itself.[1] I do not wish you to show it to any one but Bache unless you should learn^A that Mr Desor was trying to injure Agassiz at Washington in the same treacherous way in which he has ~~prev~~ done here, and in which he has so signally failed. It may be as well to state however that a full account of all the proceedings before the arbitrators has been preserved by them and will show, if called for, what the result would have been if Agassiz had not contented himself with acting upon the defensive—

There are serious threats to expel Desor from the American Academy, and it will be done if it should prove to be necessary.[2] There are queer things not yet told.

Give my kindest remembrances to him of the Coast Survey—

In the greatest haste
Yours
Ever faithfully
Benjamin Peirce

Professor Henry

Henry Papers, Smithsonian Archives.

1. The award—$100—had been made to Pierre Jean Édouard Desor for his work on Louis Agassiz's *Principles of Zoology*. Peirce enclosed a copy (in his hand) of the report of the panel that had been named to resolve a dispute between Agassiz and Desor over the authorship of scientific publications and rights to unpub-

lished data. The panel's was the third and final effort to arbitrate their dispute. In 1848, first Augustus A. Gould and Edward Clarke Cabot, and then Cabot and Cornelius Conway Felton, had awarded Desor $100 in compensation for his work on Agassiz's *Principles of Zoology*, but gave Agassiz intellectual rights to most of the disputed research. Not satisfied with these findings, Desor continued to press his claims, and also accused Agassiz of having had an affair with a domestic servant. To settle the dispute, Agassiz chose John A. Lowell, Desor named D. Humphreys Storer, and then Lowell and Storer selected Thomas B. Curtis. Upholding the earlier findings, the panel rejected any further compensation for Desor, termed his allegations of Agassiz's immoral conduct "totally destitute of foundation," and asserted that "nothing has been established in the course of this enquiry of a nature to derogate from the high personal and professional character of Mr. Agassiz." Report of Thomas B. Curtis, John A. Lowell, and D. Humphreys Storer, February 9, 1849, Henry Papers, Smithsonian Archives (quotations); Edward Lurie, *Louis Agassiz: A Life in Science* (1960; Chicago, 1966), pp. 154–161.

2. Peirce subsequently moved unsuccessfully to have Desor expelled from the academy. Lurie, p. 160.

266. TO JOHN TORREY

Washington
Feby 16th 1849

My Dear Sir

I have made enquiry relative to the passage of the bill authorizing the establishment of a mint in New York. I am rather inclined to the opinion that it will not pass though Mr Walker thinks it probably will. Should the bill pass this session I shall not fail to exert what little influence I may have, in the way of promoting your appointment. I have thus far refrained from meddleing with things of this kind but in the present case my duty as well as my inclination prompts me to interfere.

Should the bill be postponed until the next session you will be able to secure a powerful friend in Jefferson^A Davis the soninlaw of General Taylor.[1]

I would not advise however that you should make any communications to him on the subject— I have spoken to him— It may be well for you to get a letter of recommendation from the principal scientific men of the Country particularly from Boston through Dr Gray— I am not sure about Phil^d Dr Patterson is not favourable to the establishment of a new mint. Get letters from the West and South. Do all that is proper for you to do in securing the appointment—leave the result to Providence—

There is quite an alarm in the city on account of the number of robberies^B which ~~are~~ have been committed during the past week. I was informed yesterday that six persons had been attacked and that two of them had been very seriously injured. The weapon of attack in some cases is a sling shot.[2]

All the world metaphoracally speaking is expected to be here at the

Inauguration. Every thing relative to the Smithsonian is now apparently in a favourable condition.

I remain as ever
Your friend
Joseph Henry

Dr J. Torrey

Torrey Papers, Library, New York Botanical Garden.
Reply: February 21, 1849, Henry Papers, Smithsonian Archives.

1. In 1835, Davis had married Sarah Knox Taylor, the daughter of Zachary Taylor, against her father's wishes. She died only a few months later. By 1845, Davis and Taylor were back on friendly terms. *DAB,* s.v. "Davis, Jefferson."

2. A spate of robberies and assaults in mid-February—including the mugging of a War Department clerk on Twelfth Street near the Smithsonian grounds—prompted a call to "persons residing in the suburbs and more retired portion" of Washington "to be upon their guard of the nocturnal rowdy, the robber, and the assassin." To deal with the crime wave, the city councils appropriated funds for extra police protection. *National Intelligencer,* February 9, 12 (quotation), 15, and 21, 1849.

267. TO ASA GRAY

Washington Feby 21st 1849

My Dear Sir

Your letter of the 8th inst[1] was duly received by Mr Lovering[2] and I have to regret that owing to the press of business under which I am now labouring and shall continue to labour until the adjournment of Congress I had not an opportunity of giving him as much of my time as he is entitled to from his connection with you.

The Secretary of War has sent this afternoon the accompanying letter[3] which though it is perhaps not quite what you expected yet I hope it will be of much service to your Botanist.

I have just had an interview with an Officer of the Army, Major Kendrick[4] of the 2nd Artillery under orders for New Mexico who will be much pleased to collect plants for you provided you furnish him with a set of directions as to the method &c. You can address him at Jefferson Barracks near St Louis. He starts for Santa Fe but will probably make many excursions in to the country around. He is a graduate of West Point and has much taste for Science. I wrote a few days ago[5] to inform you that I could not get any encouragement relative to the appointmnt of a botanist on the Mexican[A] boundary & Major Kendrick was recommended to me at the War Department as the proper person for your object.[6] He belongs to Company B. of the 2nd Artillery. He leaves Washington in the course of a few days for St Louis.

With regard to the adoption of your Genera I scarcely know what to say. We are so pressed for funds and shall be so until the building is completed that I had concluded to begin nothing in the Report line but articles of a more popular nature. Such as the Report on Chemestry applied to Agriculture the Report on forest trees &c. Give me a particular account of the work—of the number of volumes it will occupy—of the cost of each volume including the plates of the number of copies which should be struck off—of the plan of offering it for sale[B]—of the time which would be required[C] to prepare and publish the work—Whether it should come out in volumes or in parts— I hope your good Lady has recovered and that free[D] from all interruptions you are now prosecuting with your usual ardor and success the mission allotted to you in the distribution of our duties by an all wise and benevolent Providence.

All things relative to the Smithsonian are just now in a quiet and apparently very favourable condition. You have probably seen by the papers that the Coast Survey has had a little brush but it has been made the stronger by the contest. What a noble report was that of Pierce and the other members of the committee of the Aca[dy]. It produced an excellent effect in congress[7] and was worth a hundred clap trap puffy articles such as are usually got up for the purpose of gulling the[E] members of our national Legislature.

If the scientific men of the country will only be properly united they can do much for the advance of their persuits through assistance from Congress. Politicians as a class are timid except when they have an object which they know is worthy and in the advocating of which they are sure of being sustained by authority.

All the world is to be here in the course of the next two weeks.[8] One of my very intimate acquaintances (I do not boast) has been ~~electe~~ nominated for the Secretary ship of State. I allude to Mr Clayton.[9]

Give my kind regards to Professors Pierce Guyot,[10] Gould[11] and Bond[12] and receive for yourself the assurance that I remain as

ever truly yours &
Joseph Henry

Dr Gray

If the [?~~fass~~] ↑law↓ passes congress to establish a new mint in the city of New York Dr Torrey must be appointed one of the officers. All his friends must unite on this. The appointment would be just and popular.

JH

Historic Letters, Archives, Gray Herbarium Library, Harvard University.

1. Doc. 264.
2. Charles G. Loring, Jr.
3. Not found.
4. After graduating from West Point in 1835, Henry Lane Kendrick (1811–1891) served as an assistant professor of chemistry, mineralogy, and geology at the academy until 1847, when he left to fight in Mexico. Promoted to major after the war, he was assigned to Jefferson Barracks in 1848; in early 1849, he led a march to New Mexico, the first of several expeditions under his command in that region. George W. Cullum, *Biographical Register of the Officers and Graduates of the U.S. Military Academy at West Point, N.Y.*, 3d ed. (Boston and New York, 1891), 1:595–596; *The Twentieth Century Biographical Dictionary of Notable Americans* (Boston, 1904).
5. Doc. 253.
6. We have found no evidence that Kendrick collected plants for Gray.
7. At Bache's request, in 1848 the American Academy of Arts and Sciences named Benjamin Peirce, Daniel Treadwell, Jonathan Ingersoll Bowditch, and Joseph Lovering as a committee to assess the Coast Survey's progress under his superintendence. Their report, presented on February 6, 1849, strongly endorsed Bache's "able and judicious, his energetic and economical administration of this great national work [which] raised it to the highest state of successful activity and deserved popularity." Jefferson Davis had the report reprinted as part of his remarks in the Senate debate on Benton's amendment. *Proceedings of the American Academy of Arts and Sciences, 1848–1852*, 2:124–128 (quotation on p. 128); Hugh Richard Slotten, "Patronage, Politics, and Practice in Nineteenth-Century American Science: Alexander Dallas Bache and the United States Coast Survey" (Ph.D. diss., University of Wisconsin-Madison, 1991), pp. 173, 208 note 81.
8. That is, for the inauguration of President Zachary Taylor and Vice-President Millard Fillmore.
9. John M. Clayton. *BDAC.*
10. Arnold Henri Guyot, formerly Agassiz's colleague at the academy in Neuchâtel, followed Agassiz to the United States after the revolution of 1848 led to the school's closure. He was currently delivering a course of lectures at the Lowell Institute on comparative physical geography, subsequently published as *The Earth and Man* (Boston, 1849). *DSB; Henry Papers,* 5:25n.
11. Benjamin Apthorp Gould, Jr. (1824–1896), an 1844 Harvard graduate, returned to the United States in 1848 after extensive study in astronomy in Europe, including Göttingen, where he had received his doctorate, and where he had been offered, but turned down, a professorship. He was teaching German, French, and mathematics in Cambridge. Elliott, *Dictionary; DSB; Henry Papers,* 6:342n.
12. William Cranch Bond.

268. FROM JOHN LOCKE

Washington[1] Febr. 27. 1849

Prof. Henry,
Dear Sir,

I had intended to enquire of you with regard to a report which I heard yesterday, as coming from a member of Congress which was to the effect that you had said that there were a hundred claimants for Dr. Locke's so called Invention. As you inform me that you have not studied my invention I presume this is not so. But you perceive that the station which you occupy both by appointment and by character gives vast weight[A] to every word which you utter[B] and in a crisis like the present where[c] an appropriation of 10,000 is pending would very likely turn the scale with a popular body like the congress of the United States.

Most respectfully yours
John Locke

P.S. Two notes from me to Prof Bache[2] remain unanswered by him.

Henry Papers, Smithsonian Archives.
Notation on bottom of page, in Henry's hand: "see letter 55," a reference to Henry's unsent reply (Doc. 269).

1. Locke had come to Washington ostensibly to show Henry "an electrical clock attachment, designed for the Coast Survey in case it was needed"; the survey, he later stated, had told him that it "would receive [the device] at the appraisal of Prof. Henry." Locke, *On the Invention of the Electro-Chronograph. A Letter to Nicholas Longworth, Esq. by John Locke, M.D.* (Cincinnati, 1850), p. 72.

2. Not found, although presumably one of these notes was the one of February 19, 1849, later reprinted in *On the Invention of the Electro-Chronograph.* Locke had written Bache on February 3, charging him with mismanaging the Coast Survey and with failing to control his subordinates, specifically Sears C. Walker. Bache replied on February 9 that Locke's "very offensive" letter did not deserve anything beyond an acknowledgement of its receipt (p. 34). In his letter of February 19, Locke offered an "apology" for the language of his previous letter, but again pressed Bache to state "how far certain positions assumed by Coast Survey Assistant Sears C. Walker, are authorized and sanctioned by you, as the Superintendent of that Survey" (p. 73). Locke noted in his pamphlet that Bache had never replied.

269. TO JOHN LOCKE

Washington February 27 1849

My Dear Sir

I have endeavored to keep myself as free as possible from the discussions relative to your invention and I have refrained from expressing an opinion on the subject to any member of Congress, while I supposed the matter was pending, though my opinion was several times asked. In a confidential conversation with a member of the Senate, after the appropriation had been stricken from the bill, I did say that there were several claimants for the invention, and that the appropriation was extravagant, or words to this effect. It is true, I was unacquainted with the minutiae of your claims, as presented last night by yourself, but after this conversation,, and as the matter now exists in my mind, I am still of the same opinion, and conscientiously beleive that the appropriation of $10.000 for such a contribution would do great injury to the cause of American Science, and injustice to its other cultivators.

I remain very respectfully
your obedient servant

Prfr. John Locke

482

Henry Papers, Smithsonian Archives.
In Edward Foreman's hand. Notations, in Henry's hand: "not sent" (top of page) and "Not sent the letter which called foorth this reply was withdrawn" (bottom of page).

270. FROM SIDNEY BREESE

Washington March 1ˢᵗ 1849

My Dear Sir

My connection with the Smithsonian Institution, as one of the Regents, having terminated by my resignation, I have thought proper, prior to my departure from Washington,[1] to place in your keeping this letter, fully explaining the course I deemed it my duty to pursue, when the question of a building for "an establishment for the increase and diffusion of knowledge among men" was before the board for its consideration and decision, and to invoke your recollection in regard to it.[2]—

You will remember that some of the members of the board, were strongly in favour of a moderate expenditure for the buildings. I think, the Chancellor Mr Dallas, Professor-Bache and myself were the most prominent advocates of this course, and I well remember that you heartily concurred with us. You may recollect I submitted some remarks to the board on the subject,[3] deprecatory of an extravagant, or even a large expenditure in a building, and said, if the donor, of the munificent bequest, committed to our charge, desired to perpetuate his name and his memory, by stone and mortar, or by a splendid edifice, he would not have left his fortune, to be expended in this country for such a purpose, as he could have made a greater display in his own. You will not forget that I alluded to the manner in which the Girard bequest had been expended and that I referred to some passages in Lyell's travels in America to enforce my views, and among them the following:

"It is evident that when a passion so strong as that for building is to be resisted, total abstinence alone, as in the case of spiritous liquors, will prove an adequate safeguard. In the 'old country' the same fatal propensity has stood in the way of all the most spirited efforts of modern times to establish and endow new institutions for the diffusion of Knowledge."[4]

And after stating the large sums expended, on the ornamental parts of several public buildings designed for instruction in England, and which when completed failed to accomplish the design, I read this passage from the same work.

483

"Still these collegiate buildings in support of which the public came forward so liberally, were left, like the Girard College, half finished; whereas if the same funds had been devoted to the securing of teachers of high acquirements, station, character, and celebrity, and if rooms of moderate dimensions had been at first hired, while the classes of pupils remained small, a generation would not have been lost, the new Institutions would have risen more rapidly to that high rank which they are one day destined to attain, and testamentary bequests would have flowed in more copiously, for buildings well adapted to the known and ascertained wants of the establishment."[5]

You may recollect also, that I read from the same author the history of John Lowells bequest of near $350.000—to found the Lowell Institute in which he expressly provided in his will, that not a single dollar should be expended in brick and mortar.[6]

You will also remember that I prepared a resolution nearly in the following form which I designed to introduce, but waived it on consultation with you, as there seemed no hope of its passage.

"Resolved, As the opinion of this board, the true design of the munificent donor of the Fund under its arrangement, namely "to found at Washington, under the name of the Smithsonian Institution, an establishment for the increase and diffusion of knowledge among men" can be well accomplished not by expending two hundred thousand dollars in buildings, thereby absorbing much of its active means, but rather by a cheap yet durable edifice to be erected at a cost not exceeding fifty thousand dollars, which shall be the seat of an "Establishment", first, of a set of Transactions, to consist of original papers, on the diversified subjects in the several departments of human knowledge, for which liberal premiums shall be paid, and by remunerating the authors of papers of merit which may not be entitled to premiums.

Second— By the institution of lines of research, similar to the plan adopted by the British Association, and like associations in other parts of Europe.

Third— The establishment of a fund to aid the inventive genius of the country in such discoveries and improvements in the application of science to the useful arts, as may be deemed, on examination, worthy of aid and encouragement.

Fourth— The establishment of a set of Reports annual or otherwise, and other publications, to consist of an account of the progress of all branches of knowledge—the matter of the Reports to be supplied by Collaborators eminent[A] in knowledge and science, who shall receive such premiums, or other reward ~~adequate~~ for their services as may be deemed adequate and who shall be furnished with all the Journals and Transactions of this and other countries, necessary to aid them in their labours.

Fifth— The institution of a set of lectures, by men eminent in literature and science, who may be invited to the Institution—compensation to be made for the Lectures if adjudged valuable, and published under the auspices of the Institution; and

Sixth— The establishment of a select Library, to consist—among other useful books—of the published transactions of all the learned societies of the world."

I need not remind you, that I was chiefly indebted to your suggestions in drawing up this plan and though you may not have concurred with me in all its specifications yet in its main features, and in the expenditure for a building I had as I have before stated your hearty concurrence.

Not intending any censure upon those who differed from me on the latter point, I make this statement now, in order that a knowledge of my position shall be preserved in the archives of the Institution.

Yours very truly and sincerely
(Signed) Sidney Breese

Joseph Henry
Secretary of the
Smithsonian Institution
Washington

Copy, Collection of Carl E. Coy, Sr., New Orleans, Louisiana. In Edward Foreman's hand. Reply: Doc. 272.

1. Breese had failed to win renomination to his Senate seat; under section 3 of the Smithsonian act, he lost his position as a regent when his term expired on March 3, 1849. Senator James M. Mason of Virginia was appointed to fill the vacancy. *BDAC;* Rhees, *Documents* (1901), 2:1838.

2. This was not Henry's first reading of Breese's remarks; a few days earlier, Breese had sent him a "hastily 'Scratch'd off'" draft (not found) "for correction before copying it in a fair & legible manner." Breese to Henry, February 27, 1849, Henry Papers, Smithsonian Archives.

3. Presumably at the regents' meeting of January 23, 1847, when Breese offered an amendment to a resolution relating to the selection of a plan for the building. Rhees, *Journals,* p. 22.

4. Charles Lyell, *Travels in North America, in the Years 1841–2,* 2 vols. (New York, 1845), 1:90.

5. Lyell, 1:91.

6. Lyell, 1:89.

271. FROM EPHRAIM GEORGE SQUIER

New York,
March 10, 1849—

My Dear Sir—

I can offer no apology for the liberty which I take in addressing you this letter, except the objects which I have in view, and which no one better than yourself knows how to appreciate.

In studying the archaeology of our own country, I have had my attention constantly and with increasing force directed to the Central parts of the Continent, concerning the Ancient remains of which Del Rio,[1] Du Paix,[2] Waldeck,[3] Stephens[4] and others have given us so many but so unsatisfactory glimpses. They furnish probably the most interesting subjects for archaeological investigation which the world affords. How far they may serve to reflect light upon the early history of Man in America remains yet to be determined. I am nevertheless convinced that the darkness which now envelops them may, under a properly conducted system of investigation, be in a great measure dispelled. The reasons for this belief, it is impossible, as it is at present unnecessary for me to indicate.

Suffice it to say that I have now arrived at a stage of my investigations, when it seems to me indispensible that I should carry my explorations further southward. The manifest connections betwen many of the ancient monuments of our own country and those of Mexico and Central America, are eminently suggestive, and demand further investigation. It will be curious and important to know how far they may serve to explain and illustrate each other. But apart from these considerations, there is a wide field which is yet wholly unexplored, and which there is every reason to believe is richer than any now known in objects of historical and antiquarian interests. It is not impossible indeed that there yet exist remnants of the original stock which built and occupied the vast structures of Yucatan, Palenque and Copan,[5] still secluded in the fastnesses of the interior, and like the Moquis[6] in the unexplored region above the Gila, still retaining their customs, habits and institutions slightly, if at all, impaired from what they were at the period of the discovery.

You are aware that it has, for a long period, been with me a cherished object to visit and explore these interesting regions. In this project the Venerable President of the Ethnological Society, Mr. Gallatin, and the members of the Soc. generally, have warmly sympathized.[A] Various

486

plans for carrying it into effect ↑have been↓ ~~were~~ discussed at the meetings of the Soc., but the political disturbances in Mexico and Yucatan, and the difficulty of raising the money necessary to the efficient prosecution of the enterprise, have had the effect to discourage any action, further than the appointment of a committee to take the matter in charge.

So things remained until a few weeks ago, when it was suggested by some friends at Washington, who are likely to have no inconsiderable influence under the existing administration, that as the Chargéship to Guatemala ↑will probably soon↓ ~~is likely to~~ become vacant, the appointment might be secured for myself.[7] Acting under their advice and that of my friends here, I have determined to apply for the position. If I am successful in procuring it, I shall be enabled to carry out my cherished objects, (in which my hopes and ambitions all center,) without further difficulty. Unless Govemnt aid and <u>protection</u> can be secured, no enterprise of this kind, in the present unsettled state of affairs southwards, can be successful. And as Govermt aid ad protection cannot be procured directly, I can only hope that the policy which led to the appontment of Mr. Stephens, will, in this case, be continued.[8]

I shall base my application chiefly upon Scientific grounds; for you will believe me when I say that, were the honors and emoluments of the post quadruple what they are, I would not on that account, seek to secure it.

It will of course be necessary to the success of my application to place before the Department[B] of State, testimonials from gentlemen of reputation and influence, not only in respect to general ability, but to the importance of the objects which I seek to accomplish. I have already received many warm recomendatry letters, from men eminent in a variety of depatmets, from Maine to Georgia. I enclose you copies of three of these, viz: from Messrs. Everett, Prescott and Irving.[9] I need not add, that I should be glad to receive your support also, as that of Mr. Bache, whose good opinion it is my ambition to merit. If you can in any way assist me, you will place me under renewed obligations.[10] I will not attempt to indicate in what manner this may be done, but will leave that to your own good judgment. The influence of the Smithsonian Institution, to which the tangible results of my labour would undoubtedly come, will no doubt have great weight, and I am therefore the more anxious to secure it in my favor.

I should avoid troubling you, and should certainly not think of applying for a position under Governmt, if I saw any other feasible method of accomplishing my objects.

March 10, 1849

Craving your pardon for this intrusion, and indulging the hope of hearing from you upon this matter at your Earliest Convenience[11]—

I am Dear Sir
Very Truly Your Obdt Servt—
E. Geo. Squier

Prof. Joseph Henry

Henry Papers, Smithsonian Archives.
Enclosed in Squier to Henry, March 12 (date altered from *10*), 1849, in same location.

1. Antonio del Río, *Description of the Ruins of an Ancient City, Discovered near Palenque, in the Kingdom of Guatemala* (London, 1822), which provided the first popular account of the "lost cities" of Central America. Victor Wolfgang von Hagen, *Maya Explorer: John Lloyd Stephens and the Lost Cities of Central America and Yucatán* (Norman, Oklahoma, 1948), pp. 62, 74, 149, 151–152.

2. Guillaume or Guillelmo Dupaix, whose report on his expedition to Palenque in 1807 to confirm Del Río's 1786 discovery was published as *Antiquités mexicaines, rélation des trois expéditions du Capitaine Dupaix* (Paris, 1834). Dupaix's was one of several works that Edward King, Viscount Kingsborough, translated and reprinted in his *Antiquities of Mexico*, 9 vols. (London, 1831–1848). Von Hagen, pp. 74, 78, 152; Alfred M. Tozzer, "Stephens and Prescott, Bancroft and Others," in *Los Mayas antiguos*, ed. Cesar Ramos Lizardi (Camino Al Ajusco, Mexico, 1941), pp. 35–60, especially pp. 42, 44.

3. Jean-Frédéric Maxmilien, Count de Waldeck (1766–1875), a Paris-born artist and explorer, was in London making engravings for the 1822 edition of del Río's report when he met Viscount Kingsborough, who agreed to underwrite him on an expedition to study Mexican antiquities. Eventually returning to France, Waldeck published *Voyage pittoresque et archéologique dans la province d'Yucatán* (Paris, 1838), illustrated with his own "archaeological drawings [that] were very inaccurate and most inventive." Despite its errors, the book sparked wide popular interest in the archeology of Central America. Von Hagen, pp. 152–155 (quotation on p. 155); Tozzer, pp. 36–37, 41.

4. John Lloyd Stephens, a native of New Jersey and a former lawyer turned explorer, traveled in Central America from 1839 to 1841 and from 1841 to 1842, accompanied by Frederick Catherwood (1799–1854), an English architect and engraver. They studied the ruins described by del Río, Dupaix, and Waldeck, and found other sites. Stephens published two widely-read accounts of their journeys: *Incidents of Travel in Central America, Chiapas, and Yucatan,* 2 vols. (New York, 1841), and *Incidents of Travel in Yucatan,* 2 vols. (New York, 1843). *DAB; Henry Papers, 5:*85; Tozzer; Von Hagen.

5. Located in western Honduras, near the border with Guatemala, Copán had been one of the greatest cities of the old Mayan empire. Stephens and Catherwood made the first detailed investigation of the site and its magnificent ruins. Tozzer, pp. 42, 44; Von Hagen, pp. 97–118.

6. Better known as the Hopi.

7. The incumbent, Elijah Hise (1801–1867), a Kentucky-born lawyer, had been commissioned the previous March. *DAB.*

The first person to suggest that Squier seek the Guatemalan post was apparently not a Washingtonian, as he stated, but rather Francis L. Hawks (1798–1866, *DAB*), who was then president of the University of Louisiana. Thomas G. Tax, "The Development of American Archaeology, 1800–1879" (Ph.D. diss., University of Chicago, 1973), p. 212n. Regarding the efforts made by Squier and his friends to secure the appointment, see Tax, pp. 211–213, and Charles L. Stansifer, "The Central American Career of E. George Squier" (Ph.D. diss., Tulane University, 1959), pp. 17–24.

8. In August 1839, as Stephens was preparing to embark on his first expedition to Central America, Martin Van Buren named him a confidential "special agent" to the Federation of Central America—a loose alliance among the nominally independent states of Honduras, Guatemala, Nicaragua, Costa Rica, and San Salvador—to negotiate a trade treaty and to adjudicate boundary disputes. Stephens saw the post as a means to obtain government protection at a time when the region where he was headed was still steeped in political turmoil; Van Buren viewed it as an opportunity to reward a crony who had campaigned vigorously for him in 1836. The appointment was a peculiar one, for no one in Washington knew for sure if the federation had a government, or, if it did, where it was located. Stephens never

488

found it. He subsequently advised all like-minded explorers to safeguard themselves by procuring a similar diplomatic appointment. Charles Lanman, *Biographical Annals of the Civil Government of the United States* (Washington, 1876), p. 591; Von Hagen, pp. 64–65, 79–81, 125–136; Tax, pp. 212–213.

9. Squier enclosed extracts of undated letters to him from Edward Everett and Washington Irving, and from William Hickling Prescott to Robert C. Winthrop; the enclosure is in the same location as this document. Prescott (1796–1859, *DAB*), one of the foremost historians of his day, wrote several books on Central America. Nearly fifty other individuals also wrote letters on Squier's behalf. Tax, pp. 212–213; Stansifer, pp. 22–23.

10. Believing that Henry was reneging on a promise to provide him extra copies of *Ancient Monuments of the Mississippi Valley*, Squier was much less complimentary about him in letters to other correspondents. Writing to Brantz Mayer, for example, Squier characterized Henry as "careless and neglectful," and "alto-gether the reverse of a business man, and of what the Sect. of the Smithsonian Inst. Should be." He was even harsher in a letter to George P. Marsh: "Everybody here, who has had the slightest connection with [Henry], is thoroughly disgusted ... The sooner he resigns and takes to his gallipots the better." Squier to Mayer, March 1, 1849, Gratz Collection, Historical Society of Pennsylvania; Squier to Marsh, March 1, 1849, Marsh Papers, Bailey/Howe Library, University of Vermont.

11. Writing to Henry again on March 26, Squier enclosed a letter from Jared Sparks (not found), asking that he deliver it to Secretary of State Clayton. Noting that Clayton was reviewing his application for the Guatemalan chargéship, Squier suggested that Henry might use the occasion "to say a few words on the importance of the objects sought to be accomplished in Central America." In an abstract of his reply, Henry noted that he would present Sparks's letter. Squier to Henry, March 26, 1849, Henry Papers, Smithsonian Archives; see also Desk Diary, March 28, 1849.

272. TO SIDNEY BREESE

Smithsonian Institution
March 12th 1849

My Dear Sir

Enclosed I send you a copy of the communication[1] relative to your course in the Board of Regents of the Smithsonian Institution with regard to the erection of the Smithsonian Building and I beg leave to assure you that I distinctly recollect the several facts you mention and that I can testify to the accuracy of your statements.

Your communication will be carefully preserved in the Smithsonian Archives to be called forth when the history of the Institution is to be written or when any discussion as to the Building renders it necessary.

Permit me to embrace this opportunity of expressing my acknowledgements for the support and council you have given me in the discharge of my official duties and my full concurrence in the measures you advised relative to the plan of organization of the Smithsonian Institution.

I remain very respectfully &
truly your friend & servt.
Joseph Henry

Hon Sidney Breese[A]

General Manuscript Collection, Manuscripts Division, Department of Rare Books and Special Collections, Princeton University Libraries.

1. Doc. 270.

273. FROM SAMUEL STEMAN HALDEMAN

Columbia Pa 13th March 1849.

Dear Sir:

The running of the boundary between the U.S. and Mexico would, in good hands, afford an excellent opportunity of advancing science, particularly terrestrial magnetism, which would be safe with an observer like Major Graham.[1] The region to be traversed being unknown in the departments of natural Science & Ethnography, and likely to afford new and interesting results, might be explored by the ~~same~~ ↑surveying↓ party; especially since its necessary force & slow progress w^d render unusual facilities for observation.

I mention these matters to you because your position will probably cause you to be consulted upon the subject.

Mr S. C. Walker in his recent article on the application of the electric telegraph to astronomical purposes, states his belief that the eye is more accurate than the ear in its determinations of measurement.[2] I think the relative accuracy depends entirely upon practice. If an <u>inch</u> be taken as a unit for the eye, and a <u>second</u> for the ear, and a series of short sounds be given to the latter, & of short pieces of paper to the former, during the same instant; I think the ear will determine ↑the↓ ~~its~~ fraction of its unit at least as closely as the eye. In my own case, I believe I can determine extemporaneously, without a timepiece, the length of a vowel heard in speech, in simple fractions of a second, as ⅛, ⅙,^ ¼ ¾ &c.[3]

—Very respectfully Yours
S. S. Haldeman

Profr. Joseph Henry LLD.

Henry Papers, Smithsonian Archives.
Reply: March 17, 1849, Haldeman Collection, Library, The Academy of Natural Sciences of Philadelphia.

1. James Duncan Graham (1799–1865), an 1817 graduate of West Point, was commissioned a major in the Corps of Topographical Engineers in 1838. He served on several major boundary survey projects, and was currently directing a resurvey of the Mason-Dixon line. During 1850 and 1851, he was chief astronomer and head of the scientific corps for a survey of part of the Mexican boundary. *DAB; Henry Papers, 6:*129.

2. Haldeman referred to the second part of Walker's report to Bache of December 15,

1848, wherein Walker discussed John Locke's automatic clock register and its applicability to general astronomy. Walker described how astronomical observers measured intervals "by listening to the beats of a clock or chronometer, and estimating the fraction of a second between them when any event has occurred." Noting that such a reliance upon hearing often resulted in uncertain data, Walker termed the ear "in every respect, in the subdivisions of time and space, a very imperfect organ." He asserted that Locke's automatic clock register, which marked lines on a running strip of paper so that time intervals could be readily distin-

guished, would permit greater accuracy in "every department of practical astronomy that involves the nice determination of absolute dates, or of their relative intervals in time." U.S. House, 30th Congress, 2d Session, *Electro-Magnetic Telegraph—Astronomical Observations,* House Executive Documents, No. 21 (1849), pp. 6–13 (quotations on p. 7).

3. In his reply, Henry simply characterized Haldeman's remarks as "interesting." He also thanked him for his suggestions relating to science and the Mexican Boundary Survey, and passed along some routine news about the Smithsonian.

274. TO ASA GRAY

Smithsonian Institution
Washington March 20 1849

My Dear Sir

I beg leave to inform you that Lieut Woodbury,[1] U.S.A, has left this city within a few days, to join his command, at Fort Kearney, which is about two hundred miles above the mouth of the Platte River. As he has agreed to collect, and preserve the plants of that vicinity for you, I subjoin his address to which any communication you may please to send him must be directed; viz Lieut Woodbury, Fort Kearney (via Linden) Atchison Co, Missouri.

Dr Foreman, my assistant, gave him such instructions as, default of better, would aid him in collecting and preparing the plants, but it will be best that you write to him[A] yourself, and give him such definite instructions, as you may think proper, with directions as to their transmission home.

Dr Foreman has suggested that you should furnish detailed instructions in regard to the method of collecting plants, which we may have printed, and ready to furnish on any occasion which may offer. It might be well also, to have prepared, similar instructions for the collection of other objects of Natural History—and, could you not prevail on Dr Gould and other Naturalists in Boston, to furnish us with instructions of this kind?[2] Full credit will be given to the authors.

I fear the adoption of your "Genera"[B] just at this time will be too heavy an undertaking for us, but if you can delay the publication, untill our funds will be free from the expense of the building, we can then go on with it. For the present, the Report on Forest Trees will be as much as we can do, in the way of Reports on Botany. You mention the propriety of our purchasing the stones, and I agree with you in opinion as to this. We have just paid $150, for the stones on which are engraved the 52 quarto maps of Squier and Davis' Memoir. At this rate, the stones from your genera, which might be used in the Report on Forest Trees, could not cost much, and I could advance the money for them, at almost any time.

Enclosed I send you some letters, extracts from which, you may send me, should we conclude to make any arrangement in regard to the "Genera".

> I remain very respectfully
> your obedient servant
> Joseph Henry
> Secretary of Smithsonian Institution

Dr Asa Gray

Historic Letters, Archives, Gray Herbarium Library, Harvard University.
In Edward Foreman's hand, with Henry's signature.

1. Daniel Phineas Woodbury (1812–1864), who graduated from West Point in 1836, was engaged in the construction of Fort Kearny, on the Missouri River, from 1847 to 1850. *DAB*.

2. Augustus Addison Gould (1805–1866), a graduate both of Harvard (1825) and Harvard Medical School (1830), had studied and written extensively about natural history, especially conchology and invertebrate zoology. He was curator and later corresponding secretary of the Boston Society of Natural History. *DSB*.

We are unaware of any such instructions prepared for the Smithsonian by Gould or any other Boston-area naturalist.

275. FROM FRANKLIN BENJAMIN HOUGH[1]

Somerville St Laurence Co March 23 [1849][A]

Prof J Henry.
Sir,

I herewith transmit such notes as I find in my possession, in relation to the Aurora Borealis, as I have observed ~~them~~ ↑it↓ for several years past.

In future I will transmit to the Institution[B] under your charge an[C] account of such aurorae as may be observed at this place,—if supplied with star maps, like those I have had the honor of recieving[D] within a few days.[2] I will endeavor to provide suitable magnetic instruments, as directed.

A box of minerals from this vicinity, is packed for sending to the

Smithsonian Institution, and will be delivered at Alexandria Bay, as soon as navigation on the St Laurence River, and Lake Ontario opens.[3]

The labels which accompany the specimens, refer to the volume and page of[E] the "Natural History of N.Y."[4] where they will be found noticed, or described.

I inclose with this, the figures and descriptions of of Solar haloes, remarkable for their deviation from the usual form. Should these find a place in any of the publications of the Institution, I would be grateful for one or two copies of the work that might contain them.[5]

Other miscellaneous abstracts will also be inclosed with this. Blank forms for meteorological observations have been recieved and are recieving attention.

I also inclose a copy of a "Rotary Calendar," for your library, I am aware that I have forfeited my Copy Right, by not doing this before. The duplicates, you can dispose of as you may see fit.

Should it be found to be of any scientific interest, you may if you see proper communicate it to any scientific Journal that will publish it.

I claim no privilege of Copy Right, as I expect to derive no pecuniary benefit from it.[6]

Hoping that I may be of some little service to the cause of Science by contributing my mite

> I remain
> Respectfully Yours
> Franklin B Hough. M.D.

P.S. The inclosed Calendar has never been offered for public sale, but only distributed among a few friends.

I would loan the cut to any journal that might wish to publish it.

> H.

More blank forms are needed. I would copy from my M.S.S for other months if desired.

If I had a copy of the 'list of Occultations'[7] I might perhaps make some useful observations.

Letters Received, Records of the Smithsonian Meteorological Project, Records of the Weather Bureau, RG 27, National Archives.
Reply: Undated abstract, in hand of Edward Foreman, on separate small sheet of paper attached to top of this letter.

1. An 1843 Union College graduate with a medical degree from Western Medical Reserve College, Hough (1822–1885) practiced in Somerville, New York. He later became a United States census commissioner and a founder of the American forest preservation movement.

Hough wrote or compiled some seventy-five historical or scientific works. *Henry Papers,* 5:25n; *DAB;* Elliott, *Dictionary.*

2. In mid-March 1849, the Smithsonian began distributing a *Map of the STARS near the North Pole, for Observations on the Aurora,* and a

circular, dated March 1, entitled *Instructions for Observations of the Aurora*. Both were derived from materials prepared in 1848 by the Toronto Royal Magnetical Observatory for non-commissioned Royal Artillery officers in Canadian garrisons, whom it directed "to keep a nightly register of the weather, with particular reference to the Observations of Auroras." Copies of the Smithsonian's star map and aurora circular, and Toronto Observatory's "Instructions for the Observation of Aurora" (quotation), October 11, 1848, in Volume 1, Records of the Chief Clerk, 1846–1933, RU 65, Smithsonian Archives; *National Intelligencer,* March 14, 1849. On the Canadian auroral observation program, see A. D. Thiessen, "Her Majesty's Magnetical and Meteorological Observatory, Toronto: Part XI.—Observations of Aurora Borealis and the Application of Photography in Making Magnetic Records," *Journal of the Royal Astronomical Society of Canada,* 1945, 39:360–369, 394–407.

3. The *Smithsonian Report for 1850* noted that

the museum had accessioned a "Box of Minerals and Fossils from St. Lawrence county, New York," sent by Hough (p. 41).

4. Lewis Caleb Beck, *Mineralogy of New-York; Comprising Detailed Descriptions of the Minerals Hitherto Found in the State of New-York, and Notices of Their Uses in the Arts and Agriculture* (Albany, 1842), part 3 of the *Natural History of New-York.*

5. The Smithsonian never published Hough's solar halo data. Hough included a summary of observations of solar and lunar halos in his *Results of a Series of Meteorological Observations . . . from 1826 to 1850 Inclusive* (Albany, 1855), p. 471.

6. The "rotary calendar" may have been some sort of perpetual calendar. Hough apparently believed that by not depositing a copy promptly with the Smithsonian, he had forfeited his copyright. The reply assured him that he had not.

7. That is, John Downes's table of occultations for 1849.

276. TO EPHRAIM GEORGE SQUIER

Washington
March 28th, 49

My Dear Sir

I have just returned from the State Department[1] and have been requested to ask you to come on. The mission is one which involves responsibilities of much importance and Mr Clayton has requested me to have a free conversation with you on the subject. Say nothing of this call and come on as soon as you can.[2]

I remain yours &c
J.H.

E. G. Squier

Squier Papers, Library of Congress.

1. Secretary of State Clayton had written a short note to Henry on March 28, requesting him to stop by that day for a brief visit, and to bring Bache with him—presumably to discuss Squier's application. J. M. Clayton to Henry, March 28, 1849, Henry Papers, Smithsonian Archives.

2. President Taylor commissioned Squier as

Chargé d'affaires to Guatemala on April 2, 1849. He was subsequently instructed to negotiate trade treaties with the other republics of Central America. Charles Lanman, *Biographical Annals of the Civil Government of the United States* (Washington, 1876), p. 591.

According to Thomas G. Tax, Henry never recommended Squier for the Guatemalan post.

He speculates that Henry may have been willing to allow Squier greater freedom to theorize
in his memoir on New York antiquities as
"atonement" for not recommending him. Tax,
however, apparently was unaware of this letter,

which documents Henry's intercession with
Clayton. Thomas G. Tax, "The Development of
American Archaeology, 1800–1879" (Ph.D.
diss., University of Chicago, 1973), p. 213.

277. TO ASA GRAY

Washington April 2nd
,49

My Dear Dr.

I write to suggest that in the preparation of your Report on Forest
trees you apply to the Hon Mr Marsh of Vermont for information relative to the economical value and uses of timber. He was once[A] engaged
in 'lumbering' and has I think much information on the subject.[1] I have
found him since I got under his hat a most estimable gentleman of extraordinary[B] acquirements not only in literature[C] but also in general
science.

Washington presents just now quite a contrast in appearance to that
of a month ago. The deluge of office seakers has subsided and the Hotel
keepers have again a vacation.

Professor Koeppen[2] has just finished a course of four lectures on
Greece which has been attended with full houses.[3] The lectures appear
to have taken very well though they could not be more than half understood on account of the pronounciation[D] of the Speaker.

I think courses of lectures in Washington will tend to do much good
there are in the several offices of the city many intelligent gentlemen
with small salaries who will attend with their families provided the lectures are free.[E]

We have not yet got into the new building though it has been promised to us for three months past. We shall however probably move into
it this week.[F]

I have heard since this letter was commenced that Agassiz has arrived
in the city and that he is in bad health. I will call on him and let you
know more about him before I close this letter.

When you next visit Washington cannot you bring with you some of
the large drawings of the Lowell Institute[4] and give us a few lectures on
botany or any other subject you may choose?

I have seen Agassiz he appears to have been overworked but looks much better than I expected to see him. He will remain a few days in Washington to recruit and then return to the north.

> I remain as ever truly
> Yours friend &
> Servt
> Joseph Henry

Dr A Gray

P.S. Mr Lewis Saynisch[5] of Blosburgh Tioga County Penn^a starts in a few days for for California via Fort Independence St^a Fe &c. I will request him to make a collection of plants for you.

I wish you would send me^G the instructions I requested in my last letter.

> J–H–

Historic Letters, Archives, Gray Herbarium Library, Harvard University.

1. As a landowner and sheep raiser in Vermont, Marsh had seen the destructive action of sheep on hillside vegetation, the subsequent erosion and loss of arable land, and the decimation of forests around Burlington. He had approached this problem along the lines of forest conservation as early as 1847, in an address to the Rutland County Agricultural Society. Henry's letter to Gray caused him to write to Marsh on April 25, and on May 9, Marsh sent him an outline of "an essay or a volume on the ... Economy of the forest." In it, he commented on the restorative nature of forests, and recommended a national program of forest study. David Lowenthal, *George Perkins Marsh: Versatile Vermonter* (New York, 1958), pp. 40–41, 177, 251–252; Marsh to Gray, May 9, 1849, Marsh Papers, Bailey/Howe Library, University of Vermont (quotation).

2. Adolph Ludvig Koeppen (1804–1873), a Danish professor of history at the University of Athens, came to the United States in early 1848. It is not known how long Koeppen remained in this country. Marsh to Baird, April 4, 1848, published in Caroline Crane Marsh, comp., *Life and Letters of George Perkins Marsh,* (New York, 1888), p. 119; *National Union Catalog,* s.v. "Koeppen, Adolph Ludvig."

3. Between March 16 and 30, Koeppen spoke on "Attica and Athens," mostly concerning himself with ancient Athens. Because the lecture room at the Smithsonian was not yet finished, he delivered these talks at Carusi's Saloon. Though the institution had sponsored lectures before, these were the first for which the regents had made a specific appropriation under the plan of organization; thus they may be considered the first official lectures of the Smithsonian. *National Intelligencer,* March 14, 1849; *Smithsonian Report for 1849,* p. 21; Desk Diary, March 27, 1849.

4. Gray had delivered Lowell lectures on plant physiology and botany from 1844 to 1846. To illustrate these, he commissioned—at the institute's expense—a set of impressive botanical paintings, over two meters high. Dupree, *Gray,* pp. 120, 127–130.

5. Lewis Saynish of Blossburg, Pennsylvania, was a botanical acquaintance of John Torrey's. Andrew Denny Rodgers III, *John Torrey: A Story of North American Botany* (1942; New York, 1965), p. 86; Kohlstedt, *AAAS,* appendix B.

April 2, 1849

278. TO EDWARD NORRIS KIRK[1]

Washington April 2nd
/49

My Dear Sir

I am well acquainted with Professor Guyot and fully concur with you in opinion as to his moral and intellectual character as well as to his Scientific abilities.

I have engaged him to prepare a report for the smithsonian Institution on meteorological instruments[2] and were our funds at present free to be applied to active scientific operrations we would make an appropriation to him for explorations in Physical geography. I ~~have been~~ expect[A] to see him in Washington ~~for some time past~~ before long and shall then learn more definitely the plan of operation he intends to persue during his stay in this country.

E N. Kirk, Eqr[B]

Draft, Henry Papers, Smithsonian Archives.

1. A graduate of Princeton, Kirk was pastor of the Mount Vernon Congregational Church in Boston. *Henry Papers*, 2:14n.

2. According to Henry's preface to Guyot's *Directions for Meteorological Observations, Intended for the First Class of Observers* (Washington, 1850),

the *Directions* was to be an appendix to a report by Guyot on meteorological instruments and observations. Although the report was to be published several weeks after the *Directions* in early 1850, it did not appear.

279. FROM ROBERT HARFORD HARE[1]

Linwood April 3rd/49[A]

My dear Sir

I caused the package entrusted to me to be delivered to Mr Booth[2] on Saturday Morning.[3]

My Father has no doubt acknowledged the receipt of the first vol of the Smithsonian Contributions to Knowledge.

Agreeably to our conversation I sounded H B Wallace[4] as to his willingness to contribute to your great end and found him fully inclined to take up the subject of Mental and Moral Philosophy, the one for which you esteemed him best suited, taking Moral to include Politickal[B] Philosophy. We agreed that Mackintoshs History of Ethickal Opinion was all that is necessary in the history of Mental Philosophy[5] and that there-

497

fore the first Vol or work should properly be a history of Moral and Politickal science down to the present day in order that the two subjects should stand equally prepared for periodical contributions. Should you think proper you can use this letter as the basis of any communication you may wish to make him.[6]

Have the kindness to present me to M[rs] Henry who is I hope quite well and believe that I remain with grateful recollection of your recent kind attention

Yours very truly
R H Hare

Prof[r] Henry

Henry Papers, Smithsonian Archives.
Note in Henry's hand below inside address: "Wrote to Gamble enclose Thomas B Wilson Ac[d] of Nat Siences."

1. Son of chemist Robert Hare. Edgar Fahs Smith, *The Life of Robert Hare, an American Chemist (1781–1858)* (Philadelphia, 1917), p. 33.

2. Presumably James Curtis Booth of Philadelphia.

3. March 31.

4. Horace Binney Wallace (1817–1852) had studied under both Henry (in the Princeton class of 1835) and Robert Hare (as a special chemistry student, ca. 1836–1837). He also read law, but rather than practicing any of these professions, he devoted himself to writing. Wallace became an acknowledged legal commentator, having published numerous books of case analysis in conjunction with John

Innes Clark Hare, R. H. Hare's brother. *DAB; National Union Catalog.*

5. James Mackintosh, *A General View of the Progress of Ethical Philosophy, Chiefly during the Seventeenth and Eighteenth Centuries* (Philadelphia, 1832, and many other editions). This work was originally commissioned in 1828 as one of the preliminary dissertations to the seventh edition of the *Encyclopaedia Britannica.* Mackintosh's work was only indirectly a history of mental philosophy, presenting an analysis of the nature and sources of virtuous action in the individual.

6. The report never appeared.

280. TO JOHN TORREY

Washington
April 7th 1849

My Dear Dr

Agassiz has just left our house for the Railway for Phil[d] to return to Boston. He has been here several days but has not been in very good health. He is however much better than when I ↑he↓ came on. We have enjoyed his company very much and have had several long conversations with him on the subject of the means of improving the condition of science in our country.[1] He strongly advises me to urge either Gray or yourself to prepare a report on the present state of philosophical botany.[2] Dr Gray is engaged on a Report on Forest Trees and it will not do for me to ask more than one at the same time from the same person. I must therefore again ask you to prepare the article. Cannot you talk off your lectures on the subject to Eliza or one of your other Daughters while she takes down what you say in short hand or rather I should say quick hand? Or could you not induce Dr Holton[3] to employ his phonography in this way I would allow him a small sum for compensation if he would be of any use to you.

The bill as you know for the establishment of a new mint in New York was lost. It will however probably pass in another Session. Professor Renwick is an applicant for the situation of Director which if he succeeds in getting for himself[4] one of his sons will be provided for in one of the offices of the Establishment.[A]

All things just now in this city are in a quiet condition the Office seekers have "sloped"[5] and the cabinet is now allowed to breath a little less laboriously.

What think you of the appointment of Mr E G Squier as charge de fair to Guatemala. The noteriety of the Smithsonian publication has done him some service and if he will now discharge his duty with prudence and integrity as I trust he will do, there is a fine field open to him for real distinction.

We are all well though Mrs H. has been a little ailing the weather is beginning to be quite warm. I found the sun this morning rather oppressive.

> With kind regards to Mrs Torrey
> I remain as ever truly
> Your Friend &c
> Joseph Henry

Dr John Torrey

P.S. How do you come on with the plants of oregon[6]— Fremont[B] has had a hard time during the past winter.

Torrey Papers, Library, New York Botanical Garden.

1. According to Henry's Desk Diary, Agassiz advised Henry on the production of reports by means of collaborators, and on work in natural history, especially that of Jacob Whitman Bailey. He promised to prepare a report on natural history himself, if possible (it never appeared). Agassiz further advised Henry on the character of museum collections in natural history, recommending a museum of American animals, represented in all developmental stages from embryo to adult, and a full set of geological specimens, especially comprising tertiary fossils "from Maine to Alabama." He agreed to produce a "programme of collections," which Henry eventually published as an appendix to his 1849 report to the regents. Desk Diary, April [1], 2, 5, 7, and [8], 1849 (quotations from entries of April [1] and 7, respectively); *Smithsonian Report for 1849*, pp. 24–26.

2. Henry's Desk Diary of April 7 states that he asked Torrey to prepare a report on morphology. In this context, *philosophical botany* apparently meant a reference to the application of principles of natural philosophy to plants: plant physiology and morphology.

3. Probably Charles Alexander Holton, who sold phonetic books on Broadway in New York. New York City Directory, 1848.

4. James Renwick, Sr., never secured a position at the United States Mint. As early as 1846,

he had lobbied Henry for a recommendation from the Princeton faculty for the position of director of the proposed New York Mint. Renwick to Henry, January 22, 1846, Henry Papers, Smithsonian Archives.

5. Slang for *departed* or *decamped. Oxford English Dictionary.*

6. Torrey's descriptions of the plants of Oregon and California for the publications of the Wilkes Expedition.

281. FROM EDWARD C. HERRICK[1]

Yale College Library,
New Haven, Conn
Apr. 7, 1849.

Sir,

I have delayed a reply to the proposal contained in Prof. Jewett's letter of Febr. 2,[2] until I might be able to complete the Statistics of our Library in answer to the inquiries of your Circular.[3] Could I command the necessary time I should be glad to prepare a historical sketch of the progress of discovery respecting shooting stars, for it is a subject in which I still feel a lively interest, & to the fuller understanding of which I hope yet to contribute something by future observation & research. My present occupations & engagements are however so pressing that I can scarcely keep pace with them, & I am compelled to lay by ↑aside↓ several matters of scientific inquiry which I had commenced. This state of things while it continues, must prevent my engaging in any new undertaking. I ought to say moreover that it has been mentioned to me, that Professor Olmsted intends to write some sketch of the kind proposed, & if so, I should be unwilling to interfere with what might seem to be his proper field.[4]

Among the engagements which can not be dispensed with, is a regular attention to the Aurora Borealis; for as my record began eleven years since, it has become worth while to keep it up, if any law of periodicity is ever to be deduced from it. I make a record every evening, entering negatives as well as positives. I shall of course most cheerfully engage in the system of observation on the A.B. proposed in the Circular of the Sm. Inst.[5] I can not now however observe the electrical & magnetical changes during Aurorae, & indeed one person can hardly look out for all the particulars you indicate. The "Instructions" are full, but they do not insist sufficiently on accurate time, without which many of the observations are worthless, as for instance on the altitude of the two ends of a streamer. In the first Section, N° 7, <u>north</u> should be south:— a typographical error which you have prob. noticed & corrected ere this. Magnetical observations during auroras are important but I fear that rude apparatus will furnish rather uncertain materials, & I am inclined to think we must look for help chiefly to regular magn. observatories.

Electrical observations are exceedingly necessary, & it is surprising how little we can find on record respecting the electr. state of the air during Auroral exhibitions. But in order to know what is really due to the Aurora, ought not observations to be made regularly at other times, & indeed every day, along with the ordinary meteorological observations? Could not captive balloons be employed advantageously? The aurora of Nov 17th last (one of the most extensive ↑on↓ record,) produced "marvellous effects" on the magn. telegraphs in various parts of Europe, (See South^n Lit. Mess. Richm^d Mch. 1849, p. 179,)[6] but such effects were noticed at the Station in New Haven a year or two earlier, & are alluded to in a letter printed soon after in the Bulletin of the Acad. at Brussels.[7] I should be glad to be informed what sort of effects ↑on the telegraph↓ may be looked for, & whether they may not be made serviceable.

Previous to receiving your Circular I had engaged to co-operate with Capt. Lefroy, of Toronto, & to send him my notes; & previous to this I had made an agreement with three persons nearly on this meridian to observe in concert, principally with a view to determine the elevation of arches & streamers. No very good case has occurred since our organization.

I am, very respectfully
Yr. obed^t Servt
E. C. Herrick.

Prof. Henry,
Secretary of the Smithsonian Institution.

Letters Received, Records of the Smithsonian Meteorological Project, Records of the Weather Bureau, RG 27, National Archives.
Reply: Doc. 283.

1. Herrick was librarian of Yale College, and had an interest in entomology and meteorics. *Henry Papers*, 4:312n.

2. Not found. Presumably Jewett's letter concerned the Yale library, but also communicated Henry's request to prepare a Smithsonian report on meteors.

3. Doc. 231.

4. Denison Olmsted did not write an overview of meteors.

5. *Instructions for Observations of the Aurora.*

6. The Paris correspondent of the *Southern Literary Messenger* noted a dispute in the French National Institute over the effects of the aurora on telegraph lines. Carlo Matteucci had sent the institute an account from Pisa stating that the aurora of November 17, 1848—which was observed in as widely dispersed places as California, Cuba, and Smyrna in Turkey—had produced the "marvellous effects" to which Herrick referred. His communication was treated with skepticism, until U. J. J. Le Verrier supported it by a letter from the telegraphic engineer of the London and North-western Railway, stating that this aurora had disabled his telegraph for many hours, an effect he had often seen. "From Our Paris Correspondent," *Southern Literary Messenger,* 1849, *15*:178–179;

E.C.H. [Edward C. Herrick], "Aurora Borealis of Nov. 17, 1848," *Silliman's Journal,* 1849, 2d ser. 7:293–295.

7. "Sur les aurores boréales, les étoiles filantes et la quantité de neige aux États-Unis, en 1846 et 1847," *Bulletins de l'Académie royale des sciences, des lettres et des beaux-arts de Belgique,* 1847, *14* (part 1):419–424, a letter from Herrick to Adolphe Quetelet, was presented at the meeting of May 19, 1847.

Henry later made use of this information, as well as that which Herrick supplied in a letter of May 31 (same location as this letter), in his comments on Angelo Secchi's paper on the aurora borealis at the 1849 meeting of the American Association for the Advancement of Science. AAAS *Proceedings,* 1849, 2:11.

282. EXCERPT, HENRY DESK DIARY

[April 8,][A] 1849[B]

[...] Organize the[C] Corps of Collaborators[1,D]— Bring the matter before the American Association.[2]

Dr Gray
& Torrey } Botany

Geology
    Hall[3]   Descript Geology
    Rogers[4] Dymanical Geol.
    Marthe.[5] ~~Tech~~ ↑Echonom↓ Geology

For Paleontolegy[E] Invertebrate animals
    Hall

Of the vertebrates
    Agassiz
    Wyman[6]

Special Mineralogy Cristalography &
    Dana[7]

Zoology

Entomology { LaCount[8]—Descrip
Dr Haldeman[9]   Concology
Dr Harris[10]—Morphology
Dr Gould[11]—Concology[F]

Anthropology   Morton[12]
Vertebrate ↑in genral↓ Agessiz
Ornithology   Gamble[13,G]
                    Cassin[14,H]

Zoophites   Dana
Comparitive Anatomy

                    Dr Wiman[I] ↑&↓
                    Dr Leidy[15] Phil<u>d</u>
Herpetology   Dr Holbrook[16,J]

Henry Papers, Smithsonian Archives.

1. Henry here revived an idea that had formed part of his earliest plans for the Smithsonian: establishing a corps of collaborators to prepare periodic semi-popular reports on the different branches of knowledge. Henry planned to offer support to his collaborators, mostly by supplying journals in their respective fields. But he also offered a stipend and full credit for what was essentially science journalism. Although for two years he had promoted the production of reports under Smithsonian auspices—for example, his work with Beck, Loomis, Guyot, and Gray, and his recent attempts to recruit Torrey and Agassiz—his efforts were generally unsuccessful. Agassiz's recent visit seemed to have spurred Henry to ask for advice on his system and to regularize his corps of collaborators, at least in natural history.

Henry Papers, 6:498–499, 624; *Smithsonian Report for 1847,* pp. 175, 182–183; Desk Diary, April 5 and [22], 1849.

2. Henry made no such presentation to the American Association for the Advancement of Science and indeed never constituted such a corps.

3. James Hall.
4. Henry Darwin Rogers.
5. William W. Mather.
6. Jeffries Wyman.
7. James Dwight Dana.
8. John Eatton LeConte, Jr.
9. Samuel Haldeman.

10. Thaddeus William Harris (1795–1856), librarian at Harvard College and from 1837 to 1842, lecturer in natural history there. Harris's reputation was primarily as an economic entomologist, from his work on the geological and natural history survey of Massachusetts of the early 1830s. Elliott, *Dictionary.*

11. Augustus Addison Gould.
12. Samuel George Morton.

13. William Gambel (1823–1849), a naturalist from Philadelphia, who had traveled extensively with Thomas Nuttall. Although he collected in many different branches of natural history, his fame came from his study of birds of the American West, especially of California. Elliott, *Dictionary.*

14. John Cassin.

15. Joseph Leidy (1823–1891), an 1844 graduate of the University of Pennsylvania Medical School, an anatomist, and currently a lecturer in physiology at the Medical Institute of Pennsylvania. Recently he had begun studies in comparative anatomy of paleontological specimens at the Academy of Natural Sciences in Philadelphia. *DSB.*

16. John Edwards Holbrook (1794–1871), a founder of and professor of anatomy at the Medical College of South Carolina, in Charleston. He had an international reputation as a zoologist on the basis of his *North American Herpetology,* 5 vols. (Philadelphia, 1842). Elliott, *Dictionary.*

283. TO EDWARD C. HERRICK

Washington April 9th
1849

My Dear Sir

Your letter of the 7th[1] has just been received and I hasten to answer it while the subject is prominent in my mind.

I do not think that Prof Olmsted intends to prepare an article on shooting stars. If this were his intention he would have mentioned it to me in our late communications.[2] He is about to engage in the preparation of an account of the active period of the aurora in which we are now living near the close.[3] I hope therefore that you will favourably entertain the proposition of making a Report on the shooting stars.[4]

I am much obliged to you for your remarks on the aurora the word north was a mistake in copying the article before it was sent to the press. From some observations made with an apparatus as crude as the one described in the circular[5] I have known^ good results ~~to~~ obtained.

I was at one time very much interested in the study of the aurora but after my removal to Princeton I had no opportunity of making observations trees and hills of considerable elevation shut off the view to the north and besides this I was under the impression that the aurora exhibited itself less frequently at Princeton than in Philadelphia. I am inclined to believe that ~~that~~ the aurora is sometimes a local phenomenon visible only a few miles from the place at which it is most active. You have probably made some observations on this point.

I am much interested in the fact entirely new to me which you mention with reference to the effect of the aurora on the telegraph. When I wrote the paragraph of the circular which refers to the electrical effects of the aurora the idea in my mind was that possibly an induction effect might be observed at the moment of the shooting up of of a beam by the divergency of the leaves of the electrometer in connection with the wire.[6] A[B] phenomena of this kind would require no comparative observations but would manifest its connection with the auroral beam by the by the simultaneous divergency of the leaves. If the aurora is attended with a general ↑electrical↓ excitement of the atmosphere in the position of greatest activity then the effect ~~of~~ on a long insulated wire say from Toronto to Washington would be a current from the former to the latter place but this I think would be too feeble to be detected otherwise than by a delicate galvanometer. The effects you mention must have been inductive like those I have described in Silliman's Journal as exhibited on the telegraph wires during a thunder storm.[7] I shall be pleased to hear from you on this or any other subject.

I remain truly yours &c
Joseph Henry

E. C Herrick Esq

Herrick Papers, Manuscripts and Archives, Yale University Library.
Reply: May 31, 1849, Letters Received, Records of the Smithsonian Meteorological Project, Records of the Weather Bureau, RG 27, National Archives.

1. Doc. 281.
2. Not found.
3. This appeared as *On the Recent Secular Period of the Aurora Borealis*, 1856, SI Contributions, vol. 8 (Washington, 1856).
4. In his reply, Herrick declined to take on further scientific projects, because of his duties as librarian and as treasurer pro tem of Yale.
5. Henry's "Instructions for Observations of the Aurora" (Washington, [1849]) specified a simple magnetometer, comprised of a magnetized plate suspended in a glass box, with a mirror on one of its surfaces. By means of a fixed spyglass anchored at a distance of some fifteen feet away, the observer focused on a graduated scale reflected by the mirror. Small motions of the plate were easily observable as shifts of the scale. With slight variations of arrangement, one could observe changes in magnetic declination and horizontal intensity.
6. The electrical apparatus was a long wire attached to a simple gold-leaf electroscope.
7. "On the Induction of Atmospheric Electricity on the Wires of the Electrical Telegraph," *Silliman's Journal*, 1847, 2d ser. *3*:25–32 (a reprint of Henry's communication to the American Philosophical Society, and published in its *Proceedings*, 1843–1847, *4*:260–268).

284. TO ELIAS LOOMIS

Washington April 12th 49

My Dear Sir

Your report[1] came safely to hand last week but I have not as yet had an opportunity of examing it, I hope however to be able to do so in the course of a few days. Dr Bache has just started for the south to be absent two or three weeks.[2] He will read your Report when he returns.

I hope you are getting on smoothly in Princeton and that you have found the position as pleasant as you anticipated. A ridiculous hoax was republished in the Union[3] for which I gave the Directors[4] a Scolding. The publication was however made in good faith on the supposition that the whole was sober earnest.

I suspect the article was written by a graduate of the college who attempted or rather did something of the kind last year.

Hoaxes of the kind show the profundity of the ignorance of the community on every[A] thing pertaining to scientific knowledge though it is supposed that there is much information among the multitude on such subjects.

I remain truly
Yours &c
Joseph Henry

Professor Loomis
P.S. I have heard of some designs to induce you to leave Princeton.

J.H.

Loomis Papers, Beinecke Rare Book and Manuscript Library, Yale University.

1. On astronomy.

2. Bache was measuring a survey base line on Edisto Island, on the South Carolina coast. *Coast Survey Report for 1849*, p. 43.

3. Possibly the article in the March 27 edition of the *Washington Daily Union* entitled "Electric Light," which claimed "BRILLIANT PERMANENT LIGHT, WITHOUT COMBUSTION, WITHOUT HEAT, AND WITHOUT COST!" The article, from the New York correspondent of the *National Intelligencer*, detailed a new carbon arc light that had been described in Britain. In addition to providing a steady source of illumination, the new invention relied on a process that made the chemical products from the galvanic battery that powered it worth more in trade than the components from which it was fabricated. Thus, "the light developed *costs literally nothing*." The gas companies of London were already in a panic, it was reported.

4. Thomas Ritchie was the sole proprietor of the *Union*. "Journalism in Washington," *Washington Star*, October 10, 1891.

285. FROM BENJAMIN PEIRCE

Harvard University April 14 '49

My Dear Professor Secretary.

I did not dare write an answer to your enquiry when I could let you have Neptune,[1] until after an event had occurred, of which the residual phenomenon is a fine hearty boy.[2] Before I had seen how the mother,[3] who was quite an invalid, would pass through the ordeal, I did not venture to make any arrangements for the future. But Heaven's blessed ether has carried her safely through; and, as the only return which I can make for the favour, I am now working as hard as I can upon Celestial Mechanics. Uranus and Neptune are ↑now↓ my meat and drink, and I shall be greatly disappointed if they are not ~~completed~~ consumed within^A three or four months. They were stale food, at first; and for more than a year, I have not been able to look at them without a feeling of satiety and consequent loathing. I had to wait until the appetite should return; and a long journey which I have recently taken into Analytic Mechanics, as well as some sharp drives upon comets[4] have reinvigorated me and my fondness for them is now as strong as ever. I thank you, with all my heart, for your liberality in regard to the employment of an assistant, and shall certainly avail myself of it, if I possibly can. Bache (Give him my love) had already told me of this offer but almost all the numerical work is so combined with the theoretical investigations as to make the employment of an assistant a difficult thing. I must also add that I know of no one, who is sufficiently unoccupied for my service, and who would not be too slow a coach.

I am delighted that things are going so well at Washington. You and Bache deserve to receive mural crowns[5] from your scientific fellow-citizens for the good, which you have done there— Bond,[6] who has just returned, is greatly charmed with the Smithsonian Secretary. George's new comet[7] promises to be very interesting on the 24th inst., at which time its distance from the earth will only be about ten millions of miles. George has just been observing Metis,[8] which seems to him a very difficult object, and I am very much astonished to hear that it has been seen since its ~~opp~~ conjunction at the Washingto[n] observatory. Can this be true? Could a ↑so↓ few degrees of latitude make so much difference? I wish you would enquire of Walker if it has really been seen at Washington, and tell him that Gould would be very much obliged to him for the informmation.[9]

Bye the bye, what an astonishing success Walker has had with his ephemeris![10] He richly deserved it for the labour which he bestowed upon the computations.

> Most Sincerely and faithfuly
> Your Friend
> Benjamin Peirce

Joseph Henry LL.D–
P.S. I have some interesting investigations about comets to tell you and Bache about—

Henry Papers, Smithsonian Archives.

1. The article planned for the Smithsonian Contributions to Knowledge.

2. Herbert Henry Davis Peirce, born April 11, later a noted diplomat. *The National Cyclopaedia of American Biography*, 27:273–274.

3. Sarah Hunt Mills Peirce. *DSB*, s.v. "Peirce, Benjamin."

4. Peirce probably referred to investigations to determine whether comets were indigenous to the solar system—formed when the planets were—or came from outside. He pursued this question by detailed analysis of cometary orbits. Peirce had published a list of known orbits three years before in the *American Almanac and Repository of Useful Knowledge for 1847* (Boston, 1846). His conclusion that very few comets had hyperbolic orbits pointed to comets being component parts of the solar system. He presented his findings at the 1849 meeting of the American Association for the Advancement of Science ("On the Connection of Comets with the Solar System," AAAS *Proceedings*, 1849, 2:118–122).

5. A special crown given the soldier who first climbed the wall of a besieged city. *Oxford English Dictionary*.

6. William Cranch Bond, probably in Wash-

ington in connection with the Coast Survey. *Coast Survey Report for 1849*, p. 19.

7. Discovered on April 11, 1849, by George Phillips Bond (1825–1865), William Cranch's son and assistant at Harvard College Observatory. Elliott, *Dictionary; Silliman's Journal*, 1849, 2d ser. *7:*449; *8:*428.

8. The asteroid Metis was discovered by Andrew Graham of Ireland on April 25, 1848. *Silliman's Journal*, 1848, 2d ser. *6:*438.

9. Whether Metis had been observed at the Naval Observatory by this time is uncertain, but James Ferguson of that observatory made ex-

tensive observations from September 1849 through January 1850, which Benjamin Apthorp Gould published in the first volume of his *Astronomical Journal* ("Observations of Metis," 1849–1851, *1:*17–18, 29–30).

10. Walker had just completed his ephemeris of Neptune for the years 1846 through 1849. On April 12, Henry had given his approval to publish the work, which appeared as a separate pamphlet in late May, and then as an appendix to the SI Contributions, vol. 2 (Washington, 1851). Desk Diary, April 12 and May 23, 1849.

286. TO JAMES P. ESPY

Smithsonian Institution
April 23 1849

My Dear Sir

The Meteorological correspondence continues to increase and will be soon sufficiently extensive to occupy one person continuously. Various questions are frequently asked which require investigation. What instructions do you give with regard to the method of ascertaining the mean temperature of the day?[1]

What would you think of the proposition of having prepared a lithographed engraving of the clouds according to Howard's classification?[2]

Did you make any arrangement with regard to a supply of Thermometers? We have calls for them almost every day.[3]

I hope that Mrs Espy continues to improve; please give her my kind regards. Mrs Henry would join me in what I write but I dictate this in one of the rooms of the Smithsonian Building.

We are now unpacking the apparatus and shall soon be in a condition to carry on a comparison of instruments and all other things relative to Meteorology, more vigorously.

Mr R. F. Astrop in a letter of recent date[4] asks the following question "How can I procure a copy of The Philosophy of Storms."[5] Please give him the proper directions. ↑We have just heard from Chamberlain, who promises to bring on the apparatus which includes the Nephelescope, in the course of two weeks.↓[6]

Very respectfully and truly
Your obedient Servant

Profr. Espy
Harrisburg

Draft, Letters Received, Records of the Smithsonian Meteorological Project, Records of the Weather Bureau, RG 27, National Archives.
In Edward Foreman's hand. Replies: April 25 and 30, 1849, in same location.

1. We have not found Espy's early Smithsonian instructions for making and reducing meteorological investigations, nor do we know whether he prepared any. However, in 1842 he helped establish the directions for army meteorological observers. In these instructions, the daily mean temperature was defined as the average of the observations at sunrise and 3 P.M. Thomas Lawson, *Army Meteorological Register for Twelve Years, from 1843 to 1854, Inclusive* (Washington, 1855), p. vi.

2. Luke Howard (1772–1864), a London chemist and meteorologist, in 1802 developed a system of cloud classification like that of Linnaeus for the living world. Coining such terms as *cirrus, stratus, cumulus,* and *nimbus,* Howard established the basic system of empirical classification in meteorology thereafter. *DNB.*

In his reply of the thirtieth, Espy counselled Henry to "go on with it . . . if you can see your way clear, in getting it made in a manner intelligible to our correspondents." Although Espy went on to express his doubts, Guyot's *Directions* included two lithographed engravings of cloud formations. *Smithsonian Report for 1850,* p. 18.

3. According to his reply of April 25, Espy had begun to order thermometers from MacAllister of Philadelphia, which he tested and then purchased for $1.25 each.

4. The letter, addressed to Henry or Espy and dated April 1849, is in the same location as this document. R. F. Astrop, of Diamond Grove, Brunswick County, Virginia, a military man, wrote an account of a trip he had recently taken in northern Mexico. He was a meteorological correspondent from 1849 to 1861. Fleming, *Meteorology,* p. 175.

5. Espy's *The Philosophy of Storms,* published in Boston in 1841.

6. The communication has not been found. Nathan B. Chamberlain (1808 or 1809–1878) was an inventor whose instrument-making firm in Boston often provided equipment for the Harvard science faculty. Contrary to Henry's expectation, he did not ship the instruments until June. *New York Times,* June 17, 1878; Desk Diary, June 11, 12, [17], and 22, 1849; Rhees, *Journals,* p. 474.

287. TO CHARLES ELLET, JR.

Smithsonian Institution
April 24th 1849

My Dear Sir

It is contemplated to construct a foot bridge over the canal in front of the Smithsonian building,[1] and the idea has occurred to me that a wire one would be the cheapest and best looking. Can you give me any information as to the cost—the mode of construction—the purchase of the materials &c &c.

The canal is about 6̶0̶ ↑70↓ feet wide and as the bridge is for foot passengers it need not be more than three ↑or four↓ feet wide.

When are we to receive the memoir on the wire bridge over the falls. The second volume of the Smithsonian Contributions is just about to be commenced by the printer though[A] it will not be completed until the end of the year. I should be pleased to receive your memoir as soon as convenient.

The institution is now in as prosperous a condition as I could reasonably hope for and I think notwithstanding much more has been spent in ornamental architecture than should have been the funds will be sufficient to do much good.

> I remain with much
> respect truly yours &c
> Joseph Henry

Charles Ellett Jr
Wheeling Va

Ellet Papers, Department of Rare Books and Special Collections, University Library, University of Michigan.
Inside address in another hand, possibly Edward Foreman's.

1. There were bridges at Fourth, Seventh, Twelfth and Fourteenth streets. The institution proposed a bridge at Tenth Street, opposite the Smithsonian Building.

On April 6, the day that Henry began to move into the east wing, he decided to petition the common council for a bridge. Henry was concerned about the public programs of the institution, a lecture series by Edward Hitchcock of Amherst College being scheduled to commence April 30. The city erected an iron bridge several years later. Desk Diary, April 6, 20, 27, and 30, 1849; October 5, 1850; Rhees, *Journals*, p. 702.

288. TO EPHRAIM GEORGE SQUIER

Smithsonian Institution
April 24 1849

My Dear Sir

I am most anxious to have a set of Meteorological observations made in Guatemala, but perhaps it might be best to send the instruments round Cape Horn. The boiling apparatus you mention,[1] I am not sure you will find as convenient as you anticipate. Its character for much accuracy has not been fully established; and for portability, it has not much to boast of over the Barometer. The bulb of the Thermometer is necessarily very large & from the inertia of the mercury, is very liable to be broken, whilst the observations are far less conveniently made than those with the barometer. Green[2] does not keep them on hand, but makes them to order. The cost of one is $40.

We have ordered from Edinburgh an instrument for measuring the direction and intensity of the Earthquake, for the Expedition under Lieut Gilliss.[3,A] I know not what will be the cost, of it will however be paid for by the Secretary of the Navy. In default of a better instrument, a hemispherical vessel such as an ordinary wash bowl of a white color, would serve the purpose for observations of this kind. The bowl being partially filled with molasses, or some sticky substance, will record the effect of the Earth wave. The direction of the motion will be indicated by a point on the side of the vessel which is the apex of the stain of the wave of molasses, and the intensity of the shock by the distance up the sides of the bowl to which the molasses was thrown.[4]

Your letter[5] has been delayed, and to save time I have concluded to send the wood cuts you mention directly to New ~~York~~ Haven from whence they can be returned to me.[6] Before you start I shall expect to receive your paper on the Explorations in Western New York.

Very respectfully
Your obedient Servant
Joseph Henry
Sec. Smithson[n] Institut[n]

E G Squier
New York

Squier Papers, Library of Congress.
In Edward Foremans's hand, with Henry's signature.

1. A hypsometer.
2. James Green.
3. In a letter of October 25, 1848, Gilliss had applied to Edward Sabine for assistance in procuring geophysical instruments. He in turn directed the question of design and construction of the seismometer to James David Forbes of Edinburgh, who had published "The Theory and Construction of the Seismometer" (*Transactions of the Royal Society of Edinburgh*, 1844, *15*:219–228). The instrument proved inadequate, however.

Gilliss to Edward Sabine, October 25, 1848, and February 19, 1849, BJ3/25, Letters from Americans re Magnetic Observatory in US, 1839–1854, Sabine Papers, Records of Kew Observatory, Public Record Office, London; Gilliss, *The U.S. Naval Astronomical Expedition to the Southern Hemisphere, during the Years 1849–'50–'51–'52*, U.S. House, 33d Congress, 1st Session, House Executive Documents, No. 121, 4 vols. (1855–1856), *1*:105, 508.

4. Squier did make observations of earthquakes, especially one of October 27, 1849. Although he reported the direction the earth wave moved, there is no indication that he used a seismometer. E. G. Squier, "On the Volcanoes of Central America, and the Geographical and Topographical Features of Nicaragua, as Connected with the Proposed Inter-Oceanic Canal," AAAS *Proceedings*, 1850, *4*:101–122, especially pp. 110–111.

5. Not found.
6. Squier had evidently requested Henry's assistance with a paper he was publishing in *Silliman's Journal:* "A Monograph of the Ancient Monuments of the State of Kentucky" (1849, 2d ser. *8*:1–14). That article was illustrated with two woodcuts, which Henry supplied directly to Benjamin Silliman in New Haven. Desk Diary, April 25, 1849.

289. FROM JOHN HENRY ALEXANDER

Prof. Henry
&c &c &c

Baltimore 30 April 1849.

My dear Sir,

I just heard on Saturday[1] that there was another Richmond[2] in the field in the person of our friend Renwick of N. York.[3] I am sorry for this; because he may interfere with Lord Castlecomer[4] considerably. He has divers good qualifications which I think I estimate justly. At the same time he is a little tête têtue; and deficient in that branch of science so necessary for the Patent-Office—Law—which I applied myself to not altogether unsuccessfully I believe for the regular term of three years.[5]

I sh[d] have invoked his testimony in my own behalf; but abandoned the idea principally because his son Henry is already in the Examiners' room which might have made any committal apparently indelicate and possibly embarrassing.

I write now chiefly to suggest to your Highness this fact in order that you may work, as your hand finds to do, accordingly. I write also to Bache who, I hope, has returned from the sunny South[6]— If he has, please counsel together for your humble servant.

It is quite likely that through Marsh, a means may be contrived for your armed intervention with the Sec[ys] so as to save your scruples and modesty.[7]

In the absence of Mr. Ewing, I had no occasion to be in Wash[n]; and have been still farther kept at home by the sickness of my children—three of whom I found in bed when I returned. It was only the measles and in a mild form; and I thought last week we were quit, but yesterday another, the youngest, was taken with what I suppose will eventuate in the same disorder. My leaving home, therefore, until it becomes imperative, is among the things doubtful, at present.

Hoping that you have been [spared] any simila[r][A] or other annoyances and commending myself to your kind remembrance

I remain, dear Sir,
Very faithfully
J H Alexander

Henry Papers, Smithsonian Archives.

1. April 28.
2. A reference to Henry Tudor, Earl of Richmond, who at the Battle of Bosworth Field in 1485 defeated Richard III to become king of England.
3. James Renwick, Sr., a candidate for the

post of commissioner of patents, which was turning over in the transition from Democratic to Whig rule.

4. The allusion has not been determined; as seen below, Alexander referred to himself.

5. Alexander had studied the law in a private office after his precocious graduation from St. John's College, Annapolis, at the age of fourteen, and before devoting himself to science. *Biographical Memoirs of the National Academy of Sciences*, 1877, *1*:216.

6. Bache had been in South Carolina, but was in Washington during the first week of May. Desk Diary, May 1 and 3, 1849.

7. The appointment lay with the new secretary of the interior, a former Whig senator from Ohio, Thomas Ewing (1789–1871), under whose control the Patent Office was placed upon the organization of the Interior Department in 1849. Prior to this the office was under the secretary of state. *DAB;* Robert C. Post, *Physics, Patents, and Politics: A Biography of Charles Grafton Page* (New York, 1976), p. 118.

290. FROM WILLIAM SCOTT COLQUHOUN[1]

Saluria[2]
30th April 1849

Sir,

In my last[3] acknowledging your enclosures of celestial maps tables &[c] I reiterated my enquiry as to the cause of Solar Spots.[4]

I am aware of the theory that ~~they~~ the dark center or nucleus of the spots are beneath the level of the Suns spherical surface and that the shady zone or umbra[5] which surround them is nothing else but the shelving sides of the luminous matter of the sun reaching from its surface in every direction down to the nucleus: and that Solar spots are vast excavations in this luminous matter of the Sun the nucleus being the bottom and the umbra the shelving sides of the excavation. That in the revolution of the Sun on its axis these Spots have been seen to disappear from the Suns western limb and reappear on the opposite or eastern side of the Suns disc. It was absent from the 24th Nov until 10th Dec[r] being sixteen days or half a revolution of the Sun on its axis showing the period of the Suns rotation on its axis to be thirty two days.[6]

In this theory it will be seen that the great objection to it arises from the doubtful assumption of "shelving sides of the luminous matter of the Sun." Presuming the "luminous matter of the Sun" to mean the Suns atmosphere it is inconceivable how its tangibility could admit of such an interference. Why does the theory suppose these so called excavations are occasioned by the workings of some sort of elastic vapor which is generated in the dark Globe of the Sun whose dark body had been uncovered and closed again by the encroachments of the so called luminous matter?

Doctor Herschel details the results of his investigations and says the fluidity or gaseous character of the Suns atmosphere is established by this theory—that the Suns Atmosphere is altogether in a state of commotion or instability—agitated, accumulating into masses like waves whose summits, now round, now in ridges constitute bright places which when seen through a telescope have the aspect of a mackarel sky, and that these excavated Spots or openings to the dark body of the Sun have been blown out from below by some explosive or deflagrating energy of the upheaving Power of the Sun.

While I admit it the height of Presumption in me to offer to the National ↑or↓ Smithsonian Institute (and that too without argument) a different aspect of Solar spots I trust you will appreciate the effort as coming from one who for many years has made the subject his study—Briefly then Sir instead of excavations these spots are the nucleus and tails of Comets attracted by the sun, and remaining visible, until the encroachments of the Suns fiery atmosphere closes them[A] from view forever.[7]

I am Sir
Your ob[t] Ser[t]
W. S. Colquhoun

Joseph Henry Esq
Secretary of the Smithsonian Institute
Washington City

Letters Received, Records of the Smithsonian Meteorological Project, Records of the Weather Bureau, RG 27, National Archives.
Reply: Draft, possibly in Charles P. Russell's hand, May 23, 1849, on second page of this letter.

1. Colquhoun (b. 1791 or 1792 in Virginia) had been an army officer (1819–1829) and then United States Agent for the removal of the Choctaw Indians (1829–1832). During the Mexican War he was commissioner of subsistence and subsistence agent (May 1846 to August 1848). Until mid-1849, he lived along the Gulf coast of Mexico and Texas, when he moved to Washington because of the cholera. He was listed in Washington in the 1860 census.
Charles K. Gardner, *A Dictionary of All Officers . . . in the Army of the United States,* 2d ed. (New York, 1860); Eighth Census of the United States, 1860, District of Columbia (NARA microfilm M653, reel 103, frame [581]).

2. Once located on the tip of Matagorda Island, Texas, the town is apparently no longer extant. J. Thomas and T. Baldwin, eds., *A Complete Pronouncing Gazetteer, or Geographical Dictionary of the World,* 2 vols. (Philadelphia, 1858).

3. Not found.

4. We surmise that Colquhoun saw Henry and Espy's meteorological circular (Doc. 229) in a newspaper or periodical. On February 25, 1849, he wrote to John Y. Mason, secretary of the navy, referring to it and presenting observations relative to sunspots and the weather. In that and subsequent letters he asserted that his observations showed a correlation between numerous sunspots and wet and stormy weather, and, conversely, few sunspots and dry weather. Although he wrote giving an account of a hurricane that crossed the Gulf coast in May 1849—which caused Espy to write back for further details—weather clearly took a second place to sunspots. Colquhoun's direct observation of the sun with an eyeglass had left him virtually blind by 1851, but he continued to press his theories and to call on the Smithsonian to investigate and to confirm them, so that stormy weather might be predicted "to the end that the farmer and the navigator may be prepared to meet the disasters which may arise

from such causes by being apprised of their first appearance." Colquhoun to Mason, February 25, 1849; to Espy, May 9, 1849; and to Henry, June 28, 1849, and April 17, 1851 (quotation); and a gloss of Espy's reply, dated June 30, on Colquhoun's incoming letter of May 9; all in the same location as this letter.

5. The *penumbra*, according to current usage.

6. The theory was of William Herschel, for which see *Henry Papers*, 6:145n, and many contemporary sources, for example, Robert Grant, *History of Physical Astronomy* (London, 1852), pp. 220–227. Colquhoun believed that sunspots were obstructions to the sun's light which were caused by comets or by the transits of stars, which he thought were small opaque bodies

similar to planets (for which see his letter to Mason, February 25, 1849).

7. Henry's reply acknowledged the limits to knowledge about sunspots, but stated two facts known with certainty: that sunspots are indentations in the surface, and that (on the basis of his and Stephen Alexander's researches—APS *Proceedings*, 1843–1847, 4:173–176) they are cooler than the surrounding surface. Henry stated that he considered Colquhoun's theory "novel," yet unsatisfactory, and encouraged him to cooperate in the meteorological project. He specifically requested information on storms called *northers*. Henry's letter elicited Colquhoun's of June 28, which reiterated his theory of comets as causing sunspots and supplied information on Texas storms.

291. FROM EMMA WILLARD[1]

Troy April—1849

To Professor Henry, Director of the Smithsonian Institute.

Sir,

She who addresses you, thinks she has a right to presume that her name is not unknown, to a person, acquainted, not only with the range and present condition of the sciences, but with that great cause—the cause of education, and the means and agents by which it has been in our country advanced; and particularly that of female education, in which our country is well known to have the prominence over others. In the temple of national education your post is, Sir, at the very pinnacle. You superintend an Institution given by Providence, whose object is to aid the mature mind of the nation in its bringing forth new sciences, or improvements upon old, for the advancement of ↑the↓ present and future.

I come before you, Sir, as an American to whom it has pleased Him, who chooses the weak things of this world to confound the wisdom of the wise, to reveal a portion of his physical truth before unknown. And no truth ever discovered is more intimately connected with the physical well being of man, than the one to which I allude, viz,—that Respiration, ~~producing, or~~ generating heat, at the lungs—an expansive power is there produced, which is the principal efficient cause of the blood's circulation.[2]

This theory I have proposed and sustained in "A Treatise on the Motive Powers which produce the Circulation of the Blood", published in a small volume, 1846, by Wiley & Putnam, and herewith presented for your perusal. The number[A] of "The Living Age"[3] accompanying, "contains a copy[A] of a Review of my Treatise, which, soon after its publication, appeared in the London[B] "Critic".[4]— When the high, impartial character of that ↑widely extended↓ periodical is regarded,—and when it is considered that ↑its editors↓ being Englishmen thus review the work of an American—being men, they thus speak of a woman, and all this, unasked—unsolicited—Professor Henry will I doubt not regard it as an authority of great weight; and one which of itself would justify him in listening to the petition, which it is the object of this communication to make.

As the professed[C] discoverer of a new principle[D] in Physiology,[E] highly important if true, and at least so far sustained as to "bear "upon its face a strong similitude of truth" and become "eminently entitled to the serious attention and examination by ↑the test↓ experiment of all who profess or take an interest in physiological science", I come forward to plead the intention of the generous Smithson, that persons in just such such a situation as mine, should be furnished with the means of bringing to the test of experiment,[F] new and important principles of science; and what science relating to man's earthly interests is so important to him as that which will give him a new and before unthought of control over his respiration, and the flow of his blood, ~~and furnish him with~~ ↑teach him↓ the rationale of many of the ordinary phenomena of existence, heretofore regarded as mysterious and unaccountable, and that[G] furnish him with new rules for the preservation of health, and for the removal of disease.

To you, Sir, is, as I suppose,[H] assigned such a power over the Smithsonian fund, that you could if you thought fit allow me to have an apparatus made to test the principles of this theory of the circulation allowed by many, and denied by none to be original. Such a use of the fund would fulfil the intention of the donor, & do honour (as I fully believe) to those who conduct the institution. Such an apparatus as I wish to have made, would I believe not only test principles laid down in my work on the circulation but lead ↑to↓ applications of the principles, which might be of great importance to health and life.

Should Professor Henry wish for some means of ascertaining what can be said against this theory by an ingenious medical writer, disirous to put it down, such an ~~one~~ ↑article↓ will be found, in the New York Journal of Medicine published either late in 1846 or early in -47, and also my reply to it, published in the March ↑(1747)↓ Number of the same Journal.[5]— The editor of the Journal was at that time Dr. Charles A. Lee[6] and he was understood to be the author of the artfully-woven attack on my theory. After my reply, he wrote me a letter in which he says "I consider your reply as extremely able, and well-reasoned and calculated to stagger the faith of some who have heretofore slighted your theory." ↑The Rev'd↓ Dr. Robert J. Breckenridge[7] says in a note to me that having read my work "with great attention"—"he must say that the theory of Mrs. Willard seems to him eminently ingenious, and to say the least full of probability". What I want is to change in all sound minds, this feeling of probability to one of entire certainty; so that the mass of error which now exists, and is even taught to children may be done away, and truth prevail.

    With the most profound respect—

Emma Willard.

Henry Papers, Smithsonian Archives.

1. A pioneer of women's education, Emma Hart Willard (1787–1870) had founded the Troy (New York) Female Academy (now the Emma Willard School), the first academy for women in the United States. It began accepting pupils in 1821; she gave up direct oversight of the institution in 1838 to travel, lecture, and work on education, especially in common schools of New York and New England. Willard was also instrumental in bringing mathematics, natural science, and geography—subjects she first taught herself and then her students—into women's education. Her 1809 marriage to physician John Willard gave her access to works of medicine and physiology, and a person with whom she could discuss these subjects, which she studied lifelong. *DAB;* Lois Barber Arnold, *Four Lives in Science: Women's Education in the Nineteenth Century* (New York, 1984), p. 49.

2. Willard "was so obsessed with the theory of Circulation by Respiration, worked so much over it during the remainder of her life, and made such courageous efforts to have it accepted by medical men that her family and friends often referred to her 'unfortunate mania' on the subject." Alma Lutz, *Emma Willard: Pioneer Educator of American Women* (New York, 1964), p. 118.

3. The reference is to *Littell's Living Age,* 1846, *11*:442–445.

4. *The Critic,* 1846, 2d ser. *4*:361–363 (the issue of September 26, 1846). This review was in what was essentially a periodical journal for literature, and is more properly termed a notice. It consists of extensive quotations from Wil-

lard's book, both to delineate her theory and to give her exhortatory advice to young women to preserve their health by attending to proper respiration and circulation.

5. The September 1846 issue of the *New York Journal of Medicine* printed an anonymous review of Willard's book that stated that the theory was "wholly untenable. . . . The cause . . . is insufficient to produce the effects" (pp. 239–240). Nonetheless the reviewer sought to praise Willard, calling her a "lady of masculine understanding, a good writer, an indefatigable student, and a most instructive companion" (p. 238) and commended her work in teaching women. The journal, contrary to its usual policy, printed Willard's response in the March 1847 number. She reasserted her theory, called upon Mill's canons of invariable antecedent and concomitant variation for support, liberally cited Cuvier for authority in physiology, and restated the vitalist position that physiological studies on dead or wounded animals were in no way decisive in understanding living creatures.

"[Review of] *A Treatise on the Motive Powers Which Produce the Circulation of the Blood*, by Emma Willard," and "Reply of the Authoress, to a Criticism, Published Sept., 1846, in This Journal, on a Work Entitled 'A Treatise on the Motive Powers Which Produce the Circulation of the Blood,' by Emma Willard," *New York Journal of Medicine,* 1846, *7*:233–240, and 1847, *8*:196–204, respectively.

6. Charles Alfred Lee (1801–1872), a physician and teacher of medicine, was a founder as

well as the editor of the New York Journal. *DAB.*

7. Robert Jefferson Breckenridge (1800–

1871), a prominent Presbyterian clergyman and reformer of the Kentucky state schools. *DAB.*

292. TO THOMAS EWING

Smithsonian Institution
May 1st 1849

To the Hon. Secretary of the Home Department
Dear Sir

I have just received a letter from Dr Charles T. Jackson of Boston, asking me to express to you my opinion of his scientific character, and it gives me much pleasure to comply with this request.[1]

Dr Jackson is a man of talents, of learning and of practical skill, in the line of Chemistry Geology and Mineralogy. His Reports on the Geology of Maine and of New Hampshire, are documents which evince great ability and abound in interesting and useful information. He has acquired a reputation throughout the civilized world, for his suggestions in reference to the use of Ether, as an agent for lessening pain.

I presume his fears are groundless, in regard to attempts to remove him from the Survey of the Public Domain, before he has concluded his operations. Such a course would derange the whole work, and would be in my opinion a cause of much regret.[2]

Very Respectfully
Your Obedient Servant
Joseph Henry
Sec. Smithsonian Institution

Letters Received, Records of the Division of Appointments, Records of the Office of the Secretary of the Interior, RG 48, National Archives.
In Edward Foreman's hand, with Henry's signature.

1. Jackson wrote that his former assistant, John Wells Foster, was trying to replace him as head of the Lake Superior survey. He asked Henry to speak to Ewing "& let him know that the Scientific World will never sanction the removal of a Geologist from office for political purposes . . . ." He noted that although he was in fact a Whig, he would "not urge political reasons, but stand on scientific merit alone." Jackson to Henry, April 25, 1849, Henry Papers, Smithsonian Archives.

2. Although Jackson was paranoid, in this instance his fears were justified. His subordinates had accused him of spending little time in the field, not conducting analyses, and not preparing a report, as well as appropriating the work of others, misusing government funds, drinking too much, and exhibiting symptoms of insanity. After two seasons of field work, he was removed in mid-May and replaced by Foster and Josiah Dwight Whitney, another former assistant. *DSB; Full Exposure of the Conduct of Dr.*

Charles T. Jackson, Leading to His Discharge from the Government Service, and Justice to Messrs. Foster and Whitney, U.S. Geologists ([Washington, 1851]);

David J. Krause, *The Making of a Mining District: Keweenaw Native Copper, 1500–1870* (Detroit, 1992), pp. 176–193.

293. HENRY DESK DIARY

TUESDAY, May 1st.[A] 1849[B]

Wrote to Dr Jackson[1] and also in his behalf to Mr Ewing.[2]

To Prof Davies about Pt. O.[3]

Mr Bradley[4] rendered account of expenditures for last month.

Dr Foreman is now engaged in constructing a large map for meteorology.[5]

Consultation with Mr Renwick relative to new Lecture room willing to make the changes indicated by myself.

Met Dr Bache this afternoon by appointment to examine the acoustic phenomena of the room of the House of Representatives— Sound reflected from the roof and circular sides—principal foci at a b c d. Hear-

ing perfect when speaker is in rostrum—

When word is spoken at b echo distincly heard at same place but not at a also echo from C not at D though a whisper at a is heard at b and one at D is heard at C.[C]

All the phenomena exhibited in the Hall of Rep. in accordance with well established principles of sound— No echo is heard unless the sound travels more than 100 feet going and returning.

The canal of the ear is narrow and all sounds from every side enters nearly in the same direction hence if a reflecting wall is near the primary sound and its echo consper to produce a single effct.

No remedy for the evils of the Chamber of the House which would be effectual— Glass cealing would improve the audition—the walls pannelled and Draped would also be of use.[6]

Mr Squire starts in a few days for central America. He will sind me the memoir on New York mounds by express. The drawings on wood. They are by a Mr Chapin.[7]

The blocks I lent him are now with Mr Bartlett. Will be with the others.

Mr Squire wants blanks for observations on meteorology.

Will probably establish one at Nigaragua ↑or↓ Guatemala and perhaps both.

Henry Papers, Smithsonian Archives.

1. Charles Thomas Jackson; letter not found.

2. Doc. 292.

3. Letter not found. In Charles Davies's reply of May 5 (Henry Papers, Smithsonian Archives), he wrote that although he appreciated Henry and Bache's support of him to become commissioner of patents, he had to refuse to be a candidate.

4. William A. Bradley.

5. Henry mentioned the map in his annual report for the next year:

> For the better comprehension of the relative position of the several places of observation, now embraced in our system of meteorology, an outline map of North America has been constructed, by Prof. Foreman. This map is intended also to be used for presenting the successive phases of the sky over the whole country, at different points of time, as far as reported to us, and we have been waiting for its completion, to commence a series of investigations, with the materials now on hand, relative to the progress of storms. [*Smithsonian Report for 1850*, p. 19.]

Henry had alluded to telegraphic weather reports, which were to supply the current data for the map, in several earlier diary entries. On January 30 and 31, he noted a letter to, and conversation with, Henry O'Reilly accepting his offer of making his telegraph lines available for meteorological reports; on February 9, he mentioned a letter from Matthew F. Maury about the use of the telegraph for meteorology and remarked: "I have had in my mind a fine scheme with the telegraph—Instantaneous observations on the aurora—on the thunder storm the beginning of storms &c." Desk Diary, January 30, 31, and February 9, 1849 (quotation).

If this is the same map later on public display in the Smithsonian Building, it was apparently not used to transmit weather information to the public until 1856:

> The first practical application which was attempted of the principle we have mentioned was made by this Institution in 1856; the information conveyed by telegraphic despatches in regard to the weather was daily exhibited by means of differently colored to-

kens, on a map of the United States, so as to show at one view the meteorological condition of the atmosphere over the whole country. [*Smithsonian Report for 1865*, p. 56.]

After telegraph reports were received each morning, small disks of different colors symbolizing various weather conditions were hung on pins indicating places of observation. At some point the disks were modified to show the direction of the wind. Henry hoped the map would clarify recurrent weather patterns and facilitate weather prediction. According to Fleming, telegraphic reporting triggered a shift of primary focus in meteorology from theoretical concerns to prediction of the weather. Fleming, *Meteorology*, pp. 141–145; J. Cecil Alter, "National Weather Service Origins," *Bulletin of the Historical and Philosophical Society of Ohio,* 1949, 7:139–185; *Smithsonian Report for 1858*, p. 32; Joseph Henry, "Meteorology in Its Connection with Agriculture: Part IV. Atmospheric Vapor and Currents," *Report of the Commissioner of Patents for 1858: Agriculture* (Washington, 1859), pp. 480–481; Joseph Henry, ["On the Application of the Telegraph to the Premonition of Weather Changes,"] *Proceedings of the American Academy of Arts and Sciences,* 1857–1860, 4:273–274.

6. The large House chamber, termed "a singularly bad one for all purposes of hearing" by Charles Dickens in 1842, was plagued by echoes which prevented members from being heard while speaking from their seats. Benjamin Latrobe and later Robert Mills had unsuccessfully proposed or tried various remedies involving changing the shape of the room by raising the floor, suspending a false ceiling, or altering the walls. Emily Ann Thompson, "'Mysteries of the Acoustic': Architectural Acoustics in America, 1800–1932" (Ph.D. diss., Princeton University, 1992), pp. 24, 37, and 41–53 (quotation on p. 44); Glenn Brown, *History of the United States Capitol,* 2 vols. (Washington, 1900), 1:71–73.

7. Possibly John R. Chapin (1823-post 1907), a designer and illustrator who worked in New York City from 1844 to 1860. Smithsonian Daybooks, vol. 1, p. 68; George C. Groce and David H. Wallace, *The New-York Historical Society's Dictionary of Artists in America, 1564–1860* (New Haven, 1957), p. 120.

294. FROM JOHN WISE TO JOSEPH HENRY AND JAMES P. ESPY

Lancaster May 1st 1849

M[essrs] Henry & Espy

Gentlemen— I received a circular from you with two meterological Journal sheets, dated Nov. 1st 1848[1] to which I would reply that I will with pleasure do all I can to swell the sum total of human knoweldge. If you should in time to come consider this place an "important locality" I will be happy to make such observations for you as you may direct. Until[A] then I will pursue the observations as closely as the limited supply of instruments I have in possession, with a natural propensity in the inductive Philosophy, will enable me.[2]

I have a double pleasure in the pursuit—it enables me to give while it incites me to receive knowledge. Have you ever conceived the Idea of a great Astronomical atmospheric current in the higher regions of the air? That the Earth, and likely all planets, are not necessarily solid, but hollow?[3] The whole economy of Nature implies this. Now if gravitation is governed by the quantity of matter in a body, and the Earth is hollow, would not a delicate spiral spring balance indicate the difference between the Earths surface and a height two miles from it, which is considerably more than we could attain by going inside the surface. I ask this question from you for information—whether gravitation is a law of weight, or of electrical attraction. At all events it will be worth the while of trying should I ever ascend again. And if you have any new Ideas, or well established old ones concerning this point, they might be suggested to me, with advantages in future accruing therefrom.

I have forwarded three monthly journals of the weather, which I presume have reached their proper destination. I have also received two celestial maps for Auroral observations, which I will attend to as the Aurora will enable me.[4]

I remain Gentlemen your devoted fellow citizen
and servant to human knowledge
John Wise.

Letters Received, Records of the Smithsonian Meteorological Project, Records of the Weather Bureau, RG 27, National Archives.
Reply: Doc. 296.

1. See Doc. 229.
2. Wise was a Smithsonian meteorological observer from 1849 to 1851. *Smithsonian Report for 1868*, p. 81.

3. Henry had publicly ridiculed the hollow earth theory of John Cleves Symmes in his 1826 inaugural address at the Albany Academy. Symmes theorized that the earth was hollow

521

and open at the poles. *Henry Papers*, 1:171; 3:128n.

4. Wise sent an auroral observation to

Henry in a letter of July 13, 1849 (same location as this letter).

295. HENRY DESK DIARY

[May 6,][A] 1849[B]

Plan of lectures

The plan which I have concluded to adopt is that of calling to Washington men distinguished for their original researches not professed lecturers. Though by this course we may not succeede in amusing yet we shall not fail to instruct our audiance. The lectures of Dr Hitchcok are a good sample of what the[C] audience may expect plain unaustentatious truthful—without exageration and such as is wll calculated to inspere the confidence of the audience.[1]

I shall mainly depend upon the lecturers from abroad[2] to give the popular exhibitions and reserve my own lectures for classes who may wish to attend to special courses and also to the explanation of particular phenomena new discoveries and new inventions.[3]

We may adopt the plan followed at Boston[4] of giving lectures in the day time.

Henry Papers, Smithsonian Archives.

1. Edward Hitchcock delivered a six-part series on geology beginning on April 30 and ending on May 11. The lectures were the first to be delivered in the lecture room in the east wing of the Smithsonian Building and drew large and attentive audiences. Rhees, *Journals*, p. 473; *Smithsonian Report for 1849*, p. 21.

2. That is, lecturers Henry invited to come to the Smithsonian, not foreigners.

3. In his "Programme of Organization," the paragraph related to lectures read:

The Secretary and his assistants, during the session of Congress, will be required to illustrate new discoveries in science, and to exhibit new objects of art; also distinguished individuals should be invited to give lectures on subjects of general interest. [Section II, paragraph 16.]

The first part was not carried out in any formal way, although in his 1860 report (p. 54), Henry noted that he gave a series of lectures on exper-

imental physics to local schoolteachers. An accomplished lecturer himself, Henry clearly did not follow Faraday's model at the Royal Institution. In the early reports, he took pains to point out that the lectures were suggested by Congress in the legislation establishing the Smithsonian and that although they appeared to the public "one of the most prominent objects of the Institution, . . . they really form the least important feature of the plan adopted" (*Smithsonian Report for 1850*, p. 25). He asserted that "local lectures are too limited in their influence to meet a liberal interpretation of the will of Smithson" (*Smithsonian Report for 1852*, p. 28). Initially surprised by the amount of interest in the lectures, he came to recognize how much they contributed to cultural and intellectual life in Washington, as well as their public relations function for the Smithsonian. Henry invited experts in various scientific and literary fields to deliver the free, evening lectures, eventually coming to prefer short courses by each lecturer. The Civil War curtailed the program, which came to an abrupt halt in January 1865 when the lecture room burned. Smithsonian annual reports, 1849–1864 (under "Lectures" in the secretary's report); Lucy Unsworth, "Lecturing at the Smithsonian Institution, 1846–1870," unpublished paper in the files of the Joseph Henry Papers.

4. That is, at the Lowell Institute.

296. TO JOHN WISE

Smithsonian Institution
May 8ᵗʰ 1849

My Dear Sir

The ~~problem or~~ inquiry ↑with↓ regard to the hollowness of the interior of the earth could not be solved by any variation of gravity, ~~on the~~ ↑above the↓ exterior surface, for it can be mathematically demonstrated that the attractⁿ of a solid globe & also of a hollow one are the same as if all the matter of each were concentrated in its centre. The Law of diminution of gravitation as measured above the Earth would be the same in both cases. A ~~delicate~~ Spring Balance, ~~wd~~ if sufficiently delicate would indicate a difference of the weight of a body suspended from it at diffᵗ Elevations. But this as I have said bfre would ~~be~~ ↑give↓ no information as to the hollowness or solidity of the Earth.

I have no doubt that there are great currents in the upper regions of the Atmosphere, and particularly the return currents of the Trade winds which ↑should↓ blow continually from SW. to NE. Should you conclude to make another aerial voyage I should be pleased to suggest some observations.

Very Respectfully
Your Obedᵗ Servᵗ

John Wise Esqr

Sec. Smith. Institution.

Draft, Letters Received, Records of the Smithsonian Meteorological Project, Records of the Weather Bureau, RG 27, National Archives.

On the same sheet of paper as Wise's letter to Henry of May 1; in Edward Foreman's hand. Previously printed in John Wise, *A System of Aeronautics* (Philadelphia, 1850), p. 262, and Wise, *Through the Air: A Narrative of Forty Years' Experience as an Aëronaut* (Philadelphia, 1873), pp. 393–394.

297. FROM EDWIN HAMILTON DAVIS

Chillicothe May 8th. 1849

My Dear Sir

Your kind favour of the 24th inst[1]— reached me in due time— It affordes me some satisfaction to know that Mr. S.[2] cannot boast of your name among the list of worthies recommending him to office— I had almost come to the conclusion that impudence and perseverance will accomplish most things— My intercourse with the world of late has not impressed me with a very high sense of its justice; yet there are a few honorable exceptions— All I have to say about the appointment is, that I hope he will not disgrace the Country—

I expect to furnish my ethnological map for your next volume, but should like to visit some of the localities before[A] finishing it, which will require some <u>money</u> and about six weeks of time.[3] I also intend to complete surveys of the few remaining works in this State; and then if I continue to pursue the subject, to go on and accomplish the same in each of the Western States—; but to tell you the truth I have some idea of cutting the subject all-together, for thus far it has resulted in little else than losses and vexation.

I was sorry to learn through Mr. Sherwood of N.Y. that you had granted permission to Mr. Sqr. to use the Lith. stones to strike off 40 sets of plates. Mr. S. had received most of his share before I left N.Y. I was in hopes you ↑would↓ hold back until we ascertained the exact number of the extra copies. That he wanted them for this purpose I am satisfied, for that is near the number of ext. besides Mr. Jenkins writes me this week that I can have my share of them by paying for the binding and <u>one dollar per copy for plates</u>—

Have you seen the articles in the North American Review,[4] and Ethnological Journal of London.?[5]— They are so outrageously <u>unjust</u> and <u>ex-parte</u> as to defeat ~~themselves~~ their intentions— I console <u>myself</u> with the idea that no honest or unprejudiced mind could give such a review— Its whole character and peculiar markings are so unmistakably <u>Squirish</u> as to provoke a smile of derision and contempt from every one acquainted with the circumstances[6]— I sent you last week Judge Hall's view of the matter[7]—and this week Mr. Ed. Mansfield reviews the <u>reviewer</u> with much justice and great severity[8]—you will receive a copy <u>in</u> a few days— It requires quite an effort to remain silent under such circumstances; in fact, I may do myself injustice by not exposing him, for the publick will have a right to suppose he has done everything, if I remain silent, and in this way give consent to the statements—

My Meteorological Journals shall be sent or I will bring them on when I go East— I should have been there before this if Mrs. D.[9] had been entirely well—

Who is our Representative at Peru?[10] If he was only dissatisfied or would resign, then, as antiquarians are now in favor, might not I stand a chance to distinguish myself among the huacas of the Incas.

I should be pleased to hear from you as frequently as it may be convenient for you write— Please present my respects to Mrs. H. and permit me to remain—

> Most respectfully yours
> E. H. Davis

To
Jo[s] Henry Sect.
Smithsonian Institution⎫

Henry Papers, Smithsonian Archives.

1. Not found; Davis obviously meant to write "ult" (April 24), not "inst" (May 24).

2. E. G. Squier.

3. Davis's ethnological map was never published by the Smithsonian. In an 1865 letter to Henry, he described the precedents for it and its evolution from a map of mural remains to one recording the location of tribes over the whole continent. He urged Henry to produce a "much better ethnological chart" by soliciting the contributions of ethnologists in the field. "On Ethnological Research," *Smithsonian Report for 1866,* pp. 370–371; *DAB.*

4. That is, a review of *Ancient Monuments* that appeared in the *North American Review,* 1849, 68:466–496. According to William Frederick Poole, *Index to Periodical Literature* (Boston, 1882), s.v. "Monuments, American," the reviewer was Charles Eliot Norton (1827–1908, *DAB*).

5. Three notices appeared in the *Ethnological Journal,* 1848–1849: 1:177–183, 286–288, 376–388. The reviewer was presumably the editor, Luke Burke.

6. Although the reviews were highly favorable, they almost totally ignored Davis's role as co-author. Norton mentioned him only once, as aiding Squier in his research (p. 466). Pointedly identifying Squier as the sole author of the memoir, he praised Squier's "good judgment" with which he "indulges in no uncertain speculations" (p. 490), and his goal of "present[ing] the simple truth rather than what might excite attention as extravagant or wonderful" (p. 492). He also hoped that Squier would "proceed in investigations which no other is fitted to accomplish so successfully" (p. 495).

In the *Ethnological Journal,* Burke not only gave Davis's name as "H. Davies," but also asserted:

> it is obvious that Mr. Squier is the presiding genius of the whole undertaking. He is not merely a joint explorer, but is also the arranger of the materials collected, and the writer of the entire work. He has, besides, prepared all the plans, drawings and illustrations. [p. 288.]

7. Not found. James Hall (1793–1868), formerly a circuit judge in Illinois, was a Cincinnati banker and author. *DAB.*

Hall's comments may have been in a letter. We have not found any published remarks by him on reviews of Squier and Davis. In his *The West: Its Soil, Surface, and Productions* (Cincinnati, 1848), pp. 165–166, he referred to Davis as a personal acquaintance of many years and mentioned the forthcoming memoir.

8. Edward Deering Mansfield (1801–1880) was a Cincinnati author and newspaper editor. *DAB.* We have not found his review of the reviewer.

9. Lucy Woodbridge Davis, whom Davis married in 1841. *DAB,* s.v. "Davis, Edwin Hamilton."

10. John Randolph Clay (1808–1885) had

been chargé d'affaires in Peru since 1847 and was later minister there from 1853 to 1860. *The* *Twentieth Century Biographical Dictionary of Notable Americans* (Boston, 1904).

298. FROM BENJAMIN H. GREEN[1]

Princeton May 9ᵗʰ 1849

Prof Henry
Dear Sir

I Return You my thanks for Your kindness to Mᵣ Allen[2] when at your place in the month of March last.

And would inform You that I and my Associates are negociating[A] A Contract for Coating the wires from Jersey City to Philᵃ and the greatest dificulty we have to contend with is to Satisfy them, of the usefulness and durability of our Composition. Now as Mᵣ Allen Showed you the receipt for the Component[B] parts of our Composition, and as Mᵣ French[3] will Call on you in the Corse of a week—to Consult you in regard to its Merits, I wish that you would give him Your Candid opinion upon the Subject. And in Case we effect A Contract, I Shall feel bound for this and past favors to Send you by Mail A one hundred dollar bill—if you Can influence them to believe that this Coating will last ten years, (or Thereabouts,) our point will be Established and no doubt our designs Consumated.[4] For fear you May have forgotten the ingredients of our Composition, I will Send below the receipt For its Parts,—and would Remark that, that the Rubber used in it, is Manufactored at Newark in a Manner, that the Atmosphere will not Decompose it in the least—(Gooyears Patent).[5] If you deem it proper you may tell Mᵣ French the ingredients of our Composition— Regarding this letter as Strictly Confidential.[C]

I am yours Most
Respectfuly
Benjamin. H. Green

P.S

By the way of Experiment I have Coated two miles or more on the line Betwene Princeton and Trenton and I find the machiene performs the work in the Moost Perfect posible manner Thoe not So Speadily as was anticipated.

I Should be pleased to have you See its performance.

Also I Erected 50 yards or upwards at my place and coated it with my Composition on the 20ᵗʰ of March and leaveing it Exposed, it appears by

Examening it to be as firm a coating as any thing I Ever yet Saw Applyed to Anything.

Therefore it would afford me great Sattisfaction[D] to have my Machiene (and Composition) Introduced for the Public Good.

Not meaning by this to use any Deception in any one Particular as it has allways been my aim to build up that, that was Usefull.

Receipt

Dissolve 3 pounds of Asphaltum in one gallon of Camphene add to it half a gallon of the Solution of India Rubber and when well mixed add half a gallon of Copel Varnish

Henry Papers, Smithsonian Archives.
Note at left margin of first page in Henry's hand: "Bribery—Angry reply."

1. Benjamin H. Green, of Benjamin H. Green & Company, was a resident of Princeton. He is listed in the 1870 census as a sixty-seven-year-old carpenter. He held an 1841 patent for a door fastening and had recently patented the apparatus for coating telegraph wires which is discussed in this letter. Benjamin H. Green & Company circular, May 15, 1849, Henry Papers, Smithsonian Archives; Ninth Census of the United States, 1870, New Jersey (NARA microfilm M593, reel 871, frame [430]); Edmund Burke, *List of Patents for Inventions and Designs, Issued by the United States, from 1790 to 1847* (Washington, 1847), p. 55; U.S. Patent 6,012, January 9, 1849.

2. B. Allen of No. 1 Bridge Street, New York City, according to Green's circular.

3. Benjamin B. French, who was affiliated with the Magnetic Telegraph Company. Robert Luther Thompson, *Wiring a Continent: The History of the Telegraph Industry in the United States, 1832–1866* (New York, 1972), p. 190.

4. Although we have not found Henry's reply, he apparently wrote Allen on May 31. Allen wrote back on June 8 (Henry Papers, Smithsonian Archives), to "ask Pardon for Past Offences, and [to] assure you that we did not mean to do any thing inconsistant with truth and Honour." In a note on Allen's letter, Henry characterized it as an "apology for offering bribe." On Green's circular, which included testimonials from James Renwick, Sr., and James R. Chilton and a reference to an endorsement by Royal E. House, Henry wrote "ordered my name stricken off." Henry was not mentioned in the circular, which touted the composition's rust-preventative and insulating abilities.

5. Charles Goodyear's famous 1844 patent for rubber. *DAB*.

299. FROM T. ROMEYN BECK

Albany. May 10, 1849.[A]

Joseph Henry Esq
Dear Sir

M[r] Hawley rec[d] your first letter[1] in due season, but he has not been very well & found a difficulty in meeting the rest of the Committee. I now address you in his behalf.

We very cordially agree in your proposition that the S. Inst. & the

Regents[2] join in procuring the Necessary Instruments for Meteorological ~~Instruments~~ ↑observations↓ & the Regents would be very happy, if they could be purchased by you in their behalf.[3]

The plan, so far as it is at present decided upon, is to have not more than 12 Stations throughout the State—the instruments all must have are a Thermometer—Barometer—Rain Guage—& such others as you may point out. We should be very glad to have your suggestions as to what is further necessary.

We propose to have the new System go into Operation on the 1st of Jany 1850. I have been so pressed with the preparation[B] & printing of Annual Reports of every kind—& with the superintendence of the State Library, that I have not been able as yet to bestow the necessary attention on the matter.

The liberal Appropriation of the Legislature for two years, ($1500 for each year) is such, that the fault will be ours, if a comprehensive & practical System be not established. I think we can muster some 10 or 12 Observers throughout the State, who with proper instructions, will make valuable returns.

We shall rely greatly on your advice, & are ready to fall in as a state detachment of the U States Corps of observers—under your general rules & directions.

With my respectful regards to Mrs Henry

I remain, Dear Sir
very truly Yours
T. Romeyn Beck

NB. We rec^d last year from Dr Mahlmann of Berlin,[4] the official Instructions to Observers throughout the Kingdom of Prussia. The Rev. Edward Robinson of New York has translated them for the Regents, & they will appear in the Appendix to the Annual Report.[5] I shall send you an early copy.

Letters Received, Records of the Smithsonian Meteorological Project, Records of the Weather Bureau, RG 27, National Archives.

Reply: May 19, 1849 (draft, in Edward Foreman's hand, on separate sheet of paper tipped in preceding third page of Beck's letter).

1. Not found.

2. That is, the regents of the University of the State of New York.

3. At the suggestion of Simeon DeWitt, the regents had established a meteorological system in 1825 in which the academies in the state were required to make observations with thermometers, rain gauges, and weather vanes, and transmit them to Albany for publication in the annual reports of the regents. Henry shared the direction of the system with Beck until he left for Princeton in 1832. In 1849, the regents appropriated $3,000 over two years to improve the observations. They continued to support the network with appropriations of $800 per year until 1863. Fleming, *Meteorology*, pp. 118–120; *Henry Papers*, 1:106–107, 5:24n–25n.

4. Carl Heinrich Wilhelm Mahlmann (1812–

1848), first director of the Prussian Meteorological Institute, established in 1847. C. Kassner, "Carl Heinrich Wilhelm Mahlmann," *Meteorologische Zeitschrift*, 1912, 29:309–318.

5. Mahlmann's "Official Instructions for Observers at the Meteorological Stations in the Kingdom of Prussia," appeared as an appendix to the 1849 report.

300. TO ALEXANDER DALLAS BACHE

Washington May 11ᵗʰ[–12] 1849

My Dear B,

Your kind note from camp was duly received[1]— Mrs H. and myself had concluded that you had found gloomy times in your canvas house the weather has been so inclement since you left. I have not much to communicate— TheᴬA appointment of the commissioner of Patents you have probably seen in the papers. It is said that the President was so set on the appointment of Ewbanks[2] that the friends of Alexander were obliged to give way. I regret that A. was not appointed though a worse man than Ewbanks might have been selected. Mr Burke will probably go into the Union. The inducement on the one hand is the emolument ~~of~~ ↑from↓ the paper and on the other the prospect of a seat in the U.S. senate.[3] He is much displeased with Wilkes who was very friendly while seeking to get his brothinlaw[4] appointed.

The new building of the patent office will cut through the greenhouse and the plants must be removed. Wilkes informed me that the secretary of the Interior intended to give them in immediate charge to the Smithsonian but that he (W) proposed a better plan namely that Brackenridge the gardener should be appointed public gardener and that the plants under his care should be removed to the point of land belonging to the mall directly under the capitol hill. I called on the secretary relative to this matter ↑did not find him in↓ but heard from his secretary that there was no thought of giving the plants to the Smithsonian. I therefore concluded to say nothing on the subject and let the matter take any course W– and the secretary might think fit to give it.[5]

The rumour is that Butler Kingᴮ has received the appointment of the chargé ship to Chilli and that on the strength of this he has gone to California.[6] Mr Marsh has been promised something else.[7]

I have had a visit from Professor Guyot of cambridge[8]—he regretted that he had not seen you. He is about publishing his lectures on Physical geography[9] and did not learn that you had made observations on the gulf stream until the work was finished— He has just started on his return— The last lecture of Dr. H.[10] is to be given this evening they appear to have increased in interest and the attendance has in no degree fallen off.— The number on Wednesday night was greater than on any previous evening— I have drawn his money ↑(150 Dolls)↓ to day and he starts in the early train tomorrow— The sum paid is not very large yet the Dr appears well[C] satisfied with it and the attention his lectures have received. He gave an extra meeting to those who wished the rocks and minerals to be found in the vicinity named. There was quite a number of persons in attendance the larger portion probably teachers.

Dr H with Professor Guyot and myself made an excursion yesterday to the falls of the Patomac,[11] we were much pleased with the phenomena exhibited; the water has worn a gorge, 60 feet deep and nearly a mile long. The rock being primative the effect is nearly as wonderful as that at niagara.

Renwick presented the several plans of the lecture room, to Genl.[D] Totten. He chose the one with the orator on the side— The expense of this, and the first plan, being the same. I am convinced by the course of the architect in relation to this business, that he is not to be trusted. He at first, brought to me, an estimate of several hundred dolls. extra in making the change. I then told him, I would have nothing to do with the change if there was any extra expense to attend it. The same evening, at the lecture, I was informed, that the contractors, had concluded to do it, for the same as the cost of the first plan— Before Gen Totten he affected to know all about your curve of sight,[12] and I presume would have given it, as his own, had I not been present.

Dr Foreman has been sick, for a few days past, with chills and feever. He thinks they are the effects of previous exposure— The Smithsonian rooms however have been very uncomfortable during the past week. The furnaces give scarcly any heat, in our rooms, above the Laboratory.

I have not seen Mr Walker[13] since you left. He could not come to our house on ~~frid~~ saturday,[14] on account of a meeting of the bible society[15]— I have seen Mrs Emory[16] every evening— I have always thought her a very sensible lady, and she has lost nothing in[E] my opinion by her course on[F] this occasion.

I dined on monday evening at Mr Seaton's in company with a Mr Flower, from England. Mr Ewing and Mr Gales,[17] were also of the Company— I was somewhat amused, with a little developement of character, which exhibited itself in Mr Gales. Speaking of the Daguerreotype he remarked, that it was not new—that the impressions made on the eye, of a living ox, were perceptable after the animal was dead— I stated, that the fact was not one of Philosophy Positive, whereupon the efficient editor, of the intelligencer, declared,[G] that he would prove the fact to me, by the authority of some of the first philosophers, of this and the last century. I thought no more of the matter, but was surprised the next day, to receive a communication, from the gentleman, in manuscript, and anothe in type,[18] printed for the occasion, in which, several authoraties were cited, to prove the position, not the one he advanced, but that an optical image was impressed upon the eye.[19] As I was going to the Smithsonian I called at the office, and was much diverted, with my reception. The sapient editor had entirely demolished the poor philosopher, but with a magnanimity, worthy a more important conquest, he had concluded, not to trample too rudely on his prostrate, antagonist— When I apologised for not answering his communication in writing—the answer was, 'there is no answer required; I did not expect one. When I pointed out, the error of his position, he appeared considerably annoyed, but soon rallied and reinstated himself with himself by giving me an account of what a wonderful man of science he had been, at the age of 18— With Mr Ewing I had not an opportunity of saying much.

Mr Flower the Enlishman was a desciple of free trade and once during the dinner mounted his hobby and gave a violent excathedra lecture on the absurdity of restrictions at which the company looked aghast said not a word and changed the subject as soon as possible. Dr. H lectures this evening on the connection of Geology and Theology. We are to have a gathering of the clergymen on the occasion— His lecture on bird tracks was to me the best he has given.[20]

I have thought of inviting Alexander of Baltimore to give a few lectures on Physical Geography. He has paid attention to this subject and from something he said I think he would be pleased to come before the public in this ↑way↓— How would a lecture on weights and measures, do for him next winter? I have thought, of inviting Dr Davis, to give a few lectures, on the ancient monuments, of the mississippi valley to ofset the honors which have been paid to Squier.

11ᴴ o'clock PM Dr. H. closed his course of lectures this evening—the house was more crowded than on any other evening. The Dr appeared to improve as he went on. The last lecture was written in full and the closing remarks were received with much enthusiasm.[21] He referred to the scientific institutions of this city namely to the Smithsonian—the coast survey—the observatory—the Patent office—the topographical and engineering bureaus—but—unfortunately forgot to mention the National Institute.[22] The Dr appeared well pleased with his success and

531

though his expenses must have been about 100 Dolls he was not dissatisfied with the 50 Dolls which would be found in his purse on his return.

The new Commissioner of Patents has come on— Mr Burke whom I saw at the lectures is very much softened in his feelings towards him and spoke rather kindly of him—

Peale appears pleased with the appointmt and thinks Ewbanks will succeed very well.

Perkins[23] has returned Alvards paper on tangents with the report that it is not new though the solutions have considerable merit.[24]

May 12th Mr Ewbanks has just called. I gave him an account of our course with regard to the appointment. That we had named Mansfield[25] Alexander and himself that Prof Davise[26] was our first choice—that we were much pleased with his appointment though we had recommended Alexander. Burke will go out in about 10 days. He was on the point of starting for the Hill to pay his respects to you when I informed him that you had left for the field.

Mr Espy has just come in his wife is considerably better though no person has any hopes of her but himself she has a cancer of the womb which is attended with frequent hemorrages. He will remain here some time unless called away by the illness of his wife. Mr Espy begs to be remembered kindly to you and says that he feels deeply grateful for all your kindness to him.

Professor Jewett requests me to inform you that your invitation to dinner did not reach him.

As ever yours sincerely
Joseph Henry.

Henry Papers, Smithsonian Archives.
In Henry's hand, with closing and signature by Harriet; following the signature is a note from Harriet to Nancy Bache, May 14, 1849. Reply: Doc. 301.

1. Not found. Bache was at Marriott's station, near Annapolis. *Coast Survey Report for 1849,* pp. 29–30.

2. Thomas Ewbank (1792–1870) was a self-educated manufacturer, inventor, and author who had left England for the United States in 1819. Commissioner of patents until 1852, Ewbank doubled the number of patent examiners and revised procedures to speed up examinations. *DAB.*

3. Edmund Burke, who had been a newspaper editor in New Hampshire before becoming a congressman and then commissioner of patents, became co-editor of the *Washington Union* in late May. The *Union* was "unwaver-ingly Democratic." He was not elected to the Senate. *National Intelligencer,* May 30, 1849.

4. James Renwick, Sr.

5. Wings were being added to the Patent Office Building along Seventh Street and Ninth Street. The greenhouse was relocated to the foot of Capitol Hill in 1851. Douglas E. Evelyn, "The National Gallery at the Patent Office," in *Magnificent Voyagers: The U.S. Exploring Expedition, 1838–1842,* ed. Herman J. Viola and Carolyn Margolis (Washington, 1985), p. 240. Henry recorded the conversation with Wilkes and his meeting with the secretary of the interior in his Desk Diary entries of May 7 and 9.

6. King did not get the Chile appointment

but went to California on behalf of President Taylor to investigate the prospects of statehood. The appointment went to Balie Peyton (1803–1878, *BDAC*), a former congressman from Tennessee. *Who Was Who in America: Historical Volume, 1607–1896*, rev. ed. (Chicago, 1967); *BDAC*.

7. On May 29, George P. Marsh was appointed minister to Turkey, in which position he served until the end of 1853. *BDAC*.

8. According to Henry's Desk Diary entries of May 10 and 11, Guyot promised his report on meteorological instruments by the end of the month; recommended the translation of the first two volumes of the history of geology published by the Société géologique de France (Étienne-Jules-Adolphe Desmier Archiac, *Histoire des progrès de la géologie de 1834 a 1845* [Paris, 1847–1849]); proposed a memoir for the Smithsonian on the erratic blocks of the alps; and suggested that the Smithsonian begin work on a report on the physical geography of North America by collecting all known data on heights, magnetic lines, and climatology. Henry agreed to advance Guyot a small amount for "topographical observations in different parts of our country," beginning in New England (May 10).

9. Guyot's *Earth and Man: Lectures on Comparative Physical Geography in Its Relation to the History of Mankind,* trans. C. C. Felton (Boston, 1849), was based on lectures delivered at the Lowell Institute.

10. Edward Hitchcock.

11. Great Falls, about fifteen miles above Washington. Henry noted in his Desk Diary for May 10 that they collected rock specimens.

12. In his 1856 presentation to the American Association for the Advancement of Science, "On Acoustics Applied to Public Buildings," Henry mentioned the desirability of arranging the rise of the seats in the Smithsonian lecture room according to Bache's "panoptic curve," which "enables each individual to see over the head of the person immediately in front of him." AAAS *Proceedings*, 1856, *10*:134.

13. Robert J. Walker.

14. May 5.

15. The Washington City Bible Society, an auxiliary of the American Bible Society, was founded in 1828 with the goal of furnishing Bibles to those who did not have them. Washington City Bible Society, *Seventy-Six Years of the Washington City Bible Society* (Washington, [1904]), p. 3.

16. One of Bache's younger sisters, Matilda Wilkins Bache Emory (b. 1819). Leonard W.

Labaree, ed., *The Papers of Benjamin Franklin* (New Haven, 1959–), *1*:lxv.

17. Joseph Gales (1786–1860), Seaton's brother-in-law. Gales and Seaton published the *National Intelligencer*, for which Gales wrote most of the editorials. *DAB*.

18. Not found.

19. Gales may have misunderstood a demonstration in optics texts which used the eye of a recently killed ox or other animal to show the inversion of images on a retina. See, for example, David Brewster, *A Treatise on Optics*, ed. A. D. Bache, 3d American ed. (Philadelphia, 1833), p. 243, and Isaac W. Jackson, *An Elementary Treatise on Optics* (New York, 1848), pp. 105–106.

20. Hitchcock's major work in paleontology was his study of huge fossil footprints in the Connecticut River Valley. He concluded they were caused by birds, but paleontologists now attribute them to dinosaurs. *DSB;* Edwin H. Colbert, *Men and Dinosaurs: The Search in Field and Laboratory* (New York, 1968), pp. 37–41.

21. A letter to the editor by "Sigma" in the May 18 *National Intelligencer* described Hitchcock's course as an "intellectual treat," whose object

> was not to make a personal display, but to convey, in as direct and intelligible a manner as possible, as much of a noble science as the circumscribed limits of a few brief lectures could impart.

The writer noted that the last lecture was the best and was frequently interrupted with "irrepressible bursts of applause."

22. As reported by Sigma, Hitchcock concluded by applauding the rise of Washington as a center of science, led by the Smithsonian, and "the patronage and active co-operation of so many of the heads of the departments of the Government and members of Congress in the promotion of science."

23. George Roberts Perkins, professor of mathematics at the New York State Normal School. *Henry Papers, 6:*167n.

24. Presumably an early version of the Alvord paper Henry published in 1856: *The Tangencies of Circles and of Spheres*, 1856, SI Contributions, vol. 8 (Washington, 1856). Benjamin Alvord (1813–1884) was an infantry officer who served on the frontier for many years. *DAB*.

25. Presumably Edward D. Mansfield, a West Point graduate (1819) and lawyer in addition to being a newspaper editor. *DAB*.

26. Charles Davies.

301. FROM ALEXANDER DALLAS BACHE

May 16. [1849][A] Wednesday.[B]

My dear friend

Congratulate me the seasons have resumed their course the solstice has come, & brought the most welcome reply[1] to my note of the equinox.[2] This unseasonable rain, wind, & cold will no doubt now give place to dryness, genial breezes, & mildness, gentle spring etherial mildness come![3]

Thank you for the journalizing. It would do me so much good if you would write me thus a line from time to time!

We will get on well with Ewbank. He is an honest man. No lecturing on Coast Survey or Weights & Measures, or on Smithsonian by outsiders. What will be done for Alexander? Has Davies answered you?

Humphreys[4] mentioned the little [...] which D[r]. Hitchcock gave the C.S. inter [?alies]. It was gratifying.[5]

Have indexed such a heap of miscellaneous, scientific papers & found so many lost ones.

To day worked at determining value of micrometers of instruments terrestrially. Transit nearly on merid. Preliminary tables worked up. Marks in their places. Nearly ready to begin. Such has been the state of sky & weather.

I have been greatly exercised on the subject of the Girard College. Am appealed to by many who think I might aid in putting matters right & yet know that I have not a particle of influence. Hart it seems will come forward again & Reed looks on. More anon.[6]

To day I had a racy account of the discovery of the Antarctic Continent from Lieut: Alden[7] U.S. Navy. Such scientific frauds as he narrated! Alas, Alas! He says that on the award of that medal Ross resigned his place as V.P. Geogr. Soc![8] Had you heard this.

Vidi's aneroid barometer is worth looking into. I have bought two for the C.S.[9] Love to you & yours.

Yours ever
A.D.B

Come & see us on Saturday?

Henry Papers, Smithsonian Archives.

1. Doc. 300.
2. Not found. The solstice and equinox were the times at which Jacques Babinet once proposed to correspond with Henry. *Henry Papers,* 4:240.

3. The last phrase is from the first line of the poem "Spring," part of James Thomson's *The Seasons* (1730).
4. Andrew A. Humphreys of the Coast Survey. *Henry Papers,* 6:439n.

5. Among the government departments contributing to the rise of Washington as a scientific center, Hitchcock mentioned the Coast Survey, "whose extent and importance are but feebly implied in its name, and some of whose ramifications it were very desirable should be permanently continued when the literal Coast Survey shall be finished." *National Intelligencer,* May 18, 1849.

6. Joel Jones resigned the presidency of Girard College on June 1, 1849, after only eighteen months in office. Herrick referred to the subsequent selection process as "much casting about on the part of the Board of Directors." Cheesman A. Herrick, *History of Girard College* (Philadelphia, 1927), p. 41.

7. James Alden (1810–1877), who had sailed with the Wilkes Expedition, was an assistant on the Coast Survey. *DAB; Coast Survey Report for 1849,* pp. 41–42, 66.

8. The Royal Geographical Society awarded Charles Wilkes a gold medal in 1848 in honor of his discoveries in the Antarctic. James Clark Ross, who disputed Wilkes's claims, was never a vice-president of the society. For the contro- versy between them, see M. J. Ross, *Ross in the Antarctic: The Voyages of James Clark Ross in Her Majesty's Ships* Erebus & Terror, *1839–1843* (Whitby, Yorkshire, 1982), chapter 11; David B. Tyler, *The Wilkes Expedition: The First United States Exploring Expedition (1838–1842)* (Philadelphia, 1968), chapter 11; and William Stanton, *The Great United States Exploring Expedition of 1838– 1842* (Berkeley, 1975), pp. 309–314; Paula Lucas, Archivist, Royal Geographical Society, private communication.

9. Bache referred to the aneroid barometer in his annual report as "promising," and proposed to test it further. Joseph Lovering of Harvard performed the tests and found it wanting for "nice scientific investigation." He cautioned against trusting it until "its peculiarities are better understood." In his 1850 report, Henry termed the aneroid barometer unreliable, especially for large changes in atmospheric pressure. *Coast Survey Report for 1849,* p. 18; *Silliman's Journal,* 1849, 2d ser. 8:288–290, and 1850 (Lovering), 2d ser. 9:249–255 (quotations on pp. 252 and 253); *Smithsonian Report for 1850,* p. 19.

302. FROM LEWIS C. BECK

New Brunswick May 19 '49

My dear Sir,

Your letter of the 14th inst. was duly received & I have also to acknowledge the receipt of your letter of 3 or 4 weeks since.[1] Contrary to my usual practice I have delayed answering that letter, until the present time, but I have an apology to offer for my delinquency which I hope will be satisfactory:

During my absence at Albany the house which I have occupied for eleven years was sold, with the large lot on which it stands. On my return, I found that I should have to look for a new domicile, but I supposed that this would not be a matter of much difficulty. To my surprize, however, I found that as the 1st of April Approached I was still with the^A prospect of having no 'local habitation.' At lenth, however, I succeeded in renting the only place which seemed to be at all suitable & I am now agreeably disappointed in my new residence, which is nearly opposite to Steele's Hotel within a hundred yards of the Depot; so that when you or yours will do us the favour to pay us a visit you will find the locality at least a convenient one. Now after this long story you may imagine what a <u>worry</u> it has been to me to get books, 5000[B] minerals, & traps of all sorts, ready for a move. It took us 3 weeks to get ready for a start, & we have been 2 weeks more occupied in arranging matters in our new residence—

This is apology No 1. To this I have to add that the Breadstuff Investigation so completely absorbs my time & thoughts that I have little leisure for any thing else. Last year I worked very hard at it, because I felt anxious to satisfy Mr Burke & the public of the utility of the Researches— But I laboured under the difficulties[C] of a new undertaking & the fact that samples did not arrive until late in the season. It has so happened that, soon after I sent in my Report several[D] large boxes arrived containing nearly 100 samples from various parts of the world. At first I felt almost discouraged at the amount of labour before me; but I began & have steadily persevered, during all my moving, from day to day & week to week until I begin to "see my way through it." Still my mind is so much on this work that it is very difficult for me to draw it off. The fear that those who have the direction of this matter at Washington will think that I do not ~~not~~ <u>earn</u> the Appropriation induces me to do more perhaps than I should feel myself called upon, under other circumstances, to do.

This long statement must be my excuse for any seeming neglect in regard to your letter & for the reply that I am now to make in regard to the Report on Agricultural Chemistry. The plan is marked out & a good deal done toward filling it up, but I am not yet ready to go to press. The fact is that in addition to other reasons I begin to feel more & more timid about publishing. If I were to give my <u>real</u> sentiments in regard to this matter, I know it would not suit. I hope soon to get at it in earnest & I shall complete it & at all events submit it to your judgement. By the way, I see that Prof. Johnston[2] has been invited to deliver an Address before the N.Y.S. Agricultural Society, & I suppose he will lecture about the Country on Agricultural Chemistry. I cannot but think that the constant invitation of foreigners, & especially Englishmen, to lecture &c. here, is unwise. They laugh at us when they go home, pick up our money & use the facts which our own men have collected. But I may perhaps be <u>ultra</u> in this respect. I am <u>thoroughly American</u> in my feelings, & this must be my excuse.

I regret exceedingly that Mr Burke has been removed. I had hoped that I should have completed my work under his direction. But such is the political world! I am not acquainted with Mr Ewbank & of course cannot anticipate what his action will be in regard to the 'Breadstuff' Investigation. I shall go on until I hear as I have done heretofore. I have not yet drawn for any part of the Appropriation for this year.

I have much more to say, but hope you will soon visit us on your way to N.Y. I shall be more punctual in my replies in future. In great haste

Yours truly

L. C. Beck

Prof Joseph Henry.

P.S. After I had completed the within letter one or two things occurred to me[E] & I therefore add a P.S.— I have never received a copy of the Report of your Regents to ~~the~~ Congress & have only seen it for a few moments. Is it possible ↑[?~~for me~~]↓ to get one? Mr. Van Dyke[3] would probably frank it to me. I am also very anxious to obtain a copy of the Report from the Acting[F] Secretary of the Treasury containing the outlines of the progress of the Geological Survey of Wisconsin & Iowa, by D. D. Owen & C. T. Jackson—published last year as Senate Executive Document No 2[4]— If you can obtain ↑these↓ without much trouble, I should esteem it a great favour, but I suppose you have many calls of this kind, & I do not wish to trespass on your time. In haste

yours, &c.

L.C.B.

I had not space in the sheet, to say any thing in regard to your proposition ~~in regard~~ about Lecturing. I am certainly flattered that you should think me worthy of such an invitation. I am totally ignorant of the Atmosphere of Washington & hardly know what kind of lecture would suit the lungs, of your audiences. I should, however, be disposed to try my hand, if you think a short popular course of 4 to 6 lectures on the "Chemistry of Nature,' would answer.[5] I delivered this course as a preliminary to one of my ↑full↓ courses at Albany two years ago & I was told that the lectures were acceptable. Certainly the audience, although small, seemed to be interested. I have also occasionally introduced one or two of the lectures into my regular courses. Should you think they would answer, I would rearrange them, post up the new things, & prepare diagrams, drawings &c. But I should like to have a talk with you on the subject. My lectures would of course come under the head of the 'Diffusion' instead of the 'Advancement' of Knowledge. But this perhaps will be no objection, as a popular audience, which I suppose yours is, is not the proper place for originalities in science. I could break out during the month of September,[G] if that time would suit— Let me know as soon as convenient, but I should prefer a

537

personal interview as my thoughts travel more rapidly than my pen can do.

yours truly
L.C.B

I have received the last years Report of the Smithsonian for which I thank you. I should be glad to get the one of this year if published. I have also received sundry blanks for meteorological observations. I am too much occupied & moreover too much of an absentee, to attend to these investigations. I have a friend, Mr David Bishop,[6] who I am in hopes will do something in this way for our locality, but the principal difficulty is the want of good instruments. I cannot but think that the better plan would have been to have selected a few good men at important places & to have furnished them with the necessary instruments. I fear that in this case as in many others, what is every body business will be nobodys, but it may not be so— You know I am in the habit of looking things "straight in the face."

Again yours
L.C.B.

Henry Papers, Smithsonian Archives.

1. Neither letter found.
2. James Finlay Weir Johnston, reader in chemistry at Durham University and director of the Agricultural Chemistry Association's laboratory in Edinburgh. *Henry Papers*, 3:325n; 6:313n, 336n.
3. John Van Dyke (1807–1878), a representative from New Jersey from 1847 to 1851. *BDAC*.
4. U.S. Senate, 30th Congress, 1st Session, *Report from the Acting Secretary of the Treasury*

[McClintock Young] *Communicating the Annual Report of the Commissioner of the General Land Office*, Senate Executive Documents, No. 2 (1847), pp. 160–174 (Owen) and pp. 175–209, 223–230 (Jackson).
5. Beck delivered the course in April 1850.
6. Probably David Bishop (1824–1876), an 1843 graduate of Rutgers. John Howard Raven, comp., *Catalogue of the Officers and Alumni of Rutgers College . . .* (Trenton, 1916), p. 99.

303. HENRY DESK DIARY

[May 20],[A] 1849[B]

How would it answer instead of medals to give books for memoirs— Let the author choose a certain number within the limit of the sum awarded let these books be stamped with the seal of the society and thus serve as a memento of the gift—
The word 'medals" should be struck from the programme.[1]

Our rewards are pecuniary as well as honorary intended to assist as well as to stimulate.

Our object is the promotion of the True the Beautiful the Old the Good.

All branches of thought are connected. Science recives from Literature its illustrations its prower of efficent diffusion gives to literature in return precision of thought illustrations and objects of description.

The means employed by the institution for the increase of knowledge are stimuli and assistances. Two combined what gives a stimulus generally gives an assistance.

A library would appear to assist and yet it is impossible for a person of ardent mind to contemplate a well selected assemblage of books or to look over a collection of original memoirs without being stimulated to add to the store.

The more rigerous the examination of memoirs the greater is the compliment paid to the writer whose productions stand the test.

The Institution may employ a translator nothing is more desirable than the diminution of isolatenedess[c] of nations in science.

Besides presenting the conclusions of scientific men in general we should diffuse the light of individual genius by the ↑occasional↓ translation of particular memoirs exhibiting methods of investigation as well as results.

Henry Papers, Smithsonian Archives.

1. Under "Details of the Plan to Increase Knowledge," medals were mentioned as one type of reward to be offered for original memoirs.

304. TO CHARLES ELLET, JR.

Smithsonian Institution
May 28[–30] 1849

My Dear Sir

Please receive my thanks for your communication relative to the bridge[1] and your kind offer to prepare the materials at your place. I have presented a copy of your letter to the Board of Aldermen of the City of Washington[2] and hope to be able soon to inform you that they have accepted your proposal.

I regret that I am unable to inform you what is the amount of rain which annually falls in this country. The most extended series of observations on this subject are those which have been made in the State of New York under the direction of the Regents of the University. I cannot say whether the average result of the whole series has been published. I think not. You can however procure this information from Dr T. R. Beck of Albany, Secretary of the Board of Regents of the State of New York. Also I am informed that a report made to the Legislature of Maryland several years ago by Col Abert, contains some information on this subject.[3] I will endeavour to procure a copy and send it to you.

I presented your plan relative to the improvement of the Navigation of the Western Rivers[4] to Profr Bache and to the late Secretary of the Treasury Mr Walker. It made a very favorable impression upon them. Another gentleman to whom I explained it thought it might have a deleterious effect upon the country in the way of producing intermittent fevers, and unless due consideration be had with regard to securing the barriers, disastrous consequences might ensue by their accidentally giving way. I do not place much importance upon these objections and am myself very favorably impressed with your scheme.

Please furnish the promised memoir at an early day, in order that it may appear in the second Volume of Contributions,[5] the publication of which has already commenced and will be finished during the present year.

> Very respectfully, your obedient servant
> Joseph Henry
> Sec. Smithsonian Institution

Charles Ellet Jr
Wheeling Va
P.S. May 30, 1849

Since preparing the foregoing letter, I have been some days out of town, and during ↑my↓ absence Dr Foreman of the Smithsonian Institution has collected the following information on the annual amount of rain, from the reports of the Meteorology of the Military stations and from other sources.

Mean Annual depth of Rain, from 4 years observations—[A]

Fort Constitution.	N. Hampshire, . . .	28.85
Watertown Arsen[l]	Massachusetts	39.69
Fort Wood	Louisiana.	47.90
" Hamilton.	N. York.	45.71
Hancock Barracks		36.92
Watervleit Arsenal	N. York.	34.22
West Point.	"	48.70

Alleghany Arsenal	Pennsylvania	28.14
Dearbornville Arsenal . . .	. . . .	31.30
Fort Brady	Michigan	31.89
" Howard		38.83
" Winnebago	. . . .	31 88
" Snelling	Iowa	30 32
" McHenry	Maryland	40.80
" Monroe	Virginia	52.55
Washington City Arsenal . .	D.C.	34.62
Fort Crawford	Wisconsin	29.54
" Leavenworth	Missouri Ter.	32.68
St Louis Arsenal	Missouri	24.12
Fort Smith ~~Ar~~	Arkansas	35.64
" Gibson	"	30.64
" Towson	"	46.73
" Jessup	. . . .	47.43
New Orleans Barracks . . .	Louisiana	51.85
Key West	Florida	31.39
Baltimore	average 8 years . . .	39.90
Boston	" 22 " . . .	39 23
Hanover	N.H.	38.00
State of N York, ...	Regents Repts, . . .	36.00
State of Ohio	. . . .	36.00

Ellet Papers, Department of Rare Books and Special Collections, University Library, University of Michigan.

In Edward Foreman's hand, with Henry's signature. Reply: See Doc. 310.

1. Not found. In his Desk Diary entry for May 3, Henry noted that Ellet recommended a wire bridge which would cost about $700.

2. Not found. Henry raised the matter again with Mayor Seaton in October but received no encouragement. Desk Diary, October 26, 1849.

3. Possibly the 1838 report Abert prepared for the governor of Maryland which was later reprinted as *Report in Reference to the Canal to Connect the Chesapeake and Ohio Canal with the City of Baltimore, by Colonel J. J. Abert* . . . (Washington, 1874). On page 27, Abert printed a table showing rainfall at Baltimore for eight years and referred to "an extensive collection of rain-tables for various parts of the country" provided to him by Richard Harlan of Philadelphia.

4. Ellet proposed that the federal government build reservoirs on tributaries of the Ohio River. He claimed that by collecting the water and controlling its release, the government could prevent floods, keep the river navigable at all times, and provide water in time of drought. Published by Henry (see next note), Ellet's proposal was the first comprehensive plan of flood control for a major American river system. Submitting his Smithsonian memoir, Ellet memorialized Congress in April 1850. Convinced of the practicability of his plan and impressed by its simplicity and cheapness, the committee to which the memorial was referred recommended an appropriation of $20,000 to conduct a survey. Although the bill passed in the Senate, it failed in the House. Ellet was more successful in winning an appointment to survey the Mississippi Delta; his 1852 report on a plan to prevent flooding there was republished along with his earlier Smithsonian piece

in his magnum opus: *The Mississippi and Ohio Rivers: Containing Plans for the Protection of the Delta from Inundation . . .* (Philadelphia, 1853). Ellet's ideas were not adopted in his lifetime. Opposition or competing approaches came from the Corps of Topographical Engineers, notably from J. J. Abert who doubted that reservoirs would prevent floods, and from A. A. Humphreys and Henry L. Abbot, who advocated levees instead of reservoirs. This "levees only" policy dominated the Army Corps of Engineers' approach for many years, only to be abruptly abandoned following a disastrous flood in 1927. Opposition to Ellet was also expressed by civilian engineers, such as W. Milnor Roberts, who opposed reservoirs on the basis of cost, insufficient rainfall, and health reasons. Ellet's proposal for using reservoirs for flood control was successfully adopted in the twentieth century as one of several complementary methods. U.S. Senate, 31st Congress, 1st Session, Senate Reports, No. 191 (1850); Gene D. Lewis, *Charles Ellet, Jr.: The Engineer as Individualist, 1810–1862* (Urbana, Illinois, 1968), chapter 6; Martin Reuss, "Andrew A. Humphreys and the Development of Hydraulic Engineering: Politics and Technology in the Army Corps of Engineers, 1850–1950," *Technology and Culture*, 1985, 26:1–33.

5. Either the previously discussed memoir on the Niagara bridge or Ellet's *Contributions to the Physical Geography of the United States. Part I. Of the Physical Geography of the Mississippi Valley, with Suggestions for the Improvement of the Navigation of the Ohio and Other Rivers*, 1850, SI Contributions, vol. 2 (Washington, 1851).

305. FROM LEWIS C. BECK

New Brunswick June 1st 1849

My dear Sir

To my surprise I this morning received a letter from Mr Ewbanks,[A] in which he informs me, "that the particular fund from which" my "compensation is derived, being exhausted for the present fiscal year, the Secretary of the Interior[1] deems it advisable, that nothing definite as respects the continuation of the Analysis be determined on, until the commencement of the next." He adds "When the subject is again taken up for consideration, the result will be made known to you."

Thus in the midst of the work it is arrested in a manner which I least of all expected. I thought it not unlikely that it would be placed in other hands, for it seems that any thing done by the preceding administration must of necessity be overturned by the present one. But I supposed that the appropriation for[B] this investigation was a specific one, which could not be diverted into any other channel. I have only to say that it is a <u>small</u> business, & is a foretaste of what the Scientific men of the country are hereafter to expect. I have toiled in this Investigation day & night for nearly 15 months, ~~& had~~ have already completed 27 analyses this year; & have made sundry arrangements for the next Report, which Mr Burke informed me would be expected by the 1st of January next. Now it seems that I am to receive no compensation for this years work & I am politely informed that the result of future deliberations will be made known to me. Such are the singular movements of political men. You know I did not apply for this <u>job</u>, if it can be so called. I considered the work an important one, & have always supposed that even if a single fact of interest was brought to light during the Investigation[C] it would more than repay the trifling expenditure which would be incurred by it. But the <u>authorities</u> seem to think differently.

I have not the vanity to suppose that there may not be other men qualified to undertake this work. I will only say that I have spared no pains to make myself Master of the Subject. Still no[D] man is a good judge of his own capacity perhaps—& I should not say a word if a better man had been selected; as it ↑is↓ a rule which I think a good one that those who can best discharge a duty should be entrusted with it.

But I have been drawn into saying more on this matter than I had intended— I shall still go on with the analyses slowly, on my <u>own</u> <u>hook</u>, & shall probably rearrange all my materials & present them in the form of a General Report to the New York Legislature. This state is largely interested in the subject of Breadstuffs not only because they are largely raised in it, but because the City of New York is the great port for shipment.

While[E] I supposed myself bound to the government by the appropriation I felt it my duty to labour diligently in this work, & ~~felt~~ ↑had↓ some doubt about engaging much in other ~~work~~ matters— This being now done, for the present at least, I shall go on vigorously with my long promised Report on Agricultural Chemistry— The plan is marked out & a good deal done towards the 'filling up!' I should like to have an hour's talk with you on the subject & hope you will be passing this way soon.

With my regards to Mrs Henry
I remain Yours truly
Lewis C. Beck

Prof. Joseph Henry.

Henry Papers, Smithsonian Archives.

1. Thomas Ewing.

306. FROM JABEZ D. HAMMOND[1]

Cherry Valley June 3. 1849

Dear Sir,

I rec[d] yesterday under the frank of the Clerk of the H.R. the anual Report of the Board of Regents of the Smithsonian Institution made to Congress last February— I have read it with deep interest tho' hastily— Altho from your Report it appears that you have submitted the "Programma of Organization" adopted by ~~y~~ the Regents to ~~men~~ great numbers of the most distinguished literary men of the Union and that they have unanimously approved of it I (humble and obscure as I am) feel compelled to say that in some respects I wish the plan of operations had been different— I am strongly impressed with the opinion that the Regents give too limited, or if I may so speak, too technical a construction of the Will of M[r.] Smithson— I can not believe that he intended that the Institution which might be created by his bounty should confine its efforts to the discovery of new truths in natural science and that the knowledge it should diffuse among men should be restricted to a diffusion of those new discoveries— You say "The only questions to be asked in considering the acceptance of a Memoir are whether it is a positive addition to knowledge resting on original research and of sufficient importance"[2] &c— These "researches" if I rightly understand the Progamma and your remarkes upon it are to be mainly if not wholly relating to things pertaining to Natural Science. By the "increase" and "diffusion" ↑of knowledge↓ among men I take it that M[r.] Smithson intended all men irrespective of any particular class[A]— Now may not knowledge be increased and diffused among the the masses of men if that which is already known shall be simplified, condensed and ~~rendered easy~~ presented in an attractive form and so as to be easily understood by all persons of common sense who are capable of reading the English language? It seems to me that a periodical publication on the plan of the Penny Magazine[3] when conducted by Lord Brogham[4] and his Associates would increase and diffuse in the aggreate a greater amount of knowledge among men, that is all men, than a publication of the investigations in relation to the new Plannet Neptune, the fragments of a large plannet between Jupiter & Mars or the discovery of a new Commet by an American Lady.[5] M[r.] Smithson evidently was a Utilitarian[6]— I admit that the subjects ~~you~~ mentioned are highly interesting and important and merit the earnest attention of men of men of leisure and profound learning; but as society now is or or can in future by any reasonable probability be expected to be,—is it to be presumed that the common mind will be able to explore the profound rescesses of natural science? I am not surprized my Dear Sir, that you who are so justly and highly distinguished for the important and <u>useful</u> discoveries which you have made in some of the Departments of natural science should feel a partiality for the encouragement of researches which may lead to other discoveries. But will the efforts of the Institution if mainly dircted to the accomplishment of such objects carry out the intentions of Mʳ Smithson based as they unquestionably were on the most en- larged benevolence and good will to all mankind? Very few will read and fewer still will understand your publications— The circulation of your Memoirs will be confined to the Proffesors in ~~our~~ Colleges and to men ~~and to men~~ already profoundly learned— Thus they will benefit one class of men but not <u>all</u> men— You are right when you say "That the bequest was intended for the benefit of men in general and that its influence ought not to be restricted to a single District or even nation"[7] but I think you ought to have added '<u>nor to any particular caste or class of men</u>—

The Programma does indeed contain one ↑Class↓ of subjects (Nº 2) which invites discussions on moral and political questions but from your Report I can not perceive that you are preparing for any action of the Institution on those subjects— If however no dissertations on political Economy, Ethnology or mental and moral philosophy are to be received and published which do not "<u>rest on original research</u>" or exhibit some new discovery in the science of Politics or mental philosophy I think you will not be able during your life to present the world with many memoirs on the subjects enumerated in the second class of the Pro- gramme—

If the knowledge of the Laws of matter be important certainly a knowledge of the Laws of mind and its phenomana must be infinitely more important—

But there are other subjects not embraced in the Programme on which the minds of men require to be enlightened, the attempt to do which by the Institution would in my judgment be quite in accordance with the Will of Mʳ Smithson— Dissertations on the proper limitations or rather on the proper intent of the powers of Government or in other words, ~~what~~ what natural rights each member of Society ought to sur- render in consideration that the residue of his rights shall be protected; and on the nature, extent and inviolability of the rights of man, <u>as man</u> might be produced and circulated by the Institution one would suppose especially during the existence of the present crisis of affairs in Europe with effects extensively and highly beneficial—

But the most efficient means of increasing and diffusing knowledge among all men—the mighty ~~leive~~ leaver which can and must elevate the masses without depressing the higher classes, I mean the system of primary schools first introduced by the Pilgrims, of New England and since adopted by most of the northern and western States of the Union and by some of the nations of Europe seems to have been entirely overlooked by the Regents of the Smithsonian Institution— This omission strikes me as the more extraordinary because I believe that the knowledge which M^r. Smithson possessed at the time he executed his Will of the great ~~and~~ and successful efforts which were then being made in many and various parts of this Country in favor of popular education by the improvement of Common Schools mainly induced him to make the Government of the United States Trustees of his munificent donation to be used for the purpose of increasing and diffusing knowledge among men— — And yet those who have undertaken to execute his will do not even allude to this powerful, and I must be allowed to add only means of diffusing knowledge among all men—

I should exhaust your patience were I to indulge myself in dilating on this part of my subject— I will therefore merely remark that in my opinion the Regents of the Institution ought without delay to establish a Professorship on Popular education—that during the whole ↑time↓ Congress shall be in Session lectures be delivered on the best mode of organizing, conducting and supporting the District School and also on the School Laws of the Several States and the Kingdom of Prussia, with suggestions in relation to what Laws ought to be enacted in every Country and especially in every State of the Union for the ~~support~~ establishment ~~and~~ support and regulation of primary schools—These lectures should be published and copies sent into every County in the U.S. I could name a ↑gentleman now a↓ Member of Congress ~~w~~ (M^r. Horace Mann[8] of Massachusetts) who ought to be appointed to such professorship—

A Normal School ought also to be established by ↑the↓ Institution at Washington and its operations witnessed personally by the Members of Congress and visitors at the seat of Government— Strange as it may seem to a Northern man I presume there will be found Members of Congress who never entered the School Room of a District School—

With great and undiminished regard I am truly Yours &c

Jabez D. Hammond

Joseph Henry L.L.D.

It is possible and indeed probable that my examination of your Report has been so hasty and superficial that I have in some instances unjustly imputed to it defects; if however I have not entirely deceived myself the Institution in order to be popular and useful (for to be useful in this Country it must be popular) must in some material respects change its plans of operation—

Henry Papers, Smithsonian Archives.
Reply: Doc. 312.

1. A member of the Board of Regents of the University of the State of New York, Hammond was a Democratic politician, lawyer, and historian. Henry knew him from Albany. *Henry Papers*, *1*:98n–99n, 122; *BDAC*.

2. *Smithsonian Report for 1848*, p. 12.

3. The *Penny Magazine* of the Society for the Diffusion of Useful Knowledge was an illustrated weekly printed in London. In any given issue, there might be articles on science, technology, current affairs, architecture, geography, or history.

4. Henry Peter Brougham (1778–1868), Baron Brougham and Vaux, was a lawyer, a member of Parliament, and an educational reformer. He formed the Society for the Diffusion of Useful Knowledge in 1825. *DNB*.

5. Maria Mitchell.

6. During the 1820s the British were greatly interested in organizing institutions for the improvement of the working classes through self-help and learning. The Society for the Diffusion of Useful Knowledge was but one example. It has been argued that James Smithson's decision to establish the Smithsonian Institution in a will prepared in London in 1826 in the midst of this explosive increase in self-culture institutions was not a coincidence. In this interpretation, Hammond's vision of the Smithsonian was closer to Smithson's conception than was Henry's. William L. Bird, Jr., "A Suggestion Concerning James Smithson's Concept of 'Increase and Diffusion,'" *Technology and Culture*, 1983, *24*:246–255.

7. *Smithsonian Report for 1848*, p. 27. The quotation comes from Henry's "Explanations and illustrations of the programme."

8. Mann (1796–1859), the great reformer of the Massachusetts public school system, which in turn served as a model for the rest of the nation, was serving as a Whig congressman. *DAB*.

307. FROM WILLIAM BACON[1]

Richmond, Mass, June 4, 1849[A]

Dear Sir,

Your note,[2] with accompanying documents was rec[d] one of the last days of April. I have read your report to the regents and the letter of Prof Loomis[3] with much interest. It appears to me, that the plan of operation you have marked out for the adoption of the Ins. is one which must meet with the approbation of all scientific (it's of no use to try to accommodate the opinions of others) men and to secure the best results from the avails of the funds. My only regret with regard to its present prospects is, that I have not the means to do more for the advancement of its prosperity, and that I am not situated so as to enjoy more extensively the benefits of the Establishment. By your researches and publications all useful Knowledge will receive a new impulse, and your Library will one day form a nucleus around ↑which,↓ men of enquiring minds will gather from all quarters for interchange of thought and the acquirement of new food for thought. It must, it <u>will</u> become a fountain from which <u>ten thousand</u> streams will flow out <u>in</u> all directions to refresh and gladden the hearts of all who will partake its bounty. I say all. Not that I infer that every one will ever visit the establishment or <u>be</u>come direct owners of all or any of its published documents, for in the present state of things it is questionable whether one in five hundred of our whole population would care to do either, unless indeed it were for any other object rather than to acquire information, yet, from those who search its tomes or investigate its researches, other streams will flow forth, whose influence, though silent as the dewfall of a ~~breathless~~ ↑breezeless↓ morning, will scatter intellectual health and happiness into every mind.

Prof Loomis' article is one that everybody, should read. His arguments are good and his reasoning upon them, in point, <u>exactly</u>, and we are prepared to subscribe to every item of it. Storms are no doubt produced and regulated by nature's laws as much as are the change of the seasons and the revolutions of spheres. And Why may we not suppose that certain indications of nature vary in different cases, to be sure, forewarn their approach, and may be turned to our benefit if we will observe their phases? I firmly believe that we have yet much available knowledge yet to gain in these matters, as well as in all other operations of nature.

But I am encroahing upon your time which may be devoted to more valuable purposes than scanning my remarks, and will only say, that I have much pleasure in forwarding you the Journal for May, which I believe is ~~nearly~~ correct, all except thermometrical notes having been taken by myself, carefully at the times. As my thermometer is broken, I have depended on the Journal of a friend in this matter, and here let me Enquire, if in order to accuracy, these instruments ought not all to be of the same manufacture and carefully compared to give true indices? I think so. I shall continue my journal in June, which will use my last blank. If you find my work acceptable you can forward more. I shall hope to exhibit less blots next time, but as I am an every day working farmer, grown so from choice, to be sure, you'l excuse them, now.

I gave a short notice of your report in one of our County papers, which I enclose, and get Mr Rockwell's M.C.[4] frank as you gave no address to which I should forward, will you give address for future returns?

If at any time you have documents, for distribution, I shall be happy to receive.

Yours very truly
William Bacon

Note. Since penning the foregoing, I find I am likely to lose the thermometrical journal for the present, so I forward, much to my regret without it.

Yours &c
W.B.

Letters Received, Records of the Smithsonian Meteorological Project, Records of the Weather Bureau, RG 27, National Archives.
Reply: Draft at end of letter in Edward Foreman's hand.

1. A farmer in the western part of Massachusetts, Bacon served as a meteorological observer from 1849 through 1863, and from 1865 through 1872. Fleming, *Meteorology*, p. 182.

2. Not found.

3. "Report on Meteorology of the United States," *Smithsonian Report for 1848*, pp. 193–207.

4. Julius Rockwell (1805–1888), a Whig from Massachusetts. *BDAC*.

308. HENRY DESK DIARY

MONDAY, June 4th.[A] 1849[B]

Met the Architect and Col. Totten at the building to determine on the change in the arrangement of the rooms of the building. The proposition being placed before Col Totten he without hesitation agreed to them.

The changes are as follows

1st The East wing to be desmantled and converted entirely into a lecture room[1] the seats curving around the speaker's table which is to be placed at the door entering from the range.

One gallery running from one front window to the other length wise in front of the speaker.

2nd The room intended for a museum[2] in the main building to be divided by a wall including on the west one south window. The room on the east thus formed to be devoted to a Cabenet of Physical instruments with a gallery around the whole room.

3rd The walls which according to the original plan formed the sides of the Hall through the building to be removed and the space enclosed thrown into the Library.

1 By these changes the library will be increased in capecity to the amount of one or rather in the ratio of 2:3.[3] A room will be furnished 65 feet long by 50 wide for the display of apparatus.

2 Between the lecture room the chemical operating rooms or in other words between the parts of the building most liable to fire a wall 2½ feet thick will be interposed. If in this iron doors are placed the danger from fire will be very much diminished.

3 A much more convenient lecture room will be providid than that given in the plan as shown in Owen's book the lecturer will be more conveniently placed and the long range of rooms for operation and the accomodation of apparatus will be behind him.[4]

4[c] By the change a lecture room which from its construction and the want of light as well as from the organization of the institution is of no value will be dispensed with and the whole capacity of the main building increase ~~by~~ in the ratio of 3 to 4.

5 By the change a lecture room will be ready for use at the time of the meeting of congress.

6 It is an important part of the consideration with reference to this change that it costs nothing. The contractor prefers to make the alteration in preference to carrying out the original plan.

Henry Papers, Smithsonian Archives.
At the end of the entry Henry later added: "The gallery afterwas it was though best to omit and if the room was not large enough to repeat the lecture."

1. Originally, the east wing consisted of a small lecture hall, seating from three to four hundred, two laboratories, and small mezzanine rooms for apparatus. Robert Dale Owen, *Hints on Public Architecture* (New York, 1849), pp. 105–106, plate facing p. 105.

2. By comparing this discussion with the report of the building committee, it is clear that "museum" is a slip of the pen for "lecture room." Rhees, *Journals*, p. 699.

3. Henry wanted to expand the library, originally designed to be on the west side of the first floor of the main building, by removing the central hallway and scrapping the principal lecture hall, which was on the east side of the main building, and was to seat eight hundred to one thousand people. Owen, *Hints*, p. 106, plate facing p. 105; Rhees, *Journals*, p. 699.

4. In Owen's plan, a speaker in the east wing lecture hall stood almost in the middle of the wing, facing north into a narrow lecture hall, with apparatus stored both in the mezzanine rooms behind him and in two large rooms in the east range to his left. Henry envisioned placing the lecturer at the west end of the room, with the two east range rooms and the new apparatus room behind him.

309. FROM RICHARD SEARS McCULLOH

United States Mint,
June 6. 1849

My dear Sir,

Although your letter of March 30[1] has long laid unanswered upon my table, I have neither been unmindful of the obligation I am under to proceed promptly with the work on Optics,[2] nor inattentive thereto. Much of my time has been spent in reading everything I could find within my reach upon the Wave Theory. And the only thing which has delayed my writing has been, that I felt unprepared to furnish the list of books, as requested in your letter, until I should have ascertained what is necessary to be imported, as well as what can be commanded here.

I consider the writings of Cauchy[3] (his Exerçices d'Analysee & de Physique Mathém.; Recueil de Mém. sur la Physiq. Mathém. 1839; Exerçices Mathématiques; Resumés Analytiques ↑Turin↓; Nouveaux Exercices de Mathématiques, Prague 1835–36—) the most important to be purchased. After these any of the memoirs of Fresnel,[4] Young,[5] ↑Malus↓[6] Biot,[7] Arago,[8] &c. which are not to be found in the public libraries of this city are requisite, and I will prepare a careful list thereof to be submitted to you.

In the Transactions of the Royal Society of Gottingen (or Berlin), there is a Treatise on the Wave Theory by Neumann,[9] which is highly esteemed by some; it should I think be translated, and I would request that I be permitted to have it done at a moderate compensation, the German language not being very familiar to me. I have an assistant now engaged at other work fully competent to the task in every respect.

Although I have declined, and prefer not to receive, any compensation for my own labours;[10] I do not hesitate to request that you will appropriate to this work on Optics whatever money you designed to offer me, to be expended in procuring the services of an assistant from time to time (discontinuously) to make calculations of a simple nature, verify numerical results, translate from German, Latin &c. &c. Any money thus appropriated to be expended with rigid economy, and strictly accounted for by me, with vouchers &c. This request I make solely for the reason that it will expedite and render more perfect the work, by relieving me of labour which can be readily performed under my eye.

In my own private library, I have the Treatises on Physics of Biot,[11]

Despretz,[12] Péclet,[13] Pouillet,[14] Young;[15] Newton's Optics; Herschel's Treatise on Light;[16] the same with Notes by Quetelet (French);[17] Powell on the Undulatory Theory applied to the Phenomena of Dispersion;[18] Pareira's Lectures on Polarized Light;[19] Moigno's Rep. d'Optiq. Mod. lst & 2[d] parts;[20] Woodward's illustrations of the Wave Theory;[21] Hunt's Treatise on the Chemical effects,[22] & Draper's papers.[23] Prof. Bache has a copy of Lloyd's Lectures on the Wave theory,[24] which he offered to lend me some time since. Airy's Mathematical Tracts[25] should be imported.

I find nothing so <u>physically</u> clear & beautiful as the memoirs of Fresnel—his elementary exposition of the Wave theory, (which was translated by D[r] Young, with notes, into English and published in the Quarterly Journal of Science)[26] is most excellent. He must, I think, be our guide & model.

Lloyd's Report to the 4th meeting of ↑the↓ British Association[27] is useful, but the labours of Cauchy are all subsequent thereto. Present my best respects to M[rs] H.

Very truly yours
R. S. M[c]Culloh[A]

I may be in Washington, in the course of a few days.

Henry Papers, Smithsonian Archives.
Reply: Notation on first page of letter in Edward Foreman's hand: "Answered by requesting Prof M[c] to make out his list of books."

1. Not found.

2. In late February or early March, McCulloh and Henry agreed to prepare jointly "a digest of optical Science." Henry recommended that the publication include a brief history and geometrical demonstration. He wanted the mathematics confined to footnotes. McCulloh to Henry, March 6, 1849, Henry Papers, Smithsonian Archives.

3. The author of over eight hundred papers and seven books, Augustin-Louis Cauchy (1789–1857) was professor of celestial mechanics at the Sorbonne. He has been acknowledged as one of the greatest mathematicians in history. In the 1830s, he developed three different theories of reflection and refraction. *DSB*.

4. Augustin Jean Fresnel.

5. Responsible for the renaissance of interest in the wave theory of light at the turn of the century, Thomas Young, who discovered the principle of interference, published extensively on physical and physiological optics. *DSB*.

6. Known for his discovery of polarization by reflection (1808) and his explanation of double refraction (1811), Étienne Louis Malus had published at least sixteen memoirs. *Henry Papers, 3:*478n.

7. Jean-Baptiste Biot, a firm believer in the corpuscular theory of light, received the Rumford Medal of the Royal Society in 1840 in recognition of his contributions to the study of polarization. Among his discoveries were the rotation of the plane of polarized light by liquids (1815) and the law of rotary dispersion (1818). *Henry Papers, 1:*88n; *3:*479n, 481n; *DSB*.

8. D. F. J. Arago was one of the defenders of the wave theory of light. *Henry Papers, 3:*390n.

9. Franz Ernst Neumann (1798–1895) was professor of mineralogy and physics at the University of Königsberg. McCulloh probably had in mind "Theoretische Untersuchungen der Gesetze, nach welchen das Licht an der Grenze zweier vollkommen durchsichtigen Medien reflectirt und gebrochen wird," *Abhandlungen der Preussischen Akademie der Wissenschaften,* 1835, pp. 1–160. In this article, Neumann attempted

to explain the passage of light from one medium to another. *DSB*.

10. In his letter of March 6, McCulloh assured Henry that he did not want any compensation for scientific work. He wrote that "money . . . has no charms for me" and that "I heartily despise it."

11. *Traité de physique expérimentale et mathématique*, 4 vols. (Paris, 1816). With the exception of the publication by Young, all the treatises mentioned in this paragraph are in the Henry Library, although sometimes in different editions. The works by Hunt and Airy are later editions.

12. César M. Despretz, *Traité élémentaire de physique*, 6th ed. (Brussells, 1840).

13. Jean-Claude-Eugène Péclet, *Traité élémentaire de physique*, 4th ed., 2 vols. (Paris, 1847).

14. Claude-Servais-Mathias Pouillet, *Éléments de physique expérimentale et de météorologie*, 5th ed., 2 vols. (Paris, 1847).

15. *A Course of Lectures on Natural Philosophy and the Mechanical Arts*, 2 vols. (London, 1807).

16. John F. W. Herschel, "Light," *Encyclopedia Metropolitana*, 4:341–586; this was available as a separate as well (London, 1849).

17. P.-F. Verhulst and A. Quetelet, trans., *Traité de la lumière*, 2 vols. (Paris, 1829–1833).

18. Baden Powell, *A General and Elementary View of the Undulatory Theory, as Applied to the Dispersion of Light* (London, 1841).

19. Jonathan Pereira, *Lectures on Polarized Light, Delivered before the Pharmaceutical Society of Great Britain; and in the Medical School of the London Hospital* (London, 1843).

20. François N. M. Moigno, *Répertoire d'optique moderne*, 2 vols. (Paris, 1847); volumes 3 and 4 appeared in 1850.

21. Charles Woodward, *A Familiar Introduction to the Study of Polarized Light* (London, 1848).

22. Probably Robert Hunt, *A Popular Treatise on the Art of Photography* (Glasgow, 1841).

23. Draper had published extensively on photography and on the chemical effects of radiant energy.

24. Humphrey Lloyd, *Lectures on the Wave-Theory of Light* (Dublin, 1841).

25. George Biddell Airy, *Mathematical Tracts on the Lunar and Planetary Theories . . . and the Undulatory Theory of Optics*, 3d ed. (Cambridge, 1842).

26. Fresnel had summarized his ideas on the wave theory of light in the "Supplément" to Thomas Thomson, *Système de chimie*, (Paris, 1822). A translation of this summary appeared under the title "Elementary View of the Undulatory Theory of Light" in *Quarterly Journal of Science, Literature and Art*, 1827, 23:127–141, 441–454; 24:113–135; 1828, 25:198–215; 26:389–407; 1829, 27:159–165.

27. "Report on the Progress and Present State of Physical Optics," *British Association Report for 1834*, pp. 295–413, which presented strong arguments in favor of the wave theory of light.

310. TO CHARLES ELLET, JR.

Smithsonian Institution
June 8 1849

My Dear Sir

Your favor of the 3d inst[1] has just been received and I hasten to assure you that I think a memoir giving an account of your explorations will be highly interesting.

I put great faith in your plans, and confidence in your judgement, and in my opinion any thing coming from you will be worth recording in a permanent form. We are however obliged to be cautious in the acceptance of memoirs, and to prevent ourselves from being overwhelmed with pseudo-scientific speculations of which we have already had sufficient offered to form several volumes, we have adopted the plan of rejecting unverified hypotheses. The author however of a paper containing valuable additions to knowledge may suggest all the practical applications which legitimately flow from his facts. If therefore it will be in accordance with your views to present your memoir under the following or some other similar title, we can get over all difficulties, in the way of accepting it; viz "Contributions to the Physical Geography of portions of the United States, with suggestions as to the means of improving the navigation of some of its principal rivers". According to this you will first give an account of your explorations, with all the facts you have gathered in regard to the descent and discharge of our rivers afterwards the practical application of these facts in the way of navigation water power &c. We will be at the expense of all the illustrations, and present to you as many copies of the memoir, seperately done up, as you may wish for distribution. Should you afterwards think fit to present a memorial to Congress,[A] any part of this memoir may be republished by you in connexion with all the details of the plans you may afterwards devise. In this way your paper will have ~~the~~ the character of a valuable contribution to science, whether the plans you propose should ever be adopted or not, and the plans themselves will receive our sanction so far as their publication by the Institution may be considered as such.

We should be pleased to receive the memoir as soon as possible, and you can reserve the other if you choose, for the volume of next year. Let me hear again from you on this subject, as soon as convenient, and give me any suggestions which may occur to you. I do not think it would be proper for the Smithsonian to publish the minute details of the proposed plans such as the construction of dams &c these should be reserved for the completion of the work or they may be more fully developed in your memorial to Congress.[A] You perceive from these remarks that I wish your memoir to the Smithsonian to assume as far as possible the character of a positive addition to science, while it gives proper promenence to your proposed plans.

I remain very respectfully and truly yours
Joseph Henry
Sec. Smithson[n] Institution

Charles Ellett, Jr
Wheeling Va

Ellet Papers, Department of Rare Books and Special Collections, University Library, University of Michigan.
In Edward Foreman's hand, with Henry's signature.

1. Not found.

311. FROM ALEXANDER DALLAS BACHE

Marriott's June 12, 1849.

My dear friend,

Thanks for the substantial mark of recollection in your bulletin[1] & books, the former read late last night as a refreshment after astronomical labours. And now to answer.

1. You left M^r. Marsh's list[2] &^{c}. here & as they are bulky & I supposed not immediately useful to you I have not returned them. Do you want them before I come say in a week. That reminds me that there is a talk of stopping the Weights & Measures[3] for want of money(!) about which I will write more further on, as if you have a chance to see Mr. Meredith[4] it may be well to urge upon him the importance of the work.

The arrangement about M^r. Marsh's books seems to me a good one.

2. I like the new arrangement which you propose very much. It is quite superior to the old. I hope you will have all in "black & white" so that no claim can be made hereafter on the building Com. or Board for extras.

You are liberal to the Library room, but not too liberal? Can you induce the architect to study the arrangements of the interior while there is yet time & to adapt them to the purposes in view?

You could not dispense with an apparatus room in the new arrangement & the library ought not to grasp at the whole floor.

3. What you say in regard to Prof. Beck[5] surprises me very much. The Sec. of the Interior[6] has yet to be made to feel the power of science. If not stopped he will do more mischief. Is not this a proper case for men of science to be informed of? Dr. Jackson,[7] the Patent Office matters & this new one savour of the ultra political School. Burn this treason! Is it not strange that enlightened men will thus act!! Morfit[8] ought to be ashamed to come in under such circumstances.

Do I understand your last you have succeeded in stopping the matter?[9]

4. Your quondam friend is out again in Hunt,[10] putting his name this time so as to be sure to do no harm. He threatens largely. Reiterates his stale slanders, making the lies in some cases more circumstantial. Between Hunt & F there lies one. Hunt said he was not at liberty to disclose the name of the writer of the first article. Fergy says he was![11]

On the top of this Davis has found Cashe's Ledge[12] so long looked for by Commodore Owen[13] & so badly determined. With his deeds against Fergie's words he is safe.

Mr. Blunt[14] writes me that he hopes the discussion will not be kept up, as the only harm Fergie's articles do with his name to them is to himself! The enemy he puts into his mouth &^{c}.

5. Thank you for the probabilities, and for the encouragement to go forward in the thorny path. A talk over the matters with you would do more to fix my ideas than in thinking over it for a month. In talking to you I always make such a clean breast of it with the advantage of friendly criticism on the thoughts.

After all does not the idea of <u>antecedent</u> probabity come in on one side & chance on^A the other.

6. So far from wondering at your delay in writing I only wonder & am glad that you write at all in the midst of so many distractions.

M^r. Walker's advice is wise & I doubt not you will be able to do the good without incurring the evil.

7. You may recollect that M^r. Walker recommended to Congress to bring the collection of the revenue under the same rules in regard to appropriations as other branches of the service. When he did so I asked him what effect it would have on the Weights & Measures to which he replied none the expense as part of the expense of collecting the revenue would be paid for from the gross appropriation just as a collector's salary would be paid. The new commissioner of the customs[15] has declared that the amount appropriated by Congress is insufficient for the expense of collecting the revenue having thrown out of view as matters of uncertain amount & therefore of <u>no</u> amount the cartage, storage &^c. &c. which were by law to be added to the sum appropriated & which Mr. Walker says will amount to from three to five hundred thousand dollars. But let that pass. A cry of necessity for retrenchment is raised & they propose declaring that <u>certain</u> expenses must be cut off.[16]

Now im primus The ex. Sec. assured me that the Wts. & Meas. had formed part of the estimated cost of collections & could not be affected by the new law.

Secundo— What right has the Sec. Treas. to say that some things are appropriated for & others not when all were equally included in the act.

Tertio, if retrenchment is necessary it should fall pro rata upon all expenses & not be applied so as to stop some works.

Quarto. If any work is to be stopped it ought not to be the only matter of science which the Treas. pays for.

Quinto. It could not have been the intention of Congress to stop the distribution of weights & meas. & balances to the states after a part had been supplied, until all were furnished.

Sexto. It is perfectly easy for the Sec. Treas. to provide for this expense if he chooses by anticipating the years' expenses, & putting it in the hands of a disbursing agent before the law takes effect.

Septimo. Very easy for him to make provision <u>if he sees the importance</u> of the work.

Octo. Cutting off the subsistance of fifteen workmen is rather inhuman in a case of doubtful propriety.

> If you see Mr. M. give him a talk.
> Love from Mrs. B & Self to Mrs. H & you.

> > Yours ever truly
> > A.D.B

Henry Papers, Smithsonian Archives.

1. Not found.
2. Of the "theoretical, historical, descriptive & critical works on the Fine Arts, of Galleries and Illustrated Works . . . and of Engravings and Etchings" which he was offering to sell to the Smithsonian for $3,000. Compiled at a cost of $4,000, the collection of illustrated books and engravings portrayed "the history of the Art of Engraving and the other Fine Arts (excepting Architecture)." Marsh thought it exceeded all other American collections in "*historical* value & interest." Copy, May 24, 1849, Marsh Papers, Bailey/Howe Library, University of Vermont (italics in original).

As we will document below, Marsh was selling the collection because of business reverses. He wanted to conclude the sale prior to his departure for Constantinople.

3. In 1843, in addition to the superintendency of the Coast Survey, Bache had been given responsibility for the construction and verification of standard weights and measures. *Henry Papers,* 5:475.

4. William Morris Meredith (1799–1873) became secretary of the treasury in 1849, succeeding Robert Walker. *DAB.*

5. A reference to the threatened termination by the Interior Department of Lewis Beck's research on breadstuffs.

6. Thomas Ewing.

7. That is, the effort to remove Charles T. Jackson from his position as head of the Lake Superior survey.

8. Campbell Morfit (1820–1897) was a chemist studying under, and working with, James C. Booth in Philadelphia. He had asked Henry for both a letter of recommendation and an oral recommendation to the secretary of the treasury for the position of chemical examiner for the Port of Philadelphia. Henry declined to write the letter, but did agree to serve as a reference. Morfit did not receive the position. *DAB;* Morfit to Henry, March 23, 1849, Henry Papers, Smithsonian Archives; Desk Diary, March 30, 1849.

9. Not yet, but on July 9 and 10, 1849, Henry visited Ewbanks, asking for an explanation regarding Beck's compensation for his analysis of breadstuffs. On July 11, Ewbanks told Henry that Beck would be supported. A week later, Beck informed Henry that he had

> received a very satisfactory letter from Mr Ewbanks in which he requests me to continue the Investigation & states that the Secretary of the Interior had no intention of withdrawing it from my hands.

Beck credited Henry for Ewing's reversal. Desk Diary, July 9, 10, 11, 1849; Beck to Henry, July 18, 1849, Henry Papers, Smithsonian Archives.

10. A reference to James Ferguson's article in the June issue of *Hunt's Merchants' Magazine and Commercial Review* ("The Coast Survey of the United States," 20:592–603), the third in a series on the Coast Survey. The first, which appeared in the February issue ("Survey of the Coast of the United States," pp. 131–149), was an anonymous attack on Bache and his handling of the Coast Survey. After praising the work of Bache's predecessor, Ferdinand Hassler, the author claimed that Bache had obtained his appointment because he "produced the greatest amount of personal influence" (p. 139), not because of his reputation as a scientist. After attacking the operations and results

of the survey under Bache, the author concluded by complaining that

> for want of the proper visitation and supervision on the part of the general government, a great public work is monopolized by a particular clique or faction, is used for mercenary or political purposes, for the indulgence of private pique, or the aggrandizement of personal and family influence." [p. 149].

Charles Henry Davis answered these attacks in the April issue ("'The Coast Survey of the United States.' A Reply to an Article, with the Above Title, in the February Number of the Merchants' Magazine," pp. 402–414). He defended both Bache's reputation and his achievements. Davis dismissed the anonymous critic as "unacquainted with the nature of a geodetic survey" (p. 404).

Ferguson's signed response to Davis, admitting his authorship of the February article, was, as Bache indicated, a repetition of many of the points initially discussed in the February article. The crux of the debate between Ferguson and Davis, personal attacks aside, was a comparison of the productivity of the Coast Survey under Hassler and Bache. Ferguson emphasized field work, while Davis defined productivity in a larger sense, including, for example, the production and distribution of charts. The two men also disagreed about how to calculate the budget of the Coast Survey: Ferguson included as part of the Coast Survey's resources the value of ships transferred to it from other agencies, while Davis counted only the direct appropriation.

11. In the June article, Ferguson claimed that Freeman Hunt, the editor of the magazine, had been given authority to disclose the name of the author of the February article if the inquirer was "personally interested in the publication" or could prove to Hunt that "any of [the article's] statements were unfounded" (p. 593).

12. A ledge in the Atlantic Ocean off the New England coast. *Coast Survey Report for 1849,* pp. 22–23, 78–79.

13. Captain William Fitzwilliam Owen, Royal Navy, had unsuccessfully searched for Cashe's Ledge three times. *American Coast Pilot,* 15th ed. (New York, 1847), p. 130; William R. O'Byrne, *A Naval Biographical Dictionary* (London, 1849).

14. Edmund Blunt.

15. Charles W. Rockwell had been named to this newly created position, which oversaw the "settlement of customs, revenue-cutter, lighthouse, and marine hospital accounts." Charles Lanman, *Biographical Annals of the Civil Government of the United States during Its First Century* (Washington, 1876), p. 509; *Guide to the National Archives of the United States* (Washington, 1987), p. 59 (quotation).

16. Until 1849, the expenses incurred in collecting customs revenue were deducted from the gross revenues, with only the net being turned over to the treasury. But on March 3, 1849, Congress passed a law at the recommendation of Secretary Walker, requiring that from June 30 forward the gross revenues were to be paid into the Treasury. Congress appropriated $1,560,000 and "such sums as under the law are paid into the treasury for drayage, cartage, labor, and storage," to cover the expenses of collecting customs revenue. This sum was based on Walker's estimate that savings of $500,000 could be realized from the over two million dollars spent in 1848 to collect customs revenue. *U.S. Statutes at Large,* 9:398–399 (quotation on p. 399); *Congressional Globe,* 30th Congress, 1st Session, 1848, 17:464.

Bache's fears were unrealized. Expenditures for the construction of standard weights, measures, and balances during the fiscal year July 1, 1849, to June 30, 1850, declined less than $200 from the previous year out of a total of over $12,000. U.S. Senate, 35th Congress, 2d Session, *Report of the Secretary of the Treasury, Communicating, in Answer to a Resolution of the Senate, a Report Showing the Amount Expended and the Progress Made in the Coast Survey, and also the Weights and Measures Furnished the Several States and Custom-Houses and Their Cost,* Senate Executive Documents, No. 6 (1858), p. 287.

312. [TO JABEZ D. HAMMOND][A]

[Mid-June 1849][A]

My dear Sir

Your letter[1] of June 3$^{\underline{rd}}$ has just been delivered to me by Mr C Denning and I beg to assure you that any thing from you will always be received by me with attention and respect. Yourself and Judge Conckling[2] are intimately associated in my mind with the history of my past life and an approbation from you of any plans I may have proposed or am endeavoring to carry into operation will give me much pleasure.

I regret that we do not see the affairs of the Smithsonian Institution in precisely the same light. Bacon has enumerated among his idols or fallacies of the mind that of the den in which every subject is presented to each individual tinged by the peculiarity of his mental habits. Though we have long been friends our trains of thought are probably distinct and to each the same subject is presented under the aspect of a different hue. I think however had you given the programme and my reports a second and more attentive perusal we would not have differed as widely as you imagine.

The organization of the Institution is not in every respect what I could have wished. One half of the whole income by the law of Congress after the erection of a large building is devoted to the formation of a Library and Museum; objects in themselves very important but which according to my original views of the subject are rather too ~~local~~ ↑local↓ in their operation. Much good however may be done in this way and as a compromise as well as a requisition of the Act of Congress I acquiesced in the d[i]vision.[B] The programme relates principally to the mode of expend[in]g[B] the remaining portion of the income and you appear to have entirely overlooked the fact that is to consist of two parts, the first to serve as a spur to the commencement of new investigations as well as assist ~~us~~ in their prosecution. The second intended for the diffusion of knowledge. You have strangely confounded these with each other and have assumed the fact not stated in the programme that the investigations and diffusion are to be restricted to Physical subjects.

By a reference to the programme it will be seen that we intend to publish principally two classes of works. The[c] first to contain account of any additions to knowledge in any of its branches which may be presented to us or which the Institution may have been instrumental in producing. The volumes of this class are avowedly not intended for popular effect and many of the papers which they contain will be of such a nature that comparatively but few persons in the world will be fully able to understand or appreciate them.

The most valuable papers have in every age been those ~~which are~~ [---] ↑read↓ ~~and~~ appreciated by the few and not the many. The Principia of Newton and the Celestial Mechanics of Laplace though of the highest importance even at this day can be read by not more than one man in 50.000. The essays of Bacon and Locke as well as the publications of most of the great benefactors of mankind were not appreciated by the many at the time they were given to the world. And this must always be the case the discoverers or he who increases knowledge must always of of necessity be a little in advance of his age. Surely you would not refuse to encourage original thought even when the will of Smithson especially refers to it under the term increase of knowledge and the practice of his own life evinces his appreciation of labours of this kind. One volume of this class our first publication has been given to the world. It is not on Physical Science but is an account of the Ancient Monuments of the Missisippi Valley. The second volume mentioned in my last[D] report contains a number of papers it is true on Physical Science but it will also contain one on language and probably several on Ethnology.

The other class of publications which you appear to have overlooked or confounded with the first are intended exclusively for the diffusion of knowledge among men and are not intended as original productions but as reports on the progress of knowledge the posting up from time to time of the various discoveries and presenting views of the present condition of the different branches of human knowledge of these is devoted to physical science and two classes to other subjects these are to be diffused as widely as our means will permit but we shall not be able fully to develope this part of the plan until the buildind is completed our income is much absorbed by the erection of the edifice.

I do not agree with you in opinion in regard to the value of Publications similar to the Penny Magazine Lord Broushams system has fallen into disuse. Knowledge to be valuable must be presented to the mind as a whole. Men must be taught to think as well as to know. A man may be a fool though his head be crammed with isolated facts.

The subject of popular education is one of the highest importance to the well being of the human race on it depends the stability of our institutions. It is however and object of to much importance and magnitude to be allowed to ~~for~~ ↑require↓ support ~~on~~ ↑from↓ the small bequest of a foreigner. ↑~~Our whole income devoted to this object would be but a drop in the ocean.~~↓ Every state in the Union owes it to itself to furnish the most ample means of instruction to every individual within its jurisdiction, to found normal and common schools as colleges and academies. I think therefore that we have acted wisely in not attempting to engage with our small means in the great subject of popular education as all we could do in this line would be but a drop in the ocean. W[e] have also no right to conclude that the promotion of primary education was intended by Mr Smithsons ↑in his↓ bequest. Had[E] he wished to benefit mankind in this way the benighted of Ireland and the besot-

560

ted of England would have offered a nearer and ampler field for his philanthropy. Mr Smithson was no utilitarian in the narrow signification of the term. His[F] mind was directed to every branch of knowledge though his own publications were exclusively of a class belonging to the increase of knowledge. They consist of about twenty original papers principally on Geology and Mineralogy.

I cannot agree with you in opinion that the Institution should devote itself to the diffusion of Knowledge to the exclusion of its increase. There are in our country thousands of institutions for the former and scarcely any for the latter and on this point I beg you will give my report a more attentive reading. While we are doind much in this country in the way of diffusing and applying science to the practical purposes of life very little is done in the line of increasing it. Our country has produced but one Franklin to five hundred Fultons, and why is this? Is the mind of our country men inferior to the stock from which it sprung? Certainly not. The cause is that there has been no encouragement given to original reserch and the wide distinction well known in other countries between the increase and diffusion of knowledge has been entirely overlooked among us. Our Institution will do[G]

Draft, Henry Papers, Smithsonian Archives.
In Harriet Henry's hand, with corrections and interlineations by Henry.

1. Doc 306.
2. Hammond's former law partner, Alfred Conkling was the federal judge for the Northern District of New York. *Henry Papers*, 1:92n–

93n; George Rogers Howell and Jonathan Tenney, eds., *History of the County of Albany, N.Y., from 1609 to 1886* (New York, 1886), p. 143.

313. TO CHARLES ELLET, JR.

Smithsonian Institution
June 18 1849

My Dear Sir

Your letter[1] of 11[t] was duly received. I am much gratified to learn by it that we so nearly agree in our views, as to the proper form of the memoir. I also concur with you in opinion as to the importance of a skeleton map for the illustration of your paper. It should be of such a size as readily to fold into our volume of Contributions—into the form of a page of 12 by 8½ inches. If you can prepare such a map it will be engraved with any other illustrations necessary to elucidate your paper.[2]

If the topographical proposition were true, which you mention, floods would be unknown in any of our rivers, an Obvious absurdity.

It has long been a favorite project of my own, to ↑form a↓ collection of all the surveys of lines of explorations for canals and railways in our country, to serve as the basis of a topographical sketch of the undulations of the surface of the United States.[3] Your memoir will be the beginning of this project.

We shall be pleased to have your paper as soon as it can be properly prepared for the press.

> I remain very respectfully and truly Yours
> Joseph Henry
> Sec. Smithsonian Institution

Charles Ellett Jr.

Ellet Papers, Department of Rare Books and Special Collections, University Library, University of Michigan.
In Edward Foreman's hand, with Henry's signature.

1. Not found.
2. We are uncertain what Henry meant by a "skeleton map." The only large form of illustrative material included in the published paper was the map which appears under the title, "Profile of the Ohio River and Some of Its Tributaries," in Ellet's *Of the Physical Geography of the Mississippi Valley, with Suggestions for the Improvement of the Navigation of the Ohio and Other Rivers,* 1850, SI Contributions, vol. 2 (Washington, 1851), between pp. 12 and 13.

3. Henry believed that the topographical map would "be of great importance in determining the effect of the configuration of the surface on the direction of the wind." Henry to Zachariah Allen, February 1, 1848, Collection 5040, Reynolds Historical Library, The University of Alabama at Birmingham.

314. TO THOMAS EWING

Smithsonian Institution
June 18 1849

To the
Hon Thomas Ewing
Secretary of the Interior
Sir

A few days since [I sent][A] you a letter[1] in behalf of the Contractor[2] of the Smithsonian Building relative to the rate of wages offered by the Superintendent of the New Patent Office buildings.[3] I am now requested by the Building Committee of the Smithsonian Institution to write to you on the same subject.

The Committee have been shown the accompanying copy of a letter from Robert Mills Esqr to the Commissioner of Public Buildings,[4] which in their opinion does not properly exhibit the facts of the case. In the first place it cannot be true that the elaborate style of Architecture of the Smithsonian edifice requires less skilfull workmen than the plain design of the Patent Office.[5] In the second place whatever may have been the actual announcement of the Superintendent of your building the fact is, that a statement was published in the newspapers that he intended to give two dollars per day,[6] and that in consequence of this statement the masons have abandoned the Smithsonian Building to the prejudice of the Institution, of the Contractor, and in most cases of the workmen themselves; many of them by their combination having been thrown out of employment. In view of these facts the Committee respectfully request that your Superintendent be directed not to derange the rate of wages justly established by the relation of supply and demand, and that when any change is deemed necessary on account of the scarcity of workmen or otherwise, it be made on consultation with the Contractor of the Smithsonian Building, and the other directors of Public Buildings in Washington.[7]

In conclusion the Building Committee disavow any intention to control wages in this city, they only wish to prevent the fitful changes which tend to produce dissatisfaction among the w[or]kmen,[A] and [?to inte]rrupt[A] the progress of the building under their c[h]ar[ge].[A]

> I have the honor to be very respectfully
> Your Obedient Servant
> Joseph Henry
> Secretary, Smithsonian Instit[ution][A]

Letters Received from the Smithsonian Institution, 1849–1879, Records of the Patents and Miscellaneous Division, Records of the Office of the Secretary of the Interior, RG 48, National Archives.

In Edward Foreman's hand, with Henry's signature. Reply: June 21, 1849, Letters Sent Concerning Public Buildings and Grounds in the District of Columbia, 1849–1863, vol. 1, Records of the Patents and Miscellaneous Division, Records of the Office of the Secretary of the Interior, RG 48, National Archives.

1. Not found.
2. Gilbert Cameron.
3. Robert Mills. He had been replaced as superintendent of the Smithsonian Building in 1848. Rhees, *Journals*, p. 696.
4. Robert Mills to I. Mudd, June 9, 1849, same location as this letter.

5. In his letter, Mills claimed that "the work at the Smithsonian Building is very different to our work, and may be performed by inferior labour."
6. The newspaper announcement has not been found. Mills told Mudd that he was paying the stone masons working on the Patent Of-

fice Building "a quarter of a dollar more per day, than is given on work, private, and of an inferior order."

7. In his reply, Ewing informed Henry that the wages would not be reduced.

315. TO THOMAS EWING

Smithsonian Institution
June 19 1849

To the
Hon. Thomas Ewing
Secretary of the Interior
Sir

I beg leave to express to you my opinion of the importance of the investigations now prosecuting by Henry R Schoolcraft Esqr under the direction of the Department of the Interior.[1]

Every thing relative to the manners customs habits and history of the aborigines of this country is of especial scientific interest, and this interest is at the present time much enhanced by the minute inquiries which have lately been instituted in almost every part of the world with regard to the peculiarities of the different races of men. The learned world looks to our country for a full account of the race that we have disposessed, and as every year renders the task more difficult, it is hoped that the investigations on the subject, now going on under the Government, will not only be continued, but that means may be afforded for their more active prosecution.

We would urge [?earnestly and] especially that the investigations be actively prosecuted at the present tim[e][A] while Mr [Schoolcraft][B] is in the vigour of physical and mental power, for we are [confident][B] that no person could be found so well qualified by long experience, habits of mind and peculiar acquirements to carry on the investigation.[2]

I have the honor to be very respectfully
Your obedient servant
Joseph Henry
Sec. Smithsonian Institution.

Henry R. Schoolcraft Papers, Library of Congress.
In Edward Foreman's hand, with Henry's signature. Copy in unknown hand in same location.

1. In 1847, the Office of Indian Affairs, then in the War Department, hired Schoolcraft to gather information on Native Americans. When the Interior Department was established

in 1849, the Office of Indian Affairs was transferred to it. *DSB; Guide to the National Archives of the United States* (Washington, 1987), p. 377.

2. The Department of the Interior did continue to support Schoolcraft. The result was his monumental *Historical and Statistical Information Respecting the History, Condition and Prospects of the Indian Tribes of the United States*, 6 vols. (Philadelphia, 1851–1857).

316. TO MILLARD FILLMORE[1]

Smithsonian Institution
June 23 1849

My Dear Sir

Accompanying this letter I send you the certificate of the Executive Committee stating that the sum of fifteen thousand four hundred and fifty five dollars and seven cents, is required for the purposes of the Institution. This sum is the amount of interest which will be due 1st July on the original bequest. It will be required to pay—first, upwards of five thousand dollars which we have overdrawn from Corcoran and Riggs[2]—second, to pay the next instalments upon the building, also due 1st July;—third, for the salaries of officers, the purchase of apparatus, books &c.

There will also be due 1st July, a half year's interest on our Treasury stock and I am informed by the Comptroller of the Treasury,[3] that it will be necessary for you to send me a power of attorney to enable me to obtain the money. It will not be necessary for us at present to sell any more U.S. Stock;[4] it is now at a high premium and will probably advance still farther.

I will send you a copy of the Hints[A] on Architecture, also a package of our reports, through the Secretary of the Senate.[5]

The workmen are now engaged in making the changes of which I spoke to you at your last visit: The East wing has been entirely dismantled. A commodious lecture room will be ready for the operations of the Institution before the next meeting of Congress.

We have received a lot of very beautiful instruments from Boston which were ordered nearly two years ago,[6] and with the donation of Dr Hare, shall be able to make something of a display next winter in the way of books and apparatus.

The weather is at present exceedingly warm in Washington, almost too much so to allow of any exertions. I shall be obliged to leave the city for a few weeks in August. When you come again to Washington it will give me great pleasure to accomodate you with rooms at our house.

> I remain very truly and respectfully
> Your obedient Servant
> Joseph Henry
> Sec. Smithsonian Institution

Hon Millard Fillmore
Vice President, U.S.

Fillmore Papers, Special Collections, Penfield Library, State University of New York at Oswego. In Edward Foreman's hand, with Henry's signature.

1. Vice-President Fillmore was elected chancellor of the Smithsonian on March 7, 1849. Rhees, *Journals*, p. 54.

2. This banking firm, established in 1840, had become the Smithsonian's banker by 1847. *DAB*, s.v. "Corcoran, William Wilson"; Rhees, *Journals*, p. 481.

3. Elisha Whittlesey. Charles Lanman, *Biographical Annals of the Civil Government of the United States during Its First Half Century* (Washington, 1876), p. 509.

4. Under a resolution of January 3, 1849, the regents authorized the chancellor and secretary of the Smithsonian to exchange $226,000 in United States treasury notes for United States stock certificates issued in their own names, and to dispose of the same as they saw fit, with the proceeds to be applied to the institution's programs. In April, Henry and Fillmore received and sold $16,000 worth of stock. Rhees, *Journals*, pp. 53, 469, 488.

5. Asbury Dickens.

6. The set of pneumatic apparatus ordered from Nathan B. Chamberlain. Rhees, *Journals*, p. 474.

317. FROM JOHN BARLOW[1]

> Royal Institution of Great Britain
> Albemarle Street
> London June 29ᵗ
> 1849

Sir

The Royal Institution of Great Britain, desiring to evince its sense of services rendered to Science, has, during many years been in the practice of inviting those Foreign Philosophers, whose^A pursuits have especially tended to advance the objects for which ↑it↓ was incorporated, to permit themselves to be enrolled among its Honorary Members.

By a recent Minute of the Managers of the Institution the number of this class has been restricted to thirty.

I have now the gratification of announcing to you that, at the General Monthly meeting of the Members of the Institution held on the 4ᵗ insᵗ, you were unanimously elected as one of its Honorary Members.

Permit me to assure you of my own gratification in being the medium of conveying a tribute so due to your scientific eminence.

> I am, with great esteem
> your most faithful servant
> John Barlow M.A.
> Sec[y] R.I

I enclose a[B] list of our Members[2] and one or two other papers which may possibly interest you.

Box 39, Henry Papers, Smithsonian Archives.
On Royal Institution letterhead.

1. The Reverend John Barlow (1798–1869) served as Honorary Secretary of the Royal Institution for almost eighteen years before retiring due to ill health in November 1860. *Notices* *of the Proceedings at the Meetings of the Members of the Royal Institution of Great Britain*, 1858–1862, 3:290.

2. Not found.

318. FROM JOHN EDWARD GRAY[1]

> British Museum
> 2 July 1849

My Dear Sir

Accept my thanks for the Exposition of Mr Smithson's Bequest. I regret to say that I fear you will find it very difficult to carry out many parts of your plan satisfactory to yourself or in a Manner that is Beneficial to Science & Literature.[A] I believe that most of the Instituions in this country have discovered that Medals & prizes are a great cause of dissention and produce very little benefit to the either to science or the person who receives them. To such a extent has this conviction[B] operated on the mind of most of our scientific men that the Linnean Society at a late meeting refused a bequest giving them a Medal for them to distribute[2] and the Royale & other Society would gladly get rid of the Medals they have at their disposal, they are directly opposed to the Principles that have been found ~~befinici~~ ↑beneficial↓ to trade, being in fact to Science what the Bounties &c were to trade but it is very odd ~~to~~ ↑how↓ [?exploitive] system ~~to~~ cling to Scientific & Litterary men which are rejected by those[C] who they are inclined to consider less informed. Hence they call[D] out for Copyright &c &c which are but the regmnants of protection. It was curious enough to see Fox[3] the MP. for Oldham speack agains the corn Laws[4] & Protections[E] & then to go an see him preside at a Meeting to render copyrights perpetual!

I sent[F] you the <u>Second letter</u>[5] only because I had sent by Mr Stevens, 2 copies of the <u>first</u> one.[6] If you have not received it from him I ↑will↓ try & procure one ↑back↓ from a͟ ↑some↓ friends[G] ↑there↓ for all I had of them I have given away.

The Commission which called them into existence finishes it work tomorrow you should procure a copy of their report when printed.[7] It is full of the most [?montrous] nonsense I ever heard and only shews what follies a number a gentlemen who ought to be better informed will listen to but they were determed to hear nobody but Mr Panizzi & fearred to enter on any subject less it should lead to the exposure of his follies & ↑his↓ ignorance of English habits & wants.

Ever Yrs truly
J. E Gray

Henry Papers, Smithsonian Archives.

1. Keeper of zoology at the British Museum, Gray met Henry in London in 1837. *Henry Papers*, 3:229n.

Gray was writing in response to Henry's letter of June 13, 1849, Gray Papers, American Philosophical Society. In that letter, Henry acknowledged receipt of Gray's "second letter" (see below), informed him of his election as secretary of the Smithsonian, and reminded Gray of their meeting in 1837. He enclosed a copy of the "Programme of Organization" and promised a copy of *Smithson's Bequest . . .* (Washington, 1848).

2. In 1846, the Linnean Society of London received a bequest from one of its fellows to provide a gold medal for the best contribution in each volume of its *Transactions* by a fellow. The society rejected the bequest because it felt the awarding of the medal would not benefit science and could lead to dissatisfaction within the society. A. T. Gage, *A History of the Linnean Society of London* (London, 1938), pp. 45–46.

3. William Johnson Fox (1786–1864) was a member of Parliament, 1847–1863. *DNB*.

4. Originally passed in 1815, the Corn Laws prohibited the import of grain until the domestic price had reached a designated level. They became identified with issues of free trade versus protectionism, manufacturing interests versus agricultural interests, and liberals versus conservatives. In 1846, Parliament passed a measure phasing them out over three years.

R. K. Webb, *Modern England: From the Eighteenth Century to the Present* (New York, 1975), pp. 152–153, 267–271.

Fox was a strong supporter of the repeal of the Corn Laws.

5. John E. Gray, *A Second Letter to the Earl of Ellesmere on the Management of the Library of Printed Books in the British Museum* (London, 1849).

6. John E. Gray, *A Letter to the Earl of Ellesmere on the Management of the Library of Printed Books in the British Museum* (London, 1849). Henry had asked for a copy of this publication in his letter to Gray.

7. In 1847, a Royal Commission, chaired by the Earl of Ellesmere, was appointed to investigate complaints made by library patrons against the Keeper of Printed Books, Antonio Panizzi (1797–1879, *DNB*). Panizzi had begun revising the library's catalog in 1839, with the objective of producing a complex alphabetical catalog, but had only finished with the letter "A." Many scientists had stopped using the library because of the limitations of the catalog. Gray argued for specialized subject catalogs, developed by individuals knowledgeable in each subject. Panizzi also had closed the stacks to all but library staff; scholars wanted a return to open access. It was a conflict between the librarians seeking the ideal, all-encompassing catalog for the national library, and the scientists desiring a system which served their pur-

poses by reflecting how they worked. The commission's report, published in 1850, supported Panizzi. Albert E. Gunther, *A Century of Zoology at the British Museum through the Lives of Two Keepers, 1815–1914* (London, 1975), pp. 116–125.

319. TO JOHN TORREY

Smithsonian Institution
July 19th 1849

My Dear Dr.

Mrs Henry and myself are much indebted to your good Lady for ↑her↓ generous and considerate attention to my motherinlaw.[1] It was well that the Old Lady found so kind a friend or she might have been in a bad way. Though she is quite smart for a person of her age yet she is too infirm to be trusted much alone or even with a servant since she does not know her own condition of mind and body and would attempt to direct in cases where she would require the direction of others. We were pleased to learn that she had given up the idea of going to Albany such a journey at this season of the year would have been very hazardous.

I do not recollect of having received any letter from you relative to the Fremont plants which I have not answered. I have no objections to having the plates printed by Endicott[2] and shall be much pleased to have them under your eye. It may however perhaps be best to make a bargain with the printer before hand. My experience thus far in the Smithsonian leads me to be cautious in dealing with all workmen. I am sorry to say that I have found scarcly any[A] who have very precise notions of morals in dealing with the agent of a public Institution.

We shall start for the North if nothing prevents about the first of Aug. William will probably go to Princeton[3] the beginning of next week.

We are all well but have almost roasted with the heat "done brown" brains coagulated and juices dissipated. We have a very pleasant house but very hot— Last summer I felt but little inconvenience from the heat in Washington for though the temperature was high we had in my other position a constant breeze. We have however had some very scorching days this summer.

I remain as ever
truly yours
Joseph Henry

Dr Torrey

P.S I am requested not to tell that William is to leave for Princeton next week. He wishes to surprise his Grandmother—so you will please to know nothing of the matter or in other words not to read that part of my letter.

All things in the Smithsonian are in a peaceful condition. I am making great changes i[n]^B the building—remodelling [the]^C interior so that that ass Dr Owen the chemest who attempted to plan the whole building would not know his rooms. The building Committee have given me liberty to make what changes I choose provided I do not increase the expense of the Edifice. The architect is quite willing to make any changes I may suggest because he says the interior of the building is not his. It belongs to Dr Owen. I cannot make it what it ought to be but I can very much improve it.

J–H–

Torrey Papers, Library, New York Botanical Garden.

1. Maria Alexander. Henry was writing in response to Torrey's letter to him of July 16, 1849 (Henry Papers, Smithsonian Archives), which related that Mrs. Alexander had had "an attack of vomiting." Mrs. Torrey, who was present, had nursed her, then brought her to the Torrey home to recover.

2. William Endicott was a New York City lithographer. *Henry Papers, 5*:305n. In his letter of July 16, Torrey complained that he had written Henry "two or three weeks ago in relation to the plates of Fremont's paper."

3. William Henry was entering Princeton as a freshman. He would board with Stephen Alexander. *Catalogue of the Officers and Students of the College of New Jersey* (Princeton, 1850), p. 15.

320. TO GEORGE PERKINS MARSH

Smithsonian Institution
July 19th 1849

Dear Sir

Mr Pearce has signified his assent to the proposition of purchasing the books[1] and I am therefore able to send you the accompanying certificate which I hope will answer your purpose.[2] If it should not please return it, and I will send you another.

A work containing the information you require has lately been published under the direction of Sir. J. F. W. Hershel entitled the Admiralty manual of scientific enquiry.[3] I have a copy which I can send you provided I have the address of Mrs Marsh in Brooklyn. It contains an interesting map of the general currents of the oceans.[4] These you will be readily able to refer to the trade winds and the deflecting influence of the eastern side of islands and continents.

I scarcely know to what point of inquiry to direct your attention observations of almost any kind are valuable if accurately made and faithfully recorded. A record of the quantity of rain that falls in the different seasons of the year—of the number and direction of motion of thunder storms—of the appearance of the aurora would be interesting. I will send you a set of blanks and queries relative to meteorological observations.[5]

I regret that Miss Crane[6] is not able to finish the translation of the Report[7]—and I fear with the distraction of mind necessarily produced by the arrangements for leaving your country for so long a time it will be impossible for you to do much in the way of translation.[8] I shall however be much obliged to you for any thing you may be able to accomplish before you sail. The book and the manuscript may be left at Putnam's—New York. Please inform me of the number of pages you have completed in time for me to transmit the amount to which you will be entitled[9]— I am about to prepare a report on the present state of knowledge on atmospherical electricity[10] and perhaps it will be best to translate what the report may contain on that subject.

I intend to leave Washington for the north about the 1ˢᵗ of Aug. and shall be in New York in a few days after. We shall probably meet then. I will call at Putnam's and shall probably be able to hear from you there.

> With kind regards to
> Mrs M & her sister
> I remain truly yours &c
> Joseph Henry

Hon G P Marsh

Marsh Papers, Bailey/Howe Library, University of Vermont.

1. Although a majority of the executive committee of the regents favored purchasing Marsh's books, the committee refused to act without the approval of James A. Pearce, who was absent from the June 27 meeting. Charles C. Jewett to Marsh, July 3, 1849, same location as this letter.

2. It did not. According to Jewett's letter to Marsh of July 31, same location, Marsh had asked Henry to alter the certificate, which Henry did. The altered certificate, not found, was enclosed with Jewett's letter.

3. John F. W. Herschel, ed., *A Manual of Scientific Enquiry; Prepared for the Use of Her Majesty's* *Navy; and Adapted for Travellers in General* (London, 1849). It consisted of a series of articles on the practice of science, ranging from astronomy to zoology, each written by an expert in the field.

4. In the article on hydrography, at the end of Appendix No. 1, between pp. 96b and 97.

5. According to the *Smithsonian Report for 1851*, p. 76, Marsh had a Smithsonian thermometer at Constantinople.

6. Lucy Crane was the sister of Marsh's wife. She lived with the Marsh family until her marriage in 1850 to the Marsh family's personal physician, Frederick Adolph Wislizenus (1810–

1889, *DAB*). David Lowenthal, *George Perkins Marsh: Versatile Vermonter* (New York, 1958), pp. 96, 117.

7. On May 11, 1849, Lucy Crane was paid $30 for translating an unspecified German memoir on diamagnetism. Smithsonian Daybooks, vol. 1, p. 67; Desk Diary, May 11, 1849.

8. Marsh was renowned for his knowledge of German. Lowenthal, p. 92.

9. Marsh refused payment. See Doc. 324.

10. Henry did not publish such a report for another decade, when it appeared as the fifth part of his "Meteorology in Its Connection with Agriculture," *Report of the Commissioner of Patents for 1859: Agriculture* (Washington, 1860), pp. 461–524.

321. FROM ROBERT WILSON GIBBES

Columbia July 20th 1849

My dear Sir,

The alarming increase of Cholera[1] I fear will seriously interfere with our meeting at Cambridge.[2] It was my intention to be there, and I am much disappointed at finding that I must give it up.[3] My friends are opposed to my going, and, altho' I have no personal fears of it, I feel[A] that, as it is a matter of pleasure and not of necessary business, I ought to practise self-denial. Is it possible to postpone the meeting for a month, and have it at Boston, if inconvenient to the Professors at Cambridge to meet during their college session?

I have received the proof sheets of our publication,[4] in which are many errata. I sent on a list to be appended, but have not learned whether it has been done. The next publication must be better managed, and my impression is that a phonographic reporter should be engaged for each section, so as to have the whole reports immediately prepared for publication.[5] Much of the interest in[B] the proceedings is lost by the delay in the publication.

When will your next volume be issued? I have a communication which I intend for the Association, which might come in as new—a short paper of five or six pages (with a single plate) on the remains of a fossil Rhinoceros found in S.C.[6]—the first time on the American Continent. I have only the horn and part of the nasal bone and cranium of the left side—, though I may in the fall procure other bones. It is a new species.

I have written to D[r] Elwyn[7] to send a copy of the Proceedings to each member who has paid his contribution—and to the prominent scientific institutions of the country— The remainder will be subject to the order of the Association.

Do me the favor to drop me a line as to your opinion about the meeting.

respectfully & truly
yrs
Robert W Gibbes.

Prof. J. Henry.

Henry Papers, Smithsonian Archives.

1. The intensity of the cholera epidemic of 1849 peaked in the Northeast around the end of July, then fell off rapidly. Charles E. Rosenberg, *The Cholera Years: The United States in 1832, 1849, and 1866* (Chicago, 1962), pp. 110–114.

2. Of the American Association for the Advancement of Science.

3. Based on the evidence of this and another Gibbes letter to a northern correspondent, Kohlstedt concluded that he did not attend the 1849 meeting. In fact Gibbes did go to Cambridge, where he was elected one of the assistant secretaries of the meeting, gave two presentations, and participated in the discussions. Kohlstedt, *AAAS*, p. 90; AAAS *Proceedings*, 1849, 2:2, 77, 95, 193–194.

4. Gibbes chaired the publication committee for the 1848 AAAS meeting. To produce even an unsatisfactory version of the *Proceedings* of that meeting required great perseverance and commitment. Not only did he have to repeatedly solicit copies of papers from uncooperative members, but he also had to advance the necessary money to publish the *Proceedings* when the association's treasury was inadequate for the task. Kohlstedt, *AAAS*, pp. 89–90.

5. Responsibility for overseeing publication of the *Proceedings* for the 1849 meeting was given to a committee of Cambridge scientists. A reporter was engaged. See Doc. 334.

6. Neither of the papers presented by Gibbes at Cambridge dealt with a fossil rhinoceros. He did publish one of his presentations—"On Mosasaurus and Other Allied Genera in the United States"—in SI Contributions, vol. 2.

7. Alfred L. Elwyn (1804–1884), a Philadelphia philanthropist, was elected AAAS treasurer in 1848; he held the position until 1870. Trained as a physician, he was active in the American Philosophical Society and had served as its secretary. *DAB; Henry Papers*, 6:506n; AAAS *Proceedings*, 1848, 1:92; Kohlstedt, *AAAS*, p. 92.

322. TO JAMES ALFRED PEARCE

Smithsonian Institution
July 21st 1849

Dear Sir

We have sent by express line to the care of Maj R. D. Burns[1] Baltimore a copy of the Hints on architecture which I hope will be safely received.

I am obliged to leave Washington for the North on the 1st of Aug. to be absent several weeks. If perfectly convenient to youself it might be well for you to come on before that time—if not we can postpone the meeting of the executive committee until the first of oct[2] when Dr Bache will be in the city.

The most important matter to settle was that of the purchase of a part of Mr Marshs library since the receipt of your letter[3] I have informed him that the executive committee have concluded to purchase 3000 dolls worth of the books to be paid for when the funds of the Institution will allow of the disbursement. He wishes to settle up his business before he leaves the country and particularly to adjust his financial affairs. He will deposit the greater portion of the remainder of his library with the Institution until his return and indeed he would not sell any of his books were it not that he has been very unfortunate of late in the loss of a large portion of his fortune.

Funds[4] have been provided for carrying on the building and the operations of the Institution by the sail of 16,000 Dolls of the US stock, by drawing the interest 15,000 on the Smithsonian fund and by about 5000 Dolls of interest on the U.S. stock. We still own 210,000 Dolls of US stock which is now at a premium of I think 17 per cent.

We have been making great changes in the interior of the building in the way of adapting it to the wants of the institution. By these changes the capacity of the library has been increased upward of one third—a room 50 by 65 feet has been provided for apparatus and the chemical and all other operations connected with combustion cut off from the collections. All these changes are made without increasing the expense of the building indeed the contractor I think is a gainer by alterations. It appears that all the interior of the building was planed by Mr Owen and his brother—the architect excuses himself by asserting that the interior of the building is not his. I felt some hesitation at first in urging these changes on the building committee knowing that by so doing I incurred considerable responsibility but I concluded ↑if↓ that as I was certain the changes were for[A] the best it was my duty to urge their adoption. General Totten has adopted them cheerfully and agrees with me in opinon as to their importance. You may recollect that at the time of the adoption of the plan of the building Gen. Totten was in Mexico and as I had opposed the adoption of so expensive a building I was not much consulted as to the arrangements of the interior and indeed they had all been settled in New Harmony before the plan of organization of the Institution was adopted. Though the building is not what it[B] might have been in the way of adaptation still it will now be tolerably convenient and will certainly make a very imposing appearance.

Should you come to the city before I leave I shall be much please if you will become my guest. I can then have an opportunity of informing you of all the affairs of the Institution[C] and of enjoying your society.

All things relative to the operations of the Institution are as favourable as could[D] be expected— Our report appears to give good satisfaction and there is now a call for another edition.

Dr. Foreman late of the medical College of Baltimore was temporarily employed by me on the recommendation of Dr Bache to assist in some experiments. I afterwards gave him charge of the meterological department in which he is now constantly engaged. Half of his salary is to be paid by the secretary of the Navy from the appropriation for Mr Espy and the other half by the Institution.[E]

Draft, Henry Papers, Smithsonian Archives.
Henry notation on top of first page: "Substance of letter to Mr Pearce."

1. A merchant. Baltimore City Directory, 1847–1848.
2. The next meeting of the executive committee was not until December 21. Rhees, *Journals,* p. 475.

3. Not found.
4. Beginning with this paragraph, Henry is informing Pearce of the events at the June 27 meeting of the executive committee, which Pearce missed. Rhees, *Journals*, pp. 472–475.

323. FROM ALEXANDER JONES[1]

3 Hanover Street
New York July 21st 1849

Professor Henry
Dear Sir.

I have intended for sometime writing to you; but having no plan digested for obtaining Meteorological Observations by Telegraph[2] that I could recommend, has caused me to delay writing ~~to you~~ ↑till now.↓

By the way of experiment I obtained the inclosed observations yesterday and the day before, over a large tract of country in this state, which although not as complete as such observations ought to be, yet they are interesting.

I am induced to believe that if the Government or the Regents of the Smithsonian Institute were to supply every Telegraph Station in the united States with suitable instruments, very correct and extensive observations might be simultaneously obtained over the greater part of the united States, by which the existence and progress of storms could be accurately noted and their course duly ascertained.

I would suggest, that New York should be made a central point, at which, all the reports should be ~~ob~~ received, duly registered, and duplicates of the same supplied to your Institute daily, and to such newspapers for publication as might be disposed to share in in the expense of obtaining the Reports. The Press of this ↑city↓ & Boston; (both of ~~whom~~ ↑which↓ I serve with Telegraph Reports from all points of the country daily) I feel assured as they are the wealthiest and most enterprizing;^A would willingly participate in the arrangement.

Indeed, some of the leading papers of this city have already expressed their willingness to contribute to the establishment of such observations & ~~by~~ ↑to↓ pay a fair share of the expense for the privelidge of publishing the results of the same.

Each Telegraph Office could be supplied with Thermometers Barometers, Rain guages, and if necessary Aneometers, with other appliances deemeed important— I think an arrangement can be made with all the Telegraph Companies, to have the observations recorded and transmitted to a central point, such as this^B city; for the bare amount of Tolls on the same. Duplicates of observations sent by Telegraph should be sent by mail, for^C the correction of errors; and to go through, in case of derangement on the part of the wires.

In a future letter, I will endeavour to give you a rough calculation of the probable expense of tolls for transmission, to gether with the total number of Telegraph Stations in the United States, at which instruments should be placed, ↑in order↓ to insure information over the the greatest area of the Continent at the same moment ↑or period of time.↓

In the meantime, I will take it as a favour, if you will drop me ↑a line↓, stating, in reply, your opinion of my suggestion!

> While I have the
> Honor to Remain
> Yours Very Sincerely
> & Respectfully
> A. Jones, M.D.
> Telegraph Reporter
> & Agent for the
> New york
> Associated Press

PS. The instruments distributed could ↑be↓ held as the property of the Institute, or of the Government subject to be returned, or delivered up when called for.

A.J

Letters Received, Records of the Smithsonian Meteorological Project, Records of the Weather Bureau, RG 27, National Archives.

1. Trained as a physician, Jones (ca. 1802–1863) worked for the New York Associated Press, an organization of six city newspapers that shared the cost of gathering domestic news

via the telegraph. *DAB;* Robert Luther Thompson, *Wiring a Continent: The History of the Telegraph Industry in the United States, 1832–1866* (Princeton, 1947), pp. 224–226; Fleming, *Meteorology,* p. 142.

2. In January 1848, Jones published a proposal for "daily and hourly reports of meteorological phenomena, by telegraphic messages from all parts of the country which are in telegraphic communication with New York" as a commercial venture. Apparently it was a failure. *Silliman's Journal,* 1848, 2d ser. 5:297.

324. TO GEORGE PERKINS MARSH

Smith. Inst. Aug 1st, 49

Dear Sir

I sent you yesterday another certificate and a note[1] to be used with reference to the business of the library which I hope will answer your purpose.

I now write to thank you for your uncalled for liberality in offering the translation on which you are engaged free of cost to the Institution. I shall not fail to give you due credit in presenting the result of your labours to the public.

I trust your interest in the Institution will not cease with your absence from the country. Will it not be compatible with your views and duties to prepare for us a Report on the present state of the Otoman Empire?[2] If so I will make a formal request that you do so.

I would also suggest that before you leave the country you will address to me a letter in favour of our friend Prof Baird as a suitable person should one be required to fill the post of naturalist to the Institution.[3]

Can you not interest Mr Choat in his behalf?[4] Do not fail to speak of his knowledge of modern Languages and the general philosophical character of his mind. To carry on the operations of the Institution we require the labours of an original investigator and not a mere curator of a museum. The Smithsonian should produce the same effect on science that the Royal Institution through the labours of Young[5] Davy & Faraday has done.

With kind regards to Mrs Marsh and her sister[6] I

remain truly yours &—
Joseph Henry

Hon George P. Marsh.

Retained Copy, Henry Papers, Smithsonian Archives.
Reply: August 4, 1849, in same location.

1. Not found.

2. Marsh promised in his reply to prepare a memoir on "some subject connected with Turkey," but never did so. However, while traveling in the Middle East, he did send several communications on scientific matters to Henry, some of which were published anonymously as "Notes on Vesuvius, and Miscellaneous Observations on Egypt," *Silliman's Journal*, 1852, 2d ser. *13*:131–134.

3. Marsh's recommendation for Baird has not been found, but his reply stated that he was enclosing it.

The Marshes and Bairds became family friends through their wives—Mary Helen Churchill Baird and Caroline Crane Marsh—who had known each other since their school days in Vermont. Knowing that her husband wanted to get a position at the Smithsonian, Marsh advised Mary Baird early in 1847 that he would do whatever he could to assist him, promising to secure "the good will" of regents Hilliard, Evans, and Choate, as well as of Jewett. E. F. Rivinus and E. M. Youssef, *Spencer Baird of the Smithsonian* (Washington, 1992), pp. 36–42 (quotation on p. 42).

4. In his reply, Marsh noted that Choate, to whom he had introduced Baird "some years ago," had been "much interested in him & will sustain him."

5. Thomas Young.

6. Lucy Crane.

325. TO BENJAMIN SILLIMAN, SR.

Princeton Aug 8th 49

My Dear Sir

Enclosed with this note I send you a letter and a table of result of experiments on rail ways[1] for our young friend Mantell.[2] I presume you are acquainted with his present address and that you will forward the letter to him. The table may be retained by you until he returns to New-Haven— Mrs Henry and myself became much interested in the young gentleman and shall hope to see him again before he leaves the country.[3]

You have probably, before this received a notice[4] of your election as an honorary member of the Smithsonian Institution and I hope you will be induced to take a lively interest in its operations. The members elected at this first meeting[5] were

> Dr. Hare.
> Dr. Silliman
> Washington Irving, Esq.
> Hon Alb[t] Gallatin.[6]

We shall probably divide the honorary members into sections and limit their number. Though they have no voice in the expenditure of the funds of the Institution they are requested to advise as to the operations of the establishment.

I think it probable that copies of the Contributions will be presented to the honorary members and that you will thus receive a copy on other grounds than those presented by E. G. Squier. Without authority this gentleman, whose moral faculties, appear not to have been quite as fully developed as his intellectual, has informed several persons that they are to apply to the Institution for copies of his paper. Besides allowing the authors to strike off an edition of 500 copies for sale on their own account the Regents gave to them for distribution or sale as they might see fit 200 copies additional.

I shall hope to meet you at Cambridge[7] next week and in the mean time

> I remain as ever very
> truly your friend
> & servant—
> Joseph Henry.

Prof. Benj Silliman.

Daniel C. Gilman Papers, Ms. 1, Milton S. Eisenhower Library, The Johns Hopkins University. Reply: August 21, 1849, Henry Papers, Smithsonian Archives.

1. Neither the letter nor the table has been found.

2. Reginald Neville Mantell (1827–1857), son of British paleontologist Gideon Algernon Mantell (*DSB*), had recently concluded an apprenticeship with the noted civil engineer, Isambard Kingdom Brunel (*DNB*). He traveled to the United States in the summer of 1849, hosted by Silliman, who was an old friend of his father's. Sidney Spokes, *Gideon Algernon Mantell* (London, 1927), pp. 161, 202–203, 216–219, 251; R. N. Mantell to Henry, July 6, 1849, Henry Papers, Smithsonian Archives.

3. Mantell had stayed with the Henrys for a few weeks in the spring and summer of 1849. "Our family appeared to have lost one of its members," Henry wrote after Mantell left. Henry to Mantell, June 29, 1849, Gideon Man-

tell Papers, Alexander Turnbull Library, Wellington, New Zealand; Mantell to Henry, July 3, 1849, April 4, 1850, both in Henry Papers, Smithsonian Archives.

4. August 1, 1849, in same location as this document.

5. That is, of the Establishment of the Smithsonian Institution.

6. Gallatin died on August 12, 1849. In his reply to Henry, Silliman noted that the ranks of honorary members were "already thinned by death," adding that Gallatin "when elected could not be expected to wear the honor long."

7. As Silliman wrote in his reply, an "afflictive cause" (his wife's chronic illness) prevented him from seeing Henry at the American Association for the Advancement of Science meeting in Cambridge. See also Spokes, pp. 216, 218.

326. TO ALEXANDER DALLAS BACHE

Princeton Aug. 8th /49.

My Dear B,

We arrived at this Place on Saturday last[1]—left Washington on Thursday—stopped at Phil[d] over Friday—saw Dr Dunglison[2]—found him confined to bed with a violent attack of the gout— Visited Mr Dallas was about starting with his family for Bordentown—looked very well

579

appeared in good spirits— His eulogy of the late President[3] has taken remarkably well—is to be printed for general distribution— Mr D. showed his good sense and prudence in this Eulogy—it was rather a difficult job considering the past[4]— I am informed that Mr Fillmore stands in the same relation to the President of the whig party[5] and that Mr Calhound was in the same condition under Gen. Jackson.[6] The vice President is the heir apparent and may on this account engender feelings of no friendly kind. Mr Dallas expressed himself well pleased with the condition of the Smithsonian and feels confident it will now go on without molestation. Almost all our friends were[A] out of the city— I saw none other except Dr. Bethune[7]—heard him preach on Friday and went with ↑him↓ on the Rail way to Princeton—he was going to N.Y. Had a very pleasant chat on the way, including an account of the doings at Cambridge the Dr's speach[8] your demand of the payment of a debt due one of your ancestors &c. Dr. B. thought he would be at the meeting of the association though this would depend on the condition of his Wife's health.[9]

The weather has been excessively hot in Washington—all my energies have been prostrated. We had a meeting of the Institution, the evening before I came a way— You have probably seen an account of it in the Intelligencer.[10] Mr Seaton promised to publish the notice—I have not seen it myself but hope it was done properly—the notice was prepared by myself though I know not whether it was published as it prepared. The Meeting went off very well[11]— The President and other gentlemen present appeared well pleased with the condition of things relative to the Institution. The building[B] is now going on quite rapidly and will be enclosed (the main part) this fall— The East & West Wings will be entirely finished in the course of two months.

I had an interview with Mr Clayton in which he requested me to explain to you the condition of affairs which led to the appointment of Fremount to the boundary commission.[12] He said that as he would probably not see you in some time and might not have an opportunity to give you the explanation in person he wished me to give it to you. The following is the substance of his remarks. The boundary commissioner had turned out a worthless fellow—had drawn more than 30,000 Dolls of the appropriation before reaching the place of his destination.[13]— That no account of the organization of the commission had been given to the Present administration that he (Clayton) did not know that Emory was the surveyor— Had he known this he would have given him the charge of the business[14]—that he knew Fremont to be a[C] man of talents and of the proper <u>kind</u> of knowledge that he was on the spot or near it and therefore he was appointed and not for the purpose of conciliating Mr Benton. I give you the remarks as near as I can recollect in their order and substance. The interview was short but before I left he put into my hands a communication from Mr Bancroft relative to the petitions sent through him from the Smithsonian Institution in regard to Professor Schumacher.[15] He insisted on my taking it with me to read at my leisure. I found however that the paper contained other matter which perhaps was not intended for my eye—I I therefore left strict orders that the document should be returned next day to Mr Clayton's house. I have learned through Dr. Halsted a graduate of Princeton that the Commission of the boundary survey were not in a very harmonious state. The commissioner had picked up a woman of ill fame at New-Orleans and had taken her with him. Col. Emory was disgusted with this conduct and had refused to allow his men to escort the woman. Dr H. has lately returned from Panama. I saw your mother[16] the day before we left—she said Mrs Emory expected her husband to return.

I start for Cambridge on Friday the day[D] after tomorrow and shall expect to meet you there. Mrs H half inclines to go with me and I think will do-so provided she can get ready— Capt. Davis was in Washington before I left and gave me an account of what he denominated a glorious time with you at Cambridge. He is in good spirits with regard to the Almanac— All his suggestions have been adopted by the Secretary of the Navy and the prospect is that the work will be conducted on liberal principles and will be an important aid to the developement of the scientific talents of our Country.[17]

I spent one evening at the "Seaton Station"[18] in attempting to detect currents in the earth but without success.[19] The clock arrangement of Saxton for breaking contact appears to operate well.[20] The new machine[21] so far as it has been tried, fully answers the purpose, I am informed that it will give the time true to the $1/100$ of a second[22]— I regret that the difficulty in connecting the lines[E] has rendered the use of the telegraph not as available as could be wished—

I have received a long communication from LeFroy giving me a detailed account of the apparatus and method of using the photographic magnetometer.[23] I shall write to London for a set of the apparatus immediately.[24]

I have been much disappointed in not getting my galvanometers repaired in time for my northern trip. I gave the parts which were broken to Chamberlain of Boston who assured me that he could repair them with but little trouble and that he would return them to Washington in the course of a few day[25] but since then I have heard nothing of them though I have written twice[26] to make enquiry.

I shall take with me a thermopile, and hope to be able to borrow a galvanometer in Boston.

You have heard of the accident which took place on the rail way near Princeton last week—all the sufferers are now expeted to recover though the company are much blamed for the carelessness in which the accident resulted.[27]

Capt. Cook's[28] family are at the Water Gap on—the Delaware—Mr Walker[29] is still at Schooley's Mountains[30] doing wonders in the way of rolling[F] nine pins.— Princeton is delightful at this season of the year— no cholera[31] and general good health prevails— Loomis it ↑is↓ rumored has received a call to return to N.Y. University and by some in Princeton it is thought he will accept. His wife does not appear well pleased with Princeton. He has not yet returned and nothing definitely is known as to the precise state of the matter.[32] Mr Alexander is well— and in good spirits—I must not tell you that there is some prospect of his entering into partnership for life with the daughter of one of his neighbours.[33] James W Alexander has returned to Princeton and is in the chair of Dr. Miller[34]— Dr Hodge made kind inquiry after you. He is not in good health and is considerably troubled about his wife who has gone admidst the cholera, to see her daughter[35] in Danville Kt.

I shall be much disappointed not to see you at the meeting—You will I hope be there and present your paper on the theory of probabilities[36]— Also I think an account of Saxtons machine should be presented.[37] Dr. Locke has published, I am informed, a pamphlet.[38] I sent him a copy of the speed letter with the remark that he was mistaken in his facts as given in his letter to me.[39] I have now given you all the scraps of information I can think of and as my paper is full I must close with the assurance that I am as

Ever truly yours
JH—

Bache Papers, Smithsonian Archives.
Notation at the top of the first page, in Bache's hand: "(Private)."

1. August 4.

2. Robley Dunglison, professor of the institutes of medicine at Philadelphia's Jefferson Medical College. *Henry Papers*, 6:23.

3. George M. Dallas, *Eulogy on the Life and Character of the Late President James K. Polk* (Philadelphia, 1849).

4. Dallas eulogized Polk as a kind, broadminded, dignified patriot, but he privately viewed him as intolerant, devious, and unstable. The relationship between the two men began well enough, but soon deteriorated. Dallas became increasingly embittered as Polk refused to heed his advice on appointments, ignored his views on expansionism, kept him outside of his inner circle, and snubbed him at

social functions. By the end of 1848, the two men were barely speaking to one another. John M. Belohlavek, *George Mifflin Dallas: Jacksonian Patrician* (University Park, Pennsylvania, 1977), pp. 100–106, 109–111, 131–133.

5. Millard Fillmore's tenure as Zachary Taylor's vice-president was a "humilating experience" for him. Fillmore was all but ignored in decisions about patronage. Taylor also embraced a staunch antislavery position rather than heed Fillmore's advice to compromise with proslavery Southerners. Elbert B. Smith, *The Presidencies of Zachary Taylor & Millard Fillmore* (Lawrence, Kansas, 1988), pp. 58–63, 159–163 (quotation on p. 162).

6. Cordial at first, the relationship between Vice-President John C. Calhoun and President Andrew Jackson soon soured. Calhoun believed that Jackson was favoring Martin Van Buren over him as his heir apparent. Jackson suspected that Calhoun was involved in the effort to force Treasury Secretary John H. Eaton out of the Cabinet. The split between Calhoun and Jackson widened over the issues of nullification and states' rights, culminating with Calhoun's resignation in 1832 after Jackson threatened military intervention against South Carolina. Robert V. Remini, *Andrew Jackson*, 3 vols. (New York, 1977–1984), 2:101–102, 214–215, 232–247, 292, 305–309; 3:8–14.

7. George Washington Bethune, a Presbyterian minister in Philadelphia and a trustee of the University of Pennsylvania. *Henry Papers*, 3:341n; 6:20n.

8. Bethune spoke to Harvard's Phi Beta Kappa Society on July 19. According to Bache, who traveled to Cambridge to hear the address, "the catholic doctrine on science, morals, & patriotism which he preached did my heart & head good." Bethune, *The Claims of Our Country on Its Literary Men* (Cambridge, 1849); Bache to Henry, July 26, 1849, Bache Papers, Smithsonian Archives.

9. Mary Williams Bethune's poor health led the Bethunes to move to Brooklyn, where her husband became pastor of the Middle Dutch Church, in the fall of 1849. *DAB*, s.v. "Bethune, George Washington"; Robley Dunglison, *An Obituary Notice of George W. Bethune, D.D.* (Philadelphia, 1862), pp. 4, 10.

10. The *National Intelligencer* of August 3, 1849, reported on the first meeting of the Smithsonian Establishment, held on August 1, 1849.

11. Henry described the institution's plan of organization and the progress made in implementing it. W. W. Seaton presented "an account of the disbursements of the Institution and the state of its funds." Rhees, *Journals*, p. 771.

12. On June 20, 1849, John C. Frémont was appointed to replace John B. Weller (see next note) as commissioner on the joint United States–Mexico Boundary Commission. William H. Goetzmann, *Army Exploration in the American West, 1803–1863* (1959; Austin, Texas, 1991), pp. 162–165.

13. In January 1849, President Polk named John B. Weller (1812–1875, *DAB*), a former Democratic congressman and recently defeated gubernatorial candidate from Ohio, as commissioner on the Mexican Boundary Commission. Weller left for California in February, but was stranded in Panama until mid-May. Late in June, Clayton sent him a letter via Frémont, informing him of his recall, ostensibly for being extravagant and for not supplying the State Department with expense accounts and a list of employees. (While technically correct, the allegations were politically motivated, emanating from Whig opposition to Weller.) Frémont never passed on the letter, however, and Weller, who had finally reached California, began his survey operations. In the interim, administrative overview of the commission was shifted from the State to the Interior Department. Interior Secretary Thomas Ewing, a political foe of Weller's from Ohio, fired him on December 19, 1849. After Weller was elected to the Senate from California in 1852, he forced a congressional inquiry into the whole affair. The ensuing scandal culminated in the suspension of the boundary survey. Goetzmann, pp. 157–167, 186–193; Robert V. Hine, *Bartlett's West: Drawing the Mexican Boundary* (New Haven, 1968), pp. 3–4, 81–84.

14. The boundary commission's official surveyor was Andrew B. Gray, who had little topographical experience, but was allied with railroad interests in his native Texas. Much of the actual surveying work, however, was carried out by William H. Emory, the commission's chief astronomer, along with other officers from the Corps of Topographical Engineers. Emory—Bache's brother-in-law—had been rumored to be a leading candidate for the position of boundary commissioner in 1848, but Polk made the selection on political grounds. The news of Frémont's appointment to replace Weller came as "an insult to Emory, who had been [the] chief witness against the Pathfinder [Frémont] in his famous court-martial trial following the Mexican War." Goetzmann, pp. 158, 160–162, 165–166 (quotation on p. 165); Hine, pp. 3–4.

15. It was in Henry's capacity as president of the American Association for the Advancement of Science, rather than as Smithsonian secretary, that Clayton gave him a dispatch sent by

George Bancroft, United States minister to Great Britain, with permission to share the dispatch with the AAAS. A portion of the message related to "the safety and prosperity of the illustrious Astronomer [Heinrich Christian] Schumacher" (AAAS *Proceedings*, 1849, 2:66).

In 1848, war had erupted between Denmark and two rebellious provinces, the duchies of Schleswig and Holstein, halting funding for the royal observatory at Altona, in Holstein. In recognition of "the debt which the whole astronomical world owes" Schumacher, director of the observatory, "academies of science, and philosophical societies of all civilized countries . . . protested, in the name of Science, and urged their respective governments to interfere" on his behalf (AAAS *Proceedings*, 1849, 2:66). In this country, the American Academy of Arts and Sciences drafted a circular of support for Schumacher in March 1849 and solicited similar letters from other scientific institutions, including the Smithsonian. The Smithsonian executive committee, at its meeting of April 6, 1849, directed Henry

> to express to Professor Schumacher [their] views . . . on the importance of the services rendered by the Altona Observatory, as a centre of astronomical research, and the Astronomischen Nachrichten, as a means of diffusing astronomical information throughout the world, and their earnest hope for the sake of the progress of Astronomy that both will be continued. [Rhees, *Journals*, p. 472.]

Henry's letter has not been found; however, it and other letters reached the Taylor administration, which "promptly responded to the call, by addressing itself both to the Danish and to the Schleswig Holstein authorities" (AAAS *Proceedings*, 1849, 2:66). Both the provisional government of Schleswig–Holstein and the Danish monarchy assured the State Department of their intention to support the Altona Observatory.

"Correspondence in Relation to the Altona Observatory," AAAS *Proceedings*, 1849, 2:65–68; American Academy of Arts and Sciences, *Proceedings*, 1848–1852, 2:146. See also P. S. Laurie, "The Society and the Year of Revolutions," *Quarterly Journal of the Royal Astronomical Society*, 1970, 2:120–125.

16. Sophia Burrell Dallas Bache. *Henry Papers*, 2:112.

17. On March 3, 1849, Congress appropriated funds for a *Nautical Almanac and Astronomical Ephemeris*. While the almanac technically fell under the Naval Observatory, the act provided for a separate superintendent who would report directly to the secretary of the navy, and also for an office outside of Washington. In part, this reflected the desire of Bache, Henry, and other leaders of the American scientific community to have the almanac guided by "the ablest astronomers of the country . . . under a superintendent whose scientific character shall command the confidence of mathematicians." More to the point, Bache and Henry wanted to ensure that Matthew F. Maury had little say over the appointment of staff for the almanac. When funding became available for the almanac in July 1849, Navy Secretary William Ballard Preston named Charles Henry Davis as its superintendent; Davis asked his brother-in-law, Benjamin Peirce, to be his assistant. Under their guidance, the almanac office evolved into a new center for governmental science at Cambridge.

"Some Remarks upon an American Nautical Almanac," *Silliman's Journal*, 1849, 2d ser. 7:123–125 (quotation on p. 124); Charles Henry Davis, *Remarks upon the Establishment of an American Prime Meridian* (Cambridge, 1849), p. 1; *Coast Survey Report for 1849*, p. 72; Dupree, *Science in the Federal Government*, pp. 106–108; Bruce, *American Science*, pp. 178–180.

18. Located north of the Capitol Building, this Coast Survey station was the base of Sears Cook Walker's telegraph operations. Henry visited it on July 24. *Coast Survey Report for 1849*, pp. 6, 30–31; B. A. Gould, Jr., "On the Velocity of the Galvanic Current in Telegraph Wires," *Silliman's Journal*, 1851, 2d ser. 11:67–82, especially p. 68; Desk Diary, July 24, 1849.

19. Henry may have hoped to use the Seaton Station telegraph lines and a large galvanometer to confirm the findings of British civil engineer William H. Barlow. In 1847, Barlow noticed that the magnetic needles of the Midland Railway's telegraph were disturbed whenever the telegraph wires were connected to the earth, and that the deflection varied during the day. He concluded that the magnetism was the result of currents on the surface of the earth whose direction varied diurnally, and suggested that these currents caused variations in the motion of the horizontal needle. Desk Diary, July 24, 1849; W. H. Barlow, "On the Existence of Alternating Diurnal Currents of Electricity at the Terrestrial Surface, and Their Connexion with the Diurnal Variation of the Magnetic Needle," *British Association Report for 1847*, part 2, pp. 21–22. On Henry's earlier interest in earth currents, see *Henry Papers*, 6:187, 422, 537.

20. Saxton's automatic clock interruptor consisted of a platinum tilt hammer activated by a cam on the clock pendulum rod. Ac-

cording to Walker, who had it installed on the dead-beat escapement clock at Seaton Station, "it has broken the circuit for forty days without interruption, and has in no instance deviated in an appreciable amount from its losing rate of one-tenth of a second per day." AAAS *Proceedings,* 1849, 2:182–192 (quotation on p. 188); Gould, pp. 73–77.

21. Henry was referring not to Saxton's clock interruptor, but rather to the automatic clock register which he developed in 1849. It consisted of a sheet of paper which was wrapped around a drum that revolved on a screw axis "so that the traces are made upon a perpetual spiral." Each side of the paper recorded up to two hours' worth of observations, far more than was available with other telegraphic registers. AAAS *Proceedings,* 1849, 2:189–192; Elias Loomis, *The Recent Progress of Astronomy; Especially in the United States* (New York, 1850), p. 235 (quotation).

22. That is, the effective limit of resolution using a telegraphic register that would enable "the eye [to] readily distinguish the exact value of the numbers of whole seconds." According to Walker, with a scale in which a one-inch line was equivalent to one second of time, "the probable error of the reading of the fractions of a second . . . will not be greater than one hundredth of a second." Sears C. Walker to Alexander Dallas Bache, December 15, 1848, in U.S. House, 30th Congress, 2d Session, *Letter from the Secretary of the Treasury, Transmitting a Report of the Superintendent of the Coast Survey, Relative to Local Differences of Longitude and Astronomical Observations Generally,* House Executive Documents, No. 21 (1849), p. 5.

23. Dated July 14, 1849, Lefroy's original letter has not been found, but a copy is in the Bache Papers, Smithsonian Archives. Lefroy described the declination magnetometer invented by Charles Brooke (1804–1879, *DNB*), a British surgeon and fellow of the Royal Society, which had recently been put into service at the Toronto Observatory. It consisted of a suspended bar magnet and a mirror which reflected light from a camphine lamp through a lens and onto a sheet of sensitized photographic paper wrapped around a glass drum that was driven by the hour hand of a clock. When developed, the paper showed a twenty-four hour record of magnetic variations.

Henry had recently obtained a sample register from the magnetometer through an associate of Lefroy's, William James Smythe (1816–1887, *DNB*), a Royal Artillery captain stationed in Nova Scotia, who visited him in Washington in June. Smythe also brought letters from Lefroy to Henry (not found) and Bache, in which

he urged the Smithsonian to obtain its own self-registering magnetometer as "much of the interest of such a register depends upon having another wherewith to compare it" (Lefroy to Bache, June 19, 1849, Bache Papers, Smithsonian Archives). On June 27, the Smithsonian executive committee authorized Henry to procure one. Henry wrote Lefroy on June 30 (letter not found) of the Smithsonian's plan to acquire it, which prompted Lefroy's reply of July 14. Although he described the magnetometer in detail, Lefroy advised Henry to come see it for himself. Henry replied on July 30 (letter not found) that he intended to order one from England; presumably, he also informed Lefroy of his plan to visit the Toronto Observatory in September.

In addition to Lefroy's letters, see Desk Diary, June 27, and July 2 and 30, 1849, and Rhees, *Journals,* pp. 474–475. Lefroy's article, "On the Application of Photography to the Self-Registration of Magnetical and Meteorological Instruments," *Silliman's Journal,* 1850, 2d ser. 9:319–334, described the magnetometer and other self-registering apparatus.

24. We have not found such a letter.

25. In 1847, Henry ordered a "set of galvanometers for electricity of different intensities" from Heinrich Rühmkorff (see Doc. 37). When the order arrived at the Smithsonian in April 1849, all the galvanometers were found to be broken. Rather than return them to Rühmkorff for repair, Henry sent them to Nathan Chamberlain in Boston, hoping to have them done before he left for Bache's Coast Survey camp near Portland. He called on Chamberlain after arriving in Boston on August 10, only to find that the galvanometers were still not ready. Desk Diary, April 10, June 22, July 30, 1849; Bache to Henry, July 26, 1849; Henry to Edward Foreman, August 10, 1849, Henry Papers, Smithsonian Archives; Rhees, *Journals,* pp. 471, 473 (quotation).

26. Not found, but written on June 22 and July 30, 1849, according to Henry's Desk Diary entries of those dates.

27. On the morning of August 2, a southbound passenger train derailed north of Princeton when a switch was left open, killing two persons and injuring over a dozen others. *National Intelligencer,* August 6, 1849.

28. Probably William Cook.

29. Robert J. Walker.

30. A "celebrated watering place" on the Delaware River, seventy-two kilometers (forty-five miles) north of Trenton. J. Thomas and T. Baldwin, eds., *A Complete Pronouncing Gazetteer, or Geographical Dictionary of the World,* 2 vols. (Philadelphia, 1858).

31. Henry was vigilant, yet philosophical, about the epidemic:

We know not however what place is to be safe from the dreadful disease which is now afflicting our world and it behooves every one to keep his house in order and to be ready for departure at a moments warning. The only source of tranquility is a full reliance on the assurance that all things will be ordered for the best who put their trust in the Great Disposer of all events.

Henry to Charles Hodge, July 13, 1849, Charles Hodge Papers, Manuscripts Division, Department of Rare Books and Special Collections, Princeton University Libraries.

32. Loomis's wife, the former Julia Elmore Upson, was indeed "so disconsolate at Princeton that [he] saw no prospect of living happily there." In deference to her, Loomis returned to his old post at New York University. *Henry Papers*, 5:128n; Loomis to Henry, November 8, 1849, RH 3464, Rhees Collection, Huntington Library.

33. Caroline Forman, the daughter of William Forman, married Stephen Alexander in 1850. Elliott, *Dictionary;* Hageman, *Princeton,* 1:276.

34. James Waddell Alexander replaced Samuel Miller (*Henry Papers,* 2:438) as professor of church history and government at Princeton Theological Seminary. *Princeton Catalogue,* pp. 132, 403.

35. Sarah and Mary Hodge, respectively. Charles Hodge to Henry, July 6, 1849, Henry Papers, Smithsonian Archives.

36. At the AAAS meeting, Bache discussed the utility of the theory of least squares for geodesy. He asserted that it was of little advantage over a simple average for "deriving the most probable values of the angles" in primary triangulations. AAAS *Proceedings,* 1849, 2:102–105 (quotation on p. 105).

37. This was done by Sears Cook Walker, who discussed his use of Saxton's apparatus to conduct telegraphic experiments for the Coast Survey. AAAS *Proceedings,* 1849, 2:189–192.

38. John Locke, *Documents Relative to the Electro-Chronograph, Invented by John Locke, M.D., . . . in the Year 1848* (Newark, 1849).

39. John James Speed, Jr. (1803–1867), a one-time associate of Samuel F. B. Morse's, worked as a telegrapher in Ithaca, New York, and later moved to Detroit, where he became president of the Western Telegraph Company. In 1847, while still in Ithaca, Speed asked James Rodgers, a New York City clockmaker, to build a clock interruptor of Speed's design which would enable clocks on telegraph lines to keep the same time. It consisted of a platinum tilt-hammer driven by the teeth of a wheel placed midway between a clock's minute and escapement wheels. Two years later, when Sears Cook Walker called on Rodgers to obtain a clock interruptor for the Coast Survey, he was shown the one Rodgers had built for Speed. Walker ordered one for the survey, but had it modified so that the tilt-hammer ran off the minute wheel. He used both Speed's and Locke's devices for telegraphic readings of star transits. Locke subsequently maintained that Walker had plagiarized his idea in modifying Speed's device.

In a letter to Henry of March 1, 1849 (Henry Papers, Smithsonian Archives), Locke asserted that his tilt-hammer clock interruptor "was invented by me two years before it was invented by Speed." On March 26, 1849, he sent Henry another letter (same location) in which he repeated his claim of priority and insisted that Speed's "rude clock with its ruder hammer" had "never [been] intended for any electrical purpose whatever." We have not found any replies from Henry to these letters. By the "Speed letter," Henry may have been referring to a letter of Speed's to him that we have not found.

Thomas W. Herringshaw, *Encyclopedia of American Biography of the Nineteenth Century* (Chicago, 1905), s.v. "Speed, John James"; AAAS *Proceedings,* 1849, 2:188; John Locke, *On the Invention of the Electro-Chronograph . . .* (Cincinnati, 1850), pp. 13–17, 35–38; "Telegraphic Operations of the Coast Survey.—Velocity of the Galvanic Wave," *Silliman's Journal,* 1849, 2d ser. 8:142–144.

327. FROM JOHN HENRY ALEXANDER

Prof Henry
&c &c &c

Baltimore 9 August 1849

My dear Professor

I had fully hoped and purposed to have joined you at Cambridge next week; but I have been called off by some professional engagements just at the very period and have to turn my steps Southward next week. I will not say that this is unfortunate, tho' it is disappointing; for I cannot think that the Association would be any the better for my attendance and I will not forego opportunities of returning to a profession which the state of my family compelled me hitherto too much to neglect.

If not called off, I had intended to have contributed to the meeting a memoir on the Geology of Maryland; not so much of abstract text as of explanations to numerous profiles which I have prepared and which drawn thro' Our Territory in various directions will together exhibit a very complete section of its Formations. I don't know if the views of the publishing Committee include such illustrations of their Transactions—wch nevertheless, I c^d if necessary have executed here in stone very satisfactorily and cheaply: But I send you one[1] which I have hastily traced off that you may see for yourself. If you fancy it, and it is [?fecundior artem][2] you may include me among the contributors under title of Illustrations of the Geology of Maryland. The paper will not be at hand to be read; but I shall have it ready long before the accouchement of the Transactions if they undergo such a gestation as they did last time. Who read the proofs then I don't know; but the ingenuity displayed in distorting proper names in my poor Resumé of geography[3] is worthy of a better cause and quite remarkable.

You may remember that you lent me an Egyptian Catalogue of Abbott,[4] which I supposed you were in no hurry for but which I sh^d have returned sometime ago except for the long and severe illness of my friend Cohen[5] to whom I gave it for inspection and for marking the articles identical in the two collections. The gem of the Cairo collection is the ring of Shoufo (Cheops)[6] which I believe I shewed you; and with a facsimile of which I shall seal this letter if I can lay my hand on it. This, I suppose, is valued at £7000 or £8000 itself.

When I return you the Cairo Catalogue it shall be accompanied with one of ours which Cohen purposed making out and actually begun before his illness.[7]

I see that you have not much apprehensions from cholera in Wash.ⁿ; on our part, we are in hopes that it will pass over us entirely. Is Bache with you I have not heard from him for a long time.

> With best wishes regards
> faithfully
> J. H. Alexander

Henry Papers, Smithsonian Archives.

1. Not found.

2. Literally, "fruitful to science."

3. Alexander's "Brief Notice of Geographical Explorations and Researches during the Year 1847 and a Part of 1848," which he communicated to the 1848 American Association meeting, reviewed international work in the field. AAAS *Proceedings*, 1848, *1*:102–123.

4. Henry Abbott (1812–1859), a British army physician, served in Egypt during the Syrian War and thereafter practiced medicine in Cairo. While in Egypt, he "found it an agreeable pastime to dive into the tombs of the ancients and rescue from the hands of the many pilferers such objects as appeared to me worthy of notice." By about 1851, when his family emigrated to the United States, Abbott had accumulated 1,118 objects for his "Museum of Egyptian Antiquities." Strapped for cash, he placed the collection on public display in New York City and tried to sell it to several institutions (including the Smithsonian), a goal he did not realize before his death. It was not until 1860 that the New-York Historical Society raised sufficient funds to purchase the collection, where it remained until 1937, when the Brooklyn Museum acquired it. Although Abbott asserted "that every article . . . is of undoubted antiquity," later studies revealed that some of the objects in his collection were recent fakes.

We have not found the catalog to which Alexander referred.

[Abbott], *Catalogue of a Collection of Egyptian Antiquities, the Property of Henry Abbott, M.D.* (New York, 1854), pp. [iii]–viii, 72 (quotations on p. [iii]); *Catalogue of the Egyptian Antiquities of the New York Historical Society* (New York,

1915), p. [iv]; John A. Wilson, *Signs & Wonders upon Pharaoh: A History of American Egyptology* (Chicago, 1964), pp. 35, 39, 213; Henry to Frederick West Holland, September 11, 1851, Autograph File, Houghton Library, Harvard University.

5. Mendes Israel Cohen (1796–1879) worked in his family's banking firm in Baltimore until 1829, when he left on a six-year tour of Europe and the Mediterranean. While in Egypt, he began collecting Egyptian antiquities; before returning to Baltimore, he gathered approximately seven hundred objects to form the first such private collection in the United States. In May 1849, Alexander lobbied Henry to have the Smithsonian purchase it, but both then and on at least one other occasion, the institution declined to do so. The Johns Hopkins University acquired the collection from Cohen's family in 1884. Henry to Holland (cited above); Alexander to Henry, May 5, 1849, Henry Papers, Smithsonian Archives; Wilson, pp. 38, 217; The Walters Art Gallery, *The Taste of Maryland: Art Collecting in Maryland, 1800–1934* (Baltimore, 1984), p. 10.

6. This gold signet ring bore the name of Cheops, builder of the Great Pyramid at Giza, inscribed in "minutely accurate, and beautifully executed" hieroglyphics. Abbott, pp. [v], 67, 69 (quotation on p. 67).

7. Alexander may have meant the "meticulously annotated catalogue, in which Cohen recorded the provenance of each piece" in his collection. Never published, it survives in manuscript form in the Cohen Collection (MS 251.3) at the Maryland Historical Society. *The Taste of Maryland*, p. 10 (quotation); Maryland Historical Society, private communication.

328. TO EDWARD FOREMAN

Princeton Aug 10th 49

Dear Dr,

Your letters[1] have been duly received and I am much indebted to you for your attention to the affairs of the Institution. I am off this morning for Cambridge after being detained here much longer than I intended.

1 I have in my possession the pamphlet on Physical forces[2]—the binder sent it to me the day before I left— Mr Russell[A] is mistaken as to the destruction of the pamphlets he alludes to the Report on organization.

2 The letter to the mexican Minister[3] can remain until I return.

3 If Mr Barringer[4] returns give him a copy of the 1st vol of Contributions for Arago[5] also one for Mr. Rush our Minister to France. I have seen the article in the Intelligencer and am well pleased with it.[6]

4 Breguet[7] has a copy of the book on the telegraph it was translated and published in Paris by Vattemere.[8]

5 Capt Davis' paper[9] is a very difficult one to analize— I will return your paper as soon as I can find time to study the article.

6 Send on the account of Gideon[10] and I will certify it—

7 Acknowledge in your own name the letter to Mr John A Savage[11] and inform him that no curator is to be appointed until the building is completed.

8 Send the Spanish book's to Mr Calderon de la Barca[12] agreeably to the instruction of his letter[13]—

9 Acknowledge in my absence the recipt of Mr Jagers book on Zoology.[14]

10 Send the package of letters and accounts relative to the account of E. O. Jenkins of New York done up in stout paper by express prepaid to ~~my~~ me care of Wiley (or Putnam I forget which the publisher of Owens book[15]) to be left until called for— I will call for the package when I return from the north and settle ↑the↓ account.

11 Send all packages or letters after this date to the care of Dr. Gray Cambridge.

12 Mrs Henry has at present no directions to send relative to the house.

13 Write to Mc Cullouh of the Custom house[16] to send the meteorological instruments or ask him what has been done with them since they have not been received in Washington—

Send copy of Report to Chancellor Johns[B] of Delaware.[17]

To   Prof Hope⎫
Prof Loomis ⎪
  "   Mc Lean ⎬ Princeton
    Forsythe   ⎪
Dr Schenck[C] ⎭ Princeton

Make copy of the book relative to the distribution of the 1ˢᵗ vol Contributions.

I am off in a few moments and at present can think of nothing more.

Yours truly,
Joseph Henry

Dr. Foreman.

Henry Papers, Smithsonian Archives.

1. Not found.
2. Presumably William R. Grove's *On the Correlation of Physical Forces: Being the Substance of a Course of Lectures Delivered in the London Institution, in the Year 1843* (London, 1846), an annotated copy of which is in the Henry Library.
3. Letter not found. Luis de la Rosa (d. 1856) had been minister from Mexico since 1848. Charles Lanman, *Biographical Annals of the Civil Government of the United States* (Washington, 1876), p. 619; *Enciclopedia universal ilustrada Europeo-Americana.*
4. Daniel Moreau Barringer (1806–1873), a former representative from North Carolina, recently had been commissioned minister to Spain. *DAB;* Lanman, p. 609.
5. Barringer had promised to hand-deliver the volume "as a present from the Institution to Arago." Henry to Foreman, August 6, 1849, Henry Papers, Smithsonian Archives.
6. Presumably the article in the *National Intelligencer* of August 3, 1849, reporting the first meeting of the Establishment of the Smithsonian Institution.
7. Louis F. C. Breguet, a Paris instrument maker. *Henry Papers,* 6:81n.
8. Alfred Vail, *Le télégraphe électro-magnétique américain . . .* (Paris, 1847), trans. Hippolyte Vattemare. He was the eldest son of Alexandre Vattemare. *DAB,* s.v. "Vattemare, Nicolas Marie Alexandre."
9. Charles Henry Davis's paper on tidal geology, which was a continuation of his 1848 presentation to the American Academy of Arts and Sciences (for which see Doc. 330). It was later published as *The Law of Deposit of the Flood Tide: Its Dynamical Action and Office,* 1852, SI

Contributions, vol. 3 (Washington, 1852). See also *Smithsonian Report for 1851,* p. 14.
10. J. & G. S. Gideon, a Washington printing firm, had done considerable job work for the Smithsonian, including Henry's "Programme," Sears Cook Walker's ephemeris of Neptune, and John Downes's occultation tables. The account to which Henry referred was in arrears for about $240, with some bills outstanding since 1847; it was not settled until February 1850. Desk Diary, July 27, 1849; Smithsonian Daybooks, vol. 1, pp. 101–102.
11. Letter not found.
12. Ángel Calderón de la Barca (1790–1861), minister from Spain since 1844. Lanman, p. 623; *Diccionario de historia de españa.*
13. Not found, but relating to his willingness to take charge of books destined for Spain—presumably referring to copies of the first volume of SI Contributions. The Real academia española, the Real academia de la historia, and the Academia de los ciencias naturales, all in Madrid, received copies. Desk Diary, July 20, 1849; *Smithsonian Report for 1850,* p. 75.
Henry was concerned over the slow progress in sending copies of the first volume to Europe. As he noted in late July, "The Books for Europe except those intended for England and the north of Europe have not yet been sent. The delay has caused me much uneasiness." Desk Diary, July [22], 1849.
14. Benedict Jaeger, *Class Book of Zoology . . . with a List of the Different Species Found in the State of New York* (New York and Philadelphia, 1849).
15. George P. Putnam.
16. James W. McCulloh, Jr., the brother of Richard Sears McCulloh, was an appraiser

in the New York City customs office. *Henry Papers*, 6:364.

17. Kensey Johns, Jr. (1791–1857), a Princeton graduate (1810) and chancellor of Delaware from 1832 until his death. *DAB*.

329. TO EDWARD FOREMAN

Cambridge Aug 25th 1849

My Dear Sir,

The association adjourned on Tuesday[1] afternoon after a very interesting session. The attendance was large and the number of papers greater than at any previous meeting. The result augours well for the prospect of american science. I do not thing that any meeting of the kind in this country or Europe surpassed this in the number variety and importance of the papers presented[2]— An extra or rather special meeting is to be held on the 19th of March next in charleston at which I am to preside. The affairs of the Institution are under the direction of the same officers[3] until the end of the year. Bache has been chosen President for the next year. The annual meeting is to be at New Haven.

During the session of the association I was so much engaged in the duty of my office that I was able to attend to nothing else[4] and therefore your letters[5] have been unanswered— Since the adjournmt I have been confined (for two days) to the house with an affiction of my bowells though I have been almost constantly occupied in adjusting the affairs of the association and settling with Dr Gray and Agassiz the details of their publications in the Smithsonian— Mrs Henry arrived in cambridge on Thursday and will accompany me to Dr Bache's camp.

We intend to start for the coast survey camp on monday[6] the 28th— I cannot say how long I shall remain there probably a week or two— I shall then go across the country to albany— Should any thing of much importance occur please writ[e][A] to me Care of Dr Gray and he will forwar[d][A] the letters to the Station.

Send copies of the Report to the
following persons

James[7]
Judge Philips[8] Cambridge Mass
E. S Dixwell[9] Cambridge
Mr Andrews Norton[10] Cambridge
Hon J. G. Palfrey Cambridge
George B. Blake[11] Boston

August 25, 1849

Hon Nathan Appleton Boston
Professor Felton[12] Cambridge
Professor Foster Do[13]
Professor Walker[14] Do
Professor Farrar[15] Do
James K. Mills[16] Boston
Dr George Engelmann[17] St Louis.

I will answer all your letters in order as soon as I can find a moment of leisure to do so. Every momoment since my arrival in Cambridge has been occupied. Gideons bill requires discretion and its parts referred to different appropriations— I sent you a set of the Reports so far as they were made out. I will order the remainder to be forwarded— The Paper of Secchi[18] was found—the photographic Specimen came to hand[19]— I am called to meet an engagement

Yours truly
Joseph Henry

Dr Foreman

Henry Papers, Smithsonian Archives.

1. August 21.
2. Despite Henry's fears that the cholera epidemic would deter many from coming to Cambridge, 128 people attended the second meeting of the American Association for the Advancement of Science—nearly 40 more than at the first meeting, and more than twice the average attendance at meetings of its predecessor, the Association of American Geologists and Naturalists. The number of presentations—140—also represented a significant increase over the 56 of 1848 and the 37 of 1847 (the last AAGN meeting). "The great improvement both in the quantity and quality of the matter offered over any previous year," noted *Silliman's Journal,*

> was very observable to those who have followed the sessions of this body from its origin in the Convention of Geologists at Philadelphia in 1840, to its present enlarged and comprehensive form of usefulness. It was obvious that the Association had now become truly national in character, and had taken deep hold of the feelings of men of science and investigators in all departments of knowledge.

Henry to Foreman, August 13, 1849; AAAS Circular, October 5, 1849, both in same location as this document; Kohlstedt, *AAAS,* pp. 66–76, 121–122, 201; *Silliman's Journal,* 1847, 2d ser. 4:427–429; 1848, 2d ser. 6:393–395; 1849, 2d ser. 8:311–316 (quotation on p. 311).

3. Namely, Henry as president, Eben N. Horsford as secretary, and Alfred L. Elwyn as treasurer. AAAS *Proceedings,* 1849, 2:vii.

4. Henry kept a busy schedule during the week-long AAAS meeting. As president, he opened the meeting and presided over its general sessions; he also attended its sections of general physics and of mathematics, physics, and astronomy. He made three formal presentations. On August 16, he discussed the self-registering magnetometer at the Toronto Observatory. At the general session on August 17, he read a letter from the president of a telegraph company about electrical phenomena observed during a thunderstorm, using it as "the basis of a communication . . . in relation to atmospheric electricity" (AAAS *Proceedings,* 1849, 2:200; neither the letter nor the communication was printed). At the meeting's concluding general session, on August 20, Henry spoke "On the Application of the Principles of Acoustics to the Construction of Lecture-Rooms, &c." (AAAS *Proceedings,* 1849, 2:432; the paper was not printed).

Henry also offered extemporaneous comments—some quite lengthy—in the discussions of others' presentations. Following Angelo

592

Secchi's communication on the aurora borealis (see note 18), for example, Henry commented on the connections between auroras and atmospheric electricity, reported his and Bache's observations of a peculiar auroral display on the night of August 13, and discussed the Smithsonian's plan to gather data on auroras as part of its meteorological program (AAAS *Proceedings,* 1849, 2:11–12). During the discussion of Daniel Kirkwood's letter on an analogy in the rotational periods of the primary planets, Henry offered some remarks "on the origin of the primitive state of matter called the nebular hypothesis, and on the gradual diminution of the primitive quality of caloric from excess of radiation over absorption" (AAAS *Proceedings,* 1849, 2:220). In the discussion of Joseph Lovering's presentation "On a Curious Phenomenon Relating to Vision," Henry spoke at length, citing examples of the illusion of apparent motion in bodies at rest. He related an experience he had shared with two of his daughters in 1845 as they stood on a wharf watching a canal boat (see *Henry Papers,* 6:345–346). He asserted that such illusions arose through "the instinctive generalizing tendency or law of the mind, which leads us to believe that what has happened, will happen." They showed, he said, "how necessary it was to learn to see. The senses never deceive; the error is always in the mind. The mind draws wrong conclusions from the evidence of the senses" (AAAS *Proceedings,* 1849, 2:374–376, 377 [quotations on pp. 376, 377]).

5. Not found.

6. August 27.

7. Presumably James Henry.

8. Willard Phillips (1784–1873), a former probate judge in Suffolk County, Massachusetts, and onetime owner and managing editor of the *North American Review. National Cyclopaedia of American Biography,* 7:541–542.

9. Epes S. Dixwell, a Cambridge teacher, was a AAAS member. Cambridge City Directory for 1850; AAAS *Proceedings,* 1849, 2:xii.

10. Norton (1786–1853), a biblical scholar, had taught for many years at Harvard, most recently as Dexter Professor of Sacred Literature at the divinity school from 1819 to 1830. *DAB.*

11. A Boston dry goods merchant, George Baty Blake had been one of Henry's cabinmates on his voyage to England in 1837. *Henry Papers,* 3:184–185.

12. Cornelius Conway Felton.

13. We have identified no such professor at Harvard. Henry may have committed a slip of the pen while thinking of his old friend, John Foster, of Union College in Schenectady.

14. James Walker (1794–1874), Alford Professor of Natural Religion at Harvard since 1839. *DAB.*

15. John Farrar, formerly Hollis Professor of Mathematics and Natural Philosophy at Harvard. Henry Papers, *1:227; 2:462.*

16. A Boston dry goods merchant. Boston City Directory for 1849–1850.

17. A German-born physician, Engelmann (1809–1884) emigrated to the United States in 1832 and settled in St. Louis, where he became a botanist by avocation. A close associate of Asa Gray and John Torrey, he recruited many collectors to gather specimens for them in the trans-Mississippi west. *DAB;* Elliott, *Dictionary;* Dupree, *Gray,* pp. 97–98, 156–160.

18. Angelo Secchi (1818–1878), an Italian-born Jesuit, was studying astronomy at the Collegio Romano in 1848 when the Jesuits were ordered out of Rome. He went first to a Jesuit college in Stonyhurst, England, and then to Georgetown University in the District of Columbia, where he taught mathematics and natural philosophy while continuing his astronomical studies at its observatory. When the expulsion order was lifted in 1849, he returned to Rome, where he became director of the Collegio Romano observatory.

The paper to which Henry referred was Secchi's communication to him of April 12, 1849, describing luminous auroral phenomena that he had observed on October 17, 1848, while in Stonyhurst, and hypothesizing on their origin. Henry termed the communication "one of considerable interest," in that "it contains a number of ingenious suggestions, which may lead to new results." *DSB;* Henry to Foreman, August 13, 1849, Henry Papers, Smithsonian Archives; "Aurora Borealis," and discussion of same, AAAS *Proceedings,* 1849, 2:2–12 (quotation on p. 11).

19. Henry displayed a sample register, produced by the Toronto Observatory's photographic self-registering magnetometer, in his presentation of August 16. He left the register behind in Washington, and Foreman had to send it by express to him. Henry to Foreman, August 10, 1849, Henry Papers, Smithsonian Archives.

330. TO EDWARD FOREMAN

Cambridge
Aug Monday
27th 1849

My Dear Sir,

I start this morning for Dr Baches camp— Mrs H. accompanies me. I will write from there and until I give farther directions please send your letters to the care of Dr Gray— Give me an account of all events— I regret to learn that Mr Russell is not able to attend to his business. If he does not come to the Institution it will be best to send the books with Mc Peak to his house to be acknowledged— Have the boxes containing Mr Marshes books arrived? Chamberlain had not finished the repairing of the galvanometers— He is now engaged on the apparatus of Dr Hare and is making it look as good as new[1]— I have seen Mr Jewett several times[2] and on saturday visited his Fatherinlaw's family in Roxbury[3]— Almost every moment of my time has been occcupied since I came to this place either in the business of the Association or in that of the Smithsonian. As President of the former I have been obliged to stop to settle up the affairs of the meeting. With reference to the Smithsonian I have my hands full. Dr Gray is going on with the the drawings of Trees for our report— Agassiz is preparing his paper on the cetacian remains and Peirce is engaged on his memoir on Neptune— Gould is recasting the latter part of his report on the discovery of Neptune.[4] The Association recommended to the Smithsonian the preparation and publication of a scientific manuel of observation and research the arrangement of ↑the plan of↓ which has occupied considerable time in the way of discussion.[5]

Mrs H has packed up all my papers so that I cannot refer to the several items in your letters. I will do so however as soon as I get settled in Bache's camp. The last letter I have received from you was one which came to hand on saturday with a letter[6] from Bishop Potter.*

I have been much gratified with the general approbation with which the operations of the Smithsonian have been received at the north and the good feeling which prevailed in the association with reference to the Institution. Bache was also delighted with the approbation expressed as to his labours on the coast survey and the support and assistance he may count on from the inhabitants of New England in sustaining the work.[8]

*One since accompanying a letter from Dr Silliman.[7]

How are you getting on with the arrangement of the letters?[9]— I have visited the New Laboratory at Cambridge and am much delighted with it. Every part is admirably arranged[10]— I will give you an account of it when we meet— Hosfords plan of teaching is that of Leibig[A]— the student is put at first through the course of what is called the 100 bottles— ~~100~~ different substances are put in 100 bottles which the students are directed to examine and ascertain the ~~names~~ contents[11]—

Capt.[B] Davis' paper has been noticed in the last number of the N.A. Review[12]— Should you see any thing in the papers which relates to the smithsonian please inform me of it.[13] The news papers I presume come to you regularly and are filed— How is the building getting on?— — Renwick[C] will be on about this time—I regret that I had not arranged more definitely ~~the~~ with him the form of the plastering behind the speaker.

I remain as ever truly
Yours &—
Joseph Henry

Dr. Foreman

Henry Papers, Smithsonian Archives.

Small ink "x's" appear in the left margin, adjacent to the text reading "Smithsonian the preparation," "Bache was also delighted," and "every part is admirably arranged." Neither the authorship nor the significance of these marks is apparent. Reply: Perhaps Foreman's letter of September 4, 1849, in same location.

1. In June, Henry had sent Chamberlain a box of Hare's apparatus for cleaning and repair. Rhees, *Journals*, pp. 472–473; Desk Diary, June 19 and 20, 1849.

2. Henry and Jewett met on August 25 and again the following day, to discuss the status of the negotiations for the purchase of G. P. Marsh's library. Jewett to G. P. Marsh, August 26, 1849, Marsh Papers, Bailey/Howe Library, University of Vermont.

3. Jewett was married to Rebecca Green Haskins, the daughter of Ralph and Rebecca Haskins of Roxbury, Massachusetts. Joseph A. Borome, *Charles Coffin Jewett* (Chicago, 1951), p. 30.

4. Benjamin Apthorp Gould's *Report on the History of the Discovery of Neptune* (Washington, 1850) was originally intended as part of Elias Loomis's report on the progress of astronomy, but Henry decided to publish it separately (see Doc. 337). Gould's was the first of the Smithsonian's "reports on the progress of knowledge" to appear. These reports were aimed at a more popular audience than that reached by the Smithsonian's Contributions to Knowledge, but were to be based on solid scholarship. As Henry observed, Gould's fifty-six-page pamphlet was heavily annotated, giving "copious references to authorities ... which will render the work interesting to the professed astronomer as well as to the less advanced student." *Smithsonian Report for 1849*, p. 18.

5. On August 20, 1849, at a general session of the American Association for the Advancement of Science meeting in Cambridge, Gray presented three resolutions. He called for a manual or set of manuals giving "directions for properly observing phenomena in every department of physical science, and for making collections in natural history"; asked that the Smithsonian undertake the project; and offered the association's cooperation. The AAAS adopted the resolutions at the next day's general session, but left open the question of whether a set of manuals, or a single volume of directions, was intended. AAAS *Proceedings*, 1849, 2:272–273, 356–357 (quotation on p. 273).

6. None of these letters have been found.

7. Foreman's letter has not been found; Silliman's letter, dated August 21, 1849, is in the Henry Papers, Smithsonian Archives.

8. At an evening session on August 16, Bache spoke "On the Progress of the Survey of the Coast of the United States." After he finished, Edward Everett remarked on the need to show support for the survey. The following day, he, Benjamin Peirce, and Alexis Caswell were appointed a select committee "to express an opinion on the importance of the work." Its report, read at the general session of August 21, warmly praised both the survey and Bache's superintendency. An accompanying resolution was adopted, terming the survey "highly creditable to American Science," beneficial "to the Commerce and Navigation of the country," and "eminently entitled to the continued favor of Congress." AAAS *Proceedings*, 1849, 2:162–178, 357–360 (quotations on pp. 178, 360).

9. Finding that the volume of his incoming mail was increasing rapidly—due largely to the Smithsonian meteorological project—Henry decided to arrange his letters "inorder that they may be bound." He later expressed surprise at the number of letters—some four thousand—that Foreman reported finding. Desk Diary, July 30, 1849 (quotation); Henry to Foreman, September 12, 1849, in same location as this document.

10. Modeled after laboratories that Eben Norton Horsford had seen in Europe, the new chemical laboratory of Harvard's Lawrence Scientific School included an analytical laboratory, a large lecture-hall, several smaller work or storage rooms, a library, two apartments, and a private laboratory and residence for the use of the Rumford Professor. Although not fully completed and lacking some apparatus, the chemical laboratory had been in use since the fall of 1848. *Report of the Committee of the Overseers of Harvard College, Appointed to Visit the Lawrence Scientific School, in 1849* (Cambridge, 1850), pp. 4, 8, 21; Margaret W. Rossiter, *The Emergence of Agricultural Science: Justus Liebig and the Americans, 1840–1880* (New York and London, 1975), pp. 74–81, especially pp. 76–77.

11. The "hundred bottles" was an exercise that Horsford and other first-year students performed in an introductory course on qualitative and quantitative analysis that was taught by Heinrich Will, Justus von Liebig's assistant at Giessen. In the preface he wrote for the American edition of a textbook of Will's, Horsford described the exercise's goal as "the progressive development of the taste and capacity for chemical analysis, and of the love of order and neatness." Heinrich Will, *Outlines of the Course of Qualitative Analysis Followed in the Giessen Laboratory*, ed. and trans. August Wilhelm von Hoffmann (Boston, 1847), pp. iii–iv (quotation); see also Rossiter, pp. 60–63, 79, and 218 note 23.

12. Charles Henry Davis's "Memoir upon the Geological Action of the Tidal and Other Currents of the Ocean," communicated to the American Academy of Arts and Sciences in November 1848 and published in its *Memoirs*, 1849, 2d ser. *4*:117–152, was favorably reviewed in the July issue of the *North American Review*, 1849, *49*:257–269.

13. In his letter of September 4, Foreman informed Henry that other than printing an occasional item on the progress of the building, "the daily press . . . finds nothing for comment on the Smithsonian or its affairs."

331. TO EDWARD FOREMAN

Mount Independence
Near Portland
Maine
Sept [3], 1849[A]

My Dear Sir

Your letters[1] accompanying the letters of Bishop Potter[2] Rhumkorff[3] Professor Hackley[4] &c have been duly received at this place. I am much gratified to learn that all things are going on smoothly at Washington.

I leave Dr Bache's camp this morning after spending in it nearly a week most delightfully and profitably— I would remain longer but that I have so much to attend to else where.

I wish you would enter the name of John W. Freeman Falmouth near Portland ↑Maine↓ on the list of our Meteorologists. Send to him a set of blanks a copy of the Report and such other documents as pertain to the observations. I have found him an intelligent man & will I think make a good observer.[5] He resides within a quarter of a mile of this Station and therefore his latitude and long will be accurately determined.

Chamberlain has finished the repair of the screws and other parts of the Galvanometers so that we will try them and if they do not work well we will send them to Paris.

I always feared that some of our documents were left in the Capitol and gave Mr Mc Peak charges to see[B] to them.

My illness was not the result of any indescretion[C] in the way of sensual indulgence but of an epidemic which was generally prevailing in Boston and its vicinity and the excitement and fatigue of the meeting.

I think I shall be able by my visit to strengthen the bonds of the Smithsonian Institution and to enlarge my own ideas of its usefulness by my travels.

Drirect the letters you may send to me after the receipt of this to Albany Care of James Henry State Street. I shall start from Boston for Albany probably tomorrow to meet our little girls who have gone with their Uncle Prof Alexander to that city— Mrs Henry is with me— I shall start from Albany if I am not detered by the Cholera for Toronto to study the minutia of the photographic Magnetometer. I have concluded on this after talking ↑over↓ the whole matter with Dr. B. We have come to the conclusion that we can make some improvements on the apparatus and that a visit to Toronto will be expense of time and money well applied to the cause of science.

Dr B informed me that he had attempted to make an analysis of Davi's[6] Paper but did not succed to his satisfaction[D]— Do not fail to keep me posted up on the affairs of the Institution as you have done— I will return you the letters after I get back so that you may be as minute and as free in your remarks as you choose. Dr B and his wife have both expressed very kind feelings towards you and your's.

Chamberlain will send on a box of apparatus[7] which will probably arrive before I return—

I wrote to Col. Seaton[8] about a week ago asking him to send me a schedule of the receipts and expenditures of the Institution during the present year which I may place before Mr Fillmore at the time I ask him to put his name to the certifacate selling the United[E] States Stock[9]— In his last letter to me[10] ↑he↓ stated that such a schedule aught to be presented to him. I think you will find his letter to me amoung the letters at Washington. It was received I think some time in July last. I wish you would make a copy of this and present it to Mr Bradley the post master— Get the schedule from him and send it to me at Albany[11]— You may offer to assist him in making it out.

The funds of the Smithsonian in the hands of Corcoran[12] are now I presume exhausted but Corcoran will allow us to overdraw[13] provided we pay him interest and this we can afford to do because if we sell stock we loose the interest on this at the moment of sale the affair is therefore as broad as it is long. There is just now a temporary depression in the value of stock[14] and I would rather hold on a little. Money is abundant in England and hence our stock must continue to rise.

Please send me by express pre paid 10 copies of the last Report of the Institution.

In copying the letter of Mr Fillmore you may omit the part which relates to his accepting the invitation to my house—this is private matter—

You have not informed of the result of the experiment of Prof Espy.[15]

I remain truly yours
Jos Henry

Dr Foreman

Henry Papers, Smithsonian Archives.

1. Not found.

2. Not found, but presumably in reference to the forthcoming convention of the Friends of Education. See Alonzo Potter to Henry, September 17, 1849, Henry Papers, Smithsonian Archives, and Doc. 336.

3. Not found.

4. Not found, but from Doc. 333, a favorable review of a memoir for SI Contributions. Charles William Hackley (*Henry Papers,* 5:357n) was professor of mathematics and astronomy at New York City's Columbia College.

5. We have found no additional information on Freeman, who belonged to a locally prominent family of farmers and bankers whose progenitors had been among the first settlers of Falmouth. He never became a meteorological observer for the Smithsonian. George Thomas Little, ed., *Genealogical and Family History of the State of Maine,* 4 vols. (New York, 1909), 2:905–907.

6. Charles Henry Davis.

7. That is, the Hare apparatus that Chamberlain had been cleaning and repairing.

8. Letter not found.

9. In mid-September, while visiting Buffalo, Henry left a certificate with Fillmore to sign for the sale of $10,000 worth of stock; Fillmore signed the certificate, but was unable to have his signature witnessed, and the sale could not be effected until late October. Together with the premium on the stock due to the rising value of government securities, the sale netted the institution $11,287. Desk Diary, September 13 and 18, and October 22, 1849; Rhees, *Journals,* pp. 475, 485, 488.

10. That is, from Fillmore; letter not found.

11. Henry gave such a statement to Fillmore when he visited Buffalo. Desk Diary, September 18, 1849.

12. William Wilson Corcoran (1798–1888), a Georgetown merchant, commission broker,

and partner in the banking firm of Corcoran & Riggs. He became one of the nation's leading philanthropists. *DAB*.

13. Even with the proceeds from the stock sale, the institution's account with Corcoran & Riggs was overdrawn by some $3,500. Desk Diary, October 22, 1849.

14. The stock market had been slightly depressed for several months, due in part to "the usual inertness of the summer," but also to "the languor of cholera" and reduced foreign demand for American stocks. Stock prices began rebounding in September 1849. *Washington Weekly Union*, September 1, 1849.

15. Espy hoped to demonstrate that rain could be induced artificially by the controlled burning of woodland. He believed that if carefully-spaced fires were set in the central United States during the summer, strong updrafts would be generated, producing rain in the East. He had lobbied unsuccessfully since the mid–1830s to get state or federal funds for a full-scale test of his theory. In the spring of 1849, however, having secured an appropriation to continue his federal meteorological work, Espy began planning to try the experiment on a much smaller scale. He arranged for a woodlot owner near Alexandria, Virginia, to clear twelve acres of timber and burn several large bonfires. The test was set for late July. Henry was openly skeptical about its prospects, since "the conditions necssary to success are to many to occur simultaneously unless by unhoped for good luck." As he anticipated, the test failed. Although Espy hoped to repeat the experiment, he apparently never did so. Espy to Henry, April 30, May 29, 1849, Letters Received, Records of the Smithsonian Meteorological Project, Records of the Weather Bureau, RG 27, National Archives; Henry to Foreman, August 10, 1849 (quotation), Henry Papers, Smithsonian Archives; Desk Diary, July 21, 1849; *Henry Papers, 6:*303; Clark C. Spence, *The Rainmakers: American "Pluviculture" to World War II* (Lincoln, Nebraska, 1980), pp. 9–21.

332. TO ASA GRAY

Revere House
saturday morng
Sept 8th 49

My Dear Dr

I regret that after remaining in Boston since monday night I am obliged to leave this morning in the train for Albany without seeing[A] you— I expected to be detained but two days and to have spent a day with you—but I was not released until yesterday[1] at 2 o'clock and then I was obliged to do some business which occupied me until night when I was so fatigued I was obliged to go immediately to bed— Mrs Henry proposed each morning since Wednesday to go to Cambridge without me but I expected to be releived every afternoon and hence she delayed her visit that I might accompany her.

The cloak which was left at your house probably belongs to Dr A D Bache. He has lost a dark blue one with velvet collar and plaid lining with holes in the back eaten by a mouse. Please send the cloack to Mr Bond the astronomer who will forward it to Dr. Bache— By mistake Mrs Gray's vail was put into the carriage[B] when we started for Portland— We leave this to be sent to you by the omnibus to Cambridge—

599

Please put the "etna"[2] into the bundle with Dr Bache's cloak with a paper attached on which is written "from J. Henry."

I return you with this the letter[3] from Lieut Alvord relative to the polar plant[4]—I have no faith in the success of the experiment he wishes tried. It is however very easily made. Borrow from Lovering a strong  horse shoe magnet and carefully approach[C] the two legs of the magnet to the point of one of the leaves so that a leg may be on each side. If any action takes place it will be shown by the tip of the leaf being attracted by the one pole and repelled[D] by the other as shown in figure 2. If no action 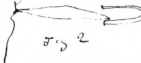 takes place the leaf will remain as in fig 1. Care must be taken that the motion be not produced by the disturbance of the air and to prevent this two panes of glass may be used as screens one on either[E] side of the leaf the magnetic action is not intercepted by glass.[5]

I also send you a letter from Baily which he requests should be referred to you. Please give me your opinion of the proposition which it contains[6] and return the letter to me at Albany. I am obliged to hurry[F] ~~back~~ to albany inorder that I may make a visit to the observatory at Toronto before I return to the south. Bache and myself have concluded to have constructed immediately for the smithsonian a set of self registering magnetic apparatus and inorder that there may be no difficulty in using them it is thought[G] best that I accept the invitation of the Director of the Observatory[7] that I should visit him for a few days for that purpose.

I gave my testimony in the telegraph case unwillingly and as I stated in the introduction only in obedience with the authority of the law— I gave a brief history of the discoveries in electricity bearing on the telegraph—an account of my own experiments and of the communications I have had with Mr Morse on the subject.[8] The result of the trial I think will ↑be↓ doubtful—He claims too[H] much but I am not certain that the law will sustain his[I] right to the use of electricity & magnetism for making and recording marks though in justice I do not think it ought to do so.[9] I was detained on account of the difficulty in verifying dates by the publications[10] and was obliged to s[p]end two days with Mr chase[11] in the Library of the Academy.[12]

Mrs Henry joins me kind regards to Mrs Gray and in grateful acknowledgements for your unwearied attention to us. We shall ever remember our visit to Cambridge as one of the most pleasant periods of our lives— Let me hear from you as frequently as convenient.— With the assurance that I remain as ever

> Your friend I am your obt Servt.
> Joseph Henry.

Dr. A. Gray

Historic Letters, Archives, Gray Herbarium Library, Harvard University.
Reply (misdated "Saturday 7, Sept. 1849," but postmarked September 8, which was a Saturday): Henry Papers, Smithsonian Archives.

1. That is, when Henry finished giving a deposition in the case of *Morse* v. *O'Reilly* (see below).

2. An apparatus that used a spirit-lamp to heat liquid in a dish.

3. Not found.

4. Also known as the "compass plant" (*Silphium laciniatum*), this member of the daisy family, found in the American prairies, derived its common name from the tendency of its leaves to orient themselves along a north-south axis. Benjamin Alvord, who was one of the first to collect and describe the plant, reported on his and others' observations of its apparent polarity in a letter to Henry (in his capacity as president of the American Association for the Advancement of Science) dated July 28, 1849, which Gray read at the AAAS meeting. Although Gray was willing to credit the testimony, he argued that the effect was due to the leaves exposing their faces to sunlight, rather than to any polarity or electrical current in the plant itself. Henry reserved any judgment on the nature of the phenomenon, calling the plant "a subject worthy of careful and precise investigation." *DAB*, s.v. "Alvord, Benjamin"; Alvord, "The Polar Plant, or Silphium Laciniatum," and discussion of same, AAAS *Proceedings*, 1849, 2:12–18 (quotation on p. 18).

5. Gray replied that Alvord's letter had left him with too little confidence "to induce me to try the simple experiment."

6. Although J. W. Bailey's letter is not found, it is apparent from other sources that he was acting as an intermediary between the Smithsonian and his close friend William Henry Harvey (*Henry Papers*, 5:270n), an Irish botanist and authority on algae, who had recently arrived in the United States on an extended visit. Harvey offered to collect marine flora along the East Coast and to prepare detailed descriptions and drawings of the specimens; in return, the institution would bear the cost of publishing his materials. Gray enclosed with his reply a letter to Henry (which, like the cover letter, was misdated September 7) in which he formally endorsed Harvey's plan, observing that "that family of plants remains to be investigated and illustrated, and if Prof. Harvey does not do it it will long remain undone." To defray expenses, the institution published Harvey's *Nereis Boreali-Americana: or, Contributions to a History of the Marine Algae of North America* in three parts between 1852 and 1858. *DNB*, s.v. "Harvey, William Henry"; Henry to Bailey, October 5 and 23, 1849, Bailey Papers, Boston Science Museum; *Smithsonian Report for 1850*, pp. 12–13.

7. J. H. Lefroy.

8. Henry's deposition was sworn before George S. Hillard, United States Commissioner for the District of Massachusetts, in Boston on September 7, 1849. His testimony was sought by the defense for an appeal of the verdict in the case of *Morse* v. *O'Reilly*, which had been decided by the United States Circuit Court for the District of Kentucky in Frankfort, Kentucky, on September 11, 1848. Morse's agent, Amos Kendall, had charged O'Reilly with patent infringement for installing the Columbian telegraph on his line from Louisville to New Orleans. O'Reilly's counsel had argued that Morse's patents were no longer valid, that his patent claims were too inclusive, and that the Columbian and Morse telegraphs operated on different principles. The court found for Morse, granting an injunction against O'Reilly's use of the Columbian telegraph. In seeking Henry's testimony for the appeal, O'Reilly's counsel hoped to demonstrate that his prior research on electromagnetism and its application to telegraphy cast doubts on the originality of Morse's invention and on the validity of his claims.

Henry testified that Morse's main accomplishment was that he had assimilated the discoveries of other researchers and applied them to "the invention of a particular instrument and process for telegraphic purposes." While he declined to state the extent to which Morse's telegraph constituted an original invention, Henry was direct on two points: that it was "based upon the facts discovered by myself and others," and that Morse had never "made a single original discovery, in electricity, magnetism, or electro-magnetism, applicable to the invention of the telegraph." He deferred passing judgment on the difference between the Morse and Columbian telegraph, having had no opportunity to examine and compare both machines.

Henry's deposition is reprinted in *Smithsonian Report for 1857*, pp. 107–117 (quotations on p. 113); see also *Smithsonian Report for 1857*, p. 90; Desk Diary, September 4, 1849; Robert Luther Thompson, *Wiring a Continent: The History of the Telegraph Industry in the United States, 1832–1866* (Princeton, 1947), pp. 145–155; Carleton Mabee, *The American Leonardo: A Life of Samuel F. B. Morse* (New York, 1943), pp. 297–301, 307–308; *First Telegraph Case before the United States Supreme Court . . . Sketch of the Opening Argument of R. H. Gillet, on the Appeal of O'Rielly from the Decision of Judge Monroe in Kentucky* (New York, 1853), especially pp. [3], 5–6.

9. The Kentucky district court refused to hear O'Reilly's appeal. He appealed to the United States Supreme Court, which heard arguments in 1852, but did not issue a ruling until 1854. In a four-to-two decision, with Chief Justice Roger Brooke Taney writing for the majority, the court held that Morse was not the "original" inventor of the electromagnetic telegraph, but that his own invention *was* original, and his patents were valid. The court stated, however, that Morse had no exclusive rights to the use of electromagnetism for telegraphy. The court also found that the Columbian telegraph had infringed on Morse's patent. Mabee, pp. 312–314; *First Telegraph Case*, p. [3].

10. As Henry observed in his deposition, he had to prepare for his testimony "without my notes and papers, which are now in Washington." In his testimony, Henry alluded to several of his own and others' publications, referring specifically to his article, "On the Application of the Principle of the Galvanic Multiplier to Electro-Magnetic Apparatus, and Also to the Developement of Great Magnetic Power in Soft Iron, with a Small Galvanic Element," *Silliman's Journal*, 1831, *19*:400–408. *Smithsonian Report for 1857*, pp. 107–117 (quotation on p. 107).

11. Salmon Portland Chase (1808–1873), O'Reilly's counsel, had practiced law in Cincinnati, Ohio, since 1830. He recently had been elected to the United States Senate. *DAB; Smithsonian Report for 1857*, p. 90.

12. That is, the American Academy of Arts and Sciences.

333. TO EDWARD FOREMAN

Albany Sept 10ᵗʰ 1849

My Dear Sir,

After being detained in Boston from Monday night until saturday morning[1] on account of the electrical telegraph we arrived here on saturday night—

Enclosed[A] I return you Troop's bill[2] with my name to that part of it which is charged to the Smithsonian. The other part must have the name of Prof. Espy attached.

I think it will be best to send all the packages relative to Meteorology to be franked by the secretary of the Navy. You can address a note on the subject to Mr Harding[3] and he will I am sure will attend to the business for us—

Mr Espy's experiment ended as I expected it would in <u>fame</u>. I have received the account from Mr Seaton which I wished to transmit to Mr Fillmore.

I presume since Prof Hackley has reported favourably on Prof Strong's paper we may[B] consider it fit for a place in the Smithsonian Contributions.[4]

As to the paper on Tidal geology[5] I think it may remain as it is until we meet. Prof. Bache informed me that he had attempted to analize the article but had not succeeded.

I had the pleasure of an introduction to Washington Irving when I passed th[r]ough New York on my way to the North. He appeared much gratified with the compliment of his election.[6]

I will make inquiry as to the cost of coal when I return through Phil[d].

That there are enimies of the SI. in and out of Congress is not new— We shall so endeavour to conduct matters that the enemies should be friends and leave the result to Providence taking care however to do all in our power to defend ourselves from the attacks which may be made.

The copies of the Reports have not yet arrived. They will probably be received in a few days.

I shall write to Stevens of London as soon as I return and get from him a detailed account of his doings relative to the Smithsonian.[7]

Please inform Gen. Totten that I put the bills relative to the engravings of Owen's book in the way of payment three months ago—immediately after I received them from him.[8]

Some of your letters have miscarried. I have not received the one[9] containing the names you mention relative to the distribution of the duplicates of the Exploring expedition collections. With this distribution the S.I. has nothing to do.[10]

I am pleased to learn that the building is making good progress— I do not understand the remark relative to the door behind the lecture table— It was never intended to close this up—

I left Mr Jewett in Boston he is engaged with his catalogue.[11] I cannot inform to day whether I shall start for Toronto or not— I have telegraphed to Mr Marsh this morning to meet me in albany but have not as yet received an answer.[12] Perhaps I shall be obliged to go with him to New York when he comes on to make arrangements about his books.

I am to see Dr Beck[13] about the menteorological observations of the State of New York tomorrow.

Since writing the paragraph at the top of the page I have received an answer to my note to Mr Marsh. He will meet me tomorrow at 11 o'clock.

We started from Boston at 8 o'clock on Saturday morning and arrived at Albany at ½ past six a distance of 200 miles— We must have stopped at least two hours on the way— We found our children all except Will at this place— I am called on by some gentlemen and therefore I must close.

as ever yours—
Joseph Henry

Dr Foreman

Henry Papers, Smithsonian Archives.

1. September 3 through 8.

2. J. V. N. Throop had engraved brass stamps and seals for the Smithsonian's meteorological project. Smithsonian Daybooks, vol. 1, pp. 74, 82.

3. Lauriston B. Hardin had been register to the secretary of the Navy since 1831. *Register of the Commissioned and Warrant Officers of the Navy of the United States . . . for the Year 1849* (Washington, 1849), p. 2.

4. Theodore Strong (*Henry Papers*, 2:436–437), professor of natural philosophy and mathematics at, and vice-president of, Rutgers College, submitted a "purely mathematical" paper "on a new method of solving cubic equations." The Smithsonian never published it. *Smithsonian Report for 1849*, p. 10.

5. By Charles Henry Davis. See Doc. 328.

6. That is, as an honorary member of the Smithsonian.

7. Henry's letter has not been found. He had learned of Stevens's recent activities from Foreman, who sent an extract from the London *Literary Gazette* of July 14, 1849, stating that the Smithsonian had "instructed" Stevens to give free copies of the first volume of SI Contributions "to the libraries of the different literary and scientific Societies of the United Kingdom." The article also noted that he was seeking a remission of the customs duty on the volumes. Foreman to Henry, September 4, 1849, Henry Papers, Smithsonian Archives.

8. Foreman had informed Henry that a "Mr. Weingartner" had sent J. G. Totten another bill for work on some lithographs for R. D. Owens's *Hints on Public Architecture*. (In July, Totten sent Henry a claim from an unidentified lithographer, presumably the same person.) Adam Weingärtner (or Weingaertner), of New York City, engraved three lithographs of the Smithsonian Building for the book. Foreman to Henry, September 4; Totten to Henry, July 12, 1849, both in Henry Papers, Smithsonian Archives; George C. Groce and David H. Wallace, *The New-York Historical Society's Dictionary of Artists in America, 1564–1860* (New Haven, 1957); R. D. Owen, *Hints on Public Architecture* (1849; New York, 1978), p. [xiii].

9. Not found.

10. At its meeting in Cambridge, the American Association for the Advancement of Science directed its standing committee to memorialize Congress to distribute "to different learned Societies of our country" duplicate specimens from the United States Exploring Expedition, which were "at present lying useless in the cellars of the Patent Office" (AAAS *Proceedings*, 1849, 2:207). After seeing a newspaper account of this proposal, Foreman apparently assumed that the Smithsonian would oversee the distribution. He suggested to Henry "that by a proper disposal of [specimens] through exchanges," the institution could achieve Agassiz's goal "of collecting all the species, fossil & recent of the fauna of N. America," and observed that the members of the National Institute might also participate in the distribution. Foreman to Henry (cited above).

11. Presumably Jewett's proposed general catalog of the books in leading American libraries. He was preparing a card file of titles culled from existing catalogs, including those of the Cambridge Public Library and the Cambridge Law Library. Rhees, *Journals*, p. 477.

Henry met Jewett on September 7 and gave him a certificate for G. P. Marsh, stating the Smithsonian's intention to purchase his library for $3,000, payable in three years or less, "provided that Mr Choate should declair as a Lawyer & a friend that [Henry] could legally give such a document." Desk Diary, September 11, 1849 (quotation); Jewett to Marsh, September 7, 1849, Marsh Papers, Bailey/Howe Library, University of Vermont.

12. On Henry's meeting with Marsh on September 11, see Doc. 336.

13. T. R. Beck.

334. FROM EBEN N. HORSFORD

Cambridge, Sept. 20. 1849—

Dear Sir,

The Publisher of the Traveller has addressed to me the following note: Sir, I am informed by Mr Parkhurst (the Reporter) that there is matter enough to make between 400 and 500 pages of the "Proceedings at Cambridge". My offer to you was to give you the pamphlet at 50 cents per copy provided it made 320 pages[1] and at the <u>Same proportion</u> if it made less.

Shall I by this arrangement be at liberty to charge the same proportion if it makes more than 320 pages? The proportion will be the actual cost of paper, composition and Press work.

Yours truly
R. Worthington.[2]

The Local committee[3] was called at my house last evening to consider the matter and after considerable discussion, the Secretary was instructed to enclose a copy of the above note to the President and Treasurer.[4]

The bills for printing Circulars—for Stationery &c will amount to about $50. That added to the obligations already incurred will amount to $350. An Addition of $200 or $250. to meet the expense of the excess of printing (for I think Mr Parkhurst's estimate is low rather than high) will make $550 or $600[5]—

Shall we stop at 320 pages? Shall we abridge (a very difficult and very delicate task) or shall we complete the publication as commenced, of the whole, original papers, discussions and all?

The early attention of the President to this subject is important. A copy of this letter has been addressed to the Treasurer. Meanwhile the publication of the Proceedings advances. About 50 pages are already struck off—

Very respectfully
and truly yours
E. N Horsford
Sec. of the A.A.

Prof Henry
President of the A.A.

P.S. If the Proceedings shall go on ↑to completion↓ will the President or Dr. Elwyn give a note of instruction to be handed to the Publisher of the Traveller?[6]

Henry Papers, Smithsonian Archives.
Reply: October 3, 1849, Horsford Papers, Rensselaer Polytechnic Institute Archives; draft (same date): Henry Papers, Smithsonian Archives.

1. H. M. Parkhurst provided stenographic coverage of the American Association for the Advancement of Science meeting at Cambridge for the *Boston Daily Evening Traveller.* His coverage was detailed (according to Edward Foreman, the clippings "fill[ed] a book of over 70 page[s] large octavo & double columns"), but the division of the meeting into concurrent sections, together with the large number of papers read, kept him from recording many of the remarks in full. On August 18, the AAAS approved a resolution of its standing committee, asking that members submit abstracts, or revise their remarks as reported by the *Traveller,* within two weeks after the adjournment of the meeting; the committee also contracted with Henry Flanders & Company to print the proceedings as a 320-page pamphlet. Foreman to Henry, September 4, 1849; AAAS circulars, August 22, and October 5, 1849, all in Henry Papers, Smithsonian Archives; *Boston Daily Evening Traveller,* August 15–21, 1849; *Cambridge Chronicle,* August 23, 1849; *Silliman's Journal,* 1849, 2d ser. *8:*444, and 1850, 2d ser. *9:*454; AAAS *Proceedings,* 1849, 2:206.

2. Roland Worthington (1817–1898) owned the *Boston Daily Evening Traveller,* published by Henry Flanders & Company. The newspaper was highly regarded for its coverage of local literary and scientific activities. George Worthington, *Genealogy of the Worthington Family* (Cleveland, 1894), p. 333; Joyce Ann Tracy, Curator of Newspapers and Periodicals, American Antiquarian Society, private communication; *Silliman's Journal,* 1849, 2d ser. *8:*444; advertisement in AAAS *Proceedings,* 1849, 2:[460].

3. That is, "the local committee who were appointed to superintend the publication of the proceedings," namely, Jeffries Wyman, Louis Agassiz, Benjamin Peirce, Charles H. Davis, Asa Gray, Henry D. Rogers, and Horsford. AAAS circular, October 5, 1849, Henry Papers, Smithsonian Archives.

4. Alfred L. Elwyn.

5. The October 5 circular gave the association's obligations as $500 to print a longer volume, and $100 "for extra press labor, stationery, postage, &c."

6. In his reply, Henry wrote that he was hesitant to judge on the advisability of proceeding with the publication "without knowing what funds are in the treasury of the Association." He promised, however, to recommend to the Smithsonian regents that the institution purchase two hundred copies of the report (at fifty cents each) for foreign distribution. If this amount and whatever funds were obtained from members proved "sufficient to defray all the expenses," Henry continued, "then I would say, go on." (He subsequently proposed to the board that the institution purchase one hundred copies at $1 each; he personally subscribed for twenty copies. Desk Diary, November 6, 1849; Rhees, *Journals,* p. 478.)

The association's funding shortage and a printers' strike in the fall of 1849 delayed the appearance of the proceedings until mid-1850. Nearly five hundred pages long, it comprised "a volume of abstracts rather than one of full papers," although some shorter papers and communications were printed in full. *Silliman's Journal,* 1850, 2d ser. *9:*454 (quotation). See also Kohlstedt, *AAAS,* pp. 90–91.

335. FROM WILLIAM WIRT PHILLIPS[1]

New York Sept 25th 1849

My Dear Friend

I have just signed a call for a special meeting of the Trustees at[A] Princeton College—to receive the resignation of Prof. Loomis & if the way be clear to appoint a successor[2]— His wife I believe has never been satisfied & I understand cannot become reconciled to Princeton. It occured to me that possibly you might be induced to come back to us—

having tried both places ↑you↓ are better able to judge between them than you were before— There is nothing like <u>experiment</u> after all— I have always thought that you & your family might enjoy more comfort at Princeton than at washington & I cannot see why you might not be as useful in the one place as in the other— The atmosphere of Washington is political & very worldly—but of this you know more than I do— You may think me very foolish to have thought of the possibility of your return—if so I trust you will pardon me— I can only say I judge as for myself—it is possible for men to change their mind & whilst we ought to be willing to make sacrifices for the sake of doing good—where other things are equal—we have a perfect right & owe it to our familie[s]ᴮ to go where we can be most comfo[r]tableᴮ— I write this in perfect confidence—without consulting with any one & will so regard whatever you may communicate— Should your return be out of the question that will be the end of the matter— If you would entertain an application from the Trustees I am sure it would be made unanimously ♭ not only but with the most cordial & earnest desire to have you among us & that they would do every thing in their power to contribute to your comfort & usefulness— I do not ask any pledge but only whether you would reconsider the question of duty & of preference between the two places should it be proposed to you & in what form would it be most acceptable?[3]

With great Respect I remain
affectionately & truly yours
W. W. Phillips

Henry Papers, Smithsonian Archives.

1. A New York City minister, Phillips had been a Princeton trustee since 1829. *Henry Papers*, 2:103n.

2. The notice for the special meeting was also signed by Princeton president James Carnahan and five other trustees. At the meeting, Loomis's letter of resignation was read and accepted, and Richard Sears McCulloh was elected to succeed him as professor of natural philosophy. Trustees' Rough Minutes, October 24, 1849, Princeton University Archives, Seeley G. Mudd Manuscript Library, Princeton University.

3. We have found no indication that Henry seriously considered Phillips's suggestion to return to Princeton. On the contrary, he favored McCulloh from the outset. He described him as "better adapted for the place than Loomis was," and, as a Maryland native, less likely to face prejudice from Princetonians who disdained anyone "born on the east side of the Connecticut." Henry to John Torrey, November 13, 1849, Torrey Papers, Library, New York Botanical Garden.

336. TO ALEXANDER DALLAS BACHE

Washington Oct 23rd 49

My Dear B.

I have been looking with anxiety for some time past for your return from the north and I have been quite disappointed to learn to day from one of the Coast survey men that you are not expected until next month[1]— In consequence of this information I have resolved to inflict on you one of my prolex epistles which though they may be of but little value to you in the reading afford me considerable pleasure (when once they are commenced) in the writing.

After we parted from you & your's on Mount Independence we were detained in Boston with the telegraph testimony until Saturday morning[2]— We left you on monday[3]— During my stay in Boston I had several interviews with Mr Jewett who informed me that Mr Marsh was so hard pushed for funds that he could not get away from the country that the certificate I had given him to the effect that the executive committee had resolved to purchase 3000 Dolls worth of his library was of no use— Mr Marsh requested that I would give him a more definite statement and this on condition that Mr Choate should give me his opinion ~~that~~ in favour of the act I concluded to do— This opinion was given in a letter to me from Mr Jewett[4] I however on more mature reflection did not like the transaction though I do not think it could have lead to any bad result though there was a possibility that it might. I therefore telegraphed Mr Marsh when I arrived in albany to meet me in that city and that I would arrange the business with him. I proposed that I should advance 1500 Dolls half the sum from funds raised by myself and that the remainder of the money would be sent to him after the meeting of the Regents next year to this proposition he very willingly agreed. He would have been obliged to sacrifice at least 500[A] Dolls of the 3000 to raise the money. He expressed himself very warmly withregard to your offer of assestance[5] and said that he had exacted a promise from his successor in Congress that he would watch over the the interest of the Coast survey—the southern[B] astronomical expedition and the Smithsonian Inst.[6] In the whole course of his life he had never been so much impressed with the liberalizing influence of Science over trade than on the present occcasion— It appears that he had purchased some years ago as one of a company a number of debts of the bank of the U.S. which had proved entirely worthless that the company had refused to pay the bank and that a law suit had just terminated against them which had swept off all the personal property of Mr M.[7]

The books are now deposited in the Library of the Institution and Mr M and his family are probably by this time in Europe.

After settling the business with Mr Marsh I started (on Wednesday) for Toronto[8] but owing to the derangement of all the ordinary means of travel in the Western part of the State of NY on account of the great agricultural fair at Syracuse[9] I was nearly four days in reaching my place of destination. I passed through Syracuse there met Washington Hunt the late member of congress[10] who informed me much to my surprise that Hunt the Philosopher from West Point who figured at the Cambridge meeting is his younger brother!![11]— I had no conversation with him relative to the communications made by his brother to the association[12]— I also heard the Lecture of Johnston the agricultural chemist[13] who we met in London—he made inquiry for you and said he intended to visit Washington before he returned to England.[14] I had but a few moments conversation with him just after his lecture.

My visit to Toronto was very gratifying and instructive. Le Froy gave me very particular information relative to the Self registering apparatus and I do not think I shall find any difficulty in the manipulations of the sensitive paper. I have received within a few days from him a list[15] of articles to be procured from London the remainder to be manufactured in this Country— He ↑Le Froy↓ requested me to present his thanks to you for your kind attention to his friend Capt Smythe Who[c] was highly gratified with your politeness to him in Phil[d] He also requested me to inform you that he had never received a copy of your Girard observations[16] and to ask you by what conveyance they had been sent.

On my way to Albany I passed through Buffalo spent an eveng with George Clinton who expressed himself gratified with your remembrance of him in sending[D] your Report. From Buffalo to Albany I passed over a line I had not traversed before since 1826 and then the travel occupied me 15 days in a canal boat. I now passed over the same distance in 15 hours. This is the go a head age—

On my return to Albany I hastened with my family for Princeton and leaving them there made my way to Washington to attend to the affairs of the S.I. Found all things in a proper condition the building much advanced and business accumulated—remained 2 weeks in Washington then returned to Princeton & New York to meet Professor Guyot and Dr Beck[17] inorder to establish the system of meteorology of the state of N.Y. Owing to the bad weather the committee did not assemble as early as I supposed they would and indeed Dr Beck could not attend. The business detained me much longer than I expected and the details proved very difficult of adjustment— Prof. Guyot is to visit the several stations and to instruct the several observers in the use of the instruments. The barometers were constructed by Greeen and for the price 20 Dolls are I think very good ones. They are all to be compaired with a standard from Newman which fortunately arrived in New York while I was there.[18] It was ordered for the S.I. last winter you can see it at Green's^E shop [...]^F Broadway upstairs— Green of Baltimore is the person to whom I allude—he has moved to New York— On my way to Washington the second time I stopped a day in Phil^d and was surprised to learn that I had been elected one of the Vice Presidents of the Educational convention through the influence of Dr Potter who would have made you President had you been there[19]—

Draft, Bache Papers, Smithsonian Archives.
Reply: October 29, 1849, Henry Papers, Smithsonian Archives.

1. Bache did not return until about November 10. Desk Diary, November 10, 1849.

2. September 8.

3. September 3.

4. September 10, 1849, Henry Papers, Smithsonian Archives.

5. Both Henry and Bache had offered to advance Marsh $500 from their personal funds against the eventual sale of his library to the Smithsonian. C. C. Jewett to Marsh, August 26, 1849, Marsh Papers, Bailey/Howe Library, University of Vermont.

6. Marsh was succeeded by James Meacham (1810–1856), a Whig, who served as a Smithsonian regent for four years, 1852–1856. He authored an extremely critical report on the Smithsonian, as a result of the institution's change of policy towards the library and collections in 1853. *BDAC; Smithsonian Report for 1853*, pp. 247–296.

7. Many factors contributed to Marsh's insolvency. He had at one time been well-off, chiefly through his wife's wealth. He invested in a wide variety of enterprises, including the Burlington, Vermont, branch of the Second Bank of the United States under a state charter in 1835, when Jackson broke up the bank. That same year Marsh also incorporated to build and run a woolen mill. Natural disasters took their toll on this enterprise, but the tariff of 1846, which reduced protection for American woolen goods while retaining a high rate on imported raw wool, put him out of business. "He sold out at a ruinous loss." David Lowenthal, *George Perkins Marsh: Versatile Vermonter* (New York, 1958), pp. 40–43 (quotation on p. 43).

8. Henry's meeting with Marsh was on Tuesday, September 11; he departed for Toronto on September 12. Desk Diary, September 11, 12, 1849.

9. The New York State Agricultural Society's annual fair was held from September 11 through 13. An event of almost national scale, at its height it attracted an estimated one hundred fifty thousand people, including such celebrities as Henry Clay, Vice-President Millard Fillmore, Governor Hamilton Fish, Horace Greeley of the *New York Tribune,* and other national and state figures. *Albany Evening Journal,* September 12–15, 1849.

10. A Whig from New York State, Hunt (1811–1867) served in the Twenty-Eighth through Thirtieth Congresses. *BDAC.*

11. Edward Bissell Hunt (1822–1863), a graduate of West Point, had at this time completed three years as acting assistant professor of engineering at that institution. In 1851 he would join the Coast Survey. *Biographical Memoirs of the National Academy of Sciences,* 1895, 3:29–41; *Proceedings of the American Academy of Arts and Sciences,* 1862–1865, 6:310–312.

12. "Remarks on Terrestrial Thermotics," AAAS *Proceedings,* 1849, 2:135–140.

13. J. F. W. Johnston, "The State of Agriculture in Europe: An Address," delivered September 12, and published in the *Transactions of the New York State Agricultural Society,* 1849, 9:24–52.

14. In January and February of the following year, Johnston did visit Washington, where he gave three lectures at the Smithsonian on "Science Applied to Agriculture." *Smithsonian Report for 1850,* p. 26; Desk Diary, January 29 and 31, February 2 and [3], 1850.

15. Not found.

16. Bache's *Observations at the Magnetic and Meteorological Observatory, at the Girard College, Philadelphia*, printed as U.S. Senate, 28th Congress, 2d Session, Senate Documents, No. 97 (1845), 3 vols., and as a separate offprint by Gales and Seaton of Washington in 1847.

17. T. Romeyn Beck.

18. Henry had ordered a standard barometer from noted instrument maker John Frederick Newman of London, who had made the Royal Society's standard. *Henry Papers*, 3:151n; *Smithsonian Report for 1849*, p. 14.

19. On October 17 in Philadelphia, the first convention of the Friends of Public Education (or Friends of Common Schools; the name varies) elected Henry one of five vice-presidents, along with Alonzo Potter. Horace Mann was president of this group, which by 1851 had organized as the American Association for the Advancement of Education. *Proceedings of the National Convention of the Friends of Public Education* (Philadelphia, 1849), p. 8. *Proceedings of the American Association for the Advancement of Education*, 1851, 1:3.

337. TO ELIAS LOOMIS

Smithsonian Institution
October 30 1849

My Dear Sir

Since my return to Washington I have been so much engaged in clearing off the business accumulated in my absence that I have not been able to write to you on the subject of your report until to day.

Your memoir on Astronomy was read sometime in April last by Profr Bache and myself, and although my mind has since been so much occupied on other subjects that I do not recollect the particulars of the criticisms yet on the whole we did not fully accord with you as to what the article should be, and particularly the part relative to the Planet Neptune we thought would require recasting. On account of the delicacy of this part of the Subject, and in order to get the opinions of others with reference to it, I requested Dr B. A. Gould to furnish me with a sketch which would meet the approval of Pierce and the astronomers at Cambridge. This I intended to submit to you, if it met my approbation, to be incorporated in your report but the article was so full that I afterwards concluded to accept it as a seperate report,[1] and to request you to give us an account somewhat more extended of the three last divisions of the subject, towit—

> Additions to our knowledge of comets.
> Additions to our knowledge of fixed stars.
> Progress of Astronomy in the United States.

I hope this arrangement will meet your approbation. It will releive you from the preparation of a part of the Report which will be very liable to criticism, and which were it possible I would gladly not meddle with at all. Gould's first sketch was returned to him for alteration, and I have not yet read the second which has lately been received. I have put into the hands of a translator ↑of↓ this place, Struve's Report on the Stellar Universe, published in 1847.[2] This I presume will not interfere with your report, and will serve to give a general view of the opinions on the subject down to the time at which you commence. Please inform me on this point.

It was the opinion of Dr Bache and myself that the history of the progress of Astronomy in the United States should not be confined to the history of American Observatories and the determination of the Longitude by magnetic Telegraph, that it should also include at least a breif notice of the labours of Rittenhouse (See Dr Pattersons Address before the American Philosophical Society)[3] of Ellicott[4] and others, down to the present time. The following is a list of names to be referred to, as they occurred to us at the time of reading the memoir.

Observers &c
Capt Charles Wilkes U.S. Navy
J. H. Alexander Eq Topograph[l] Survey of Maryland
Capt Talcot U.S. Army[5]
Profr. Courtenay University of Virginia
Profr Nicollet (Deceased)[6]
———— Mason New Haven (Deceased)[7]
Lieut Gilliss U.S.N.
Dr B. A Gould Cambridge
Geo M Justice Philadelphia[8]
Profr E Loomis New York
~~Mason and Dixon.~~ Profr S. Alexander, Princeton, Occultations & Eclipses
Jos. Roberts (Deceased)[9] See Am[n] Philosoph[l] Trans[ns]
Samuel J Gummere Burlington N.J.[10]
Edward. C. Herrick New Haven.
Robert. T. Payne Boston[11]
Profrs[A] ↑J. Henry &↓ S. Alexander[B] Princeton (Heat of Solar Spots)
Profr Coffin National Observatory[12]
Profr Hubbard   ″   ″
———— Boutelle Coast Survey[13]
Profr Barnard Tuscaloosa, Alabama.[14]
Profr. Jas Curley Observatory Georgetown.[15]
Cap

Instrument Makers
_____ Young, Philadelphia[16]
Alvan Clark Boston[17]
Henry Fitz Jr New York[18]
Amasa Holcomb Southwick Mass.[19]
Joseph Saxton Coast Survey.[20]

Topographical Corps
Col. J D. Graham
  ″ J. C. Fremont
  ″ W. H. Emory
Capt [...]^C Lee[21]

Publications
American Almanac[22]
United States Almanac[23]
Nautical Almanac
Downes Computations
Paynes Occultations[24]
Gibbes Occultations[25]

Public Surveys
Coast Survey of the U. States
Survey of the State of Massachusetts[26]
Texian Boundary
North Eastern Boundary[27]
Latitude and Longitude Gulf of Mexico.[28]
Light Houses.[29]

For other names see index to Sillimans Journal, Transactions and proceedings of the American Academy and American Philos. Society.— also early Transactions of the Royal Society of London, for an account of the observations of Winthrop[30] and of Mason & Dixons Line. It would be well for you to drop a line to each of the^D abovementioned persons, or if you will prepare a circular I will have it printed for you.[31] Copious references to authorities should be given at the bottom of the page. Dr Bache has written a sketch of the Astronomical part of the Coast Survey[32] which he will furnish you at any time.

I remain very respectfully and truly Yours
Joseph Henry
Sec Smithsonian Institution

Profr. E. Loomis

Loomis Papers, Beinecke Rare Book and Manuscript Library, Yale University.
In Edward Foreman's hand, with Henry's signature.

1. Benjamin Apthorp Gould, *Report on the History of the Discovery of Neptune* (Washington, 1850). John G. Hubbell and Robert W. Smith concluded that the probable reason that Henry and Bache gave the commission to Gould was that Loomis's account "was not as favourable to [Benjamin] Peirce as they wanted. . . . Henry and Bache wanted no doubt about who was 'right.'" "Neptune in America: Negotiating a Discovery," *Journal for the History of Astronomy*, 1992, *23:*261–291, especially pp. 281–282 (quotation on p. 282).

2. *Études d'astronomie stellaire: Sur la voie lactée et sur la distance des étoiles fixes* (St. Petersburg, 1847), by Friedrich Georg Wilhelm Struve (1793–1864, *DSB*). No English translation of this work appeared.

3. Most likely Robert M. Patterson's "Discourse," delivered at the American Philosophical Society's centennial celebration, May 25, 1843. The talk was a history of the society and presented David Rittenhouse's work of observing the transit of Venus in the 1760s. APS *Proceedings*, 1843, *3:*3–36.

4. Andrew Ellicott conducted state boundary surveys, being especially noted for his work in western New York State; he also surveyed the District of Columbia. *Henry Papers, 3:*303n.

5. Andrew Talcott (1797–1883), an 1818 graduate of West Point, from 1832 to 1836 had been astronomer for determining the boundary between Ohio and Michigan. Currently he was chief engineer on the Richmond and Danville Railroad. George W. Cullum, *Biographical Register of the Officers and Graduates of the U.S. Military Academy . . .* , 3d ed., 3 vols. (Boston, 1891), *1:*186; Christine Roysdon and Linda A. Khatri, *American Engineers of the Nineteenth Century: A Biographical Index* (New York, 1978).

6. Joseph Nicolas Nicollet, a French astronomer and immigrant, had extensively surveyed the upper Mississippi Valley. *Henry Papers, 5:*283n.

7. Ebenezer Porter Mason (1819–1840) had accompanied James Renwick in a survey of the northeastern boundary and was Denison Olmsted's assistant at Yale. A young astronomer of promise, he had completed a book just before his death, *Introduction to Practical Astronomy: Designed as a Supplement to Olmsted's Astronomy* (New York, 1841). *Silliman's Journal*, 1841, *40:*407–408; Elliott, *Index*.

8. A supporter of the Central High School Observatory and a promoter of a city observatory for Philadelphia. *Henry Papers, 6:*349n.

9. Joseph Roberts, Jr. (1793–1835), an actu-ary and cashier, keeper of the Friends' Observatory in Philadelphia, and teacher of mathematics and natural philosophy for the Friends, ca. 1824–1835. On two occasions he had observed and reported on solar eclipses as a member of special American Philosophical Society committees. *Henry Papers, 2:*296, 325; Marion Elderton, comp., "Biographical Register of A.P.S. Members," APS Library.

10. Samuel James Gummere (1811–1874), a mathematician and astronomer, who, with his father, John Gummere (*Henry Papers, 1:*59n), revitalized the school at Burlington, New Jersey, that the elder Gummere had run between 1814 and 1833. *DAB;* Elliott, *Dictionary*, s.v. "Gummere, John."

11. Robert Treat Paine, an attorney and astronomer of independent means. In 1840, Paine was appointed chief engineer of the Massachusetts Trigonometrical Survey, whose astronomical work he completed with distinction. *Henry Papers, 2:*302n; Elliott, *Dictionary*.

12. John Huntington Crane Coffin (1815–1890), an astronomer at the Naval Observatory since 1844, did extensive observations with the mural circle. Elliott, *Dictionary*.

13. Charles O. Boutelle, formerly of the Northeastern Boundary Survey and since 1844 on the Coast Survey. *Henry Papers, 5:*476n.

14. Frederick Augustus Porter Barnard (1809–1889), severally professor of mathematics, natural history, and chemistry at the University of Alabama. At both this institution and his subsequent one, the University of Mississippi, Barnard was noted for founding observatories. He was also an astronomer for the Alabama and Florida Boundary Commission. *DAB*.

15. James Curley (1796–1889), an Irish immigrant and Jesuit priest, taught natural philosophy, mathematics, and astronomy at Georgetown College, 1831–1879. He was the founder and director of its observatory and in 1847 made a precise determination of the latitude of Washington. Elliott, *Dictionary*.

16. William J. Young, who had most recently constructed the equatorially mounted refracting telescope for Gilliss's Chile expedition. J. M. Gilliss, "Observations of the Planets Mars and Venus. . . . Introduction. Description of the Observatory," *The U.S. Naval Astronomical Expedition to the Southern Hemisphere, during the Years 1849–'50–'51–'52*, U.S. House, 33d Congress, 1st Session, House Executive Documents, No. 121, 4 vols. (1855–1856), *3:*xlvi.

17. Alvan Clark (1804–1887), in a varied life

that included careers in engraving and portrait painting, was a telescope maker, especially known for his fine lens grinding. He sold his first telescope in 1848. Elliott, *Dictionary.*

18. Henry Fitz (1808–1863) operated a photographic studio in Baltimore from about 1840 to 1845, when he moved to New York to work as a telescope maker. He ground the lenses for the Gilliss expedition instruments. Elliott, *Dictionary;* Gilliss, *3:*xlvi.

19. Amasa Holcomb, whose work came to prominence in the 1830s, was noted for his reflecting telescopes. *Henry Papers,* 2:408n–409n.

20. Joseph Saxton was a Philadelphia inventor who had a productive career at the United States Mint in Philadelphia, and, since 1843, at the Coast Survey, where he designed and produced accurate surveying equipment. *Henry Papers,* 2:159n–160n.

21. Thomas Jefferson Lee (ca. 1806–1891), of the West Point class of 1830, was a member of the Corps of Topographical Engineers and author of *A Collection of Tables and Formulae Useful in Geodesy and Practical Astronomy* (Washington, 1849). Cullum, *1:*451–452; Roysdon and Khatri.

22. *The American Almanac and Repository of Useful Knowledge* was published annually by Gray and Bowen of Boston between 1830 and 1861. Robert Treat Paine did the astronomical calculations for the earlier volumes.

23. Probably *The United States' Almanac, or Complete Ephemeris,* published by E. H. Butler of Philadelphia between 1843 and 1845, whose astronomical calculator was John Downes. Similar titles were published from the early national era onward. Milton Drake, comp., *Almanacs of the United States,* 2 vols. (New York, 1962), 2:1169, 1174, 1180; *National Union Catalog.*

24. Paine was famous in the astronomical community for his extensive observations of occultations and eclipses, which eventually ran to over two thousand instances. "Robert Treat Paine," *Proceedings of the American Academy of Arts and Sciences,* 1885–1886, 21:532–535.

25. Most probably a reference to Lewis R. Gibbes's observations of lunar occultations, 1848–1854, for which he invented a mechanical calculator in 1849 or 1850 to give approximate times for the astronomical events. He apparently only published tables of occultations in the local newspaper. Gibbes, "On the Occultator," *Silliman's Journal,* 1869, 2d ser. 47:191–193; Gibbes to William Cranch Bond, December 11, 1851, Bond Papers, Harvard University Archives.

26. This work was done from 1830 to 1838,

in connection with the preparation of a map of the commonwealth; it was later confirmed by Robert Treat Paine. Elias Loomis, *The Recent Progress of Astronomy; Especially in the United States* (New York, 1850), p. 211.

27. James D. Graham surveyed both the United States–Texas and United States–Canada borders, in 1839–1840 and 1840–1843, respectively.

28. The Florida reefs and keys presented special difficulties of surveying for the General Land Office, as well as being hazards to navigation. The Coast Survey began a survey of the area in 1849, under the provisions of a special congressional appropriation. Part of the survey's efforts included the establishment of an astronomical and magnetic observatory near Key West, where Julius E. Hilgard made determinations of latitude, longitude, and magnetic direction and intensity. *Coast Survey Report for 1848,* p. 9; *Coast Survey Report for 1849,* pp. 7, 46–49; C. Albert White, *A History of the Rectangular Survey System* (Washington, [1983]), p. 111.

29. Perhaps a reference to the 1842–1843 project of I. W. P. Lewis, civil engineer to the United States Light House Establishment, to determine the positions of lighthouses by astronomical means as an aid to navigation. U.S. Light-House Establishment, *Compilation of Public Documents and Extracts from Reports and Papers Relating to Light-Houses, Light-Vessels, and Illuminating Apparatus, and to Beacons, Buoys and Fog Signals, 1789–1871* (Washington, 1871), pp. 337–388.

30. John Winthrop, the colonial astronomer chiefly known for his observations of the transits of Venus in 1761 and 1769. *Henry Papers,* *1:*96n; Elliott, *Dictionary.*

31. No such circular has been found.

32. Not found.

Loomis took many of these suggestions, but incorporated them in a book which he published independently, not as a Smithsonian report: *The Recent Progress of Astronomy; Especially in the United States* (New York, 1850). He apparently disliked Henry's removing from his scope the discovery of Neptune, for his book began with a chapter entitled "Recent Additions to Our Knowledge of the Planetary System," which was chiefly devoted to Neptune. It continued with three further chapters on the topics that Henry mentioned above. However, Loomis did not follow Henry's stricture about providing "copious references to authorities"; his book contained no references at all.

338. TO EPHRAIM GEORGE SQUIER

Smithsonian Institution
October 30 1849

Hon. E. G. Squier
Dear Sir

Your communication was received by me on the 20th October and the memoir will bear that date in the Transactions of the Institution.[1] It has been referred to a commission[2] and will be put to press as soon as possible after it has been reported on. A package containing the wood-cuts was received sometime since from Mr Bartlett, and is now in N. York ready to be put into the hands of the engraver.[3]

A bill has been presented to me for meteorological instruments, from Mr Pike.[4] I informed you at the time of our last communication[5] that I could not then furnish you with instruments, and that I did not think that you would be able for some time to come to make any use of them. I will pay this bill however on condition that you will send us regular reports on the Barometer, Thermometer, direction of the Wind &c from some fixed point in central America.[6] You may probably find some persons connected with the religious institutions who would undertake to keep the record. Since you have two Barometers you may perhaps be enabled to establish two stations.

In sending statues, or other specimens of ancient art it will be well to forward them to us by the vessels belonging to the U. States, otherwise the expense may exceed that which the Smithsonian Institution can appropriate to Collections in this line.[7] If an order for this purpose be required I presume I can procure one through the Secretary of State.

I am pleased to learn that your mission has been successful. Your position is a very important one and requires prudence as well as enterprise and talent, to discharge properly its duties. With my best wishes for your success I remain,

Very truly your obedient Servant
Joseph Henry
Sec'y Smithsonian Institution

Squier Papers, Library of Congress.
In Edward Foreman's hand, with Henry's signature.

1. The communication is not found, but it was probably a cover letter to the manuscript of *Aboriginal Monuments of the State of New-York*, 1850, SI Contributions, vol. 2 (Washington, 1851), whose title page does bear that date.

2. William W. Turner and Brantz Mayer (1809–1879, *DAB*), a Baltimore lawyer, founder of the Maryland Historical Society and author of works on Maryland and Mexican history. Squier, p. 2.

3. Sarony and Major of New York, according to the printed plates.

4. Benjamin Pike, either senior or junior, instrument makers of New York. *Henry Papers,* *1:*305n.

According to the *Smithsonian Report for 1851,* p. 76, Squier took two barometers and two thermometers with him at Smithsonian expense, instruments that James Green usually supplied.

5. Not found.

6. What are presumed to be Squier's meteorological observations, covering the months of April and May of 1850, survive in Folder "Meteorological Observations Nicaragua 1849," Box 20, Meteorological Project, RU 60, Smithsonian Archives.

7. When in 1850 Squier did ship back from Nicaragua statues and other ethnographic material, he apparently used commercial shippers, who nonetheless donated their costs. *Smithsonian Report for 1850,* pp. 23, 78–80.

339. TO ORMSBY MacKNIGHT MITCHEL

Smithsonian Institution
October 30 1849

My Dear Sir

I have been absent from Washington for two weeks organizing a system of Meteorological observations for the State of N. York. On my return I found your communication of the 11th of October[1] on my table.

Dr Bache has not yet returned to Washington and until he arrives we cannot have a meeting of the Executive Committee. My own judgement is that your application for assistance is a proper one, and that if the income of the Institution would warrant the appropriation, it should be made.[2] This opinion is independent of any personal feeling I may have in regard to yourself—though your character as an accurate observer must form a part of the data on which the opinion is founded. The question therefore in my mind is not as to the merits of the proposition but whether the Smithsonian Institution is able at present to make the appropriation. You have no idea of the number of applications which are made to the Institution for assistance with regard to scientific investigations, and the small amount of income we can devote at present to purposes of this kind. Until the edifice is finished one half of the whole ~~of the whole~~ interest of the original bequest will constitute the building fund,[A] one half of the remainder is to be applied to the Library and other collections, leaving for our publications, lectures, researches, &c not more than four or five thousand dollars a year. From this you will perceive that if we do not immediately agree with your proposition it is because our means forbid and not because as you would seem to infer we do not properly appreciate its value.

I beg to repeat in this letter my conviction of the importance of the improvements you have made in the methods of recording Astronomical observations and I hope that the means will be liberally provided for reducing all your plans to practice. If you can make it convenient to lecture at Washington this winter I think you might make your visit subservient to your proposition as well as the general interest of science.[3]

> I remain very truly
> Your friend and servant
> Joseph Henry
> Sec'y Smithsonian Institution

Profr. O. N. Mitchell

Collection of F. K. Mitchel, Center Sandwich, New Hampshire.
In Edward Foreman's hand, with Henry's signature.

1. Not found.

2. Mitchel had asked for "1000 Dolls per year for catalogue of stars" from observations at the Cincinnati Observatory. Desk Diary, October [28], 1849 (quotation); Rhees, *Journals*, p. 477.

3. Mitchel did not lecture at the Smithsonian until the 1855–1856 season. *Smithsonian Report for 1855*, p. 35.

340. TO SPENCER FULLERTON BAIRD

> Smithsonian Institution
> Nov 1st 1849

My Dear Sir,

During my absence at the north my letters were forwarded to me and amoung the numbe[r] was one from you which by accident was mislaid at Princeton and has just now come to light.[1] I regret that it has so long remained unanswered.

After leaving Cambridge, I made a short visit to Prof. Bache and then went to Toronto U.C. to confer with Capt Lefroy relative to the cooperation of the observers in the British provinces in our system of meteorology and also to get some instruction in the manipulation of the self registering photographic magnetic instruments. My visit was highly gratifying I rceiveed all the information I desired and the assurance of a hearty cooperation in all the operations of the Smithsonian Inst.

The state of New York has appropriated 3000 Dolls for improving its system of Meteorology and has given the system principally in charge to the Smith. Inst. Mass will probably follow this example[2] also the Surgeon General of the US[3] will probably order the several new Military Posts to be furnished with instruments in accordance with our plans.[4] I have procured a standard barometer from London and after considerable discussion have settled upon a forms of instruments and observations to be generally used. I have engaged Green of New York formerly of Baltimore to make the barometers and thermometers & Pike & son of the same city to construct rain gages snow gages & wind vanes. The arrangement of this matter has occupied much of my time since I saw you last.

The affairs of the Institution appear to be in a favourable condition and I think it probable that the building will be finished before the expiration of the time mentioned in the contract provided the Contractor can procure the money for the purpose.

Mr Marsh found some difficulty in arranging his business before he started. We purchased or agreed to purchase 3000 Dolls worth of his library and he deposited a portion of the remainder with us— Before he left he put in my hands a warm letter in your favour[5] to be used at the proper time.

I am much obliged to you for the information relative to the german Reports. The appendix to the work you mention should be translated and published.[6] I was not well pleased with the American Edition of Müller.[7] The body of the work gave several principles which were due to me though no credit was given. The American Editor should have done better justice.[8]

What progress are you making in the translation and publication of your german Lexicon.[9] I have seen one part. The execution is beautiful— Cannot you furnish me in time for my report with an account of what you have done in the way of Natural History with the small appropriation given you for researches & collections in this line[10]—give it to me in such a form that I can use ↑in↓ it ↑in↓ or rather append it to my report.

Shall we not see you in Washington this winter?—

I remain truly yours &—
Joseph Henry

Prof Baird

Baird Papers, Smithsonian Archives.
Note on reverse of last sheet in Baird's hand: "Ask Henry to mention the principles for which he should be credited. Matter much the same." Reply: Doc. 341.

1. Not found.
2. Massachusetts set up a similar system, beginning in 1851. *Smithsonian Report for 1850,* pp. 16–17.

3. Thomas Lawson (1781 or 1785–1861), surgeon general from 1836 until his death. *DAB.*

4. Lawson assigned to Thomas G. Mower (1789 or 1790–1852), a surgeon in the United States Army, the general direction of the army's cooperation with the Smithsonian. On the same day as he wrote Baird, Henry wrote to Mower (not found) requesting assistance (as Mower put it in his response) "in extending the meteorological observations of the medical department of the army." Mower offered his help, reported that the Mexican War had disrupted the regular observations, and stated that, although entrusted to army doctors, the observations were often shunted off to hospital orderlies. This seemed to offer an opportunity for Smithsonian direction over a far-flung set of observers, who, moreover, would have their own instruments. Alexander S. Wotherspoon, an assistant surgeon in the Surgeon General's Office, was placed in charge of immediate supervision and reduction of the data; he had met Henry just two days before, and then written to give a list of military posts where meteorological observations were taken and places where the army would soon be established, so that Henry could know the extent of army efforts. Beginning in 1850, army meteorological registers were routinely directed to the institution. However, a formal system of cooperation under Smithsonian direction was never worked out.

Fleming, *Meteorology,* pp. 110–114; *Smithsonian Report for 1850,* p. 17; Desk Diary, October 30 and 31, 1849; Mower to Henry, November 27, 1849, Letters Received, Records of the Smithsonian Meteorological Project, Records of the Weather Bureau, RG 27, National Archives; *List of Members of the American Philosophical Society* ([Philadelphia, 1865]), p. 36; Charles K. Gardner, *A Dictionary of All Officers . . . in the Army of the United States,* 2d ed. (New York, 1860), pp. 332, 498.

5. Not found.

6. Presumably Johann Heinrich Jacob Müller's *Bericht über die neuesten Fortschritte der Physik, in ihrem Zusammenhange dargestellt,* 2 vols. (Brunswick, 1849–1851). About 1852, announcements appeared of the publication—under Smithsonian auspices—of a translation of this work, but it finally came out as parts of four successive annual reports of the Smithsonian: *1855*:311–423; *1856*:357–456; *1857*:333–431; and *1858*:372–415. *DSB; List of Works Published by the Smithsonian Institution, Washington* ([Washington, 1852]), p. 4.

7. The 1848 revised Philadelphia edition by Lea and Blanchard after the 1847 London edition of *Principles of Physics and Meteorology,* a translation of Müller's *Grundrisse der Physik und Meteorologie, für Lyceen, Gymnasien, Gewerbe- und Realschulen, sowie zum Selbstunterrichte* (Brunswick, 1846). Müller (1809–1875), the professor of physics at the University of Freiburg in Breisgau, made a reputation translating, editing, and writing textbooks, patterning his first after C.-S.-M. Pouillet's noted *Éléments de physique expérimentale et de météorologie* of 1827. *DSB.*

8. Henry is not mentioned in the work, although it dealt with a full range of electric and electromagnetic phenomena. For instance, it discussed induction—including self-induction (ascribed to Faraday on p. 473), simple electric motors, thermopiles, and the telegraph. The omissions would have been particularly galling, as the unidentified American editor inserted long sections of his own supplementary material, for instance, on the telegraph (pp. 459–463).

9. Thanks to George Perkins Marsh, Baird had gotten the job of translating the Brockhaus *Bilder Atlas zum Conversations Lexicon,* a popular illustrated encyclopedia. New York publisher Charles Rudolph Garrigue had first offered the job to Marsh, who in turn recommended his protégé, whom he had tutored in German. The work appeared in parts, starting in 1849, as J. G. Heck, *Iconographic Encyclopaedia of Science, Literature, and Art,* trans. and ed. Spencer F. Baird. By 1851, the work was complete with four volumes of text and two of plates. David Lowenthal, *George Perkins Marsh: Versatile Vermonter* (New York, 1958), p. 92.

10. Baird had written Henry in early June 1849, requesting funds for collecting and shipping natural history specimens for the Smithsonian museum, chiefly "reptiles, fish, and fossils." Baird planned the work in connection with his collaboration with Louis Agassiz on the fish of North America. In his reply Henry authorized $75. For about three weeks beginning the middle of July, Baird and companions explored the Shenandoah Valley and the regions around White Sulphur Springs. He collected mammalian bones and seined for fish in the Shenandoah, James, and Greenbriar watersheds, discovering both new species and new locales for known ones. However, severe illness cut short his collecting activities. Baird to Henry, June 9, 1849, printed in William Healey Dall, *Spencer Fullerton Baird: A Biography* (Philadelphia, 1915), pp. 187–188; Henry to Baird, June 13, 1849, Baird Papers, Smithsonian Archives; Baird to Henry, August 11, 1849, Henry Papers, Smithsonian Archives; Rhees, *Journals,* p. 473. The short account in *Smithsonian Report for 1849,* p. 19, presumably refers to Baird's trip.

341. FROM SPENCER FULLERTON BAIRD

Carlisle, Nov. 3″, 1849.

Dear Sir,

Many thanks to you for your kind letter of Nov. 1st and for the information therein contained. You must have been kept pretty busy this fall between your gigantic plans for the advancement[A] of meteorological science, and the affairs of the Smithsonian Institution building. I think we are now in a fair way to have many knotty problems solved with regard to the mutual connection and causes of many natural phenomena. There certainly is no way in which the will of the founder of the Smithsonian Institution as to the increase of knowledge, can be more effectually carried out, than in taking charge of what no individual or even ordinary society could grasp. I consider the day as not very distant when many of the most interesting questions in natural and physical science shall be solved by the agencies set in motion by the Institution, yourself at the head. How[B] easy to call upon the trained meteorological correspondants for information upon other subjects, the distribution and local or general appearance of certain forms of animals, vegetables, or minerals; the occurrence of certain diseases over the entire country; the spread and rate of progress of a pestilence as small pox, cholera, or yellow fever through the land; the range of action of noxious insects, as the Hessian fly, the cotton or tobacco worm &c., with an infinity of others. I have long dreamed of some central association or influence which might call for such information, digest it, and then publish it in practical form to the world, and I see that my dream is not far from realisation.[1] Pennsylvania should not be behind hand with Massachusetts and New York in their aids to science; she[C] will I hope follow their example when she realises that an example has been set her by states with whom she has endeavored to compete in plans[D] for universal education.[2]

There is quite an interesting article on Meteorology in the Bilder Atlas, which I have already translated, but have not had ↑yet↓ transcribed for the printer. It may occupy some 100 pages of the Iconographic Encyclopedia.[3] I would be much gratified if you would read it over and note[E] any errors which may have crept in or been retained. I have finished the matter of about 700 pages of the whole American edition, having rendered nearly 300 last month. If I can continue at the same rate for several months longer I shall be through with it. Translating scientific matters is with me a labor of love, and when I finish the work I am at I shall miss a pleasant occupation.[4] If you do not check my presumption, I may come upon you for permission to help you in your physical investigations by translating[F] or digesting matters of german science. I could do much more than I now accomplish but for the—, to me—odious labor of preparing two lectures weekly in the department of Chemical philosophy. I can make no researches for want of the proper apparatus, and the endless repetition of old and threadbare facts is, to say the least, tiresome.

Will you not send me a note of those matters in Müller's Physics in which proper credit has not been given to you for discoveries and observations made? The text of the Natural philosophy of the Bilder Atlas is much like that of Müller, although rather fresher, and I would wish to do you justice in your own country.[5] I have already made sundry corrections in the subject of electromagnetism, but some inaccuracies I may have overlooked. I ~~have~~ ↑shall↓ endeavor[G] throughout the ~~entire~~ entire work to do full justice to American Savants, when it has not already been done. If you have time, I would beg for a memorandum of this kind as the Natural philosophy is now being printed, and I would wish to make any necessary corrections in time.[6] I regretted exceedingly that your absence this fall prevented me from taking advantage of your kind offer[7] to read over the Mss. of the Physics.

I send an account of expenditures, for freight of specimens, liquor used, and some other items. Part of the whiskey bill is for amounts received prior to Jan. 1st 1849, but I thought it best to send in the entire account. Dickinson College[H] would pay about half of it, but I think it best not to let the College have any claim upon the specimens, although it was understood, at the time of my depositing my collections, that Sundry expenses were to be paid by her for the use of the specimens in their free exhibition to the students. The specimens received are by no means represented by the amount of their cost. A large number of very rare or new and exceedingly valuable forms in[I] natural history are embraced in the series. Never have I obtained half as much in the same time as since April 1st, of this year. I am overloaded with treasures, duplicates of great value, and uniques. In fact, I am greatly at a loss to know where to stow all my goods. I wish they were all transferred to the cool cellars of the Smithsonian building.

Would you consider it indelicate importunity in me,—as such I am afraid you will consider it, to ask whether you will recommend the appointment of curator this winter. I feel more and more desirous of escaping from my toils here, which I should do, were I so fortunate as to be selected for the post. I am afraid that with the limited attendance of students this year that it will be impossible for the treasurer of the College to pay the full amount of salary ($1000). Next spring too, my father-in-law, Gen. Churchill, breaks up his establishment here and leaves Carlisle as a residence,[8] in which event my own convenience and facility[J] of investigation and study will be greatly curtailed, by the necessary restrictions of a boarding house. I can at any time make arrangements for a substitute in the college, ~~although~~ to take charge of the uncompleted portion of the year (collegiate). My plan would be if I were appointed from the 1st of January, or even the 1st of July, 1850, to transport most or all specimens to Washington ↑in the spring↓ and after remaining there for a while, to go North and explore the region in the North of New York, the wildest portion of the[K] United States, ~~and~~ there to collect specimens of all kinds, and to make such observations of various kinds as might be in my power.[9] Professor Guyot intends visiting the same region, and the explorations belonging to our mutual departments would be appropriately carried on together. I have many connections in the Adirondack region, and have already visited it, although several years have elapsed. Before I started I could put matters in train for calling in collections from various parts of the country by the distribution of appropriate circulars. Could I but ask in the name of the Smithsonian Institution for objects of interests, their acquisition would be much easier than it is now. If you could not spare as much as $500 per annum for expenses, I could do a great[L] deal with half the sum. This amount with $1000 for myself would not be a heavy drag upon the funds, for a year or two. I may have opportunities now for making collections which may not or ↑may↓ never recur; and I would like to commence working the great machinery which I trust I can set up, for making a true and genuine collection of objects of science. I am afraid I have wearied your patience by what I have written, but hope you will forgive my prolixity and importunity, in regard[M] to what is a somewhat vital matter.

I would be proud to furnish a report of progress in collecting natural history objects this year, but would it answer in case of no appointment being made this winter? Would it not suggest to many the idea of the situation, and would you not be overwhelmed with applications for the curatorship, or by agitations for the same object? Do you wish for a more particular bill of items than is found in the accompanying account of expenditures?

Very truly and Sincerely Yours
Spencer F. Baird.

P.S. Shall I draw on you for the amount of the bill or will you forward it.

Baird Papers, Smithsonian Archives.
Reply: Doc. 351.

1. As assistant secretary of the Smithsonian, Baird pursued this idea and used the meteorological correspondence network to gather natural history data. James Rodger Fleming, "Meteorology at the Smithsonian Institution, 1847–1874: The Natural History Connection," *Archives of Natural History,* 1989, *16*:275–284; *Smithsonian Report for 1851,* p. 51.

2. Both Massachusetts and New York early on had made provisions for state support of free public education not based on need. The fight for Pennsylvania state support of schools for all, not just the poor, took place in the mid-1830s. Only after a bitter struggle did a voluntary system emerge in 1834, where counties could apply for state support upon their own funding of free public schools. For details on these and other plans, see Lawrence Arthur Cremin, *The American Common School: An Historic Conception* (New York, 1951), especially pp. 91–110.

3. "Meteorology" occupied pages 358–430 of the first text volume of J. G. Heck, *Iconographic Encyclopaedia of Science, Literature, and Art,* trans. and ed. Spencer F. Baird, 6 vols. (New York, 1851).

4. Baird's translating was rather more an exercise of correcting translations made by others. He apparently paid thirty-seven cents per page for rough translation out of the dollar per page that publisher Rudolph Garrigue paid to him. Baird to George Perkins Marsh, March 11, 1849, Marsh Papers, Bailey/Howe Library, University of Vermont.

5. Henry enclosed a brief sketch of his work in connection with the electromagnetic telegraph in Doc. 351.

6. Not strictly speaking "Natural Philosophy," but rather "Physics," which occupied pages 175–430 of the first volume.

7. No evidence of this offer has been found.

8. Sylvester Churchill (d. 1862), of Woodstock, Vermont, was a brigadier general in the United States Army. Around May 1, 1850, he undertook a tour of inspection of artillery posts from Kansas to Maine. F. B. Heitman, *Historical Register of the United States Army, from Its Organization* (Washington, 1890); David Lowenthal, *George Perkins Marsh: Versatile Vermonter* (New York, 1958), p. 91; Baird to Henry, April 20, 1850, Baird Papers, Smithsonian Archives.

9. Baird undertook an ichthyological expedition to northern New York and Vermont in July and August, 1850, collecting specimens for the Smithsonian. *Smithsonian Report for 1850,* p. 45.

342. FROM ARNOLD GUYOT

Cambridge Mass. 7[–8][A] Novembre 1849

Cher Monsieur

En réponse à la lettre que vous m'avez fait l'honneur de m'adresser le 1er Novembre,[1] j'ai l'honneur de vous transmettre un modèle de régistre météorologique tel qu'il me semblerait utile qu'il fût tenu par les observateurs qui recevront la série complète des instruments. Les autres peuvent laisser en blanc les colonnes qui leur sont inutiles. Je vous demande la permission, Monsieur, de vous dire les motifs de la distribution que j'ai adoptée.

1° Je pars du principe que chaque feuille doit être un document complet et indépendant, qui doit porter avec lui tous les renseignements nécessaires pour corriger & utiliser directement les observations qu'elle contient. Elle doit donner les dâtes, le lieu, la position géographique l'altitude de l'observatoire, la nature et les corrections des instruments, leurs variations accidentelles, enfin la signature personnelle de l'observateur qui donne à la pièce son authenticité & la place sous la responsabilité d'un nom.

2° L'ordre dans lequel se suivent les colonnes ~~est celui~~ indique celui dans lequel les instruments doivent être observés. Le thermomètre extérieur avant d'ouvrir la fenêtre pour mouiller le[B] psychromètre; le thermomètre du Baromètre, avant que l'approche de l'observateur ait ~~fait~~ modifié sa température; puis le vent, l'état du ciel &. et en dernier lieu le psychromètre, qui aura eu le temps de prendre sa température.

3° L'observateur doit se faire une règle invariable d'inscrire dans le journal l'indication de ses instruments, telle que la donne leur lecture immédiate, sans faire aucune correction de tête. Les valeurs corrigées doivent donc avoir une colonne à part, comme c'est ici le cas pour le Baromètre. Cependant le nombre des thermomètres rend les doubles colonnes impraticables. Aussi doit on tendre à fournir aux observateurs des thermomètres assez exacts pour que leurs indications puissent être admises sans corrections. Ayant le moyen de corriger l'erreur du zéro dans l'instrument même, & la météorologie ne pouvant répondre d'une erreur de température d'un demi degré, il ne sera pas très difficile d'arriver à ce résultat. Quant au psychromètre ce sont les différences seules qui importent, et tout instrument de ce genre dont les Deux thermomètres ne marchent pas d'accord, doit être rejeté. Les colonnes de ce dernier instrument sont nombreuses, mais il est essentiel pour découvrir les erreurs accidentelles que les éléments complets soient réprésentés.

4° La colonne des vents admet comme l'un des éléments essentiels, la direction d'où viennent les nuages. La discordance entre la direction des courans d'air près de terre et dans les diverses hauteurs de l'atmosphère, est un fait beaucoup plus ordinaire qu'on ne l'imagine et qui me parait d'une grande importance pour l'étude de la loi des orages et de la rotation des vents. Dans le dernier coup de vent du 30 8bre, j'ai vu encore trois courans très déterminés souffler simultanément, aux différentes hauteurs, dans les directions différentes, S. OSO & NE. pendant une bonne partie de la matinée.

5° Pour éviter les copier & diminuer les chances d'erreurs qui en sont la suite, il me parait utile que chaque feuille donne une place pour les moyennes essentielles. Une colonne perpendiculaire est réservée pour les moyennes diurnes de chacun des éléments, et des colonnes horizontales pour les moyennes de chaque groupe de 5 jours. Ces colonnes ont en outre l'avantage de couper la série des chiffres & de faciliter les additions et la formation des moyennes. La dernière feuille du mois donne des colonnes pour les moyennes mensuelles par heures & les moyennes générales. Les observateurs étant munis des tables nécessaires, il faut espérer que les réductions se feront ↑par eux↓ jour par jour, ainsi que le calcul des moyennes. Ce travail↑, qui↓ est peu de chose pour chacun d'eux, les intéressera à leurs observations en leur donnant les résultats et en facilitera grandement la publication.

6° Chaque mois se compose de trois feuilles, portant un N° d'ordre. Le modèle que j'envoie représente la troisième et dernière feuille. Elle contient sur la 1re page onze jours, au lieu de dix, pour les mois de 31 jours. On éviterait cette inégalité en continuant la division par 5, sans égard pour les mois, comme le fait le système Prussien,[2] mais à tout prendre, j'ai pensé qu'il valait mieux conserver le groupement par mois civils. Les deux premières feuilles n'en contiendront que dix et l'espace réservé aux abréviations^C sera plus large. Elles n'auront pas non plus le résumé mensuel, au revers, du reste↑, sauf les jours du mois↓ elles seront semblables à la 3me. Il sera bon de les faire imprimer chacune à part, afin d'imprimer aussi à leur place, les jours du mois & les heures.

7° Le nombre des observations pour chaque jour étant fort limité, il faut engager les observateurs à les multiplier beaucoup, pendant la durée des orages et des états inusités de l'atmosphère. Le revers de la feuille présente des colonnes pour cet usage.

8° Pour éviter les erreurs provenant d'un mauvais placement de chiffres, il sera bon de ligner légérement tous les intervalles à le façon du modèle que je joins à la feuille.

9° Les feuilles ne seront pas cousues en cahiers dans le centre, mais seulement sur les bords à l'endroit marqué (O), puis pliées en deux et placées dans un portefeuille de même grandeur, format petit infolio, garni d'attaches. On peut en envoyer à chaque observateur deux séries de 36 pour une année, l'une pour le journal original; dont^D il enverra, successivement chaque mois, les feuilles à Washington, l'autre pour la copie qu'il gardera pour lui.[3] Il recevra en outre quelques feuilles supplémentaires en cas d'accident.

10° Chaque observateur devra être fourni en outre d'un livre blanc Q^{to} ou grand Oct° pour y inscrire les remarques particulières et les descriptions détaillées de phénomènes qui ne trouveraient pas de place dans les régistres. Par ex. une aurore boréale est indiquée dans le régistre à sa dâte, et le régistre renvoie pour la description à la page du Livre de Remarques. Les résumés d'époques météorologiques et les comparaisons d'époques entr'elles, pourront aussi y trouv[er]^E place. Ce Book of Remarks pourrait avoir la forme dont je joins ici un modèle.

Vous voyez, Monsieur, par ce tableau que je penche pour adopter comme heures d'observations celles qui ont été proposées par Humboldt[F] & Mahlmann pour le royaume de Prusse,[4] par Lloyd,[5] et que les observations de Toronto[6] prouvent être suffisantes pour obtenir de bonnes moyennes dans le Nord des Etats Unis.

Ce nombre d'observations est sans doute insuffisant pour l'étude de variations diurnes des éléments météorologiques, et celle de la loi des orages. Mais ce dernier inconvénient sera bien diminué et même plus que compensé, si les observateurs ajoutent volontairement des observations extraordinaires pendant les orages. Quant à tel aux oscillations régulières, il faudra s'en remettre à quelques observatoires spéciaux, auxquels on pourra attacher deux observateurs au lieu d'un, en ajoutant les heures supplémentaires recommandées par Lloyd & Humboldt 10 AM & 6 PM pour la température & l'humidité 10 AM et 4 PM pour le Baromètre.[7] Cette dernière perspective me ferait préférer décidément la série de 6. 10. 2. 10 à celle de 7. 11. 3. 11 que propose le Cap. Lefroy.[8] En[G] adoptant celle-ci, ou bien les heures supplémentaires ne seraient pas placés à des intervalles égaux, comme ait désirable, ou bien elles tomberaient sur les heures beaucoup moins favorables pour l'étude des phénomènes, 11^{hm} & 7^{hs}. De plus les heures de 6. 2 & 10 s'accordent avec les heures du lever, du dîner & du coucher et semblent gêner l'observateur le moins possible.

Au reste cette question des heures d'observation est pendante pour l'Amérique aux différentes latitudes. Les résultats des observations de Girard Collège analysés, jetteront du jour sur cette question.

Quant aux tables psychrométriques, après nouvel examen, mon intention était de vous proposer d'adopter comme les meilleures les tables de Haeghens, dans l'Annuaire Météorologique de France.[9,H] Vous les trouverez à la page 114 du volume. Mr Haeghens tient compte, comme vous pouvez le voir par les pages qui précèdent les tables, de tous les travaux faits sur cette matière, et spécialement de ceux de Mr Regnault.[10] Elles tiennent compte Les tables sont aussi commodes qu'aucune de celles qui ont été publiées et d'une exactitude très suffisante, comme vous le verrez par les différences verticales & horizontales de la colonne des tensi[on]s[I] et de celle de l'humidité relative. De plus elles s'appliquent au thermomètre[J] couvert d'une couche de glace. Je les tiens pour préférables à toutes les autres. Aussi je n'hésiterais pas à proposer que les psychromètres, du moins, fussent gradués en degrés centrigrades. C'est une excellente occasion, d'ailleurs, de familiariser les observateurs avec cette échelle, et il ne peut en résulter aucun inconvénient puisque l'échelle n'est ici qu'un moyen d'arriver à l'évaluation de l'humidité relative, qui des deux façons s'exprime en centièmes.[11] Si toutes fois vous pensez qu'il fût nécessaire d'offrir les tables en mesures anglaises, je serais bien aise que M[r] le Cap. Lefroy se chargeât de transformer les tables de Haeghens. Mais j'avoue que pour ma part, j'aurais jugé ce travail superflu. Je ne serais point d'avis d'admettre les trois échelles dans[K] les mêmes tables, comme il le propose; il faut éviter tout chiffre qui n'est pas directement utile à l'observateur qui en fait usage; ~~Cela de~~ ce serait diminuer la clarté & augmenter les chances d'erreurs. Il vaut mieux que chaque table soit à part & complète.

À propos de thermomètres; je viens de recevoir de mon ami M[r]: Ch. Martins[12] la nouvelle que Bunten fils, auquel, j'avais commandé un thermomètre spécimen, est mort dans l'intervalle.[13] Mr Martins m'indique comme le meilleur fabricant actuel de thermomètres Mr Fasteret,[14] qui travaille sous la direction spéciale de Mr Regnault. Il ferait, s'il le faut, d'excellents psychromètres.

Pour la réduction du baromètre à 32° F. les tables de Delcros, dans l'annuaire Met. d France, sont d'une grande commodité et donnent à vue, sans addition, pour chaque dixième de degré centigrade sa valeur de la correction. Mais elles supposent l'échelle métrique.[15] Pour la division anglaise, les tables contenues dans le Report of the Committee of Meteorology de la Soc: Royale de Londres 1840 pag 82, sont suffisantes;[16] quoique elles ne donnent la[B] ~~correction~~ valeur de la correction que de degrés en degrés, il est facile de faire à vue une petite interpolation pour les fractions de degrés.

Je crains de ne pouvoir revoir la traduction & livrer mon rapport[17] avant mon retour de la tournée que je vais commencer. Mais pendant ce tems, je pourrais vous envoyer, si vous le désirez, les instructions spéciales, qui accompagneront les tableaux blancs que l'on enverra aux observateurs.[18] On peut prendre pour base celles de Mahlman, que j'ai trouvées fort bonnes et auxquelles il n'y aurait que peu de modifications à faire. Comme elles sont traduites dans le Report des Régents de l'Univ. de N York, elles peuvent fort bien servir pour le premier moment.

Les 36 thermomètres de Green que j'ai emportés ici ont fort bien soutenu les épreuves que je leur ai fait subir jusqu'a présent. Les écarts ne passent guère ½ degré. Je finirai aujourdhui ces comparaisons, dont j'ai tenu régistre par Numéros.

En réponse à une lettre que je lui ai adressé la semaine dernière, Mr J Green m'a dit que 8 des baromètres nouveaux sont prêts et que les autres, qui doivent être réparés, seraient prêts au commencement de cette semaine. Je vais donc partir pour New York afin de les comparer Samedi & Lundi. Je comparerai aussi le Newman du Columbia College.

Le Newman du Smithsonian Instit, déposé chez Green, se trouve marquer beaucoup plus bas que celui de l'Observatoire de Cambridge,[19] que j'ai comparé de nouveau avec soin & qui s'accorde avec le Barom. typal de Delcros & de Paris. Je vais le soumettre à de nouvelles comparaisons; il semble avoir pris peut être un peu d'air cependant comme il sonne encore Assez bien, ce ne peut être la cause de la différence assez forte qu'il présente. Ces discordances dans des instruments réputés parfaits, prouvent toujours plus la nécessité[L] des[M] comparaisons directes. Si je vais à Toronto, je ne manquerai pas de constater le rapport du Newmann de l'observatoire avec les autres.

Le paquet que j'expédie contient encore une note sur la répartition des postes Météorologiques dans l'Etat de New York, résumant les résultats de notre conférence à ce sujet à Princeton;[20,N] je ne sais si vous attacherez quelque importance à ce petit document que je serais mieux en état de faire après avoir vu par mes yeux les localités.

J'attendrai à New York dès Lundi vos directions, Monsieur, sur les points suivans.

Faut-il établir des instruments ↑à Erasmus Hall (Flatbush) et↓ dans la ville de New York, et dans quelle localité? ou avec qui faudrait-il m'en[O] entendre?[21]

Ne faut-il pas me rendre immédiatement auprès du M[r] ~~F.~~ T. Romeyn Beck pour arrêter définitivement le choix des stations et voir combien il sera possible d'en établir avant l'hiver?

Je vous prierai de plus de vouloir bien me donner quelque direction pour mon argent de voyage, et d'avoir la bonté de me donner deux mots d'introduction pour Mr T. R Beck, et en cas, pour M[r] le Cap. Lefroy.[22]

Mon adresse à New York est Of. A. G.   care of A. Mayor
                                        22 Maiden Lane

J'ai regret, Monsieur, de n'avoir pu vous envoyer tout ceci plus tôt; mais j'ai travaillé jour et nuit depuis une quinzaine, pour être en état de m'absenter pendant plusieur semaines. Veuillez, Monsieur, recevoir l'expression de ma haute considération & de mon entier dévouement.

Ar[d] Guyot
Prof

Prof. J. Henry, Secretary
Smithsonian Institution[P]

Folder "Letters from Prof. Guyot, 1849–50," Records of the Smithsonian Meteorological Project, Records of the Weather Bureau, RG 27, National Archives.
English translation: Appendix.

1. Not found.

2. See [Carl Heinrich Wilhelm Mahlmann], "Official Instructions for the Observers at the Meteorological Stations in the Kingdom of Prussia (Translated from the German)," *Sixty-Second Annual Report of the Regents of the University of the State of New-York* (Albany, 1849), pp. 264–265.

3. Henry's marginal notation at this spot on the English translation states: "Sent to Albany also."

4. That is, 6 A.M., 2 P.M., and 10 P.M., credited by Mahlmann to Alexander von Humboldt (1769–1859, *DSB*), the great Prussian physical geographer and naturalist. Mahlmann, p. 261.

5. Humphrey Lloyd prepared the portion relating to fixed observatories of the *Report of the Committee of Physics and Meteorology of the Royal Society Relative to the Observations to Be Made in the Antarctic Expedition and in the Magnetic Observatories* (London, 1840). This work contained detailed observing instructions. However, for meteorological observatories not making magnetic observations, he recommended four times for observation, the hours of 3 A.M., 9 A.M., 3 P.M., and 9 P.M., and not the hours which Mahlmann—and Guyot, below—recommended. This and other discrepancies, noted below, indicate another set of Lloyd instructions, possibly the revised edition of 1842, which we have not located. *Report Relative to Observations*, pp. 51–52, 56; Edward Sabine, *Observations Made at the Magnetic and Meteorological Observatory at Toronto in Canada. Vol. 1—1840, 1841, 1842* (London, 1845), pp. 10–13.

6. In accordance with the committee report, meteorological observations at British colonial magnetic stations such as Toronto were made at the time of magnetic ones: every two hours around the clock. *Report Relative to Observations*, pp. 36, 51–52; Sabine, passim.

7. For Humboldt's recommendation, which Guyot used, see Mahlmann, pp. 261–262; Lloyd did not refer to supplemental observations in the *Report Relative to Observations*.

8. We have not found the source of Lefroy's proposal.

9. J. Haeghens (d. 1853), a Parisian meteorologist and professor at the agricultural institute at Versailles, was one of the compilers and preparers of the *Annuaire météorologique de la France*, the four volumes of which appeared in Paris between 1848 and 1852. The psychrometric tables appeared in the first volume.

10. Henri Victor Regnault (1810–1878),

professor of chemistry at the École polytechnique and professor of physics at the Collège de France, had been commissioned in 1842 by the minister of public works to provide standard determinations of the physical constants of water vapor and other gases. *DSB*.

11. Guyot's suggestion was not followed. By 1850, his *Directions for Meteorological Observations* (for which see below, note 18) was neutral with respect to Fahrenheit and centigrade temperature scales. But Smithsonian meteorological observers' forms from the 1850s show that thermometric and psychrometric observations used Fahrenheit's scale only. Fleming, *Meteorology*, pp. 84–85.

12. Charles-Frédéric Martins (1806–1889), botanist, a professor on the medical faculty at Paris, and a cofounder with Haeghens and A. Bérigny of the *Annuaire météorologique de la France. World Who's Who in Science; Poggendorff.*

13. Bunten of Paris was a well-known instrument maker, who produced, among other items, standard thermometers. Arnold Guyot, "[Report on Establishing a New System of Meteorological Observations]," *Sixty-Third Annual Report of the Regents of the University of the State of New-York* (Albany, 1850), p. 282; Deborah Jean Warner, National Museum of American History, private communication.

14. J. T. Fastré manufactured physical apparatus and was active in Paris until the early 1870s. Deborah Jean Warner, private communication.

15. J. Delcros, described as a former officer in the corps of geographical engineers, prepared barometric tables in the *Annuaire météorologique de la France* for 1849, but Guyot referred more specifically to these tables' continuation by Haeghens. The former tables were only graduated by degree, while the latter were by tenths of a degree, though for a smaller range of pressures.

16. Royal Society of London, *Report of the Committee of Physics, Including Meteorology, on the Objects of Scientific Inquiry in Those Sciences* (London, 1840), a revision and extension of the report cited above, note 5.

17. Guyot's promised report on meteorological instruments.

18. This became Guyot's *Directions for Meteorological Observations, Intended for the First Class of Observers*, published by the Smithsonian in 1850, the standard instructions for those who had a full range of instruments. The work was still prefaced by Henry's commitment to pub-

lish the full report, of which the *Directions* were to form an appendix.

19. That is, of the Harvard College Observatory.

20. During Guyot and Henry's meetings in New York and Princeton, October 11–16, they set the positions of twenty stations throughout New York State. Guyot's report to the New York regents of the following March specified five regions: New York City and maritime, eastern and Hudson Valley, Adirondack, western, and Great Lakes. By that time, he had provided instruments to seventeen stations in the first four regions. Desk Diary, October 13, 1849; Guyot, "[Report on a New System of Meteorological Observations]," pp. 283–284.

21. Erasmus Hall, Flatbush, Long Island,

was one of the operating stations by 1850. The observer there was Thomas Morris Strong (1797–1861), pastor of the Dutch Reformed Church from 1822 and a local historian. *Smithsonian Report for 1852*, p. 81; Thomas William Herringshaw, *Encyclopedia of American Biography of the Nineteenth Century* (Chicago, 1905).

22. These letters of introduction have not been found. However, Guyot visited the Toronto Observatory for several days beginning December 6, for the purpose of comparing instruments with that observatory's standards; he favorably impressed J. H. Lefroy. Lefroy to Edward Sabine, December 15, 1849, BJ3/39, Lefroy to Sabine Correspondence, 1848–1851, Sabine Papers, Records of Kew Observatory, Public Record Office, London.

343. TO EDWARD SABINE

Smithsonian Institution
Washington Nov 7th, 49

My Dear Sir

Your very acceptable letter of Oct 12[1] was duly received and I am much gratified to learn from it that you think well of our efforts to "increase and diffuse knowledge among men". I sent you a copy of our programme some time since with the request that ↑you↓ would favour me with any criticism with reference to it which might occur to you. To this I have not received an answer but I shall consider the remarks in your letter as an approval of the general plan. The programme is not in every respect what I could wish. There were many persons to be consulted and we were consequently obliged to make some compromises to satisfy all parties. Mr Bache and myself wished to establish the[A] institution on the most liberal plan; namely that of doing the greatest good to the greatest number and to diffuse the benefits of the ~~the~~ benevolent bequest of Smithson among men of every clime. We[B] were however obliged to give way in part to local influence and to acquiesce in the expenditure of more money (↑from↓ the income, not the principal) for the erection of a ↑building↓ than was necessary. Perhaps however the plan which has been adopted may in the long run prove the best—that, with the great diversity of opinion among the Regents, it is the best that could be passed at the time I am sure. _____ Thus far it has succeeded as well, and indeed better, than could have been expected and the institution is beginning to secure the confidence and support, of all intelligent persons in this country.

We have sent a copy of our first volume[2] to the Royal society and you will much increase my indebtedness to you, by exerting your influence to induce the society to put us on its exchange list.[3] We have a second volume in the press which I trust will be as interesting as the first and from present appearances we shall be able to publish one volume a year, so that the society will not be a loser[C] by the exchange— We shall also be much gratified to receive a copy of the observations published under your direction[4] and of the Reports of the British Association. Be so good as to inform me whether the Association[D] receives donations of books; not having a local habitation I have concluded that it has no library.

The magnetic apparatus as soon as it arrived or at[E] least before it was unpacked was lent to Col. Emory of the mexican boundary commission to be used in the course[F] of his survey of the line between the new possessions of the U.S. and Mexico.[5] He has already made a series of observations with it which I hope will be found of sufficient interest to repay you in some degree for the trouble of superintending its construction.

The standard barometer from Newman came safely and is now put up in the shop of an intelligent and skilful[G] workman,[6] whom we have employed to construct a large number of barometers for the system of observations about being established under the direction of the Smithsonian Institution. Newman has not informed me whether the instrument was compared with the standard of the Royal society.

We have received from Jones two sets of selfregistering thermometers—wet bulbs[7] and radiating instruments. I am sorry to say that the black bulb thermometers[8] were both broken in the transportation though they were packed in sand. I doubt the propriety of this kind of packing though the sand will resist external pressure. I think it will transmit an impulse sufficient, as in this case, to break the heavy bulb from the stem of a thermometer. All the other articles came safely though they were in the same box. Perfectly elastic packing is the only safe one for brittle and heavy instruments.

I visited a few weeks ago, Toronto, and spent[H] a day or or two most delightfully with Capt Lefroy. He is a most admirable fellow thoroughly imbued[I] with the spirit of science. He instructed me in the manipulations of the process of preparing and using the sensitive paper for the self registering photographic apparatus and gave ↑me↓ muc[h][J] valuable information, the result of his experience, in the use of meteorological instruments.

I was highly pleased with your friend Capt Smyth who favoured us with a short visit at Washington. He appears to have been much amused with a visit we made to our yankee king, General^K Taylor. The^L republican simplicity of the government at Washington contrasts strikingly with the formal courts of Europe. Should you meet with ~~him~~ ↑the Capt↓ please give him my kind regards.

> I remain with much respect,
> very truly your friend & servt.
> Joseph Henry.

Lieut. Col. Ed. Sabine
R.A. For Sec R.S.

Sabine Papers, Library, Royal Society of London.
Draft: November 6, 1849, Henry Papers, Smithsonian Archives.

1. Not found.
2. Of the Smithsonian Contributions to Knowledge.
3. Sabine was foreign secretary of the society. By 1850, the Royal Society was exchanging its publications with the Smithsonian. *Smithsonian Report for 1850*, p. 76.
4. The reference is to any of the numerous published meteorological and magnetic observations of the British foreign observatories at Toronto, Van Diemen's Land (Tasmania), the Cape of Good Hope, and St. Helena.
5. Jones's portable declinometer, along with other portable magnetic instruments, was later transferred to James Duncan Graham and a duplicate set commissioned for the Smithso-

nian, paid for by the government. *Smithsonian Report for 1850*, p. 23.
6. That is, James Green.
7. Psychrometers.
8. These are the "radiating instruments" mentioned just above. The large blackened bulb was part of a thermometer configured to hold a maximum temperature. The instrument was designed to measure the heat of the sun's direct rays. Later models enclosed the blackened bulb in a vacuum, to prevent its being altered by passing air. Negretti and Zamba, *A Treatise on Meteorological Instruments: Their Scientific Principles, Method of Construction, and Practical Utility* (London, 1864), pp. 85–86.

344. TO GEORGE BIDDELL AIRY[1]

> Smithsonian Institution
> November 14 1849

Dear Sir.

Your letter of 20th of October[2] has just been received. We are much gratified with the terms of commendation in which you have thought proper to express yourself with reference to the first Volume of the Smithsonian Contributions to Knowledge.[3]

You will find in the Volume an account of the programme of organization of the Institution which has been provisionally adopted and it would give me much pleasure to receive from you any criticism or suggestions in reference to it which might tend to facilitate the object of the benevolent founder of the Institution, viz the <u>increase</u> and <u>diffusion</u> of knowledge among men.

The American ambassador, the Hon Mr Laurence[4] will, we presume take charge of the volumes you purpose presenting to the Institution, and transmit them to us in safety.[5]

I lately made a visit to the observatory of Toronto and was highly gratified with all the arrangements of Capt Lefroy for observations in Magnetism and Meteorology. As soon as our building is sufficiently advanced for the accommodation of the Photographic registering apparatus, we shall order a set from Europe.

We are endeavoring to establish an extensive series of meteorological observations, under the direction of the Smithsonian Institution which shall embrace as far as possible the Continent of N. America. We purpose employing three classes of observers—one to register only the face of the sky, the direction of the wind, and beginning and ending of storms; another to give in addition the temperature; and the third, furnished with complete sets of instruments, to observe all the important meteorological phenomena. It is believed we shall be able to collect data sufficient for settling the mechanical phenomena of American storms, viz, whether they consist of horizontal gyrations, or of upward and inward motions towards a single axis, or of motions in all directions towards a vertical plane; or whether they partake sometimes of all these characters.

We are also endeavoring to collect the statistics of railway and canal explorations, which now cover a[A] considerable portion of the vast territory of the United States, in order to add to our knowledge of the topography of the country; we also intend further to improve our knowledge of this branch of science by barometrical measurements along our mountain ranges.[6]

The Coast[B] Survey of the U. States is making good progress under the admirable superintendence of Dr Bache, though I am sorry to say that it is likely to receive some opposition during the next session of Congress and that probably attempts will be made to change the whole plan of organization and place the work in charge of officers of the Navy, who, though well skilled in the duties of their profession are not well qualified for the peculiar duties of an exact topographical survey of this kind; which as you well know should be entrusted to no one but a person of profound scientific attainments, combined with executive talents of a high order. Yourself and other gentlemen of eminence in science would do good service to the cause in which you are interested by expressing your opinion of the importance of the work, of the plan of its present organization, and of the fitness of Dr Bache for its direction.[7]

I remain very respectfully your obedient Servant

Joseph Henry
Sec. Smithsonian Institution

G. B. Airy Eq Astronomer Royal[C]
P.S. Accompanying this letter I send you a copy of my report to the Regents of the Institution in which you will find an account of all our operations.[8]

J.H.

RGO 6/371 ff97ʳ–98ᵛ, Airy Papers, Royal Greenwich Observatory Archives, Department of Manuscripts and University Archives, Cambridge University Library.
In Edward Foreman's hand, with Henry's signature and postscript.

1. Airy (1801–1892) had been Astronomer Royal and director of the Royal Greenwich Observatory since 1835. He made the observatory into a model of careful and accurate stellar observation. *DSB*.

2. A retained copy (RGO 6/57 f33ʳ⁻ᵛ) is in the same location as this letter.

3. Airy had written: "if every succeeding volume shall equal the first in interest, they will form the most remarkable series of works ever published."

4. Abbott Lawrence.

5. Airy had offered the published astronomical, meteorological, and magnetic observations of the observatory from 1836 and asked the name of the Smithsonian's agent in London through whom he could send them. The *Smithsonian Report for 1850*, p. 75, indicated that the institution had received an exchange from the Royal Observatory at Greenwich.

6. According to Henry's 1849 annual report, he had instituted a letter-writing campaign to solicit the survey data for canals and railways from private hands. He hoped to supplement this information with barometric readings on mountains to aid in determining their heights, much as Arnold Guyot had done in New Hampshire. His stimulus in this project was Charles Ellet's proposed memoir, published as *Of the Physical Geography of the Mississippi Valley,* *with Suggestions for the Improvement of the Navigation of the Ohio and Other Rivers,* 1850, SI Contributions, vol. 2 (Washington, 1851). Henry envisioned the preparation of similar papers and an accurate physical map of the country. We have not found any of the letters that Henry sent out, nor is there any further indication that this project continued. *Smithsonian Report for 1849,* pp. 15–16; see also Doc. 313.

7. Henry anticipated trouble similar to that which arose in February of 1849. No such challenges were made to the survey in the next session, but apparently he and Bache nonetheless solicited expressions of support from eminent foreign astronomers and geodesists. We have not found a letter from Airy, but Alexander von Humboldt, François Arago, and Heinrich Christian Schumacher all wrote to offer their support for leaving Bache in control of a civilian operation. Hugh Richard Slotten, "Patronage, Politics, and Practice in Nineteenth-Century American Science: Alexander Dallas Bache and the United States Coast Survey" (Ph.D. diss., University of Wisconsin-Madison, 1991), p. 173; *Report on the History and Progress of the American Coast Survey up to the Year 1858, by the Committee of Twenty Appointed by the American Association for the Advancement of Science* (n.p., 1858), pp. 83–84.

8. That is, the *Smithsonian Report for 1848*.

345. FROM LOUIS AGASSIZ

Cambridge 19. 9.[1] 1849.[A]

Dear Sir,

I have been trying during the whole week past, to steal an hour to write to you or rather to read my paper[2] over before I send it, but have not yet been able and so I will at least answer your questions now as there are some which admit of no delay.[3] Prof. Harvey's lectures before the Lowell Institute are among the most instructive I have ever attended.[4] He is full of his subjects and imparts both precise and far reaching information. His delivery is less fluent however than you should expect from a gentleman so[B] well informed and so thoroughly master of his subject. But there is such a simplicity and candor about him that this deficiency is soon forgotten to make room to the ↑gratifying↓ impression ↑left↓ by[C] his profound knowledge.

My paper on the Classification and metamorphoses of Insects has now been ready for some time; but I want to read it over again to correct all the little deficiencies of redaction which have no doubt escaped my attention as long as I was more engrossed with the subject itself than with the form in which it is put. There will be but one plate to that paper. The next on embryology of Ascidiae with the recent investigations respecting cellular growth is far advanced.[5] I may perhaps send both together.

It will give me great pleasure to deliver a series of lectures before the Smithsonian Institute this winter. I have thought the fittest subject for about four lectures, if you want as many, were a more extensive development of those views which I brought out in my evening adress before our Association in August,[6] which might also be condensed into fewer lectures if you prefer it, or extended into more if you wish me to do so,[7] by introducing some new results I have arrived at quite recently respecting the geographical distribution of animals, showing that geographical distribution has direct reference to structure and gradation of types throughout the animal kingdom. As I never write my lectures I can easily accomodate some of these subjects to your plans, as soon as I know the time you will allow me. I should like to deliver them immediately before or soon after the meeting in Charleston.[8] As they want me to deliver also some lectures there I will immediately write to D\u1d63 Hollbrook[9] to ascertain what time they would prefer.

The swedish paper for translation I shall send with my Manuscript. About the report upon the radiated Animals[10] I wish to know if you have decided upon the form in which you will publish the book and the

636

plates. It is of importance ↑for me↓ to know it soon, as I shall be influenced in the selection of the illustration by the size of the plates. Recently I have made quite extensively use of the system of phonography to write the results of my investigations. As soon as I have done with a series of experiments I have a phonographer come to me and in the course of a few hours I dictate what would cost me days to write. It has occurred to me that if you could allow me the services of such a man to write my report I might finish it in ↑a↓ much shorter time, than if I have to do all the writing myself. The expense amounts to about ten dollars for a number of pages equaling the contents of a printed sheet of 16 8° pages like those of the report of our Association[11] printed in Philadelphia. It were a very desirable assistance to me; but you will perhaps find it too expensive. If you grant it I should morover request you to pay the bill of this man, as I get along, having not myself the means of advancing much money. I[n] a few days I shall have some pages ready to try the types for the nomenclatural part of the letter press.

Will you allow me to remind you of the claims of Prof. Baird to a preference in your election of a Conservator of the Museum in the Smithsonian Institute. I do not know a scientific man in this country to compete with him for such an office as he is equally conversant with the manual operations required in such a station, as with the wants of an establishment of that kind. The numerous specimens I have received from him have again and again satisfied me that he understands also how and what to collect.[12]

Believing I have now answered all your questions I remain

With high regard
Your sincere friend
L Agassiz

Prof. J. Henry, Washington.

P.S. On reading your letter again I find I ought to mention, that you may advertise my lectures as a Course on the Morphology of the Animal Kingdom. As for Prof. Harvey's ability to prepare a paper upon the Algae of the United States I can only say that he stands uppermost among the modern Algologues and that there is not yet even a nominal catalogue of the species of this family found in this country published.

Henry Papers, Smithsonian Archives.

1. That is, November 19.
2. Presumably, given the discussion below, *The Classification of Insects from Embryological Data*, 1850, SI Contributions, vol. 2 (Washington, 1851).

3. Henry's questions were posed in a letter which we have not found.
4. William Henry Harvey lectured in America in 1849 and 1850. From late October through early December 1849, he gave the

Lowell Institute lectures, which Agassiz faithfully attended. Harvey also collaborated with Jacob Whitman Bailey in the production of the algae volume of the Wilkes Expedition publications. *Henry Papers,* 5:270n; *DNB;* W. H. Harvey, *Memoir* (London, 1869), pp. 184–191.

Henry had apparently asked about Harvey's ability to give lectures in the Smithsonian series. He was commissioned to do so, and in March 1850 he spoke on marine algae and vegetable morphology. These lectures were published later as "Substance of a Course of Lectures on Marine Algae," *Smithsonian Report for 1855,* pp. 87–130. *Smithsonian Report for 1850,* p. 26; Desk Diary, March 19, 21, and 23, 1850; Harvey, p. 209.

5. This proposed paper was based on Agassiz's presentation to the American Association for the Advancement of Science at the 1849 meeting: "On the Embryology of Ascidia, and the Characteristics of New Species from the Shores of Massachusetts," AAAS *Proceedings,* 1849, 2:157–159. It never appeared as a Smithsonian publication.

6. "On Animal Morphology," AAAS *Proceedings,* 1849, 2:411–423.

7. Agassiz's series encompassed three lectures, from February 26 to March 1, 1850, entitled "The Unity of the Plan of the Animal Creation." *Smithsonian Report for 1850,* p. 26; Desk Diary, February 25, 1850.

8. That is, the March 1850 meeting of the American Association for the Advancement of Science.

9. John Edwards Holbrook.

10. This report never appeared.

11. That is, the AAAS.

12. Agassiz wrote to Baird the same day, informing him of the encouragement he had provided. Baird Papers, Smithsonian Archives.

346. TO JARED SPARKS

Smithsonian Institution
November 20 1849

My Dear Sir

I write to you this morning for the purpose of requesting that you will not forget your promise of addressing me some remarks to be placed before the Board of Regents on one of the propositions of the programme of organization of the Smithsonian Institution, viz that which refers to Historical researches and accurate surveys of places, celebrated in American History.[1] The next meeting of the Board will be held on the second of January 1850.

In order to assist in supporting the Astronomical Journal lately established at Cambridge, I shall propose to the Regents of the Smithsonian Institution, to subscribe for a sufficient number of copies to supply the principal foreign observatories.[2]

I trust that the Corporation of Cambridge will also contribute something towards this object, which cannot fail to redound to the honor of the venerable institution entrusted to their care.[3]

I remain very respectfully
Your obedient Servant
Joseph Henry
Sec. Smithsonian Institution

Jared Sparks LLD.

Sparks Mss 153, Sparks Papers, Houghton Library, Harvard University.
In Edward Foreman's hand, with Henry's signature.

1. In the "Programme of Organization," under the rubric of increasing knowledge, this was one example of a topic for which the institution could provide funds to stimulate research. We have found no further activity on this subject, however.

2. On November 14, Henry had written to the editor, B. A. Gould, requesting a list of foreign observatories to which the journal would be distributed; he proposed his plan to the executive committee on December 21, 1849. The Smithsonian subsequently took twenty subscriptions. Rhees, *Journals*, pp. 477–478; Desk Diary, November 14, 1849; Henry to Sparks, April 14, 1852, College Papers, Second Series, vol. VIII, Harvard University Archives.

The idea for this journal began in an exchange of letters between Benjamin Peirce and Alexander Dallas Bache, the first proposing "an astronomical and mathematical journal on purely scientific principles with out any popular element," the second amplifying on the original idea. Public discussion and promotion—in which Henry took a part—came at the August meeting of the American Association for the Advancement of Science. J. S. Hubbard proposed establishing an American astronomical journal, to be "the embodiment as it were of American Astronomy." It was to be based on the model of Schumacher's *Astronomische Nach-*

richten, and Gould was intended as editor. On the motion of Benjamin Peirce, the physical section of the association approved the idea and appointed a select committee to carry it into effect, comprising Henry; Peirce, C. H. Davis, and Gould from Cambridge; Bache and Sears C. Walker from the Coast Survey; and Maury, Hubbard, and J. H. C. Coffin from the Naval Observatory. In the fall, the committee issued a printed prospectus, and gathered support from the American Philosophical Society and the American Academy of Arts and Sciences. The journal began publication in November 1849.

Peirce to Bache, June 7, 1849, Bache Papers, Smithsonian Archives; Bache to Peirce, June 14, 1849, Bache Scrapbook, Peirce Papers, Houghton Library, Harvard University; J. S. Hubbard, "On the Establishment of an Astronomical Journal in the United States," AAAS *Proceedings*, 1849, 2:378–381 (quotation on p. 380); "Circular [and] Prospectus [by B. A. Gould et al.]," reprinted in *Silliman's Journal*, 1849, 2d ser. 8:449–450; D. B. Herrmann, "B. A. Gould and His *Astronomical Journal*," *Journal for the History of Astronomy*, 1971, 2:98–108, especially p. 104.

3. Sparks had recently been elected president of Harvard. No evidence exists that Harvard contributed to the support of the journal.

347. TO ASA GRAY

Smithsonian Institution
Nov 21st 1849

My Dear Dr

Your favour of the 19th has just been received.[1] We shall be much pleased with a short course of lectures from Professor Harvey on his return from the South[2] if he cannot give them when he first visits Washington. We cannot pay much, the drafts on our income on account of the building have left us for the present in rather low water. We can pay 25 dolls per lecture and any expenses which may be incurred on account of illustrations. Prof. H. could give us three lectures in a week and would therefore not be long delayed in this city.

I regret to learn that Sprague[3] is unwell and that he comes on slowly with his drawings. I hope you will keep him alive, he is too valuable a man to be allowed to slip off the stage for want of attention to his physical condition—

The second volume of contributions is in the press. Eight memoirs have been received and accepted. I have concluded to print each memoir seperately after the plan adopted by the academy of Brussels.[4] I do not think there will be any difficulty in the way of reference, if on each memoir we give the vol, and the number of the article in the vol.

I hope you will not draw on me again, if possible, until the 1st of Jany we shall then have from interest upwards of 20 thousand Dolls.[5] The building has been pressed on very rapidly this fall inorder to close it in previous to the begining of winter.

I would be pleased with an account of the progress you have made in the Report on trees to present to the Regents at their next meeting which takes place on the 1st Wednesday (the 2nd) of Jany. Also an account of the explorations of Wright, and any ~~other~~ suggestions ~~which~~ which you may be pleased to communicate.[6]

I have spoken to Professor Jewett relative to Michaux and he agrees with me that it will be best for you to secure the copy you mention for the Library of the Institution, you can have the use of it for the preparation of your report.[7]

All things relative to the Smithsonian appear to be in good condition. Our[A] 1st volume has[B] been well received abroad, and all the learned societies of Europe, from present indications, will exchange with us.

The box containing the articles you sent was recived a few days ago; the books presented by yourself have[C] been deposited in the Library, and will be acknowledged.

I am rejoiced to hear that the health of Mrs G has improved, and I shall not fail to inform Mrs H of the message to her. Dr Hare is at the table with me while I am writing this letter[8] and bids me give you and your good Lady his kind regards and to assure you that there have been but few days of his life more pleasant than those which he spent at your house. Dr Torrey's youngest daughter[9] is to spend the winter with us; She is expected at the opening of congress. Shall we not have the pleasure of a visit from Mrs Gray and yourself this winter? Cannot ~~not~~ you favour us with a course of at least 3 lectures— We shall, I think, be able to make your time[D] pass agreeably in Washington and both Mrs H and myself would be delighted to have you for our guests.

> I remain as ever your friend
> & servant
> Joseph Henry

Dr Asa Gray

P.S. Please sign the accompanying account and return it to us. The allowance for Sprague without farther explanation may produce some difficulty in auditing[E] the account.[10]

J–H–

P.P S.[F] Enclosed I send you samples of shavings from died wood for examination under the microscope.

J–H–

Historic Letters, Archives, Gray Herbarium Library, Harvard University.
Marginal note by Gray opposite fifth paragraph: "Write 25 Decr."

1. Henry Papers, Smithsonian Archives.
2. According to Gray's letter, in mid-December Harvey was heading to Florida and Jamaica, not to return until spring.
3. Isaac Sprague.
4. That is, in the *Mémoires de l'Académie royale des sciences, des lettres, et des beaux-arts de Belgique.*
5. Gray had applied to Henry for funds to reimburse him for support of Charles Wright's natural history expedition to the Southwest.
6. Gray communicated information on Ferdinand Jacob Lindheimer, Augustus Fendler, and Wright, which Henry worked into the *Smithsonian Report for 1849*, pp. 23–24.
7. Gray had requested the purchase of François Michaux's *The North American Sylva, or, A Description of the Forest Trees of the United States, Canada, and Nova Scotia*, the first English-language edition, published in Paris and Philadelphia, 1817–1819, 6 vols. in 3, a translation by Au-

gustus L. Hillhouse of *Histoire des arbes forestiers de l'Amerique septentrionale* (Paris, 1810–1813).
8. Hare had arrived on November 17 for a ten-day visit. He presented Henry with his memoir on the explosiveness of nitre that would eventually form part of the second volume of the SI Contributions; sold the institution some scientific books and periodicals; and made arrangements about the apparatus he had donated. Desk Diary, November 17, 21, 22, 23, 27, and 28, 1849.
9. Margaret A. Torrey.
10. Sprague was preparing drawings and engravings for Gray's report on forest trees. The specific invoice Henry mentioned has not survived, but Sprague would first be paid in February 1850 for this work. Gray to Henry, September 7, 1849, Henry Papers, Smithsonian Archives; Smithsonian Daybooks, vol. 1, p. 105.

348. TO MATTHEW FONTAINE MAURY

Observatory Nov 27th 1849

My Dear Sir

I regret that I do not find you at the observatory— I have brought with me Mr Walker's paper on the Planet Neptune[1] which I wish to exhibit to you and to request that you will make any changes in it you may think fit. You will find a paper in the 1st Section containing a statement which I propose to insert in the preface of the article[2] which I hope will do justice to the observatory and obviate all difficulty— The changes which you may propose in the memoir may be communicated to me and I will take the responsibility of making them.[3]

> I remain very truly
> Your obt servt
> Joseph Henry

Lieut Maury
Super of the Observatory

Letters Received by the Naval Observatory, Records of the Naval Observatory, RG 78, National Archives.
Reply: December 3, 1849, Letters Sent by the Naval Observatory, Records of the Naval Observatory, RG 78, National Archives.

1. A draft of Sears C. Walker's *Researches Relative to the Planet Neptune,* [1850], SI Contributions, vol. 2 (Washington, 1851). This draft has not been found.

2. The published work contained no preface.

3. In his reply, Maury strongly objected to the proposed paper for not giving enough credit to the Naval Observatory and to him for his direction of Walker while the latter was in his employ. In particular, referring to Walker's search in older star catalogs for previous sightings of an object that could be identified as Neptune, Maury wrote: "Mͬ Walker was directed to do this. It was his duty—he was paid for it—and that he might do it the better, he was excused from working at the Instrument." However, if the paper were recast so as to give the observatory justice,

> I will as a personal favor to yourself, and to give you a practical proof of the impression which your course in the matter has made

upon me, consent that an account of the labor of the Observatory in this matter shall be given to the world in the Smithsonian Contributions.

Otherwise, Maury would feel compelled to object to the Smithsonian publication. (The fact that the Naval Observatory's printing of its *Astronomical Observations* for 1846 had recently burned in a fire, precluding the observatory's publication until 1851 and thus after the Smithsonian's, added to Maury's frustration.)

Henry and Maury met to discuss the work, the result of which was Henry's shortening and recasting of the memoir by the end of the year. In the published article, sections of pages 10 and 18–19 were apparently rewritten to show the more active involvement of Maury and others at the Naval Observatory.

In addition to Maury's reply, see Henry to Maury, December 21, 1849, in same location as this letter; and Maury to Henry, December 26, 1849, in same location as reply.

349. FROM JOHN TORREY

Princeton, Decͬ 1st 1849.

My dear friend—

Your letter of Novͬ 14th[1] was received in due time. You were to call that same evening to converse with him[2] respecting the Mexican Boundary Commission. I trust that something favorable was elicited from him. As our Government cannot <u>directly</u> [?fun] ↑promote↓ science, we must be constantly on the watch for opportunities to give it collateral aid by obtaining the appointment of good men to exploring & other expeditions.[3]

You probably misapprehended my last letter[4] in relation to two botanical works. One of them, (namely Endlicher & Martiuss plants of Brazil)[5] I am a subscriber for—but the other (Nuttall's N. American Forest Trees)[6] I have not— The latter I greatly wished to use & cannot afford to purchase: The former is the one I wished you to assume (for the Smithsonian) the subscription of.[7]

If I can possibly get all the drawings for my botanical paper—so long promised you—done in time, I shall be glad to have it printed in the 2nd vol. of the Sm. Contributions, so as to have the matter disposed of. I am now urging Gray to forward the drawings & he has promised to do his best—

I herewith send you Endicotts estimate for printing the plates, & also a sample of the paper which he proposes to use. Some of the plates are ready to strike off—& you thought that Endicott might do the printing if his terms were favorable. I think you will find no fault with the estimate here enclosed.

You have probably been informed by Mr Brackenridge of his visit to Princeton. He came to shew his mss of a work on Ferns, which he has long been preparing for the US. Exploring Exped[n] He brought also a quantity of his splendid folio plates. I think his work will do himself & our country great credid.[8]

Madge is all ready, but I have not yet concluded about her escort. Bobby Horner[9] was to have gone to Washington about the opening of Congress, but my damsel don't like to put herself under his care. It seems that Miss Martha Dod[10,A] is also going to the Seat of Government—to spent part of her time there with you. The two girls may go on there together, & I believe Miss D. expects to find some protector in Philadelphia.

Why don't you get some well-educated & obliging young man to be your assistant Secty? After he became acquainted with your business & habits, he could spare you a large part of the time now given to your correspondence & leave you the opportunity of making some researches.[11]

I hope Mrs. Henry will not find Madge a burden to her— Give her Mrs. Torrey's love & my kindest regards—

Yours cordially
John Torrey

Henry Papers, Smithsonian Archives.
Reply: December 26, 1849, Torrey Papers, Library, New York Botanical Garden.

1. The letter is dated November 13 (Torrey Papers, Library, New York Botanical Garden).

2. Secretary of State John M. Clayton.

3. Henry replied that the corps was already full when he spoke with Clayton and that W. H. Emory's subsequent departure from the commission left it "in a more unfavorable condition for doing any thing in the way of original research and exploration."

4. Not found.

5. S. F. L. Endlicher and K. F. P. von Martius, eds., *Flora Brasiliensis*, 15 vols. (Munich, 1840–1906).

6. Thomas Nuttall, *The North American Sylva*, 3 vols. (Philadelphia, 1842–1849), an appendix to a new edition of Michaux's work of the same title.

7. In his November 13 letter, Henry promised to take the books for the Smithsonian library although he could not pay for them until the next year.

8. Brackenridge's *Filices, Including Lycopodiaceae and Hydropterides* appeared in two parts: the text in 1854 and the plates in 1855. Both Torrey and Gray revised the manuscript prior to publication. John Hendley Barnhart, "Brackenridge and His Book on Ferns," *Journal of the New York Botanical Garden*, 1919, *20*:117–124.

9. Robert E. Hornor, owner of the *Princeton Whig* and a pillar of the Whig Party in New Jersey. *Henry Papers*, *5*:137n.

10. A daughter of the late Albert Baldwin Dod and later wife of Edwin Augustus Stevens (1795–1868, *DAB*).

11. In his November 13 letter, Henry had complained of the amount of time taken up by correspondence. In his reply of December 26 he continued:

> With the duties of an architect—a financier—an accountant a director of researches—an editor &c&c my time is pretty fully occupied.— I have however the assistance of a gentleman [Edward Foreman] who devotes all his time to the duties of the office and renders the most important service— still we can scarcely keep up with the correspondence and discharge the other duties which devolve on us.

350. FROM SPENCER FULLERTON BAIRD

Carlisle, Dec. 1, 1849.

Dear Sir,

It is with great reluctance that I interrupt you at a time when you must be so busy as now, but your own experience of printers has no doubt long ago informed you of the fact that they greedily devour copy. I have been holding back the Mss. of the article on Magnetism until I could hear from you as to the precise points in which your name ought to be mentioned in connection with the history of the Science. Am I right in giving the following as your discoveries, or rather is there anything else which I have omitted? 1st The application of electro-magnetism to the construction of large magnets; 2^d The suggestion of electro-magnetism as a motive power: 3rd The discovery of secondary or induced currents: 4 What is the precise relation in which you stand to the electro magnetic telegraph. 5th The^A discovery of the action of atmospheric electricity on the telegraph wires.[1] In these days of conflicting claims of different nations, I am very anxious that America shall have all the credit she deserves among her own children, and I hope that you will not hesitate about assisting me in this matter on account of your known reluctance to advance your own claims.

Did you receive a letter I wrote[2] in reply to your last,[3] about four weeks ago? If not, I am afraid you will think me very remiss, in not answering. Serious complaints are made of our Postmaster of the way in which he mismanages his business, and there is good ground of presumption that the letter may still be lying in the office here. You asked me[B] whether I could not furnish you with a brief report of operations with the funds entrusted to my care for Natural History purposes, and the progress which I had made in collecting. May I repeat what will seem tiresome to you, if you have received my letter of Nov. 3ᵈ?— I would be very happy to make[C] such report if you thought that in the event of no election of curator this winter, its publication would not draw down upon you a host of impracticable applicants for similar grants which might worry you excessively, as well as start new claimants and applications without number for the curatorship. It might too, excite a jealousy in the minds of the trustees as to my making collections for any other institution than this College. I refer more particularly to collections other than those made during the Virginia trip, although they would have no right to any such feeling ↑and I would not hesitate on that account↓: Please let me know as to this matter, if not too late. I have very recently received the finest collection of European reptiles and fresh water fish, I ever saw; by far the best in the country. I also obtained some additional fossil bones from the Susquehanna, embracing remains of the extinct elk. I challenge comparison now as to my collection of fossil northern vertebrates.

As the meeting of the regents approaches, I become more and more anxious, and uneasy as to result, especially as not knowing whether you have concluded to make the nomination this winter or not.[4] My position here is becoming more and more distasteful to me every day, and now that Prof. Allen has been carried off to the Presidency of Girard College,[5] I have lost my only congenial associate. I look forward too, with feelings of actual dread, to the time when I shall have to commence chemical lectures, which will take place ↑early↓ next year, or as soon as I have finished Natural Philosophy. This, is a delightful pursuit to me, but the drudgery of preparing illustrations in Chemistry which will leave scarcely an interval of time to devote to pursuits more congenial, after[D] fulfilling my obligations as an editor, is exceedingly painful in anticipation. I want now to be busied in laying the foundation of a valuable and (in this country) unique cabinet of comparative anatomy, by adding to what I already possess, the skeletons of the domestic animals. Every time too, that I hear the cry of fire in the streets, I am in an agony of apprehension lest the frail wooden building in which I keep my treasures may take fire, and I thus lose what I feel cannot well be replaced ↑and what would be so secure in the cellars of the Smithsonian building↓. I also want to take advantage of the brief period during which our troops will be in Florida,[6,E] to visit that country, and take advantage of my connections with many of the officers as well as of my relation to the Inspector General,[7] to start a series of collections, by which I think more could be done in elucidating the Natural History of that remarkable peninsula, than has been yet[F] accomplished. In particular I wish to secure a perfect suite of skeletons and other preparations, young and old of the manatee, an exceedingly interesting cetacean, of which but two specimens are within my knowledge, ↑as in collections↓ and these not perfect.

Would not the fact that the Smithsonian Institution had a large collection of objects of Natural history, ready to place in her rooms as soon as they were ready for their reception, be the best reason for not taking charge of the collections of the exploring expedition? With a large room perfectly or nearly empty, and an increasing fulness in the Patent office, might not a greatly to be deprecated action of Congress be invoked, which should[G] have for its object to compel you to take charge of these collections, and which it might be difficult to refuse? Whereas with an indigenous collection, any attempt at foisting those in question, upon you, might be met by showing that if you did take charge of them you could not keep them separate from your own but, would be obliged to merge all together. This, the pride of the Navy and of the Savants of the Expedition would never permit and a powerful interest would be enlisted in keeping the Expedition specimens out of your control. And at any rate, your possession of a curator would not be any reason for your assuming the charge of that[H] expensive collection, to support which, would require a goodly amount of funds, which perhaps can not well be spared for some years.

Bear with me, dear Sir, in my importunity with which I know you can sympathize. I need not deny that I am very desirous of the immediate appointment, and at the same time I know that with the kindest feelings towards myself, you will do what you think is your duty. I would fain hope that duty will be a good[I] friend to me in this emergency. The election might be made to take effect on the first of July, if not in January; and even in this case I can make such arrangements as will give me my liberty before July, so as to permit me to commence active service. I feel well assured that Prof. Jewett will cordially agree to an early nomination. In the hope that I have not wearied you by this interminable letter I remain

Very truly Yours
S. F. Baird.

Henry Papers, Smithsonian Archives.
Letterpress copy: Baird Papers, Smithsonian Archives. Reply: Doc. 351.

1. Baird mentioned Henry in connection with all of the above except the suggestion of electromagnetism as a motive power. The effect of lightning on telegraph wires was in the meteorology section, as was Henry's suggestion of an "excellent, safe, and economical plan" of lightning protection. J. G. Heck, *Iconographic Encyclopaedia of Science, Literature, and Art,* trans. and ed. Spencer F. Baird, 4 vols. (New York, 1851), pp. 339, 342, 351, 419, 421.

2. Doc. 341.

3. Doc. 340.

4. Jewett had written Mary Baird on November 29 to report on a conversation with Henry about Baird's appointment. Jewett informed her that if Henry was successful in getting the regents to devote some of the building fund to active operations for two years, he thought Baird would be appointed at the next meeting. Baird Papers, Smithsonian Archives.

5. William Henry Allen (1808–1882), professor of mental philosophy and English literature at Dickinson College, had just been elected president of Girard College. He served until 1863, then resumed the presidency in 1867 and held it until his death. *DAB;* Cheesman A. Herrick, *History of Girard College* (Philadelphia, 1927), pp. 41, 141–150.

6. Although there were federal troops permanently stationed at forts in Tampa and St. Augustine, a much larger number had recently been sent to Florida in response to two attacks in July in which outlaw Seminoles killed three white men and looted and burned several houses and a store. Although negotiations resolved the immediate crisis, the troops remained in the area for some time. James W. Covington, *The Billy Bowlegs War, 1855–1858: The Final Stand of the Seminoles against the Whites* (Chuluota, Florida, 1982), pp. 9–15.

7. Sylvester Churchill, Baird's father-in-law.

351. TO SPENCER FULLERTON BAIRD

Smithsonian Institution
Dec 11th 1849

My Dear Sir

I have no doubt that you are very anxious to learn the state of the Smithsonian affairs particularly with reference to the probability of your appointment at the next meeting of the Board, and I regret that with my present engagements I am unable to go into a full exposition of all the facts bearing on the question. From present appearances I do not think there is any prospect of your being appointed at the approaching meeting though if the state of the funds are no worse than I think they are something more may perhaps be allowed for collections.[1]

You know that inorder to increase the principal of the Smithsonian fund the Regents resolved to defer the full operation of the Institution until after march 1852. They wished and still ↑wish↓ to be able to state to the public that after completing the building and getting the Institution under way they have added 150 thousand dolls to the original fund. Every proposition which interferes with this plan is received with coolness. The plan was originnaly suggested by the probability[A] that I was about to resign the office of Secretary and it was afterwards modified so as not to bring in Professor Jewett until the ↑completion of the↓ building was completed. This part of the plan was warmly opposed by Mr Jewett and his friends, and I think justly, because he had been appointed to commence his duties three years before the above mentioned time. The plan was adopted and Professor Jewett was brought in 3 months before the time mentioned in his appointment and in consequence of this I asked at the last session of the Board that an additional appropriation might be made for the active operations of the Institution, this hower was reluctantly granted and was finally considered favourably on account of the advance in the value of the stock which formed the principal part of the building fund— All the appropriations of the present year have been expended and besides this a portion of the Library of Mr. Marsh, to the value of 3000 Dolls, has been purchased. The purchase was made in the first place with the idea that the money need not be ↑was not to be↓ advanced on it until the end of three years. Mr Marsh however found it impossible to make his arrangements for leaving the country with ↑out↓ receiving at least a part of the money and inorder to prevent dificulty I advanced 1500 Dolls on my own account, and promised to propose to the Board that the whole should be paid at the begining of the next year. From the above statement you will perceive that we shall be much streghtened next year unless the Board conclude to abandon the financial[B] scheme they have adopted.

I can assure you that it would give me much pleasure to nominate you to the office of naturalist were there any prospect that the nomination would, at present be for the best interest of the Institution or that it would be acted on by the Board. I have told you that you are my choice and if nothing occurs to change my opinion of your character of which I see not the slightest prospect I shall nominate you to the Board ↑in due time↓. You must recollect howev (and I know you do) that in all the appointments I must be governed by what I conceive to be the best for the Institution. I shall know no friendship in the choise and if you are elected it will be because, all things considered you are the best man; you will therefore owe your election to your own reputation— though I shall nominate you with the understanding that you will assist in carrying out the plan of organization of the Institution set forth in the Programme.

Enclosed I send send you a sketch of my connection with the telegraph[2] and also accompanying a phamphlet containing some of my discoveres in Electricity[3]—My time is now so much occupied that I am unable to give you an account of my researches in other branches of science.

> I remain truly your
> friend &—
> Joseph Henry

Prof Baird
P.S. I have attempted to write to you three times before this.

Baird Papers, Smithsonian Archives.
Note in margin of last page, in Edward Foreman's hand: "Please sign the bill herewith sent." Reply: December 14, 1849, Henry Papers, Smithsonian Archives.

1. In his reply, Baird asked if Henry would have time to see him in Washington in a week or two to discuss "the operations of the Institution, and the business of collecting," requesting specifically whether he could store some of his rapidly accumulating specimens in the cellar of the Smithsonian Building.

2. Probably the one-page history filed with Henry's letter to Baird, April 23, 1850, Baird Papers, Smithsonian Archives.

3. Possibly Henry's "Contributions to Electricity and Magnetism. No. II.—On the Influence of a Spiral Conductor in Increasing the Intensity of Electricity from a Galvanic Arrangement of a Single Pair, &c.," *Transactions of the American Philosophical Society*, 1837, 2d ser. 5:223–231.

352. [TO MARY H. GILL][1,A]

Smithsonian Institution Dec. 12th, 1849.

We are on the whole well pleased with our residence in this place, and have formed a number of pleasant acquaintances. Washington however during the session of Congress is a place of unrest. The position I now occupy is one of great responsibility and labor and its duties have occupied nearly all my thoughts for the last three years. I regret that I have been so much withdrawn from the pursuits in which by long study and experience, I was best qualified to make advances. I am however reconciled to the change, from the consciousness that I am in the way of doing much good. I have a wide sphere of influence and the difficulties with which I am surrounded serve to stimulate exertion. I have been obliged to study the moral philosophy of my position with care, and constantly to act in accordance with principles which I have well considered. Few can imagine the difficulty of properly administering an important trust, connected with government. Honesty of purpose is not sufficient in a situation of this kind; prudence, firmness and moral courage also are requisite, and the latter can not be expected in any case, where the proper course of action is not clearly marked out in the mind of the incumbent. Men in office are sometimes really to be pitied; they desire to do right but know not what the right is, amidst the perplexities which surround them; or, another difficulty—the right and best course they may distinctly see, and yet they may not be able to pursue it, because they are controlled by others, outvoted and so compelled to do not what they would but what they can, towards effecting their purposes. The last three years of my life have formed a season of almost constant struggle to direct the affairs of the Smithsonian Institution so as to produce the greatest amount of good. Though I have not in all cases been able to accomplish all I wished I have reason to be thankful that I have done as much as I could have reasonably expected, and more than my friends hoped for. I am making my answer to your acceptable letter[2] the means of indulging my egotism; you requested however to be informed of my present position.

Mary Henry Copy, Henry Papers, Smithsonian Archives.

1. An unidentified correspondent who may have been a former neighbor of A. D. Bache's in Philadelphia. *Henry Papers*, 5:391n.

2. Not found.

353. REPORT ON ORMSBY MacKNIGHT MITCHEL'S EXPERIMENTS

Smithsonian Institution
Dec. 13th 1849[A]

I have examined Profr. Mitchell's experiments on the transmission of Electricity, and as far as I can make out the arrangements, from his very brief account of them, I think they are very ingenious; though to my mind the results are not conclusive with reference to any of the hypotheses[B] he has mentioned.[1]

In every case he employs, for indicating the time, the developement of magnetic force in soft iron. The objection to this method is, that the developement of magnetism itself is a process which requires time for its completion. The length of this time depends, probably, on the intensity and the quantity of the current, and also on the character of the iron. Besides this, a single disturbance which may be considered the element of a wave, is not sufficient to produce an appreciable magnetism; it requires a series of these forming a short current to pass around the iron before the magnetism is fully develloped. Again, the developement of the magnetism of a peice of iron surrounded with a part of the wire of a long circuit[C] is retarded by the adverse action of the initial secondary induced current, in the wire, which increases with the length of the circuit; and also the magnetism of the same iron is prolonged at the time of the breaking of the circuit by the terminal secondary induced current.

Wheatstones Experiments are not open to these objections[2] and since he has proved beyond doubt that the spark appears last at the middle of a long wire, I am inclined to the hypothesis that the beginning of the disturbance, called an Electrical current, is simultaneously progressive from either pole of the battery and arrives in succession at corresponding points of each branch of the wire, reaching the middle point last.

I think it probable that different results would be produced in these experiments ↑if↓ the marks on the revolving disc were made with the decomposing arrangement used by Bain in his Telegraph.[3]

Joseph Henry

Letter Books, 1849, vol. 6, "Miscellaneous," pp. 292–293, General Correspondence of Alexander Dallas Bache, Records of the Coast and Geodetic Survey, RG 23, National Archives.
In an unknown hand, with place, date, interlineation, signature, and possibly alterations by Henry.

1. It is unclear exactly what Henry was evaluating. Mitchel was cooperating with Coast Survey efforts directed by Sears C. Walker to measure the velocity of electricity in order to be able to make corrections for distance between widely separated observing stations which used the telegraph to record longitude and astronomical observations. Although Charles Wheatstone had determined a figure for the speed of a static electric discharge through copper wire, the Coast Survey needed to determine the speed of electricity using galvanic electricity through iron telegraph wires such as were then in use. Mitchel's reports of his work just prior to this include a November 10 report to Bache (*Coast Survey Report for 1849*, pp. 72–78); a November 16 communication: "On the Velocity of the Electrical Wave or Current, Through a Metallic Circuit," *Astronomical Journal*, 1851, 1:13–16; and a report of November 28 for which we have found only Henry's evaluation (Henry Papers, Smithsonian Archives). Mitchel was also in direct correspondence with

Bache: on December 14, Bache sent Henry a letter from Mitchel for his "consideration" (Henry Papers, Smithsonian Archives). Henry was evidently being consulted for his expertise in electromagnetism.

Mitchel reported in the published article that he slightly modified his automatic clock register to measure the velocity of electricity. He made one of two recording pens part of a local circuit. The other could be switched between a 960-kilometer-long circuit using the telegraph lines between Cincinnati and Pittsburgh and a local circuit. While the first pen was driven by a clock and recorded clock-beats or seconds on a revolving metal disk, the second was activated by a receiving magnet and recorded the time of an event. Mitchel made various adjustments, for instance in battery intensity, and came up with a figure roughly ten times lower than Wheatstone's. Although he expressed confidence in the results, "as every care was taken to eliminate all possible sources of error" (p. 16), he hoped to continue the experiments "at dif-

ferent hours of the day and night, at different seasons of the year, and through different
media" (p. 16).

Philip S. Shoemaker, "Stellar Impact: Ormsby MacKnight Mitchel and Astronomy in Antebellum America," (Ph.D. diss., University of
Wisconsin-Madison, 1991), pp. 182–184; *Coast
Survey Report for 1849*, p. 31; B. A. Gould, Jr.,
"On the Velocity of the Galvanic Current in
the Telegraph Wires," AAAS *Proceedings*, 1850,
4:71–100.

2. In his determination of the velocity of
electricity, Wheatstone used spark gaps rather
than a mechanical device activated by electro-
magnetism. *Henry Papers*, 2:491–493.

3. See Doc. 171, note 4. Although using the
Bain electrochemical telegraph eliminated the
problem of the "pass-time," the time it took for
the armature to close the local circuit, it introduced other errors. Gould, pp. 85–86.

354. FROM LOUIS AGASSIZ

Cambridge 31 X'[1] 1849.[A]

Prof Henry.
Dear Sir,

Besides my official answer[2] allow me to add a few lines to apologize
for not answering your kind letter[3] and delaying sending my MSC.[4] But
I have lately received two large works upon subjects indirectly connected with my paper, which I must have read before I can give up my
MSC. for the press. It shall however be finished without much further
delay.

I have ↑probably↓ to be in Washington in the course of February to
look over the fishes of the Ex. Exp if Capt Wilkes agrees to a proposition
which I have made to him, about them.[5] If it is convenient to you we
might select the same period for my first lectures in Washington. I have
of course a large number of diagrams which I shall take on with me to
illustrate my subject, and I trust your lecture room is provided with a
large blackboard. So that nothing more were wanting. Pray let me know
if this is acceptable to you.

What would you say if I were not to come alone, but as a married
man? The fact is that I am engaged to Miss Lizzie Cary[6] and very very
happy to be so. It is one more connection with this country and your
friendship tells me that you will not be sorry to learn it. Mention it if
you please to ↑the invisible↓ Dr Bache.

With high regard
your sincere friend
L Agassiz

Henry Papers, Smithsonian Archives.

1. That is, December 31.

2. Not found, but possibly the letter excerpted as "Communication from Professor Agassiz, Relative to the Formation of a Museum," *Smithsonian Report for 1849*, pp. 24–26.

3. Not found; in his Desk Diary entry of November 22, Henry noted writing to Agassiz about "lecturing papers Report."

4. *The Classification of Insects from Embryological Data*, 1850, SI Contributions, vol. 2 (Washington, 1851). According to its title page, the article was finally received March 6, 1850.

5. After involved negotiations, Agassiz agreed to work on the fish collections of the Wilkes Expedition in Cambridge. Although he completed a two-thousand-page manuscript by

1861, Wilkes was unable to get Congress to appropriate funds for publication. George E. Watson, "Vertebrate Collections: Lost Opportunities," in *Magnificent Voyagers: The U.S. Exploring Expedition, 1838–1842*, ed. Herman J. Viola and Carolyn Margolis (Washington, 1985), pp. 66, 69.

6. Elizabeth Cabot Cary (1822–1907), a member of several prominent Boston families, later Agassiz's biographer, and a founder of Radcliffe College. Agassiz, whose first wife died in Switzerland in July 1848, met her in 1847 through Harvard classicist Cornelius C. Felton, who was married to Elizabeth's sister, Mary. Edward Lurie, *Louis Agassiz: A Life in Science* (1960; Chicago, 1966), pp. 166–175; *DAB*.

355. FROM SAMUEL TYLER

31ˢᵗ Dec: 1849.
Frederick City Maryland

My dear Sir

I herewith send you the work of my friend the late Dʳ Harrison[1] of New Orleans. You will please keep the book as long as your convenience may require.

I have also sent a copy of my work on the Baconian Philosophy[2] with a note, for Sir D. Brewster, which you were kind enough to offer to send to him. The note is open that you may see it.

After my return here, I looked over Newton's Principia, in order that I might contrast it with the Physio-philosophy of Oken,[3] while both works were fresh in my mind. And what cogent testimony does the contrast afford, in favour of the inductive method, in unraveling the intricacies of nature! Newton's whole argument is professedly based upon phenomena. The mathematical principles necessary for the physical investigation setforth in the first & second books, are avowedly based upon the laws and conditions of certain motions and forces observed upon the earth. Then, in the beginning of the third book, four rules of inductive reasoning are laid down; then six summaries of phenomena are stated, upon which the reasonings are to be based: and then from this experiential basis, "the frame of the system of the world" is demonstrated. Amidst all the intricacies of mathematical demonstration, Newton, with a vigilant caution most marvelous never for a moment looses sight of phenomena. Induction is throughout the Principia, the logical centre and logical circumference, within and around which, all the demonstrations revolve. It has always filled me with an aspiring sympathy with all that is great in intellect, when I have dwelt upon this sublime argument and seen how, in the wonderous logical combinations, all the mathematical principles and deductions are subordinated to phenomena; and my feet have stood firmer in the inductive method.

While I had Newton in my hands, I looked at Emerson's defence of the Principia, to find the passage which a remark of yours brought to my mind in our conversation about ontology. In speaking of the argument of Leibnitz against empty space drawn from his metaphysical doctrine of "a sufficient reason," Emerson says: "So this world-maker will not agree to leave any room or free space for bodies to move in; and in this he is as dogmatical as if he had been originally one of God Almighty's privy council."[4]

Emerson, though a rough, was a very clear headed man. One of the clearest statements, in a few words, of the inductive method to be found, is in the preface to his "Principles of Mechanics."[5] Indeed, to the modern mathematicians we are indebted for[A] many of the clearest statemts of the inductive argument, and of the perennial[B] nature of the philosophy which it builds up. All are acquainted with the admirable views of Maclaurin in the first part of his commentary on the philosophy of Newton.[6] And even on the continent of Europe, in the beginning of the last century, Prof. J. Christ Sturmius of the university of Altorf had a remarkable insight into the modern logic both in physics and mathematics. In his "Mathesis Enucleata" he says that the mathematical method of the Ancients was as inferior to that of the moderns as their physical was.[7] This fact has not be sufficiently dwelt upon in the history of science. For it is well to note that the Synthetic method of the ancient mathematicians could never have rendered to physics the aid which the analytic method of the modern mathematicians has.[C] But the passage in the "Mathesis Enucleata" which chiefly attracted my attention, is this: "they also (the ancient mathematicians) made use of a certain sort of Analysis, whereby they found out those Theorems and Problems; and which, to raise the greater admiration in their readers they afterwards studiously concealed, and kept to themselves."[8] Sturmius here repudiates the pretended a priori character of the Synthetic method of the ancient mathematicians, and charges them with disingenuousness in concealing the anlysis by which they obtained their first principles. How applicable is this remark to the Physio-philosophy of Oken. All the doctrines in physics, which he pretends to have excogitated from the native conceptions of the reason, are but the experiential inferences from observation. Whatever is true in his philosophy, he has borrowed from the sciences, and whatever is false, is but his own <u>empirical</u> notions however he may disguise the matter to himself or to others.

Since my return home, I have been sick from the effects of a cold, and am still so. This together with engagements will compel me to forego the honor of lecturing in the Smithsonian Institution this season. Next season, if we like, I will do so. And I hope to be able to show, how entirely the philosophy of common sense has triumphed over all others, and now stands vindicated to reason.[9] A popular and practical form can be given to the subject. The rains of heaven do not more universally water every province of nature, than does ~~the~~ philosophy every province of thought. Therefore, points of contact betwen it and lower problems of thought must exist, and give it practical bearings.

> I am dear Sir very truly
> Your servant & friend
> Sam.⌐ Tyler

Prof: Joseph Henry

Henry Papers, Smithsonian Archives.

1. John Harrison, *An Essay towards a Correct Theory of the Nervous System* (Philadelphia, 1844), a presentation copy of which survives in the Henry Library. John Hoffman Harrison (1808–1849) had been professor of physiology and pathology at the Medical College of Louisiana and editor of the *New Orleans Medical and Surgical Journal* from 1845 to 1849. Thomas William Herringshaw, *Encyclopedia of American Biography of the Nineteenth Century* (Chicago, 1905).

2. Probably the second edition of Tyler's *Discourse of the Baconian Philosophy* (Frederick, Maryland, 1844).

3. Lorenz Oken (1779–1851), a German Romantic philosopher, natural scientist, and author of a system of *Naturphilosophie. DSB.*

4. William Emerson, "A Defence of Sir Isaac Newton against the Objections That Have Been Made to the Several Parts of the Principia," in *The Mathematical Principles of Natural Philosophy by Sir Isaac Newton*, rev. and corr. William Davis, trans. Andrew Motte, 3 vols. (London, 1819), *3*:192. Emerson (1701–1782, *DNB*), an English mathematician, made the remark in response to the claim of Leibnitz that God would not have left empty space but would have filled it with matter, which was in opposition to Newton's assertions that "all the great bodies in the world move in free space" and that "all bodies have pores or open spaces in them" (p. 191).

Leibnitz's critique of Newton was part of a famous philosophical debate between him and Samuel Clarke in the early 1700s. Leibnitz derived his views on space from his principle of sufficient reason, arguing that "the more matter there is, the more God has occasion to exercise his wisdom and power," and concluding "there is no vacuum at all." H. G. Alexander, ed., *The Leibniz-Clarke Correspondence* (1956; Manchester, 1970), quotation on p. 16.

5. Perhaps the following passage:

> For he [Newton] admits nothing but what he gains from experiments, and accurate observations. And from this foundation, whatever is further advanced, is deduced by strict mathematical reasoning.

This was in contrast, Emerson wrote, to the systems of other philosophers, which were "nothing but hypotheses, conceits, fictions, conjectures, and romances, invented at pleasure, and without any foundation in the nature of things." William Emerson, *The Principles of Mechanics*, 2d ed. (London, 1758), quotations on p. iv.

6. Colin Maclaurin, *An Account of Sir Isaac Newton's Philosophical Discoveries* (London, 1748). Maclaurin (1698–1746, *DSB*), a Scottish mathematician and natural philosopher, was a strong supporter of Newton.

7. J. Christophorus Sturmius, *Mathesis En-ucleata: or, The Elements of the Mathematicks,* trans. J. R. (London, 1700), preface, paragraph I. Sturmius wrote that just as

a blind deference to, and superstitious Veneration of Antiquity, and especially of *Aristotle,* has hindered the growth and progress of Natural Philosophy, . . . so without doubt Mathematicks also, . . . would have arrived long since to a higher pitch, and by this time have surpass'd those Limits, which now we admire its arrival to.

Sturmius, or Sturm (1635–1703), had been professor of mathematics and natural philosophy at the University of Altdorf. *World Who's Who in Science.*

8. Preface, paragraph VIII.

9. For Tyler and Scottish Common Sense philosophy, see *Henry Papers,* 6:563n.

FROM ARNOLD GUYOT

Cambridge Novr 7 1849.

Dear Sir

In reply to the letter which you did me the honor to address to me on the 1ˢᵗ November I have the honor to transmit to you a model of a meteorological register which appears to me useful for the observers to keep who shall receive a complete set of instruments—others may leave the columns blank which are useless to them. I beg permission to point out to you the motives which urged me to the distribution which I have adopted.

1. I set out with the principle that each sheet ought to be a complete and independent document carrying on its face all the marks necessary to correct and render useful directly the observations which it records. It should give the date, place geographical position, the altitude of the place of observation, the nature and the Corrections of the Instruments their accidental variations, finally the personal signature of the Observer which gives the piece its authenticity & places it under the responsibility of a name.

2 The order in which the columns follow indicates that in which the instruments ought to be observed. The external thermometer before opening the window to moisten the Psychrometer the thermometer of the Barometer before the approach of the observer has modified its temperature, then the Wind, the State of the Sky &c and in the last place the Psychrometer which will have had time to assume its proper temperature.

3 The observer should make an invariable rule to inscribe in theᴬ journal the ~~readings~~ ↑indications↓ of his instruments given by their immediate readings without making any mental Correction. The corrected values should have a seperate Column, as that in the case of the Barometer. The number of thermometers however renders double columns impracticable. It is likewise understood that thermometers will be fur-

nished to observers sufficiently exact so that their indications may be received[B] without Corrections. Having the means of correcting the zero point in the same instruments &[C] the meteorologist not being able to record an error in temperature of ½ a degree, it will not be very difficult to arrive at this result. As to the Psychrometer these are the only differences which are important, and every instrument of this kind of which the two thermometers do not entirely accord should be rejected. The columns of this last instrument are numerous, but it is essential to discover accidental errors that every element be represented completely.[D]

4 The Column for winds admits of many essential elements, the direction whence the clouds come, the disagreement between currents of air near the surface and at different heights of the atmosphere is a fact much[E] more common than we imagine and which appears to me of a great importance for the study of the laws of storms and the rotation of winds. During[F] the last blow of 30th October I saw three very distinct currents blowing simultaneously, at different heights and in different directions from S. W.S.W & N.E. during a considerable part of the time.

5.. To avoid copying and to diminish the chances of error consequent upon it, it[G] appears to me useful that each sheet should give a place for ↑the essential↓ <u>means</u>. A perpendicular column is reserved for the daily means of each of the elements, and horizontal columns for each groupe of 5 days. These columns besides have the advantage of diminishing the number of decimals and of facilitating addition & formation of the means. The last sheet of the month gives columns for the monthly means by hours & the general means. The observers being furnished with the necessary tables, it is to be hoped that the reductions will be made by them day by day as also the calculation of ↑the↓ means. This labour will be a small thing for each of them will interest them in the observations, giving them the results and facilitating greatly in their publication.

6 Each month is composed of three sheets ~~bearing~~ a numbered[H] in order. The model I send represents the third and last sheet. It contains on the ~~first~~ ↑last↓ page 11 days, in place of 10, for the month of 31 days. This inequality is avoided by continuous division by 5 without respect to months, as in the Prussian system, but taking it all together I have thought it would be better to preserve the grouping of the civil month. The two first sheets will contain but 10 days each, and the space reserved for abbreviations will be larger. The will not have the monthly resumè on the back, with this exception except the days of the month they resemble the third. It will be well to have them printed separately

in order to print likewise in their places the day of the month & the hours.

7. The number of observations for each day being very limited, it is expedient to induce observers to multiply them especially during storms and in unusual states of the atmosphere. The back of the sheet presents columns for this use.

8 To avoid errors from placing the decimals badly It may be well to rule light lines in all the spaces as is shown on the model which[I] accompanies the sheet.

9 The sheets need ↑should↓ not be ~~cut~~ ↑stitched↓[J] in the center but in the margin at the place marked[K] (o) for if folded in two and placed in a portfolio of the same size it may form a small volume provided with strings. There may be sent to each observer two series of 36 sheets for each year, one[L] of them for the original journal to be returned each month[M] to 👉 Washington, the other as a copy to be kept by him. He should receive besides other ↑supplementary↓ sheets in case of accident.

10 Each observer should likewise be furnished with a blank book in large 8vo to write down particular remarks and ↑detailed↓ descripti[on]s[N] of Phenomena which find no place on the register. As for instance an aurora Borealis is indicated ↑by a date↓ at[O] a place in the register which refers for a description of it to a page in the book of remarks. The resumè of meteorological epochs & the comparison of these with each other may likewise find a place in it. The Book of Remarks may have a form such as accompanies this letter.

You perceive Sir, by this table that I propose to adopt as hours of observations those proposed by Humboldt & Mahlman for the Kingdom of Prussia, by Lloyd, and which the Observations at Toronto prove to be sufficient to give good means in the northern part of the U.S.

This number of observations is undoubtedly too small for the the study of the daily variations of meteorological elements and that of the law of storms. But this last inconvenience will be much diminished & ~~in some degree~~ ↑even more than↓ compensated for, if the observers would voluntarily add extra observations during storms. As to regular oscillations they should be confided to ~~regular~~ ↑certain special↓ observatories, to which two ↑observers↓ instead of one should be attached, adding the supplementary hours recommended by Humboldt & Lloyd—10 AM and 6 PM[P] for temperature & humidity, 10 AM & 4 PM for the Barometer. This last view ~~appears to~~ ↑causes↓ me decidedly ↑to↓ prefer[Q] ~~to~~ the series 6, 2, 10 to that 7, 3, 11 which Capt Lefroy proposes. In adopting the latter the supplementary hours will not be placed at equal intervals as would be desirable or they would fall upon hours much less favorable for the study of the phenomena 11 & 7. Moreover the hours of 6, 2, 10 agree with the hours of rising, dining and going to rest, and would seem to incommode the observer the least possible— For the rest this question of hours of observation is unsettled, for America, in different latitudes. The results of the Girard College observations if analysed will throw light on this question.

With regard to Phychrometric[R] tables, after a new examination my intention was to propose to adopt as best the tables of Haeghens, in the Annuaire Meteorologique de France. You will find them at page 114 of the Volume. M. Haeghens takes into account all the labours of others on this subject & especially of M Regnault as you will see by the pages which precede his tables. The tables are likewise as convenient as any which have been published and of very sufficient exactitude[s] as you may see by ~~the differences of~~ the Vertical & horizontal ↑differences of the↓ Column of Tensions and of that of relative humidity. Moreover they apply to a thermometer covered with ice. I hold them to be preferable to all others. I likewise do not hesitate to propose that the psychrometers, at least, be graduated according to the Centigrade Scale. It is an excellent chance moreover to familiarize observers with this scale, and no inconvenience can result from it since the scale is but one of the ~~moye~~ means of arriving at the valuation of the relative humidity which in two ways expresses itself in 100[ths]. If you always think it necessary to ↑offrir↓ keep the tables in English measures I am quite assured that Capt Lefroy will charge himself with transforming the tables of Haeghens, but I confess for my part, I should be sorry to see this superfluous labour performed. I do not advise ↑you↓ to admit the three scales in the same tables ~~as he proposes~~. We must avoid every decimal which is not directly useful to the observer who makes use of it. It will diminish the ↑perspicuity↓ and increase the chance of errors. Each table should be seperate and complete.

In reference to Thermometers I have[T] just ~~about to~~ received[U] of ↑my friend↓ M Charles Martin the news that Bunten J[r] of whom I ordered a specimen Thermometer is since dead. M. Martin assures me that the best living maker of thermometers is M. Fasteret who works under the special direction of M. Regnault. He can make, if he please, excellent Psychrometers.

For[V] the reduction of the Barometer to 32°F the tables of Delcros in the Annuaire de france are of great convenience & give at sight without addition for each 10th of a degree (Centigrade) the value of the Correction, but they suppose the use of the metrical scale. For the English division the tables contained in the Report of the Committee on Meteorology of the Royal Society of London 1840 page 82 are sufficient though they give the Value of the Correction only ~~degree by~~ ↑for each↓ degree—it is easy to make at sight an interpolation for fractions of degrees.

I fear I shall be unable to revise the translation and deliver my report before my return from the journey which I am about to commence. But during this time I can send ~~it~~ to you, if you desire ↑the↓ special instructions which accompany the ~~tables~~ blank forms to be sent to observers. We may take those of M. Mahlman as a basis, I have found them very good and in which but few alterations need be made, as they are translated in the Report of the Regents of the Unv^y of N. York. They may very well serve for the first movement.

The 36 Thermometers of Green which I brought here have very well sustained themselves under the trials to which I have hitherto submitted them. The ↑écarts↓ variations do not exceed ½ a degree. I shall to day finish the comparison of which I have kept a register ↑par [?pamiers]↓.

In reply to a letter which I addressed to him last week Mr Green has said that 8 of the new Barometers are ready and that the others to be repaired will be ready at the beginning of this week. I shall therefore set out for N York to compare them, on Saturday or Monday. I shall compare them also with the Newman of Columbia College.

The Newman of the Smithso^n Inst^n at Mr Greens is marked much lower than that of the University of Cambridge as I have made the comparison with care and which accords with the ↑standard(?)↓ Barometer of Delcros &^W of Paris. I am about to submit it to new comparisons. It seems to me that probably it has taken in a little air. But as it sounds ve[r]y^N well, this cannot be the cause of the difference which it presents. The differences ~~of~~ in Instruments reputed perfect—every day proves the necessity of direct comparisons. If I go to Toronto I shall not fail to establish a comparison between the Newman of that observatory and the others.

The packet now forwarded also contains a note on the division of the State of New York into Meteorological stations, reviewing the results of our conference on the subject at Princeton. I do not know if you attach much importance to this document as I shall be in better condition to decide after seeing the places with my own eyes.

I shall await your directions at New York on Monday and [...]^X on the following points.

661

Should Instruments be established at Erasmus Hall (Flatbush) in the City of New York and in what spot—with whom shall I confer?

Shall I not repair immediately to D^r T Romeyn Beck to ~~stop~~ ↑fix↓ definitively upon the choice of stations and to see how it will be possible to establish them before ↑the↓ winter.

I beg you likewise to give me some orders concerning my travelling expenses and to have the kindness to send me a line of introduction to Dr Beck and (in case of need) for Capt Lefroy.

My address at New York is

A Guyot care of A. Mayor

22 Maiden Lane.

~~P.S.~~

I regret sir to have been unable to send you the whole sooner but I have worked day and night for a fortnight, to be in condition to absent my self for some weeks— Be pleased to receive the ~~expression~~ ↑assurance↓ of my highest regard and devotedness.

A Guyot

Prof^r

Prof J Henry
Smithson^n Institution

Folder "Letters from Prof. Guyot, 1849–50," Records of the Smithsonian Meteorological Project, Records of the Weather Bureau, RG 27, National Archives.

Translation of Doc. 342. In the hand of Edward Foreman, who presumably did the translation. All corrections and interlineations appear to be by Foreman. In some cases, he wrote a French word or words above the line and left a space on the line for the English equivalent.

❧ TEXT NOTES ❧

Doc. 1

A. Moved from end of letter.
B. Altered from *receit*
C. Altered from *to*
D. Interlineation in ink.
E. Altered from *this*
F. Altered, possibly from *everaye*

Doc. 2

A. Altered from *1846*
B. Altered from *lesst*
C. Altered from *thg*
D. Altered from *germ*
E. Altered from *your*
F. A two-centimeter break separates this paragraph from the following in the original.
G. Altered from *ussful*
H. Paper torn.

Doc. 3

A. From internal evidence.
B. Altered from *Gothick*

Doc. 4

A. From the postmark and internal evidence.
B. Altered from *plessant*
C. Paper torn.
D. Altered from *f*
E. Altered from *Eaton*
F. Henry left a 12.5-centimeter space between this paragraph and the next for the address.
G. Remainder written in left margin, beginning on first page.
H. Altered from *littles*
I. Altered from *attentions*

Doc. 5

A. From internal evidence.
B. Altered from *G*
C. Altered from *thi*
D. Altered from *it*

E. Altered from *c*
F. Altered from *f*
G. Altered from *Grants*
H. Altered from *im*
I. Altered from *will*
J. Altered from *of*

Doc. 6

A. From internal evidence.
B. Altered, possibly from *aneedote*
C. Altered from *i*
D. Altered from *homes*

Doc. 7

A. Altered, possibly from *attendendy*
B. Altered, possibly from *no*
C. Altered from *m*
D. Altered from *considerably*
E. Altered from *peared*
F. Altered from *bulding*
G. Altered from *goee*
H. Altered from *resemple*
I. Altered from *chesapeaq*
J. Altered from *him*
K. Altered from *Louissa*
L. Altered from *y*
M. Altered from *trial*
N. Altered from *Jugge*

Doc. 8

A. From internal evidence and the postmark (January 25).
B. Altered from *for*
C. Altered from *mis*
D. Initial parenthesis deleted.
E. Altered from *anoy*
F. Altered from *p*
G. Altered from *beang*
H. Paper torn.

Doc. 9

A. Altered from *i*

Doc. 10

A. From internal evidence.
B. Altered from *s*
C. Altered from *of*
D. Altered from *p*
E. Altered from *ex*
F. Altered from *naamely*
G. Altered from *B*
H. Altered from *c*
I. Altered from *Crettenden*
J. Altered from *mee*
K. Altered from *professional*
L. Altered from *yours*

Doc. 11

A. Missing from this and one of the variant copies, but present in the other.

Doc. 12

A. Written in left margin of first page.
B. Altered from *do*
C. Ink blot.
D. Altered from *probably*
E. Altered, possibly from *flith*
F. Altered from *S*
G. Altered from *surround*
H. Moved from above the dateline.
I. Written sideways in margin to left of illustration.

Doc. 13

A. Altered from *29*
B. Altered from *terminaded*
C. In the original, preceded by angled double lines and written at an angle to signal a break with the text above.
D. Altered from *busille*
E. Altered from *f*
F. Altered from *pracfical*
G. Altered from *esseemed*

Doc. 14

A. Altered from *didd*
B. Altered from *bi*

Doc. 15

A. Altered from *ar*

Doc. 16

A. From internal evidence.
B. Altered from *my*
C. Altered from *a*

Doc. 17

A. Altered from *eather*

Doc. 18

A. Ink blot.
B. Altered from *p*
C. Altered from *dyppeptic*

Doc. 19

A. Altered from *he*
B. Altered from *h*
C. Altered from *leisure*
D. Altered from *h*

Doc. 20

A. Day altered from *19*
B. Ink blot.

Doc. 21

A. Altered from *myself*
B. Altered from *paggases*
C. Altered from *are a*
D. Altered from *one*
E. Altered from *has*
F. Altered from *They are*
G. Altered from *collecting*
H. Altered from *Synonymy*
I. Altered from *in*
J. Altered from *may*
K. Period altered from comma.
L. Altered from *swedish*
M. Altered from *ra*
N. Altered from *washington*
O. Altered from *th*
P. Altered from *could*
Q. Altered from *or of*
R. Altered from *success*
S. Altered from *P*

Doc. 23

A. From internal evidence.
B. Altered from *g*

Doc. 24

A. From internal evidence.
B. Altered from *s*

Doc. 25

A. Day altered from *19*
B. Altered from *to*

Doc. 26

A. According to Jewett's reply, the outgoing copy was dated March 24.

Doc. 27

A. From outside address.
B. Altered from *refered*
C. Altered from *which*
D. Altered from *the*

Doc. 28

A. Altered from *an*
B. Dash altered from comma.
C. Altered from *a*
D. Altered from *s*

Doc. 29

A. Altered from *entre*
B. Altered from *conclusive*
C. Altered from *a*
D. Altered from *this*
E. Altered from *l*

Doc. 30

A. Altered from *of*
B. Altered from *s*

Doc. 31

A. Altered from *it*
B. Altered from *my*
C. Altered from *board*
D. Altered from *evers*

Doc. 32

A. Altered from *in*
B. Altered from *shuch*

Doc. 33

A. Altered from *or*

Doc. 34

A. Altered from *widthth*

Doc. 36

A. Altered from *duch*
B. Altered from *lense*
C. Center of word erased.
D. Altered from *in*
E. Altered from *making*

Doc. 37

A. Altered from *burried*
B. Altered, possibly from *pilgramage*
C. Altered from *fou*
D. Altered from *loose*
E. Altered from *newton*
F. Altered from *thoughts*
G. Altered from *should*
H. Altered, possibly from *90*
I. Altered, possibly from *gulpth*
J. Altered, possibly from *derived*
K. Altered from *from*

Doc. 38

A. Altered from *this*
B. Altered from *number*

Doc. 39

A. Altered from *pony*

Doc. 40

A. Moved from end of letter.

Doc. 41

A. Altered from *immage*
B. Altered, possibly from *ea*

Doc. 42

A. From internal evidence.
B. Altered from *are*
C. Remainder not found.

Doc. 43

A. Altered from *assistant*
B. Altered from *subscribing*
C. Altered from *reports*
D. Altered from *g*
E. Altered from *t*

Doc. 44

A. Altered from *attemppted*

Doc. 46

A. From internal evidence.

Doc. 47

A. Altered from *J*
B. Alternate reading: *20*
C. Altered from *two hours*

Doc. 48

A. Altered from *bound*
B. Altered, possibly from *I*
C. Altered from *G*
D. Altered from *d*
E. Remainder written in margin.

Doc. 49

A. Altered from *the*
B. Altered from *thout*
C. Hole in paper.

Doc. 50

A. Altered from *f*
B. Altered from *to*

Doc. 51

A. Altered from *A*
B. *3 O'clock* altered from *12*
C. Hole in paper.
D. Altered from *on*
E. Altered from *Lagrange*

Doc. 52

A. Altered, possibly from *ere*
B. Comma altered from dash.

Doc. 54

A. From internal evidence.
B. Altered from *coure*
C. Altered from *fourth*
D. Remainder not found.

Doc. 55

A. From the postmark and internal evidence.
B. Postmarked Philadelphia.
C. Altered from *owen*
D. Altered from *L*
E. Altered from *Frasier*
F. Altered from *Dallass's*

Doc. 56

A. Alternate reading: *internal*

Doc. 58

A. From internal evidence.

Doc. 59

A. From internal evidence.

Doc. 60

A. Moved from end of letter.
B. Moved from bottom of first page.

Doc. 63

A. Altered from *to*
B. In a darker ink and in Henry's hand.

Doc. 64

A. Altered, possibly from *does*
B. Altered from *hower*
C. Altered from *E*
D. Altered from *f*
E. Altered from *if*
F. Postscript written in margin.

Doc. 66

A. Altered from *a*
B. Altered, possibly from *three*
C. Altered from *of*
D. Altered from *all*
E. A partial Mary Henry Copy (in the same lo-

cation as the original) has instead of the following (to "Were I to consult . . . "): "Also I have been repeatedly informed or reminded that time and opportunity for scientific research would be much greater in Philadelphia; and this is quite true."
F. Approximately fifteen words crossed out.
G. Alternate reading: *desirable*
H. Altered from *Position*
I. Approximately three words crossed out.
J. Remainder in Henry's hand.
K. Remainder written in margin.

Doc. 67

A. Altered from *objectionably*
B. Altered from *not*
C. *and author* altered from *did not*
D. Altered from *by*
E. Altered from *prese*

Doc. 69

A. Altered from *f*
B. Altered from *late*

Doc. 71

A. From internal evidence.
B. Altered from *on*

Doc. 72

A. Altered from *attend*

Doc. 75

A. Altered from *appearence*
B. Altered from *writter*
C. Altered from *an*
D. Altered from *u*
E. Altered from *tuo*
F. Altered from *redolves*
G. Altered from *allg*

Doc. 76

A. Altered from *D*

Doc. 77

A. Altered from *the*
B. Altered from *wh*
C. Altered from *dillute*

D. Altered from *tranversely*
E. Altered from *globale*

Doc. 78

A. Day altered from *7*

Doc. 80

A. Day altered from *7*

Doc. 81

A. Altered from *bowells*
B. Altered from *too*
C. Altered from *woud*
D. Altered from *Lucindass*
E. Remainder not found.

Doc. 82

A. Altered from *g*
B. Altered from *is*

Doc. 83

A. From internal evidence and Henry's reply.
B. Altered from *as*
C. One or two missing words.
D. Altered, possibly from *is*
E. Altered from *f*

Doc. 84

A. Altered from *ca*
B. Altered from *Mr*
C. Altered from *Gibbs*

Doc. 85

A. Moved from end of letter.
B. Altered from *off*
C. Altered from *T*
D. Altered from *a*

Doc. 86

A. Altered, possibly from *have*

Doc. 87

A. Moved from end of letter.

Doc. 88

A. From Henry's file note on the other copy.
B. Altered from *bank*
C. In the copy, *none*
D. Altered from *Galltin*
E. In the copy, *450*
F. Altered from *sacrafice*
G. Altered, possibly from *carrying*
H. Altered from *out*
I. Paper torn.
J. Altered from *myse*
K. Altered from *kinds*

Doc. 89

A. Altered from *metalic*
B. Altered from *lighting*
C. In the original this paragraph is separated from, but marked as continuous with, the preceding paragraph.

Doc. 90

A. Altered from *unplesant*

Doc. 91

A. Altered from *king*
B. Altered from *from*
C. Altered from *n*
D. Altered from *the*
E. Altered from *have*
F. Paper torn.
G. Altered from *C*

Doc. 92

A. Altered from *was*
B. Altered from *orr*

Doc. 93

A. Altered from *of*
B. Altered from *placede*
C. Altered from *Colledge*
D. Altered from *is*
E. Moved from top of first sheet.

Doc. 95

A. Variant copy: "I still however adhere to the opinions expressed in my former letter, that the fixture will tend to attract the lightning of the clouds, and that no protection

which human foresight can suggest will render the building as safe as one on which there is no increased tendency of the lightning to fall."

Doc. 99

A. Altered from *examinations*

Doc. 100

A. Altered from *accompaniement*

Doc. 102

A. Altered from *lenses*
B. Altered from *hight*
C. Altered from *on*
D. Altered from *boy*

Doc. 103

A. Altered from *Vanderbilt*
B. Altered from *explanation*
C. Altered from *o'clc*
D. Altered from *intelligentleman*
E. Altered from *r*
F. Altered from *influen*
G. Altered from *mor*
H. Altered from *female*
I. Remainder written in margin.

Doc. 105

A. Altered from *that*
B. Altered from *complete*
C. Remainder written in margin.

Doc. 106

A. From internal evidence and file note.
B. Partially eaten away by ink.

Doc. 107

A. Ink blot.
B. Pencilled quotation mark preceding this word.
C. Altered, possibly from *necessessarly*
D. Pencilled quotation mark.
E. Altered from *Maurey*

Doc. 108

A. Altered from *seems*
B. Lieber left half a page blank before resuming.

Doc. 110

A. Remainder written in margin.

Doc. 111

A. From the file note and internal evidence.

Doc. 112

A. Altered from *a*
B. Remainder written in margin.

Doc. 113

A. Day altered from *17*
B. Altered from *orrange*
C. Altered from *in*

Doc. 114

A. One word cancelled by Henry before he cancelled the whole sentence.

Doc. 115

A. Altered from *Geologic*

Doc. 116

A. From provenance and internal evidence.

Doc. 118

A. Altered from *O*
B. Altered from *important*

Doc. 119

A. Altered from *individual*
B. Altered from *disuade*
C. Ink smeared.

Doc. 121

A. Altered from *procurring*
B. In pencil in left margin: *(2)*
C. In pencil in right margin: *(3)*
D. Altered from *hole*
E. Altered from *communication*
F. Altered from *shall*
G. Scribe's addition.
H. Cancelled material altered, possibly from *I assure you*
I. Altered from *felings*

Doc. 122

A. Altered from *in*
B. Altered, possibly from *buy*
C. Altered from *mee*
D. Paper torn.
E. Altered from *pressin*
F. Altered from *Library*
G. Semicolon altered from dash.
H. Altered from *f*
I. Altered from *Libraries*
J. Comma altered from dash.
K. Altered from *there* or *these*
L. Altered from *clerical*
M. Altered from *This*

Doc. 123

A. Altered from *co*

Doc. 124

A. From internal evidence.
B. Altered, possibly from *in*
C. Remainder not found.

Doc. 125

A. Altered from *This*
B. Altered from *at*
C. Altered from *congress*
D. Altered from *or*
E. Altered from *his*
F. Altered from *Board*
G. Altered from *thing*

Doc. 126

A. Moved from end of letter.
B. Moved from end of letter and day altered from *28*
C. Altered from *&*
D. Altered from *one*

E. Altered from *the*
F. Altered from *subject*
G. Altered from *in*

Doc. 128

A. Written in side margin.

Doc. 129

A. Paper torn.
B. Altered from *boston*

Doc. 131

A. Altered from *deed*
B. Remainder written in margin.

Doc. 133

A. Altered from *1847*
B. Altered from *Vol*
C. Altered from *without*
D. Altered from *e*
E. Remainder written on verso and recto of brief partial draft dated January 2, 1848.
F. Alternate reading: *ingenerous*
G. Altered from *R*
H. Altered from *f*
I. Squier left a 2.5-centimeter space between this line and the next for the title.
J. Altered from *wh*

Doc. 134

A. Outlined in ink.
B. Altered from *serves*
C. Altered, possibly from *valuables*
D. Altered from *owen*
E. Altered from *in*
F. Altered, possibly from *ap*
G. Remainder written in margin.

Doc. 137

A. From the postmark (January 16) and from internal evidence.
B. Altered from *ratter*
C. Altered from *nearer*
D. Altered from *occulcations*
E. Altered from *referted*
F. Altered from *feell*
G. Altered from *o*
H. Altered from *Monomanaa*
I. Altered from *s*

J. Altered from *I*
K. Partially obscured by seal.
L. *on Monday* altered from *tomorrow*
M. Altered from *t*
N. Followed by a fifteen-centimeter space for the address.
O. Altered from *fathers*
P. Altered from *tile*

Doc. 138

A. Altered from *Stahls Blacks Lavoisiers Newtons Amprees Dufays*
B. Altered from *Dy*
C. Altered from *Consisttntly*

Doc. 139

A. Altered from *yours*
B. Altered from *obt*

Doc. 140

A. Altered from *untll*
B. Altered from *as*
C. Altered from *etc*
D. Hole in paper.
E. Altered from *of*
F. Altered from *letters*

Doc. 141

A. Comma added by Henry.

Doc. 142

A. The first *16* is altered from *15*; the *th* is in Henry's hand.
B. Altered from *Memoir*
C. Altered from *a*
D. Altered from *committee* (Henry's hand).
E. Altered from *the*
F. Henry's hand.

Doc. 143

A. Altered from *supply*

Doc. 144

A. Year pre-printed on cover; day and month pre-printed on top of page.
B. Altered from *w*

C. Altered from *the*
D. Altered from *would*

Doc. 145

A. Moved from upper left margin.
B. Altered from *rether*
C. Altered from *wast*
D. Altered from *Is*

Doc. 146

A. Altered from *the*
B. Altered from *critics*
C. Altered from *met*

Doc. 147

A. Altered from *f*
B. Altered from *rase*
C. Passage moved from reverse side of page.

Doc. 148

A. Day altered from *28*
B. Altered from *preettly*
C. Altered from *Squire*
D. Paper torn.
E. Altered from *yo*

Doc. 149

A. Altered from *Wᵐ*

Doc. 151

A. Paper torn.

Doc. 152

A. Correction of day from *8ᵗʰ* based on date of executive committee meeting in first paragraph.

Doc. 153

A. Altered from *judgement*

Doc. 154

A. From file note and internal evidence.

Doc. 155

A. Altered from *of*

Doc. 156

A. Altered from *imediately*

Doc. 157

A. Hole in paper.
B. Paper torn.

Doc. 158

A. Altered from *P.M.*
B. Altered from *artile*

Doc. 159

A. From file note and internal evidence.

Doc. 161

A. Sabine brace in the margin of the next paragraph, with marginal note: "Ordered May 5th."

Doc. 162

A. Altered from *defenite*

Doc. 163

A. From internal evidence.

Doc. 165

A. Date changed from manuscript designation of *9*; from internal evidence.
B. Altered from *hope*
C. Altered from *Nichol*
D. Altered from *L*

Doc. 166

A. Altered from *off*
B. Rest of page blank.
C. Altered from *placee*
D. Altered from *be*
E. Altered from *is*
F. Altered from *cha*

Doc. 167

A. Altered from *of*
B. Altered from *begining*
C. Altered from *I*
D. Altered from *g*
E. Altered from *k*

Doc. 169

A. Altered from *retuned*
B. Altered from *March*
C. Paper torn.
D. Altered, possibly from *a*

Doc. 170

A. Paper and ink worn away.
B. Altered from *gentleman*
C. Altered from *owen*

Doc. 171

A. Altered from *boy*
B. Altered from *b*

Doc. 173

A. Month illegible and year lacking; supplied from file note and internal evidence.
B. Paper torn.

Doc. 174

A. Altered from *write*
B. Altered from *memor*
C. Altered from *p*
D. Originally after *I have*
E. Altered from *propers*

Doc. 175

A. Altered from *these*
B. Altered from *should*

Doc. 176

A. Day altered from *18*
B. Altered from *Pie*
C. *are appended* altered from *is appendded*
D. Altered from *g*
E. Altered from *kinds*

Doc. 177

A. Altered from *h*
B. Altered from *became*
C. Altered from *an*
D. Altered from *D*
E. Altered from *it*
F. Altered from *puting*
G. Altered from *p*
H. Altered from *for*
I. Altered from *An*
J. Altered from *gives*
K. Altered from *Dry*
L. Altered from *Bos*
M. Altered from *H*
N. Altered from *have*
O. Altered from *c*
P. Altered from *o*
Q. Altered from *a*
R. Altered from *reaction*
S. Remainder written in margin.

Doc. 178

A. Altered from *magnify*

Doc. 179

A. From internal evidence and notations in Bache's hand.
B. Altered from *saught*
C. Altered from *set*
D. Altered from *in*
E. Altered from *of*
F. Altered from *owen*
G. Altered from *national*
H. Altered from *departe*
I. Altered from *Vate*

Doc. 180

A. Altered from *an*
B. Altered from *donations*
C. Altered from *that*
D. Altered from *from*
E. Paper torn.
F. Comma altered from dash.

Doc. 181

A. Altered from *h*
B. Altered from *reminiscendes*

Doc. 183

A. Altered from *smoothey*

Text Notes

Doc. 184

A. Altered from *Saturdy*
B. Altered from *hime*
C. Altered from *if*

Doc. 187

A. Altered from *speacial*
B. Altered from *Ma*

Doc. 188

A. Altered from *trustees*

Doc. 190

A. Altered from *y*
B. Altered from *presice*
C. Altered from *exet*
D. Altered from *Do*
E. Altered from *be*
F. Altered from *to*

Doc. 191

A. From internal evidence and Henry's reply.
B. Altered from *Drawings*
C. Altered from *pa*

Doc. 192

A. From file note and internal evidence.
B. Altered from *speciments*

Doc. 193

A. Altered from *firt*
B. Altered from *o*
C. Altered from *at*
D. Altered from *dr*
E. Altered from *ouht*
F. Altered from *draftsmans*
G. Altered from *convexing*
H. Altered from *streets*
I. Altered from *p*
J. Altered, possibly from *unwortey*

Doc. 195

A. Altered from *articles*
B. Altered from *almoot*
C. Altered, possibly from *thier*

D. Altered from *sucessson*
E. Altered from *wile*

Doc. 196

A. Altered from *works*
B. Altered from *encouragment*

Doc. 197

A. Altered from *Seeriotyped*
B. Altered from *Doct*

Doc. 198

A. Altered from *printes*
B. Altered from *B*
C. Altered from *gest*

Doc. 199

A. From internal evidence.
B. Altered from *offict*
C. Altered from *don*
D. Altered from *galery*

Doc. 202

A. Altered from *hours*
B. Altered from *March*
C. Altered from *capital*
D. Altered from *s*
E. Altered, possibly from *howe*
F. Altered from *rackets*
G. Altered from *Demorrats*

Doc. 203

A. Altered from *for*
B. Altered from *to*
C. Altered, possibly from *diserned*
D. Altered from *your*
E. Altered from *Erening*
F. Altered from *she*
G. Altered from *o'olock*
H. Altered from *rong*
I. Altered from *find*
J. Altered from *will*

Doc. 204

A. Altered from *Squir's*
B. Altered from *caracter*

673

Doc. 205

A. Altered from *as*
B. Altered from *reom*
C. Altered from *a*
D. Altered from *revew*
E. Altered, possibly from *now*
F. Altered from *By*
G. Altered from *mattrasses*
H. Altered from *establishing the*

Doc. 207

A. Altered from *of*
B. Altered from *stry*

Doc. 208

A. Altered from *as*

Doc. 209

A. Altered, possibly from *memtry*
B. Altered from *rept*

Doc. 210

A. Altered from *a*
B. Altered from *excepted*
C. Altered from *Pr*
D. From this word through the end of the body of the letter, Henry wrote over his text a second time.
E. Altered from *decyphering*
F. Altered from *chyrography*

Doc. 212

A. Altered from *a*
B. Altered from *reciprocal*

Doc. 213

A. Altered, possibly from *l*
B. Altered from *such*

Doc. 214

A. Altered from *think*
B. Altered, possibly from *desended*
C. Altered from *pertains*
D. Altered from *They*
E. Altered from *vallue*
F. Altered from *Y*

G. Remainder written in margin.
H. Altered from *cou*

Doc. 215

A. Altered from *leasure*

Doc. 216

A. From internal evidence.
B. *important that* altered from *importantant*
C. Altered from *befefo*
D. Altered from *our*
E. Altered from *general*

Doc. 217

A. From internal evidence, handwriting, a file note, and provenance.
B. Altered from *at*
C. Altered, possibly from *booksfelders*
D. Remainder not found.

Doc. 218

A. Altered, possibly from *prep*
B. Altered from *obl*
C. Altered from *accompany*

Doc. 219

A. A larger than normal space precedes the next sentence.
B. Altered from *the*
C. Paper torn.
D. Altered from *its*

Doc. 220

A. From position in letterbook and internal evidence.

Doc. 221

A. Obscured in binding.
B. Altered from *Savants*

Doc. 222

A. Altered from *know*
B. Altered from *should*

Doc. 223

A. Altered from *contributions*

Doc. 224

A. Altered from *objectionable*

Doc. 225

A. Altered from *contributions*

Doc. 229

A. From file note in Coffin's hand.
B. Altered by hand from *observation*

Doc. 230

A. Paper torn; possibly 5
B. Altered from *Homes*
C. Paper torn.
D. Remainder not found.

Doc. 232

A. Moved from left margin.

Doc. 233

A. From internal evidence.
B. Altered from *saed*

Doc. 234

A. Altered from *they*
B. Altered from *Secretary*

Doc. 235

A. Altered from *ferely*
B. Altered from *successfull*
C. Altered from *Neather*
D. Period altered from comma.

Doc. 238

A. Hole in paper.
B. Altered from *a*
C. Altered from *k*
D. Altered from *storm,*
E. Altered from *up*

F. Altered from *chesapeake*
G. Altered from *into*

Doc. 239

A. Altered from *amounts*

Doc. 240

A. Day altered from *17*
B. Altered from *def*
C. Altered from *y*

Doc. 241

A. Altered from *national*
B. Altered from *withouy*

Doc. 242

A. Comma altered from period.
B. Altered from *espidition*
C. Altered from *sacretary*
D. Altered from *cool*

Doc. 243

A. Altered from *imployed*
B. Altered from *enteres*

Doc. 244

A. Altered from *th*
B. Altered from *all*

Doc. 245

A. Altered from *phenomina*
B. Altered from *phenominon*
C. Altered from *a*
D. Altered from *aparatus*
E. Altered from *mulitiply*

Doc. 246

A. Hole in paper.

Doc. 247

A. Altered from *express*

675

Doc. 248

A. Altered from *correspond*
B. Altered from *5*
C. Altered from *of*

Doc. 249

A. Altered from *a*

Doc. 250

A. Altered from *meterrological*

Doc. 251

A. From internal evidence; Lieber dated the letter *48*

Doc. 254

A. Paper torn.
B. Altered from *payed*
C. Altered from *as*
D. Altered from *deferent*
E. Altered from *46*

Doc. 255

A. Altered from *absorbes*
B. Altered from *a*
C. Altered from *leg*

Doc. 256

A. Altered from *coast*

Doc. 257

A. Altered from *cl*
B. Altered from *the*
C. Altered from *marsal*

Doc. 258

A. Altered from *I*
B. Altered from *are*
C. Altered from *tak*
D. Altered from *op*

Doc. 259

A. Altered from *high*
B. Altered from *appropriations*
C. Followed by a blank line with two dashes in the left margin.
D. Altered from *so*
E. Altered from *d*
F. Altered from *will*

Doc. 260

A. Paper torn.
B. Altered from *the*
C. Altered from *acceptible*

Doc. 261

A. Altered from *directions*
B. Altered from *positton*
C. Altered from *other*

Doc. 262

A. Altered from *feel*

Doc. 263

A. Altered from *incouragement*
B. Altered from *or*
C. Altered from *botany*

Doc. 264

A. Altered from *litter*
B. Altered from *meteorllogical*
C. Altered from *200*
D. Altered from *lettl*
E. Altered from *King*

Doc. 265

A. Alternate reading: *hear*

Doc. 266

A. Altered from *D*
B. Altered from *roberies*

Doc. 267

A. Altered from *Mexico*
B. Altered from *sail*
C. Altered from *requred*

D. Altered from *freed*
E. Altered from *to*

Doc. 268

A. Altered from *weeght*
B. Altered from *as*
C. Altered from *when*

Doc. 270

A. Altered from *en*

Doc. 271

A. Alternate reading: *sympathised*
B. Altered from *department*

Doc. 272

A. Altered from *Breeze*

Doc. 273

A. Altered from ⅛

Doc. 274

A. Altered from *y*
B. Altered from *g*

Doc. 275

A. From the title of the volume into which the letter is bound.
B. Altered from *as*
C. Altered from *such*
D. Altered from *receiving*
E. Altered from *in*

Doc. 277

A. Altered from *one*
B. Altered from *extraortinary*
C. Altered from *litterature*
D. Altered from *pronouncitition*
E. Altered from *freee*
F. Altered from *m*
G. Altered from *on*

Doc. 278

A. Altered from *expecting*
B. Moved from facing page.

Doc. 279

A. Moved from end of letter.
B. Altered from *Political*

Doc. 280

A. Altered from *S*
B. Altered, possibly from *Fremontt*

Doc. 282

A. Undated entry between April 7 and 9, 1849.
B. From title page.
C. Altered from *our* or *an*
D. Altered from *Colaborators*
E. Altered from *Paleontalegy*
F. Altered from *Colcology*
G. Altered from *Camble*
H. Altered from *Da*
I. Altered, possibly from *Liman*
J. Line moved from bottom of previous column.

Doc. 283

A. Altered from *know*
B. Altered from *a*

Doc. 284

A. Altered from *an*

Doc. 285

A. Altered from *before*

Doc. 287

A. Altered from *thoughs*

Doc. 288

A. Period altered from comma.

Doc. 289

A. Paper cropped.

Doc. 290

A. Altered, possibly from *it*

Doc. 291

A. Altered from *Copy*
B. Leading opening quotation marks deleted.
C. Altered from *discov*
D. Altered from *principal*
E. Altered from *Physiooogy*
F. Altered from *experimentent*
G. Altered from *those*
H. Altered from *suppose*

Doc. 293

A. Preprinted.
B. From title page.
C. The remainder is on an undated page between entries of Saturday, April 28, and Monday, April 30, in two columns erroneously dated Monday.

Doc. 294

A. Altered from *untill*

Doc. 295

A. Undated entry between May 5 and 7.
B. From title page.
C. Altered from *this*

Doc. 297

A. Altered from *f*

Doc. 298

A. Altered from *negotiating*
B. Altered from *composition*
C. Altered from *Confidentialy*
D. Altered from *Pleasure*

Doc. 299

A. Moved from end of letter.
B. Altered from *preparations*

Doc. 300

A. Altered from *the*
B. Altered from *Kind*
C. Altered from *will*
D. Altered from *Col*
E. Altered from *of*
F. Altered from *in*
G. Altered from *declaired*
H. Altered from *10*

Doc. 301

A. From internal evidence.
B. Word moved from end of letter.

Doc. 302

A. Altered from *o*
B. Altered from *4000*
C. Altered from *diffuculties*
D. Altered from *a la*
E. Altered from *my*
F. Altered from *acting*
G. Altered from *september*

Doc. 303

A. Undated entry between May 19 and 21.
B. Altered from *isolatenes*

Doc. 304

A. Leaders (spaced periods) in the following table have been standardized.

Doc. 305

A. Altered from *Ewbak*
B. Altered from *from*
C. Altered from *Invistigation*
D. Altered from *not*
E. Altered from *When*

Doc. 306

A. Altered from *classes*

Doc. 307

A. Moved from end of letter.

Doc. 308

A. Preprinted.
B. From title page.
C. Altered from *5*

Doc. 309

A. Remainder written in margin.

Doc. 310

A. Altered from *congress*

Doc. 311

A. Altered from *in*

Doc. 312

A. From internal evidence.
B. Paper torn.
C. Altered from *the*
D. Altered from *re*
E. Altered from *Hh*
F. Altered from *He*
G. Remainder not found.

Doc. 314

A. Paper torn.

Doc. 315

A. Hole in paper.
B. Paper torn.

Doc. 316

A. Altered from *hints*

Doc. 317

A. Altered from *h*
B. Altered from *our*

Doc. 318

A. Altered from *Littrature*
B. Altered from *convition*
C. Altered from *a*
D. *they call* altered from *these calling*
E. Altered from *Proctions*

F. Altered from *send*
G. Altered from *friend*

Doc. 319

A. Altered from *non*
B. Hole in paper.
C. Covered by seal.

Doc. 321

A. *I feel* altered from *still*
B. Altered from *of th*

Doc. 322

A. Altered from *were*
B. Altered from *I*
C. Altered from *sm*
D. Altered from *I [...] be*
E. Remainder not found.

Doc. 323

A. Altered from *enterprize*
B. Comma erased.
C. Altered from *to*

Doc. 326

A. Altered from *are*
B. Altered from *buildings*
C. Altered from *i*
D. Altered from *Day*
E. Altered from *line*
F. Altered from *rooling*

Doc. 328

A. Altered from *Russel*
B. Altered from *John's*
C. Altered from *Schencks*

Doc. 329

A. Paper torn.

Doc. 330

A. Altered from *Leebig*
B. Altered from *Dr*
C. Altered from *renwick*

Doc. 331

A. Dated September fourth, but actually written the day before, based on Henry's Desk Diary for September 3, 1849, and on Doc. 332.
B. Altered from *seet*
C. Altered from *indescreso*
D. Altered from *statisfaction*
E. Altered from *Ue*

Doc. 332

A. Altered from *see*
B. Altered from *st*
C. Altered from *approache*
D. Altered from *repeled*
E. Altered from *eather*
F. Altered from *huray*
G. Altered from *thoughe*
H. Altered from *to*
I. Altered from *a*

Doc. 333

A. Altered from *Inclosed*
B. Altered from *mad*

Doc. 335

A. Altered from *of*
B. Paper torn.

Doc. 336

A. Altered from *3000*
B. Altered from *southearn*
C. Altered from *he*
D. Altered from *send*
E. Altered from *green's*
F. Left blank.

Doc. 337

A. Altered from *Profr*
B. Altered from *Alaxander*
C. Left blank.
D. Altered from *these*

Doc. 339

A. Comma altered from period.

Doc. 341

A. Altered from *in*
B. Altered from *So*
C. Altered from *and*
D. Altered from *s*
E. Altered from *not*
F. Altered from *dir*
G. Altered from *endeavored*
H. Altered from *college*
I. Altered from *of*
J. Altered from *facilities*
K. Altered from *Un*
L. Altered from *good*
M. Altered from *regrard*

Doc. 342

A. From repetition of place and later date at bottom of letter.
B. Altered from *les*
C. Altered from *abbé*
D. Altered from *l'autre*
E. Hole for binding.
F. Altered from *humboldt*
G. Altered from *Et*
H. Altered from *france*
I. Hole for binding; reading from appended English translation.
J. Altered from *psychromètre*
K. Altered from *sans*
L. Altered from *nécessités*
M. Altered from *de*
N. Altered from *Wash*
O. Altered from *s'en*
P. Internal address repeated at bottom of first page.

Doc. 343

A. Altered from *an*
B. Altered from *we*
C. Altered from *looser*
D. Altered from *association*
E. Altered from *b*
F. Altered from *s*
G. Altered from *skilled*
H. Altered, possibly from *saw*
I. Altered from *imbude*
J. Obscured by paper guard.
K. Altered from *general*
L. Altered from *the*

Doc. 344

A. Altered from *so*
B. Altered from *coast*
C. Moved from bottom of first page.

Doc. 345

A. Moved from end of letter.
B. Altered from *to*
C. Altered from *of*

Doc. 347

A. Altered from *I*
B. Altered from *was*
C. Altered from *has*
D. Altered from *tame*
E. Altered from *crediting*
F. Altered from *P.S*

Doc. 349

A. Altered from *dod*

Doc. 350

A. Preceding 5 altered from *6*
B. Altered from *in*
C. Altered from *au*
D. Altered, possibly from *to me*
E. Altered from *f*
F. Altered from *e*
G. Altered from *might*
H. Altered from *this*
I. Altered from *k*

Doc. 351

A. Altered from *po*
B. Altered from *finan*

Doc. 352

A. From Mary Henry notation: "Extract from letter to Miss Gill."

Doc. 353

A. Place and date moved from end of letter.
B. Altered from *hypothesis*
C. Altered from *current*

Doc. 354

A. Moved from end of letter.

Doc. 355

A. Altered from *to*
B. Altered from *perenial*
C. Altered from *have*

Appendix

A. Altered from *this*
B. Altered from *rea*
C. Altered from *no*
D. Altered from *compleetly*
E. Altered from *more*
F. Altered from *In*
G. Altered from *It*
H. Altered from *number*
I. Altered from *whice*
J. Altered from *stiched*
K. Altered from *marqued*
L. Altered from *One*
M. Marginal notation under drawing: "Sent to Albany also"
N. Hole in paper.
O. Altered from *in*
P. Altered from *AM*
Q. Altered from *preferable*
R. Altered from *Physhrometric*
S. Altered from *exacticude*
T. Altered from *am*
U. Altered from *receive*
V. Altered from *From*
W. Altered from *at*
X. Left blank in original.

Under a name, "letter from" signifies a letter from that person to Henry, while "letter to" indicates a letter from Henry to that person. When Henry is neither sender nor recipient, the names of both parties are given. In the case of Henry, "letter from," followed by a list of names, indicates letters to Henry; "letters to," Henry's letters to various recipients. Subentries are so arranged that letters and documents precede the customary alphabetical listing.